The Decline of American Communism

A VOLUME IN THE SERIES

COMMUNISM IN AMERICAN LIFE
Clinton Rossiter, General Editor

BOOKS PUBLISHED TO DATE:

The Roots of American Communism by Theodore Draper
The Communists and the Schools by Robert W. Iversen
The Decline of American Communism by David A. Shannon

David A. Shannon

THE DECLINE

A History of the Communist Party

OF AMERICAN

of the United States since 1945

COMMUNISM

Harcourt, Brace and Company, New York

To
J. R. S. and E. J. S.

This book is one of a series of studies of Communist influence in American life. The entire survey has been made possible through the foresight and generous support of the Fund for the Republic. All of us who have taken part in it are grateful for this exceptional opportunity to study the most confused and controversial problem of the age and to publish the results exactly as we find them.

CLINTON ROSSITER

PREFACE

For more than a decade, the American people have been concerned about the presence of an active, organized, and dedicated Communist party in their midst at a time when relations between the United States and the Soviet Union have been strained and mutually suspicious. This concern has given rise to a flood of oratory and print on the nature and purposes of Communism, some of which has been intelligent, dispassionate, and informed, and some, perhaps most, inadequately researched, hysterical, and dangerously wide of the target. Yet this book is the first devoted exclusively to a history of the Communist Party of the United States itself during the years it has caused the greatest anxiety, the years since World War II.

The American Communist Party's recurrent political and ideological shifts result in explosions that bring to light many hidden facts. This book is a history of the party from the 1945 upheaval, which ejected Earl Browder from leadership, through the biggest explosion in the party's career, detonated by Khrushchev's speech on Stalin's crimes and the Russian intervention in Hungary, an explosion that rocked the party from early 1956 to early 1958. This book is not a guide to the detection of Communists, but a history of the party itself in the postwar years. The story of the American Communists since 1945 is, in a sense, a complete story, for it has a beginning, a middle, and an end.

In the writing of any book one becomes indebted to others, but I am embarrassed as I contemplate the number of people who have helped me to write this one. To all of them I express my gratitude.

My thanks to my colleagues and the administrators of Teachers College, Columbia University, for affording me a leave from teaching to do research for this book and to the Fund for the Republic for the financial assistance that made the leave feasible. My thanks also to the Graduate School of the University of Wisconsin for a summer-session salary grant that enabled me to spend full time for a summer finishing the book.

My colleagues in the study of Communism in American Life, which has been sponsored by the Fund for the Republic, were stimulating, helpful in criticism, and generous of time. I owe special thanks to Clinton Rossiter, director of the project, but all of the following aided me: Theodore Draper, William Goldsmith, Daniel Bell, Daniel Aaron, Ralph Roy, Nathan Glazer, Moshe Decter, Earl Latham, Robert Iversen, John Roche, and Joel Seidman. George Rawick and Mrs. Nancy Goldsmith assisted me for a time in research.

Many people who were either participants in this book in some way or another or who helped me in some manner with their special knowledge corresponded with me, allowed me to interview them, or both. They were of inestimable help. They were: C. B. Baldwin, Jack Barbash, Bruce Bliven, Merle Brodsky, Earl Browder, Joseph Clark, Joseph Freeman, John Gates, Max Gordon, Nissen Gross, Mrs. Gilbert Harrison, Dorothy Healy, Philip Jaffe, Mrs. Ida Landau, Val Lorwin, Curtis MacDougall, Joseph Starobin, Michael Straight, Irwin Suall, Norman Thomas, Rexford Tugwell, Henry Wallace, and David Williams. I also had some interviews with Communist rank-and-file members who prefer to remain anonymous.

Finally, I owe thanks to my wife, Jane Short Shannon, who helped in many ways, above all by reading the manuscript in all its stages with a kindly and encouraging attitude and yet with a coldly critical eye.

DAVID A. SHANNON

Madison, Wisconsin
March, 1959

CONTENTS

PART ONE

THE AMERICAN COMMUNIST PARTY: POSTWAR READJUSTMENT

We are the most consistent opponents of imperialism and the staunchest champions of American-Soviet friendship. Consequently, we cannot accept the viewpoint of those who find both the U.S. and the U.S.S.R. responsible for the increased war danger. We maintain, as a matter of fact and record, that the Wall Street interventionists and bipartisan warmongers alone are to blame for the real and growing danger of a new world war.

       —EUGENE DENNIS *to the fourteenth national convention of the Communist Party, August 1948.*

ONE: NEW LEADER AND NEW LINE

W hen the war in Europe ended
with Germany's surrender in May 1945, the American Communist Party was at its peak, with between 75,000 and 85,000 members. In 1944, the Communists had recruited more than 4,000 new members a week. It had money of its own as well. Far from being the recipient of "Moscow gold," it was able to send funds to Communist parties abroad. It enjoyed a measure of prestige in at least some sections of society and of indifference in others. A public-opinion poll taken soon after the war revealed greater toleration toward Communists than there had ever been earlier, a reflection, to at least some extent, undoubtedly, of the regard with which Americans generally held the military exploits of their Soviet allies. The party had widespread influence beyond its own boundaries. Between one-fifth and one-fourth of all the members of the Congress of Industrial Organizations (C.I.O.) belonged to unions led by Communists or men close to the party. The party could count upon one-third of the votes of the C.I.O. executive board. The Communists had some strength at the polls. In November 1945, they elected two members of New York's city council on their own ticket, and two other city councilmen, elected on the American Labor Party ballot, worked hand in glove with the Communists.

Today, the Communists look back upon their power in 1945

wistfully. Their party has become a shambles. The membership has left in droves. There is one acknowledged party member for each twenty-five of 1945. The party has fewer dues-paying members than it had when it split off from the Socialist Party of Eugene V. Debs in 1919. Today, the party is almost bankrupt. It has been forced to stop publication of its daily newspaper, to close its schools, and to trim its staff to the quick. The Communists have lost almost all their influence in the trade unions. The C.I.O. has expelled the Communist-controlled unions and then raided their membership until almost no one is left. No longer do Communists make a good showing at the polls. In the fall of 1957, a Communist candidate for the New York City council received only 1 per cent of the district's vote. Instead of prestige or even toleration, Communists today receive social ostracism. It goes almost without saying in today's politics that the Communists are universally despised.

In 1945 the outlook for the American Communists had never been brighter; by 1959 it had never been darker.

What had happened in that decade and a half? Why did the Communists decline to political insignificance? The answer involves some factors beyond the party's control, and some factors within its control, decisions of the party leadership that proved disastrous from the party's own point of view. The *coup de grâce* came, ironically, not from America, but from Moscow.

This book is a description of the Communist Party's decline after 1945.

PATRIOTS ALL: THE WARTIME LINE

During the last months of the war, when victory seemed within the Allies' grasp, the foreign policy of the Soviet Union toward its Western comrades in arms gradually changed from uneasy alliance to hostility. The change was apparent at the Yalta conference in February 1945. Inevitably, the changed direction of

Moscow's policies would have a jolting impact on the American Communist Party.

But American party leaders detected no departure in Russian policy until they discovered in May that an important French Communist official, Jacques Duclos, had published the previous month in one of his party's magazines, *Cahiers du Communisme*, a biting criticism of the American party's wartime line. Duclos was especially critical of the 1944 decision of the top American leader, Earl Browder, to dissolve the Communist Party and re-make it into the Communist Political Association, the C.P.A. This criticism from abroad awakened the American Communists to a realization that the postwar world they had anticipated was not the one foreseen in Moscow. No criticism such as that Duclos had written, they thought, could have been made without the approval of the Soviet Union. Duclos was too important a leader in too important a Communist Party to have made such criticisms of a sister party without being sure of his position in Moscow.

The Communists' wartime line was a curiosity in the history of American Communism. After the Nazi invasion of Russia, their emphasis was upon national unity to win the war against fascism, now a "peoples war" instead of an imperialist adventure. They submerged their traditional criticisms of American capitalism until they were, on many issues, to the right of many non-Communist liberals. A minor detail at the 1944 convention, which founded the C.P.A., indicated a great deal about their mood and tactics. Browder sprinkled professional singers through the audience so that the assembly could sing what Browder still calls "the best rendition of 'The Star Spangled Banner' ever performed by a large amateur group." [1] It was in this nationalistic all-out-for-unity mood that Browder, in a Bridgeport, Connecticut, speech, offered to "clasp the hand" of the junior J. P. Morgan in the unlikely event that that gentleman, dead for nine months, proved himself to be a progressive capitalist member of what the Communists called "the democratic anti-fascist coalition." [2] Not only in such peripheral matters, but on issues of significance to Communists—

race relations, organized labor, and political action—the wartime Communist line revealed itself.

Traditionally, the Communists have been, in their own way, vigorous champions of the rights of minorities, although Communist policy toward minority racial groups has vacillated more than is generally known. During the war, however, the Communists soft-pedaled this issue. California Communists endorsed the federal government's removal of the West Coast Japanese to what were euphemistically called "relocation centers" in the country's interior. American Communists did not help Negro leaders in their efforts to pressure the administration to end color segregation in the armed forces, and they criticized Negro militants. Indeed, in early 1941, before the German invasion of Russia, when the American Communists' slogan was "The Yanks Are Not Coming," the Communists had opposed A. Philip Randolph and his "March on Washington" movement, which wrung from Franklin D. Roosevelt the executive order establishing the Fair Employment Practices Commission.[3] During the war, the Communists took the position that unity for the war effort demanded that racial discrimination be at least temporarily tolerated if not condoned.

The Communists adopted a similar attitude toward trade-union militancy. American workers during the war encountered only opposition from the Communists when they considered strikes or slowdowns against grievances. *Political Affairs,* the official magazine on Communist theory (called the *Communist* until the party dissolved and set up the C.P.A.), proclaimed that to strike or even to permit a strike "would be a crime against the war effort. . . . Co-operation on the basis of the nation's war-time program alone has provided the solution of the workers' problems." Communists in the United Auto Workers tried unsuccessfully to persuade the membership to accept piecework and incentive pay to increase production. On one occasion in San Francisco, when longshoremen protested to their union that employers required them to load more cargo into the freight slings than they considered safe, Harry Bridges ordered the men to put even more in the slings.[4]

In 1944, the Communists vigorously supported Roosevelt's re-election, and, after the election, Browder expressed his gratification and warned against independent political action: "We must discourage every project of organization of new parties . . . the lesson of this election campaign points toward reducing the number of parties and not increasing them." Browder was not disappointed, as were some New Dealers, at the refusal of the Democratic convention to renominate Henry A. Wallace for vice-president. "I think . . . it is probably fortunate for the country and for Wallace that he was not nominated in this past election." In early 1945, when Edward Stettinius, a former president of United States Steel, replaced Cordell Hull as Secretary of State, many liberals were alarmed. But not the Communists. The New York newspaper *PM* expressed its displeasure with the appointment and was rebuked by the Communists for being "irresponsible." Browder urged "unconditional support" of Roosevelt's national war-service proposal, which would have made liable for military or industrial service all able-bodied men and women; many liberals opposed it.[5]

The C.P.A.'s postwar strategy called for a continuation of the wartime line. Browder, in *Political Affairs,* predicted Russian-American harmony after the war, despite the obviously deteriorating relations in the last months of the European war, which he described as *"a conflict of mood and opinion but not a conflict of interest."* As Browder saw it, there were but two alternatives to continued Russian-American harmony: war, which would be "military and political insanity"; or armed peace, "another name for diplomatic and economic war without drawing the military conclusions." The West would reject both alternatives because they would "cancel all prospects for a rapid extension of the world markets so vital for America's postwar economy." [6]

If Browder's crystal ball was cloudy, his followers did not perceive it. They filled out the details of the Communist line for the postwar period to conform to Browder's general position. Postwar universal military training, "the most effective and democratic method by which the United States can build and maintain a military establishment geared to the needs of the post-war world," was a plank in the Communist platform for the world of peace. It was a pity indeed that the American people had not heeded George Washington's advice and established universal military service in 1790. Labor was urged to extend its no-strike pledge. Postwar strikes, Communists believed, would only endanger the goal of full employment. Furthermore, strikes would prevent the maintenance of high wartime take-home pay. The Communists were to maintain the C.P.A. and not reconstitute the old party, wrote the Communist organization secretary, John Williamson. The C.P.A. was the "most indispensable weapon" in maintaining "national unity in the post-war period, including the long-time collaboration of Communists in the democratic coalition." [7]

The Communists' rationale for this whole soft line was that there were profound changes developing in American capitalism. The war against fascism, as the Communists saw it, was making the American business community, or at least a large part of it, democratic and responsive to the needs of the whole nation. Here and there, reactionary capitalists remained, but they were on the defensive, even in retreat: the "decisive sections of the American capitalist class have abandoned the old policy of hard-boiled reaction and imperialism, and are seriously trying to adjust themselves to the democratic currents and needs of the nation at war." With such a development, obviously the Communist position toward the capitalists would have to change. "The problem," wrote Browder, "is no longer how to combat the whole bourgeoisie but how to strengthen the progressive against the reactionary sector. . . ." [8]

EARL BROWDER VERSUS WILLIAM Z. FOSTER

But, said Jacques Duclos, this wartime line of Browder's was "revisionist" nonsense, and the American Communists saw his "letter" as an international signal to scuttle the Browder position and adopt a harder line, although Browder wrote an introduction to the *Daily Worker* translation of the Duclos letter in which he tried to minimize the differences between his position and that of Duclos. For weeks, the American Communists were in turmoil. The national board met in almost continuous session in the last half of May 1945. The pages of the *Daily Worker* carried discussion from any Communist who wanted to write, quite in contrast to periods of normal party stability, when the membership was quiet on all important matters and nothing suggested anything but perfect party unanimity. When equilibrium again came to the American Communists, confirmed by their special emergency convention of July 26-28, there was a new reconstituted party organization, a new leadership, a partial outline of a new line, and, most important, a new leftist mood.

The two antagonists in this ideological duel were Earl Browder and William Z. Foster. Foster was the most important Communist leader to oppose Browder in the national board meetings following the *Daily Worker*'s translation of the Duclos letter. He had been in and around leftist politics for almost a half-century. Born in March 1881, in Taunton, Massachusetts, the son of an Irish immigrant father and a mother of English-Scottish background, Foster grew up in the Philadelphia slums, quit school at the age of ten, and worked at a variety of jobs all over the country, as a dock worker, a seaman, a streetcar conductor, a lumberjack, and a farm hand. In 1901, he joined the Socialist Party of Eugene Debs, which expelled him in 1909. He then went into the Industrial Workers of the World, where he tried unsuccessfully to persuade the Wobblies to join the American Federation of Labor and "bore from within." In 1912, Foster formed his own organization, the Syndicalist League of North America; it lasted two years. Another short-lived organization followed. During the war, he rose within the American Federation of Labor in Chicago as an organizer in the meat-packing industry. In 1919, he came to national prominence as the A.F. of L. leader of the violent but unsuccessful steel strike. The next year, he founded still another of his own organizations, the Trade Union Educational League (T.U.E.L.), spurned at first by the American Communists but accepted by the Russians' Red International of Labor Unions, or "Profintern," at its first congress in Moscow in July 1921. No Communist when he went to Moscow in 1921, Foster returned to the United States to join the American party and, at the Profintern's direction, to be the head of the American Communists' labor branch. T.U.E.L., the American section of the Profintern, had its headquarters in Chicago; the central political office of the Communist Party was in New York. Thus Foster moved into the American Communist organization as a top leader. In 1928 and 1932, he was the Communists' candidate for the Presidency.

But in the 1930's, Earl Russell Browder had passed Foster and become the number one man in the Communist Party. Browder was a complex and contradictory person. Born in Wichita, Kansas, on May 20, 1891, the son of a teacher and the grandson of a Methodist circuit-riding minister, he never fully lost—apparently did not want to lose—his Kansas ways. He made many trips to Moscow, he served the Comintern as one of its agents in China, he married a Russian, and he was proud of his friendship with certain leaders of the international movement, particularly Georgi Dmitrov. Yet he continued to speak in the flat accents of a Kansan (he pronounced the word "cadre" to rhyme with ladder), and he dressed like a small-town Midwestern businessman of a generation ago (even with long underwear tucked neatly inside his socks). Although in his political career he was ever sensitive to the wishes of the Soviet Union, he remained something of an American nationalist. He is likely today to tell strangers a few minutes after meeting them how proud he is of the way Americans have treated his three sons, who are disinterested in politics.

Foster had chafed under Browder's party leadership during World War II. His heart had not been in the party's wartime line. He opposed the idea of Communist co-operation with "sections of the bourgeoisie." In January 1944, Foster had declared his dissent in a letter to the Communist national committee. But neither this letter nor any other indication of Foster's disapproval reached print until after the Duclos letter. Browder, of course, opposed publication of Foster's views, and Foster was not sufficiently sure of himself to fight the Browder machine. He did not come out into the open until the Duclos letter made him confident of Russian support. During the war, he had published articles that agreed with the Browder line, even after the early 1944 letter of dissent to the party's national committee. Indeed, as late as June 1945, two months after the Duclos affair, *Political Affairs* carried a Foster article that included these words: "By far not all American capitalists favor a policy of aggressive imperialist expansion. Large numbers of them followed the general Roosevelt line. These more far-sighted elements among the capitalists, the Kaisers, Krugs, Nelsons, etc., realizing that their class interests dovetail with the nation's interests and understanding that any attempt of the United States to go it alone in the world would result in sure disaster, are accepting the general policies laid down at Teheran and Yalta." Foster's acknowledgement of "more far-sighted elements among the capitalists" implied the same distinction among capitalists that Browder had made, and the distinction was the basic tenet from which the whole Browder soft line flowed. Further, Foster's statement that the "class interests" of the capitalists "dovetail" with the nation's interests was a good example of the kind of "revisionism" he was already pledged to stamp out.[9] His article was diametrically opposed to his position at the national board discussions in his efforts to depose Browder. This was not the first time, however, that the mechanics of Communist publication could not keep pace with Communist ideological change.

Foster had two important lieutenants in his struggle against Browder: Eugene Dennis and Robert Thompson. Dennis, born Francis X. Waldron, Jr., was also of Irish extraction. Reared in the Pacific Northwest, Dennis had got into the labor movement as a teamster and had joined the party in 1926 after a strike of agricultural workers in California. The party sent him to the Lenin School in Moscow, from which the Comintern sent him to China. Arriving back in the United States in the mid-1930's, Dennis became a member of the party's national committee and state secretary of the Wisconsin organization. His work there attracted Browder's attention, and he moved Dennis into the national office. Browder's protégé turned against his sponsor; in the process, Dennis made himself the party's number two man.[10]

Unlike most party leaders, Thompson had little political or trade-union experience. Barely thirty years old when he became Foster's lieutenant in charge of eliminating the influence of Browder and the Browderites, Thompson had spent much of his adult life as a soldier. He had been a member of the Abraham Lincoln Brigade and had fought and been wounded in the Spanish Civil War. As a staff sergeant infantry platoon leader in New Guinea in World War II, he had earned the Distinguished Service Cross. He received a medical discharge long before the end of the war. The ruthlessness and toughness of a good infantryman were the qualities Thompson brought to the battle against Browder. During the party upheaval, Thompson was heard to say to a friend who found it difficult to vilify Browderite friends that he did not find it difficult at all—"just like killing Japs." Thompson's reward for his services in routing the Browder heretics was one of the most important positions in the party, state secretary of New York, by far the biggest of the state organizations and, with its offices at the national headquarters on East Twelfth Street, the most influential.[11]

Neither Dennis nor Thompson could lay claim, as did Foster,

to Marxist purity and opposition to Browder's "revisionism." Dennis had written articles in the spring of 1945 in which he saw eye to eye with Browder about the postwar world, and Thompson felt obligated to take considerable space in one of his attacks on Browder to describe how he had been misguided. In language reminiscent of a repentent backslider from a total-abstinence pledge, he explained: "I conditioned myself to swallowing an opportunist gnat and as is inevitable in such cases wound up by swallowing elephants." [12]

On June 2, 1945, the national board of the C.P.A. adopted a draft resolution entitled "The Present Situation and the Next Tasks," which became the basis of the Communists' official discussion and which, slightly amended, became the main resolution passed by the special party convention, July 26-28. The draft resolution was a thorough repudiation of Browder and his wartime soft line, as well as an outline of the new line.[13] From the time the draft resolution passed the national board, Browder was in actuality no longer the top Communist leader. He remained a member of the C.P.A.'s thirteen-member national board and of the national committee (of which the national board was an executive committee), but he had been repudiated. The special national convention dissolved the C.P.A., re-established the Communist Party of the United States of America, the C.P.U.S.A., and refused to elect Browder to its national committee. After the convention, Browder was just another rank-and-filer, and a disgraced one at that. Several months later, in February 1946, the party expelled him altogether.

The fundamental difference between the old Browder line and the new Foster line was the denial of progressive tendencies in capitalism. The Communists now said American capitalism was inherently reactionary and imperialist; those who defended it or the policies of the government, in their eyes only the instrument of reactionary imperialists, were retrograde. If the defenders of American policies were honored leaders of the working class, their defense proved only that they were "misleaders" of labor.

From the premise of the inherently reactionary nature of capitalism and its agencies, it followed that Communists should do all in their power to fight capitalists rather than to collaborate with them in any kind of alliance.

The Communists did not discard the idea of alliance with non-Communists who were not staunch defenders of capitalism or of American policy—especially foreign policy. The "democratic antifascist coalition" should become even stronger. To the Communists, the unity of all noncapitalist working-class groups was paramount. Co-operation with non-Communist labor, farmer, and Negro groups remained one of the Communist goals.

The Communists had once referred to "the united front of struggle from below." In a similar mood, the Communists hoped to woo the masses away from their "misleaders." Whereas the party had once refrained from attack on many popular leaders, or had spoken kindly of them, they now would attack them if they supported governmental policies or were outspokenly anti-Communist. Thus, Walter Reuther now became an object of Communist scorn and vilification; Walter White, of the National Association for the Advancement of Colored People, who supported American foreign policy, now was labeled a hateful betrayer of his people. The Communists were not prepared to pull out of unions that had anti-Communist leaders; they would try to overthrow them instead. However, they did maintain "dual organizations" against the N.A.A.C.P. The new coalition was to be an alliance, but one with a difference. It never really developed.

For some time, there were ideological lags and even internal inconsistencies in the Communist position. The Communist draft resolution, for example, contained an endorsement of the Labor-Management Charter which United States Chamber of Commerce President Eric Johnston, C.I.O. President Philip Murray, and A.F. of L. President William Green had signed in early 1945, until a revision made after the resolution's passage by the C.P.A. national committee.[14] Endorsement of a document written in part by an officer of the National Chamber of Commerce was obviously at odds with the new line. The endorsement was withdrawn from the document's final draft, but a plea for an extension of federal aid to small business remained. James S. Allen, one of the party's theoretical writers who strongly favored a hard line, was justified somewhat in calling the draft resolution "full of inconsistencies, contradictions and confusion." [15]

The new line did jell before 1945 was over. Communists soon learned what ideas they could express and what ones they should banish.

RIGHT AND LEFT DEVIATIONISTS

Back in the 1930's, the Browder party's two ideological bogies were, on the right, Jay Lovestone, expelled from the party in 1929 for professing the heretical view that special American conditions and traditions required a unique Communist party, and, on the left, the Trotskyists. Now, after World War II, Browder himself became the bogy on the right of the line; an assorted collection of former Communist extremists, lumped under the label "left deviationists," became the bogy on the left.

When Browder was toppled from the leadership, he remained a party member in his party club or branch, the lowest party echelon, until his expulsion from the party. The decision to expel came from the top rather than from the rank and file. On January 27, a convention of the Manhattan party passed a resolution urging the national committee to expel him; the next day, the Bronx convention passed the same resolution. Only then did Browder's party club in Yonkers take any action against him, ousting him on February 12. Browder did not bother to appeal the decision. He did not even go to the club meeting to defend himself. On February 13, the national committee affirmed the Yonkers club's action, adding that the party "must root out all vestiges of revisionism and all rotten liberal attitudes toward Browder and the conciliators of Browderism." [16]

The new leadership kept a sharp suspicious eye on Browder, worried lest he split the movement or try to recover his former position. But Browder's first concern was to make a living from a mimeographed newsletter he called *Distributors Guide*. A group of businessmen whom Browder described as "periphery sympathizers" of the party promised him support, and his first issue appeared on January 5, 1946. The circulation was very small, and since it contained nothing but Browder's analyses of economic conditions and international events, neither of which was anything new to veteran readers of the Communist press, there was nothing in the venture to threaten the new leadership's security. The leadership was nevertheless alarmed. It threatened to expose the business supporters of *Distributors Guide* as Communist sympathizers if they did not withdraw their support—even Communists find occasional advantage in Red baiting—and the newsletter quickly collapsed.[17] Browder's next venture was a trip to Moscow, and the new leadership panicked.

He had decided to go to Moscow "just to see what was going on." [18] He denied then and has denied since that the purpose of his trip was to appeal his removal from party leadership.*

The State Department granted Browder a passport and the Soviet Government granted him a visa. He left New York by plane on April 26, 1946. The next day's *Daily Worker* carried

---

* The New York *Times* of September 15, 1946, quoted Browder as saying there was no "shadow Comintern" to which he could have appealed, and that Duclos in 1945 had never intended his article "as an intervention of international leadership." Browder's argument was that Duclos had "washed his hands of responsibility for the results, which is something no kind of international leadership could do." He also quoted Duclos, as reported in the London *Daily Mail,* as saying that American Communists were "an immature and uninfluential group." Foster cabled Duclos on September 16, saying that Browder had used Duclos' name to discredit the American party. Duclos replied that the London paper had distorted what he had said but did not reply to the main point of Browder's assertion (*Daily Worker,* September 21, 1946). This was a curious byplay; Browder, who obviously was removed from office by international intervention, denied the real intent was to remove him; and Foster, who could never admit that it was Communists from abroad who had elevated him to power, argued by implication that the orders had come from overseas.

the headline BROWDER LEAVES FOR STOCKHOLM TO EXTEND ANTI-PARTY INTRIGUE. Dennis said the trip was "calculated . . . to create confusion and uncertainty in the ranks of the Party." The party secretariat hastened to issue an official statement calling Browder "an unreconstructed revisionist . . . a social-imperialist . . . an enemy of the working class . . . a renegade . . . [and] an apologist for American imperialism." [19]

Browder arrived in Moscow on May 6, received a warm welcome from minor Russian officials, and moved into a three-room hotel suite provided by the Russians. Then nothing happened. He called upon several Soviet officials, all of whom were cordial but careful to avoid discussion of anything important. Years later, Browder reported the impression that there were "wheels within wheels," all of which were in motion, and said he did not understand what was happening in the Russian leadership. On May 20, a group of Browder's friends and acquaintances arranged a lavish dinner at a Moscow restaurant to celebrate his fifty-fifth birthday. The feast began in midafternoon. By about eight o'clock, Browder felt his part in the celebration had gone too far, and to escape further vodka toasts he slipped out and returned to his hotel. There in his suite was a very impatient messenger from the office of the foreign minister, Vyacheslav Molotov. Browder was to be ready for an interview with Molotov by ten o'clock that night. "Apparently the only person in Russia authorized to talk to a foreigner was Molotov." Browder drank a quart of black coffee and went for a long walk. When Molotov's limousine came for him, he was ready for what he thought would be "a historic crisis in my life."

In a conversation ten years later, Browder recalled that there were three people in Molotov's office during the interview—Molotov, Browder, and an interpreter. Molotov, who had returned that day from a foreign ministers' conference in Paris, asked Browder to state his mission. Browder first asked if the Communist International, or Comintern, dissolved technically in 1943, were to be re-established. Molotov said it would not be. (The next year, the

Soviets founded the Communist Information Bureau, or Cominform.) Browder then talked about what he thought could be done in the world if there were Russian-American co-operation; he maintained such co-operation was possible. He enumerated his many criticisms of Foster's leadership of the American party and described the kind of party and movement he thought there should be in the United States. According to Browder, Molotov listened intently but did not indicate by word or facial expression what he thought of Browder's position. After an hour, Molotov asked him to elucidate further on certain points, and Molotov's questions indicated that the foreign minister understood him perfectly. As midnight approached, Molotov said he was very tired and, without revealing his own views in any way, brought the interview to an end. Browder arose, and Molotov said casually that on his desk was a proposal that Browder be appointed the American representative of the Soviet book-publishing industry. Was Browder interested? Browder said he would accept the appointment, for it would prove to the world that he was a friend of the Soviet Union.

Browder's venture as representative of Soviet publishing proved as disastrous as the *Distributors Guide* venture. For several years, an American woman Communist had been in business as the Soviet representative for fiction and photographs, leaving only nonfiction for Browder to try to sell to American publishers. Browder invested and lost his savings. He sold only a few scientific works to American publishers. In 1949, he canceled the contract, sold the office furniture to pay the last month's rent, and went out of business. There was no market in the United States for Russian books, and, said Browder, "By that time I wasn't sure I was a friend of the Soviet Union anymore anyway." [20]

When the American press released the news of Browder's appointment, Foster announced the party would intensify the fight against Browderism. The party had already done a great deal to eliminate Browderism from its ranks. It had expelled Browder's brother and one of its wealthy angels, A. A. Heller, whose money had helped to establish International Publishers, which publishes

Communist books.[21] But now anti-Browderism became a frenzied ritual. Nearly every issue of *Political Affairs* denounced "Browder revisionism." [22] The editors of *Political Affairs* even managed to work a condemnation of Browder into an article about May Day celebrations.[23]

In July 1948, Browder humiliated himself by asking his enemies in the party to reinstate his membership. In a letter to Alexander Trachtenberg, of the cadre and review commission, the office charged with the party's "internal security," Browder said that Tito's recent defection from the Soviet orbit was a serious threat to Communism, and added, "In such a moment all other considerations must give way to the necessity of unity of the world movement and the protection of its achievements. . . . The enemy camp, making use of my expulsion from the Party, now tries to manipulate with my name to extend their disruptive efforts. This is a weapon to which they are not entitled; my only desire is to strengthen the camp of peace, democracy and socialism."

Robert Thompson assumed the task of handling the case. He got the floor at the national convention in August 1948, read the Browder letter, and to the delegates' applause called the communication "an attempt . . . thinly disguised by demagogic phrase-mongering about Tito" to further Browder's "anti-Party factional activities" and his "anti-Marxist bourgeois political line." The delegates unanimously rejected Browder's application for membership.[24]

No Communist dared say anything that could be construed as "rightist" Browderism. And this was important to Foster, for there were top Communist leaders who had once been close to Browder. Dennis, for example, had been Browder's right hand, a fact that Foster could never forget. Dennis lived that down only after years of party conformity. Foster elevated Dennis to the job of general secretary of the party in 1946 when the anti-Browder campaign was at its peak, gaining for himself the administrative assistance he needed because of his own age and poor health. Dennis was now beholden to him. Rooting out "revisionism" and "rotten liberal attitudes toward Browder" bolstered Foster's position in the party; it also seriously limited the party's flexibility. It had to be cautious about doing anything that could be interpreted as Browderite.

The Communist leaders inflated "leftist tendencies" into another bogy. Here and there within the party, small groups of "superleftists" now argued that Foster's leadership was as "revisionist" as Browder's. In the fall of 1946, the party initiated a wave of expulsions. Among the first "left deviationists" expelled were the writers Bruce Minton and his wife, Ruth McKenney, author of *My Sister Eileen*. In August 1945, the Mintons had written a letter to the editors of *New Masses* criticizing it for its "reformist editorial policy" and resigning as contributing editors. The following spring, after several exchanges of letters, *New Masses* had dropped the Mintons from its masthead. In September 1946, the state committee of Connecticut expelled them "for conducting a factional struggle against the line of the Party and its national leadership" and warned the membership to beware of those who "resort to ultra-revolutionary phrase-mongering and factionalism." [25] The Mintons then dropped out of the Communist movement altogether, but others who were expelled organized little splinter groups and published bitter criticisms of the party's leadership.

The primary Left-deviationist groups were these: the New Committee for Publications, which published *NCP Report* beginning in the fall of 1946, with Carolyn Burkhart as chairman and Lyle Dowling as editor; the PR Club CP (Expelled) of the Bronx, which published *Spark: A Marxist Monthly* beginning in April 1947, and which consisted largely of the family of a man named Earl Price; the Maritime Committee for a Communist Party, which operated on the New York waterfront with William F. Dunne, Sam Darcy, and Charles Keith as leaders; a small group in California under the leadership of Harrison George and Verne Smith; and a short-lived group in Queens, the Workers Freedom League, led by Bert Sutta, an expelled section organizer. None of these Left deviationists had ever been in the party's top leadership, but some of them had been in the party for years. In 1948, some of these groups succeeded in forming an alliance, and published *Turning Point,* which as late as 1956 was occasionally on sale at a few newsstands in mid-Manhattan.

The spectacle of the party lashing out at these Left deviationists with all the furious epithets at its command was both comic and tragic. It was comic because the groups were quite unimportant, a handful of fanatics armed with no more than revolutionary indignation and mimeograph machines. They polemicized against one another almost as vigorously as they did against the party leadership, each maintaining that it and only it had the true message. These little sects were no more than gnats to the party itself, but the party treated them as a major threat. Communist writers took pages and pages for diatribes against the "renegade cliques," the followers of "semi-Trotskyism and unprincipled Leftist adventurism," and "degenerate factionalists." The national board even hinted darkly that the Left groups were a plant of "reaction": "It would be odd if reaction did not seek to combine its attacks against our Party from without with attempts at organized disruption from within." [26]

The party went to great lengths to quell the Left deviationists. The strange story of Francis Franklin is revealing. Franklin was a Communist graduate student at the University of Virginia in the late 1930's. Browder met him at Charlottesville and thought he had promise, and Franklin soon came to New York City. He taught American history at the Jefferson School, the party's adult-education institution, but in 1947 was fired for "disruptive activities." Finally, his section expelled him after he had distributed an open letter to the party membership charging the leadership with Browderite tendencies. He began then still another leftist mimeographed periodical, *Towards Socialism,* with which he engaged in the esoteric polemics of the deviationist fringe. Then, quite without warning, his periodical announced in October 1949 that the whole venture was a mistake. The party was not what it should be, but the way "to Bolshevize" the party was to work within it rather than to criticize it from the outside. Another fringe periodical told its version of the story under the headline FRANCIS FRANKLIN TURNS RAT. "F. F. . . . is now ready for a deal. He has lists, he has correspondence with expelled and CP members. . . . He has put in his bid to become the National Committee's 'finger man.' " [27]

But the spectacle was also tragic in that the party cast out some old men who had sacrificed much for the Communist movement only to find themselves ostracized in their old age. Among these old men was Verne Smith, who had come into the party from the I.W.W. in the 1920's and had served for years on the *Daily Worker* and the *Daily People's World,* the party paper published in San Francisco. Another was Bill Dunne, who had been coeditor of the *Daily Worker* when it began publication in 1924. Another was Harrison George, who had joined the Socialists in 1910 and the I.W.W. in 1914 and become a charter member of the Communist Party in September 1919, joining from his cell in Leavenworth Penitentiary.[28] An interesting case was that of Max Bedacht, who began his Marxist associations in Europe in 1902 and continued them in the party of Debs after he came to the United States in 1908. In 1919, he was on the executive committee of the Communist Labor Party, one of the left groups that split from the Socialists. For years, Bedacht was president of the International Workers Order, one of the party's most important fronts. When Browder was removed, he aspired to a higher position in the leadership, but Foster kept Bedacht in the I.W.O. Bedacht was spoiling for a fight. He found it in 1946. He charged that the party's plan to establish an old people's home for each of the several nationality groups in the I.W.O. was "bourgeois nationalism." For two years, he harped on this theme, and in October 1948, the party expelled him. He moved to New Jersey and became a poultry farmer.[29] These old men were classic "true believers," dedicated revolutionaries. Now when their lives were almost over they found themselves rejected and despised by the party they had helped to build. The movement devoured its own.

The Communist leadership and the party line were secure from internal dissent. The party could quote Lenin against both the Left and the Right: from *"Left-Wing" Communism: An Infantile Disorder* against the left bogy and from *What Is To Be Done?* and several other works against the Browderite witches. The party used Lenin, who was nothing if not flexible, to help make the Communist line rigid. By 1948, the American Communists had set themselves such tight ideological boundaries that they had little room in which to turn around. When the crisis came in Moscow after the death of Stalin, the American Communists could break out of their ideological box only by tearing their party to pieces.

FOREIGN-POLICY LINE

The most important part of the entire Communist line was its position on foreign policy. Minor aspects of the line on domestic matters could change a little, but the line on foreign policy, with its defense of the Soviet Union and its attack on American policies, was a firm anchor. The positions of non-Communist labor and Negro leaders on foreign policy became the touchstone to determine whether the Communists would support or criticize them.

The rationale of the Communist line was that American capitalism and capitalists were inherently reactionary and imperialist. Their reasoning was straight from Lenin's "classic," *Imperialism,* which argued that imperialism was the last inevitable stage of capitalism. As domestic capitalist economies become incapable of absorbing their product, argued Lenin, capitalists seek markets and investment opportunities overseas. Overseas adventures bring the various national economies into conflict and result in war. Foster acknowledged the argument's source: ". . . the United States is an imperialistic country . . . the most aggressive empire in the world. This country displays all the features characteristic of imperialist capitalism as analyzed by the great Lenin." [30]

To the Communists, of course, it followed that such imperialism must be fought tooth and nail. To do otherwise, to their way of thinking, would be to compromise with evil.

Dozens of Communist editorials, articles, and speeches alleged that it was American policy to 1) protect and extend capital investments—"Anglo-American international cartel investments"; 2) reduce the Soviet Union to weakness and to isolate it from the rest of the world—"the policy of hostile encirclement"; 3) make the defeated Axis powers American satellites; 4) "resurrect a decadent feudal-reaction" everywhere and keep democracy to a minimum—"Washington likes what Franco is doing in Spain and wants all of Europe to follow the Franco model"; 5) establish American hegemony over the colonial areas breaking away from the British, Dutch, French, and Belgian empires; 6) strengthen its grip on Latin America; 7) operate the United Nations as its instrument for extending its strength and reducing the power of "the peaceloving peoples"; and 8) force Great Britain into a junior partnership with American imperialism.[31]

Another fundamental assumption of the Communist foreign-policy line was that the Soviet Union was not imperialist, that it was, on the contrary, anti-imperialist and the major defender of peace and democratic values on the world scene. The Communists inverted Lenin's dictum on imperialism, that imperialism is the last stage of capitalism, to argue that the Soviet Union, not being capitalist, could not possibly be imperialist. Foster put it this way: ". . . the charges of 'red imperialism' against the U.S.S.R. are ridiculous on their face. Imperialism . . . is the final stage of capitalism. . . . The U.S.S.R., on the other hand, is fundamentally non-imperialist. The Soviet Union has no capitalism and hence no capitalist monopolies to drive it into policies of oppression and exploitation of other peoples. In consequence, Soviet policy, dictated by the structure of the socialist regime itself, is inevitably one of peace and friendly collaboration with other nations."[32]

When critics of the Soviet Union pointed out that, despite what

Lenin said about imperialism, the U.S.S.R. had in fact expanded a great deal beyond its 1939 borders, the Communists had a complicated reply. The Soviet Union had expanded, they granted, but they ignored its influence in the Eastern European "democratic people's republics." But when one considers the territories that "were forcibly torn away from it after the war of 1904-05 and after World War I," Russia was actually "80,000 square miles smaller than the country was forty years ago." [33] The Communists conveniently failed to mention the fact that Czarist Russia was an imperialist power. Besides, Communists insisted, the Soviet Union had only "liberated" oppressed peoples near its borders.

Given the assumptions that the United States was guided by imperialist motives and that the Soviet Union was "inevitably" peaceful and friendly, it was simple for the Communists to determine "correct" positions as world events developed. They merely criticized whatever the United States proposed and supported whatever the Soviet Union proposed.

The American Communists have always maintained, however, that their policies are dictated by American interests rather than Soviet interests. Eugene Dennis's open letter to the attorney general of the United States in 1947 revealed Communist thinking on this subject: "I grant you that on more than one occasion the position of the American Communist Party on foreign affairs has in one or another aspect coincided with the foreign policy advocated by the USSR. So what? It was in each instance in accord with the interests of the United States and all democratic peoples." [34] The whole question of whether American Communists were motivated in their foreign policy by American interests as they understood them or by Soviet interests is unrealistic, because to them it is inconceivable that the true interests of the United States "and all democratic peoples" would not be the same as the Soviets'.

Still, the vigor with which Communists put their argument that "Socialism in the Soviet Union is the highest form of democracy" suggested that they protested too much.[35] One can sense a certain embarrassment in the *Daily Worker* editorial writer who wrote about Stalin's unanimous popular election to the Supreme Soviet in 1946: ". . . we can hear the snickers from the professional enemies of socialism. These pygmies cannot possibly imagine that every voter in Stalin's district thinks he should be elected. But why not? He is universally admired and liked.[36]

Stalin's seventieth birthday in December 1949 taxed the resources of Communist writers. The American Communists published nine articles of praise of the Russian dictator in the magazine section of their Sunday *Worker,* the editors of *Political Affairs* devoted an entire issue to extolling various aspects of his genius, and the party's national committee sent him special birthday greetings. It was no easy matter to write something that stood out from the others. Foster confessed his failure. "Stalin's revolutionary achievements are so many that it would be impossible even to list them in a brief article like this." But Alexander Bittelman tried. "Stalin's greatness and genius stand out so clearly and beautifully that progressive humanity has no difficulty in recognizing them. . . . To live with Stalin in one age, to fight with him in one cause, to work under the inspiring guidance of his teachings is something to be deeply proud of and thankful for, to cherish." [37]

Communist writings bristled with devil theory. Why had the wartime alliance of the United States, Great Britain, and the Soviet Union collapsed? "The reactionary trusts and their political spokesmen . . . are striving to substitute a so-called United Nations combination, in reality a reactionary combination of large and small capitalist states, under American hegemony, in place of the solidarity and cooperation of the Big Three unity." [38] And why did not the "big American and British imperialists . . . want to live and work harmoniously with the USSR?" Because "they see the Soviet Union as the bulwark of world democracy, the friend of all oppressed peoples," which would block their efforts to dominate the world. When the U.N. Security Council considered the matter of Soviet troop movements near Iran in 1946, Foster said the whole affair was just "another manufactured world crisis," part of an effort to ring the Soviet Union with imperialist military bases.

"They want to reduce that country to their sway, to put it in its place, so to speak, as they are now proceeding to do with the lesser capitalist countries of the world." [39]

The Communists identified Winston Churchill's famous "Iron Curtain" speech at Fulton, Missouri, as a part of the conspiracy; it was a "chapter in a whole series of American imperialist provocations against the American people themselves and against the Soviet Union." [40] As for the Iron Curtain itself, the Russian policy of denying Western journalists free access in Eastern Europe sprang from a desire to maintain harmony between the Soviet Union and the Western powers. Imperialist Western reporters would only poison the well of Big Three unity. In the past, said Foster, the Soviets had extended to Western journalists "every facility to observe what is going on in the new land of Socialism only to have these correspondents once they have put foot outside of the USSR launch the most outrageous broadsides of attacks and slanders against the country whose guests they were." [41]

American concern with Russian espionage was altogether artificial, claimed the Communists. When the House Committee on Un-American Activities was trying to get Gerhart Eisler to testify early in 1947, Eugene Dennis claimed the committee was "Cooking up for the United States something akin to the 'Reichstag fire' conspiracy." "A crude plot to whip up hysteria against any reasonable calm discussion of atomic disarmament," said the editors of the *Daily Worker* as they coined a new slogan, "A spy scare a day keeps disarmament away." [42] When the Canadians revealed the existence in their country of a Russian wartime espionage ring, the *Daily Worker*'s foreign editor declared, "Some miserable stooge— no doubt planted in the Soviet Embassy . . . another brush in the current attempt to make all the English-speaking people believe that we cannot cooperate with the Russians." [43]

The year 1947 saw two new developments in American foreign policy, the Truman Doctrine and the Marshall Plan. Since late in the war, the anti-Communist government of Greece had been harassed by Communist guerrillas, and the British had given the

Greek Government financial and military support, probably preventing Greece from moving into the Soviet orbit. In February
1947, the British notified Washington that its internal economic
problems and its troubles in the shaky empire made it imperative
that they pull out of Greece. Fearing that without continued support for the Greek Government, the Communists would soon control Greece and possibly also Turkey, President Harry Truman
went to Congress to ask for an appropriation of $400,000,000 to
be used for economic and military support to the Greek and Turk-
ish governments. In the course of his speech, Truman said it should
be American policy "to support free peoples who are resisting attempted subjugation by armed minorities or by outside pressure."
This became known as the Truman Doctrine.

A few months later, Secretary of State George C. Marshall described at the Harvard University commencement a program that
came to be known as the Marshall Plan. He suggested that the
United States offer economic aid to any European government, including the Soviet Union and those under its influence, in order
that the European economy might revive and "permit the emergence of political and social conditions in which free institutions
can exist." Europeans, rather than Americans, were to work out
the details, and they should understand that Marshall Plan aid
would be the last from the United States in the foreseeable future.
The response from Western Europe was enthusiastic; the economies of those nations were in truly desperate condition. The Russians themselves raised only minor objections until the European
foreign ministers' meeting in July. In April of the following year,
the Marshall Plan became law.

Many Americans were worried about the Truman Doctrine and
the Marshall Plan, new departures in American policy. A great
many continued to believe, as had their fathers and grandfathers,
that involvement with foreign countries should be no more than
temporary, the sooner ended the better. Defenders of democracy
were concerned about the Truman Doctrine's support of the conservative Greek regime although they wanted Greece to remain

outside the Soviet sphere. Defenders of old-fashioned capitalism were disturbed by the prospect of some of their tax money going for Marshall Plan aid to the Labour government of Great Britain.

The Communists aimed considerably more fire against the Marshall Plan than the Truman Doctrine, although the Truman Doctrine was the more vulnerable to Communist criticism in a variety of ways. It was more openly anti-Soviet than the Marshall Plan, it bolstered an undemocratic regime in Greece, and since it did not involve the co-operation of the European powers as much as the Marshall Plan, it was easier to charge it with domination of foreign countries. But the Truman Doctrine became law quickly, before the Communists could organize a major campaign against it. Truman made the proposal on March 12 and signed the bill on May 22. The Marshall Plan, on the other hand, took ten months from announcement to enactment, giving time for Communists the world over to follow the Russian lead in denouncing it.

Yet the Truman Doctrine came in for its share of Communist attack. It was a doctrine of "unabashed imperialism [that] flows from the 'get tough' program of the biggest monopoly capitalists." Further, it was "an attempt to make a big new advance for American imperialism," an advance that would provide a base for the "possibility of eventual attack" on the Soviet Union.[44]

The American Communist attack on the Marshall Plan was massive. Communist periodicals made the plan the major object of attack for months, and so vigorous was the party's opposition that it made the Marshall Plan a major issue of conflict between the Communist unions and the national C.I.O. leadership and thereby hastened the day of Communist isolation from the labor movement.

Perhaps one reason for the unusual vehemence of Communists everywhere against the Marshall Plan, aside from the fact that the plan obviously would work to the long-term disadvantage of the Communist parties of Western Europe, was that with the plan the State Department had outsmarted the Soviets. Marshall's Harvard address left the door wide open to Soviet-bloc participation in the plan, and he underscored the point in a press conference a few days later. The strategy was that Moscow would refuse to participate but that it would be put in an embarrassing position by so doing. The strategy worked perfectly. Had the strategy backfired, had Moscow permitted Warsaw, Bucharest, Budapest, and the other Communist capitals to undertake Marshall Plan agreements, the State Department would have been in a precarious position. Many observers doubted that Congress would have voted the necessary funds. And it may be that the Soviet Union considered calling the State Department's bluff. At the beginning of the meetings of the European foreign ministers at Paris in July, Soviet Minister Molotov's objections to the plan were only minor, but a telegram from home reversed his mood to his usual truculence.

The Communist position on the Marshall Plan was that it was just another imperialist maneuver, "a cold-blooded scheme of American monopolists to establish their ruthless domination over harassed world humanity," as Foster put it,[45] but imperialism with a difference: the plan was a deliberate attempt to rebuild the German war potential and pave the way for a resurgence of Nazism. One of its purposes was "support of the German Nazi industrialists," and such an alliance would only lead to the rise of anti-Semitism in the United States and "an emerging native fascism." [46]

If the Marshall Plan was indeed a Wall Street gambit to extend control over the economies of Western Europe, as the Communists claimed, then the Communists were up against the obvious question of why the capitalists of Europe, in defiance of Lenin's theories, should want Marshall Plan aid. The Communists answered that the Western European capitalists, though still devilishly clever, were in retreat. "The 200 families of France and the monopolists of Britain today deliberately chose 'junior partnerships' with the American trusts in the hope that they will succeed in preserving capitalism and in assuring for themselves a sizeable share of the profits." [47]

Curiously, the Communists failed to criticize the Marshall Plan as being partially motivated, as it was, by the beneficial effect it would have on the American economy. Both American management and American labor foresaw the salutary effect that Marshall Plan orders, a kind of federal subsidy, would have on the economy, and they rushed to Washington to partake of the largesse. The shipping industry, for example, both labor and management, got a provision into the act requiring that at least half of all Marshall Plan goods had to be sent in American ships. Communists argued instead that the Marshall Plan would bring depression. "The Marshall Plan takes every possible step, in the name of recovery, to see to it that the European standard of living is drastically reduced. . . . Every major provision of E.R.P. blocks recovery." The resulting European depression would hasten an American depression, always "just around the corner," the Communists asserted. Using an argument reminiscent of Republican campaign literature in the 1920's, the party asked, "What will Phil Murray tell his steel workers when the steel corporations attempt to use the low-paid German workers as strikebreakers by transferring orders to their Ruhr plants?" [48] The Communists never made clear whether the Marshall Plan would hurt American workers with imported depression or imported manufactures, but, in any case, their opposition to the plan was clear.

In response to each development of foreign relations after the Marshall Plan, the Communists continued to reflect Russia's line of criticism. Early in 1949, the United States, Canada, and ten nations of Western Europe signed an agreement creating the North Atlantic Treaty Organization. The twelve nations agreed to coordinate their military organizations and to take common action in the event of an Eastern attack. To the Communists, who called the treaty the "North Atlantic War Pact," N.A.T.O. was another "advance in the domination of American ruling class circles. . . . Wall Street now has a new instrument to advance its insane program for world domination." Capitalism's governmental puppets had heightened the "danger of an atomic war instigated by Wall Street. . . ." [49] President Truman's Point Four program, announced in his inaugural address in January 1949, was a "scheme

. . . to spread the Marshall Plan over the colonial and semi-colonial world. The general economic aim of these proposals is to help bolster up the shaky American economic system . . . to secure financial domination over the colonial and semi-colonial areas, and to build up more military allies for the planned war against the U.S.S.R." [50]

The Communists were as critical of American foreign policy for Asia as they were of the policies for other parts of the world. The purposes of America's China policy, the Communists charged, were the same as its European policy: to encircle and isolate the Soviet Union, to support reactionary regimes, and to reduce the area to the status of "an American tool and appendage." Furthermore, it was American policy to be "soft" on the conquered Japanese just as it was "soft" on the Nazis, which not only revealed the true political sentiments of American imperialists, but afforded them allies against the Russians.[51] When one reads the Communist attacks on the China policy of President Truman and Secretaries of State Marshall and Dean Acheson before the Chinese Communist victory and the "Asia First" attacks on these officials after that victory, one wonders if the two groups were writing about the same people.

For all the Communists' articles hailing Chinese Communist military victories, their attacks on American Far Eastern policy, their abuse of the Chinese Nationalists, and their filiopietistic pieces about Mao Tse-tung, their inspiration and interest lay in Eastern Europe rather than in Asia. To all but a relatively few Americans, Chinese history and the Chinese civil war were a confusing jumble; not fully understanding, most Americans knew only they did not approve of the Chinese Communists. No more sophisticated on these matters than the rest of the population, the American Communists knew only that they and Mao Tse-tung were on the same side.

In the most serious and lasting split in the Communist world to date—the break between Yugoslavia and Russia in June 1948—the American Communists supported the Russians without hesitation. Although the American party was not a member of the Cominform—when the Cominform was established in the fall of 1947 the American party stayed out "because of the present political situation in the United States" [52]—it jumped on Tito as heavily as did any of the Cominform members. Until Tito's excommunication, the American Communists had praised him, and the party had officially backed Yugoslavia in the Trieste dispute with Italy; when Foster returned from a trip through Europe in early 1947, he made a glowing report on Tito and Yugoslavian socialism.[53] After the break, however, Foster and Dennis were quick to belabor Tito for having "deviated from Marxism-Leninism," and they managed to publish their statement in the first issue of the Cominform newspaper to appear after the schism.[54]

In 1945, the American Communists had perceived that the Russian view of the postwar world had changed drastically. Consequently, they abolished their soft wartime line, overthrew their leadership, and developed a new and harder line more in keeping with their understanding of Russian desires. The internal consistency of their new line did not always shine brightly, but they were consistent in their support of the Soviet Union. In guiding and adjusting themselves as world events developed, the American Communists never took their eyes away from the red star in the East.

TWO: THE PARTY LINE FOR AMERICA

In July 1946, at a routine meeting, the Communist top leadership echelon—the national committee—heard Max Weiss deliver an abstract theoretical report called "The Struggle on the Ideological Front." Weiss had been a leader of the Young Communist League before the war; now he was moving up to the heavyweight class as a party theoretician. There was little that was original in his report, but Weiss ably put into a few pages the fundamental theoretical position of the new line. Through his report, as through the line in general, ran two main threads: the devil-conspiracy theory as an interpretation of the drift of events; and a swing to the left.

The "devils" behind American domestic policy were the same ones who made American foreign policy: Wall Street and its agents, commonly called "lackeys," "puppets," or "tools." As the monopolists were imperialist abroad, they were reactionary, even inclining toward "fascism," at home. And they were as cunning at home as they were abroad. According to Weiss, they were currently engaged in a propaganda campaign to inculcate "a pragmatic contempt for theory among the masses," and they had been quite successful in their sly campaign to popularize the term "management" and take the more personal word "boss" from circulation. "It is time we threw off the 'management' veil and helped the

34

workers uncover the face of the enemy—the trusts, the 60 families!" [1]

The devil-conspiracy theory explained facts that conflicted with basic Communist theory. The Communists had always begun with the assumption—only occasionally explicit—that political virtue resided in the proletariat. But the proletariat did not always behave virtuously by Communist standards. There was, for example, its "pragmatic contempt for theory," or at least for Communist theory. How could this ideological deficiency of the inherently virtuous be explained? The explanation was to blame the bourgeoisie for corrupting the proletariat. Communists used the same method to explain racist attitudes among workers: the bourgeoisie had "infected" the workers with the "virus of white chauvinism."

The Communists clearly had shifted left. That is to say, they were less inclined than they had been to compromise or water down their Communist principles in order to achieve immediate goals short of the ultimate aim of a Soviet America. Yet they were acutely aware that to shift too far left or to appear to be too far left would endanger their position with the groups whose support they needed—the labor movement, non-Communist political liberals, and the Negro movement for equality. Yet they did isolate themselves—as they admitted after the damage was done. There seem to be three main factors in the party's becoming isolated. First, and most importantly, the Communists put their main effort into propaganda and agitation to persuade other Americans to their pro-Soviet views about United States foreign policy. To the Communists, foreign policy had nothing to do with their being in a leftist or rightist, "hard" or "soft" stage; the party always followed their Russian comrades in foreign policy. From 1941 to mid-1945, the United States and Russia were military allies. During these years, the consistent American Communist support of Russia's foreign policy did not harm the party's relationships with non-Communists because the primary aim of Russia's policies was also the main objective of American policies. Indeed, the American party's identification with the Soviet Union actually lent it prestige during the war years, when the might of the Red Army and the tough resistance of the Russian people against the Nazis earned the respect of most Americans. But after the war, American and Russian foreign policies were in conflict, to put it mildly, and the American Communists' support for Soviet foreign policy became a serious disadvantage in their efforts to influence non-Communists on any matter. Second, after the war, the Communists became increasingly negligent, even reckless, about maintaining their bridges to the non-Communist publics whose support, or at least whose neutrality, they vitally needed. Third, the drift of the general non-Communist population after the war was undeniably to the right, toward acceptance of the *status quo,* abandonment of the demand for social reform that characterized the 1930's, perhaps even return to the dominant social values of the years before the Great Depression. While non-Communists drifted right, the Communists shifted left.

One essential Communist tactic to minimize the danger of self-isolation while making a turn to the left was their attempt to build a "broad coalition of all democratic and antifascist peoples" against "the postwar program of Wall Street [which] is directed against the people of our country, no less than against the democratic forces the world over." [2] The tactic required that the Communists not appear to be too far left for popular acceptance; the party understood the problem, the necessity of waging "its fight in such a manner as to achieve the maximum unity—unity within the C.I.O., unity of C.I.O. with A.F. of L., the Railroad Brotherhoods, the miners, unity of labor with the farmers, the Negro people, the veterans." [3] But the party had other devices as well in its effort to make itself attractive to non-Communist "democratic and antifascist peoples."

One device was to intensify the courtship of some middle-class elements that the party had begun in the 1930's. Immediately after the war, the Communists made quite a play for support from middle-class professionals and intellectuals in their belief that "the Battle for the Middle Class is a central issue." The Left Wing president of the United Office and Professional Workers of America, Lewis Merrill, declared there was "no future for creative workers, whether they are in the sciences and professions or elsewhere, in a country completely dominated by the policies of monopoly industry and monopoly finance." The pitch for professionals reached a peak with the republication of an article by the British Communist and scientist J. B. S. Haldane. Haldane described the Soviet Union as a professional's paradise and promised professional people that if they were good at their jobs in a Communist society "you would have more power and more responsibility than you have now." [4]

Another device was to concentrate on issues that they actually scorned as bourgeois reforms. During the summer of 1946, the *Daily Worker* incessantly editorialized in favor of price controls because the cause was popular among non-Communists whose alliance Communists wanted. Party members participated in neighborhood tenants' councils, and they worked hard for rent controls and public housing. In a self-critical mood, the party confessed it had not done enough to "mobilize the American people in the fight for progressive taxation." [5]

Still another method was to exploit some of the style and flavor of the Browderite–Popular Front period of the party but in a different context, to use some of Browder's more successful techniques for different ends. In Browder's era there had been the slogan "Communism is twentieth-century Americanism." The slogan disappeared, but the sentiment did not. The Whitmanesque "We too sing America" theme became even stronger for a few years after the war. There was even an attempt to install pragmatic old Benjamin Franklin, the symbol of the self-made man and the author of Poor Richard's capitalistic homilies, into the pantheon of Communist heroes.[6] Ever prone to glorify the common people in its art—Communist artists had a special weakness for big-muscled, square-jawed men and big-hipped, peasant women as subjects—the movement now went all out for folk music. Back in 1929, during the textile strike at Gastonia, North

Carolina, the Communists had discovered folk music in the person of a little hillbilly striker named Ella May Wiggins, the mother of five children who was killed by a policeman. Browder was a man with small-town Kansas musical tastes and a former flute player in the town band who still gets the instrument out occasionally. He had always encouraged folk music, and after Gastonia the song took root in the movement.[7] But in the postwar era, folk music flourished in the party as it never had before. Guitars were everywhere, and the party member who did not appreciate Pete Seeger, a singing "peoples' artist," was an independent soul indeed.[8]

But for all their Popular Front tone, the Communists had no intention of watering down their Marxism–Leninism in the coalition they hoped to build, of compromising their goal of winning the American masses to "a Socialist outlook." On the contrary, their support of such reformist measures as progressive taxation, public housing, and price and rent control—New Dealish measures, in general—was a trap for non-Communist liberals and a device by which they hoped to further acceptance of Marxism–Leninism. Foster put it this way, using the example of labor: "Organized labor can and should support many of the economic reforms and make-work projects of the New Dealers or Keynesians. . . . Lenin long ago taught the workers to support reforms as by-products of the general class struggle. But, as Lenin also taught, the unions cannot, save at their own peril, accept the general conclusions of these reformers that their proposals will put the capitalist system upon a healthy and progressive basis." Dennis, in a 1946 report to the party's national committee, was a little more candid, saying that "we have correctly warned against and opposed raising the issue of Socialism in the U.S.A. as an immediate slogan of action. But . . . *what is on the order of the day* is the issue of educating and winning millions of American workers and anti-fascists *to a Socialist outlook* . . . the mass education of the American working masses toward the attainment of Socialist consciousness." Perhaps Gilbert

Green, one of the younger members of the national committee, expressed the idea most clearly and succinctly during the up-heaval after the Duclos letter. "Even when we support certain reform measures advanced or supported by liberal-bourgeois forces, we are duty bound to make perfectly clear to the work-ers and the people that these measures are inadequate . . . while propagating socialism as the ultimate answer." [9]

The Communists recognized that winning the American masses to "a Socialist outlook" would not be an easy task, but they thought a severe economic depression was imminent, and depres-sion would facilitate their task and help them to victory. With depression would come a sharpening of the class struggle, and the workers would soon understand that the "superficial reforms of the New Dealers or Keynesians cannot solve basic problems which grow out of the decay of the capitalist system." The work-ers would then accept the leadership of the Communist party, "the vanguard party . . . integrally linked with the masses, not separated from them, helping them to move forward [to social-ism] and leading them in their forward movement." [10]

The balance of this chapter discusses Communist attitudes and actions on five aspects of American society on which the party took a strong position in the years after the war: the health of the American economy, organized labor, religion, literature, and the Negro. Examination of the Communist position on these five subjects reveals the party's reliance upon the Soviet Union for guidance even on matters peculiarly American, shows the quality of thinking that characterized the party leadership, and indicates much about the party's internal power structure, its methods, and its style.

ANOTHER GREAT DEPRESSION?

During the war, Communists had been optimistic about the post-war economy even when most other people were apprehensive.

During the last days of the European war, Dennis had written optimistically of "the possibility of achieving an expanding post-war domestic economy and a growing world market . . . as well as a constantly rising standard of living. . . ." [11] But then Duclos tipped the party over into a somersault, and the same American economy suddenly was filled with indications of impending doom. The facts were the same but the shape of the lens through which Communists saw them had changed.

Classic Marxism maintains that cyclical convulsions are inevitable in a capitalist economy, and, in their reaction against Browderism, the Communists clutched at this tenet with tenacity. Communists were by no means alone in predicting an economic crisis. Theoretical economists, businessmen, and labor leaders of all shades of political opinion were anxious about a downswing in the business cycle with the end of the war, and they had some justification for their fears. After all, the American economy had emerged from depression only with the advent of war.

The Communists were far more reckless in their predictions of depression than the academic economists. As the postwar boom took shape, they vacillated between denying that prosperity really existed and insisting that the depression was just around the corner. Every tremor in the stock market they heralded as the advent of a crash. When the stock market quivered in early September 1946, the editors of the *Daily Worker* plastered their front page with big type: "Wall Street Hit by 1929 Jitters. Another drop in stock prices . . . which heralds the volcanic eruption to come . . . sharpest drop since 1940. But it is only the beginning. Even before the promised postwar paradise has had a chance to materialize, the inner rottenness of the present social system shows itself. The ghost of the coming crisis stalks the Stock Exchange." [12]

Communists argued that Keynesian measures might delay the depression but could not avert it, though they might minimize the effect of the depression when it came. [13] They ignored programs like the Full Employment Act of 1946, the G.I. Bill of Rights, and the "52-20 clubs," and insisted that business had rejected Keynesian measures because it actually wanted a depression. Foster said businessmen believed "an eventual economic crisis, after an orgy of profitmaking, would advance their overall reactionary plans. . . . They are convinced that with ten or fifteen millions of workers unemployed and half-starved they, patterning after Hitler, would be able to mobilize these hungry multitudes for struggles against democracy in this country and for imperialist aggression abroad." Of course, the capitalists were wrong in thinking that the hungry would turn to fascism. "In a great economic crisis, with the workers in their present militant mood all over the world, things would certainly turn out very differently than the reactionary capitalists now calculate. . . ." [14]

The postwar years moved on, and no depression came; but the Communists continued to predict economic ruin. "It may not take more than two or three years, if that long, before the bottom drops out of the domestic market," said a 1946 party pamphlet. Three years later, the depression was still on its way. The number of predicted unemployed varied from Foster's "ten to fifteen million" to "perhaps thirty million" and "tens of millins." [15] Not until the crisis in the party after the downgrading of Stalin in 1956 was there any hint in Communist literature that their economic "perspective" was faulty, and the article that appeared then was labeled "A Discussion Article" to indicate that the ideas expressed, while they might be considered seriously, were not official. [16]

Why the Communists persisted in their predictions of an imminent major depression is a complex question. No small part of the explanation is the fact that Russian economists insisted that the American economy simply could not behave the way it actually was.

Late in 1946, Eugene S. Varga, an outstanding Soviet economist, published a book entitled *Changes in the Economy of Capitalism as a Result of the Second World War.* [17] Varga was an eminent figure in Russian academic circles. Born in Hungary in 1879, he had become a professor of political economy in Budapest during World War I. In Hungary's Communist regime after the armistice, he was People's Commissar of Finance. When the Hungarian Communists fell from power, he went to Moscow, and in 1929 he became chairman of the Institute of World Economics and World Politics. Varga also enjoyed a considerable reputation abroad. Early in 1944, an American business newspaper published a translation and condensation of one of his articles on postwar currency stabilization.[18] American Communists knew his writings well. He had written regularly for *Inprecorr,* the Comintern journal, during the 1920's and 1930's. In early 1946, *New Masses* published a translation of one of his articles that had appeared in a Russian magazine.[19]

Varga's book was a dry piece of economic analysis—he said in his preface that the book "is not easy reading"; but it attracted world-wide attention. The main question discussed was how the capitalist economies would develop in the postwar era; the book was based on extensive data, much of it from published official material.[20]

Varga discussed the impact of the war upon the American economy and predicted the economic future of the United States. The war had impoverished the capitalist economies of Europe, but those of the United States and, to a lesser extent, Canada had been "really enriched." They had become technologically more efficient during the war. Labor conditions in America had been better in the war years than they had been in Europe, civilian consumption had been markedly better, and industrial production had approximately doubled while production in Europe, particularly in Germany, had declined. Because of these conditions, the United States would not suffer a crisis of underproduction after the war such as Europe would; on the contrary, there would be an economic upsurge for two or three years after the war. But all was not to be rosy for the United States, by any means. The postwar boom would be followed by a crisis somewhat longer than the depression of 1920-21, to be succeeded by an economic cycle less like the cycle of 1921-29 than that of the "special type of depression" which America had after 1929. In general, the postwar period would see a "deepening of the general crisis of capitalism," against which capitalist recovery methods would prove ineffective.

In January 1945, Varga's work had been discussed by prominent Soviet scholars at his institute. The assembled scholars had several carping criticisms to make, but Varga proceeded with his book. In May 1947, twenty leading Soviet scholars gathered again to criticize the finished product. Their meeting was quite an impressive show, and they were merciless in their criticism. In their eyes, Varga had not been sufficiently anticapitalist or anti-American. One of the critics revealed much when he charged that Varga should have given a "clearer" and "more optimistic" answer as to when exactly the "longed for . . . collapse of capitalism" would occur. The scholars were mild compared to the attacks that were to come in the Soviet press. The tenor of the attacks was revealed in *Bolshevik,* February 15, 1948: Soviet economists must be "free of bourgeois objectivism." The American press had noted Varga's writing before all the stir and had characterized it as vigorously anti-American, but it was not anti-American enough for Stalin's postwar society. Varga was "non-Marxist" and "reformist." [21]

Remarkably, Varga did not immediately capitulate before his critics. He defended his main points at the May 1947 meeting, conceding only that he may have made minor errors that did not affect his general conclusions. He stuck to this position for two years before the attacks and the humiliation became too much for him. He was removed as head of his institute. In the Soviet journal *Problems of Economics* in 1949, he recanted completely. [22]

The American Communists reprinted in *Political Affairs* a translation of one of the attacks upon Varga predicting that a severe American depression was imminent. They also printed a translation of one of Varga's *mea culpa* articles, a piece embarrassing even to read, so abjectly did the author strip himself of

all dignity. He was as critical of himself for defending his book
for two years as he was of the book itself.[23]

The year Varga recanted, American party intellectuals held a
"Conference on 'Managed Economy,' the 'Cold War,' and the
Developing Economic Crisis" at the party's Jefferson School.
They demonstrated they were not Vargas. Party Chairman Foster
could not attend the conference, but he sent the group a communication that was quite explicit about what the conference's
conclusions should be. For two days, the intellectuals pondered
—and came to the recommended conclusions: the new Great
American Depression was still just around the corner.[24]

THE LINE FOR LABOR

Since the Communists saw a major depression about to strike
America, bringing with it social conditions advantageous for their
party, it was imperative to strengthen their position in preparation. And of all elements of the American public, none was so
important to the Communists as organized labor, for without
considerable direct strength and influence in the labor movement,
a Communist party is nothing in an industrial nation. The core
of Communist theory is the proletariat, and throughout the Western world the trade union is the institution that most directly
and clearly represents industrial workers. Wherever in the Western world there are vigorous Communist parties, the parties have
major strength in the trade unions. Western Communist parties
that have failed conspicuously have done so primarily because
they failed to develop a strong and lasting base in the trade-
union movement.

Communists got a foothold in the C.I.O. soon after its foundation in the mid-1930's. C.I.O. President John L. Lewis needed
experienced organizers, particularly for the industries with little
tradition of unionism. Unorganized workers were ripe for recruitment. The Communist Party and other left political groups were

more than willing to offer organizers, and Lewis and other C.I.O. leaders were willing to use the Communists' experience. The C.I.O. leaders did not anticipate that the Communists would use their position to further their own ends. Lewis thought he could use the Communists and not be used by them. He asked David Dubinsky, of the International Ladies Garment Workers Union, when Dubinsky protested the use of Communists, "Who gets the bird—the hunter or the dog?"

In industries where strong unions existed before the birth of the C.I.O., like coal mining, the Communists made little progress. Neither did they gain much in the industries in which Lewis or Sidney Hillman or other established union officers led the organization of workers, such as steel and textiles. But in others, where there was a legacy of union radicalism, like nonferrous mining and smelting or in those like electrical appliances, municipal transport, maritime, and, to a lesser degree, auto, where there was almost no unionism at all and where established C.I.O. leaders did not themselves organize, the Communists were able to establish almost immediate control. Ironically, the vacuum which the Communists filled existed at least partly because the A.F. of L., which was noisily anti-Communist, failed to organize the unskilled workers of basic industry.[25]

A survey of Communist strength in the C.I.O. will come in the next chapter. Suffice it for the moment to say that at the end of the war, from one-fifth to one-fourth of the C.I.O. membership was in unions controlled by Communists or pro-Communists, that several important state and city C.I.O. councils were under Communist influence, and that there were Communists or fellow travelers in significant posts on the national C.I.O. staff.

Almost immediately after the end of the war, there began a wave of strikes unlike any the United States had ever experienced. In 1946, labor set a record for man-hours lost by strikes. The basic reasons for the strikes were many: the release from the generally observed wartime no-strike pledge, which had built up irritation and discontent; a desire to affirm that a unionized

America was really here to stay, and to prevent an antiunion drive from management like that which followed World War I; a wish to maintain wartime take-home pay, swollen by overtime; and a will to raise real wages in the face of steadily mounting prices. The party did all it could to capitalize on the strike wave.

The party now had two designs for the labor movement: to exploit the labor-management crisis to bring about greater labor unity; and to extend the economic fight to politics generally. Repeatedly, the party urged that a national labor strategy committee be set up representing all the major branches of labor—the C.I.O. the A.F. of L., the railroad brotherhoods, and the independent unions. This committee, the party argued, should direct national wage policies and co-ordinate strike strategy. Such a committee, it fondly hoped, would prove to be the nucleus of a united labor movement and an instrument with which the party could extend its influence. A united labor movement would have an important job to do in the economic field, but the real struggle, the party argued, was in politics. Only through political action could come, for example, "the fight against monopoly prices, against monopoly dictation of prices." [26]

But things did not develop to the party's liking at all. Despite the heat of the struggle in the postwar strikes—the strike of the auto workers against General Motors lasted for 118 days—and despite the vacillating policies of the Truman administration toward the strikes, policies that the Communists hopefully thought would disrupt the C.I.O.'s marriage to the Democratic Party, the tide was against the Communists in the trade unions. In fact, the tide of popular opinion generally was turning against the Communists in 1946. Anti-Communism was growing rapidly, a product of the cold war. Early in the year, there was a crisis in the United Nations over the U.S.S.R. and Iran. In March, Winston Churchill delivered his "Iron Curtain" speech, and although the speech did not have as warm a reception as it would have had a year or two later, it was influential. In August, Communist Yugoslavia shot down two American planes, and passions began to grow hot. Throughout the year, apostate Communists told their stories to Congressional committees and to the press. A sharp fight raged between the Communists and the non-Communists over control of a new veterans' organization, the American Veterans Committee. And in November, the voters responded to the new conservative mood that had come over them and elected the first Republican Congress since 1928.

Communists found themselves fighting a losing defensive battle rather than an offensive in organized labor. At the March convention of the United Automobile Workers (C.I.O.), by a narrow vote the vigorously anti-Communist, social-democratic Walter Reuther wrested the presidency of the union from the Communist-supported incumbent, R. J. Thomas. The Reuther group had not won control of the union's executive committee, but the Communists' campaign against Reuther had ended in defeat. Throughout the C.I.O., pressure increased for a purge of Communists from union office.

By the time the C.I.O. met in its annual national convention in Atlantic City in November 1946, the battle between the Communists and the anti-Communists in the organization was too hot to be ignored. The party, of course, wanted no mention of the conflict. Recognizing that they did not have a chance of getting any pro-Communist resolutions from the convention, the best the Communists could hope for was that there would be no anti-Communist resolutions. But as it developed, anti-Communist resolutions were passed, and, ironically, the Communists at the convention voted for them. They even helped to write them.

At a convention of a national labor federation, as at a political convention, the real work is done off the convention floor in committee meetings. At the meetings of the executive board, composed of the presidents of the C.I.O.'s constituent unions, before the convention opened, it became evident that the Communists were going to have a difficult time. The executive board passed a set of amendments to its constitution designed to tighten the national organization's control over the state and local C.I.O.

councils, measures obviously aimed at restraining the activities of
the Communist-dominated councils, of which New York City's
and California's were the most important. Strategic retreat seemed
the best course for the Communists. They remembered the ad-
monition of the party's labor secretary, John Williamson: "We
must avoid tactics that separate the Left and progressive forces
and organizations from the mass of the labor movement." [27]

A factor in the distance of the Communist retreat was the
complex personality of the C.I.O.'s president, the widely respected
Philip Murray. Murray was no ordinary man, or one easy to understand. A Scottish immigrant and coal miner, he had risen in
the ranks of John L. Lewis's United Mine Workers. When the
C.I.O.'s Steel Workers Organizing Committee organized the steel
industry, the mild little man with the Scottish burr was in the
middle of the fight. He became president of the United Steelworkers of America, holding the respect of all factions. A de-
vout Roman Catholic and personally strongly anti-Communist,
Murray was also libertarian. He did not like the Communists in
the C.I.O., but he believed that so long as they were good unionists and adhered to C.I.O. principles they had a right to C.I.O.
membership and to their opinions. Furthermore, although he had
come to be what he was through struggle and had helped to lead
the C.I.O. to what it was through conflict, he was a man of peace.
He did not like feuds, especially feuds that might endanger the
position of the C.I.O. Murray arranged for a compromise between the Communists and the anti-Communists, which was not
as anti-Communist as some wished or as the Communists feared.

Without consulting anyone first, he brought up the matter at
a meeting of the executive board before the convention opened.
He explained that the C.I.O. had been attacked as Communist-
dominated and that in the recent elections candidates had tried
to win votes on the issue. He had stated categorically before that
the organization was not dominated by Communists, but now he
wanted action from the executive board and from the convention
that would refute the allegations. In typical fashion, he appointed

six members of the executive board, three "lefts" and three "rights," to study the matter and report their recommendations back to the full board. The three "rights" were Walter Reuther, Milton Murray, of the Newspaper Guild, and Emil Rieve, of the Textile Workers; the three "lefts" were Ben Gold, of the Furriers and an acknowledged party member, Michael ("Red Mike") Quill, of the Transport Workers Union, and Abram Flaxer, of the State, County and Municipal Workers. The special committee brought back a compromise, and their resolution received a unanimous vote from the presidents of all the constitutent unions.

Before reading the resolution before the convention on November 18, Murray gave an obviously extemporaneous speech which briefly explained the resolution's background, its purpose, and his interpretation of it. The resolution, he told the delegates, "should not be construed to be a repressive measure, calculated to do certain things of a repressive nature, but it does provide definitely certain charts and certain courses, that when this subject matter is disposed of, should be and in fact must be adhered to within the councils of the National CIO and all of its affiliates." While at Atlantic City, many people had told him and written him "that this organization of ours should indulge itself in the extravagances of repressive legislation. As the President . . . I should like to be distinctly understood that I am definitely opposed to any form of repression in this movement of ours." But, on the other hand, "there should be strict adherence" to the resolution. He ended on a note that showed his personal view of the party: "It [the resolution] portrays rather vividly this Union's allegiance to one country, and that is the United States of America."

He then read the resolution, of which these are the significant parts:

In our efforts to win economic security and social justice and to unite our movement against the forces of reaction and the enemies of democracy, we reaffirm our faith that these goals can be achieved for the American people through the democratic process and without sacrificing any of our basic human freedoms. . . .

In pursuit of the principles set forth herein and adopted by the CIO Executive Board, we, the delegates . . . *resent and reject efforts of the Communist Party* or other political parties and their adherents *to interfere in the affairs of the CIO*. This convention serves notice that we will not tolerate such interference. [Italics added.]

President Murray put the resolution to a voice vote, and it was unanimously adopted. There was no debate.[28]

Reaction was mixed. *Time* published a photograph of an aging, brooding, and tired Murray walking Atlantic City's boardwalk. Murray, *Time* said, had compromised, but the Communists had suffered a setback. The New York *Times* saw the resolution as a Communist defeat, and published a cartoon of Murray sweeping Communists from the house of labor.[29] The *Jewish Daily Forward* of New York, which had been fighting Communists since the early 1920's, accused Murray of running away from a battle with the party. The Communist rank and file was bewildered. How could it be, they asked themselves, that the presidents of the "left-led" unions, as they were called in the Communist press, assented to a resolution that implied the party interfered in C.I.O. matters and that this interference was resented? The *Daily Worker* hastened to explain. The resolution was unfortunately necessary, the labor editor explained, to prevent "a knock-down and dragout fight, sharpened division and possibly splits in the C.I.O, more factionalism, possible purges—just what the reactionaries have been looking for hopefully." The editors cheerfully headed their editorial "A Rebuff to Reaction." Ten days later, after seeing how most people had regarded the resolution as a rebuff to the Communists, the *Daily Worker* was not quite so cheerful. George Morris, the paper's labor columnist, wrote, "I don't know of a single Communist who does not feel that the C.I.O. yielded unjustly to reactionary hysteria. . . ." But then, in bold-face type, he said that "there can be no doubt of the correctness of the action of the Communists and all 'lefts' in the convention by their agreement to vote for the statement after they succeeded in eliminating all the major damage that the right wing sought to include in it. That is how a united front works." [30] But not all the damage had been eliminated, and certainly that was not the way the party wanted to see a united front work.

To explain the fact that the Communists in the labor movement were on the defensive, the party fell back upon its devil-conspiracy theory. Big business was corrupting the labor movement, and the devil's imps were the social democrats; big business used social democrats to do its dirty work in labor circles. "It is a noteworthy fact that Wall Street imperialism finds it useful and necessary to build up . . . Social Democratic labor leaders . . . for its own reactionary purposes. . . . Social-Democrats pose as progressives. . . . They are, in fact, masked reactionaries who perform their disruptive role in their own distinctive way." No term was too harsh for a social democrat. Foster called Norman Thomas a "drum major for imperialism," Victor Riesel's labor column a "pipeline" from Wall Street, and Riesel himself a "Pinkerton." [31] Riesel by 1946 was no longer a social democrat, but since he had once been managing editor of the *New Leader* when it was published by the Social Democratic Federation, he was fair game. But it was another former social democrat, Walter Reuther, who drew the lion's share of Communist abuse. To the Communists, Reuther's rise in the union was proof that "the bourgeoisie resorts to methods of hot-house cultivation and forced growth to produce the needed crop of Social-Democratic spokesmen who may assume leadership in its behalf within labor's ranks." [32]

Working with the social democrats, of course, were the party's special demons, the Trotskyites.[33] And in the years after the war, the Communists rediscovered a forgotten or neglected enemy, the Vatican.

THE PARTY AND RELIGION

It is clear that the party after the war hardened its opposition to religion. It became more opposed to organized religion than it had been, or at least it now expressed its opposition openly, and it also became more outspokenly opposed to religion itself as distinct from religious institutions.

Meanwhile, the American people in general were moving in the opposite direction. There had been a resurgence of religion in the United States since Pearl Harbor. Granted that some of the resurgence reflects appearance rather than reality, granted that there is a secular motivation for some people's religious activities, and granted that there is a considerable amount of re-ligiosity in the United States with only a superficial religious sig-nificance, nevertheless, there seems to have been a growth of truly religious thought and feeling.

The Communists were most disturbed about Roman Catholi-cism. Historically anti-Marxist, Roman Catholics constitute a very large part of the American working class. To offend these work-ers' religious sensibilities while trying to attract them ideologically would seem to be poor tactics, but that is the course the Com-munist Party took. During the Browder period, the party had played down its antireligious views and had developed the "out-stretched hand policy" toward Catholics. Now the party withdrew the outstretched hand. "We must avoid our error of the past in which we told ourselves that we were extending the 'outstretched hand,' when clerical reaction was offering us a mailed fist," wrote the editor of *Political Affairs*. "That illusion was part of the Browderite roseate prospect of the progressive postwar role of 'enlightened imperialism.' " [34]

The Roman Catholic Church was certainly vigorously anti-Communist; in the early 1950's, some prominent American Cath-olic clerics and some diocesan newspapers allowed their anti-

Communism to push them into unthinking extremism that often endangered civil liberties.

To Communists, the Church of Rome was a tool of Wall Street and imperialism. "With Social-Democracy . . . now greatly diminished in strength as compared with the period following World War I, imperialism leans increasingly upon the Vatican. . . . Today the Vatican shares with Social-Democracy the task of ideological mobilizer of the masses on the side of imperialism and its anti-Soviet crusade." [35] Foster, in an antireligious chapter no American Communist leader would have permitted himself in the previous decade, declared in his 1949 book, *The Twilight of World Capitalism,* that "the Catholic Church . . . is a most militant champion of capitalist reaction; it is a major force in the present attempt of Wall Street imperialism to preserve the capitalist system by setting up a fascist world under American domination." [36]

Had the Communists restricted their criticism to the Church's leaders, making a distinction between religious institutions and religious feeling, they might have made a little progress in their "struggle . . . to drive a wedge between the reactionary Heirarchy and the masses in the Church." [37] But the Communists directed their fire at religion itself as well. Foster approvingly quoted Marx on religion as "the opium of the people" and wrote that as capitalism conquered feudalism, "The capitalists quickly came to realize that . . . they had to have religion . . . to pacify so far as possible their inherently rebellious workers." Foster was as harsh toward Protestantism and Judaism as toward Catholicism. He found any religious faith a "superstition." [38]

But despite the party's antireligion, there remained, both within the party and around its fringes, a few religious people, even some ministers. There is a rather strong tradition in the United States of religiously inspired economic, social, and political reform that has at times been radical. This tradition has been strongest within Protestantism—there was a significant group of Protestant ministers in the old Debs Socialist organization—but the tradition is present also within Judaism and, to a lesser degree, within Catholicism. What strength the Communists have had among church people has been largely the tag end of this historic tendency. Others have been attracted by the party's emphasis on peace, although Communist motivation on the peace issue was hardly that of Christian pacifists. Some Negro churchmen have been in and around the party.

Religious Communists, however, have never been important leaders in the party. They have been only window dressing. Their advice and their point of view have never gained party acceptance. For example, when William Howard Melish, former rector of a Brooklyn Protestant Episcopal church who had a weakness for Communist fronts, advised that "The progressive movement has a lot to learn about the potential of a Jewish-Christian tradition," [39] his words went unheeded. Early in 1947, the editors of the *Daily Worker* stopped publishing the column of Eliot White, a Massachusetts Episcopalian clergyman and party member who had contributed a column to each Saturday edition for years.

The party did not even attempt to use religion as a weapon in the class struggle, as it tried to do with art and literature.

"ART IS A WEAPON"

In art and literature, as in other fields, the Communists went off in one direction after the war while the rest of the population went in the other. The party longed to see a rebirth of the proletarian novel, of "proletarian culture" generally, which had enjoyed a vogue in the 1930's. But no such movement developed. Most American writers, painters, and musicians turned away from social themes altogether. Since the war, writers—and readers—have concerned themselves to an unusual degree with such themes as the individual's adjustment, or maladjustment, to his environment and to his search for self. The novel has tended to become more psychoanalytic than social.

With the slogan "Art Is a Weapon" and all that this implied, the party failed badly to discern the drift of American thought. Indeed, the party failed to recognize some developments in recent cultural history that particularly concerned it. The proletarian novel, as Granville Hicks has reminded us, was not a really popular art form even at its high tide in the 1930's. These novels did not sell well, and leftist writers complained that publishers discriminated against them.[40] The party might well have heeded the reception of one of the last serious proletarian novels to be published, Ruth McKenney's *Jake Home,* which appeared in 1943.

Jake Home was published three years before Ruth McKenney was expelled from the party. She was undeniably a competent writer. Her light novel *My Sister Eileen* had been a commercial triumph, and her *Industrial Valley,* an only slightly fictionalized account of how unionism came to northeastern Ohio, had been exciting reading despite its partisanship. But *Jake Home* deserved and got a poor reception. Reading it today, one wavers between incredulity and hilarity, and readers in 1943 thought little better of it. The New York *Times* reviewer insisted upon treating the book as a burlesque. Clifton Fadiman, while commenting there was some good writing in the novel, objected to its "dated ideology." Even Browder, who was revered in the book to the point of embarrassment, thought it was "awful, simply awful." [41]

But the party leadership after the war ignored the previous reception and quality of proletarian novels and called upon Left Wing artists to rush in and satisfy the developing demand for "people's culture." Foster advised them: "The next years will show a tremendous resurgence of progressive spirit in every cultural field . . . awakening masses and peoples will increasingly demand the voice of every kind of artist in their struggle against reactionary capitalists, especially big American capital. Hence our Party must be fully prepared to play a vital leading role in the broad cultural movement of the people. . . ." [42]

Despite the changing tide of taste, Communist writers might have been able to gain a hearing if they had written works of artistic merit. The party was so insistent that "people's culture" reflect the party line exactly—as Albert Maltz soon discovered—that it sacrificed art for ideological purity.

Albert Maltz, today known as "The Pope" in the Communist expatriate colony in Mexico where he lives, had written such movies as "This Gun for Hire," "Destination Tokyo," and "Pride of the Marines," the sum of which was something less than a rich cultural experience. He had written some books which indicated talent. Early in 1946, *New Masses* published an article of his that was essentially a plea for the integrity of the Left Wing artist. He argued that a literary work must be judged on its artistic merits rather than on its ideology. He praised the writings of non-Communist and anti-Communist leftist novelists like James T. Farrell, Lillian Smith, and Richard Wright, saying that "Writers must be judged by their work, *not* by the committees they join." He deplored Farrell's committees, but said they did not detract from Farrell's stature as a writer.[43]

The reaction to Maltz's article was immediate and devastating. The party's national committee was in session in New York the week the article appeared. In giving the main report to the committee, Dennis stressed the "purity of theory [which] devolves upon every leader and member of the Party, upon every Party organization, institution and publication. . . ." Thoughts of impurity reminded Dennis of Maltz. "The need for exercising great vigilance against the smuggling of hostile ideas into our midst is brought home to us by the current issue of *New Masses,* which prints a bourgeois-intellectual and semi-Trotskyist article on the subject of the Party and the writers, an article which advocates 'citizenship' to Trotskyite writers in the camp of the Left. That this could have been published in a magazine professing a Marxist viewpoint only serves to warn us of the immensity of the task before us in the struggle we must wage against rotten-liberalism and an enemy-class ideological infiltration." [44]

Communist writers were quick to get the point. Mike Gold, a *Daily Worker* columnist with pretensions to the title of Great

Proletarian Novelist, was the first to attack. "Albert Maltz seems to have let the luxury and phony atmosphere of Hollywood at last to poison him." This was no time to be wishy-washy toward anti-Communists, because "The capitalists are plotting . . . to establish an American fascism as a prelude to an American conquest of the world." Joseph North soon joined the attack. So, too, did Howard Fast. Maltz's Hollywood colleagues Alvah Bessie and John Howard Lawson jumped on their fellow scenarist.[45]

In 1947, Maltz, as one of the "Hollywood Ten," was to stand firm in his beliefs and defy J. Parnell Thomas and his House Committee on Un-American Activities. But in 1946, he neither stood firm nor defied the attacks of his friends and the party leadership. He recanted, utterly and abjectly. He crawled. Under a particularly arty photograph of himself, with a strong light behind his head à la Hollywood, Maltz published an article, ironically called "Moving Forward," in the *Worker:* "I consider now that my article—by what I have come to agree was a one-sided, non-dialectical treatment of complex issues—could not, as I had hoped, contribute to the development of left-wing criticism and creative writing. I believe also that my critics were entirely correct in insisting that certain fundamental ideas in my article would, if pursued to their conclusion, result in the dissolution of the left-wing cultural movement." Before he concluded the article in the next day's edition, Maltz had even taken to task anyone who had defended him.[46] The "art is a weapon" campaign could now go on, purged clean of "rotten-liberalism." By the fall of 1946, this "weapon" theme had gone so far that the *Daily Worker*'s sports editor, Bill Mardo, was saying, "Yes, sports is a weapon," as he organized a basketball league for Left Wing trade-unionists.[47]

In such an intellectual atmosphere, it was not surprising that art did not develop. *New Masses* lost whatever sparkle and zest it ever possessed, and it never approached the level of ferment of the old *Masses* before World War I. When the old *Masses* advertised "Read the Masses and Enjoy the Revolution," it meant it. But *New Masses* took everything with ponderous seriousness, especially itself. In the spring of 1947, *New Masses* merged with *Mainstream* to become *Masses & Mainstream,* but it picked up no intellectual spark in the process. Its publishers estimated its circulation at 5,600.

The banality of the product that resulted from the "art is a weapon" campaign is difficult fully to describe, but a synopsis of a short story that appeared in the *Daily Worker* on Christmas Day, 1946, will suffice. The story was written by Herb Tank, a strong-armed seaman with literary aspirations who later became Harvey Matusow's bodyguard, and it was about "Jerusalem Slim and the Twelve Bindlestiffs." "A long time ago there was this Carpenter, a tall slim fellow. That's why I call him Slim. Well, this Carpenter Slim plied his trade somewhere around the Mediterranean ports. In some burg called Nazareth, I think." His career eventually alarmed "the fat boys." "The big boys over in Rome didn't like it at all. 'Got to get rid of this agitator,' they said. 'Got to put an end to this radical talk.' One of the big wheels among the fat boys put his goon squads on the job. They went fishing around the twelve bindlestiffs figuring they ought to be able to buy at least one of them off."

"Sure enough, one of the twelve bindlestiffs was ready to rat for a price. And his price was cheap, too. Then the vigilantes, the stormtroopers, turned on the radical Carpenter and they lynched Him."

This was American Communist culture in the postwar era. In 1949, this story was deemed worthy of inclusion in an anthology of the best pieces to appear in the *Daily Worker* in twenty-five years.[48]

THE PARTY AND THE NEGRO

The Communist Party after the war misread the aspirations of American Negroes as badly as it failed to detect new currents in religion and literature. The party wrongly predicted the direction

American Negroes were to take in their fight for the elimination of racial discrimination and pursued policies that tended to isolate it from the main stream of the Negro movement.

Since 1945, the Negro's fight for equal rights has been a most significant part of social history. Much, very much, remains to be done, but clearly the Negro has come a long way toward full citizenship since 1945 in the achievement of such gains as abolition of racial segregation in the armed forces, the near elimination of lynching, state fair employment practices laws, and the recognition by white politicians of the potency of the northern Negro vote. There have been important partial victories: the acceptance of Negroes in more and more fields of economic activity, the decline of racial discrimination in public transportation, and, most important, the Supreme Court's decision on racial segregation in the public schools.

The Communist Party, however, has contributed almost nothing to the winning of these achievements. (Curiously, Communists abroad have had an indirect salutary effect on the American Negro question. Part of the motivation behind white acceptance of Negro reforms is embarrassment in the ideological cold war and a desire to win the confidence of colored people in Asia and Africa.) The party, in fact, lost almost all its influence in the Negro movement at precisely the time when Negroes were making their greatest advance since post-Civil War reconstruction. In 1956, the Communists admitted as much.

The party became virtually isolated from the Negro movement, and the isolation was a disaster from the Communists' point of view, for ever since the late 1920's, they had put a major emphasis upon winning Negroes to their cause. The reason for the Communist concern for influence among Negroes is easy to discern. Here was a tenth of the population which, with perhaps the exception of the American Indians and some Latin Americans, was the most exploited and oppressed minority group in the United States, a group relegated because of its color to what a nineteenth-century Englishman would have called "the lower orders." Its attraction to Communism appeared to be a relatively simple matter. There was always some kind of an outrage against decency and democracy to which the Communists could point and say to Negroes, "Look what the white capitalists are doing to you; join us to end your degradation." That American Negroes have for the most part ignored and resisted the Communists, have refused to be an easy mark, speaks much for their common sense and their integrity.

Back in the 1920's, the American Communists had paid their Russian comrades the supreme compliment of imitation when they adopted a policy called "national self-determination for the Negro people in the Black Belt." This jargon meant that in a Soviet America there would be in the most heavily Negro populated part of the South an autonomous Negro republic, or—and here the Communists hedged a little—Negroes would be enabled to create such a subrepublic if they so wished. Stalin had developed theories on the Soviet "national question." The Soviet empire was composed of a considerable variety of nationalities, a Union of Soviet Socialist Republics, in which, theoretically, each nationality constituted an autonomous republic bound together in the union by socialist brotherhood. There was a vast difference between Stalin's theory and Stalin's practice, but the American Communists refused to see a difference. The Soviet national republics were actually considerably less autonomous than, say, Texas. But for the American Communists nothing would do but that they apply Stalin's theory to the American Negro.

Another aspect of the Communists' adoption of the slogan was that it afforded them an opportunity to point up a supposed parallel between the American Government and the Negro on the one hand and, for example, England and India on the other. The slogan was partly a device for crying "imperialism."

Needless to say, the idea of an autonomous Negro republic, with the kind of supersegregation that would involve—"Red Crow," its opponents labeled it—proved less than a howling success in attracting American Negroes to the party. Nor had the idea much appeal for whites. After the swing to the Popular Front idea in the mid-1930's, the party let the national self-determination slogan go unused, although they did not officially abandon the theory.

What attraction the party had for Negroes was a result of its "practical" Negro work, its coming to the aid of Negroes who were victims of some kind of injustice. For this kind of work, some of which was carried on quietly and unheard of among the whites and some of which received the most blatant publicity, non-Communists and anti-Communists owe the Communists due credit. If the party's purposes were cynically to capitalize on tragedy (and they were), if the party inflated instances of injustice beyond the facts of the case (and it did), and if the party made difficult the resolution of cases by its very presence and thereby added the "Red issue" to the Negro's burden (and again it did), still the party fought vigorously when too many Americans sat complacently on their hands and clucked disapproval. The Communists dramatized the Negro issue, whatever their purpose, and brought cases to attention that otherwise might never have been noticed beyond a few restricted circles.

During World War II, the Communists dropped national self-determination even as a theory. Browder explained in the party's magazine. ". . . we Communists . . . faced the possibility that the Negro people, disappointed in their aspirations for full integration into the American nation, might find their only alternative in separation and in the establishment of their own state in the Black Belt. . . . We raised this as one of the rights of the Negro people, in case the Negro people found this was the only way to satisfy their aspirations." But now, Browder continued, "The crisis of history has taken a turn of such character that the Negro people . . . have found it possible to make their decision once and for all. Their decision is for their complete integration into the American nation as a whole, and not for separation." [49]

In the 1945 reaction against Browderism, it was perhaps inevitable that the Communists should change their line on the Negro question. They changed it officially after over a year of discussion —back to the old national self-determination line.

Statements of dissatisfaction with Browder's Negro position began to appear almost immediately after the publication of the Duclos letter. James W. Ford, a Harlem Negro who had been the party's candidate for vice-president in 1932 and 1936, was one of the first to start the line in the new direction. Before the party's special convention, Benjamin J. Davis, Jr., a Negro New York City councilman elected on the Communist ticket and the party's most important Negro leader, brought back national self-determination into the discussion. Since Davis had once said that he, as a Negro, should have seen the wisdom of dropping national self-determination before Browder did, he had special penance to pay. He restored the hoary old slogan.[50]

However, the party wanted time to formulate its position. The reconstituted party's first resolution skirted the subject of national self-determination and said only that Communists had recently "glossed over the national character of the Negro question." The resolution called for the creation of a special party commission to undertake a study of Negro conditions and trends and "in the light of Marxist-Leninist theory, to formulate a comprehensive definition of Communist policy and program on the Negro question." [51]

Claudia Jones, a young New York Negro originally from the West Indies and since deported, first endeavored to prove that the "Negro people in the Black Belt constitute a nation." The Black Belt, by her definition, was a wildly shaped territory that "stretches contiguously westward from the Eastern shore of Maryland, and lies within" every Southern state except Kentucky, Missouri, and Oklahoma. Others on the commission accepted her definitions. She took her criteria of what constituted nationality from Stalin in his *Marxism and the National and Colonial Question*. These criteria were a common language, a common history and culture, a common territory, and a common economic life. The others accepted these, but they were not unanimously in agreement with her that the Negroes did in fact meet the criteria. By ignoring the fact that Negroes and whites together met Stalin's criteria of nationality, and rejecting other criteria, she concluded that Negroes were in fact a full-fledged nation—not a potential nation, nor a developing nation, but a here-and-now nation. Being a nation and an oppressed people, Southern Negroes bore, then, the same relationship to American imperialism as the Indonesians and the Indians bore to Dutch and British imperialism. Apparently defining "national self-determination" to mean the choice of Negroes to move either toward integration or toward territorial separation, a choice she vehemently insisted American Negroes had not yet made, she concluded that "the right to self-determination of the Negro people in the Black Belt" should be raised as a *"programmatic demand"* but not as a "slogan of immediate action." If the distinction was fuzzy, it was not uniquely so in Miss Jones's confused article.[52] Max Weiss followed with an article entitled "Toward Clarity on the Negro Question," a quality sorely needed at that point. What Weiss wanted was clear enough. He wanted a black republic, immediate redrawing of Southern electoral boundary lines, and a redivision of the land ownership.[53]

But other commission members were not so sure of the wisdom of a black republic. Francis Franklin, hardly sounding like the Left deviationist he was alleged to be some months later, warned that Negroes *"definitely do not want even to hear"* about any kind of separation. Their *"passionate desire"* was for equality and integration. Yet Franklin did not reject national self-determination in all circumstances.[54] Doxey Wilkerson, easily the best-qualified member of the commission by his experience and education, held a master's degree from the University of Kansas and had been a professor at Virginia State College and at Howard University. As a trained Negro social scientist, he had been an assistant to Gunnar Myrdal when Myrdal had done the work for his important book on the American Negro question, *An American Dilemma*.[55] Wilkerson wrote that consideration of American Negroes as a nation offered only "political insights," arguing that they had the characteristics of a nation only "in rudimentary form." "The overwhelming majority of the Negro people," he warned, "abhor and reject any proposal that they separate—in any form whatever, even temporarily—from the American nation as a whole." To revive self-determination in the Black Belt as a slogan or to affirm the idea as the party's theoretical position "would be theoretically incorrect and . . . tactically disastrous." [56]

In a few years, Wilkerson would be in a position to say, I told you so, but in 1946 he fought a losing battle. People with considerably more stature in the party than he—Wilkerson had not been a member for long—made it clear that Wilkerson was "incorrect." James S. Allen, a white man widely respected as a party theoretician, led the campaign against Wilkerson. Perhaps part of the reason for the sharp attack on Wilkerson was that he had written his article after Foster had already published an article on the subject taking the opposite side of the argument.[57]

In December 1946, the party's national committee adopted a resolution on the Negro question that recognized the national self-determination idea. "In fighting for their equal rights, the Negro people are becoming more unified as a people. Their fight for liberation from oppression in the Black Belt . . . is a struggle for full nationhood, for their rightful position of full equality as a nation." Negroes might even achieve full nationhood before America became "socialist." However, "The Communist Party does not attempt to impose any specific solution in advance of the form in which the right of self-determination will be exercised; nor does it prematurely raise self-determination as an immediate slogan of action." [58] The step back to the old party position was now complete.

One can only speculate upon the leadership's motivation in reviving this ideological relic. Foster recognized that the idea had not been popular among Negroes in the past; he even conceded that the "lack of response" had amounted "in many cases to vigorous opposition." Yet he was for national self-determination. Probably a large part of their motive was to "turn the clock back" to a time before Browder had identified himself with a Negro line. Evidence for this hypothesis lies in the frequent criticisms of Browder that sprinkled the debate on the Negro question. Another possibility is that the leadership wanted to reaffirm its orthodoxy to the international movement. Stalin, who undoubtedly knew less about American Negroes than the worst-informed American party member, was cited as the supreme authority several times in the discussion. Foster and Jones were particularly fond of quoting "that great expert on the national question, Stalin." [59]

And it is possible that the new Negro line was an attempt, although a clumsy one, to exploit both the movement for integration and the strain of Negro nationalism that does exist in black America. A reader of the general Negro press cannot fail to detect a current, although not a strong one, of color nationalism. This may have been a foggy idea in the back of Foster's head when he wrote that "the orientation of the Negro people is first, toward full participation of their national consciousness." [60]

Whatever their motivation, the policy of national self-determination, even if not waved "as an immediate slogan of action," proved again to be a soggy dud in the Negro community. The Communists could truthfully deny that their resolution said anything about segregation into a black republic, but the precise nature of the party's position was too abstract, too much like walking an intellectual tightrope, to be popularly understood. And the Negro community hated anything that smelled the least bit like separation. Whatever attraction the party had for Negroes after the war was because of its practical work and despite its theoretical position. In other words, what success it had was due, ironically, to a pragmatic attitude rather than to Marxist-Leninist-Stalinist orthodoxy.

In one other respect, the party hurt itself among American Negroes. It attacked respected and popular Negro leaders with all the calumny it could muster. The Communists' favorite target was A. Philip Randolph, once a Norman Thomas Socialist. At various times, Communists called him a "demagogue," an "imperialist," a "saboteur" of FEPC, and a "secret ally" of Senator Theodore Bilbo. Dr. Ralph J. Bunche was not held in respect among Negro Communists. A Negro columnist for the *Daily Worker* wrote that

Bunche had won the Nobel peace prize only "for his services to the western imperialist warmongers." [61] Comments such as these would have been better calculated to win friends in the Mississippi Democratic committee than to attract support in Harlem and in Chicago's South Side.

Nor did the party's open effort to capture the N.A.A.C.P. advance its purposes. The effort merely drew counterattacks from N.A.A.C.P. leaders, who speak for American Negroes with more authority than any other group. Seldom have the Communists allowed to appear in print such an open statement of intention to infiltrate an organization as was Henry Winston's advice to the party on the N.A.A.C.P. [62]

As if all these tactics were not enough self-inflicted wounds, the party began even during its 1945 crisis to forge a weapon with which in just a few years it would create havoc in its own ranks. Ben Davis started it all in July 1945 with one sentence: "We have relaxed vigilance against white chauvinism even in our own ranks for which we are paying dearly." [63] "White chauvinism" was Communist jargon for prejudice against Negroes. Davis's idea grew quickly. "The Present Situation and the Next Tasks" called for "a vigorous struggle to root out every manifestation of open or concealed white chauvinism in our own ranks." The following winter, Dennis ordered the members "to burn out the infamy of white chauvinism" among them, and the resolution on the Negro question of December 1946 repeated the cry: "By its own actions, the Communist Party must set an example before the whole labor movement . . . white chauvinism within its ranks, whether it manifests itself openly or in concealed form, must be systematically combatted and expunged." [64] All this talk of white chauvinism, the term Communists invariably used, within the party itself must have made Negroes a little wary about what kind of people the Communists were. The results were to become worse from the party's own point of view. In 1949, the campaign to stamp out white chauvinism within the party was to become a full-fledged witch hunt, a purge with disastrous results.

The reconstituted Communist Party's postwar line on America did not serve it well. The Foster leadership badly misjudged the health of the American economy, had to go on the defensive in the labor movement, offended many Americans' religious sensibilities, saw its cultural program lapse into banality, and flew in the face of what it itself recognized to be the temper of the Negro movement. Here and there, individual party members saw the way things were going and protested—or just quietly quit the party.

The top leadership, however, insisted it was right. "There are . . . those," said Henry Winston to the national committee in 1947, "who draw the conclusion that our Party is moving against the stream. . . . Can it be said that such is the situation today? . . . it is not true that our Party is moving against the stream. Indeed, the very opposite is true. Our Party is moving with the great body of democratic-minded Americans. . . . It is only by thus correctly estimating the situation in our country today that we can be in a position to speak to the rank and file, to the millions, and win them for the program of our Party." [65]

THREE: PARTY ORGANIZATION, PARTY STRENGTH, AND PARTY LIFE

*L*ike other organizations in the United States, the Communist Party had an elaborate constitution, which, if carefully examined and explained, reveals a great deal about the party's structure and methods. The party's zeal for organizational efficiency and its tendency toward bureaucracy were so great that it frequently ignored the letter of its constitution. Nevertheless, making due allowances for operational deviations, the constitution is basic to an understanding of the party.

Few rank-and-file members had more than a slight familiarity with the party constitution. In the summer of 1956, during the party's great crisis over the downgrading of Stalin, one member wrote the *Daily Worker* suggesting that it print the constitution in full since few members had ever possessed a copy of it and many had never read it. Several days later, he wrote again, repeating his request, adding that when his party unit had decided to have a discussion of the constitution it had been unable to obtain a copy even when members went to the next higher party echelon.[1]

The constitution began, conventionally enough, with a preamble of generalities.[2] The preamble described the organization as "the political party of the American working class, basing itself upon the principles of scientific socialism, Marxism-Leninism." The party attached itself to the American democratic tradition, to the "traditions of Jefferson, Paine, Lincoln and Frederick Douglass, and the great working class traditions of Sylvis, Debs and Ruthenberg." In actuality, the party was far closer to Ruthenberg than any of the others. Ruthenberg was a Cleveland office worker who helped to split the Communists off from the Socialists in 1919, later became the party's number one leader, and was buried in the Kremlin wall in 1927. The preamble also pledged the party's support to a number of reforms which most liberal Republicans and Democrats would support, but declared that American problems could be solved finally only through socialism, "the highest form of democracy." The preamble described the party's mission as the education of the working class for socialism through its everyday struggles.

The party constitution made a vague and ambiguous disclaimer of revolutionary intent and advocacy of violent overthrow of the United States Government. Article II stated that the party's purpose was "the establishment of Socialism by the free choice of the majority of the American people," but the document said nothing on the question of whether this "free choice" was to be exercised by the ballot and other constitutional means or by the use of force outside of law. In the discussion of "different roads to socialism" that developed in the party's 1956-57 crisis, in which some Communists urged that the party renounce revolutionary force, the implication was clear that theretofore the party had not envisaged constitutional methods. The constitution also declared that "adherence to or participation in the activities of any clique, group, circle, faction or party which conspires or acts to subvert, undermine, weaken or overthrow any or all institutions of American democracy" was grounds for immediate expulsion from the party. The party, however, never used this clause. The clause could have been invoked against the left deviationists who were expelled, but, instead, those leftists were always charged with rejection of party discipline.

Most of the party constitution pertained to organization. The basic unit in the party was the club, which sometimes was still called by its older names, the "branch" or "local." The Communists did not use the term "cell" after the 1920's. With a few exceptions, all members belonged to a party club. The exceptions were a few members at large, or "floaters." Not even rank-and-file members knew who the floaters were.[3] There were three categories of party clubs: community clubs, shop clubs, and industrial clubs. The community club was to provide leadership in such community problems as housing and education, but it was to do so in such a way as to perform its primary "task of promoting the systematic socialist education of the people." In other words, community clubs exploited local problems as a way to propagandize.[4]

To the party leadership, the shop club was the most important basic unit. Composed of party members who worked within a single factory or plant, "It [provided] the best method for the Party to keep in constant touch with the most important section of the working class and to defend the economic and political interests of labor and the nation." The industrial club was a special and infrequently used device. Members of industrial clubs were workers within a number of shops in the same industry. If Communist membership in the industry increased sufficiently, a number of shop clubs superseded the industrial club.[5]

The national leadership was eager to increase the number of shop clubs and thereby increase its influence in industry, especially basic industry, vital to any revolutionary organization. National organization secretaries hammered away at this "concentration policy" in their reports, emphasizing its importance and complaining about its relative lack of success. In November 1945, for example, John Williamson, the national organization secretary until he became national labor secretary in mid-1946, proposed that "six of our most experienced and leading comrades" be sent as special organizers to work in the basic industries of Youngstown, Gary, Flint, McKeesport, Toledo, and Kansas City. Where the concentration policy had a measure of success, the party considered the results gratifying. It claimed that if it had not been for Communists on the New York waterfront, the 1945 longshoremen's strike would have been lost in a day or two. "Instead, it was able to last eighteen days and as a result forced economic concessions . . . and organized a force for democracy within the union and against [Joseph P.] Ryan." The party asserted that the concentration policy stimulated labor militancy. During the 1946 steel strike, Williamson declared, "In Indiana Harbor, where we had a live and active mill branch, the vote for the strike was 18 to 1. In South Chicago, in the big mill where we have long had influence and today have a branch that functions fairly well, the vote was 12 to 1. In Gary, however, where we were slow in organizing mill branches and in developing Party work, the strike vote was only 5 to 1." [6]

Above the clubs were the state organizations and whatever other levels between the state and the local the party wanted to create. The larger state organizations, the New York and the California, for example, had two and sometimes three levels of organization between themselves and the club. New York had city, county, and section organizations. In the Coney Island area of Brooklyn, for example, there were several clubs, which together constituted the Coney Island section, which was part of the Brooklyn or Kings County organization. The county organization, in turn, had the city organization between itself and the state party. So many links in the chain of command, of course, made it extremely difficult for a club to exert influence upward through the rest of the organization. But a centralized corps of professional party workers, or "cadres," made command efficient from the top down.

The area embraced by a party club or section depended upon how densely concentrated was the membership. Particularly in New York City, a club might embrace only a neighborhood; but in smaller cities there might be only one club in the community. In some parts of New York there were enough party members in one apartment building to constitute a club. Isadore Begun, Bronx County chairman, gloated over one building in which there were ten members: "Just think, if you want to call a meeting all you have to do is knock on the steam pipe." [7]

The party constitution empowered the national organization with authority to create districts from two or more state organizations. Thus, the national body created the New England district, of which the Massachusetts party was the most important. National headquarters also, without express constitutional authority, divided the Pennsylvania organization into two districts, one centered in Pittsburgh, the other in Philadelphia.

In theory, the highest authority in the party was the national convention, but in fact, it was the national secretariat of four or five leaders at national headquarters. The top leaders displaced the convention through a variety of techniques. One was to ignore the constitutional injunction for a national convention every other year. A national convention met in July 1945 to reconstitute the party and adopt the constitution, but three years elapsed before the next convention, in August 1948. Another convention met in December 1950, but after that there was none until February 1957. However, even the conventions were routine meetings under the top leadership's direction. At no convention until that of February 1957 was there any important dissent from the views of the national leaders, and then the dissent came because the national leadership itself was divided. Moreover, sometimes national headquarters simply ignored or reinterpreted resolutions passed by the national convention.

Each national convention elected a national committee, composed of members from all over the nation, who were expected to meet at least three times annually. The national committee elected a national board, later called the national executive committee, formerly called the political bureau, or politburo, to act in its behalf between meetings. The constitution made no provision for a secretariat, but this smaller group of the national board actually ran the party's day-to-day activities. Thus, there were three levels of leadership at the national level besides the national convention. In 1945 and early 1946, the secretariat was composed of Foster, Dennis, Thompson, and Williamson. In July 1946, Henry Winston, a thirty-five-year-old Negro veteran, born in Mississippi, who joined the party in Kansas City in 1930, moved up into the secretariat.[8]

The party's high degree of centralization was entirely in keeping with established Communist practice and theory. Grigori Zinoviev in 1920 laid down "democratic centralism" as one of the "Twenty-one Conditions for Admission to the Communist International," and centralism, if not "democratic" centralism, has been an essential feature of the American Communist Party ever since. The constitution of 1945 used the words "democratic centralism" only once, and then in a manner that emphasized democracy rather than centralism: "In accordance with the principles of democratic centralism . . . Communist Party members shall be involved in the formulation of major policies and shall have the right and duty to examine the execution of policies."

Theoretically, democratic centralism was a system of organization in which each party echelon elected the next higher echelon and agreed to abide by the decisions of the higher body. In practice, elections by lower bodies were minimized and control was emphasized. In other words, the Communist Party was organized from the top down rather than the bottom up; it was centralized rather than democratic. A textbook for new party members put it this way: "The Party is one unified whole. . . . Once a decision is made, the minority is subordinate to the majority in its execution. . . . The lower organizations must carry out the decisions of the higher organizations." [9] In this respect, the party was organized more like a military organization than a political party.

The Communist Party differed importantly from other parties, even other leftist parties, in the amount of power granted to party employees. In the Socialist Party of Eugene V. Debs, for example, the most important and powerful men in the party were not on the party's payroll. Those who were on the payroll, the national office force and the organizers, were functionaries, in the pre-Communist sense of the word, rather than policy makers. But the reverse was true in the Communist Party. The people who made all the major decisions were on the party payroll. The most important Communists were full-time, professional revolutionaries, making their living at party activity. This fact had important implications for the operation of the party.

For one thing, professional direction of the party tended to make the party the most centralized and bureaucratic organization in the history of American politics. The fact that a Communist official's salary came from party headquarters on the ninth floor of 35 East Twelfth Street, New York City, made him realize that the party's real power resided there, no matter what the constitution said about the party club. He realized that to differ with the ninth floor on any important matter might mean expulsion or dismissal, and for an expelled party functionary the economic road was rocky indeed.

The fact of centralization of authority in the hands of a few professionals also affected the decisions of the party. Had the power distribution within the party been more nearly like that of other political groups, and had leaders of the so-called "mass organizations" or Communist trade unions exercised real power within the party, its policies might have been somewhat different from what they were. But the trade-union leaders exercised little if any power in the party. Quite the reverse: they either followed the professionals' desires in political matters, and to a lesser degree in strictly trade-union matters, or they bolted the Communist movement altogether. The professional party leaders insisted that they be followed, and they offered no alternative but withdrawal from the party. The party might have been able to hold on to its trade-union following in the postwar decade if it had followed the will of the Communist trade-unionists rather than insisting upon the reverse.

Finally, the fact that the party's top leaders were not really dependent upon popularity, even acceptance, in the rank and file tended to separate them from the membership. To a politician of the major parties, nothing is so important as broad support within

his party, but not so in the Communist Party. Communist leaders
mend no fences. In the party upheaval of 1956, a Negro woman
member from the Bronx described the relations of the top leaders with the ordinary membership rather eloquently if inelegantly:
"How many of you have been introduced to a leader of the party
for about a dozen times and have him or her look at you and smile
each time and say so nice to know, so nice to know [?] You know
after the second or third time you begin to wonder if there is something wrong with you, but after the sixth or seventh time you begin
to wonder, period . . . it's not that they see so many people, it's
because they don't see and know the membership. . . . I think
that communist leaders are the worst snobs I have ever known." [10]

Another important characteristic of the Communist Party's
organization was the high degree to which the party's professional
personnel could be shifted about over the country for a variety
of functions. In theory, and to a considerable degree in practice,
the party was as efficient, as flexible, as capable of manipulation
as a commando battalion. The analogy to military organization
is one that Communists themselves used in such terms as "united
front" and "cadre." In military usage, a cadre is a permanent staff
of trained soldiers around which new units may be built. In Communist usage, a cadre was a trained party employee, a "full-timer,"
a standardized part at least theoretically capable of functioning well
in any community or task.[11]

For all their power, party leaders were poorly paid. No one
ever got rich, or even economically comfortable, as a professional
Communist. When the federal Social Security Administration in
1956 attempted to revoke old-age benefits based on Communist
Party wages, it revealed that the highest salary Foster ever received
from the party was $73 a week. His annual party salary in the
period after the war ranged from $2,340 to $3,180. Perhaps he
also supplemented his salary by the sale of his books, which the
party press touted shamelessly. *Daily Worker* staff men received
the minimum American Newspaper Guild wages, $60 a week just
after the war, later raised to $75 and then to $85. New York

State leaders and most national leaders received about the same pay or a little more than the *Daily Worker* employees. Leaders in states where the party was weak received less. All in all, Communist leaders lived very modestly. Many of them were able to get along only because their wives worked. Surely it was not financial gain that induced men to make the party their career; nearly all of them could have made better incomes in business or the professions.[12]

Above the whole complex party structure stood the international Communist movement. That the national leadership was subservient to international Communism, ultimately to Moscow, will be demonstrated time and again in this book. But there is some question as to just how the international leadership made its wishes known to the American party. Until the party, officially at least, withdrew from the Communist International, or Comintern, in 1940, to meet the letter of the Voorhis Act, there is no question but that there was a Comintern representative, in common party speech the "Comintern rep" or "CI rep." [13] There may have been CI reps to the party, or their equivalent, since 1940. Soon after Louis Budenz dramatically quit the party and the managing editorship of the *Daily Worker*, he charged that Gerhart Eisler, a German, was the post-Comintern equivalent of a CI rep. The party, of course, was extremely secretive about its international connections, and Eisler denied the charge. After some complex criminal litigation, Eisler jumped bail and went to East Germany. Since the Eisler case, there have been no official charges of the presence of a CI rep, but this negative evidence by no means proves that such a representative has not existed. Budenz charged also that Dmitri Z. Manuilsky, a Soviet representative to the United Nations, had acted as an international representative to the American party in 1945.[14]

Actually, however, whether there has been a CI rep or the equivalent in the United States since 1945 is an academic question. The precise means of communication between the Soviet Union and the American Communists are not so important as the fact that there was communication. In nearly all circumstances, a CI rep, a courier, or an "open wire to Moscow" was unnecessary, and there is not conclusive evidence in the public record that such means of communication have existed since 1945. American party leaders in nearly all cases had no real need for direct communication with the Soviets; there was sufficient information about Russian policy in Communist Party newspapers and magazines from abroad and in other publications accessible to them and to anyone else who made an effort.[15] Apparently, American party leaders on more than one occasion relied upon the United States "bourgeois press," particularly the New York *Times,* for information about Soviet developments.

Was there—is there—a party "underground"? Both informed and uninformed persons have made such charges. The Communist "underground" has been used to mean: 1) the "review commissions," both national and state, intended to expose police agents in the party and to maintain party discipline; 2) espionage or sabotage activities connected more or less directly with Soviet intelligence services; 3) secret party activities that do not necessarily involve espionage or sabotage; and 4) the method of party organization adopted in 1949 and 1950 in an effort to minimize the effectiveness of Federal Bureau of Investigation agents. The last will receive further attention in Chapter VII.

The review commissions played the role of the party's "internal security" agency and have therefore been compared to the Soviet Cheka or NKVD. Indeed, the NKVD and the review commissions had the same function if not the same power. Communist Party members could be charged with many offenses, and, if found guilty, they could be censured, removed from leadership, or expelled. The offenses ranged from "conduct unbecoming a member of the Party" to "personal or political relations with enemies of the working class and nation." The party club was to sit in judgment upon an accused member, and the accused had a constitutional right of appeal to the next higher echelon. In practice, only rarely did a club find a member innocent, and appeal was futile.

Charges by a review commission nearly always resulted in the disciplining of the party member. The party did have a problem. Court trials had proved that the F.B.I. had agents among the Communists, and the party had no recourse but to try to discover them. Yet to be effective, the review commissions had to operate secretly at least part of the time.

The most important kind of underground was engaged in espionage or sabotage in the service of the Soviet Union. There is overwhelming evidence in the public record of Soviet espionage in the United States before and since 1945. The most publicized cases had to do with espionage before or during World War II, notably the Alger Hiss, Klaus Fuchs, and Julius and Ethel Rosenberg cases. But three other convictions dealt with espionage committed since the end of the war: the Coplon-Gubichev case, the Soble case, and the Abel case.

On the night of March 4, 1949, F.B.I. men arrested Judith Coplon and Valentin Gubichev in New York City as Miss Coplon was in the act of passing to Gubichev some reports she had prepared based upon information she had gleaned from F.B.I. documents in her position with the Department of Justice in Washington. Miss Coplon, a graduate of Barnard College, was a United States citizen by birth. Gubichev was a Russian national, a New York employee of the United Nations. Miss Coplon was tried in 1949 for stealing documents from her government department; she and Gubichev were tried together in early 1950 for conspiracy to commit espionage. The core of Miss Coplon's defense was that she was having a love affair with "Gubie," as the tabloid newspapers insisted upon calling him. Gubichev was living in New York with his wife, also a Russian national. Juries in each trial found the defendants guilty as charged. At the request of the Department of State, Gubichev received a suspended sentence requiring that he leave the United States within two weeks. Apparently, the Department of State hoped for reciprocity for American nationals who had been convicted of espionage in Communist countries. Two months after her second conviction, Miss Coplon married one of her attorneys. In December 1950, a higher court reversed the decision against her on technical grounds. She had been arrested without a warrant, and information obtained by illegal wire-tapping had been used against her. The higher court's decision was concerned only with due process of law rather than with the facts of the case, upon which two juries had found Miss Coplon guilty.

In January 1957, the Department of Justice brought indictments against Jack Soble, his wife, Myra, and Jacob Albam for espionage committed since the war. Each admitted his guilt. In June 1957, the Immigration and Naturalization Service, at the F.B.I.'s behest, arrested Colonel Rudolf Ivanovich Abel of the Soviet secret police. Abel was tried and convicted of espionage.[16]

These cases make clear that there has indeed been Soviet espionage in the United States since World War II. They do not, however, establish a direct connection between the American Communist Party and espionage for the Soviets. None of the convicted had been a member of the Communist Party of the United States. Gubichev and Abel were Soviet citizens. The Sobles and Albam appear to have been coerced into espionage by fear for the safety of relatives in Russia. Judith Coplon was the only American convicted for postwar espionage that was apparently the result of ideological conviction, but there was no evidence at her trial to indicate she had been a member of the Communist Party.

This is not to say that there was no link between the American Communist Party and Soviet espionage apparatus in the postwar period; it is only to say that such a connection has not been made a matter of public record. The detection of espionage is a police function, the responsibility particularly of the Federal Bureau of Investigation. The F.B.I. quite understandably does not reveal all it knows or suspects, for to do so would jeopardize its opportunities to investigate further. Public statements of federal officials responsible for the detection of espionage indicate that considerable Soviet espionage has existed which has not been made public. In 1953, the head of the Internal Security Division of the Department of Justice revealed that his office had under investigation 766 espionage and 261 sabotage cases, and F.B.I. Director J. Edgar Hoover told reporters that year that "Enemy espionage rings are more intensively operating now than at any other time in the history of the country." [17] But beyond such statements as these and the above-mentioned convictions, there is no further evidence of espionage in the United States in the public record.*

During and before the war, the party served as a recruiting ground for espionage agents. This is clear from the public record. Whittaker Chambers and the Rosenbergs went into espionage work directly from the party. Judith Coplon apparently had friends who were party members, and she was on the periphery of the movement herself. The other people convicted for postwar espionage evidently had no connection with the American party. There is some evidence to indicate that if confidential sources were available it could be documented that the party has continued to serve as a recruiter since World War II as it is known to have done before 1945. In his 1958 book, *Masters of Deceit,* F.B.I. Director J. Edgar Hoover wrote that "by the early 1940's there was a definite lessening of direct Soviet dependence on the U.S. Party for espionage assistance." He also made the point that the party's "most important" contribution to Soviet espionage was recruit-

---

* On September 28, 1956, in a letter to Louis Nichols, Assistant to the Director of the F.B.I., I asked for what information the F.B.I. could give me about the Communist Party, both its underground and the open party, that was consistent with national interest for me or any other citizen to know. J. Edgar Hoover's reply, dated October 5, 1956, was as follows:

Dear Professor Shannon:

The letter dated September 28, 1956, with enclosure which you wrote to Mr. L. B. Nichols has been brought to my attention.

Although I would like to be of assistance, I feel sure you will appreciate the situation which prevents me from doing so when it is explained. The FBI is strictly a fact-gathering agency, and we are not empowered to divulge information from our files since they are confidential and available for official use only.

The rules governing this phase of our operations are not flexible, of course, and this situation precludes me from complying with your request.

Sincerely yours,

[Signed] J. Edgar Hoover

ment. But, using a source apparently not a matter of public knowledge, he also wrote, "In one major apparatus detected by the
FBI . . . twelve of seventeen participants had been Party members." [18] Certainly, if one may speculate, it would seem that Soviet
intelligence officers would look to the United States Communist
movement for recruits as a matter of convenience; a Communist
or party sympathizer might be assumed to have the emotional and
intellectual motivation necessary. On the other hand, once recruited, a spy seems to sever all connection with American Communists and to work only with other Soviet agents. From the point
of view of both the Soviets and the American party, it would seem
only common sense to keep spies away from known Communists
to minimize the possibility of detection.

To summarize, there has clearly been Soviet espionage in the
United States in the recent past. We must presume that it continues. There is no documentation in the public record of a direct
connection between the party and espionage in the postwar period,
but such a connection may well have existed. In view of the party's
ideological commitment to the Soviet Union and of the known
record of Soviet espionage in the United States and elsewhere,
those responsible for the internal security of the United States
are wise to keep a vigilant eye on Communist activities.

Concerning the third kind of underground, activities that were
secret but not necessarily related to espionage, again there is little
evidence. It has been charged that the party operated an "underground business empire" to raise money and to further its interests within the business community. The "empire" was headed by
Robert William Weiner, usually called William Weiner, who from
1938 to 1940 was the party's financial secretary. In 1940, Weiner,
under his original name, Warszower, was convicted of passport
fraud along with Earl Browder. Because he had a serious heart
condition, the federal government did not imprison him, fearing
he might die in prison and become a party martyr. In May 1950,
the federal government moved to deport him as a subversive alien,
but both Russia, Weiner's country of birth, and France, the nation

from which he last embarked for America, refused to accept him. The Immigration Service did not intern him, again for fear of his dying while in government hands. Weiner's business investments for the party, it has been alleged, extended into many kinds of enterprises—from a night club (Café Society Uptown) to export-import houses—in a complex series of firms.[19]

Earl Browder has stated that while he was the party's head, Weiner did indeed make financial investments for the party. The organization had excess funds in the late 1930's and during the war, and Weiner invested these to get a better return than could be obtained from conventional management of organization funds. That these investments involved the party in bourgeois enterprise does not seem to have bothered the leadership. On the other hand, Browder maintained that the business operations were not extensive and that the published charges were grossly exaggerated. He did not know what happened to the investments after he was removed from leadership in 1945, but he presumed that they had been liquidated as the party became increasingly hard-pinched for money in the late 1940's. It seems quite unlikely that the party had extensive investments as late as the mid-1950's, when there was much evidence, such as the closing of party schools and the decline of its press, to indicate that it was in desperate financial condition. Yet as late as January 1959, the party expelled a Brooklyn party leader who was reported to have absconded with perhaps as much as $250,000 and gone abroad. Such a large sum probably would have been in investments of some kind.[20]

BROADENING THE PARTY'S INFLUENCE

If the party had never been able to radiate influence beyond its own membership, it would not have been a significant force in American life. But it was always able to reach certain non-Communists, mobilize them to an extent, and manipulate them for the party's advantage. The party had three main kinds of institutions for extending its influence: front organizations, party schools, and the party press.

There were many kinds of party fronts. Some were important (the International Workers Order) and some were not (the Quad City Committee for Peace). Some were more or less permanent (the Civil Rights Congress) and some were temporary (Committee for the Defense of the Pittsburgh Six). Some had broad and general objectives (American Slav Congress) and some were very limited in their purposes (American Committee for the Settlement of Jews in Birobidjan, Inc.). Some were created by the party (Veterans of the Abraham Lincoln Brigade) and some were established by non-Communists and subsequently captured by Communists (North American Committee to Aid Spanish Democracy). Besides the fronts proper, there were organizations that were only partially infiltrated by Communists. Some of the target organizations were able to repel Communist infiltration and influence (American Veterans Committee, National Association for the Advancement of Colored People, American Civil Liberties Union); other targets proved more vulnerable but were never completely captured (Southern Conference for Human Welfare). All kinds of fronts and target organizations had one thing in common, however: they provided an opportunity for Communists to mobilize people outside the party for support of one or more of the party's aims. Party fronts were by far the most important device the Communists had for the magnification of the party's influence.

A brief examination of the International Workers Order (I.W.O.), an organization primarily for immigrant workers and easily the largest Communist front in the postwar period, reveals the advantages that fronts had for the party. The party founded the I.W.O. in 1930, when Communists and other Left-Wingers split off from the Workmen's Circle, a Jewish social-democratic fraternal organization. Recognizing the opportunity to reach vast immigrant groups, the Communists pushed I.W.O. work hard. The I.W.O. became a powerful organization through the sale of life-insurance policies (incidentally, they were excellent ones), agitation against prejudice toward minority groups, and the exploitation of immigrants' interest in their country of origin and their cultural nationalism. At the I.W.O.'s high tide in 1947, it had 184,398 members holding insurance policies in the sum of $122,234,513. There were fourteen constituent organizations of various nationality groups in the I.W.O., of which the largest by far was the Jewish Peoples Fraternal Order. There were also 261 general lodges for English-speaking members, most important in the Negro communities of New York and Chicago, and to a lesser degree among French, Norwegians, and Chinese.[21]

The I.W.O. held many advantages for the party. Most importantly, it afforded the party a degree of access to foreign-language groups, which together form a significant part of the American working class and which, because of their relative isolation from anti-Communist American culture, seemed to the party to be a fruitful field for activity. The insurance policies brought the immigrants into the organization, and once there the Communists could go to work on them ideologically, developing sympathizers and even recruits. I.W.O. leaders spread the Communist line as clearly at the organization's meetings as ever did the *Daily Worker*.[22] The I.W.O. provided the party with mailing lists, which was no insignificant matter when one considers that nearly a million people were associated with the I.W.O. at one time or another. The party used the I.W.O. to give a distorted impression of support for its line. When I.W.O. conventions passed resolutions supporting the party's position on various matters, the Communists pointed to the resolutions and said that here was the view of 185,000 people. It was nothing of the sort, of course, because most I.W.O. members were apolitical people who had no understanding of the resolutions and who were in the I.W.O. solely for its capitalistic insurance benefits.

Important, too, was the financial aid the I.W.O. gave the party. Most front organizations were a drain on the party's financial resources, but with the I.W.O. the situation was reversed. The I.W.O.

subsidized the Communist press, which chronically pleaded for more money, with frequent large advertisements. During the period 1944-46, the I.W.O. paid the *Daily Worker* over $30,000 for advertising, and over $35,000 to the *Freiheit,* sometimes called "the Yiddish *Daily Worker.*" In 1946 alone, the I.W.O. spent $37,570.48 for advertising in various Communist periodicals.[23] Furthermore, the I.W.O. paid Communist cadres the best wages in the Communist movement, and thereby relieved the party of a financial obligation. It is also quite probable that the party collected salary kickbacks from Communist cadres in the I.W.O., as it was known to do in the 1930's. All in all, it was a dark day for the party when in 1950 the State of New York rescinded the I.W.O. charter and took over the administration of the insurance program itself.

An individual's membership in a party front may mean any number of things, including almost nothing at all. All kinds of people belonged to Communist fronts and for a vast variety of motives. Many were party members. Many were fellow travelers, people who were sympathetic with some or all of the party's aims but for some reason—fear, inertia, a principled reservation about the party, unwillingness to accept party discipline, or a calculated design to escape the stigma of actual membership—did not actually join the party. But the important front groups contained thousands who were neither party members nor fellow travelers. Many went into front organizations with at least a dim awareness that Communists were active in the front but feeling that the Communists' presence did not present a serious matter. To some people on the Left, the party represented the extremity of their own leftist tendencies; they were not willing to follow their own tendencies, but they were willing to co-operate with Communists on matters that were important to them. Other front members were even mildly anti-Communist but thought the effectiveness of the front in some cause or other outweighed the handicap of the Communists' participation. Still others joined front groups utterly unaware of Communist activity in the front, believing that these people sometimes accused of being Communists were actually genuine progressives being smeared by reactionaries. Some people stayed in organizations after they had become fronts in order to fight the Communists.

The party's incessant cry of "Red baiting" tended to keep non-Communists in front organizations. Any kind of criticism of the American party, of the Soviet Union, or of anything Communist, even if temperate, inevitably brought from Communists the charge of Red baiting. The Communists argued that all criticism of Communists or Communism was "fascist," asserting that it divided the opponents of fascism and thereby strengthened reaction. Since Hitler and Mussolini had indeed done what Communists accused all critics of the party of doing, the Communist Red-baiting cry, which amounted to "fascist baiting," had some effect.

The various "schools of Marxist studies" were one of the Communists' most effective devices for recruiting and propagandizing. Immediately after the war, there were several of these schools, five of them in the metropolitan New York area alone: the Jefferson School of Social Science, the School of Jewish Studies, the George Washington Carver School in Harlem, the Walt Whitman School of Social Science in Newark, and the Tom Paine School of Westchester. Others were the Samuel Adams School in Boston, the Tom Paine School of Social Science in Philadelphia, the Ohio School of Social Science in Cleveland, the Abraham Lincoln School in Chicago, the Joseph Weydemeyer School of Social Science in St. Louis, the Michigan School of Social Science in Detroit, the Pacific Northwest Labor School in Seattle, and the California Labor School in San Francisco.

Of these schools, the Jefferson School was the biggest and most important. Started in 1944, when two smaller institutions merged, the Jefferson School had more than 45,000 students in its first four years. Its building at Sixth Avenue and Sixteenth Street was so busy that the directors opened another "campus" in the Brownsville section of Brooklyn in 1946 and conducted extension courses all over the New York metropolitan area.[24] Ostensibly, the school had no direct connection with the party, but actually the relationship was very close. Instructors and other officials were party members, and the fact that instructors were dismissed when they got into difficulty with the party indicates that party conformity rather than academic distinction was the primary criterion for faculty membership. Surely, the illusion that the Jefferson School was independent of the party was difficult to retain when national party headquarters moved into the school's building in the early 1950's.

In some respects, the Jefferson School was only an adult-education center with a Communist slant. There were courses in art appreciation, American history, trade-unionism, philosophy, health, and literature. But there was also in the school an Institute of Marxist Studies, which taught a three-year course in Communist theory. The institute was part of the training of members for party leadership.

Besides the more or less permanent party schools, the party occasionally established temporary schools for the ideological indoctrination of new party members. In 1947, for example, there were at least two such temporary schools in Harlem, the Harlem Leadership Training School and the Maceo Snipes School. Most Negroes who joined the party did so because of the party's practical work for Negro rights rather than for any Marxist reasons. Consequently, when Negroes discovered the true nature of the party, they very commonly dropped out, thereby causing a more rapid membership turnover rate for Negroes than for the membership as a whole. In order to keep Negroes in the party, ideological indoctrination was a necessity, and the Harlem schools tried to provide it through fifteen hours of instruction in basic Communist ideology. These schools made no pretense of being adult-education centers.[25]

The party press served many functions: it propagandized among non-Communists, it provided an instrument for party building, it educated party members, it served as a bulletin, and it even, on rare occasions, served as a forum for discussion of divergent opinion. To American leftist groups, a newspaper or periodical is indispensable. Indeed, some leftist groups are hardly anything more than a list of subscribers to a fugitive journal. The party recognized the importance of its press and made sacrifices to keep it going and strengthen it. The party poured a great deal of money into the *Daily Worker,* which never was able to support itself after the war. In 1947, for example, the party budgeted $222,000 to make up the paper's deficit.[26]

Curiously, as important to the movement as was the *Daily Worker,* the party was never able to get even a majority of members to subscribe to it. Nearly all Communists read the *Worker,* the *Daily*'s Sunday edition, available by separate subscription, but the total circulation of the *Daily* was usually about one-third of the party's membership. Federal postal laws require that publications using second-class mail and appearing more frequently than monthly publish a sworn statement of their circulation in the first issue to appear in October. The *Daily* did not always observe this law closely—from 1946 through 1948, it did not publish its circulation—but the law forced it to publish some useful data. In 1945, the *Daily*'s average circulation was 22,220. It grew to 23,400 in 1949. The Sunday *Worker* had a circulation of 67,066 in 1946, 67,566 in 1947, and 64,348 in 1948.[27] The primary reason for the failure of most of the membership to read the *Daily* was probably that as a newspaper it was sadly deficient. It could not hope to compete with the general press in news coverage and features, although it tried. And as a propaganda sheet, the *Daily* was usually abominably dull. Anyone familiar with the party's position, as were most of its readers, seldom found anything in it that was surprising. The *Daily* was as predictable as the tides. Communists not only did not read the *Daily,* but they were openly critical of it. In 1946, the editor complained that he had "even heard of discussions in Party organizations where the paper was actually condemned as if it were a paper belonging to the enemy." [28]

The *Daily* had internal difficulties, too. For years, it did not have really effective editorial management. Browder had been the editor in chief, but actually he had little to do with the paper's day-to-day activities. When Louis Budenz was managing editor, much of the political direction came from Jack Stachel, a national committee member, but Stachel did not bother himself with journalistic routine. There had not been a *Daily* editor who was both an able journalist and a top political figure in the party since the days of Clarence Hathaway in the 1930's.

When Budenz left the party in October 1945, the *Daily* staff asked the ninth floor for the appointment of someone with party power who was really interested in journalism. Dennis in time appointed Morris Childs, whose qualifications were meager on both scores. The staff grumbled about Childs's appointment, but, typically, it did nothing but grumble. Childs's appointment did not sit well, either, with the extremely "hard" leadership of the New York State organization, Thompson and Davis. Childs's health was not good, and he knew he was looked upon with disfavor. When he returned from covering the Moscow foreign ministers' conference in early 1947, he asked the ninth floor for a leave of absence. At the June 1947 meeting of the national committee, Dennis announced Childs's leave of absence and moved the appointment of John Gates, a national committee member and the head of the party's veterans commission. Gates did not have journalistic experience, although he proved to be a capable editor, but he did have a stronger position in the leadership than either Budenz or Childs. The *Daily* staff was satisfied with his appointment.[29]

The *Worker,* somewhat larger than the *Daily,* containing even a magazine section in the years just after the war, was considerably more useful to the party. Its news columns summarized some of the more important stories that had appeared in the *Daily* the previous week, and the columnists saved some of their better material for it. But as important as the *Worker*'s content was its method of distribution. Though copies were sold by mail and on newsstands, the party worked hard at personal delivery to make contact with non-Communists. Every party club was expected to order a bundle of *Worker*s each week. Then, on Sunday, the club would hold a "Sunday mobilization" to distribute the papers, selling them from door to door, hoping to interest new people. "We look upon the Sunday mobilization not only as a means of selling papers but as a means of getting the Party into homes of the community." Conscientious Sunday mobilizers carried subscription blanks and recruiting cards with them.[30]

On the West Coast, the party's paper was the *Daily People's World,* published in San Francisco. The *World* tried to maintain the fiction that it was not a party paper, but only a Left Wing labor sheet. It is true that the *World* did not concern itself as much with strictly party matters as did the *Daily Worker,* but the difference was due partly to the fact that the California party in general tended to look inward at itself less than did the party in New York. But the *World* was the party's paper, nevertheless. It carried the *Daily Worker* columnists, and staff men moved back and forth between the two publications. Periodicals intended only for Communist eyes frankly disclosed the connection of the *World* to the party. In 1946, a party organization report praised the California party for having the *World* "on the agenda for every meeting," and another periodical announced that "The Communist Party of California has just launched a drive for 10,000 *People's World* subscriptions and renewals in the next four months." [31]

In 1947, the party began a weekly paper in Detroit, the *Michigan Herald,* but the venture soon failed, and the party fell back upon the device of a special Michigan page in copies of the *Worker* mailed to that state.[32] The special page for local matters was also used at various times for New England, eastern Pennsylvania, western Pennsylvania, the South, Ohio, and Chicago (the DuSable edition).

Some foreign-language newspapers followed the Communist line. Of these, the *Morning Freiheit* of New York, a Yiddish daily published in the same building that housed party headquarters and the *Daily Worker,* was the most important. Its circulation in 1947 was 20,911, roughly the same as the *Daily Worker*'s.

The party also had a few magazines. The party itself published

Political Affairs, a monthly devoted to Communist theory and official definitions of party line. As a monthly, *Political Affairs* was not required by law to publish its circulation figures, but in 1946 it conducted a drive to raise its circulation to 12,500.[33] *New Masses,* later *Masses & Mainstream,* followed the party line in literary and general cultural affairs, trying to reach a broad audience. *Jewish Life,* which once had been published by the New York State organization, was an English-language periodical devoted to Jewish culture. There were also the organs of the various front organizations, notably *Fraternal Life,* published by the I.W.O. and the *American Slav,* published by the American Slav Congress.

The party maintained two firms, International Publishers and New Century Publishers, for books and pamphlets. The party established International in the 1920's, partly with money given by A. A. Heller. Heller, a Communist and a successful businessman, had recently sold his air-reduction firm to a larger competitor. This Communist publishing house, founded with capitalist profits, specialized in Marxist "classics." New Century, headed by Weiner, specialized in party pamphlets. Both firms were very busy. In 1946, the Communists published through these houses over two million copies of their publications, and midway through 1947 they were running ahead of 1946.[34]

INDICATIONS OF PARTY STRENGTH

The best single index of the party's strength is the number of members it had. Fortunately, the size of its membership rolls at different times can be determined with reasonable accuracy. To determine Communist influence precisely is another matter. We can only note indexes of Communist strength or weakness and generalize from them.

Earl Browder has stated that when he was removed from leadership in the summer of 1945, there were from 75,000 to 80,000

C.P.A. members, and John Williamson roughly verified Browder's estimate in a report in late June 1945. The year 1944 had been a banner year for recruiting. The Communists that year enrolled an average of 4,275 new members a month. Many of these new converts soon quit, but there is no record of how many did so.[35]

Apparently, however, this large party was not well organized and efficient. Dues payments were irregular. Before the war, dues payments had averaged 85 per cent, but they declined to 71 per cent in the last six months of 1944 and to 58 per cent in the first five months of 1945.[36] The leadership complained about the lack of effectiveness and the ideological backwardness of many members. "In Detroit, where two-thirds of the membership is less than a year in the organization, and where not even 10 per cent has been in the organization for a number of years, many of the tasks handed down to the clubs are either not tackled at all or inadequately fulfilled." In Detroit, "the cadres are not only without previous experience as club leaders . . . they are in the majority new members themselves. Most of the club leaders in Detroit are not ten steps ahead of the members, and the average member differs little in political development from a progressive trade unionist." Chicago and New York, where there were over 5,000 members of long standing, who had been in the party for years, had another kind of difficulty: in those centers, the experienced members tended to do all the work, leaving the recruits untrained.[37]

Inevitably, many members left the movement during the 1945 upheaval. Some sided with Browder and quit. Others were formally expelled, and still others were informally dropped. Browder estimated that between 20,000 and 30,000 left the party in the first few months after the upheaval, and his estimate again is borne out by other evidence.[38] In late 1945, the party conducted a membership registration, the best way for the organization to do its membership bookkeeping. The registration showed the membership to be about 53,000. But in 1946, the Communists conducted a vigorous recruiting campaign and enrolled about 20,000 new members during the year, bringing their total to about 73,000, only slightly less than there had been in the C.P.A. before the Duclos letter.[39]

Foster's boast in January 1947 that the party had then more members than ever before in its history reflected more a pride in his leadership than a scrupulous regard for fact, but the party was undeniably vigorous. In April 1947, Communists made 110 local radio broadcasts and two national network broadcasts. In March and April, they distributed 4,500,000 leaflets.[40]

The party was also quite successful at raising money. When, in March 1947, Secretary of Labor Lewis B. Schwellenbach proposed outlawing the Communist Party, the party responded with an "Operation Fighting Fund" and hoped to raise $250,000 in twenty-five days. It obtained that sum in only twenty days, whereupon it set a new goal, $300,000 higher.[41] San Francisco Communists collected $6,667.95 at a mass meeting called on three days' notice, and they were especially proud of their ability to get "regular contributions from non-Party contacts." [42] All in all, early 1947 appears to have been the high tide of Communist strength in the postwar period.

The party enabled itself to grow in 1946 and early 1947 by exploiting every possible grievance of any significant group. The housing situation was particularly acute at that time, and the Communists capitalized on the situation to the hilt.

For example, there was the case of Michael Gorglione, a resident of New York's Greenwich Village with no particular political convictions. He and his wife, each of them elderly, had a rent-free apartment in exchange for his services as superintendent of the fifteen-tenant building. In April 1946, the landlord fired Gorglione and, without a court order, had the Gorgliones' furniture moved into the street. The couple, who had a son in the Navy, had nowhere to go. A small crowd of Villagers, apparently not Communists, saw the eviction, became angry, and moved the furniture back into the apartment. At this point, the Communist Party moved into the situation. Mrs. Clarina Michelson, the local section organizer, "mobilized" the neighborhood. She prepared and distributed leaflets explaining the case, rallied the support of fifty

neighborhood leaders, including the Gorgliones' priest, and per-
sauded the landlord that the tenants were satisfied with Gorglione's
work. The landlord consented to rehire the elderly Italian and to
let the couple continue to live in the building. The Gorgliones
were naturally grateful for the party's work in their behalf, which
had some similarity to the kind of "social work" Tammany Hall
had once been famous for, and Mrs. Gorglione expressed her
thanks at a public meeting of the Greenwich Village section. At
the meeting, two young Italian-Americans joined the party because of the Gorglione episode, and scores of others became more
kindly disposed toward the Communists.[43]

Even more successful was the party's exploitation of the de-
plorable housing situation in the Harlem tenements. In May 1946,
the Abe Lincoln party club of Harlem staged a mass meeting on
housing at the corner of Lenox Avenue and 117th Street, in the
heart of Harlem. From this meeting there grew the United Harlem
Tenants and Consumers Organization, operated by Communists
but with a considerable non-Communist following. Tenement
dwellers were happy to join the organization if it promised to improve their housing conditions, and, once in the tenants' group,
they were likely targets for Communist recruiters. The party got
all twenty-three tenants of one particularly bad building into the
tenants' organization, and recruited fourteen of these into the
party. Similar tactics were successful in the Bronx. Joe Jackson,
Chairman of the Melrose club of the Bronx, reported that the
party had done extensive recruiting through a tenants' organization. "Two houses are solidly Communist, from cellar to top floor.
Concentration, brother." The Chicago party had similar but less
spectacular results in the heavily Negro South Side.[44]

Other issues proved fruitful to the party. Many employers in the
Bedford-Stuyvesant area of Brooklyn, a Negro neighborhood, refused to hire Negroes. With only a few people, the Communists
there in 1947 began a campaign to change the employers' minds.
The issue was popular in the neighborhood, and non-Communists
did much of the picketing of offending stores. Many shop owners

capitulated, and in the process the party got thirty neighborhood recruits. The party also did its utmost to capitalize on the wave of strikes in 1946. The Jefferson School sent a chorus around to picket lines to sing party songs and distribute free copies of the *Daily Worker,* and John Williamson urged members to exploit strikes to the fullest, to "understand that now is the time to recruit." [45]

The party's organizational secretaries were careful to avoid revealing much in their published reports about the party's membership composition, but they let slip quite a bit at times. We can, for example, determine the party's geographical distribution with considerable accuracy. The party was overwhelmingly urban, and it was strongest in the very big cities. The bigger the city, the more concentrated was Communist strength. An estimated one-third or a little more of the national membership was in New York City alone. The borough of Manhattan in June 1947 had 11,080 party members, more than any industrial state, such as California, Illinois, Ohio, Michigan, or Pennsylvania.[46] In June 1946, the *Worker* inexplicably printed a table showing the extent of recruiting done in the first five months of the year, with a breakdown by states and regions. The New York party acquired over 6,000 new members. California was next with 1,598, and Illinois next with 1,175. Texas recruited more than western Pennsylvania, 276 to 174, and Louisiana more than Wisconsin, 125 to 111, but, in general, the South did not have much of a movement. Montana recruited only three, Utah only eight, and North and South Dakota, New Mexico, Arizona, and Wyoming none at all.[47]

Good statistics on the class or occupational composition of the party are not available, but it is obvious that the membership was not strong among those who toiled in mines, mills, and factories. The Communists tried hard to expand their working-class membership. In recruiting drives, it set itself quotas of industrial workers—Ohio in 1946, for example, was to fill three-fourths of its recruit quota of one thousand with industrial workers—but the party had to admit, "In such states as New York and California [the two most important] . . . the present membership is not predominantly working class in composition. . . ." [48]

Nor is it possible precisely to describe the party's ethnic composition. In the years just after the war, Negroes proved relatively easy to recruit. Rose Gaulden, a Harlem party leader, reported that a few people even walked into Harlem party headquarters without any previous contact and said they wanted to join. One-third of the 1946 recruits were Negro. But, once recruited, Negroes did not stay. "We attract the Negro people because of our militant fight on issues which concern them. But we have not yet found the medium to train and hold our new members." [49] The Communists had some strength, but not much, in the New York Puerto Rican community. Puerto Rican migration to New York increased tremendously after World War II, but Communist strength among these people declined just as they were becoming a significant part of the New York population. In November 1952, the party regretfully announced "a drop of 80% [among Puerto Ricans] in the past few years." Typically, the party put the blame for the loss on Browder. [50] A significant proportion of the membership was Jewish, although statistics are not available. The Yiddish *Freiheit* had almost as much circulation as the *Daily Worker,* but this fact does not mean much—many readers of the *Freiheit* were not party members and there were unquestionably many Jewish *Daily* readers. Nor are there statistics on the numbers of party members who were immigrants or of recent immigrant background. It is likely that there was a higher proportion of immigrants in the party than in the national population, but it is questionable that the proportion was higher than that of the cities where the party was strongest.

Strong as the party was in 1946 and 1947, it had a great deal of "fat" in it; it had the same kind of organization problems it had had in 1944. The organization secretary complained constantly about the failure of many members to behave in an accepted Bolshevik manner. Winston regretted that in building mass movements too many party members became so deeply involved in whatever struggle there was at the moment—housing, the campaign against passage of the Taft-Hartley Act, strikes, or whatever—that they slighted their strictly party duties. "There is a tendency . . . to place the Party in the background. In practice, the Party becomes a secondary matter; everything else is primary and the Party is secondary." And many members were quite inactive. The Negro members were especially lax about party work. Winston even asserted, "The bulk of the [Negro] membership we never see from one registration to the next." [51] Very significantly, the rate of dues collection was poor. In the first quarter of 1947, slightly less than half the party members were up to date in their dues payments.[52]

In late 1947 and early 1948, the party's membership began to shrink rather seriously, and the party was never able to reverse that downward direction. The Communists reached the pinnacle of their postwar influence in the Wallace movement of 1948, but their own organizational strength had already begun to wane. When the party met in its fourteenth national convention at New York in early August 1948, Organizational Secretary Winston had to report a decline in membership to slightly more than 60,000, a net loss of roughly 13,000 in eighteen months.[53] Neither the Communists nor their opponents realized it at the time, of course, but the long, slow ebb tide of the American Communist Party had begun.

THE COMMUNISTS AT THE POLLS

The Communist Party ran candidates for public office on its own ticket in several elections in the first few years after the war. These elections give the kind of statistics a historian likes to have, but it is difficult to determine precisely what the significance of a Communist vote is. When a Communist identified as such on the ballot made a poor showing, then obviously the electorate did not have significant Communist sympathies. But when a Communist made a good showing at the polls, what is signified? It possibly could mean that those who voted for the Communist candidate endorsed his position. It possibly could mean that many voters had a vague sympathy for the party's aims. And it possibly could mean that many voters were dissatisfied with the major-party candidates and voted Communist only because they had no other way to express their dissent. But it is clear that when a Communist running on his party's ticket received many votes those who voted for him, at the least, were not so anti-Communist that their attitude toward the party overrode other considerations.

A vote for a Communist or a pro-Communist on the ticket of some other party—New York's American Labor Party, for example—or in a nonpartisan election, such as many school-board elections, does not necessarily indicate support for the candidate as a Communist, because the voter might not have been aware of the candidate's Communist connection. Ohio Communists rejoiced in 1947 when A. R. Krchmarek polled 64,264 votes in the nonpartisan Cleveland school-board election even though he lost. Krchmarek was not widely known as a Communist then and was not identified as such on the ballot. It is probable that his Slavic name reaped him more votes than his party affiliation, since he was the only candidate on the ballot who had an East European name. Similarly, an Oakland, California, Communist named Emma Stanley received 23,087 votes to her opponent's 33,176 in a 1947 school-board election, but she was not identified as a Communist on the ballot. Another California school election is the best example of this kind of Communist electoral success. In 1950, when the popular mood of the nation clearly was anti-Communist, Bernadette Doyle, chairman of the Communist organization in San Diego County but not labeled as a Communist on the ballot, polled 605,-393 votes, 26 per cent of the total, for the post of state superintendent of public instruction. The fact that she was a woman and had a distinctly Irish name probably was the reason for her strong showing.[54]

Not surprisingly, the Communist Party made its best voting rec-

ord in New York City, and New York was the only city in the
nation to elect Communist officials after the war. From 1937 until
1947, New York had a complicated proportional-representation
system of elections to the city council, and under this system the
Communists enjoyed a measure of success. In 1937, Peter V.
Cacchione, of Brooklyn, ran for the city council and missed election by only about 300 votes. He won election in 1941 and again
in 1943, when Benjamin J. Davis, Jr., of Harlem, also won on
the Communist ticket. Each was re-elected in November 1945,
Cacchione by the largest vote possible under the proportional-representation system. Two candidates of the American Labor Party
(A.L.P.)—Mike Quill and Eugene P. Connolly—also won city
council seats in that election. When Cacchione died in office in
1947, the party and the city council engaged in a spectacular has-
sle over his council seat. The New York City charter provided that
when a councilman died his political party would name his suc-
cessor for the balance of the deceased's term, but in New York
one could not enroll with the election board as a Communist, and
Cacchione had not enrolled as a member of the A.L.P., as had
most Communists. Through this technicality, the council refused
to seat Simon Gerson, whom the Communists named to take
Cacchione's place. In November 1949, after Davis had been convicted under the Smith Act, the council ousted him under the city
charter provision that prevented convicted felons from holding
office. New York's voters in a 1947 referendum abolished pro-
portional representation, and after that the party never again made
a significant showing.[55]

In the 1946 Congressional and state elections, the New York
Communists supported A.L.P. candidates, but they ran two candidates for state office on their own ticket—Robert Thompson for
state comptroller and Davis for state attorney general. Thompson
received 85,088 votes and Davis 95,787. An analysis of their votes
reveals about what one would expect: the overwhelming majority
of their vote came from the poorer neighborhoods of New York
City. In Manhattan, the assembly districts with a significant Com-

munist vote were the Lower East Side, Harlem, and the extreme northern West Side. In Brooklyn, the Coney Island area, East New York, and the poorer parts of Flatbush turned in the highest Communist votes. The heaviest Bronx Communist vote came from the assembly districts just to the east of Webster Avenue, and the only Queens district to report a significant Communist vote was the area along the East River just north of Newtown Creek. But nowhere were the Communist candidates a threat to the major-party candidates. The Communists ran best in East New York, where they polled 3,495 votes. Democratic candidates customarily poll about 40,000 there.[56] All the neighborhoods with a significant Communist vote were low- or lower-middle-income areas with a high proportion of Negro or immigrant inhabitants.

No other part of the country returned such large Communist votes, but Boston's twelfth ward, Roxbury, a generally poor neighborhood with a considerable Negro and immigrant population, was a source of many Communist votes immediately after the war. In 1946, William Harrison ran for the Massachusetts General Court, the lower house of the legislature, on the Communist ticket and polled 3,124 votes, one-sixth of the total. The following year, a Communist candidate for city council from that ward received one-fourth the vote cast.[57]

California was the only other area to poll an important Communist vote. In 1946, the Communists conducted a write-in campaign for Archie Brown for governor, and he received 22,206 votes. Governor Earl Warren, with both the Republican and Democratic nominations, under the California cross-filing system, polled over 2,300,000, but Brown's total for a write-in candidate was fairly strong. The distribution of Brown's vote indicated where California Communist strength lay: he received 13,949 votes in Los Angeles County and 6,842 votes in San Francisco and Contra Costa Counties, both in the Bay area.[58]

Elsewhere in the country, Communist candidates did very poorly. The Communist candidate for governor of New Jersey in 1946 received only 4,031 votes from a total of 1,414,527 cast, and over three-fourths of his vote came from the counties adjacent to New York City. Michigan's Communists in 1946 nominated an extensive slate, but their most successful candidate, Abner W. Berry, a Negro comrade later to be a *Daily Worker* columnist, polled only 3,120 votes for secretary of state. In Indiana, in 1946, none of three statewide Communist candidates polled as many as a thousand votes, running behind Socialist and Prohibitionist candidates. Colorado Communists in 1946 made a frank bid for the Negro and Mexican vote by nominating one of each for their only candidates, but each polled only about 2,000 votes.[59]

Many conclusions might be reached from this quick survey of Communist voting power, but one that stands out is that except for a few large cities, notably metropolitan New York and Los Angeles, the Communists were unable to poll enough of a vote to cause majority-party candidates to look twice. Obviously, even in the two years of its relative strength immediately after the war, the party would have been hopelessly naïve to have entertained ideas of coming to power under its own name by the ballot box or of influencing any significant part of the electorate through its candidates' electoral activity. This the party realized, and it put its electoral emphasis upon creating other political parties in which it could work for its own ends. The high tide of this "coalition" policy was to come in 1948, and a former vice-president of the United States was to be the stalking-horse.

THE PARTY AND THE TRADE UNIONS

No survey of Communist strength would be complete without some attempt to estimate the number and influence of party followers in the trade-union movement. As noted in Chapter II, most of the trade unions in which Communists were influential were in the C.I.O.

The unions ultimately expelled from the C.I.O. as Communist

dominated and thus followers of policies inimicable to the labor movement were the following: United Electrical, Radio, and Machine Workers of America (U.E.), easily the largest of the "left" unions, and the third largest C.I.O. union, with a 1947 membership of about 500,000; Farm Equipment Workers (F.E.), about 65,000 members; International Longshoremen's and Warehousemen's Union (I.L.W.U.), the Harry Bridges union, with 75,000 to 100,000 on the West Coast waterfront and in the Hawaiian pineapple and sugar industries; American Communications Association (A.C.A.), a union of about 10,000 members with contracts in the telegraph field; International Union of Mine, Mill and Smelter Workers (Mine, Mill), 108,000 members in 1947, most of them in the Rocky Mountain nonferrous-metal industry but with some significant contracts in the eastern brass industry; Food, Tobacco, Agricultural, and Allied Workers of America (F.T.A.) with a membership in 1947 of 46,700; National Union of Marine Cooks and Stewards (M.C.S.), led by Hugh Bryson, about 7,000 members, mostly in Pacific shipping; International Fishermen and Allied Workers of America, a West Coast union of about 10,000 members; International Fur and Leather Workers Union, usually called the Furriers, Communist dominated since the mid-1920's, about 85,000 members; United Office and Professional Workers of America (U.O.P.W.A.), about 45,000 members in 1947; and the United Public Workers of America, another white-collar union, about 85,000 members.

There were four other important C.I.O. unions in which Communists had considerable power until the unions ousted the Communists from leadership or the leaders themselves broke with the party: National Maritime Union (N.M.U.), Joe Curran's union, which broke from the party in 1946-47; United Furniture Workers, which defeated a Communist-supported slate of officers for the first time in 1950; the Transport Workers Union (T.W.U.), the union of the fabulous "Red Mike" Quill, which broke in 1948; and the United Shoe Workers of America, which defeated the Communists in a 1946 struggle.

A few unions had a significant Communist caucus that could not fully control the organization. Most important of these was the United Auto Workers (U.A.W.). Until 1947, the R. J. Thomas–George Addes–Richard Leonard faction, which had the support of the Communists, controlled the U.A.W.'s executive board, although the anti-Communist Walter Reuther became U.A.W.'s president in 1946. The United Retail, Wholesale, and Department Store Workers Union had a noisily anti-Communist national leadership, but its large District 65 in New York, headed by Arthur Osman, was firmly in the Communist camp until well into the 1950's. Other such unions were the United Gas, Coke, and Chemical Workers of America, the United Packinghouse Workers, and, briefly, the Amalgamated Clothing Workers, for whom John Abt, in the 1950's to become the party's most heavily worked attorney, was counsel immediately after the war.

The Communists also controlled some of the state and city C.I.O. councils. Of these, the most important were the ones in New York City and California, but the party's followers were in every significant state and local council and had effective control in such places as Milwaukee, St. Louis, Detroit, and Minneapolis. The party's main purpose in these councils was to exploit the C.I.O.'s strength and prestige for party-line resolutions.

The party had its followers in the C.I.O. national office until 1947-48, when the C.I.O. began to clean house. Most important of these were Leonard Howard ("Len") DeCaux, a New Zealand-born graduate of Oxford, editor of the *CIO News,* and director of the publicity department, who resigned his post July 15, 1947, and Lee Pressman, who resigned as C.I.O. counsel in February 1948. Soon after the outbreak of the Korean war, Pressman testified before the House Committee on Un-American Activities that he had been a party member in the 1930's, and he clearly was close to the party after he was no longer a dues-paying member.

No A.F. of L. international union was under the control of Communists, but in New York City and Los Angeles there were strong locals under Communist domination. In Los Angeles, pro-

Communists or Communists controlled several of the numerous "Hollywood unions." In New York, the Communists controlled the painters' local, had considerable power in the local of the Hotel and Restaurant Employees' International Alliance, and had influence in the International Typographical Union local. There were many Communists in the International Longshoremen's Association—the party recruited 120 from the Brooklyn docks in the summer of 1947—but they never exercised any real power in the organization.

Not all or even most of the union leaders the Communists liked to call the "Left-Progressives" were members of the party. Among those who freely announced their party membership were Ben Gold and Irving Potash, of the Furriers, and Hal Simon, of U.E. Many of the Left leaders were more or less open about their activities around the edge of the party but did not assert actual membership. For example, Lewis Merrill, president of U.O.P.W.A. was until 1947 a trustee of the Jefferson School and a contributing editor of *New Masses,* and Max Perlow, general secretary-treasurer of the United Furniture Workers, was an open supporter of *Daily Worker* money-raising campaigns. Still others—R. J. Thomas, of the U.A.W., was a conspicuous example—were not Communists and did not accept the party's views but did accept the support of Communist fractions in their unions. Some union leaders were Communist in every respect but actual dues-paying membership. Harry Bridges is a case in point. In the many deportation proceedings against Bridges, the prosecution was never able to prove its contention that Bridges was a party member. He probably was not. But, for all practical purposes, his union was Communist led.[60]

The question of how much control the Communist Party could exercise over the Left union leaders was another matter, for the Left leaders were frequently torn between what the party wanted and what their union membership would allow. Not even in the most Communist of the C.I.O. unions was there ever a majority of members who were sympathetic to the party. Most union members were usually unconcerned with their leaders' political activities, but were anti-Communist when their political passions became aroused. The Left union leaders, therefore, had to tread softly, had to be careful lest their membership get the impression they were marching to the beat of the Twelfth Street drum. Sometimes, also, the leaders' loyalty to the party conflicted with their loyalty to their union. Mike Quill, for example, had his differences with the party over the five-cent subway fare in New York. The *Daily Worker* constantly battled against proposals to increase the fare, calling an increase a tax on the poor instigated by the real-estate interests,[61] but if Quill were to get a significant wage increase for his union members, there had to be an increase in the fare. What particularly irked Quill was that Gold and Potash, of the Furriers, old hands at extracting wage increases for their well-paid members at the expense of consumers, were against a fare increase. Finally, after differences with the party on other issues, Quill denounced the Communists in early 1948.

Still another factor preventing the party from using the Left trade-unionists as effectively as it could manipulate its political cadres was that some of them were using the party, rather than the reverse. In some unions, one could not rise in the union leadership unless one were a Communist or a pro-Communist, and some young men on the make joined for opportunistic reasons with no real ideological commitment. A disgusted former maritime worker in California summarized the situation well in labor slang: "After the unions were organized and put on a paying basis, then the scramble began for pie-card jobs. It was common knowledge in some unions that the only way to get elected to office was to get the support of the Left. So a lot of petty larceny opportunists, or just plain wishy-washy pie-cards, joined the Left and got themselves elected with criminal consequence later on."[62] The loyalty of an opportunist was as easily lost as it was gained.

Evidence that the party could not control the Left union leaders as it wanted to is seen in the frequent complaints of John Williamson, who became the party's labor secretary in mid-1946. Although Williamson tried to direct his forces at national C.I.O.

conventions from caucuses in his hotel room,[63] he was unable to get all the Left leaders consistently to toe the mark. In his reports, he complained bitterly about the Left leaders' behavior, attributing it to "Browder revisionism [which] left deep imprints in the thinking and practices of our trade union cadres." [64] Very likely the Left union leaders did yearn for the Browder period, when the party line had more frequently coincided with the beliefs of their union members.

The party's main handicap in the C.I.O., however, was that even if it could have made the Left union leaders behave like automatons it still would not have rallied a C.I.O. majority. Since the Communists were a minority, they had to accomplish their ends through co-operation with, or at least with the tolerance of, the non-Communists. They had to build and maintain what they so fondly called the "Left-Center coalition." The center, symbolized by Phil Murray, just would not go along with the Left when the party pressed for C.I.O. endorsement of its position on the Marshall Plan and the Wallace candidacy. In other words, the Communists' trouble was in their line. The non-Communist center in the C.I.O. steadily became the anti-Communist center, and, later, the results for the party were disastrous.

"THE LIFE OF THE PARTY"

A consideration of the special problem the Communists faced just after the war of how to handle returning Communist servicemen reveals a great deal about "party life." About fifteen thousand Depression-generation Communists went into the armed services during the war, and it was important to the party that these thousands return to the fold. The Communists created a special veterans committee, which put out a pamphlet to explain the Browder upheaval to the returning soldiers. They ran special classes for veterans. They had each club compile a list of returning party veterans, send the list to national headquarters, and call personally upon each veteran to "integrate" him back into the organization as quickly as possible. In May 1947, they sponsored the First (and last) National Encampment of Communist Veterans of World War II in Washington. But their special efforts failed. When an estimated one-third of the Communist veterans were back home, Robert Thompson confessed, "It is clear that a large percentage of these already discharged Party and YCL [Young Communist League] veterans are not being reached." [65]

The basic reasons why the party failed to recover many of its returning servicemen were very much entangled with two other basic party problems, neither of which the party ever fully faced nor even clearly recognized. The first of these problems was the dilemma of immersion into "party life" versus contact with people outside the party and the Left Wing movement. The second problem was that of the postwar drift—perhaps rush is a better word—to middle-class ways of life, such as the urban migration to the suburbs.

Active party members in the big cities lived a special kind of life, by the party's design somewhat isolated from the main stream of American life. To be an active member in New York, for example, was not just to be affiliated with a political group; it was to become fully involved, immersed, in a movement that permeated almost every aspect of life. Members read party literature and frequently not much else; their social life was largely limited to other members; nearly all their free time was taken by some kind of party work; when they went to the movies, they went to a Russian film at the Stanley rather than to see the neighborhood theater's Hollywood product; their cultural interests became the studied and synthetic folk culture of Pete Seeger and the hootenany, the self-conscious proletarianism of the *New Masses,* and the muscular primitivism of Hugo Gellert. The party spirit even entered family relationships, and such phrases as "a progressive marriage," to indicate the marriage of two Communists, and "a Communist home" were common.

The term "Communist home" requires special explanation. Two items from the *Daily Worker* in one 1947 month reveal the meaning clearly. A letter to the editor began, "We are a group of children, 10 to 11 years of age, who call ourselves the Roosevelt Club after a great man. Since there are many anti-labor bills, we feel it is our duty to help support the Daily Worker in fighting fascism. . . . We are enclosing with this letter $22.15 which we hope you will accept." [66]

The other item deserves full quotation:

If our Party-building drive can use a mascot, I hereby nominate the four-year-old daughter of the Hy Wallachs. This incredible daughter of the veteran section organizer is a Quiz Kid with a social conscience, the vanguard of the infant masses.

Vicky has invented a game called "Section," which all the kids on the block play. The game starts with 'lections to the Section "exec" (Vicky's always chairman) and lesser committees. Dire is the threat of being removed from the "exec" for scratching a playmate or other unsociable conduct. They have assignments of leaflet distribution (any scraps of paper will do) and Sunday mobilizations. The grown-ups are somewhat bewildered by some of Vicky's terms. A neighbor recently called on Mrs. Wallach to find out what Vicky had in mind when she called her daughter "undisciplined."

While "Section" is a game of fascinating words and forms, it is not entirely without content. After a brief "Section" meeting, the kids dispersed to their homes to urge a boycott of the anti-Negro film Song of the South.[67]

The reason that Communist leaders stimulated this kind of a Communist home and urged this special kind of party life was that it was a powerful force against backsliding and contamination by non-Communist ideas. It deepened the commitment of party members. To leave most organizations is a relatively simple matter, but to leave the Communist Party was to wrench one's very roots, to change one's whole life, to lose one's friends, to become an outcast.

While this kind of isolation had certain advantages for the party, it also had real disadvantages. Because most of their life was within the party and they had relatively little experience with outsiders, Communists were often unqualified for "mass work," for recruiting, and for co-operating with non-Communists in such "mass orgs" as the P.T.A., the co-op, or the union. It was terribly difficult for a non-Communist to respect the parents of a little Vicky. Furthermore, when a Communist did establish real contact with the outside world and with normal people—a phrase Communists themselves sometimes used [68]—the gap between the reality and their preconceptions, nurtured by years of party propaganda, was great. The release from isolation that Communists gained when they went into the armed forces was an important factor in the party's failure to regain its veterans.

Many Communist servicemen had never had friendships with non-Communists before the war, at least in their adult lives. They had never known anyone—or at least never lived with anyone —who associated the term "party line" with rural telephones rather than with ideology. The experience was disillusioning. They became aware for the first time that the "masses" were a good bit more "backward" than they had ever realized, but that the "backward masses" threw up some good specimens of humanity despite their ideology, or lack of it. Furthermore, as they saw how the workingmen of Europe and the majority of Asians lived, they began to wonder whether the lot of the workingman under American capitalism was so bad after all. Military service gave these Communists an opportunity to make a break with their pasts, and thousands of them seized it.

And the United States the veterans returned to was not the United States they had left, just as the Foster party many of them did not return to was not the Browder party they had left. The veteran had left a depression; he returned to an expanding economy. He had left a relatively stagnant society; he came back to social changes of bewildering rapidity. Thousands of young families packed off to the suburbs, to housing developments that grew almost overnight on what had been tilled fields. Families moved all over the nation. One-fifth of America's families changed their address each year. Each report of the census bureau was more startling than the last. In the general prosperity, couples who never thought they could afford children produced a crop of babies unprecedented in recent American history. Thousands of young men left home to go to college under the G.I. Bill of Rights and to begin an ascent at least part way up the social and economic ladder. This direction of American life had its effects upon the Communist party, especially upon the veterans and their generation.

"I can point to at least five couples of my acquaintance," wrote one Communist observer of social change in 1946, "who, before they had children, were active party members. When they had the first child, it became necessary to move from the city because 'you can't bring up a child in the city.' Then they lived too far out to participate in party activities. But that was not the real reason. The real reason is that they bought their home; they began to skimp here and there; mother had to do her own washing which took much more time than sending to the laundry and it saved a couple of dollars each week. The thing that happens to father is worse by far. Constantly his family needs more money. . . . He is an intelligent man . . . he has the experience to work in an administrative capacity and so he leaves the ranks of the workers. Don't tell me this is imagination. It is what I see happening all around me." [69] But the writer's plea to stay in the city and live the "party life" and create "Communist homes" fell upon many deaf ears. The Levittowns broke up most of the Communist neighborhoods of New York, where a child learned to read the *Daily Worker* at home and where a family that voted for Norman Thomas was considered reactionary. The trend that the complaining observer saw in 1946 was to grow to mammoth proportions.

PART TWO

THE
UNPOPULAR
FRONT

The present party line follows the broad path towards the people's front and people's democracy types of government now to be found in Eastern Europe. . . . Some liberals believe that a united front coalition would introduce a regime of "progressive capitalism," but this is a naive and dangerous illusion.

—WILLIAM Z. FOSTER, *The Twilight of World Capitalism*

FOUR: CREATING GIDEON'S ARMY—THE PROGRESSIVE PARTY

A month after the end of World War II, readers of *Political Affairs* got their first hint of the political plans of the top Communist leadership. An article on American politics was nearly as critical of President Harry S Truman and his five-month-old administration as it was of the most conservative wing of the Republican Party, and it ended with a preview of what was soon to become the party's official policy: "The progressive forces will have to find other political alternatives if the only choice narrows down to a hide-bound reactionary Republican Party with fascist overtones and a Democratic Party which refuses to make a real stand for a progressive program and is constantly in retreat." [1]

Party chairman Foster opened a meeting of the national committee on November 16, 1945, with a routine flailing of Browder and then yielded the floor to Eugene Dennis for the main report. The first part of Dennis's speech, a harangue against "American imperialism" and a prediction of depression, contained nothing unexpected. But soon he raised the question of a third party. He professed to see in the C.I.O., among Negroes, "among the followers of Wallace in the Democratic Party," and in the Fiorello La Guardia–Newbold Morris wing of the New York Republican Party, "a growing minority sentiment for building a national third party." One of the basic errors of the Browder line, he told the committee, was acceptance of the two-party system. Dennis did not propose establishing a third party immediately, "or even necessarily during the course of the 1946 elections," but something would have to be done before the 1948 Presidential elections. "The American people must have an alternative to the two-party strait-jacket; they must be in a position to have a choice in 1948 other than between a Truman and a Dewey or a Vandenberg." Then came the order: *"This is why it is necessary from now on to create the conditions and base for organizing a major third party nationally."* The Communists, however, must be cautious because a "majority of the labor and progressive movement still has to be convinced and won over for a third party . . . it is essential that the advocates of a third party do not weaken their cooperative relationship with those anti-fascists who do not yet favor a third party." Communists must not "abandon the struggle to mobilize the people to exert . . . mass pressure which can influence the course of the Administration," even if Truman is quite hopeless. Should Truman advance any progressive proposals, the party should support them but *"without entertaining any illusions, and without entering any long-term alliance with the Administration."* In other words, get what you can from Truman, but build a third party to defeat him in 1948.[2]

Thus, three years before the 1948 elections, over two years before Henry Wallace announced his Presidential candidacy, before Truman disappointed many liberals in 1946, even before the cold war was well under way, the Communist Party determined its 1948 electoral policy in rough outline. How the policy should be applied, the Communists had yet to decide. When, where, how, and around whom to form a third party were still open questions. Another open question, and apparently one on which there were differences of opinion among the party leadership, was whether the third party should be similar to the American Labor Party in New York, endorsing many of the Democratic candidates, including the Presidential nominee, or a completely independent third ticket. The Communists' pressure for a third party waxed and waned in 1946 and 1947, but the party leadership never swerved from this third-party goal decided upon immediately after the war.

Party hacks ground out copy urging a break with the two-party system. At times the pressure was relatively slight, and at times it was intense, but it never ceased. The associate editor of *Political Affairs,* V. J. Jerome, invoked Lenin's approval of a third party, the highest possible authority in Communist eyes. Jerome's argument was so involute and his style so verbose, even flatulent, that it is doubtful that many readers had the patience to unravel it, but his conclusion was clear: there must be a third party, "although every care must be taken against premature actions. . . ." [3] Dennis certainly was careful in a public address at Madison Square Garden in January 1946. He only touched the issue, saying the American people "can rely only on their independent strength . . . to promote independent political action of labor and all progressives in the struggle for a truly democratic domestic and foreign policy." [4]

Dennis was more explicit at the party's next national committee meeting. The party would not try to establish a third party for the 1946 elections, but "if possible—and it is preferable— steps toward forming a third party should be taken early in 1947." The question of whether the third party would endorse the Democratic nominee was still open.[5]

The party had already begun a little experiment to test the idea. Early in 1946, Samuel Dickstein, congressman from Manhattan's Nineteenth District, resigned to accept a state judgeship. The district scheduled a special election for the balance of his term. The A.L.P. first nominated an unknown, and the Democrats put up a Tammany district leader. But the Democrats soon withdrew their first man to nominate Arthur G. Klein, who had been in Congress back in the 1930's and had a good New Deal voting record. After Klein filed, the A.L.P. put in another new nominee, the well-known radio news commentator Johannes Steel.

The Communists freely announced why they got the A.L.P. to nominate Steel and make a real race. The district, running up Manhattan's East Side from the Battery to Fortieth Street, was a working-class area with a large Jewish and immigrant population, "a district well suited to test the burning issues of the day; and to register what new alignments may be in the making in the political arena." [6] Because Klein was such a strong New Dealer, Steel's candidacy was particularly significant.

There is no question that Steel was close to the Communist Party. At that time, he was a columnist for the *Daily People's World,* and he wrote for that paper throughout his campaign. He was invited to speak at I.W.O. conventions, where he peddled the straight party line.[7] In 1947, the Soviet Union gave Steel a visa to cover the Moscow foreign ministers' conference, breaking its own rule to grant visas only to the thirty-five American journalists approved by the American Government.[8]

Steel ran a very strong race. The New York C.I.O. endorsed him. So did the National Citizens Political Action Committee and the Independent Citizens Committee of the Arts, Sciences, and Professions. So did Secretary of Commerce Henry Wallace and former Mayor Fiorello La Guardia. On February 19, Klein polled 17,360 votes to Steel's 13,421. The Republican candidate, William S. Shea, received only 4,314. The election results elated the Communists.

In the fall of 1946, there was one important political development in the third-party plans. In September, Secretary of Commerce Wallace resigned under pressure after his famous foreign-policy speech at Madison Square Garden.

The Communists had always had a rather uncertain attitude toward Henry Wallace. During Wallace's first several months as Secretary of Agriculture in Roosevelt's first term, the Communists had regarded him as just another bourgeois politician—this was their view of Roosevelt and all the New Dealers—but they warmed up to him considerably during the Popular Front period after 1935. During the war, Wallace, as Vice-President, made several speeches full of the popular clichés and sentiments of the war-time Left, and the Communists began to portray him as something of a hero. They reprinted some of his speeches in their periodicals; they were delighted with his statements on his good-will tour of the Asian areas of the Soviet Union in the early summer of 1944.[9] Yet Browder never cared much for Wallace, and he had indirectly notified Wallace's personal political adviser, Howard Young, that the Communists would do no more to support Wallace's renomination for the vice-presidency than the trade unions would, and Browder did not think the unions were prepared to fight to the bitter end over the issue.[10]

Jacques Duclos, however, in his famous article of April 1945, had kind things to say about Wallace. Duclos implied that Wallace had a better record of opposing American monopoly than Browder had. After berating Browder, Duclos wrote, "In the United States the omnipotent trusts have been the object of violent criticism. It is known, for instance, that the former Vice-President of the United States, Henry Wallace, has denounced their evil doings and their anti-national policy." And then again: "The former Vice-President of the U.S., Henry Wallace, present Secretary of Commerce, said rightly that one cannot fight fascism abroad and tolerate at home the activity of powerful [reactionary] groups." [11]

American Communists were still ambivalent toward Wallace, however. In January 1946, Alexander Bittelman, a veteran second-echelon leader, regarded Wallace as the only hope of the Truman administration, praised his book, *60 Million Jobs,* and declared that Wallace "is destined to play a great role . . . if he can shed his illusions. . . ." But later in the year, the Communists were not optimistic. At a dinner meeting of the A.L.P., the *Daily Worker* said, Wallace "gave comfort to reaction. Wallace evaded the actual facts as they exist. His words were . . . a whitewash of the present imperialist course of the administration." The editorial ended: "Wallace's advice will scarcely be taken seriously by the workers and other progressives in the nation." In June, Wallace wrote an article for the magazine published by the Democratic national committee, arguing strongly against third parties, and the *Daily Worker* swarmed with protest.[12]

On September 12, 1946, Wallace delivered a speech on foreign policy at a Madison Square Garden rally sponsored by the National Citizens Political Action Committee and the Independent Citizens Committee of the Arts, Sciences, and Professions. The speech came to be of historic importance, although no one expected it to be at the time. The public that night was under the impression that Wallace's speech had the approval of President Truman. In the speech, Wallace said, "And just two days ago, when President Truman read these words, he said that they represented the policy of the administration." Before Wallace spoke, Truman had told reporters the speech had his approval.*

What Wallace actually said in his September 12 speech soon became remarkably twisted in the memory of both the American Left and the Right. Wallace stated his conviction on the necessity and possibility of peace, and he condemned a "get tough with Russia" foreign policy. But the heart of his speech was a plea for what a decade later would be called "peaceful coexistence." "Russian ideals of social-economic justice are going to govern nearly a third of the world. Our ideas of free-enterprise democracy will govern much of the rest. . . . By mutual agreement, this competition should be put on a friendly basis, and the

* There later developed a considerable controversy over the facts of Truman's "approval." Two days after the speech, Truman told reporters his earlier statement had been misinterpreted, that he had only approved Wallace's right to deliver the speech. Years later, Truman wrote in his memoirs that he had not read the speech at all before it was delivered and that Wallace had only referred to it briefly at the end of a conference on other matters on September 10. Wallace directly controverted Truman's memory. He said that he and Truman had gone over the speech page by page, that Truman "didn't have a single change to suggest," and that Truman had positively stated his approval of the speech's ideas. The question of which man's memory, if either, is accurate is interesting but not vital to this book. At the time of the speech, the public impression was that the Wallace speech had Truman's endorsement.[13]

Russians should stop conniving against us in certain areas just as we should stop scheming against them in other parts of the world." At another point in the speech, he referred approvingly to "practical regional political reservations," or, in other words, political spheres of influence.

The Madison Square Garden audience was unmistakably Left Wing. It booed and hissed when Wallace said anything it construed as critical of the Soviet Union. At one point he said that "we may not like what Russia does in Eastern Europe. Her type of land reform, industrial expropriation, and suppression of basic liberties offends the great majority of people of the United States." After this sentence, the hissing was so loud that Wallace's shouted extemporaneous remark could be heard over the radio but not in the Garden: "I'm talking about people outside New York City when I say that. Every Gallup poll will show it!"

Thereafter, because his radio time was rapidly expiring, Wallace omitted several sentences that might have drawn further vocal protest. Among them was this one: "The Russians should stop teaching that their form of communism must, by force if necessary, ultimately triumph over democratic capitalism—while we should close our ears to those among us who would have us believe that Russian communism and our free enterprise system cannot live, one with another, in a profitable and productive peace." [14]

The next morning's *Daily Worker* roundly damned Wallace. A news story, replete with editorial opinion, reported, "He attacked Republican reaction in the international field, and then proceeded to back the Truman administration, which is united with the Republicans in that field. . . . He advanced views . . . which covered up American imperialism's aggressive role." Senator Claude Pepper, of Florida, who also spoke at the Garden meeting, got the headline and favorable coverage. An editorial, entitled "Wallace Evades Issue," was quite harsh. "Wallace repeated the major fallacies advanced by most apologists for American imperialism and designed to cover up administration policy. . . . The Soviet Union should not interfere in the west, he said, and we should give her a free hand in eastern Europe. The entire concept is a false one. The struggle is between the aggressive Anglo-American imperialists who want to dominate the world and the democratic, antifascist, peace-loving peoples of the world. . . . The 'bi-partisan' foreign policy followed by the administration and now generally endorsed by Wallace is one of imperialist intervention." The next day's editorial was not quite as critical, but it declared that "Wallace glossed over the responsibility of American imperialist policy." [15]

The Communists were very unhappy with Wallace's speech; so was Harry Truman, as it soon developed. Two days after the speech, Truman told reporters he had not approved the speech. On September 18, Truman and Wallace had a conference, at the end of which Wallace told the press he would make no further statements or speeches on foreign policy until Secretary of State James Byrnes returned from the Paris peace conference. On September 19, Truman and Byrnes had a teletype conference, in which Byrnes said, in effect, either he or Wallace would have to resign. The next morning, Truman asked Wallace for his resignation, and Wallace readily submitted it.[16]

After Truman's September 14 statement to reporters, the *Daily Worker* staff had executed a quick about-face. The staff was in trouble with the ninth floor. In Dennis's words, "the Party leadership quickly, immediately, and unitedly overcame this particular, unpardonable mistake." [17] An editorial of September 15—five days before Wallace's resignation—was a little warmer toward Wallace. On September 16, James S. Allen hailed Wallace for refusing "to be browbeaten by the reactionaries into silence or into accepting . . . the program of encircling and isolating the Soviet Union." On September 17, a *Daily* editorial told the readers, "The labor and progressive movement . . . has the job of welcoming and supporting Wallace's initiative." Thereafter, the Communists were all out in their support of Wallace. By Christmas, few Communists remembered they had hissed him in the

Garden and in their newspaper. By Election Day in 1948, American conservatives had forgotten it, too.

From the very beginning of Communist third-party talk, there was a difference of emphasis between some of its harder, more leftist leaders, typified by Foster, "the old man," and more practical types, typified by Dennis and the *Daily Worker* staff. There appears to have been nothing even dimly suggesting a split, but Dennis and the *Daily Worker* staff were prone to emphasize a national third party in the image of the A.L.P., which would both co-operate with the liberal Democrats and pressure the Democratic Party to pursue "progressive" policies and nominate the kind of candidates the Communists might support. They were concerned lest they alienate independent liberals and labor leaders who were not ready to support an independent ticket. Foster, on the other hand, did not seem to care whether he alienated independent liberals and labor or not.

In two *Daily Worker* articles, Foster denounced "lesser evilism"—party jargon or "Communese" for the tendency, for example, for liberals to regard Truman as a lesser evil than Dewey. To Foster, a Truman was more dangerous than a Dewey precisely because he appeared more sympathetic to traditional labor aims, was more likely than a Dewey to attract the working class, but was fundamentally as committed to capitalism as a Dewey.[18]

But Dennis said the party could not afford to ignore the differences among major-party figures, and he clearly believed such Democrats as Wallace, Pepper, and Adolph Sabath were "lesser evils" than Truman. *Daily Worker* staff men declared it "a dangerous tendency" to see no difference between the Democratic and Republican candidates for governor of New York in 1946 —James M. Mead and Thomas E. Dewey.[19]

Eventually, the Russians resolved the difference in Foster's favor, as we shall see later, but until the fall of 1947, one could not be sure whether the Communists were for or against lesser evilism. After that, lesser evilism clearly was a kind of political leprosy.

Following the Democratic debacle in 1946, when the Republican Party won the Congressional elections for the first time since 1928 and swept most of the state elections, too, the differences between Foster and Dennis became even more noticeable. The Republican victory confirmed the necessity of a third party in both Foster's and Dennis's minds. Foster declared that the Democrats "will undoubtedly strive to put in the field a conservative Presidential candidate, but one with just enough liberal coloration, they hope, to fool the workers. . . . The only possible chance (a faint one at best) to get a progressive candidate from the Democratic Party leaders will be precisely by holding over their heads the threat of a new party." [20] Dennis was more sanguine. "It is possible, actually possible, for the third-party movement to facilitate the election of a progressive presidential ticket in 1948. Such a victory will be possible if this movement is so organized and broadened as to bring about a situation in which there can be a coalition candidate, backed by the independent and third-party forces, running as a Democrat." [21] Foster could agree with Dennis that the party "must move heaven and earth to create a united, progressive front . . . a coalition party," [22] but they disagreed as to whether such a party should or could pressure the Democratic Party or should declare a three-cornered race immediately.

But while Dennis and Foster preached their different emphases, there were developments on the non-Communist Left that were soon to puncture both their grandiose dreams.

NON-COMMUNISTS AND ANTI-COMMUNISM

The typical anti-Communist propagandist before the war was as much an opponent of social security or trade-unionism as of Communism. Indeed, he often thought social welfare legislation was Communism. Often as not, the anti-Communist propagandist was a superpatriot, like some of the leaders of the Daughters of the American Revolution or the American Legion. The typical anti-Communist congressman had close ties with the business community or represented a poll-tax district or both. The activity of these conservative anti-Communists, despite their intensity and shrillness, was quite ineffective. The Communist Party's strength and influence grew fastest in the late 1930's, when conservatives had the anti-Communist field almost to themselves.

The reasons for the ineffectiveness of conservative prewar anti-Communism are not difficult to discern. The primary reason was that the conservatives' anti-Communist message did not reach liberal and labor organizations, where the Communists naturally concentrated their efforts. In the organizations in which conservatives predominated, such as the D.A.R. and the Legion, Communist efforts were negligible, and in the organizations in which there was an opportunity directly to combat Communist influence, the conservative anti-Communists were without influence. The conservative anti-Communists were in no position to do any infighting against Communists; they could only swing at them from afar. Another reason for conservative failure was their usual "shotgun" technique. They did not aim truly at the Communists; they aimed at everything they considered left of center, and the center was to them a point somewhere among the conservative elements of the Democratic Party. Thus, for example, they occasionally called Roosevelt a Communist and frequently charged that Rexford Tugwell and other "brain trusters" were Kremlin agents. So many of their charges were ridiculously extreme, that many people tended to dismiss all anti-Communist criticism as the product of the Right lunatic fringe.[23]

There was one major exception to the conservative complexion of the anti-Communists—the Socialists or social democrats—and one small group of minor exceptions—the ex-Communist Party splinter groups. These Left Wing anti-Communists and their publications, especially the *Socialist Call* and the *New Leader,* provided more accurate and balanced accounts of the Communists than anything emanating from the conservatives, such as Elizabeth Dilling's *Red Network*. But they were few in number and insignificant in their national influence, and the fact that they were both anti-Communist and anticapitalist at the same time seemed unfathomable to the man in the street.

Few though they were, the Socialist critics of Communism were significant historically, for they created and kept alive an anti-Communist Left tradition, and from their nucleus was to grow after World War II a liberal anti-Communism of major proportions. From this tradition sprang the Americans for Democratic Action (A.D.A.) and the Liberal Party of New York.

In the spring of 1944, a group of social-democratic and liberal trade-unionists and intellectuals, led by David Dubinsky, president of the International Ladies Garment Workers Union and a former Socialist Party member, bolted the A.L.P., charged it with Communist domination and direction, and organized the anti-Communist Liberal Party. At first very small, despite their good poll for Roosevelt in 1944, the Liberals gained steadily in vote and influence. In the postwar decade, they became a potent force in New York politics, in some cases holding a balance of power between the major parties. The Liberal Party serves as a pressure upon the New York Democratic organization by providing independent liberal voters a "conscience line" on the ballot. It usually, but not always, nominates the Democratic ticket. As the liberals' anti-Communism increasingly gained followers, the A.L.P. went downhill and eventually died.

More important nationally was the founding of A.D.A. If one had to choose a date that represents a watershed in the recent history of American liberalism, one could do worse than to select January 4, 1947, when A.D.A. organized in Washington. From that day forward, American liberalism became increasingly anti-Communist, and this development had important effects upon the history of American Communism. One of the important factors in the Communist Party's isolation from the main stream of American life in recent years is the development of the *non*-Communist Left into the *anti*-Communist Left.

The development of liberal anti-Communism had been a slow, sometimes painful, and frequently bewildering process. Part of the style of American liberalism in the Roosevelt era was a soft-heartedness (and soft-headedness) toward the Soviet Union and an abhorrence of Red baiting. This frame of mind could not change overnight. Indeed, there are still some non-Communists with these values and assumptions. But they are comparatively few in number, and they have become fewer each year since 1945.

A brief account of recent left of center organizations will serve to describe the evolution of the division over the Communist issue in American liberalism. To begin with the political activities of the C.I.O., in July 1943, the C.I.O. executive board created the C.I.O. Political Action Committee (C.I.O.-P.A.C.), with Sidney Hillman, of the Amalgamated Clothing Workers, as chairman, to rally the labor vote for Roosevelt and other New Dealers in the 1944 elections. The following summer, the C.I.O.-P.A.C. set up the National Citizens Political Action Committee (N.C.-P.A.C.) to raise funds and mobilize liberals outside the trade unions, largely from the kind of people who in 1952 became known as "eggheads." Although originally intended to be only a temporary operation, the N.C.-P.A.C. decided in the spring of 1945 to become permanent and loosen its ties with the C.I.O.-P.A.C. Elmer Benson, former governor of Minnesota, became national chairman, and C. B. ("Beanie") Baldwin, who had served with Wallace in the Department of Agriculture, became executive secretary. Until 1947 and 1948, people with all sorts of political convictions were in the C.I.O.-P.A.C. and the N.C.-P.A.C. There were outright Communists, pro-Communists, liberals neutral on the Communist issue, mild anti-Communist liberals, and vigorously anti-Communist socialists of various kinds. Within the C.I.O.-P.A.C., the Communists were no more important than they were in the C.I.O. itself—a noisy and sizable minority—but Communist influence in the N.C.-P.A.C. was greater. Earl Browder had said that Minnesota's Communists worked closely with Benson in that state's politics,[24] and Baldwin remained as a top official in the Progressive Party after 1950, when almost all who were not Communists or fellow travelers had left the organization.

There was still another of the Left and labor political groups, the Independent Citizens' Committee of the Arts, Sciences, and Professions (I.C.C.A.S.P.), one of the strangest groups in the history of American politics. Founded to provide money and glamour for the cause of Roosevelt's 1944 candidacy, the I.C.C.-A.S.P. was filled with Broadway and Hollywood people and professional artists and writers; it could claim a record among political organizations for physical beauty, creative talent—and for political innocence. The political thought processes of the late Hollywood actor Humphrey Bogart are a case in point. In 1946, Bogart told a *Time* reporter he had joined I.C.C.A.S.P. because he had voted for Roosevelt in 1944 and wanted Harold Stassen for president in 1948. But if some of the members were babes in the political woods, the leaders were not. They knew precisely what they were doing. In 1946, a few members complained that the organization was rapidly becoming a Communist front. When a reporter asked I.C.C.A.S.P.'s chairman, the sculptor Jo Davidson, if this charge were true, Davidson replied, "Have you stopped beating your wife?" When Hannah Dorner, the executive secretary of the organization, who affectionately called the members "glamour pusses," was asked the same question, her reply was revealing: "Says who and so what? If the ICCASP program is like the Communist line, that is purely coincidental." [25]

Soon after Secretary of the Interior Harold Ickes resigned in February 1946, because Truman nominated oilman Edwin W. Pauley to be under-secretary of the Navy, he became executive chairman of I.C.C.A.S.P. The "Old Curmudgeon" was less than happy with his new associates, but it is significant that in 1946 I.C.C.A.S.P. could attract someone of his stature at all. He tried to resign in August, but was persuaded to remain until the 1946 elections. He quit very soon after the elections, but not before one final insulting frustration. Ickes had given a speech at Chicago in which he had said that the Soviet Union was creating international tension. The sponsors of the meeting found their mimeograph machine had conveniently broken down, and Ickes's speech was not distributed to the press. After leaving I.C.C.A.S.P., Ickes called Communism "a nonassimilable political ideology. A true progressive movement has no chance of success unless it rigidly excludes communists." [26]

On December 29, 1946, the N.C.-P.A.C. and the I.C.C.A.S.P. merged to become the Progressive Citizens of America (P.C.A.). The P.C.A. clearly was bent on a third party from its first meeting. Wallace spoke at the first meeting, and although he was still publicly committed to the Democratic Party and had campaigned for a few Democratic candidates in the recent elections, he told the new organization, to its delight, "We have less use for a conservative, high-tariff Democratic Party than we have for a reactionary, high-tariff Republican Party. If need be we shall first fight one and then the other." But when Wallace said, "We should have no allegiances outside this country," the audience was noticeably cool. The preamble of the P.C.A.'s program raised the question of a new party: "We cannot . . . rule out the possibility of a new political party. . . . We, the people, will not wait forever—we will not wait long for the Democratic Party to make its choice." And it did not wait long—exactly one year—before the P.C.A., with its claimed 36,500 members (18,000 from the N.C.-P.A.C., 18,500 from the I.C.C.A.S.P.), became the nucleus of the Progressive Party. The P.C.A.'s cochairmen were the former heads of the merged organizations, Dr. Frank Kingdon and Jo Davidson, but the executive vice-chairman, the man who actually ran things, was "Beanie" Baldwin, later Wallace's campaign manager. [27]

The division among liberals over the Communist issue was becoming sharper. In early 1946, the struggle between the Reuther and Communist caucuses in the U.A.W. was in the nation's headlines. The same year saw a fight between Joe Curran and the party in the N.M.U. In November 1946, the C.I.O. adopted its "resent and reject" resolution, and state C.I.O. organizations here and there went much further. The New Jersey C.I.O. convention adopted by overwhelming vote a strong anti-Communist resolution, and the Massachusetts organization banned Communists from its offices.[28]

A National Conference of Progressives held at Chicago in September 1946 indicated two simultaneous trends in the liberal community: liberals were disappointed with the Truman administration and the alliance of northern Republicans and Southern Democrats in the Seventy-ninth Congress and were eager to revive the New Deal spirit; and they were becoming increasingly divided over the question of Communism, both at home and abroad.

The Chicago conference embraced a wide range of political and economic opinion. The C.I.O.-P.A.C., the N.C.-P.A.C., and the I.C.C.A.S.P. issued the call to the conference, which was signed also by Philip Murray, James Patton, of the National Farmers' Union, Walter White, of the N.A.A.C.P., A. F. Whitney, of the Railroad Trainmen, and Clark Foreman of the Southern Conference for Human Welfare. Among others involved in the conference were Hannah Dorner, Henry Morgenthau, Jacob Potofsky, of the Amalgamated Clothing Workers, the vigorously anti-Communist C.I.O. Secretary-Treasurer James Carey, and pro-Communist John Abt. A few months later, one would wonder that such a diverse collection ever could have assembled in the same room. But a common anxiety about the way affairs were going in Washington pulled them together. It must be remembered that it was not until mid-1947 that Truman appeared as a champion of liberalism, after a Republican Congress afforded him a conservative backdrop. The Democratic record on price control and inflation had been poor, housing was a mess, and Truman had even asked Congress for power to draft strikers in government-seized industries into the armed forces. In 1946, it seemed to the liberals that Truman would undo everything Roosevelt had gained.

If a common anxiety pulled the conference delegates to Chicago, the Communist issue blocked their unity. Angus Cameron, then of the publishing firm of Little, Brown and later to become an independent publisher of leftist books, moved that the conference go on record urging Henry Wallace to carry on his fight. The Wallace-Truman dispute was contemporaneous with the conference. The motion passed unanimously. No one moved that the conference declare itself for a third party, for third-party advocates knew that to raise the issue would only divide the group. The Communist issue could not be suppressed despite efforts to do so. Phil Murray departed from his prepared text in his speech to say he did not want any "damn American Communists meddling in our affairs."

Murray personified the confusion of liberals on the Communist issue. His course toward anti-Communism was hesitant and painful. After his Chicago remark, he disclaimed to reporters any intention of a Communist purge in the C.I.O. Yet in a few weeks, he raised the Communist question at the C.I.O. convention and pushed through the "resent and reject" resolution. And a few weeks after that he appeared to change direction again when he requested C.I.O. officers to join neither the P.C.A. nor A.D.A. Even in 1948, when he eased Lee Pressman out of the C.I.O., he arranged for Pressman to get a lesser job.

Confused as the picture was, the differences among liberals were sharpening quickly. The Chicago conference was the last major gathering of pro- and anti-Communist liberals. The Chicago meeting appointed a "Continuations Committee" to give the conference the semblance of permanence and to call a second conference in January 1947. A second conference never materialized. By January 1947, the split in American liberalism had taken organizational form with the establishment of the P.C.A. at the end of December and the founding of A.D.A. the next week.

A.D.A.'s origins trace directly to the social-democratic anti-Communism of the prewar period. In May 1941, a group of social-democratic and liberal intellectuals organized the Union for Democratic Action. U.D.A.'s first chairman was the theologian Reinhold Niebuhr, a former Socialist Party member, and its first executive secretary was James Loeb, Jr. U.D.A. never represented more than a handful of people, and in the spring of 1946, Loeb proposed that U.D.A. sponsor a conference aimed at broadening the organization. From Loeb's proposal and U.D.A.'s support came A.D.A., progressive and as opposed to Communists as to any other totalitarians.

Many liberals, most of them Democrats, were ready to join with those who believed in a socialist democracy and in a progressive anti-Communist movement. When U.D.A. called its conference, after first carefully seeing that no Communists or pro-Communists received invitations, many of the "big names" of American liberalism responded. In the new A.D.A. were such labor leaders as David Dubinsky, Walter Reuther, James Carey, George Baldanzi, and Emil Rieve. Among former New Dealers were Eleanor Roosevelt, Leon Henderson, Wilson Wyatt, and Paul A. Porter. Several young Democratic politicians, such as Hubert Humphrey, Franklin D. Roosevelt, Jr., and Richardson Dilworth, all soon to make their marks in politics, attended the meeting. Among the intellectuals were Reinhold Niebuhr, Elmer Davis, Bishop William Scarlett, Stewart Alsop, Robert Bendiner, Marquis Childs, Morris Ernst, A. Powell Davies, Louis Fischer, John Kenneth Galbraith, Saul Padover, Arthur M. Schlesinger, Jr., and James A. Wechsler.[29]

The Communists perceived the danger to them should A.D.A. and its kind of thinking grow, and their attack was immediate. Their first argument was to deny that, by definition, it was possible to be both liberal and anti-Communist. When this failed to impress many, they fell back upon their hoary devil-conspiracy theory. The whole thing was a "social democratic plot," instigated by "Wall Street" to prepare the way for "fascism." By citing the affiliation to A.D.A. of such people as Dubinsky and Professor George S. Counts, they claimed to document an association of A.D.A. "with the top reactionaries of the country." Dubinsky and Counts were no less than "Red-baiting Loreleis trying to lure liberals into reaction's swamp."[30] The Communists persuaded few. A.D.A. grew, and Left anti-Communism gained steadily.

NEW YORK AND CALIFORNIA: A DOUBLE GAME

The Communist Party set itself two main tasks in 1947, to be accomplished simultaneously. It had, first, to build a third-party movement; and, second, to persuade Henry Wallace to accept the leadership of the new party. At both tasks the Communists were successful.

Foster kicked off the 1947 program: "The Communist Party, which played an important role in the events leading up to the big C.P.P.A. campaign [one of many historical distortions about the 1924 La Follette movement in his *Political Affairs* article], must play a much more important one in the 1948 political struggle and in the building of the third party. . . . We must . . . make the question of building the new party our major task and leave no stone unturned for its realization." The job would not be easy, but it could be accomplished if "Wc . . . master every detail of the complicated general strategy and tactics necessary to lay the foundations for victory and the new party in 1948." [31]

The difference between Foster and Dennis over whether the third party should be a third ticket or a lever against the Democratic Party remained until later in the year, and in the summer of 1947, the Communists played a rather tricky double game. The Communists were fearful that if they pushed the third-party idea too hard in New York they might split the A.L.P., which still contained the Amalgamated Clothing Workers and other C.I.O. elements with primary political loyalty to the Democratic Party. So, as Robert Thompson explained they must,[32] the Communists played the third-party tune softly in New York, never saying more than that the A.L.P. should strengthen itself as a lever on the Democrats, saying nothing about an independent third Presidential candidacy. Simon Gerson explained the whole strategy after the critical A.L.P. county conventions and state C.I.O. convention were over. "Within the A.L.P. and the progressive labor movement in New York there are people who wholeheartedly support the principle of a third party but are not convinced about the necessity for a third ticket now. It was this central issue that had to be resolved if the unity of both the A.L.P. and . . . the State C.I.O. was to be maintained. . . . How was it resolved? By the two groups—the pro-third ticket forces and those who favored a third party but not a third ticket in 1948—agreeing on the necessity of building the A.L.P. as labor's political arm in New York while deferring for future consideration the question of a third ticket. It was on the basis of this policy that the A.L.P. county organizations remained united . . . [which] would have been impossible had the Wallace-for-President issue been placed before the convention for a vote." [33]

In California that summer, the Communists played a different game. While New York Communists lay low on the issue, California's Communists went all out. New York had the A.L.P., but California had no counterpart to it. The Communist task was to create a new party so that it could either pressure the Democratic Party from the outside, consistent with Dennis's emphasis, or strike out on its own as a third ticket, as Foster desired.

The convention of the Marine Cooks and Stewards at San Francisco passed a resolution calling for the establishment of a national third party, and Hugh Bryson, the M.C.S. president, circulated unions all over the country urging similar action. Communists and other "left progressives," including many on the staff of the Bridges union, tried to get their policies adopted first by the California Democratic committee meeting in late July, but they failed utterly. In fact, the Democratic statement on foreign policy equated Communism with fascism, called for a strong military-defense program, and endorsed the Truman Doctrine and the Marshall Plan. After this defeat, Bryson, later to be convicted for perjury for swearing in a Taft-Hartley affidavit that he was not a Communist, issued a call for a conference to be held in Los Angeles on August 24.

This conference, composed mostly of California Left union

leaders, a few Left Wing Democrats, and some followers of the Townsend old-age pension plan, including old Dr. Francis E. Townsend himself, listened to Bryson harangue against Truman's foreign policy. After a great deal of vacillation in the Townsend group, the conference declared itself the founding convention of the Independent Progressive Party (I.P.P.). California had the equivalent of the New York A.L.P. Bryson held the office of organizer and temporary chairman. He brought Elinor Kahn, who had been a lobbyist for the maritime unions, back from the East to be the state director when he moved up to be permanent chairman.[34]

Getting the I.P.P. on the California ballot was a difficult matter. California law required about 300,000 signatures to a petition, and gathering signatures became the I.P.P.'s first item of business. Foster and Pete Cacchione went to California to help out their West Coast comrades, and with hard work and thorough organization, the necessary signatures were obtained. As Foster put it, "Comrades, that was a major achievement." [35]

Things were progressing well for the Communists. The third-party program was on schedule. As late as September 1947, the plan was still to use a third party as a lever against the Democratic Party. In fact, Cacchione and Vito Marcantonio talked about a fight in the Democratic primaries and state conventions for Wallace delegates to the 1948 Democratic national convention.[36] Near the end of the month, the *Worker* published excerpts from a speech Dennis had given at Madison Square Garden earlier in September. "We Communists are not adventurers and irresponsible sectarians. We are not going to isolate ourselves. We never did and do not now favor the launching of premature and unrepresentative third parties or independent tickets. Such moves can only succeed and serve the camp of progress when they arise out of the collective decision and united action of a broad democratic and anti-war coalition." [37]

Such a tone from a Communist leader would not be heard again for a long time. For at that moment, Russian Communists were laying down a new line which the American Communists would note and then press ahead for Wallace's independent candidacy. The Russians appeared to support Foster's point of view. The changed emphasis of the party in the fall of 1947 is one of the clearest examples in the postwar period of the American Communists following the Russian lead, even when the American Communists themselves recognized the disastrous effect the Russian direction could have on their own party. "We are not going to isolate ourselves," said Dennis just before the news came of the formation of the Cominform. But we did isolate ourselves, Dennis would tell the party membership nine years later, and Dennis admitted that one of the major factors in the party's isolation was its 1948 electoral policy.[38]

THE RUSSIANS, THE COMINFORM, AND AMERICAN POLITICS

On October 5, 1947, *Pravda* revealed that at the end of the previous month there had been a secret conference in Poland of representatives of the Communist parties of nine European nations. The Russian leaders at the meeting were Andrei A. Zhdanov and Georgi M. Malenkov, both of whom were very close to Stalin. Others were Milovan Djilas and Edward Kardelj from Yugoslavia, Vulko Chervenkov and V. Poptomov from Bulgaria, Anna Pauker and George Gheorgiu-Dej from Romania, M. Farkasz and Joseph Revai from Hungary, Wladyslaw Gomulka and H. Minc from Poland, Jacques Duclos and Etienne Fajon from France, Rudolf Slansky and S. Basztovanski from Czechoslovakia, and Luigi Longo and Eugenio Reale from Italy. The subsequent careers of these delegates reflect much of the recent history of international Communism, and another meeting of those still alive today would be an interesting event. But in 1947, they listened united to a speech by Zhdanov, next to Stalin probably the strongest figure in the Russian party.

The precise content of Zhdanov's speech did not become known to the rest of the world until *Pravda* published it on October 22, but on October 5, *Pravda* published the texts of the resolutions adopted at the meeting in Poland. When Zhdanov's speech appeared, it was obvious that the resolutions were no more than a condensation of his speech; they even lifted some of his phrases word for word.[39]

The conference of the nine Communist parties was to have the greatest importance for the development of international Communism—indeed, for the history of the world—for the next few years. The conference established the Communist Information Bureau, or Cominform, composed of the parties represented at the conference. The Cominform's headquarters were in Belgrade until the Tito blowup in 1948, and then in Bucharest. Its establishment symbolized a new direction in world Communism. When the Comintern dissolved in 1943, the Communist parties of the world, at least ostensibly, had been cut loose from Russian direction. That the tie was not actually severed is indicated by, among other things, Browder's removal from leadership in 1945 upon orders from abroad. But with the Cominform's establishment, the "road to socialism" to be followed by the Communists of various nations was to be the one indicated on the Russians' ideological maps.

One of the Cominform's immediate purposes was the defeat of the Marshall Plan. The conference's manifesto declared that "the imperialist camp and its directing force, the United States of America, show a growing aggressive activity. . . . The Truman-Marshall plan is only a farce, a European branch of the general world plan of political expansion being realized by the United States of America in all parts of the world. The plan of . . . subjugation of Europe through American imperialism is complemented by plans for the subjugation of China, Indonesia, and South America." Therefore, the Communist parties of the world were to "place themselves in the vanguard of the Opposition against the imperialistic plans of expansion and aggression in all its manifestations." Zhdanov was even more explicit: "A special task devolves upon the fraternal Communist Parties of France, Italy, England and other countries."

The Communist parties of Western Europe were quick to execute the order. The Paris Communist newspaper, *L'Humanité,* fairly bristled with references to *"l'impérialisme américain."* [40] The French and Italian parties conducted several strikes over the next several months in an effort to hamper the economic recovery of their nations and prevent beneficial effects from the European Recovery Program.

Much weaker than their European comrades, the American Communists also did what they could to effect the same ends. They spurred on the third-party movement, gained effective control of it, and used it in an attempt to provide propaganda for overseas anti-Americanism. Foreign Communists could point to the American third party and assert that the United States was not united behind the Marshall Plan and the rest of American foreign policy, that American policy was only the result of insidious Wall Street machination.

With the publication of the texts of the conference's resolutions, the American Communists determined to push ahead with a third-party ticket, as distinct from just a third party, come what may. The conference manifesto had a clear meaning on East Twelfth Street: "In consequence the Communist parties should . . . unite and coordinate their efforts on the basis of a common anti-imperialistic and democratic platform as well as gather around themselves all democratic and patriotic forces in their respective nations." The manifesto also declared, "The main danger for the working class at this moment lies in the underestimation of its own strength and overestimation of the force of the imperialist camp." Zhdanov was equally clear and pertinent to the American Communists: "Communists should be the leading force in the cause of drawing all anti-fascist, freedom-loving elements into the struggle against the new American expansionist plans for the enslavement of Europe." [41] Within the American framework, this could only mean a third party with a third ticket.

The American Communists understood the meaning. The issue of the *Daily Worker* that carried the text of the Cominform resolutions declared in an editorial on the formation of the Cominform that "every American who is fighting mad at the profiteering trusts here at home" should welcome "this overseas resistance to the same crowd which is rooking him and his family and trying to wreck his unions and democratic liberties. . . . The nation urgently needs a strong anti-monopoly, anti-war coalition based on the Roosevelt-Wallace line." [42]

For another two weeks, the party leadership held off from revealing to anyone, even its most trusted followers in the C.I.O., that it had determined for a third ticket as well as a third party. The reason for the delay was that revelation of the plans might endanger the Communist position in the C.I.O., which was to meet in its annual convention in Boston October 13 to 17. If one of the Communist C.I.O. leaders knew of the decision, he might inadvertently reveal too much at the convention and touch off an anti-Communist explosion. The tactic worked well. Although Secretary of State Marshall addressed the C.I.O. convention, and Murray personally favored the Marshall Plan, the C.I.O. Left managed to prevent the C.I.O. resolution on foreign policy from supporting the plan explicitly. Furthermore, the Communists at the convention prevented the question of reaffirming the previous year's "resent and reject resolution" from even being raised. [43]

The day after the Boston convention, the Left union leaders in the C.I.O. had the new line on the third ticket explained to them at a meeting in New York City. In 1950, Mike Quill, who had broken with the party in early 1948, told the details of this meeting to a C.I.O. committee in Washington when the C.I.O. was about to expel the Bridges union:

On Saturday, October 18th, 1947, the day after the [CIO] convention closed in Boston, I attended a meeting with Harry Bridges and Eugene Dennis, the General Secretary of the Communist Party, and John Williamson, Robert Thompson, the State Chairman of the Communist Party, and several others at the headquarters of the Interna-

tional Workers Order on 5th Avenue, New York City. There Eugene
Dennis told us in very blunt language to disregard everything that
happened at the CIO convention in Boston, and he especially said to
disregard the Political Action resolution because the national leaders
. . . have decided to form a Third Party led by Henry Wallace, and
that Wallace would come out in the next few weeks and announce that
he was a candidate for President of the United States on the Third
Party ticket. The Communist Party was asking all the left-wing controlled unions to start to petition and campaign now, to start the publicity, to line up endorsements for Wallace as soon as he announced
himself on the radio. . . . There was no use trying to reason with
Eugene Dennis. He was going through. So I discussed it with Gerhart
Eisler, and Eisler told me it was in the best interests of the Soviet
bloc that the Third Party should be headed by Wallace and made it
very clear to me that that was the only reason why the Third Party
ticket was gotten up.

There were no lawyers at this C.I.O. hearing to determine
whether or not the Bridges union should be expelled for Communist domination, although the witnesses were sworn, and Bridges
himself was soon given the opportunity to cross-examine Quill.
The result was real drama, Quill insisting in his Irish brogue upon
the veracity of his testimony, and Bridges, curiously never directly denying it, playing innocent and trying to get Quill to con-
tradict himself:

Q. [Bridges] Is it true you testified that at that meeting Dennis,
    Williamson, Robertson [of the Bridges union] and several others
    gave instructions to disregard the entire program of the CIO
    convention, at least the political program?
A. [Quill] That's correct. Dennis gave the instructions.
Q. Did he only mean the political program or was there addi-
    tional phases?
A. There was other items came up. . . .
Q. You couldn't be mistaken on that meeting?
A. No, I couldn't, Harry. That was something that stuck in my
    mind.
Q. I see. Couldn't be anywhere else or any other date? It couldn't
    be another year or something like that, could it?
A. No, it couldn't. It was in the afternoon of Saturday October

18th, and the God damned thing dragged out until late at night. I never heard so much talk in my life at one meeting.

Q. How did you get to the meeting?

A. I was invited there.

Q. By whom?

A. By Williamson before I left Boston.

Q. Did you invite anyone else there?

A. No.

Q. Do you recall who else was there outside of you and I, Williamson, Dennis, Bob Thompson?

A. Oh, sure I can.

Q. Let's see how many you can recall.

A. Matles, Emspak [both of the U.E.]—that fellow that screwed up the strike in the Packinghouse. What was his name? Herbert Marsh. He was there. Jim Durkin; Selly; another representative of the Communist Party, Hal Simon.

Q. Who?

A. Hal Simon. He was from UE.

Q. S-i-m-o-n?

A. Yes. I believe that's the way you spell it.

Q. Anyone else?

A. Arthur Osman; Gold and Potash and Abe Feinglass from Chicago, I don't remember any more.

Q. But there were more, you think?

A. Yes, there was. It was a big room.

Q. Do you remember anything else that was decided or on which instructions were given outside of the one thing you have mentioned?

A. No, the big thing was Wallace. I don't remember anything else.

Q. It was the program of Wallace?

A. Yes. . . .

Q. Was there any discussion of how it was to be carried out or anything like that?

A. Oh, there was a tremendous amount of discussion about setting up a labor committee of CIO and A.F. of L., getting the petition campaign carried on, getting radio time, getting the unions on record as far as possible behind them. It took a long, long time.

At another point in the cross-examination, Quill said that at the meeting "Williamson came to me and said, 'This is ours; we created it; get busy and support it.' " [44]

At the same time that the Left trade-unionists were getting the new line at I.W.O. headquarters, six hundred Communist leaders from the East and South were similarly instructed at a meeting elsewhere in the city. At this latter meeting, Henry Winston and Foster gave the new line on the third ticket.[45] The following Monday, Foster spoke on "The Meaning of the 9-Party Conference" at a well-advertised meeting at New York's Manhattan Center. He attacked the Marshall Plan, hailed the formation of the Cominform, and concluded by saying that it was time for the American Left to "open its eyes politically, unite its split forces, cleanse its ranks of Hitler-like red-baiting, cut loose from the leading strings of the Democratic and Republican Parties, and launch a great mass, anti-monopoly, progressive peace party of its own." [46]

Gone now was all thought of trying to pressure the Democratic Party into the kind of program and candidate the Communists wanted. Gone now was all idea of an A.L.P. kind of party on a national scale. An independent third ticket was now the order of the day.

The Communists' next immediate goal was to persuade Henry Wallace to declare himself an independent candidate for the Presidency of the United States. October 1947 would have been a most appropriate time for Wallace to have strengthened his ideological defenses, but, to his eventual regret, he did not.

PERSUADING HENRY WALLACE

To understand the relations of Henry Wallace and the Communists, some things about Wallace the man, one of the most puzzling figures in twentieth-century American politics, must be understood. A man of peace, he became a world figure as vice-president of a nation at war. He had a rural background and was interested primarily in agricultural problems, but his support during and after World War II came mostly from urban people. A man who became embroiled in intense political conflicts, he shrank from personal battles and tried to ignore, or forestall, or compromise strife about him. Of all Roosevelt's cabinet members, he became the symbol of radicalism, to both his friends and his opponents, yet he actually did relatively little to warrant the reputation. A man whose fame was established by his rhetoric, he was, however, quite awkward and wooden on the public platform. Strongly committed personally to a Keynesian "progressive capitalism," he became a manipulated instrument of the Communists, to whom Keynesian economic thought was anathema and to whom "progressive capitalism" was a contradiction in terms. Widely considered, with some justification, as an impractical dreamer and even a mystic, he was intensely interested in the practical and mundane subject of hybrid corn and other utilitarian genetic experiments. A cabinet member for nearly a decade and vice-president for four years, he was still remarkably innocent of American political realities and of the ways of people seeking their ends through political activity.

Henry Wallace was no Communist, and he was not sympathetic to the Communists' basic aims. But he was a relatively easy mark for the Communists. They were able to manipulate him for several reasons: he was astonishingly unknowing about Left Wing politics and methods; he was devoted to the cause of peace and sincerely believed the Truman administration to be headed toward war; and he had in his intellectual baggage many of the beliefs of liberals during the Popular Front period, particularly a fear of being charged with Red baiting, which he could not discard as easily as did many other liberals when international and domestic conditions changed after the war. Furthermore, Wallace was himself so lacking in Machiavellism that he found it difficult to recognize duplicity in others. He was a likely victim for political "con men."

Wallace's lack of knowledge about the Left often led him to make poor judgments. When he endorsed Johannes Steel's candidacy in early 1946, an action that he conceded a decade later had been unwise, he did so because he thought Steel had been an

effective anti-Nazi in his radio broadcasts. He did not know that
Steel's Democratic opponent had previously served in Congress
and had a good New Deal voting record. He did not know that
Steel was a columnist for the *Daily People's World,* and, indeed,
he had only the vaguest idea of that newspaper's nature.[47]

When conversation turned to practical politics, Wallace was
prone to let his mind wander to some other subject, perhaps to
agriculture. Michael Straight, publisher of the *New Republic,* tells
a story of a meeting of Wallace advisers with Wallace in Straight's
home in the early fall of 1947. A sharp argument developed between Straight and "Beanie" Baldwin over a critical detail of organization, and in the exchange Straight took the position that if
the Wallace camp could not gain better trade-union support than
it had, it would fail dismally. When Straight turned to Wallace to
see which side of the argument he was taking, he saw that Wallace, who had not seemed tired when the meeting began, had fallen
into a sound sleep.[48] With such disinterest in, even distaste for,
practical politics, Wallace was dangerously naïve.

In December 1946, Wallace became editor of the *New Republic,*
then published in New York. He wrote a weekly column with the
aid of an assistant, and lent his prestige to the magazine, but his
position was actually more honorific than functional. The *New
Republic* presented Wallace a stage on which to play the role of
liberal public figure.

In March 1947, Wallace first hinted broadly that he had a
third party in the back of his mind. In a speech at Garden City,
Long Island, he recalled that liberals under Wilson had succeeded
in winning the Democratic nomination in 1912, but that Theodore
Roosevelt that year had not won the Republican nomination and
had bolted the G.O.P. to run on an independent ticket. He concluded his brief review of political history with the sentence, "Liberals wonder which of these experiences will be repeated today."
In May, he told newsmen at Olympia, Washington, that he would
lead a third ticket if he thought doing so would help prevent war.[49]

Through the spring and summer of 1947, however, Wallace's

emphasis was on working within the Democratic Party rather than on forming a new party. After he returned from his highly publicized and criticized trip to England and the Continent in the spring, during which Congressman J. Parnell Thomas urged that Wallace be indicted under the Logan Act of 1799 for activities abroad contrary to the American national interest, Wallace and his advisers made a long trip throughout the United States. On this trip, made after the announcement of the Truman Doctrine but before the Marshall Plan proposal and Truman's veto of the Taft-Hartley Act, Wallace spoke to large and enthusiastic audiences. His aide "Beanie" Baldwin was active during the tour trying to line up local Democratic leaders sympathetic to Wallace, or at least opposed to Truman, and at the end of the trip, he thought he had about 120 votes for Wallace for the 1948 Democratic convention.[50] As late as September 1947, Wallace said publicly he would continue fighting within the Democratic Party to "prevent it from committing suicide," but he warned that if the Democrats continued in their present direction "the people must have a new party of liberty and peace." [51]

One cannot but wonder how much the Communists influenced his public statements. Wallace, like most other active figures in politics, relied heavily on ghost writers, increasingly so in 1948 when he was giving as many as a dozen speeches a day. From early 1947 until just before the 1948 elections, Wallace's principal ghost writer was Lewis Frank, Jr. Michael Straight brought Lew Frank and Wallace together, an act that he was soon to regret. Frank, a personable and likable young man in his late twenties, the son of a well-to-do Detroit manufacturer, had been Sidney Hillman's protégé in the New York N.C.-P.A.C., and to Straight that was recommendation enough. Straight had also known Frank in the American Veterans Committee, which was then having a sharp internal fight between Communist and anti-Communist factions. Frank had been among the Left-Wingers in A.V.C. battles and had led the pro-Communist caucus at the Michigan A.V.C. convention in the fall of 1946. Straight then thought him to be an independent leftist, not unsympathetic to the Communists but not under their discipline. In the A.V.C.'s bitter struggles, Frank aligned himself clearly with the Communist caucus in the organization's national planning committee.[52] Wallace did not then and does not now suspect Frank of being a Communist, but he was never fully comfortable in his relationship with him. In retrospect, he disapproves as "too extreme" many things Frank wrote into his speeches.[53] James A. Wechsler, now editor of the New York *Post,* who traveled with the Wallace campaign party for ten months in 1948, reported that Wallace's extemporaneous speeches to small groups were quite different in tone and content from his prepared addresses for large meetings, a fact that underlines the critical role that Frank and other speech writers played.[54]

Wallace certainly was not careful to protect himself from Communist influence, either direct or indirect. Indeed, he almost made it a principle not to ascertain if any person were Communist. Michael Straight had conversations with Wallace about the fight over the Communist issue in A.V.C. In these talks Wallace disapproved of an organization's trying to keep out Communist individuals, because such a policy would necessarily involve investigation into each individual's beliefs.[55] Wallace's responses to newsmen's questions revealed his attitude toward relations with Communists. In May 1947, in response to a query if he would accept the support of known Communists, he said, "Anyone who will work for peace is okay with me. . . . Folks have found out they don't have to be scared of the word 'communism.' We've seen folks smeared and called red. This word 'communism,' this word 'red,' seems to lose its terror." When asked if the Communists were attempting to overthrow the government, Wallace replied, "I'm no expert on the Communist Party. But the Communists I've met have been very good Americans." And in December 1947, he told a meeting of U.E. shop stewards, "I am not following their [the Comunists'] line. If they want to follow my line I say God bless 'em. I admire their utter devotion to a cause they think is just." [56]

The Communists responded warmly. May Day marchers in 1947 carried a fifty-foot photograph of Wallace through New York's streets. Speaker after speaker at the I.W.O. national convention praised Wallace, and the delegates responded with applause.[57]

Wallace also had many admirers who were not Communists or fellow travelers by any stretch of imagination. Wallace's popularity was a function of Truman's unpopularity, and Truman was a very unpopular president in early 1947. Millions of people who voted for Truman in November 1948 disapproved of him early the previous year. Thousands who later approved of the Marshall Plan denounced the Truman Doctrine, and Truman's first domestic policies compared badly with what people remembered of the ferment of the New Deal era. In the spring of 1947, a P.C.A. official in Chicago made a tour of downstate Illinois to sound out Wallace sentiment among local trade-union leaders of both the A.F. of L. and the C.I.O. His wishes may have biased his findings, but he reported, "People whom we have considered to be 'conservative' trade unionists tell me that if their choice in 1948 is between Truman and a Republican, they just would not vote. They indicated . . . that if Mr. Wallace is ever ready to declare himself, they would support him." [58] Anti-Wallace observers reported similar conditions. In the early summer of 1947, James Loeb, Jr., of A.D.A., reported to his organization after a trip through the West. Many liberals, he said, who were quite opposed to Wallace's position on many issues were supporting him anyway because they regarded him as a symbol of opposition to reaction, which they felt was growing rapidly. He further reported considerable dissatisfaction with the Truman Doctrine.[59]

And the idea of a third party was clearly in the minds of many who were not Communists or pro-Communists. As early as December 1945, some Socialist leaders had discussed the possibility of a labor party to regroup liberals and laboring men who had supported Roosevelt. The Socialist discussion brought consternation among the Communists, who thought the Socialists were preempting their own domain. The Socialists thought there was not enough mass support for such a party and let the matter drop.[60] By mid-1947, however, third-party sentiment had grown considerably. For example, in June, sixty-seven Northwestern University professors addressed an open letter to Wallace urging him to form and lead a third party. They based their plea on the premise that Truman was betraying the Roosevelt tradition, and certainly Truman was not yet the "give-'em-hell Harry" he was to become the next year.[61] As late as April 1948, the anti-Wallace editor of the *Progressive,* Morris H. Rubin, wrote, "Much as I hate to admit it, I must say that there are tens of thousands of good American progressives who aren't even faintly fellow-travelers who are lined up with Wallace." He divided these Wallace followers into four categories: liberals who find "peace of mind in any haven that doesn't belong to the major parties"; pacifists; Wallace's personal partisans; and those who were thoroughly disgusted with Truman but could not bring themselves to vote Republican.[62]

The story of Truman's gaining the confidence of the American people, particularly of the liberals, is one of the most exciting chapters of recent political history. His popularity began to grow in June 1947, the month of Marshall's Harvard commencement address and his vigorous, but overridden, veto of the Taft-Hartley Act. From that month until Election Day, eighteen months later, Truman's popularity grew steadily. And as Truman's stock rose among former F.D.R. supporters, Wallace's declined.

After the announcement of the formation of the Cominform in October 1947, the Communists intensified their pressure on Wallace, and now their object was to get him to announce his independent candidacy. Wallace slowly yielded. He had told a Labor Day audience at Detroit that his main purpose was to keep Truman from having a "blank check" from liberals. And after a speech in mid-October in which he charged that Secretary of Defense James Forrestal "and others in the Truman cabinet" constituted a "war party" leading America to destruction, he replied when asked his party affiliation, "I'm a Democrat." He predicted, however, that if Truman received his party's nomination, he would not carry ten states.[63]

Wallace moved closer and closer to a clear announcement of third-party intentions after the C.I.O. convention. In early November, he told a visiting delegation of Italian Communist women, led by Mrs. Palmiro Togliatti, that a third party would be formed "if the peace requires it." In early December, he told Cornell University students that "if it is apparent that the Democratic Party is a war party, I shall do all I can to see that there is a third party." Two days later, he said that the "people must have a choice between progress and reaction." [64] Wallace was beginning to respond to thoroughly manipulated pressure from the Communists.

Throughout the fall of 1947, delegates from Communist Party fronts and Left-led unions called upon Wallace at the *New Republic*'s offices. In the words of the magazine's publisher, "there were steady deputations led in to see Henry. Phil Murray would criticise the Third Party—on the following day a 'rank and file' delegation from some painters or auto workers local in New York or New Jersey would troop in to tell Henry that Murray did not speak for the membership." Another *New Republic* editor complained that the offices were "like Grand Central station." Wallace's anteroom frequently overflowed into the hall.[65] One group from New Jersey that came to Wallace to urge him to run was typical. It was headed by the non-Communist pacifist James Imbrie, chairman of the New Jersey Independent Citizen's League. Also in the delegation were a non-Communist publisher and a Baptist minister. But others in the group were the secretary of the American Slav Congress of Greater Newark, and local officers of Mine, Mill, C.I.O. Packinghouse, and U.E. Wallace told these groups he would run if he thought he could get three million votes on the peace issue.[66]

The problem for the Communists, then, was to persuade Wallace that he would receive strong support. In the fall of 1947—before the Soviet coup in Czechoslovakia, before the Berlin blockade, before the antics of the Communists at the Progressive Party

convention, before Truman's aggressively liberal 1948 campaign—
it was not difficult to convince Wallace that he had three million
supporters, for at that time he probably had a great many more.
If Wallace could have run for the Presidency a year earlier, he undoubtedly would have polled a much better vote than he did.

In the Chicago judicial elections in November 1947, a new
local Progressive Party received a substantial vote. Twenty-one
judgeships on the Cook County Superior Court were up for election. Of the approximately 700,000 votes cast, 113,000 were
straight Progressive, and one Progressive candidate, Professor
Homer F. Carey, of the Northwestern University Law School, received 313,000. The Communists were greatly excited by the election—3RD PARTY VOTE ROCKS CHICAGO, POLITICOS STUNNED was
a *Daily Worker* headline on November 6—but actually the significance of the Progressive vote for the 1948 national elections was
more apparent than real. The Chicago issues were not the main
Wallace issues. Two major factors in the Chicago election were
dirty politics and Jim Crow. The major parties there had for
years refused to nominate a Negro for the Superior Court, and the
Progressives had nominated well-qualified Negro attorneys. Carey's
strong showing resulted from the revelation that his bipartisan opponent was a close friend of a famous Chicago gangster's lawyer.
All the Chicago newspapers supported Carey after the association
became known. The election results, rather than the conditions behind them, impressed Wallace and the men around him.[67]

The Communists and others working with them, fearful that
Truman might make a liberal address to Congress in January and
thereby reduce third-party sentiment, did their utmost to get Wallace to declare his candidacy in December. The I.W.O. handled
the immigrant-group pressure, and the Left trade-union leaders
promised labor backing. On December 12, 1947, Albert E. Kahn,
president of the Jewish Peoples Fraternal Order, the I.W.O.'s
largest constituent organization, wrote to Louis Adamic, the leftist
Yugoslavian-American writer:

Will you join Zladko Balokovich [President of the American Slav Congress], Vito Marcantonio, myself and others in the signing of the enclosed letter?

We feel that it is of the utmost importance at this time that every encouragement be given to Henry Wallace in getting him to run for the presidency in 1948.

I'd appreciate your wiring me collect—c/o Jewish Peoples Fraternal Order, IWO, 80 Fifth Avenue, New York, N. Y.—as we want to get the message to Wallace at the earliest opportunity.

The message to Wallace will not be sent in the name of any organization but will come as a personal message from the signatories.[68]

In mid-December, the Progressive Citizens of America's national committee met in Chicago, and there was a hot debate over whether to ask Wallace to declare his independent candidacy. The principal opponents of an independent candidacy on the committee were Frank Kingdon, a cochairman of the P.C.A., Bartley C. Crum, a San Francisco attorney, and Robert W. Kenny, a former California attorney general. Those most vocal for Wallace's candidacy were Vito Marcantonio, the A.L.P.'s East Harlem congressman, John Abt, and the then Communist writer Howard Fast. The third-party advocates won the fight, whereupon Kingdon and Crum resigned from the P.C.A.

At this point, the Left trade-union leaders shifted their Wallace endorsement program into high gear. Already several Left unionists had declared for Wallace, among them Bryson of M.C.S., who was actively getting signatures to Wallace nominating petitions in California. On December 18, Kenneth Sherbell, A.L.P. state senator from Brooklyn and public affairs director of the Communist-led District 65 of the Distributive Workers, announced that forty-five New York C.I.O. and A.F. of L. local leaders had signed a letter to Wallace urging him to run. Most of the labor leaders were from the painters, the furriers, and the C.I.O. city organization. A few days later, a group of Communist Negroes in Philadelphia joined with Local 30 of the Furriers to ask Wallace to declare. On December 27, the national executive board of the Bridges union endorsed Wallace and a third party, as did two locals of the rubber workers at Akron. The next day, Ford Local 600, the largest U.A.W. local and the last one to have a strong Communist caucus, wired Wallace, "Declare yourself as a candidate for President." [69]

On Monday, December 29, Hugh Bryson and Elmer Benson, along with other P.C.A. leaders, conferred with Wallace in Chicago. After the conference they issued a press release which summarized their activities of the past two weeks: "Ever since the executive committee of the Progressive Citizens of America urged Wallace on Dec. 16 to run as an independent he has been visited by a stream of similar delegations from Eastern states." [70]

That night, Wallace, on a national radio network, announced his candidacy for the Presidency. He ended his speech with these words: "We have assembled a Gideon's army—small in number, powerful in conviction, ready in action. We have said with Gideon, 'Let those who are fearful and trembling depart.' For every fearful one who leaves there will be a thousand to take his place. A just cause is worth a hundred armies. We face the future unfettered by any principle but the general welfare. We owe no allegiance to any group which does not serve that welfare. By God's Grace, the People's Peace will usher in the Century of the Common Man."

Would Wallace have run for the Presidency in 1948 if the Communists had not exerted pressure to persuade him to run? if the Communists had opposed the idea of a third ticket? Would there have been a national third party if there had been no Communist Party? These are legitimate subjects for speculation, but only for speculation. History cannot be written in the subjunctive.

One reason to think that there would have been a third party even without the Communists is that Wallace had considerable non-Communist support when he first announced his candidacy and for a few months thereafter. Indeed, he still had the support of many non-Communists on Election Day, although he had lost many thousands during the campaign. On the other hand, there was no national organization with a third-party goal that was not dominated by Communists or people working closely with Communists, and Wallace had to have some kind of a vehicle, such as the P.C.A., from which to throw his hat in the ring. Timing must be considered in this speculation. It is unlikely that Wallace would have decided to run so many months before the Democratic national convention if the Communists and their allies had not pressured him, and in the first half of 1948, Wallace's popularity among non-Communists started to wane. But Wallace lost support among non-Communists partly because he was identified with the Communists. Certainly if there had been no Communist Party or if the Communist Party had opposed a third ticket, the situation would have been different from what it was. How different is anyone's guess.

FIVE: PROFESSIONAL SOLDIERS IN A CAMPAIGN THAT FAILED

The Communists greeted Wallace's announcement of his independent candidacy with enthusiasm. His decision to run for the presidency was "an historic challenge to a vast and sinister conspiracy against the true interests of the United States," said a *Daily Worker* editorial. A *Daily Worker* columnist went so far as to suggest that in New York the third party "may well" become the "major party."

But these same *Daily Worker* articles revealed that Communists were sensitive and defensive about Wallace's candidacy—defensive against Wallace critics who charged his candidacy would only elect a reactionary Republican, and, shrewdly, sensitive to the possibility that Wallace's advocacy of "progressive capitalism" might corrupt his Communist supporters.

The Communist counter to the argument that Wallace was insuring Republican victory was confused. Their usual reaction was to cry "lesser evilism": it made no difference whether Truman or Vandenberg, Dewey, or Taft were president. This was the argument taken in the *Daily Worker* editorial hailing Wallace's announcement: there are "only two parties now facing the electorate—the war party of the bi-partisan Truman-GOP coalition [and] the peace party of the new people's movement." But a *Daily Worker* columnist argued that Truman was so unpopular he could not win even if there were no third party, an argument that did not contest the basic point of Wallace's critics that Truman's election was desirable.[1]

Liberal Democrats in 1948 occasionally charged the Communists with deliberately seeking the election of a conservative president and Congress in the hope that the economic policies of such a government would plunge the United States into a depression and thereby improve the Communists' position. The Communists always denied the accusation, and to deny was all they could do with an allegation about their intentions.[2] The charge was probably wide of the mark. Both before and after 1948, the Communists supported legislative proposals that would have a salutary economic effect.

Having embraced Wallace for immediate political advantage, the Communist leadership took measures to prevent the membership from embracing Wallace's ideas, which were not Communist, or even Marxist. They saw the possibility that, in the heat of a campaign, Communists might begin to believe everything Wallace said. Wallace's "progressive capitalism" bothered the Communists a great deal, and they tried to offset whatever influence Wallace might wield within the Communist Party by starting a big anti-Keynes campaign. Foster declared in January that "We Communists must take up the cudgels energetically against all the Keynesian theoretical nonsense," and the comrades took up their pens, if not their cudgels, to write a whole series of anti-Keynesian pieces. By spring, a casual reader of *Political Affairs* might have reasonably wondered if the Communists were for or against Wallace. Every issue but one in the first seven months of 1948 contained at least one anti-Keynes article.[3]

Although Wallace's Keynesian views disturbed the Communists more than anything else about the former vice-president, they were critical of some of his expressed views on foreign policy as well. In May 1948, Wallace published *Toward World Peace,* a short book about his views on international relations.[4] Max Weiss wrote a twelve-page review of the book praising Wallace for his criticisms of American foreign policy but taking him severely to task for writing that the Soviet Union and the United States were "equally responsible" for the danger of war. "The danger to peace comes from one direction," wrote Weiss, "from the expansionist drive by American imperialism. . . ." He was also critical of Wallace for saying "that the [Russian] proletarian dictatorship suppresses political democracy. On the contrary, the proletarian dictatorship . . . was from the start a thousand times more democratic than the freest of the bourgeois democracies. . . ." [5] Actually, Weiss made the same kind of criticism of Wallace that the *Daily Worker* editorial writer made the day after Wallace's Madison Square Garden speech and which got him in trouble with the ninth floor. But that episode, of course, happened before the Communists had Wallace installed as the front man for the new "antifascist coalition."

More important in the long run than the ideological differences between Wallace and the Communists was the effect that Wallace's candidacy and the Communists' support of it had upon the Communist unions in the C.I.O. The Communists' support of Wallace shattered the "left-center coalition" in the C.I.O.; for the Communist unions, the Wallace movement was the beginning of the end.

The coalition began to dissolve almost immediately after Wallace's announcement. A.L.P. leaders in New York hailed Wallace's decision, and within three days, the Amalgamated Clothing Workers and other non-Communist C.I.O. unions in New York left the A.L.P.[6] At the national level, the alliance of the Murray group and the Communists broke down completely at the January meeting of the C.I.O. executive board in Washington. This was one of the historic meetings of American labor. The Left union chiefs caucused in Communist labor secretary John Williamson's room in the Hay-Adams Hotel the night before the meeting. Among those present were Mike Quill, Harry Bridges, Abe Flaxer, Ben Gold, Irving Potash, Donald Henderson, Joseph Selly, John Santo, and James Matles. Williamson instructed them to try to get a pro-Wallace resolution passed at the next day's meeting. The meeting ran over into a second day, and, at a second caucus in Williamson's room the night between the board sessions, the Left unionists reported it highly unlikely that such a resolution would pass. Williamson directed them to stall, to try to get the C.I.O. to take no position at all on the third party for another month. In about a month there was to be a special Congressional election in the Bronx in which the Communists expected the Wallaceite A.L.P. candidate, Leo Isaacson, to make a strong showing, and Williamson hoped that if the C.I.O.'s decision could be postponed, the Bronx election would influence it. At the next day's session, however, the Left unionists lost the motion to postpone. Then the board went ahead and voted 33 to 13 to condemn the Wallace candidacy. It also passed a resolution supporting the Marshall Plan.[7]

By fostering and supporting Wallace's candidacy, the Communists had brought the Communist issue to a head in the C.I.O., and they had lost the battle. But the worst for the C.I.O. Communists and pro-Communists was yet to come. Within two weeks after the January board meeting, Lee Pressman was forced to resign. In March, Murray fired Bridges as C.I.O. regional director for northern California. In two more years, the Left unions were expelled from the C.I.O. altogether, and in eight more years, there would be almost no Left unions in existence. The price to the Communists for their support of a third party proved to be very high. The Communists lost almost everything in the labor movement and gained nothing.

There appears to have been some division in the Communist Party's leadership over how hard to fight for Wallace support in the C.I.O., over how much to endanger the Left unions' position. As usual, Foster was the most extreme. Mike Quill testified: "To follow up the fear that I had of what the Communist Party were doing within the CIO, I discussed this new line with William Z. Foster . . . in the month of January, 1948. I expressed to him fears that this move will split the unions, and weaken our position locally and nationally against the employers. He said the Communist Party have decided that all the unions that it can influence within C.I.O. are to go down the line behind Wallace if it splits the last union down the middle." [8] There is other evidence to confirm Quill's testimony. Foster himself hinted that such was his position in an article that blasted Murray and other C.I.O. leaders as "labor-imperialists" who have "abdicated the working-class leadership." And John Williamson, who was close to Foster, told the Communist national committee in early February, "We Communists have always supported the idea of a united trade union movement because it is in the general interests of the workers. However, different conditions dictate different approaches. . . . It is impossible to think in terms of trade union unity on the basis of support of Wall Street's imperialist program and two-party system." [9]

Dennis, however, did not go along with Foster and Williamson on this point. He told the same national committee meeting that "we . . . oppose any sectarian tendency to convert the political struggle within the trade unions in behalf of Wallace and the new people's party into a movement to split or withdraw from the established trade union centers." [10]

Neither point of view became final party policy. Foster, according to Quill, advocated "a Third Federation of Labor" in early 1948, "carved out of the A.F. of L. and the C.I.O. in order to implement the Henry Wallace movement." [11] Such a federation was never founded. Nor did the Communist unions bolt the C.I.O.—although they were later expelled. They left the C.I.O.-P.A.C. only when the C.I.O. endorsed Truman. Neither did Dennis's view prevail, if Dennis intended that the Left unions should not go so far in their Wallace support as to evoke retaliation from the C.I.O.

The C.I.O.'s alliance with the Democratic Party was so firm and mutually advantageous that to have severed it would have been disastrous to both. The C.I.O. Communists and pro-Communists went ahead and tried to break the alliance. The result,

perhaps the inevitable result, was that they soon found themselves outside what they themselves had called the "mainstream"
of labor.

In February 1948, the Communists had no regrets about their
third-party decision. Quite the contrary. For on February 17,
in the Twenty-fourth Congressional District in the East Bronx,
A.L.P. candidate Leo Isaacson won the special election by a
nearly two-to-one majority. Isaacson received 22,697 votes to the
Democratic candidate's 12,578. The Liberal Party candidate received 3,840 votes, and the Republican ran a poor last, with less
than 3,000.[12] This February 1948 election was the high tide of
the Wallace movement.

The Twenty-fourth Congressional District was poor and ethni-
cally mixed. It was about two-fifths Jewish, but some parts of
it were primarily Irish. There was a considerable Negro and
Puerto Rican population.[13] The Communists exploited the dissatisfaction of these groups for their own advantage.

The election came before Israel's independence or Truman's
quick recognition of the new state, and many of the Jewish voters
of the district considered Truman's Palestine policy one of ap-
peasement of the British. In early 1947, the Communists themselves had advocated a binational Palestine and urged the Jews
to come "to an agreement with the Democratic Arab forces, and
even with the Arab states as such" [14]—surely an unpopular position in the Jewish community—but their line had changed along
with that of the Soviets late in the year, and they now supported
Palestine's partition and independence.[15] Isaacson's Communist
and A.L.P. workers rallied hundreds of Jewish votes with a pamphlet, published in Yiddish, charging that "Truman spills Jewish
blood for Arab oil." [16]

Isaacson polled a fairly good vote in the Irish Catholic neighborhoods. In 1946, the A.L.P. had received only one vote in ten
in the predominantly Irish election districts, but in the special
election, Isaacson carried five Irish neighborhoods and did not
do badly in others. Samuel Lubell, a political analyst who ad-

vances the interesting "urban frontier" thesis, attributed the increased Irish vote to anxiety over the changing ethnic character of the area.[17]

Isaacson carried the Negro and Puerto Rican vote by sheer hard work. There were between 800 and 1,000 Communist Party members living in the district, who worked with typical party energy, and each day the A.L.P. sent over 300 campaigners into the area. On Election Day, Isaacson had 2,000 people working for him.[18]

An election eve Isaacson rally was typical of the campaign's ethnic approach. Wallace was the main attraction at the meeting, and in his speech he concentrated on denouncing Jim Crow and Truman's Palestine policy. Other speakers were Vito Marcantonio, who had a strong Puerto Rican following in his congressional district; Paul Robeson, who pointed out that Southern white supremacists were Democrats; Isaacson himself, who is Jewish; and a young Negro veteran who had been the victim of a brutal Southern policeman. Mike Quill was on hand to plug for Isaacson in an accent that no one could mistake.[19] By thus playing for the support of minority groups, which in New York City are majority groups, the Wallace forces gained an overwhelming victory.

The Isaacson election caused jubilation in the Wallace camp and alarmed the Democrats. Two days after the Bronx election, Senator J. Howard McGrath, chairman of the Democratic national committee, in a radio speech, all but invited Wallace to return to the Democratic fold.[20] The next week, Democratic Senator Glen Taylor, of Idaho, a singing-cowboy type, cast his lot with Wallace, announcing that he would seek to be Wallace's running mate. Even to outside observers, Wallace seemed to have great strength; not enough to win the Presidency but enough to split the Democratic Party, much as Theodore Roosevelt had split the G.O.P. in 1912. The Wallace group was confident and optimistic. Many non-Communist Wallace supporters were gratified with the organizational job the Communists could produce, and the Communists were pleased with Wallace's apparent appeal.

Wallace's speeches in late 1947 and early 1948 reflected the Communist line more accurately than they ever had before. The opening for the Communists was the inadequacy of two young people.

Lew Frank, Wallace's pro-Communist principal speech writer, was a young man. He was called upon constantly to write about subjects that a more experienced and learned person would have found difficult to handle. The Marshall Plan as it was developing in Congress in the winter of 1947-48 and the Communist coup in Czechoslovakia, which occurred immediately after the Isaacson victory, were two cases in point. Frank needed help.

Help arrived in the form of a young newspaperwoman named Tabitha Petran. Miss Petran had been on *PM,* and on *Time* before that. For *PM,* she specialized in foreign affairs. Her politics is indicated by her subsequent career: after the 1948 elections, she joined the staff of the fellow-traveling *National Guardian,* and in the 1956 crisis of world Communism, her point of view was less critical of the Soviet Union than that of many *Daily Worker* writers.[21] But Miss Petran did not feel adequate to the Wallace task either. For intellectual counsel, she helped organize a "research group," which met at the Manhattan home of the wealthy Frederick Vanderbilt Field.

The research group met each week, usually on Wednesday nights, to discuss the general content of what should appear in Wallace's speeches. The group contained some people of intellectual ability. Field was an expert on East Asia and had written on that subject for *Political Affairs.*[22] Among other members of the group were Marion Bachrach, later a Smith Act defendant; Victor Perlo, once an economist for the War Production Board and the Department of Commerce; David Ramsey, a contributor to the *Communist* as early as 1936, a collaborator with Perlo in criticizing the Marshall Plan, and a person with good grounding in economics; and an expert on German affairs, Walter Schlieper, a German refugee who wrote under the name Maximillian Scheer for the Overseas News Agency, a respectable non-Communist press association. In late 1948 or early 1949, Schlieper-Scheer left the United States to work in East Berlin. In the words of the Alsop brothers, who wrote a column on the research group in March, after which it no longer functioned as a body, "Mr. Wallace thus provides the voice. Mr. Frank provides the words. But the select company to which Mr. Field plays host provides the ideas." [23] Certainly the ideas of some people in the group found their way into Wallace's speeches and other public statements.

Wallace testified against the Marshall Plan before the House Committee on Foreign Affairs in the morning of February 24, 1948. He came to the hearing with a prepared statement, which was extreme in its language and point of view. His main point was that the Marshall Plan had undergone a change since Marshall made the original proposal in June 1947, that "militarists and bankers" had converted it to a program that "could convert western Europe into a vast military camp, with freedom extinguished." The European Recovery Program (E.R.P.) would bring neither real relief nor recovery to Europe, would revive German militarism, and would cause repression and union-busting in the United States. It had already, Wallace charged, postponed the plans of the British Labour Party government to nationalize the steel industry, a charge that Jennie Lee (Mrs. Aneurin Bevan), a Labour member of Parliament, later denied. In place of E.R.P., he proposed the "Wallace plan," which envisaged American-Soviet co-operation and an expansion of the principle of the defunct United Nations Relief and Rehabilitation Administration. To a congressman's objection that such a plan would be at the mercy of a Russian veto in the U.N. Security Council, Wallace replied that the Soviets would not want to veto such a plan.

Wallace's criticisms of E.R.P. and his own recovery plan were precisely the ideas that two members of the research group— Victor Perlo and David Ramsey—had made the previous month in a *New Republic* article. The Perlo-Ramsey article had been more restrained in its language than the Wallace statement, but the ideas of the two documents coincided exactly.

That Wallace was reading someone else's words, and words with which he did not entirely agree, was indicated by his responses to questions from congressmen after he read the prepared statement. In one exchange, for example, Wallace granted that Communism was totalitarian and "a system of desperation" of hungry people. At another point in the questioning he said, "I do not think that the present administration at any time entertained any idea of imperialism of the type you are talking about—that is, world domination. . . . I don't think our military ever envisioned anything of that sort and to suggest anything of that sort is—only a madman could entertain a thought of that kind." [24]

But the Marshall Plan testimony was not the last time that the ideas of Wallace's ghost writers were to lead him into situations he would in time regret. At the time he was testifying before the House Foreign Affairs Committee, the Russians were directing events in Czechoslovakia about which he could not keep silent.

On February 19, 1948, Soviet Deputy Foreign Minister Valerian A. Zorin arrived in Prague by plane. He stayed in the city for six days, by which time the Communists had successfully accomplished their *coup d'état*. Within a fortnight, Jan Masaryk, the Czech foreign minister and one of the most respected and popular statesmen of Europe, committed suicide. American public opinion was outraged. Wallace had to comment on the Czech crisis. The position he took, Wallace was to say four years later, was "my greatest mistake." [25]

Wallace knew Czechoslovakia. He had been there in the late 1920's, and he was related by marriage to a Swiss diplomat who had served in Prague for years. Obviously, he determined much of his position on the Czech coup himself. But at the same time, he echoed the sentiments of the Communists so promptly that it is apparent he also continued to let others put words in his mouth.

In a Minneapolis speech on February 29, Wallace blamed the Czech crisis on the Truman Doctrine, saying the Soviets were merely reacting to American aggression.[26] A few days later he told newsmen essentially the same thing but characterized the whole affair as "unfortunate." This was too much for the *Daily Worker*. "But why does Henry Wallace view the advance of the people's democracy against intriguers as 'unfortunate?' Unfortunate in what respect? . . . surely this is not unfortunate." [27]

Two days after Masaryk's suicide, a *Daily Worker* columnist wrote: "Let [Americans] remember another suicide—of John Winant's, who found that postwar America was not what he hoped and expected . . . and could not endure the strain of it." Four days later, Wallace, who was then living in Winant's former home, told the press, "Maybe Winant had cancer, maybe Masaryk had cancer. Maybe Winant was unhappy about the fate of the world." [28]

In a press conference on March 17, Wallace accused the American ambassador to Czechoslovakia of having attempted to stage a "rightist coup" in Prague. The Communists had merely beaten the reactionaries to the punch. The accused ambassador categorically denied the charge, pointing out that he was not even in Czechoslovakia until after the crisis began. The Communist Party had the same position on the coup that Wallace had.[29]

Wallace has said that he arrived at his position on Czechoslovakia partly from having heard indirectly from a Czech he had long admired, Joseph L. Hromádka, the outstanding Protestant theologian of East Europe.[30] Three months before the coup, Hromádka had written in a Czech periodical, "If the reactionary elements in America were to gain complete victory, then I . . . would feel constrained . . . to stand on the side of the East." A month after the coup, Hromádka, who had been a close friend of Masaryk, wrote, ". . . we fear nothing. We look to the days ahead with hope and peace." [31]

Hromádka had fled from the Nazis in 1939 and come to the United States, where he served as Stuart Guest Professor of Apologetics and Christian Ethics at Princeton Theological Seminary. He returned to Czechoslovakia in 1947. While in America, he published *Doom and Resurrection,* a "crisis-of-our-age" sort of volume with Protestant theological overtones. The book's dedication read, "To Henry A. Wallace. A man of deep social and spiritual vision." In 1958, Hromádka received a Lenin Peace Prize from the Soviets.[32]

One cannot but wonder if another European influenced Wallace's public statements on Czechoslovakia. A man named Hermann Budzislawski told his Communist friends that he had persuaded Wallace to his position on the Czech coup. Budzislawski was a friend of Schlieper-Scheer and his colleague on the Overseas News Agency. Budzislawski wrote for the agency under the name of Donald Bell, and appeared in several important and respected American newspapers. He also was an occasional member of the research group. Budzislawski-Bell was something of a poseur, but an able man. During the war, he was Dorothy Thompson's research assistant until she discovered his Communist affiliations. He claimed to be her ghost writer, which she denied. In the late summer of 1948, Budzislawski-Bell accepted an appointment as professor of sociology at the University of Leipzig in East Germany, the institution that subsequently appointed Gerhart Eisler to its faculty.[33]

Budzislawski-Bell was known to have exaggerated his importance in the past, and it is difficult to know how much credence to give his story about Wallace. Wallace does not remember him under either of his names.[34] Budzislawski-Bell, however, may very well have influenced Lew Frank, which would not have been especially difficult, given Frank's predilections and Budzislawski-Bell's obvious familiarity with European politics.

THE PROGRESSIVE PARTY CONVENTION

Some of the Communists' official and published statements called attention to their connection with the Progressives. In the draft resolution for the fourteenth national convention of the Communist Party, published and available to the general press in late May, appeared these sentences: "The Communist Party, from the earliest days after the end of the war, understood that its traditional fight for a new people's party . . . had once more been placed by events as an immediate, practical question. . . . Because of its correct line, the Party was able to carry on effective mass work and make significant contributions to the . . . forging of the new political alignment and people's coalition." [85] The nation's press, almost unanimously opposed to Wallace, picked up this expression of self-congratulation and made the most of it. William Z. Foster, in his keynote speech to the Communist convention, held a week after the Progressive national convention, declared, "They are brazen liars who charge that the Communist Party is trying to dominate the new party or to claim the credit for its formation," [86] but the damage was already done. Furthermore, no unusual powers of observation were required to perceive that at the Progressive convention the Communists had not only tried to dominate the proceedings but had been quite successful in their effort.

Charging Communist control, liberals began to leave the Wallace camp in significant numbers even before the Progressive Party convention. Most of these defections were in the western states. When the Colorado Progressives began intensively organizing in June, the Communists made their power in the new party obvious. In early July, two prominent Denver Progressive leaders resigned from the Wallace movement, and there were more withdrawals after the Colorado Progressives named their delegates to the national convention. Among the delegates elected were Robert

Trujillo, who had run for state office on the Communist ticket in 1946, and Mrs. Arthur Bary, wife of the Communist district organizer. Another Colorado delegate was Graham Dolan, national educational director of the Mine, Mill and Smelter Workers, who himself admitted he did not know how he became a delegate, since he had not been elected. At this point, the state's most prominent Progressive, Charles Graham, a former regional chairman of the War Labor Board, quit the movement. He was to have been a member of the national platform committee, but he did not even go to the convention.

In other western states, the Communists played similar tricks with similar results. At Nevada's state convention, the Progressive state chairman, George Springmeyer, insisted the convention go on record as opposed to fascism, Nazism, and Communism. Elinor Kahn, California leader of the Wallace party, and Charlotta Bass, publisher of a Los Angeles Negro newspaper, neither of whom was even a delegate, since they were from another state, denounced Springmeyer's attitude as Red baiting. When his motion lost, Springmeyer resigned and stalked out of the hall. In South Dakota, the Progressive state committee itself criticized Wallace for "playing into the hands of the Communists and the fringe elements." [37]

The Progressive Party met in Philadelphia in late July for its first national convention. When the convention was over, the Communists had eliminated doubt about their role in the Wallace movement, and disillusioned non-Communists dropped out by the thousands. Minor party conventions are usually quiet and staid affairs. The Progressive meeting was anything but quiet or staid. For organized enthusiasm and synthetic folksiness, no political conclave was ever its equal. Pete Seeger, People's Songs, Inc., amateur folk singers, and community song leaders set the convention's tone, and their spirit reached a climax when the beaming Vice-Presidential candidate, Glen Taylor, gathered his children about him, whacked his guitar, and sang "Friendly Henry Wallace" over three national radio networks. Ten thousand New

Yorkers, brought to the convention by special trains and under effective Communist Party discipline, supplied a cheering section. Many of these people had responded to a notice in the *Daily Worker* for "all members on vacation to return immediately, and all planning vacations to temporarily cancel them. . . . Our new and urgent tasks require the fullest mobilization of all our members." [38]

But the Philadelphia convention was more than noise and folk songs. The meetings of the convention's committees and the debates over the committee's reports on the convention floor were serious matters, and they showed the extent to which the Progressive venture was a Communist operation.

The first news from Philadelphia had to do with the deliberations of the platform committee. Rexford G. Tugwell, then of the University of Chicago, was the committee's chairman; Lee Pressman was its secretary. There were seventy-two other members of the committee and several "staff assistants."

An unofficial advisory subcommittee of the platform committee had already met in New York the weekend of July 17-18 and begun work on the platform. Working under Pressman's general direction, David Ramsey, Tabitha Petran, and others prepared what became known as the "New York draft." When the full platform committee met at Phiadelphia on July 20, before the convention opened, it accepted the New York draft as a basis for its further work. The committee then conducted hearings on the platform. The high point of the hearings was the rude reception given A.D.A.'s James Loeb, Jr., when he came before the committee and challenged it to criticize Communism.[39]

The full committee appointed a five-man drafting subcommittee to make desired changes in the New York draft. Martin Popper, Executive Secretary of the National Lawyers Guild, was chairman of the drafting subcommittee. Other members were Louis Adamic, Mrs. Paul Robeson, Dean Joseph E. Johnson, of Howard University, and Professor Frederick L. Schuman, of Williams College. Schuman was ill and did not actually serve. Sitting with the subcommittee as "staff assistants" but informally functioning as members were Petran and Ramsey again, Professor Richard Watt, of the University of Chicago Law School, Paul Sweezy, and Leo Huberman.[40]

The Communist issue in various guises divided the platform committee from the beginning. Before the convention, Tugwell had discounted charges of Communist infiltration in the Progressive movement as the inevitable reaction of hostile politicians, but he began to change his mind when he saw men he knew to be Communists operating at the convention. He began a withdrawal from the Wallace movement at this point. Technically, his appointment as platform committee chairman was provisional, and when the full committee met for the first time, his first act was to ask for nominations for permanent chairman, saying he did not wish to be nominated. Popper objected and nominated Tugwell, arguing that if Tugwell did not serve as chairman, the press would interpret the action as evidence of dissension. Tugwell declined and asked for further nominations, but there were none. Tugwell backed down and served as chairman.[41]

Early in the committee's work, Cedric Thomas, a Maine real-estate man, dropped a bombshell by urging that the platform make clear that the Progressive Party was not Communist. Charles Rohrer, Progressive candidate for lieutenant governor of Indiana, supported Thomas, saying, "To the average man, Communism still stinks." The reaction to these statements was tumultuous. Thomas retreated a little and formally moved to include in the platform a statement Glen Taylor had made to the effect that the Progressive purpose was to make the economy function so well that Communism would interest no one. This was no less than Red baiting, declared Popper and Mrs. Robeson. In a maze of parliamentary technicalities, the committee defeated Thomas's motion.[42]

But Thomas was not through yet. The New York draft contained the sentence "The Progressive Party will fight for the constitutional rights of Communists and all other political groups to express their views . . ."—a plank of immediate pertinence, since the first indictments of Communists under the Smith Act had been returned just the previous week. Thomas moved that the sentence be amended to read simply "the constitutional rights of all political groups," omitting direct mention of the Communists. Red baiting again, said Popper, and the original statement won by a large majority.

Communists and those close to the party were not a majority of the platform committee, but there were enough non-Communists who agreed with some parts of the party line to allow the Communists and their close allies to write most of the platform. Had there been an organized non-Communist caucus in the committee, the platform could have been quite different. On just one point was the Communist position defeated without an appeal to higher authority or a threat to bolt. The New York draft contained a plank calling for confiscatory corporation taxes. Sweezy, a Marxist economist but not a Communist, opposed the plank, saying it was poor economics. Popper and Petran opposed him strenuously, but a majority voted with Sweezy. However, the non-Communists did not agree among themselves enough to vote together on all issues. When the non-Communist Schuman offered a long and detailed substitute on monopoly that avoided a pledge to nationalize specific industries, Sweezy opposed him, and Schuman lost.[43]

The bitterest fight in the platform committee came over the issue of Puerto Rican independence. Independence for Puerto Rico was a frequently repeated Communist demand, for the Communists hoped to make it appear that the Puerto Ricans suffered under the yoke of American imperialism. Foster had been in San Juan in March to whip up support for independence.[44] The New York draft contained a plan for Puerto Rican independence, and Tugwell vigorously objected. A former governor of Puerto Rico, Tugwell asserted there were not five hundred people on the island who were for separation from the United States. After all, New York had proved to be Puerto Rico's best safety valve, and that valve would close with independence. Tugwell proposed a plank calling for self-determination for Puerto Rico, with the Puerto Ricans free to choose either independence or full American statehood. Vito Marcantonio argued vociferously for outright independence. The East Harlem congressman declared, among other things, that "Self-determination is a term of the imperialist demogogues." The Left, of course, stood with Marcantonio, except for one amusing exception. Mrs. Robeson, perhaps getting the matter confused with "national self-determination for the Negro people in the Black Belt," came out for Puerto Rican self-determination. Looking dismayed when she saw who was for independence and who was not, she quickly changed her mind, saying she was "for independence, period." Tugwell was adamant. The committee meeting ended before the dispute was resolved. Before the next meeting, Wallace appealed to Marcantonio to yield on the issue, and Marcantonio offered no more opposition on that issue. The final platform did not contain an independence plank.[45]

There was one last battle in the platform committee. Schuman was disappointed with the final draft for its thorough condemnation of American foreign policy and its silence about Soviet policy. He prepared an amendment which read, "We demand that the United States stop sacrificing the cause of peace to industrial profits and military ambition. We demand that the Soviet Union stop sacrificing the cause of peace to territorial aggrandizement and power politics." However, someone told Schuman, correctly or not, that if this statement were offered to the convention, Paul Robeson would object from the floor and declare the second sentence untrue. Schuman thereupon modified the proposal, making it read that the threat to world peace was the "joint responsibility of the Soviet Union and the United States." Very early the next morning, Schuman and three other men saw Wallace in his hotel room and asked his support of the Schuman amendment. Wallace agreed with Schuman and told Baldwin, Frank, and Albert J. Fitzgerald, the convention's chairman and president of U.E., that he wanted the Schuman amendment in the platform. He told Baldwin to notify Pressman of his position, saying that Pressman was "the only one likely to object." The platform committee held a special session just before the platform was to be presented to the convention, and Pressman supported the Schuman amendment. Popper and several others protested vigorously for some time before Baldwin came into the meeting and said that Wallace demanded the amendment. At this point, the opposition ceased. On the convention floor, Pressman read the amendment as a "correction" to the platform draft which had already been mimeographed and distributed to the delegates.[46]

On the convention floor itself, the Communists and their close followers made their influence felt. The keynote address, delivered by Charles P. Howard, an Iowa Negro, had been written by a radio writer named Allan E. Sloane, who described himself to a Congressional committee in 1954 as a former party member and fellow traveler. Sloane also testified that he had written Wallace's acceptance speech with the aid of Millard Lampell, another radio writer, whom Sloane described as a Communist. Several weeks before the convention, Sloane told the Congressional committee, he had received a telephone call from Hannah Dorner, who said that Wallace's acceptance speech was "terrible" and asked Sloane to write another one. Sloane went to Progressive Party headquarters in New York and there encountered Lampell, his former roommate, who had recruited him into the party in 1943. Lampell said Wallace's speech was "a dog," and they proceeded to write another one.[47]

Not everything went smoothly for the Communists. There were three important incidents on the convention floor itself in which non-Communists unsuccessfully challenged the party machine: a dispute over the composition of the Progressive Party's national committee; a quite improbable and embarrassing farce over a platform plank on the Macedonians; and the so-called "Vermont resolution" on foreign policy.

The convention's rules committee, technically headed by Marcantonio but actually run by John Abt, proposed a party-organization scheme that would practically insure Communist minority domination of the party machinery. The rules committee suggested a national committee of 180 members, one-half of which would constitute a quorum. Each member could vote proxies. The feature that brought the fight on the convention floor was a device that allowed the Communists and fellow travelers from the so-called "functional divisions," such as the youth division and the labor division, to pack the national committee. The functional divisions were loaded with Communists. Hugh Bryson had proposed in the rules committee that these divisions be given sixty seats on the national committee. The non-Communists, who had "Beanie" Baldwin's support in this matter, scaled the number down to forty. But even forty of these committee members, if they were faithful to the Communist line, would assure the Communists almost a quorum majority, not counting proxies and party-line followers among other members of the national committee.

James S. Martin, cochairman of the Maryland delegation and a former New Dealer, spoke against this committee-packing proposal on the convention floor and moved to recommit the section to the rules committee for reconsideration. During the debate, Scott Buchanan, former dean of St. John's College, made a short speech in which he said, "This article allows for minority control of this party. If we want to do that, I think there'll be some of us walking out of this party." When the delegates finished booing Buchanan, they defeated Martin's motion to recommit. But the battle was not quite over. Leonard Stein, an assistant dean at the University of Chicago, moved that the sentence about the forty divisional representatives be deleted. Chairman Fitzgerald ruled his motion out of order, Stein appealed the decision of the chair, and parliamentary confusion became rampant. The upshot was that the convention adopted the rules committee report as originally presented.[48]

The Macedonian dispute was hilarious farce. The Macedonians were scattered among three nations—Greece, Bulgaria, and Yugoslavia—and some kind of support for Macedonian unification, aimed to discredit anti-Communist Greece, was a standard item in Communist statements of what the world should be. But since Tito had been excommunicated about a month before the Progressive convention, the Macedonians had allied themselves with the Tito heresy. Macedonian unification now became anathema to the Communists. But someone slipped. The New York draft contained this sentence: "We support the aspirations for the unified homelands of traditionally oppressed and dispersed people such as the Irish, Armenians and Macedonians." Someone caught the slip just before the convention adopted the platform.

The platform had been read to the convention, and the delegates had the document in their hands. Pressman got the microphone to present several "corrections" to the platform. Among them was the deletion of the Macedonians from the sentence about "oppressed and dispersed people." A delegate from New Haven, a man named Spodick, tried to get the floor to ask the reason for the deletion. Chairman Fitzgerald ruled him out of order. The press and radio men, sensing that something was afoot, began to watch closely and to ask questions. Spodick asked for the floor again, and Fitzgerald relented. Spodick wanted to know what was wrong so suddenly with the Macedonians. He had been for Macedonian unity last month, he was still for Macedonian unity, and why wasn't the platform committee? Fitzgerald looked puzzled and turned to Pressman. Pressman looked helpless. Finally, Louis Adamic, an expert on Balkan problems, came to the rescue. Adamic became a Titoist before he died, but he was anything but a Titoist then. He talked for a few minutes in language so vague that no one understood his meaning. James Wechsler reported he might as well have been speaking his native Balkan tongue. Spodick was not persuaded by Adamic's double talk. He moved that the sentence stand as originally written. Fitzgerald did not even put the motion to a vote. Very few of the delegates understood the background of the squabble, and the convention allowed the Macedonians to be "corrected" out of the platform.[49]

The most dramatic and best-publicized dispute at the convention occurred when James Hayford, chairman of the three-member Vermont delegation, arose and proposed that the following sentence be added at the end of the foreign-policy section of the platform: "Although we are critical of the present foreign policy of the United States, it is not our intention to give blanket endorsement to the foreign policy of any other nation." "Beanie" Baldwin, who was in another room dealing with another matter but keeping one eye on the television set, rushed back to the platform. He was too late. Other speakers were seconding Hayford's motion and receiving applause as well as cries about Red baiting. Pressman and others pointed out that the platform already declared the danger of war the "joint responsibility" of the Soviet Union and the United States—itself a last-minute concession. One anti-Vermont delegate declared that the amendment was "an insinuation against a friendly ally of the United States" and received greater applause than those who spoke for the amendment. After enough debate for the radio audience to understand the significance of what was going on, the convention overwhelmingly defeated the amendment by a voice vote. There was only one conclusion the radio audience could reach: the Progressive platform did give blanket endorsement to the foreign policy of another nation.[50]

The most highhanded acts of Communist manipulation at Philadelphia occurred at the convention of the Young Progressives of America (Y.P.A.), which met immediately after the main convention adjourned. Christine Walker, of Detroit, and Alvin Jones, a Negro honor student at Southern University Law School in Baton Rouge, were cochairmen of Y.P.A. Miss Walker was a member of U.O.P.W.A. and of the Wayne County Industrial Union Council, from which non-Communist locals had resigned. Jones was prone to make slips of the tongue. When he introduced Leo Isaacson to the Y.P.A. convention, he referred to him as "Comrade, no, I mean Congressman Isaacson." Later in the convention, he called for order by saying, "Comrades, comrades, quiet, please." The executive director of Y.P.A., with whom day-to-day power actually lay, was Seymour Linfield, associate general counsel of U.E., on loan to the Wallace movement for 1948.

The non-Communists in Y.P.A. were better organized than their elders. When Linfield presented the report of the convention arrangements committee, which had been delegated to suggest the convention rules and methods of electing convention officers, several delegations created a storm. They protested that the industrial states, where Communists had the greatest strength, were overrepresented on the convention committees. The proceedings bogged down in parliamentary confusion, with cries of "Point of order," "Point of information," and "I call the question" from all over the hall. In the general hubbub, Miss Walker called for a voice vote on the arrangements committee's report. The result was indecisive. She called for a show of hands, after which she announced the report was adopted. In the words of one observer at the convention, at this point "all hell broke loose on the floor. One group began to chant 'rollcall, rollcall,' while another chanted 'We want Wallace, We want Wallace.' " Then the lights went off, throwing the room into darkness, and an offstage voice introduced Glen Taylor.

The lights came on, and Taylor spoke briefly. At the end of his speech, the United States senator from Idaho accompanied himself on his guitar and sang a parody of "The Isle of Capri," a popular song of the 1930's. The parody told the story of a man who went swimming with a nude woman, encountered her husband, and left his false teeth on the Isle of Capri. After this cultural phenomenon, Wallace gave a brief speech and Paul Robeson sang.

The next day's session came to a more dignified but similarly abrupt conclusion. When a dispute arose the next afternoon, the chairman announced that the convention was presented with a choice of adjourning the session or paying the proprietors of the hall an additional fee of nearly $2,000 an hour. The convention voted to grant the Y.P.A. national council power to act as the convention's agent on all unfinished business, and the convention adjourned without even adopting a platform.[51]

The Progressive Party convention was almost a total victory for the Communists. They gained almost every objective they had sought. Some Progressives, including even those at the convention but not on important committees, failed to perceive the extent of Communist influence. Most planks of the platform and most of the speeches would have been acceptable to non-Communist liberals with only a little revision. Yet the Communists left Philadelphia with warranted satisfaction. The main reason for their victory was that they were organized and the non-Communists were unorganized and divided. There was no Progressive of stature willing to organize and lead a non-Communist caucus.

Wallace, of course, was the most prominent non-Communist in the Progressive Party, and he refused to act against the Communists. After Tugwell recognized party members working at the convention, he personally appealed to Wallace to repudiate them. Wallace did not give Tugwell a direct reply. A few hours later, Tugwell encountered William H. Lawrence, of the New York *Times,* who asked Tugwell when Wallace was going to repudiate the Communists. Tugwell replied that he was trying to persuade Wallace to reject them. Lawrence gave Tugwell a clipping that described Robert M. La Follette's strong stand against the Communists in the Progressive movement of 1924. Tugwell later showed the clipping to Wallace, saying that in his opinion La Follette had taken the true liberal position. Wallace answered, "If they want to support me I can't stop them." Yet Wallace knew the danger to his candidacy that the Communists represented. Before the Progressive convention, he had said in a New Hampshire speech, "I'm never going to say anything in the nature of red-baiting, but I must say this: If the Communists would run a ticket of their own this year, we might lose 10,000 votes, but we would gain 3,000,000." [52]

THE CAMPAIGN FAILS

After the convention, a wave of non-Communists withdrew from Gideon's army. Within a week, six New Mexico Progressive leaders, including the state treasurer and organizer, quit the movement. The same day, the chairman of the Colorado convention delegation announced his resignation. A Progressive rally in Denver attracted only two hundred people, many of whom were open Communists, and several of this small body left before the meeting was over. In early August, twelve Progressive leaders in San Mateo County, California, publicly resigned from the party, saying the defeat of the Vermont resolution had been too much for them. Thousands of other Wallaceites just quietly withdrew. Among them was Tugwell. He told a Baltimore *Sun* reporter in August, "I am an uneasy member of the Progressive party. I hope its organization and program will develop in a way that will permit those of us who are old-fashioned American progressives to go along with it." He soon decided that his hope was futile. Because of his long friendship with Wallace, he made no public statement when he left the Progressives.[53]

Apparently even some Communists saw what was happening to the Progressive Party, saw that what they had so carefully nursed along was rapidly becoming a kind of big party front rather than a real third party. But the Communist leadership persisted in its policy. "A wrong theory exists, which even permeates Left circles, that the Progressive Party reached its high point during or before its Philadelphia convention," said John Williamson at the Communist national convention in early August. Firm in its belief that the decline of the Wallace movement was a "wrong theory" rather than a demonstrable fact, the Communist convention reaffirmed positions that already were having disastrous effects from the Communists' own point of view. There was nothing wrong with the "fundamentally correct line," said Foster. The trouble was "weaknesses and mistakes . . . of a Right-opportunist character" in applying the line. As for the party's increasing isolation from the labor movement—a month later, the C.I.O. would endorse Truman and even U.E. would fail to endorse Wallace for fear of a union split—Foster only fulminated against labor's delay in recognizing "the increasingly reactionary, pro-war line of the Murray forces." [54]

The Communists had gained effective control of the Progressive Party, and they had reaffirmed their hard line at their own national convention. Given these two facts and the realities of American politics, there was only one direction the Progressive Party could go thereafter: down. As more and more non-Communists left the Wallace movement, the Communists increased their control. By October, the Communists were even trying to sell the *Daily Worker* at meetings where Wallace spoke, including, of all places, Houston, Texas. Pro-Wallace I. F. Stone had to admit in one of his columns, "The Communists are doing a major part of the work of the Wallace movement, from ringing doorbells to framing platforms. Okay if you want it that way, so they 'dominate' the party. So what? I'm just a poor dupe who can't take either Dewey or Truman." [55]

In the fall of 1948, Wallace began to suspect that the Communists were deliberately embarrassing his candidacy in order to keep the Progressive Party small and easily controlled. Josiah Gitt and Louis Adamic came to see Wallace to warn him of this possibility. Adamic was convinced that the Communists were more interested in control of the party after the election than in getting Wallace a good vote. Wallace told Baldwin of his suspicions, but Baldwin pointed out that the Communists were serving a useful organizational function at the local level. Nevertheless, in October, Wallace hired a new ghost writer whose ideas more nearly matched his own. [56]

Certainly the Communists had no desire to see the Progressive Party mushroom so that they would lose control of it, but there was little likelihood of that. The Communists actually worked as faithfully for the Wallace campaign at its end as at its beginning, and there is no evidence to support Wallace's suspicions. The Communist attitude toward Wallace and the Progressives did not change essentially in 1948. Wallace was just slow to realize—and then only dimly—what co-operating with the Communists involved. If anything, the Communists at the very end of the campaign softened their position a little. At the last minute, they acceded to the decision to withdraw some of the several Progressive Congressional candidates who were running against liberal Democrats.

These Progressive Congressional candidacies particularly irritated the anti-Communist Left. In California, the Progressives put up candidates against several liberal Democrats, among them Helen Gahagan Douglas, Chet Holifield, and Frank R. Havenner, when these Democrats refused to crossfile with the Progressives. In New York, the Progressives ran Lee Pressman against Abraham J. Multer, and in New Jersey and Pennsylvania, Wallaceite candidates ran against Charles Howell and Frank Buchanan, both Democratic liberals with labor support. In Illinois, where Progressive candidates could receive only write-in votes, Grant Oakes, President of the Left Wing Farm Equipment Workers Union, opposed Adlai Stevenson for governor, and Professor Curtis MacDougall, of Northwestern University, opposed Paul Douglas for the United States Senate. Late in the campaign, the Progressives withdrew some of these candidates, including all of them in California.[57]

The primary reason for the decline of the Wallace movement was the Communists, both at home and abroad. The American public became highly aroused against Communism during the course of 1948, and the electorate, with justification, identified the Wallace Progressive Party with the Communists.

A series of events in 1948 intensified American anti-Communist sentiment. Indeed, if foreign Communists had deliberately tried, they could not have done much more than they did to hurt the Wallace campaign. In late February came the Communist coup in Czechoslovakia. In June, the Russians began their blockade of West Berlin, and the United States Air Force retaliated with the airlift. In late June and early July, the Soviets and the Cominform excommunicated Yugoslavia's Tito. The sensational Kasenkina affair in New York occurred in August. Oksaka Stepanova Kasenkina, a teacher for the children of Russian diplomats in New York City, had defected and gone to the farm for Russian refugees operated by the Tolstoy Foundation. The Russians kidnaped her and returned her to the Soviet Consulate. On August 12, she jumped from a third-floor window of the consulate, successfully escaped, and told the whole story. That same month, Whittaker Chambers began his revelations about Soviet espionage. By Election Day, the electorate was in no mood to vote for a party it associated with Communism.

But it was not only Communist activity in the Progressive Party that diminished Wallace's following; Harry Truman played no small part in the desertions from Gideon's army. Truman conducted a campaign designed to minimize the Wallace movement. Tugwell exaggerated in his postelection analysis when he wrote, "As fast as [Wallace] occupied a forward trench, he found Mr. Truman in it with him . . ." but certainly Truman did move toward the Left during the campaign. Without attacking Wallace directly, Truman made it clear, especially before labor audiences, that a vote for Wallace was a half-vote for Dewey. He capitalized on the fear of reaction that had only a few months earlier stimulated the Wallace movement. In Detroit, for example, the president told a Labor Day audience in Cadillac Square that Taft-Hartley was "only a foretaste of what you will get if the Republican reaction is allowed to continue to grow. . . . If you let the Republican reactionaries get complete control of the Government, the position of labor will be so greatly weakened that I fear not only for . . . wages and living standards . . . but even for our democratic institutions." [58]

Furthermore, the Dixiecrat revolt hurt Wallace and helped Truman in the North. When Truman's civil-rights position was too strong for the Dixiecrats to stomach, it appealed more than ever to northern Negroes. Wallace's tour of the South, in which he refused to speak before segregated audiences and was the target of several rotten eggs, was clearly intended to gain Wallace votes in the North. But it failed of its objective. Southern recalcitrance on the race issues, symbolized by Strom Thurmond's Presidential candidacy, boosted Truman rather than Wallace.

On November 2, Harry S. Truman, "the man who couldn't win," surprised the political experts, the press, the public, and Thomas E. Dewey by winning re-election. The experts were nearly as surprised by Wallace's poor showing. Wallace received only 1,156,103 votes.[59] In April, Wallace had spoken optimistically of twenty million votes, and he had been generally conceded two or three million down until Election Day.[60] Probably, the mechanics of vote counting being what they are, there were many Wallace votes never officially reported. But even if only half the Wallace votes were counted—and the count was surely more honest than that—Wallace still ran a miserable race.

Of Wallace's total vote, well over half came from New York City and California. His total New York State vote was 501,167; in California, he received 190,381, of which 101,085 came from Los Angeles County, 21,492 from San Francisco County, and 16,853 from Alameda County (East Bay).[61] Other states with significant Wallace votes were Massachusetts (38,157), Michigan (38,955), New Jersey (42,683), Ohio (37,596), Pennsylvania (55,161), and Washington (29,745). If all Wallace voters in New York, Maryland, and Michigan had voted for Truman, Truman would not have lost those states. In Illinois, one could vote for Wallace only with a write-in, and Ohio's ballot carried only the names of Wallace electors without mentioning Wallace or the Progressive Party. Had the Progressive ticket been fully on the ballot in those states, Truman might well have lost them too.

Wallace carried only thirty of the nation's precincts. Seven of these were in Tampa, around Ybor City, inhabited largely by Cuban cigar workers. Five were in Los Angeles; the other eighteen in New York City—eight of these in Vito Marcantonio's bailiwick, which sent him back to Congress. Wallace also carried two election districts in the East Bronx, where there was a large workers' co-operative apartment house, started by Communists in the 1920's and later known as "little Stalingrad." [62] Wallace, the *Daily Worker* complained, did not even carry some of the traditionally A.L.P. "Jewish working class districts." The Democrats in those districts increased their vote more than did the A.L.P.[63]

What were the end results of this Communist venture into third-party politics? Most were on the debit side of the Communist ledger. The Communists almost completely sacrificed their position in the C.I.O. They brought to a head a crisis over Communism in the non-Communist liberal community, and the election results showed that the progress of the Left from non-Communism to anti-Communism was well developed. The Communists had bet a great deal on the establishment of a popular leftist party, and they lost the wager.

The Communists had little on the credit side of the 1948 ledger. The third party had given international Communism a propaganda weapon, an opportunity for foreign Communists to point to the Progressive Party and say that the American masses were grumbling under the yoke of their Wall Street masters.[64] The Communists had gained a little influence among some non-Communists and through them had broadened the audience for their propaganda. The party even acquired some new members from the Progressive Party, especially young people—Elizabeth Gurley Flynn reported that she had recruited four Amherst boys and five Boston students within a week [65]—but it is not likely that the recruits stayed in the party long. Total party membership declined during the year.

The Communists stuck with the Progressive Party for another four years. They saw nothing mistaken about the Progressive venture when they surveyed the 1948 election returns. On the contrary, the Communists declared, "the basis for a mass, potentially powerful, anti-imperialist coalition was created." The election results *"reinforce the view that the foundation of a national Third*

Party, capable of successfully challenging the reactionary program of American monopoly, was laid in this campaign." [66]

William Z. Foster in 1949 candidly described what Communists expected from such a third party. In a book confidently dedicated to his great-grandson, "who will live in a Communist United States," Foster spelled out what he hoped would happen if the third party had won:

> The present party line follows the broad path towards the people's front and people's democracy types of government now to be found in Eastern Europe. . . . First, we propose the regular election of a democratic coalition government, based on a broad united front combination. . . . Second, our party contends that such an anti-fascist, anti-war, democratic coalition government, once in power, would be compelled either to move to the Left or to die. With state power in its hands, it would be forced to pass over from the more or less defensive program upon which it was elected to an offensive policy. . . . Third, a democratic, anti-fascist, anti-war government, under the violent attacks of the capitalists and in its efforts to find solutions to the burning economic and political problems, if it were to survive, would necessarily move leftward, toward socialism, much as the People's Democracies of Eastern and Central Europe are now doing. Some liberals believe that a united front coalition would introduce a regime of "progressive capitalism," but this is a naive and dangerous illusion.[67]

In view of revelations Communists themselves would make in 1956 about life in the "people's democracies," the judgment of the American people in 1948 in rejecting Foster's "united front coalition" acquires a new significance. In 1956, even Communist leaders would admit publicly that their third-party venture had been a stupid mistake.

PART THREE
YEARS
OF
SUSPICION

Comrades, we are heading into some big storms.

—EUGENE DENNIS, *August 1948*

SIX: THE PARTY AND ANTI-COMMUNISM

In 1949 and 1950, the disillusion, frustration, and anxiety that had been building in the United States over the Communist issue at home and abroad burst into full, angry reaction. Each year since the war was one of shock, but 1949 and 1950 were traumatic even for that trying era.

By then the world was clearly divided into three camps—the Communist world, led by the Soviet Union; the Western world, led by the United States; and the "neutralist" Afro-Asian bloc—and the cold war was sharp. Some events of 1949 led many Americans to think they were losing the cold war, and many people thought the reverses were as much the result of internal betrayal as of foreign Communist strength.

In the spring of 1948, Chiang Kai-shek had controlled about three-fourths of China's territory and two-thirds of its population. The next year, Mao Tse-tung's Communist forces drove Chiang and his Nationalists to Formosa. Shanghai obviously would not now become what Senator Kenneth Wherry had so wildly predicted—"just like Kansas City." [1] In September 1949, President Truman announced that the Russians had exploded an atomic bomb. It was now apparent that Soviet bombers could destroy the industrial centers of the Western European nations, which had been brought into a military alliance with the United States earlier in the year. Further than that, as many an American recognized when he awakened in the night at the sound of an airplane over his home, it was possible now for the Russians to bring nuclear destruction to the United States itself.

Americans were bewildered, angry, and resentful. A few years earlier, when their fascist enemies were near defeat, the chances of postwar peace and international harmony had seemed bright. But there was no real peace, no harmony, and now another hostile dictator had power to hurt America such as Hitler had never possessed. Assured by some military leaders and others in 1946 that only American technology and science were capable of discovering the "secret" of atomic fission, many people now leaped to the conclusion that only Communist espionage, disloyalty, treachery, and a bungling, "soft-on-Communism" administration could account for the Russians having the bomb. And when Klaus Fuchs confessed to atomic espionage and the Rosenbergs were convicted, these dark conclusions were confirmed in some people's minds.

In 1946, there had been a spy sensation when the Canadian Government exposed an espionage ring which had operated during the war. In 1947, there had been the confusing Eisler case. Contemporaneous with the revelation of the Russian bomb was the story of Judith Coplon's passing classified information to Valentin Gubichev of the Soviet Embassy. The biggest headlines about espionage at the time, however, concerned the affair of Whittaker Chambers and Alger Hiss.

The Hiss case marked the end of one era and the birth of another. The whole Hiss story as it slowly unfolded was so bizarre—involving microfilms hidden in an abandoned dumb-waiter and a pumpkin, Oriental rugs, an old Woodstock typewriter, a Model A Ford, and two very strange men—that one would reject the story as too wild if one read it as mystery fiction. The evidence in the case was extremely complicated, but the main point is that relatively few Americans formed their judgment of Hiss and Chambers—at least their first judgment—on the basis of the evidence. The personalities and appearances of the two men, their careers, and the kinds of people they symbolized, rather than the evidence, influenced the judgment of most people—that, and whether one regarded himself as a friend or an opponent of the New Deal.

The Hiss case began during the 1948 campaign, when Chambers, once a Communist and a Bohemian writer, later a spy for the Soviets, and later still a senior editor of *Time,* charged that Alger Hiss, to all appearances the prototype of the young, competent, well-educated, idealistic, and liberal lawyer and junior New Deal administrator, had been a member of the Communist Party from at least 1934 to 1938. Chambers made his charges before the House Committee on Un-American Activities, whose chairman then was J. Parnell Thomas, of New Jersey. But the most prominent member of the committee in the Hiss case was a young politician-on-the-make from southern California, Richard M. Nixon. Nixon was a freshman congressman at the time, having defeated the veteran liberal Democrat Jerry Voorhis in the 1946 Republican landslide.

Faced with a libel suit brought by Hiss, Chambers broadened his charges against him, asserting now that Hiss had helped him covertly transmit classified State Department documents to agents of the Soviet Government. He produced the "pumpkin papers," and a New York grand jury indicted Hiss for perjury, the statute of limitations preventing an indictment for espionage, and early in 1949 the case went to trial. The trial ended in July with a hung jury, eight to four for conviction. A second jury found Hiss guilty, and he received a five-year sentence.

More important to us here than the details of the Hiss case was its impact upon American public opinion. The case brought to the public in a dramatic way a realization of the strength of Communism in America in the previous decade, and the contemporary political implications of the case tended to exaggerate Communist influence in 1949. President Truman during the 1948 campaign referred to the Hiss affair as a "red herring" designed to distract voters from the inadequacies of the "awful Eightieth Congress," and the public came to see the case as a struggle between Nixon, the symbol of aggressive Republicanism, critical of all things New Deal, and Hiss, the symbol of the bright young New Deal intellectual. When more evidence was brought to light and Hiss was finally convicted, more was at stake than his own career. The New Deal and the kind of liberalism it represented were now suspect to many a person who had voted for Roosevelt; and some New Deal critics, always ready to impute the worst to "that man" and what he symbolized, now felt vindicated. Then Secretary of State Dean Acheson, dapper, urbane, suspect in some quarters anyway because of his Ivy League polish, in an impolitic but compassionate statement said he would not "turn my back on Alger Hiss." Many people concluded that subversion was still rife in the federal government.

The jury found Hiss guilty on January 21, 1950. On February 3, Klaus Fuchs confessed in London. On February 9, at Wheeling, West Virginia, Joseph R. McCarthy, then a relatively unknown first-term senator, asserted he had "here in my hand" a list of 205 —or 57, as later speeches put it—names who were known to Acheson to be Communist Party members and who were nevertheless still working in the State Department. The era of McCarthyism was born. It was a violent child, destined to live about a half-decade.

McCarthyism was a whole complex of attitudes, some of them contradictory. It was militant anti-Communism, but it was also unreasoning fear and hysteria about Communism, both at home and abroad. It was exploitation of popular fear and frustration about Communism for partisan political advantage, but it was also a more general political irresponsibility. It reflected isolationist attitudes toward Europe—but not toward Asia—yet played upon the nationalist feelings of European immigrants whose homelands were behind the Iron Curtain. It was anti-intellectual, both in the sense of exalting the irrational and in the sense of animosity toward intellectual and cosmopolitan people. It appealed to the prejudices and frustrations of the relatively poor as well as to the fears of the *nouveaux riches,* particularly Texas oil millionaires. Above all, McCarthyism was an acceptance of the idea that the end justifies the means, the end being power and the eradication of the Communists, who themselves believed that the end justifies the means.

Senator McCarthy did not invent McCarthyism, and his abrupt political decline after his repudiation by the Senate in December 1954 did not absolutely end the phenomenon. Nevertheless, McCarthy—as did Hiss—came to symbolize more than he actually was. The years of the height of McCarthyism saw many wild and improbable developments. The American people swung frantically with an anti-Communist bludgeon. They used the rapier very little. The bludgeon hurt the Communists, but it hurt a great many anti-Communists too. In the effort to save democracy and liberty from Communism, the American people outraged democracy and liberty themselves. At both popular and official levels, Americans violated both the spirit and the letter of the Bill of Rights.

The federal government, under the administration of both Truman and Eisenhower, pursued an extensive campaign against Communism at home and abroad. The Truman administration instituted a security program to root out subversives from government, and the Eisenhower administration widened its scope. Congressional committees investigated almost everything and received many headlines. Congress passed new anti-Communist legislation, for example the McCarran Internal Security Act of 1950, which among other things provided for concentration camps for the internment of Communists in the event of war. And the Department of Justice brought many prosecutions under the Smith Act of 1940. By the end of 1954, ninety-two Communist leaders had been indicted and tried under that act. Four others were indicted but were fugitives at the time of their trials. Of this total of ninety-six, only three were acquitted. One died during trial, and five others had their cases severed because of poor health.

State and local governments and the people generally were also active in the anti-Communist crusade. A few states prosecuted Communists under "little Smith acts." Many instituted non-Communist oaths as a condition of public employment. At the state level, officials were apt to be extreme, even sometimes a little silly, in their anti-Communism. One member of the Indiana Textbook Commission, for example, wanted to ban school readers that included Robin Hood stories, perhaps on the theory that the Sherwood outlaw was an anticapitalist precursor of Marx and Lenin. Indiana also required professional boxers to take a non-Communist oath before practicing their trade in the Hoosier State. But government officials were only a little wilder, if any, than the public at large. The Cincinnati Reds became the Redlegs. Social clubs ostracized members who were suspected of Communist sympathies. An association of chess players expelled an officer thought to be a Communist.

American public opinion had been hostile to the Communists ever since they came into being during and just after World War I. Apparently, however, the experience of being a wartime ally of the Soviet Union softened that hostility, and immediately after World War II, American Communists enjoyed greater good will— or, rather, less ill will—from the public at large than ever before or since. A 1940 public-opinion survey indicated that nearly three-fourths of the population favored a law to forbid membership in the Communist Party. In 1946, fewer than half the people favored such action. But soon public opinion was to change again. By the early 1950's, Americans were unwilling to tolerate Communists. A careful survey made in the early summer of 1954 revealed that about three-fourths of the people favored stripping admitted Communists of their citizenship, and about one-half thought they should be jailed.[2]

All this anti-Communism hurt the Communist Party. The party suffered badly. Hampered by legislation, vulnerable to prosecution, and the object of the public's intense hostility, the Communists were in no position to advance their political program nor to expand their organization. In this climate of opinion, the opportunities for an actual, living, active Communist were limited indeed. Forces and conditions outside the party, in the real world—what Communists call the "objective situation"—put the American Communists on the defensive. The Communists had to be more concerned with their party's survival than with its advancement, and they quite naturally tended to isolate themselves from the harsh world.

Yet it was not the "objective situation" alone that brought the Communist Party to a moribund and feeble condition. When Communist parties die, or nearly die, a large part of the final illness is self-inflicted. Not even the "objective situation" of Hitler's Germany killed the German party. Years of intellectual malnourishment and ill-advised self-medication with magic rituals, complete with incantations and exorcism of demons, take their toll.

EXPECTATIONS OF FASCISM AND WAR

The Communists had two closely related ideas about the immediate future during the years of McCarthyism that underlay their line and activities on almost all matters. These basic assumptions were that the United States was on the verge of fascism nationally and on the precipice of total nuclear war internationally.

The villains, of course, were "American imperialism," "Wall Street," "the monopolies." The twin dangers of war and fascism were but two sides of the same imperialist coin. Imperialism, "especially American imperialism," was "incurably warlike." But the American masses—"labor and progressive-minded Negro and white masses"—opposed war, as did, of course, the Communist Party, the "vanguard" of the working class. The imperialists, according to Communist writers, then, had to make America fascist to put over their war program: ". . . the purpose of the fascist trend is to hasten the preparation for a war seeking Wall Street's world domination." [3]

The Communists deluded themselves with the thought that they were in actual fact the vanguard of the working classes and that they were so regarded by "Wall Street." From this delusion arose their belief that all measures directed against Communists or the party were but the opening wedge of fascism, of a program of imperialism to destroy American democracy, annihilate the labor movement, reverse the direction of the Negro toward full equality, and coerce the population to an acceptance of total war. "The anti-Communist drive cannot and will not be limited to Communists," wrote the veteran Communist Will Weinstone in 1950. "The Communists are singled out for attack first of all because they are staunch fighters for peace against a ruling class gone war mad; because they are unyielding battlers for democracy against a bourgeoisie which is turning to fascism and hates and fears every vestige of democracy. . . . But while the main edge of the onslaught is directed against the Communists . . . the anti-Communist crusade is seeking to speed the destruction of all working-class, militant, progressive organizations, and to gag all decent people." The Communists thus saw themselves in the heroic posture of the Dutch boy with his finger in the dike. If they faltered, if they were defeated and silenced, all was lost, not only for them, but for "all decent people."

The party leadership's position on whether or not war and fascism were inevitable was another of their several Scylla-Charybdis constructions. The "correct" line was that the party must sail between the Scylla of underestimating the danger the imperialists represented and the Charybdis of considering war and fascism inevitable. The consequences of Scylla were obvious, and Charybdis "can only lead to paralysis in action, to waiting about and even to feelings of hopelessness, and to attempts at liquidationism of the Party in practice." [4]

In actual practice, as apart from what they said, the party's leaders operated on the assumption that war and fascism were extremely likely if not inevitable. Their arguments admitted of no other logical conclusion. If the imperialists had their way, they would bring war and fascism. If their drive for world domination were blocked by the Soviet "peace camp," they would make war out of frustration. Either successful or unsuccessful in their expansionist program, the imperialists would bring fascism and war. The Communists had themselves in a tight intellectual box. While exhorting the membership not to let up the fight against war and fascism, which the membership might do if told the twin evils were inevitable anyway, the leadership instituted internal party reorganizations based upon the premise of the extreme likelihood of war. Surely the party's internal purges and the decision to go "underground" (to be described in the next chapter) were designed to ride out the storm of an imminent war and accompanying fascism.

There is more than a little irony in the denouement in the mid-1950's. By then the danger of war had subsided—because of changed Russian leadership and policy—and McCarthyism had declined to relative insignificance. But the American Communists, huddled in their storm cellars, talking only among themselves, had nothing to do with this outcome. All in all, the Communists' campaign against war and fascism was quite ineffective. Their worst fears—indeed, their expectations—did not materialize. The Communists were ineffective because they alienated non-Communist opponents of war and reaction and because the insincerity of their posture as civil libertarians and defenders of freedom was transparent.

A few examples will illustrate. Labor leaders, Communists thought, should be their allies. But Foster called C.I.O. and A.F. of L. leaders "blatant supporters of the current employers' program . . . splitting unions and breaking strikes at the behest of the State Department . . . tools of the warmakers." Will Weinstone called Phil Murray a "slanderer" pursuing "a craven policy." [5] Negro leaders also felt the Communist lash. Communists attacked Dr. Ralph J. Bunche "for his services to the Western imperialist warmongers," and called the anti-Communist George Schuyler "a true lackey of the monopolists." [6] Nor were Communists likely to get sympathetic understanding or co-operation from the liberal wings of the Democratic and Republican parties, which the Communists attacked more vigorously than they did

those parties' conservative wings. When Truman vetoed the Mc-
Carran Act, Will Weinstone said that Truman was just as bad
as McCarran and did not really want to defeat the measure. His
veto was "only for the record and to 'appease' and deceive the
masses." [7] And back in 1946, Wisconsin Communists in the
U.A.W. West Allis local had supported McCarthy, then an unknown conservative circuit-court judge, against the liberal Senator Robert M. La Follette, Jr., in the open Republican primary.
The *Daily Worker* was clearly delighted with La Follette's defeat. [8]

The Communist effort to pose as defenders of the Bill of Rights
was ridiculous to anyone who knew their record on freedom
within the party, let alone Communist unwillingness to grant civil
liberty to their enemies. When the Supreme Court announced its
decision in the Dennis case, upholding the constitutionality of the
Smith Act, the party's national committee issued a statement
which among other things urged the American people to "speak
out together in defense of the Constitution and the Bill of Rights"
and declared the party would "not capitulate to the bookburn-
ers." [9] The appeal had a hollow ring to people who remembered
that the Communists had supported the prosecution of the Minneapolis Trotskyists under the same Smith Act in 1942 and had
reaffirmed that position in July 1949 even while the first Communist Smith Act trial was in progress. [10] In 1946, the party had
tried to get what it called "poison books" removed from the
library shelves of New York's public schools. The *Daily Worker*
was particularly opposed to an allegedly anti-Negro novel called
Lanterns on the Levee, by William Alexander Percy. [11]

In fact, the Communists had several times used precisely the
same kind of illiberal tactics and methods that the McCarthyites
used. In 1946, the Communists heard that old White Russian
General Anton Denikin had been admitted to the United States.
They demanded that the Immigration Service explain itself and
deport the man. [12] And they had pushed the guilt-by-association
device to extreme lengths to smear an enemy. A *Daily Worker*

story in 1946 by William Allan, a Detroit U.A.W. Communist, about Walter Reuther is a case in point. Reuther, as head of the U.A.W. committee on social security, had negotiated on a group-insurance plan with "one Leo Perlman, former Czech social Democrat, who likes to be called a doctor and an insurance actuary, though he is neither." Perlman's firm was the Trade Union Casualty Co., which had associations with another insurance firm called Continental Assurance Co., which was "connected through interlocking directorates with the Chicago packing houses, Elgin Watch Co., the large Illinois banks and International Harvester." There was thus a link between Reuther and Chicago capitalists. But Allan pushed the association one step farther. On the board of Continental Assurance was the uncle of the first national secretary of America First. Thus Reuther was also consorting with Nazis. This tenuous commercial and avuncular relationship was "evidence" for Communist support of the Thomas-Addes faction of the U.A.W.[13]

The Communists invoked the memory of Jefferson and Madison when the court upheld the Smith Act. The tragedy was that the times called for genuine, rather than cynical, defenders of the Jefferson-Madison tradition of civil liberty.

THE SMITH ACT CASES

In 1940, during the period of the Nazi-Soviet pact, President Roosevelt signed the Alien Registration Act, generally known as the Smith Act, for its sponsor, Representative Howard Smith, of Virginia. The measure's Title I forbade, upon pain of fine up to $10,000 and imprisonment up to ten years, "knowingly or willfully" advocating, abetting, advising, or teaching the "duty, necessity, desirability, or propriety" of overthrowing or destroying by force or violence the United States Government or American state and local governments. Title I also forbade organizing or attempting or helping to organize "any society, group, or assembly of persons who teach, advocate, or encourage the overthrow or destruction of any such government by force or violence; or becomes or is a member of, or affiliates with, any such . . . [organization], knowing the purposes thereof." The act had first been invoked in 1942 against eighteen Trotskyists. The Eighth Circuit Court of Appeals upheld the conviction and the Supreme Court denied certiorari. Also, during the war there had been an indictment of thirty alleged Nazi sympathizers under another section of Title I, pertaining to inciting disloyalty in the armed forces. The presiding judge died after seven hectic months of trial, and the case was dropped, only to be revived in 1945. In November 1946, the District of Columbia Court of Appeals dismissed the indictment.

One other relevant background case involved William Schneiderman, chairman of the California Communists. The case was a denaturalization proceeding not involving the Smith Act. In 1943, the Supreme Court ruled that the government had not proved by "clear, convincing, and unequivocal evidence" that the Communist Party in the five years before 1927 had advocated violent or forceful overthrow of government.[14]

Then on July 20, 1948, the Department of Justice sought and obtained from a federal grand jury in New York City an indictment against the twelve members of the national board of the Communist Party under Title I of the Smith Act. The twelve national board members were: William Z. Foster, Eugene Dennis (born Francis X. Waldron, Jr.), John B. Williamson, Jacob Stachel, Robert G. Thompson, Benjamin J. Davis, Jr., Henry Winston, John Gates (born Israel Regenstreif), Irving Potash, Gilbert Green, Carl Winter, and Gus Hall (born Arno Gust Halberg). The specific charges against them were that they had conspired with one another "and with divers other persons to the Grand Jury unknown" to dissolve the Communist Political Association and to reconstitute the Communist Party of the United States, "a society, group, and assembly of persons who teach and advocate the overthrow and destruction of the Government . . .

by force and violence," and then knowingly and willfully had caused to be taught and advocated such overthrow and destruction by force or violence. The indictment did not allege the defendants had committed any overt revolutionary act—only teaching and advocating. In other words, they were not charged with a conspiracy to overthrow the government; they were charged with conspiracy to form a party to teach and advocate overthrow of the government. The twelve defendants were arrested without incident in July and were released upon bail. At the beginning of the trial, the case against Foster was severed because his health was frail.[15] Since then, the government has occasionally reconsidered trying Foster, but each time it has let the matter drop because Foster's health has deteriorated further.

The trial opened January 17, 1949, before Judge Harold R. Medina in the federal court building, Foley Square, New York City. The trial lasted nine months, dragging through an exceptionally hot summer, and did not end completely until October 21. It was, in the words of one constitutional historian, "certainly among the most turbulent and hectic in American court annals."[16] The defendants engaged five principal attorneys: George W. Crockett, Richard Gladstein, Abraham J. Isserman, Louis F. McCabe, and Harry Sacher. Dennis acted as his own attorney. In the words of Judge Augustus Hand, the conduct of the defense attorneys at the trial was "wilfully obstructive." Despite several warnings from Medina that their conduct was contemptuous, the defense attorneys persisted in baiting the trial judge and accusing him of seeking publicity, of partiality toward the prosecution, and of racial prejudice. In June, Judge Medina declared defendants Hall and Winston in contempt, and the party organized a demonstration of pickets on Foley Square and a Union Square rally of protest. At the trial's end, Judge Medina cited the defense attorneys for contempt, found them guilty, and sentenced them to imprisonment without giving them an opportunity to reply. The Court of Appeals, by a 2 to 1 vote, upheld the contempt conviction, as did the U.S. Supreme Court, by a vote of five to three. Justices Black, Douglas, and Frankfurter dissented, and Justice Clark did not participate.[17]

It was clear from the beginning of the trial that the Communists' strategy in the courtroom was to use the case as a sounding board for its general position and program and to attempt to portray American justice as a sham. For the first several weeks of the trial, the Communists challenged the validity of the jury panel, asserting that the method of selecting jurors systematically excluded Negroes, the poor, and working people. The open purpose of this unsuccessful gambit was, in Foster's words, to put "the Government, not the Communists . . . on trial." [18] But the courtroom strategy was only part of a larger strategy: to arouse mass protest against the government's case in order to pressure the administration to drop its prosecution and actually to build the party and the movement in the process.

Soon after the trial opened, the Communist national committee made a full-page announcement in the *Worker*. The headline was "THE HERESY TRIAL HAS BEGUN." A subhead continued, "But this 20th century Political Inquisition is not proceeding according to bipartisan plan. In the courtroom the accused have become the accusers." In a box on the page was an outline of general strategy: "HERE IS OUR PLAN FOR A NATIONWIDE CAMPAIGN TO QUASH THE HERESY INDICTMENTS AND PRESERVE THE BILL OF RIGHTS: 1) Speak To the People, For the People Will Decide. . . . Get All Within The Sound of Your Voice to Pass Resolutions And Send Telegrams To Attorney General Tom Clark. . . . 2) Give The People Something To Read And Pass On To Others. . . . 3) Show The People How To Act Together. . . . 4) Ask The People To Pass The Ammunition. . . . 5) Build While You Convince." A few weeks later the veteran party war horse Elizabeth Gurley Flynn wrote in one of her frequent "pep talk" articles, "There is no more telling offensive to defend the leaders of the Party . . . than for the Party to grow right now in the very period of the court trial." [19]

The party's strategy did not work. The defendants and their

counsel did not present the kind of a case to persuade a jury, and the party's activities outside the courtroom neither helped the party grow nor aroused public opinion in the defendants' behalf. Indeed, the party could not even count on its usual friends. The party had difficulty raising money for trial expenses. One of the party fronts, the Civil Rights Congress, began a campaign in the summer of 1948 to raise $250,000. By the following February, it had collected only $74,095.45. (The way this sum was spent is further evidence of the party's strategy: only $25,592.05 went for legal defense; the balance was spent on "mass agitation, tours, conferences, printing, etc.") [20] The party's defenders complained of public apathy. As "The Thin Man," Dashiell Hammett, put it, "We had a lot of people going around saying, 'I don't care how it comes out just so they get it over with.' " He blamed the "imperialist press" for this apathy.[21]

The prosecution in the trial presented a three-pronged case. It dealt at length with the circumstances under which the party had been reconstituted in 1945; it introduced as evidence of intent to overthrow the government several "classics" of Marxism-Leninism-Stalinism published or taught by the party; and it presented thirteen former Communists and F.B.I. "plants" who testified that the "classics" had been taught or that the defendants had otherwise taught and advocated overthrow of the government.

The Communist strategy not only failed in the courtroom, it failed also to arouse any widespread concern in the public at large for the civil-liberties issues involved in the case. Indeed, the Communist antics in the court tended to prevent such general concern. Their tactics certainly were not well calculated to attract non-Communists and anti-Communists to the defense of free speech for Communists, though the Supreme Court ruled in 1957 that the case did involve principles of free speech.

Perhaps the most important aspect of the trial was Judge Medina's charge to the jury. The prosecution had concerned itself only with evidence about Communist speeches and publications, the advocacy of overthrow of government, rather than overt action leading to such overthrow. Yet the first amendment to the Constitution clearly guarantees free speech and a free press, which has been judicially construed to mean no limitations unless the speech or publication presents a "clear and present danger" to the safety of the republic. Judge Medina bridged the gap between illegal action and constitutionally guaranteed speech by charging the jury that the defendants could be found guilty if they found that the defendants intended to overthrow the government by violence and force "as speedily as circumstances permit." And he removed the clear-and-present-danger issue from the jury's consideration by stating that, as a matter of law, "there is sufficient danger of a substantive evil."

The jury found the eleven defendants guilty as charged. Judge Medina sentenced them to $10,000 fines and five years' imprisonment, except for Robert Thompson, whose record of heroism in the army prompted the judge to reduce his imprisonment to three years. The defendants appealed, and in 1950 the Court of Appeals, Judge Learned Hand writing the opinion, upheld the conviction. The Supreme Court granted certiorari, and, in June 1951, found the Smith Act constitutional and upheld the convictions. Justices Black and Douglas dissented, and Justice Clark did not participate.

The Supreme Court's decision in the Dennis case is an extremely important one in the nation's constitutional history, but it need not detain us here. Suffice it to say that the opinions were varied and complicated and that the vote of the court represented an unprecedented judicial approval for restriction of speech. It is interesting to note that Justice Douglas's dissenting opinion referred to the Communists as "miserable merchants of unwanted ideas," and that two of the majority justices, Frankfurter and Jackson, wrote that the Smith Act, while constitutional, was an ill-advised and ineffective method of combating Communism.[22]

The Department of Justice sought and secured indictments of many other Communist leaders after the Supreme Court upheld the convictions of the top eleven leaders. On March 10, 1952,

Philip Frankfeld, his wife, and four other Maryland Communist leaders were brought to trial in Baltimore. All were found guilty and sentenced to $1,000 fines and from two to five years' imprisonment. Ironically, the *Daily Worker* announced Frankfeld's expulsion from the party and his wife's removal from leadership just three days before the trial began. The party's leadership accused him of "defeatism," of writing and circulating among the membership a pamphlet counter to the line of the party, and "moral degeneracy and corruption . . . double-dealing and deception." [23] Such charges certainly smacked of the party's own "thought control."

In a trial in Los Angeles beginning on February 1, 1952, and ending August 5, William Schneiderman, Oleta O'Conner Yates, Dorothy Healy, and eleven other top California Communists were convicted under the Smith Act. Although convicted, the California Communists conducted quite a different kind of defense from the one in the first trial. These defendants, in June 1957, became the first Smith Act group to receive a favorable decision from the Supreme Court.

The most widely publicized of these "second-string" prosecutions was *United States* v. *Elizabeth Gurley Flynn, et al.,* sometimes known as the "second Foley Square trial." In this trial, thirteen Communists were convicted, but a new development was Judge Edward J. Dimock's directed acquittal of two of the defendants, Isadore Begun and Simon W. Gerson, on the grounds that insufficient evidence had been presented to connect them to the indicted conspiracy. Subsequently, the convictions of two other defendants, Alexander Trachtenberg and George Blake Charney, were set aside and new trials ordered when the testimony of the principal witness against them, Harvey Matusow, was revealed to be questionable at best.

Prosecutions and convictions of "second-string" and even "third-string" Communist leaders continued through 1953 and 1954. Seven were convicted in Honolulu, five in Pittsburgh, four in Seattle, six in Detroit, five in St. Louis, and nine in Philadelphia. In all these cases there was but one acquittal.

What were the effects on the Communist Party of all these prosecutions, convictions, and imprisonments? (The question of the wisdom of the Smith Act prosecutions, which involves an assessment of their impact on civil liberties, is another question.) Certainly prosecutions under the Smith Act did not kill the party, for it was still a going concern after the frequency of new indictments declined about 1955. In that year, the F.B.I. estimated the party had 22,663 members.[24] Membership strength shrank considerably after the 1949 trial, but the party's most important membership loss did not come until 1956 and 1957, after the Smith Act prosecutions had almost ceased.

It is impossible precisely to measure the various factors causing the decline of the Communist Party in the early 1950's and say that this or that causal factor was responsible for x percentage of the party's deterioration. Smith Act prosecutions were only one among many actions and conditions that hurt the party. Among others were the further deterioration of Russian-American relations during the Korean war, the continued health of the American economy, and, perhaps most important, the ill-advised actions of the Communist Party itself.

The prosecutions obviously hurt the party. It was forced to spend for legal defense a great deal of money it would otherwise have spent for offensive, rather than defensive, activity. The trials consumed a great deal of the Communists' time and energy, which they would have preferred to use otherwise. It has been asserted that the Smith Act convictions "beheaded" the party, leaving the rank and file without effective leadership. Unquestionably, the imprisonment of the abler and more experienced leaders damaged the party's efficiency, but the most important party leader, William Z. Foster, actively led the party despite the poor health that prevented the government from pushing his prosecution. There is no reason to believe that the main direction of the party would have been different had the imprisoned leaders remained active in the leadership. The party's decision to go "underground" in 1949 and 1950, related of course to the Smith Act prosecutions, probably damaged party efficiency more than the leaders' imprisonment. It is unlikely that a considerable number of Communists severed their party connection because of fear of prosecution. Only one of the convicted Communists, Barbara Hartle, convicted at Seattle in 1953, renounced the party before the Communists' 1956 crisis, and she related that her indictment prompted her to stay in the party longer than she would have otherwise. It may even be true that the prosecutions led members to resolve to stick with the party, come what may.

"PEACE" AND WAR

In the late 1940's and early 1950's, the most prominent feature of the American Communists' outward face was their "peace crusade." "Peace," by which the Communists actually meant unstinting agreement with the foreign policy of the Soviet Union, had long been a prominent Communist demand. But in 1949 and early 1950, "peace" became the ideological hook upon which all else hung.

Foster expressed the notion of the centrality of the "peace" issue clearly in a message to the party's national committee. "Under no circumstances should we neglect the mass struggles over wages, unemployment, Negro rights, and fascism: but we must recognize that these are all bound up with the fight against war. Everything depends upon our success in this all-inclusive key struggle. To mobilize the masses to fight for peace should be the very center of the work." Then, in a passage that illustrated the party's ambiguous position on the inevitability of war, he advised that the "peace crusade" must be a long-term campaign, if not one of indefinite duration. "Regardless of any agreements that may be made to soften the cold war . . . the war danger will continue to exist. . . . That is because of the incur-

able warlike character of imperialism, especially American imperialism. The war danger will last as long as capitalism does,
and we must orientate upon this realization . . . the fight for
peace must be in the center of all our Party's work." [25]

The party's first big peace project was the Scientific and Cultural Conference for World Peace, usually called the Waldorf
Peace Conference, in March 1949. An organization called the
National Council of the Arts, Sciences, and Professions, composed of former Progressive Citizens of America members for
the most part, officially sponsored the conference, but the Communists actually organized the affair. The conference attracted an
impressive list of intellectuals as participants, indicating that as
late as the spring of 1949 the influence of Communists in the
non-Communist Left was far from extinguished.[26] In October,
the party inspired the formation in Chicago of the National Labor Conference for Peace, and in December, it was behind a
weekend peace rally in New York City's Manhattan Center.[27]

The Communist peace campaign began in earnest in the spring
of 1950; the immediate occasion for the stepped-up program was
the job of getting American signatures to the so-called Stockholm
Peace Petition. In March, the Permanent Committee of the World
Peace Congress met at Stockholm and drafted the appeal. The
chairman of this committee was the French scientist and Communist Frederic Joliot-Curie, now dead; the vice-chairman was a
non-Communist former assistant attorney general of the United
States, O. John Rogge. Other American delegates were Albert
Kahn and Johannes Steel. The petition itself was an innocuous
condemnation of the use of atomic bombs, which several million
Americans might have endorsed had it not been for the petition's
international Communist sponsorship. It did not call for the abolition of nuclear testing. The Russians still had a lot of testing to
do.

O. John Rogge's story was interesting. Rogge had criticized
both American and Russian imperialism at a peace conference
in Mexico City in 1949, and the Communists called him a slan-

derer. In early March 1950, before the Stockholm meeting, he agreed to serve as legal counsel for Tito's Yugoslavia in the United States, and he registered with the Department of Justice as required by the Foreign Agents Registration Act of 1938. Still he went to Stockholm. At a meeting of the World Peace Conference in Warsaw in November 1950, Rogge gave a speech in which he vigorously condemned Soviet imperialism. His speech caused a scene of memorable proportions. An American delegate, Charles P. Howard, who had given the keynote speech at the 1948 Progressive convention, called Rogge "not only a lawyer for Tito but . . . the advocate for the slaveholder Jefferson Davis . . . and of King George III." The staff of the Cominform's newspaper was violent in condemnation of Rogge.[28]

In order to reach their goal of five million signatures to the Stockholm petition by October 24, United Nations Day, the Communists staged the kind of organizational campaign at which they once excelled. They used their influence in the trade unions they still dominated; they created new front groups (Harlem Women's Committee on Peace, Veterans for Peace, U.S. Youth Sponsoring Committee for the World Peace Appeal); they organized conferences with noble titles; and they exploited their old front groups, like the American Slav Congress. But their effort failed to achieve the goal. At the end of the campaign, the Communists claimed only two and one-half million signatures, and that figure was unquestionably padded.[29]

Before the petition campaign was over, the United States was actually engaged in armed conflict with Communists in Korea. Early in the morning of June 25, 1950, North Korean troops crossed the thirty-eighth parallel, the boundary between the American and Russian occupation zones set by the Potsdam Conference, in a large-scale, obviously long-planned invasion of South Korea. Almost immediately, the United States, independently and through the United Nations, went to the aid of the South Koreans; within a matter of days, American soldiers were being killed as the North Koreans pushed on south.

The American Communists now faced a new situation, but the fundamentals of their position on the Korean war had already been decided. As early as 1947, the party press had begun to publish paeans to the Soviet-supported North Koreans and condemnations of the American-supported government of Syngman Rhee in South Korea. The North Koreans were peaceful and democratic; Syngman Rhee was a reactionary puppet of Wall Street.[30] Curiously, there had even been foreshadowings of some of the details of the party line on the Korean war. On the first anniversary of V-J Day, *New Masses* had carried an article on bacteriological warfare with ideas that would in time come to fruition in such *Daily Worker* headlines as "REPORT U.S. PLANES DROP MORE GERMS ON KOREA," "BACTERIOLOGICAL WAR CRIMINALS," and "EYEWITNESS DESCRIBES GERM BOMB." [31]

The Communists claimed that the whole Korean affair was part of a conspiracy of Wall Street and its agents in Washington and Seoul. In a "plot . . . as thoroughly planned as . . . the Japanese seizure of Mukden in 1931," Wall Street had entrusted Syngman Rhee to arrange the incident. John Foster Dulles was "the trigger man." The party secretariat issued a statement that even had Dulles "standing in the front lines of the puppet government trenches, giving them their marching orders." Dulles was indeed an awful person in the Communist press. The Cominform called him, under the headline "JOHN FOSTER DULLES, BANKER, SLAVEOWNER, WARMONGER," "one of the more sinister members of the imperialist gang of misanthropic fiends." [32] According to the Communists, North Korea had not invaded South Korea. Quite the reverse. Troops of "the quisling South Korean government" had "crossed all along the 38th parallel and penetrated one kilometer into North Korean territory." [33]

The purposes of the whole Wall Street plot, the Communists maintained, were the "colonial enslavement" of all East Asia and the establishment in Korea of "powerful bases from which to make war upon the new China and the Soviet Union." [34] The North Korean "guards," as the party press first called them, had foiled the imperialist plot with strong resistance. Then they counterattacked. Within six weeks, they controlled nearly all the Korean peninsula, and the "guards" became "Korean people's liberation forces." How the North Koreans were able, without previous planning and careful and extensive preparations, to launch such a major offensive was a military question the Communists did not answer—or even consider. The intervention of American-U.N. forces on a large scale, the subsequent expulsion of the North Korean army from South Korea, and the carrying of the war north of the thirty-eighth parallel only served to confirm for the Communists their interpretation of the whole conflict.

Almost from the beginning of the Korean war, there was a difference of opinion about war aims and strategy between President Truman and General Douglas MacArthur, commander of the U.N. forces in Korea. Truman wanted no more than a limited war; he tried to restrain his colorful and outspoken general, who was for more adventurous policies even should they risk involvement for the United States in a general war with Communist China or the Soviet Union. The Truman-MacArthur differences became impossible to ignore or compromise in the spring of 1951, and in April, the president removed the general from command.

The MacArthur ouster prompted a few Communists to reassess their interpretation of the Korean war, as well it should have. If the Truman administration were bent on a war of conquest in the Far East, why should it risk political disaster with the removal of the bellicose and politically important MacArthur? No important Communist, apparently, at that time prepared any thorough critique of the whole party position on war, imperialism, and American foreign policy. But at least one, Joseph Starobin, foreign editor of the *Daily Worker* and secretary of the party's commission on peace activities, quietly and privately expressed his doubts to party leaders about the validity of the party line. Neither Starobin nor anyone else led any large-scale agitation in the party. The rank and file and most leaders had no knowledge of any dissent in the national office.[35]

Lest anyone else should develop heretical ideas about the party's line, Eugene Dennis wrote a letter to the party membership on the MacArthur affair, in which he upheld the old line in no uncertain terms. The Truman-MacArthur controversy was of no real significance, wrote Dennis. The differences between the president and the general were only over tactics and pace. "The Truman Administration continues to move in its own aggressive way and at its own pace toward a global war . . . under the guise of opposing a 'third world war,' of waging a 'limited war,' the Truman Administration continues to pursue Wall Street's aggressive war policy, a criminal policy which . . . if unchecked, can only lead . . . to a third world war." The party must not relax, must not let up the struggle against a general war. Henceforth, ordered Dennis, every item *of every Party agenda in every leading committee and club must be linked with . . . an all-out struggle and campaign against the Truman and MacArthur war policies."* [36]

The Communists failed to modify their position on Korea in the slightest. Through the long truce negotiations, conducted intermittently from July 1951 until the armistice two years later; through a Presidential election in which Foster called General Eisenhower "Wall Street's speed-war candidate"; [37] through the gradual but steady fading away of old soldier MacArthur, the Communists incessantly maintained that Washington was about to launch a new world war of imperialistic conquest. Even when the final armistice was signed, the party's national committee declared that the peace was only a partial victory over "the plans of Wall Street to establish its world domination through war." Foster, never one to allow a fact to upset his theory, found little solace in the armistice. The "Wall Street planners of a third world war," he told his readers, "have been trying (and still are) to make another Spain in Korea." The State Department will yet "try to sabotage the [Korean] peace." [38]

The most important effect of the party's whole peace crusade in the long run was that it further contributed to its isolation from the publics it needed for sustenance. Besides all their work in especially constituted peace organizations—they scorned the established peace organizations such as those of religious groups and the Fellowship for Reconciliation and were in turn scorned by them—the Communists tried to use their influence in organizations founded for some other purpose. In trade unions, for example, the Communists regarded a leader's position on foreign policy as a touchstone. "A labor leader is a progressive to the degree that he stands for peace . . . and co-existence with the Soviet Union. He is a reactionary to the extent that he stands for . . . the war drive of U.S. imperialism and its anti-Soviet foreign policy. No matter how militant . . . on other questions, to the extent that he supports the war drive, he is a reactionary." [39] Communists applied the same test to Negro leaders. When the national leaders of the N.A.A.C.P. supported the Korean war, the Communists accused them of selling out for "a few paltry jobs [in] the operation of Point Four in Africa." [40] And, as will be seen in greater detail later, the Communists in the Progressive Party insisted on their position on Korea, precipitating a crisis in the Progressive organization that left it without a prominent non-Communist leader. The root of the matter was that the party accorded conformity to the international Communist line a higher priority than its own viability.

A few Communists dimly perceived the effects of the party's parochialism. There was even a guarded and fuzzy warning in the party's official magazine.[41] But warnings from their own ranks did not change party policy. The Communists were not fully to realize the consequences of their sectarianism until they were jarred by events in the Soviet Union.

With a more astute peace program, one less obviously a reflection of Russian foreign policy, the Communists might have gained some strength or at least slowed their decline. For there was widespread opposition to war in the United States as well as widespread opposition to Communism. A large part of the population was anxious and frustrated about the Korean war. Ironically for the Communists, popular desire for peace expressed itself in the election of a Republican administration, an administration headed by a war-hero five-star general and a Vice-President who made his mark in politics as a professional anti-Communist.

THE LAST DAYS OF THE PROGRESSIVE PARTY

After Wallace's showing in the 1948 elections, the Communists were slow to lose their illusions about the Progressive Party being a "mass party of the working class." Communists deplored the electorate's commitment to the major political parties and tried to convince themselves that sentiment for the Progressive Party's program was growing even if the party was not. But in 1950, they had to admit that "there is not yet a mass third party in America." [42]

Despite the ineffectiveness of the Progressive Party and despite the fact that any realistic appraisal of its future would not indicate growth, the Communist Party continued until after the 1952 elections to support and dominate the Progressive Party. The Communists, too, continued their relationship with the A.L.P. in New York, which supported the Progressives in national elections. With each group, the Communists continued their support because these "progressive" political organizations represented the best instruments then available to the Communists for amplifying the general Communist program. Within the Progressive Party and the A.L.P., there were still some leftist non-Communists, residues of the popular frontism of the mid-1930's, who would tolerate the Communists and respond to such general slogans as "Peace, Democracy, and Socialism."

Early in 1950, Henry Wallace belatedly tried to change the popular impression that the Communists controlled his party lock, stock, and barrel. At the second national convention of the party, in Chicago, Wallace said that the failure of the first convention to adopt the "Vermont resolution" denying blanket endorsement of the foreign policy of any nation had been a mistake. He went on to warn that Progressives should not take any positions that would give observers "the slightest, legitimate reason for believing that any working member of our Party puts Rome, Moscow or London ahead of the United States." [43] The convention went on to declare in one of its resolutions that the United States and the Soviet Union had both "made mistakes" in foreign policy.

This was mild enough. Neither Wallace nor the convention seriously criticized Soviet foreign policy or began any movement to remove Communists from influence within the Progressive Party. The Communists, nevertheless, refused to overlook the Progressives' slight reproach to Communist orthodoxy. The *Daily Worker* took the Progressive convention to task. "What happened at the Progressive Party convention," National Committeeman Gil Green instructed his comrades, "cannot be condoned." [44] Thus bucked up, the Communists in the Progressive Party were in no mood to compromise when the outbreak of war in Korea came.

Within a few days after the administration's decision to go to the aid of the South Koreans, the executive committee of the Progressive Party called a meeting of the full national committee for July 15. The smaller group then began on July 6 a series of sessions in preparation for the meeting of the full committee. In these meetings it became obvious that the differences over the Korean war between Henry Wallace on the one hand and the Communists and pro-Communists on the other were too great to be compromised.

There were five meetings of the executive committee before it finished drafting a statement on Korea. Not all members of the committee attended all the sessions. The members most consistent in attendance were C. B. Baldwin, Progressive Executive Secretary; James Durkin, President of the Communist-dominated United Office and Professional Workers of America; the playwright Lillian Hellman; Vito Marcantonio, the A.L.P.'s congressman; John McManus, Editor of the *National Guardian;* Paul Robeson; Arthur Schutzer, Executive Secretary of the A.L.P.; Alfred K. Stern; Henry Wallace; and Walter Wallace, who has since testified that he was then a member of the Communist Party.[45] Others who attended meetings but were not committee members were John Abt, Vaughn Albertson, Louis Burnham, Lydia D'Fonseca, and Mrs. Martha Dodd Stern.[46] After the Sterns refused to return to the United States from Mexico in the spring of 1957 to appear before a grand jury investigating espionage, Boris Morros, an American counterspy, implicated Mrs. Stern in espionage. The daughter of the late Professor William E. Dodd, American Ambassador to Germany in the 1930's, and her husband then fled to Czechoslovakia.[47]

There was a wide gulf between Henry Wallace's estimate of the Korean conflict and that of the rest of the executive committee, but Wallace's dissent from the statement drawn by the committee was not stated clearly and decisively in the committee's meetings. At the end of the July 10 meeting, according to the minutes, Wallace even expressed "provisional agreement" with the drafted statement but would reserve final decision until the next morning. The next morning, he telephoned Baldwin to say that he could not agree to the statement unless it contained four major modifications. These modifications would have changed the entire direction of the statement. The committee declined to make the changes, and thus, on July 11, 1950, Wallace severed his connection with the Progressive Party.[48]

On July 15, the entire Progressive national committee met, and by a vote of 32 to 2 adopted the statement with which Wallace could not agree. The two dissenters were Clark Foreman, of the Southern Conference of Human Welfare, and Thomas Emerson, of the Yale University law faculty. Henry Wallace did not attend the meeting because he had already in effect left the party. The statement condemned Truman's directive commanding the fleet to defend Formosa, urged that Communist China be admitted to the United Nations, and urged the U.N. Security Council to "issue appropriate orders and adopt measures" to end the hostilities and then increase economic and technical assistance in Asia. On the same day, Wallace issued a statement to the press in which he put responsibility for the conflict on the Soviet Union. "We must continue our fight . . . in South Korea until such time as Russia is willing to use her influence to stop the fighting and start . . . UN negotiations. . . . I say that Russia could stop the fighting now if she wished to do so." [49]

From the summer of 1950 on, the strength of the Progressive and American Labor parties steadily waned. The Korean war polarized political opinion: the general public more and more identified the policies of these parties with sympathy for the Soviet Union, and the Communists and fellow travelers in these parties were less and less inclined to compromise. The Progressives and Communists in California, for example, condemned Mrs. Helen Gahagan Douglas vociferously in her race against Richard M. Nixon in 1950 because she supported the war.[50] In the same election, Vito Marcantonio made "peace" the main issue of his campaign and was defeated by a fusion candidate. The 1952 Progressive Party national candidates—Vincent Hallinan for President and Mrs. Charlotta Bass for Vice-President—were almost unknown. Hallinan, a cousin of Ireland's Eamon de Valera, was a wealthy San Francisco Left Wing lawyer; Mrs. Bass had worked closely with the Communists.[51] The Hallinan-Bass ticket received only 140,023 votes, about one-fifth of 1 per cent of the total vote. Well over half the Progressive vote came from New York City, Los Angeles, and the San Francisco Bay area.[52]

After the 1952 election, it became obvious to the Communists that to continue their third-party gambit was fruitless. The "mass party of peace" had become just another Left Wing sect, only slightly larger than the Communist Party itself. The extent to which the Communists controlled the Progressive organization and the American Labor Party is seen in the subsequent history of those parties when the Communists pulled out: the Progressives disappeared altogether, and the A.L.P. failed to get enough votes in 1954 to stay on the ballot.

THE C.I.O. EXPULSIONS

The C.I.O. began in a small way to expel the Communist-controlled unions the very month Truman trounced Dewey and Wallace. The end of the road for the C.I.O. Communists was in sight after the Portland, Oregon, C.I.O. convention in late November 1948. The convention summarily ended the jurisdictional dispute between the Left-led Farm Equipment Workers (F.E.) and the U.A.W. by ordering F.E. to merge its 65,000 members into the Reuther organization within sixty days. When the F.E. leaders refused, the U.A.W. raided F.E.'s members, and F.E. disappeared anyway. At the Portland convention, President Murray gave three small Communist unions a stern lecture on their inadequacies as trade unions and threatened to deal with them more harshly in the future. These unions—the United Office and Professional Workers, the United Public Workers, and the Food and Tobacco Workers—had organized only a tiny fraction of the workers in their industries.[53]

The Communist unions did not stand together at the Portland convention. The leaders of the Food and Tobacco Workers, the Furriers, and the Marine Cooks and Stewards, all with much stronger Communist support in the rank and file than most Left unions, fought back at the anti-Communist C.I.O. leadership. They submitted and voted for a set of resolutions that sounded like a summary of the Communist line.[54] But the leaders of the bigger Left unions, more vulnerable to attack from their non-Communist rank and file, tried to compromise. Delegates from U.E., I.L.W.U., and the Furniture Workers voted for the C.I.O. majority resolution and even for the resolution rescinding the charter of the Communist-run New York City C.I.O. Council—to the exasperation of the Communist labor secretary.[55] Albert Fitzgerald, President of U.E. and the presiding officer of the Progressive convention four months before, voted for a resolution endorsing the Marshall Plan in the C.I.O. executive board and delivered a self-effacing speech on the convention floor: "I tell you frankly I do not give a damn for Russia. . . . Vishinsky and Molotov are engaging themselves in saber rattling and war mongering. . . . If President Truman makes a sincere effort to carry out his promises . . . I will tell the Progressive Party to go to hell." [56] Through such tactics, Fitzgerald managed to postpone C.I.O. action against his union and even remain a C.I.O. vice-president—for another year.

After the convention, the party's leadership stiffened the resistance of the C.I.O. Left unions. Early in January 1949, delegates of eight Communist unions met in New York and announced a "rank and file unity plan." [57] In the spring, the Communists refused a compromise in the Transport Workers Union, which, according to Mike Quill's account, would have given them a large minority on the union's executive board and the post of national secretary-treasurer. The party preferred to fight it out with Quill for a majority of the executive board. Quill utterly routed the Communists after this challenge. At the next national convention of the T.W.U., the Communists won no national offices and not a single seat on the executive board. [58] In May, the officers of nine Left unions voted as a bloc against the C.I.O. executive-board decision to withdraw from the World Federation of Trade Unions. [59] In June, the Communists, in an effort to give better co-ordination to the Left unions, started a new monthly magazine, the *March of Labor*.

Perhaps the best example of the Communists' decision not to compromise—even to counterattack and take the consequences— was in U.E., by far the most important of the Communist-controlled unions. The Communists had effectively controlled U.E. since 1941, when they elected James Matles and Julius Emspak to national office. The slow-moving and slow-thinking Albert Fitzgerald, President of the union, was not a Communist; he was only a "front man" for the Communists who ran the union. At U.E.'s national convention in Cleveland in September 1949, the Communist leadership encountered for the first time an effectively organized anti-Communist opposition, led by James B. Carey. The Carey forces represented most of the big U.E. locals, but Matles and Emspak had a majority at the convention through their control of the many small locals. The Communists got their slate of national officers elected and their resolutions adopted. Then they counterattacked. They began a purge of the anti-Communists by amending the union's constitution to empower the general executive board to bring charges against and expel individual members. The amendment empowered the Communist national U.E. officers to eliminate their opponents even when their opponents had the support of their locals.[60]

Even after the C.I.O.'s Portland convention, the Communist unions might have been able to survive in the C.I.O. if they had behaved circumspectly. After the Communist activities in 1949, however, the C.I.O. leadership resolved to make quick work of them. At the Cleveland C.I.O. convention in November 1949, the national C.I.O. majority effectively ended all Communist influence in the national body. By a large vote, the convention amended its constitution to make Communists or those who consistently followed the Communist line ineligible for C.I.O. national office, including membership on the executive board. The convention itself then expelled U.E., saying that it was no more than "the Communist Party masquerading as a labor union." The convention then amended its constitution again to empower a two-thirds majority on the executive board to expel "or take any other appropriate action against" any union whose policies and activities "are consistently directed toward the achievement of the program or purposes of the Communist Party." [61]

Soon after the convention, the C.I.O. executive board, through a series of subcommittees, began hearings on charges against the Left Wing unions. The pattern in all the hearings was to prove that the union, through its publications and resolutions, had consistently followed each turn in the Communist party's line, a relatively easy matter to prove. The C.I.O. did not try to prove that the union leaders were members of the Communist Party, a task which would have been considerably more difficult, if not impossible, but would have been irrelevant anyway. By the late spring of 1950, the C.I.O. executive board had expelled nine Communist-led unions. Communist influence in the C.I.O. was all but completely eliminated. Any Communists left were either rank and filers or, at most, local officers who thereafter could sing the party tune only softly.[62]

Being cut off from the rest of the labor movement was a severe handicap for the Communists and the unions they controlled, but worse was to come. The C.I.O. granted charters to new unions to compete with the expelled unions or allowed established C.I.O. unions to raid the Communist unions' membership. Within a few years, the Communist unions, assaulted by raid after raid, had dwindled away. By 1956, the only Communist unions with anything like their strength before expulsion were the Bridges union and Mine, Mill. A new union in the electrical industry, the International Union of Electrical, Radio and Machine Workers (I.U.E.), the Machinists (I.A.M.), and the A.F. of L.'s International Brotherhood of Electrical Workers had all but eliminated the once-powerful U.E.[63] The Bridges union and Mine, Mill were able substantially to retain their old strength because of special circumstances. Harry Bridges, despite, rather than because of, his politics, is a popular figure among West Coast dock workers. His generation of dock workers will not forget his heroic role in the 1934 dock strike, and Bridges runs a union that "delivers" in the Gompers "bread and butter" sense. There are two reasons for Mine, Mill's survival. It has a heritage of radical rhetoric that goes back to William D. ("Big Bill") Haywood and the Western Federation of Miners, for one thing, and employers prefer Mine, Mill to unions, such as the United Steelworkers, that might give them greater opposition at the bargaining table. Thus, Mine, Mill is a peculiar combination of a Red and a company union.[64]

In Communist theory, the workers in basic industry are supposed to be the core of their party's strength, the revolutionary proletariat. Until 1949-50, the Communists looked at the two million members in the unions they controlled and, with a bit of optimistic self-delusion, saw themselves as the vanguard of the working class. But by the mid-1950's, the membership of Communist-controlled unions had shrunk to about 200,000, about one-tenth of the former membership, less than 1 per cent of total American trade-union strength. Any group that professes to speak in the name of the working class with as little power in that class as the Communists have demonstrated speaks with a hollow ring indeed.

THE ROSENBERG CASE

The exclusion of Communist influence from the main stream of the American labor movement, the prosecutions under the Smith Act and other governmental anti-Communist programs, the deflation of the Progressive and A.L.P. popular fronts, and the general anti-Communist sentiments of the public, together with certain internal activities of the Communist organization, considerably reduced the strength of the Communist Party. Any index of the party's health shows a sharp decline from about 1949 to about 1953. In early February 1950, F.B.I. Director J. Edgar Hoover testified to a Congressional appropriations committee that there were at that time 54,174 members of the Communist Party. In 1953, he reported that party membership was 24,796, more than a 50-per-cent decline in three years.[65] In 1950, the general manager of the *Daily Worker* in his annual sworn circulation statement reported his paper's average circulation as 20,336, and the Sunday edition (the *Worker*) as 67,199. In 1953, these figures had fallen to 10,443 and 28,822 respectively.[66]

Despite the party's weakened organizational strength, despite the almost universal disapproval of Communist doctrines by the American people, despite the inhibitions upon Communists when they operated in public, the Communists still were able in the early 1950's to make of the Rosenberg affair one of the biggest, noisiest, and most successful propaganda campaigns in Communist Party history.

In early February 1950, Klaus Fuchs, a German-born physicist who as a naturalized British subject had worked in the United States during the war on the atomic-bomb project, was arrested for espionage. Fuchs confessed to the English authorities and told them what he knew of espionage. His testimony implicated Harry Gold, an American, who soon confessed to his role as a courier for a spy ring. Gold pleaded guilty in the Philadelphia courtroom of Federal Judge James P. McGranery, and was sentenced to thirty years' imprisonment. This sentence was the maximum imprisonment; the law provides for "death or imprisonment for not more than thirty years." Gold told the F.B.I. all he knew about the ring and implicated Julius Rosenberg, a Communist engineering graduate of the City College of New York; Julius Rosenberg's wife, Ethel; Ethel Rosenberg's brother, David Greenglass, a skilled machinist; Morton Sobell, a college classmate of Rosenberg; and Anatoli A. Yakovlev, a Russian national then presumably in the Soviet Union. When Gold's arrest was announced to the press, the *Daily Worker,* under the headline "FBI WHIPS UP NEW 'ATOMIC SPY' HOAX," declared, "By an obvious 'coincidence,' the arrest of Gold was timed to knock off the front pages the return tomorrow of United Nations Secretary-General Trygve Lie and his anticipated report of Soviet proposals to end the cold war." [67]

Greenglass confessed and revealed all he knew, as had Fuchs and Gold before him. The Rosenbergs and Sobell were indicted in August 1950, and their trial began in New York City in the court of Federal Judge Irving R. Kaufman on March 6, 1951. The burden of the prosecution's case was the testimony of Harry Gold and David Greenglass. The revelations of these two witnesses were partially confirmed by the testimony of others. The Rosenbergs denied everything. Ethel Rosenberg, when asked before the grand jury if she knew Gold and Yakovlev, had declined to answer on the grounds that her testimony might be self-incriminating. At the trial she denied she knew Yakovlev or had ever seen Gold before. Sobell pleaded not guilty, but did not take the witness stand at all; he said nothing to the jury whatsoever. The trial consumed three weeks. On March 29, 1951, after deliberating seven and one-half hours, the jury announced its verdict: the Rosenbergs and Sobell were guilty as charged. The Rosenbergs' attorney, Emmanuel H. Bloch, thanked the court, the prosecuting attorney and his staff, and F.B.I. members for their courtesies during the trial. He told the jury he was satisfied that it had examined the evidence "very carefully." Judge Kaufman sentenced the Rosenbergs to death and Sobell to thirty years' imprisonment. David Greenglass received a sentence of fifteen years' imprisonment.

The Communist press did not carry one word about the Rosenbergs until after they had been found guilty and had been sentenced. A person in the unenviable position of receiving news only from the *Daily Worker* would not have known until the day after they were sentenced that the Rosenberg case even existed. Nor did the party's Civil Rights Congress come forward to raise bail for the Rosenbergs after their arrest. When the Communists finally mentioned the case, they did not deny the Rosenbergs' guilt. The first mention, a news story, asserted that the Rosenbergs were being made scapegoats for the Korean war. An editorial three days later took the position that the sentence was what one would expect from a government "which is refusing to negotiate peace in Korea." The whole case, according to the editorial writer, was an effort "to turn the hatred of 57,000 American casualties away from the war makers in Washington toward Jews and Communists. Not since the days [of] the Czars . . . and Nazis . . . has this pogrom tactic been so brazenly used." But there was no accusation of a judicial frame-up.[68] No newspaper asserted that the Rosenbergs were innocent until four months after the end of the trial, and the charge that the Rosenbergs had been framed came then, not from the Communist press, strictly speaking, but from the fellow-traveling *National Guardian,* a publication of the New York A.L.P. begun for the Wallace movement in 1947.[69]

Why the Communists were so reticent about the Rosenberg case at first is an interesting subject for speculation. It seems likely that the Communists were quiet about the case until they were confident that the Rosenbergs were not going to confess to espionage, as had Fuchs, Gold, and Greenglass before them. To have organized and launched a big amnesty campaign and have it undermined by a confession would have been disastrous.

On November 8, 1951, seven months after the Rosenberg trial, while the case was being appealed, a group that called itself the National Committee to Secure Justice in the Rosenberg Case opened a bank account in New York City. The committee did not announce its formation until almost two months later. The president of the organization was Louis Harap, Editor of the Communist magazine *Jewish Life*. The chairman was Joseph Brainin. The most active directors of the committee were its executive secretary, David Alman, and his wife, Emily, who served as national treasurer. Alman had been a paid staff member of the New York Civil Rights Congress and the American Peace Crusade. The sponsors of the committee were a mixture of active party members, such as Herbert Aptheker, and intellectuals with several past associations in party fronts, such as W. E. B. DuBois, a few of whom enjoyed national prominence.[70] This committee organized and co-ordinated the pro-Rosenberg campaign throughout the country.

For its first several months, the Rosenberg committee's effort failed to generate much excitement except among small leftist groups in a few big cities ever ready to respond to such appeals. In the late fall and early winter of 1952, the committee stepped up its activities with more mass meetings, delegations to Sing Sing, where the Rosenbergs were imprisoned, and pickets outside the White House gates. Simultaneously, Rosenberg committees appeared in Paris and London. From then until the Rosenbergs' execution on June 19, 1953, the campaign operated at fever pitch.

Circumstantial evidence indicates that there was a relationship between the intensification of the Rosenberg campaign both in the

United States and in Europe and the case of Rudolph Slansky in Czechoslovakia. Slansky and thirteen other defendants were tried in Prague, November 20-27, 1952, and eleven of the defendants were hanged six days later. All but three of the fourteen were Jewish, and there were distinctly anti-Semitic overtones to the prosecution. Among other things, Slansky was charged with "Jewish bourgeois nationalism." The Communists everywhere were quick to deny they were anti-Semitic—they were only anti-Zionist, they asserted—but they clearly linked the Rosenberg and Slansky cases in an apparent attempt to divert attention from the Prague trial. Jacques Duclos, the French Communist leader, went so far as to say, "The conviction of U.S. atom spies Julius and Ethel Rosenberg was an example of anti-Semitism but the execution of eight Jews in Czechoslovakia last week was not." [71]

The French Communists achieved much more spectacular results with their pro-Rosenberg campaign than did their American comrades. Exploiting the legacy of the Dreyfus case of more than a half-century before, the French Rosenberg agitation emphasized the assertion that the couple were victims of anti-Semitism, a charge the major American Jewish organizations consistently rejected. Such prominent non-Communist French leaders as Cardinal Feltin, Archbishop of Paris, Edouard Herriot, President of the National Assembly, four former premiers of France, and Vincent Auriol, President of the Republic, took part in appeals for the Rosenbergs.[72] Undoubtedly, the Rosenberg agitation in France heightened anti-American sentiment, as it was intended to do.

In the last frantic days of the American pro-Rosenberg campaign, which featured motorcades, special "Rosenberg trains" from New York to Washington, and "round-the-clock vigils" outside the White House, there occurred a little-publicized incident that indicated that the Rosenberg committee and the Communists were determined to run the clemency campaign entirely by themselves and wring from it the greatest possible propaganda value. The incident involved Irwin Edelman, of Los Angeles, an erratic leftist expelled from the Communist Party in 1947. In November

1952, Edelman published a pamphlet entitled *Freedom's Electrocution,* which quite agreed with the Communist line on the Rosenberg case except that it was critical of the conduct during the trial of the Rosenbergs' counsel, Emmanuel H. Bloch. Soon after the pamphlet's publication, Edelman was expelled from the Los Angeles Rosenberg Committee.[73] The *National Guardian* refused to accept an advertisement for the pamphlet, and a letter in the *People's World* urged that Edelman be ignored.[74] Edelman interested two lawyers, Fyke Farmer, of Nashville, and Daniel G. Marshall, of Los Angeles, in his indictment of Bloch and in his suggestion that the Rosenbergs should have been tried under the Atomic Energy Act of 1946 rather than under the Espionage Act of 1917. Under the 1946 act, the death penalty or life imprisonment may be imposed only when intent to injure the United States is proved and only by recommendation of the trial jury. Using Edelman's argument, Farmer and Marshall, on June 13, 1953, five days before the Rosenbergs' scheduled execution, filed with Judge Kaufman a petition for a writ of habeas corpus. Bloch declined to co-operate with Farmer and Marshall and wired Judge Kaufman to state his refusal to be associated with the petition. Judge Kaufman denied the petition on June 15. Bloch refused again to co-operate with Farmer and Marshall when they tried to interest the Supreme Court in their argument. On June 17, two days after the Supreme Court had recessed for the summer, Justice William O. Douglas granted a stay of execution after hearing the Edelman argument. The court reconvened in extraordinary session the next day. The following day, June 19, the court vacated Justice Douglas's stay of execution. That evening, shortly after eight o'clock, the Rosenbergs were executed.[75] The Communists and the Rosenberg committee had been determined to keep the Rosenberg case activity in their own hands, where they could control it, even if this end meant rejection of a legal argument that had sufficient merit to persuade a justice of the nation's highest court to call the court into extraordinary session.

The primary motive of the Communists in the Rosenberg agitation in the United States was to broadcast the Communist opinion, central to their whole political line, that the government of the United States was controlled by "fascists" who sought to involve the nation in war, destroy the labor movement, abrogate civil liberties, eliminate dissent, and persecute minority groups. For Communists, already persuaded to the party's line, the Rosenberg case served as confirmation, and the defense agitation served to deepen personal commitments. And non-Communists moved to sympathy for the Rosenbergs by humanitarian considerations afforded the Communists an opportunity for indoctrination. From the first editorial on the Rosenberg case to the blast when the couple was executed, the Communists hammered away with the argument that the Rosenbergs were sentenced to death as a step toward outright fascism. The facts of the case itself got short shrift in Communist pages. The Rosenberg affair, the Communists repeated, was a device to channel "the hatred of the American people for the Korean war, for the 'inevitable atomic war' line of the atombomb maniacs . . . against the working-class vanguard, the Communists, the Negro and Jewish people, the labor and progressive forces generally." The Rosenbergs' trial and conviction was nothing but "a political plot to assist in advancing the McCarthyite pro-fascist reign of fear in the United States, to brutalize the population, and get it to accept the further fascization of the United States without resistance." Thus, the Communists asserted, to defend the Rosenbergs was not only humanitarian, but it was self-defense against fascism, essentially patriotic protection of American democracy. "There must be a halt to the Hitlerization of America by the Eisenhower-Brownell-J. Edgar Hoover forces working hand in glove with the swastika-minded McCarthy and his goons." [76] The opening-wedge-of-fascism theme dominated appeals directed to organized labor and to Jews, both groups that had good reasons to fear fascism. The theme permeated even the sentimentally murky poems and songs of the Rosenberg campaign. [77]

Why was it that the Communist Party, declining in size and power even while it led the Rosenberg agitation, was able to create such a big amnesty campaign and then bombard the campaign's followers with the usual Communist propaganda line? Why was it that thousands of non-Communists came sincerely to believe that the Rosenbergs had been framed, despite a trial at which defense counsel expressed no complaint about procedure and despite over two years of appeals, motions for retrials, petitions for habeas corpus, and applications for reduction of sentence which were heard seven times by the Court of Appeals and seven times by the Supreme Court? Part of the answer lies in the fairly widespread opposition to capital punishment. And a large part of the answer lies in part of the American heritage. There were skeletons in America's closet. There had been cases of injustice in the courts and discrimination against minorities. It was not difficult to persuade some people that what had happened before was happening again. Had there been no Sacco-Vanzetti case and no Mooney-Billings case and had no American Jew ever suffered persecution, it is not likely that the Rosenberg defenders would have received a serious hearing. This the Communists realized, and they worked mightily to inflate the Rosenberg case into an American Dreyfus affair. Therein lies the real tragedy in the Rosenberg case. The sins of the past are not easily lived down.

This, then, was the outward face of the Communist Party in the late 1940's and early 1950's. It clearly was in retreat. American public opinion had reached an unprecedented pitch of opposition to Communists and their ideas. The government's prosecution of Communist Party leaders and the kind of defense that the party elected to make against the prosecution had resulted in an important handicap to the party's efficiency. The manner in which the party conducted its "peace" campaign had further isolated it from the non-Communist Left and from the movement for Negro equality, and the Communists' "hard" line had contributed to the decline of the Progressive Party and the elimination of Communist influence in the decisions of the C.I.O.

Facing attack from government, from the trade unions, and

from the public in general, the Communists endeavored to appear as militant advocates of freedom and justice, as defenders of the Jeffersonian tradition of civil liberty. They sought to be regarded as the innocent victims of a society that had lost its restraint and that had forgotten a noble tradition of due legal process and fair play toward dissenters from majority attitudes. The Communists and their organizations obviously were the victims of a reaction that was sometimes disrespectful of the highest traditions of law and justice, but they were hardly innocent victims.

SEVEN: THE PARTY'S INTERNAL SECURITY

I n the trial of the top eleven leaders of the Communist Party, the prosecution brought to the witness stand F.B.I. agents who had been accepted in the party as bona fide members. In 1950, Congress passed the McCarran Internal Security Act and the Korean war began. All these events the Communists interpreted as the beginning of American fascism, which might well end in an American equivalent of the German Third Reich.

The Communists had to assume there were still other F.B.I. "Communists," as yet unrevealed, and it began immediately to strengthen its defenses. There is a bitter humor in the fact that the measures the party took to safeguard its "internal security" against its enemies were in many ways similar to the measures that federal and state governments and American society in general took to protect itself against the Communists. Both instituted loyalty checks. Both became irrationally suspicious of behavior and thought that did not conform to its norms. Both expelled and ostracized suspected individuals. Both infringed freedom in the quest for security, although the party never had afforded freedom to its own members. Both injured innocent people—that is, those who were not actually working for the enemy. One is reminded of a sentence of Edmund Wilson's in the early 1930's when he described a battle between police and Communists in New York's City Hall Park: "A gray flight of pigeons rises from the park, the only free living things in sight." [1] There were differences between the two internal-security systems, of course, and the differences were important. The Communist society had almost no restraint upon authority.

The Communist Party's system of internal security can be described under two categories; first, organizational measures to eliminate or minimize the effectiveness of police agents, or to establish an underground apparatus for a refuge in the event an open party proved impossible; second, the strengthening of ideological defenses so that the party would be intellectually pure —lean, hard, invulnerable to the erosion of outside ideas, 100 per cent Communist, not "soft on capitalism."

THE "LOYALTY" PROGRAM

The party made its first important organizational change for security early in 1949 when it stopped issuing party membership cards and quit keeping central membership lists. Soon thereafter, alarmed by their new awareness of F.B.I. agents in their ranks, the Communists launched what J. Edgar Hoover described as a "loyalty check." The party's review commissions at all party levels investigated the loyalty of every party member. There even was a subcommittee of three members of the national executive committee to investigate their fellow committee members. J. Edgar Hoover knew of the existence of this high-level subcommittee; its establishment reflected apparently well-founded suspicions. [2]

In 1950 and 1951, the party reorganized itself thoroughly in an effort for maximum security. The party clubs, the party's basic unit, had typically been composed of twenty-five to fifty members. In order to prevent a member's knowing many other members, each club broke down into several with a membership of from three to five. Written communications were kept to a minimum.

Rather than use mimeographed documents, which might find their way to F.B.I. files, party units used the blackboard extensively, erasing the messages as soon as possible. There were standing directions to destroy after reading whatever written communications were necessary.[3] The whole effort proved to be a farce and a serious impairment of party efficiency. The small clubs did not prevent members from identifying other members, because they had already known their comrades from the days before the security reorganization, and, in many cases, members of different clubs continued to see one another socially. Thus, the purpose of the system was not achieved, and the new arrangement sacrificed efficiency. Communications often became garbled in their clandestine transmission. Moreover, there were not enough dedicated and efficient Communists to lead the expanded number of party units. As a result, many clubs failed to meet regularly, had inadequate planning for their meetings, and displayed—to quote a survey of organization problems in New York—a distressing "lack of ideological and political content." [4] In sum, many ordinary rank-and-file members proved to be inept conspirators.

Another aspect of the party's security program was purposely to reduce the party's size, weeding out the suspect, the unenthusiastic, and the easily frightened. Clearly, many of the expulsions were the result of hysteria over party security and reaction to nonconformity, but a large part of the pruning of the membership was deliberate and calculated. According to the sworn testimony of a former Communist official, at one time William Z. Foster, ever an extremist, proposed reducing the membership of the party by 90 per cent and sending the remaining 10 per cent underground.[5] How many members were dropped by design is impossible to say —probably the party's top leadership itself does not know—but the organization secretary of the New York State organization in the party's self-appraisal in 1956 reported that in his state "For 'security reasons,' we also dropped a few thousand members, and so exaggerated the fascist danger by this and other security measures, that we actually menaced the continued existence of our

Party." Some members—an estimated "many, many hundreds"—
were expelled on trumped-up charges.[6] Others did not have to be
expelled. They read the words of the national organization secretary, Henry Winston, and accepted his not too subtle invitation
for the uninterested to leave the party. Winston warned that the
party's situation "makes necessary a qualitative strengthening of
the work of our Party" before he explained how easy it was to
leave: to join or leave "the ranks of the Communist Party has
at all times been a voluntary individual action based on conviction.
We will continue that concept of organization. Only those who have
been registered by the Party in the current registration [to last
another thirty days] will carry the great honor that goes with
membership in the Communist Party." Thousands already looking
for a way out grasped the opportunity. Still others, especially those
thought to be fainthearted or those who might be compromised
because of something in their past, were simply informally dropped.
They were not notified of meetings nor assigned to any tasks.[7]
These people did not quit the party; the party quit them.

The underground was one of the most important of the organizational methods adopted in quest of party security. Scores of
important party leaders left their homes, assumed new names,
and lived a clandestine existence. There were two reasons behind
the decision to go underground: to obstruct F.B.I. agents and to
form the nucleus of a party for the future should the maintenance
of the regular above-ground party prove impossible.

Those who went underground—or became "unavailables," as
they were commonly called within the party—were important
leaders but not from the very top leadership. The most important
leaders were too well known for the anonymous underground, and
lesser leaders at the club level were not trusted enough for such
assignments. But when the very top leadership went to prison in
1951 under the Smith Act, many of the unavailables automatically
moved upward in the party bureaucracy.

Those in the underground lived hard and unpleasant lives,
away from their families and friends, writing for the Communist

press under pen names, traveling a great deal, and delivering messages and attending secret meetings in the accepted Hollywood spy-film fashion.[8] But the hardships of the "unavailables" did not strengthen the party. Indeed, the whole underground venture tended to make the party more inefficient, more isolated, and more bureaucratic than it had been in the late 1940's. Clearly, the underground had important ill effects upon the party as well as for the people in it.

The Communists always denied that there was such a thing as the underground, but a published organizational report in late 1953 indirectly admitted as much. The report, itself written by someone in the underground under the pen name Alex Parker, declared that a "fairly large section of the leadership" must "work and live in a new way, under conditions . . . which guarantee the protection of the Party members and organizations." [9]

The Parker report defended the decision to go underground but obliquely revealed some of the harmful consequences of the decision. One admitted difficulty was that secrecy prevented the degree of contact between upper and lower party echelons necessary for efficiency: "Formerly, when we were able to see each other daily, use the phones at will, we never gave much thought to the content of our association. Our National Committee must . . . find ways to guarantee closer and quicker connections between the various levels of organization." Another admitted disadvantage was that the underground "bred an 'inner type' of party functionary who is often disconnected from the masses. . . . Such people are often shipped around the country from post to post by 'mail order,' " unable to give "leadership to mass work." But the unavailables became not only isolated from the "masses" but also from the party membership, thereby making the party more bureaucratic than ever. Instructions appeared as if by magic from somewhere in the underground. Much of the leadership was truly invisible, truly "unavailable," and no organization with such an isolated and yet powerful leadership could maintain even a semblance of democracy.[10]

Inefficiency, isolation, and bureaucracy were perhaps not so harmful to the party as the adverse opinion the public in general took toward the underground. Conspiracy is a dirty word in American politics, and the Communists with their underground tactics behaved very much like the conspirators their opponents said they were. Certainly the Communists did not constitute any ordinary political party in the days of the underground. Clearly, part of the reason the Communist Party came very close to being an illegal organization was that it behaved like an illegal organization.

The pursuit of men's motives is a precarious occupation at best, but it seems altogether likely that the decision for underground and other clandestine activity was not altogether rational. There was in the Communist Party a strong strain of radical romanticism that lent the underground member an aura of leftist glamour. It was not difficult for the underground Communist to identify himself with the French Communist underground against the Nazis or with the early twentieth-century Bolsheviks conspiring against the czar. Furthermore, the underground was "an opium of the Communists," a release into another world for people thoroughly frustrated by the real political world. It was natural for a romantic Communist, given his interpretation of the world about him and his frustration by it, to believe that as part of the underground he would live as a hero in Communist pages or that as a fugitive he was a modern Jean Valjean. How else can one explain the story of the four Smith Act fugitives?

In June 1951, the Supreme Court upheld the conviction of the first eleven Communist Smith Act defendants. The defendants had no further recourse in law and were to begin their sentences. Seven of them entered prison, but four became fugitives from justice: Robert Thompson, Gus Hall, Henry Winston, and Gil Green. All were married and had children. To become a fugitive meant separation from wife and family for an indefinite period, undoubtedly longer than it would take to serve their five-year sentences. (Thompson, as a war hero, had received only three years.) It does not seem likely that each of the four fugitives made his decision independently, but someone made such a decision, and it was one that would be difficult to defend on rational grounds. As fugitives hunted by police, they could have been of very little if any value to the party. The party gained nothing; the four sacrificed much. The first to be caught was Gus Hall, apprehended in Mexico in October 1951. In September 1953, the F.B.I. seized Robert Thompson in a cabin in California's Sierra Nevada mountains, along with Sid Stein, who was by then a fugitive from another Smith Act trial. Winston and Green were never caught. In 1956, when the party was in the biggest uproar of its history as a result of Khrushchev's disclosures about Stalin, they surrendered separately to federal officers in New York City. The two men never disclosed publicly where they had been. Had they gone to prison in 1951, they would have been already released. As it was, they were sentenced to additional terms for contempt of court. The decision to become fugitives doomed them to separation from their families for at least ten years. Back in 1950, when the first Smith Act case was under appeal and Green was temporarily imprisoned, Mrs. Eugene Dennis had written a lament about the longing of one of Green's children for her father. "I hold close the memory of little eight year old Josie Green . . . sitting in a corner, holding locked in her arms her father's soiled shirt just as it had been sent home from the West Street Jail; and she sat there, rocking back and forth, crooning to herself, holding that shirt in her arms." [11] There was no such political exploitation of a child's tragedy after Green had been bailed out and then holed up as a fugitive.

The fugitives and their families were not the only ones who suffered from the Communist "loyalty program." Expulsion and rejection caused unhappiness for hundreds. Expulsion is not a matter to be taken lightly for a dedicated member who has spent years in the Communist movement. To be expelled is to be abandoned by one's little society, to receive the "silent treatment" from associates of years' standing, to suffer rebuff and execration from old friends. For party functionaries and frequently for members of Communist-led unions, to be expelled meant to lose one's job.[12] Furthermore, the former Communist has a difficult time adjusting to non-Communist society. Suspect in some quarters unless he goes through the accepted rites of expiation, and suspect in other quarters if he does, the expelled Communist lives a lonely life between two worlds. Hundreds, perhaps thousands, of Communists were banished to this twilight purgatory in the early 1950's.[13] To combat expulsion was useless. The defendant in expulsion proceedings had no rights. The organ of the New York State party itself declared, "Each 'prosecutor' at an expulsion knew full well that there were a series of standard charges . . . to be put into each case . . . anti-leadership, undisciplined, anti-working class, and for the poor soul who would dare to attempt to argue his or her case, the cardinal crime of breaking the unity of the Party and . . . wanting it to degenerate into a debating society." [14] Two cases in which the party mistakenly and unfairly ostracized members whose lives had been devoted to the movement illustrate a great deal about the party's methods and devotion to the Soviet Union as well as different reactions to party rejection.

Anna Louise Strong's association with the Communist Party went back to the party's earliest history. She became a party specialist on Asia, and for thirty years her articles appeared in the party press. In early 1949, Miss Strong was in the Soviet Union, writing a series of articles under the title "Tomorrow's China," which were published in late January and early February in the *Daily Worker*. Then, for reasons never explained, the Russians arrested her as a spy and on February 21 deported her to the United States. The American Communists, embarrassed at having published her articles almost until her arrest, tried to atone for their sin by vilifying her. The first Smith Act trial was then in progress, and Miss Strong sent the Civil Rights Congress a check for $1,000 for its defense fund. She endorsed the check, "For the American Communists who are getting as raw a deal from American justice as I got from the USSR, from a fellow victim of the cold war." At the "request" of Eugene Dennis, the Civil Rights Congress returned the check. Dennis said, "The noteworthy efforts

of the CRC [Civil Rights Congress] to defend the Bill of Rights
. . . would be harmed, not helped, by tainted money." A few days
later, Elizabeth Gurley Flynn, who had the reputation in the party
of the "rebel girl" mellowed into a kindly grandmother, attacked
Miss Strong as "arrogant and egotistical." It was, said Mrs. Flynn,
"no wonder the Russians were at the end of their many years of
patience with the erratic highhanded Miss Strong, about whom
they obviously know more than they are telling." [15]

Miss Strong, grown old in Communist service, took her calumny
without retaliating. She settled down in California to await a better
day, still devoted to Communist principles. Seven years later, when
the Russian leaders themselves said that Stalin had been a criminal
paranoiac, the American party leaders again accepted the single-
minded and patient Miss Strong.[16] And she again accepted the
American, Chinese, and Russian Communists.

John Lautner did not accept his own treatment from the party
so quietly. Lautner was born in Hungary and came to the United
States when he was eighteen. He became a naturalized citizen in
1926 and a Communist Party member in 1929. From 1930 to
1932, he worked in the party's national group activities in Cleveland and Detroit. Early in 1933, he became a full-time party functionary as a section organizer in New York City, where he remained
until he moved up to district organizer of West Virginia. Late in
1940, the party sent him to its National Training School, and
when he finished he became the national secretary of the party's
Hungarian National Bureau. In 1942, he went into the army and
stayed three years, the last year of which he served in the army's
psychological-warfare program in Italy. After the war, he resumed
his life as a professional Communist and worked up to greater
positions of power. In May 1947, he became head of the New
York review commission, charged with the administration of the
party's internal security. In September 1948, the party added to his
duties by making him a member of the national review commission.[17]

In September 1949, in Budapest, the Communist Hungarian

Government tried a Communist leader, Laszlo Rajk, on charges of espionage in behalf of Tito, the United States, and Great Britain. The trial in Budapest was to have repercussions on the American party and to bring about the expulsion of John Lautner. When Lautner had been in Italy during the war, there were a few members of the British army attached to his unit, among them a Hungarian named Charesyez. Charesyez "confessed" at the Rajk trial that he was an agent of Tito and testified that Lautner had first introduced him to Titoists in Italy during the war. Thus, Lautner was suspected of being part of an anti-Communist spy ring. In 1956, the Hungarian Communists themselves confessed that the entire Rajk case had been a frame-up, and they restored Rajk to their list of heroes—posthumously.

Lautner was not aware of the testimony in Budapest concerning him until January 1950. The American Communists devoted a great deal of attention to the Rajk case; the *Daily Worker* of October 4, 1949, used four full pages to reprint part of the trial record, and *Political Affairs* carried a favorable review of a collection of documents relating to the case published by the Hungarian Government.[18] But these accounts did not mention Lautner. There were, however, American Communists who knew that Lautner had been implicated, and they were determined to get rid of him. They took as further "evidence" of Lautner's guilt the fact that, as head of the New York review commission, he had not detected that Angela Calomiris, who testified for the government in the first Smith Act trial, was an F.B.I. spy.

In December 1949, Louis Weinstock, a Communist leader for years, approached Lautner, who was still unaware of the suspicions about him, at a *Daily Worker* fund-raising bazaar at the St. Nicholas Arena in New York. Weinstock suggested that Lautner should go to Hungary. Lautner said he could not afford such a trip, and Weinstock replied that he would raise the necessary money and get Lautner a trade-union job in Hungary. He urged Lautner to get a passport. A few days later, Robert Thompson also urged Lautner to get a passport, and Lautner made application for one. The

State Department denied the passport because of Lautner's Communist affiliation.

In later years, Lautner told the following story under oath in a number of trials and hearings. In January 1950, after Lautner had been out of circulation with a brief illness, the party treasurer, Jack Kling, told Lautner they had some work to do in the Midwest. Lautner wrote his mother in Youngstown, Ohio, that he would see her Sunday afternoon, January 15. He left New York by train Friday night, January 13, arriving in Cleveland the next morning. Early that afternoon, he met Kling at Cleveland's Union Station. Lautner and Kling spent the afternoon at a show, then were picked up by a car and taken by a circuitous route to a house in the Kingsbury Run section of Cleveland. Kling told Lautner to go down to the basement. In the basement were two men, whom Lautner did not know, armed with guns, knives, and rubber hoses. They ordered Lautner to undress, and the men searched his clothes. Then Kling came downstairs with the driver of the car, Saul Wellman, a Detroit Communist leader, and Joseph Brandt, a leader of the party in Ohio. They had a wire recorder and a device they said was a lie detector, which they strapped to Lautner's arm. They asked him if he were a C.I.A. agent, what his relationship was to Noel and Herman Field, and to whom he had talked about underground plans. They shook a Hungarian newspaper in his face and said, "We know you." In Lautner's words, "I was threatened time and time again that if I don't come clean I will never leave that place." When they learned that his mother was expecting a visit from him the next day and that he had registered at a Cleveland hotel, Kling, Wellman, and Brandt went upstairs. When they returned in a few minutes, their attitude had changed. One of the men originally in the basement put a gun to Lautner's ribs, and Kling told him to write down what he dictated. Lautner wrote in pencil Kling's dictated "confession" that he was a paid anti-Communist spy and that he had received a fair hearing on the espionage charges. Brandt insisted the statement be rewritten in ink. Lautner rewrote it. Kling then announced that the "hearing" would continue the next day, Sunday, and that Lautner should meet them at the Mayfair Restaurant on Euclid Avenue. Kling and Brandt departed. Lautner complained that he was cold and asked for his clothes. When he got them back, he found that fifteen dollars, his gloves, and the State Department letter refusing him a passport were missing. He was then taken by car to a city bus stop.

Such was Lautner's loyalty to the party and his intelligence that he thought the whole affair in the basement "was a way of testing me or something like that." The next day, he actually went to the Mayfair Restaurant and waited for Kling for an hour and a half. When Kling failed to appear, Lautner went to Youngstown to see his mother. He returned to New York, Monday, January 16. The next morning, Lautner read in the *Daily Worker,* "The National Review Commission approves the recommendation of the subcommittee which examined the case of John Lautner and hereby expels him from the Communist Party as a traitor and enemy of the working class." Not until then did Lautner realize what had happened. Still he wanted to remain in the party. A few days later, he wrote a letter to Alexander Trachtenberg, chairman of the national review commission, to protest his expulsion and ask for a hearing. To insure delivery of the letter, Lautner had his brother take it to Trachtenberg personally. Trachtenberg never replied.

It took months for Lautner to get his bearings. When he did, he was not as patient with the party as Miss Strong was. He was angry for being falsely accused and expelled. "I was not a revisionist. I was a loyal and devoted Party member up to the time I read my expulsion." In September 1950, eight months after his expulsion, Lautner wrote to the F.B.I. volunteering to tell what he knew about the Communist Party.[19] Subsequently, he became a most effective witness for the government in trials and hearings involving Communists.

All in all, the Communist organizational defense methods were disastrous from the party's own point of view. An exaggerated estimate of the danger of American fascism, blind adherence to the methods and style of foreign Communist parties, and a romantic emotional predilection for the bold, heroic stance combined to produce, in the end, a shrunken organization, inefficient and isolated. The process left a trail of personal tragedy and bitterness, some of which was to be effectively directed against the Communists. But the underground and mass expulsions were no more disastrous for the party than the other aspect of its defense mechanism, the campaign for ideological purity.

THE CAMPAIGN AGAINST HERESY

At a meeting of the state committee of the Communist Party in New York in the spring of 1956, after Khrushchev's speech denouncing Stalin had triggered a crisis in the American Communist movement, one of the committee members found release from years of party suppression in a vigorous condemnation of the Communist Party's undemocratic and relentless smothering of intellectual dissent. He was especially critical of "the ideological purification processes which were literally brainwashing." [20] He was referring to the mental-purification program the party undertook in 1949 and 1950 as an integral part of its fortification against outside assaults. In its intensity, its intellectually repressive extravagance, its fever for detecting and routing heretics, the Communist Party's striving for purity made the contemporaneous tendency toward conformity in American society at large seem pale in comparison.

The Communists were systematically thorough in their campaign. In March 1950, Foster, in a message to the party's national committee, deplored "what I consider to be the greatest of all the weaknesses of our Party, namely its lack of systematic theoretical work." [21] Within a week, the leadership exerted pressure to enroll more party members in classes in Communist theory at party schools. Robert Thompson, leader of the New York organization, ordered that "all clubs take immediate steps to mobilize its members to take courses at the [Jefferson] School, at its annexes, and at the School of Jewish Studies." Each club should assign one additional member to attend party schools, preferably in courses on the Soviet Union, on Marxism and the Negro question, and on Marxism and labor. His injunction to the party clubs to take action was clear: "This statement should be read, discussed and acted on immediately at every club meeting." [22]

More important than the party's effort positively to develop "correct" ideology through education, however, was its campaign negatively to eliminate heresy. In this campaign, not even Foster himself was immune. Dennis related "that a number of us in the National Committee have called attention to certain faulty or unhappily formulated statements in some of Bill's writings. . . ." Such suspicion of Foster had been misguided, Dennis confessed; Foster had received the imprimatur of important foreign Communists and was obviously acceptable. "We have . . . noted that his book *Twilight of Capitalism* received very favorable comment in the great Marxist-Leninist journal, *For A Lasting Peace, For A People's Democracy!* And we took cognizance of the fact that this same book has been published in abridged form in tens of thousands of copies by our great brother Party, the Communist Party of Italy." [23]

The list of banned ideas and attitudes in the Communist index was a long one, but the two that received the greatest fire in the party's age of suspicion were Freudianism and color prejudice. The party's anti-Freudianism was interesting for its intellectual justification, and its attitude toward prejudice was noteworthy for its extremism.

There are a great many people who have reservations about the validity of Freudian psychiatry and who deplore the facile popular interpretations that have become common in this age of oversimplified Freudianism. But only the Communists interpreted the popularity of Freudianism as an anti-working-class plot of bourgeois imperialism. And only Communists had a basically conspiratorial motive for their opposition to Freudianism. Throughout the Communist denunciation of psychiatry, no matter what the explicit argument, ran the fear that Communists would go to psychiatrists and reveal secrets about the party. The anti-Freud campaign was at least partly a security measure.[24]

Criticisms of psychoanalysis began to become common in Communist periodicals in 1950. Milton Howard had a series of articles on Freudianism in the *Daily Worker* early in the year, and *Masses & Mainstream* devoted some space to the subject. The antipsychoanalysis campaign got official leadership endorsement in the March 1950 meeting of the party's national committee. Henry Winston, in his report at the meeting, condemned the "reactionary bourgois philosophy and practice which violates every principle of working-class ideology. . . . The fight to mold Communist thinking must be developed resolutely in a struggle against these subjectivist, idealistic, Freudian concepts, which, in essence, are anti-working class, anti-Communist, and tend to undermine a class struggle approach to social and individual problems." In June, Mrs. Eugene Dennis wrote, "As a mother and a Communist I reject such tripe. . . . Freud be damned!" [25] The war was on.

There is a fundamental conflict between dialectical materialism and Freudianism which Communist philosophers could have fruitfully explored and clarified. The Communists, however, fell back upon their convenient theory of capitalist conspiracy.

In the "general crisis of capitalism," one Communist article argued, "bourgeois ideologists" are forced to "invent theories which are calculated to conceal the naked brutality of imperialism's aims by giving them a 'scientific' facade." Capitalism had already degraded "social science into an ideological instrument justifying mass impoverishment, imperialist war, and fascist cannibalism." "Bourgeois psychology" was no more than another "insidious instrument at the disposal of the monopolist ruling class." "The most widespread and dangerous form of this shoddy bourgeois psychology," the argument went, "is Freudian psychoanalysis . . . [and] it is not accidental that the Wall Street dominated United States . . . has become the center for the dissemination of Freudianism."

The only answer to emotional distress was communism: "In the Socialist Soviet Union, where exploitation of human beings has been abolished . . . the source of the insecurities, the conflicts, and the mental anguish chargable to capitalism has . . . been eliminated." [26]

The task of developing an intelligent Communist critique of psychoanalysis fell to the Russians. In the summer of 1950, a group of Soviet psychologists met for a symposium. This group also rejected Freud, but they advanced the discussion by reviving the conditioned–reflex psychology of Ivan Pavlov. Pavlov offered a way to reconcile psychology with materialism. His work on the functioning of the cerebral cortex provided a materialist base for psychology; psychology became an aspect of physiology. In 1951, the Russians published the papers presented at the symposium in English,[27] and in due time the American party responded. In September 1952, *Political Affairs* discovered Pavlov, explained the implications of his work, and touted him as the new answer to Freud.[28]

After the party developed its theory of psychoanalysis as a façade for imperialism, psychoanalytic terms became anathema in Communist circles. To use such terms indicated an infection of bourgeois ideology, an infection dangerous to intellectual purity which must be eliminated. The Communist novelist Howard Fast was to learn that the use of such terms was forbidden. In his *Spartacus,* a novel about a slave revolt in ancient Rome, Fast had used such terms as "inner struggle" in his fictional glorification of class struggle. For such deviation from 100-per-cent Communism, Fast was subjected to personal abuse and his book was criticized in the *Daily Worker* for, among other things, having too much "of the destructive influence of Freudian mystifications." [29]

Far more important for the development of the party and far more repressive was the party's campaign to stamp out "the virus of white chauvinism." The campaign against white chauvinism within the party became a full-scale internal witch hunt, as hysterical, as disrespectful of justice, and as ridiculously self-defeating as any hunt for Communists in non-Communist American society.

The Communist purge on the question of anti-Negro prejudice was a natural and logical development from the party's past. The Communists had long realized that American Negroes represented an opportunity and a challenge unique to a Communist party in a capitalist country. And, as related earlier, the party's line on the Negro had vacillated back and forth between a peculiarly Stalinist kind of Negro nationalism and a militant struggle for Negro rights and equality as Americans. After World War II, the party had gone back to its earlier Negro nationalism position, which tended to isolate Communists from the main stream of the Negro's movement for equality and integration. It was natural, then, for Communist energies in behalf of Negroes to become directed inward, within the party, rather than outward, against the many unhappy conditions and forces in American life that discriminated against and exploited the colored 10 per cent of the population. It was perhaps inevitable in a purification campaign that any manifestation by a Communist of prejudice against Negroes should make him suspect as a carrier of a bourgeois virus.

The metaphors "carrier" and "virus" are not invented here. These were terms Communists themselves used frequently as an integral part of their explanation of Negro prejudice. In Communist theory, the proletariat is inherently virtuous and the bourgeoisie is the source of all evil. Communists did not recognize that in the South and elsewhere lower-income groups are more vehemently anti-Negro than people more comfortable economically, but they did recognize that there was prejudice against Negroes among American workers. The Communists tried to explain away this worker prejudice, which embarrassed their basic theory, as an infection deliberately introduced by the bourgeoisie. For a party member, then, to be infected indicated that he was not really a good Communist.

The Communists' barrage against discrimination outside the party was not nearly so rewarding as their efforts had been in the

1930's. In 1950 and 1951, they made a major matter of the conviction and execution in Mississippi of Willie McGee. It is probably true that Communist support for McGee served to reinforce Mississippi's determination to execute him, but it is also probably true that if it had not been for Communist activities in McGee's behalf, the case would have been little noticed nationally. The biggest Communist effort against Negro oppression generally since the war was the petition the Civil Rights Congress submitted to the General Assembly of the United Nations charging that America's treatment of Negroes constituted a violation of the UN's convention on genocide. The petition was an obvious effort to discredit the United States in the eyes of the colored peoples of the world and to furnish ammunition for the Soviet bloc's anti-American propaganda program. Although Americans may not justifiably take pride in their Negro relations, the charge that the Government of the United States deliberately pursued a genocidal policy toward its Negroes was too fantastic to be effective among people who knew America.[30]

The party's campaign against white chauvinism got started in early 1949, at precisely the time the trial of the first Smith Act defendants began at Foley Square. Pettis Perry, Secretary of the national Negro work commission, was the director of the operation. "Pete" Perry had been born on a tenant farm in Alabama in 1897. When he was ten, he started to work picking cotton. At twenty, he left the South and bummed around the country on freight trains, working sporadically at a variety of unskilled jobs. In 1932, he settled in Los Angeles, and soon thereafter, having become involved in the defense compaign for the Scottsboro boys, joined the Communist Party. Like many another Southern Negro, his formal education had been poor, and he was only barely literate when he became a Communist. The party opened new intellectual vistas for him: "I practically learned to read by reading the *Communist Manifesto* and *Capital.*" He rose steadily within the party in California as a "full-timer," becoming in the 1940's a member of the committee responsible for California and Arizona. In 1948, he moved to New York to become director of the national party's Negro work.[31] Perry was ideal as the person in charge of the campaign against white chauvinism: as one who had grown up in semifeudalism and whose only intellectual experience was in Communism, he was militant; as a true Negro proletarian as well as a Communist, a relatively rare phenomenon, no white Communist of less humble origins was in a position to challenge him.

Innocent actions or words very quickly became interpreted as manifestations of prejudice. One of the first incidents occurred at the special office the party established early in 1949 to turn out propaganda in defense of the Smith Act defendants then on trial. One night, a white girl typist who was very busy asked another girl in the office, a Negro comrade who was not then occupied, to go out and bring back coffee. The colored girl took offense at the request and brought charges of white chauvinism against the typist.[32]

Fairly important party leaders soon learned they were not immune. Isadore Begun, Bronx County party chairman and a member of the state committee, and two of his subordinates were removed from leadership in the spring of 1949 because of alleged white chauvinism. Begun had given a speech at a Harlem testimonial affair for a Negro woman trade-unionist comrade. The speech was, Robert Thompson wrote in *Political Affairs,* "devoid of any appreciation of the political significance of the holding of such an affair in honor of this Negro trade-union leader." Begun "descended to the level of telling a dirty joke, which, under the circumstances, was a chauvinist act. The nature of this act was all the more serious in its character and consequences because the offense was against a Negro woman, a member of the most oppressed section of the Negro people." [33] For this offense, the state committee removed Begun from all his party posts, reprimanded him, and assigned him to special "control tasks" in Bronx Negro work. A loyal party member for more than twenty years, Begun did not rebel. In a spirit of abject contrition, according to the *Daily Worker,* he "fulfilled his control tasks . . . with merit, achieving a greater Communist understanding of the Negro question as a national question." After doing penance for a year, Begun was restored, although his restoration apparently did not end the problem in the Bronx. Years later, a comrade complained, "The Bronx Party was paralyzed for over three years with a series of removals of the County leadership on charges of white chauvinism." [34]

The party disrupted itself in several districts over these charges. The vice-chairman of the Wisconsin party, Fred Blair, was suspended because of "weakness in combatting 'white supremacy' ideas." Southern white Communists were more than usually suspect. Charges against leadership in Louisiana and Texas "almost wrecked" the party there, and in Georgia the party disappeared altogether in a white-chauvinism controversy. [35]

The campaign led the party to absurd lengths. The party forbade members to take vacations in Florida and thus earned the antagonism of a considerable number of formerly friendly members of the Furriers' Union and District 65 who had been accustomed to Miami vacations in the off-season. [36] In the summer of 1951, the party moved its national headquarters away from the *Daily Worker* building, just below Union Square, to the heart of Harlem. [37] Publishing a drawing of a Negro minister "with distorted features" was found to be white chauvinism, and for this offense the editors of the Sunday *Worker* publicly apologized. They also apologized for publishing a drawing of a nonsegregated dance which had shown Negro men dancing with white women but had failed to show white men dancing with Negro women. [38] Howard Fast was forced to write a public apology for allowing one of his characters in *The Proud and the Free,* a novel of the American Revolution, to use the term "nayger." To use the words "boy" or "girl" in referring to Negroes became suspect, and some Communists even objected to the use of "black" and "dark" as in such phrases as "black despair" or "dark future." [39]

Obviously, things had got out of hand. The effort to eliminate white chauvinism had become a spasm of hysterical suspicion which damaged the party's effectiveness. Still, the party did nothing to call off the farce so long as Pettis Perry remained in command. In 1950, he had been elected to the national committee, and in 1951, when the Supreme Court ruled in the Dennis case and the top eleven leaders either went to prison or took off for the woods, he and Gurley Flynn and Foster became the party's ruling triumvirate. Not until Perry's conviction as one of the "second-string" leaders in early 1953 did any top leader try to correct the excesses of the white-chauvinism spasm. Finally, in July 1953, Foster himself acted.

He published in *Political Affairs* an article on "Left sectarianism" in the fight against white chauvinism. He by no means condoned any white-supremacist thought in the party, but he did assert that "our Party must achieve a more realistic definition of what constitutes white chauvinism than is now the case." He also pointed out that there was such a thing as "Negro bourgeois nationalism." To make sure his new definitions of what really constituted white chauvinism and what constituted "Left sectarianism" on that issue were understood, he ended his article with a series of textbookish study questions.[40] The wilder aspects of the white-chauvinism campaign soon disappeared.

The hysteria ended but it left its mark upon the party. By 1953, there were fewer Negroes in the Communist Party, both in absolute numbers and in percentage of total membership, than there had been any time since 1937.[41] Instead of making the party more attractive to Negroes, the furor had actually driven them out. A 1956 survey by the New York State organizational secretary concluded that "gross distortions in the fight against white chauvinism in the Party . . . tended to create an unreal estimate of rampant white chauvinism in the Party. What Negro would want to associate with such a Party?" [42]

In fact, the entire party defense program—underground, small and secret clubs, and emphasis on ideological purity—backfired. Recruitment of new members all but ceased. The party was more interested in apprehending heretics in its ranks than in recruiting.

By 1953, only 43 per cent of the membership had been in the party less than ten years and 60 per cent were between the ages of thirty-five and forty-five, the Depression generation. For reasons that are obscure, the party had also driven out more men than women. In 1953, women party members outnumbered their male comrades, and in community organizations of the party, as opposed to industrial organizations, women constituted three-fourths to nine-tenths of the membership. And, finally, the party's emphasis on security tended to isolate the Communists. Instead of working among non-Communists, party members huddled together where they felt more secure, either entirely within the party or in front organizations where party membership was no handicap.[43]

In 1953, it became obvious to the party leaders that some changes had to be made. Furthermore, after the nineteenth congress of the Soviet party late in 1952 and Stalin's death a few months later, Russian emphases were changing. The American party, however, modified its approach only gradually. It failed to make any major and dramatic changes until there were major and dramatic developments within the Soviet bloc, and nothing really dramatic happened until February 1956, when Nikita Khrushchev addressed the twentieth congress of the Soviet party on the sins of Joseph Stalin.

PART FOUR
THE
AGE
OF
KHRUSHCHEV

"Humanity has lost the greatest man of our time. . . . Stalin meant that a new era had dawned for mankind. . . . As humanity bids him farewell, his vision will grow brighter with the generations." —Daily Worker *editorial, March 6, 1953, the day after Joseph Stalin died.*

"Stalin was a very distrustful man, sickly and suspicious. . . . The sickly suspicion created in him a general distrust even toward eminent Party workers whom he had known for years. Everywhere and in everything he saw 'enemies,' 'two-facers' and 'spies.' Possessing unlimited power he indulged in great willfulness and choked a person morally and physically. . . . And how is it possible that a person confesses to crimes he has not committed? Only in one way—because of application of physical methods of pressuring him, tortures, bringing him to a state of unconsciousness, deprivation of his judgment, taking away of his human dignity. In this manner were 'confessions' acquired."—NIKITA KHRUSHCHEV *to Twentieth Congress, Communist Party of the Soviet Union, February 24, 1956, as reported in the* Worker, *June 10, 1956.*

EIGHT: SLOW THAW IN THE COLD WAR

In October 1952, the Nineteenth Congress of the Communist Party of the Soviet Union met at Moscow, the first such meeting since the 1930's. Stalin had just published his *Economic Problems of Socialism in the U.S.S.R.* and set a slightly modified line for the congress to ratify. Stalin played down the conflict between the "socialist" and capitalist camps, suggesting "peaceful co-existence," and emphasized "contradictions" between the capitalist nations which, he hoped, would bring acute conflicts among them. There seemed to be a shift from "cold war" to "cold peace." Following the congress, Communist parties of Western Europe became increasingly hostile toward American influence in their countries and tried to form popular fronts for "peace" in an effort to intensify the "contradictions."

Stalin died March 5, 1953. The Russians had no constitutional or traditional arrangement for succession to the real seats of power, and the next several months saw a series of top officials rise and fall before Nikita Khrushchev emerged as the new Russian dictator. Khrushchev, thus far at least, has been more moderate and restrained than was Stalin in his last twenty years or so. Even while the struggle for power within the Soviet Union was in progress, there was the beginning of a "de-Stalinization" process. Overt terror declined. In July 1953, the Russians announced the removal—and subsequently the execution—of Lavrenti P. Beria, chief of the secret police. Many political prisoners from the Stalin era were released. Clearly, a greater degree of personal security for Russian Communist leaders and other important Russians began to develop soon after Stalin's death. The new leaders, especially Khrushchev, displayed more flexibility and a relative moderation, both in foreign and domestic affairs.

There were changes, too, in the United States. The strength of the American "radical right" began to wane in the spring of 1954 when the Army-McCarthy hearings were televised into millions of homes. Senator McCarthy finally hanged himself on the plenitude of rope which the "modern Republican" administration allowed him, and before the televised hearings had ended, comedians were making jokes about "point of order." A few months later, the Senate of the United States formally repudiated the junior Wisconsin senator, and McCarthyism faded as a major political force.

With something of a thaw in both the U.S.S.R. and the U.S.A., relations between the two countries improved a little. In July 1953 came the signing of the Korean truce, and the war that was not a war (but that killed 25,000 American soldiers, nevertheless) at last came to an end. In May 1955, East and West finally agreed to a peace treaty for Austria, and that summer Khrushchev and President Eisenhower conferred at Geneva. Their "summit conference" brought no new agreements, no new era of East-West harmony, but the mere fact that the American and Russian executives had met indicated that the cold war had eased somewhat. Observers noted a "Geneva spirit." The summer of 1955 also saw the visit of a delegation of Russian agricultural experts to the lush cornfields of Iowa and the spectacle, unthinkable three years before, of conservative little corn-belt towns vying with one another for the opportunity to play host to Russians at Gargantuan fried chicken and ice-cream dinners.

With all these developments, it was inevitable that the American Communist Party should modify its position on a variety of matters, that there should be a change in the direction of the Communist line. Developments in the Soviet Union had never failed to make an impact upon the United States Communists; they were now to do so again. But for three years after Stalin's death, there were no dramatic and sudden changes, nothing comparable to the changes of line in 1939, 1941, and 1945. The changes were so gradual, so piecemeal, that they generated little excitement. The changing direction of the Communist Party was a slow drift rather than a fast current, hardly perceptible to outsiders at any given moment. Even party rank and filers had to look back to old landmarks and measure the extent of their drift before they realized they had moved at all.

A bare beginning of a shift in the party line came in December 1952, before Stalin's death—but after the nineteenth Soviet party congress—with a "Draft Resolution on the Situation Growing out of the Presidential Elections." Two months later, *Political Affairs* carried an article which contained the admission that "in the past few years our Party has suffered considerable isolation from the masses." In June 1953, the party leaders made sure the membership understood the importance of Stalin's last work as well as the pedigree of the draft resolution by publishing as a special supplement to *Political Affairs* a "Reader's Guide" to Stalin's book, complete with pedantic study questions and directions on how long to study each part.[1] These first deviations from the party's postwar Left orthodoxy were not in response to new conditions or developments in America or in American-Russian relations, for there had not as yet been any important new developments. They were in response to the nineteenth congress and to a recognition—but only a dimly perceived recognition—that the party's postwar line had led it into a blind alley.

The draft resolution, as published in late 1952, even contained an admission of error from the party's leaders, the first time the leadership under Foster had granted it could have been mistaken: "It was incorrect to have favored the departure of the Wallace forces without masses from the Democratic Party. Every effort should have been made to encourage the Wallace forces to fully unfold the struggle for peace to its conclusion within the Democratic Party in a determined effort to influence the mass base of that party." In the resolution's final form, adopted in the summer of 1953, the leadership watered down its admission of error. "The mistakes made by the Party" were not now attributable to the leadership, but to "strong sectarian tendencies within its ranks." [2]

After Stalin's death, the pace of the party's drift toward greater moderation quickened a little. When Foster wrote his article calling for an end to the wild excesses of the campaign against white chauvinism within the party, he denounced "Left distortions" and "sectarianism." In September 1953, he made the flat-footed assertion that the party's "most predominant handicap is a Left-sectarianism, which . . . has tended to shrink back upon itself and to neglect mass work on various fronts." [3] With such statements as these, it was to be only a matter of time before the comrades would again reach to their bookshelves for Lenin's *Left Wing Communism: An Infantile Disorder,* a document that had lain undisturbed and forgotten since several old Bolsheviks had been railroaded out of the party on charges of Left deviation soon after the war.

The softer post-Stalin line began to jell with the publication and adoption in 1954 of a draft of a new party program, "The American Way to Jobs, Peace, Democracy (Draft Program of the Communist Party)." Both a magazine article and a pamphlet,[4] the draft program emphasized what leftists had once called "immediate demands" rather than a new social order: "the Communist Party emphasizes that the issue at the present time is not Communism. The choice before our people today is peace, security, democracy versus the grip which the monopolists have on the country and their plans of fascism and war." The document made a great effort to establish the party as "American." The name of the program itself emphasized this national approach, and the writers of the program took pains to picture their party as "the inheritor and continuer of the best in American democratic, radical and labor thought and traditions. Its devotion to the true national interests of the American people is the source of its deep and abiding patriotism." The draft program advocated "a peaceful path to Socialism in the U.S.," declared that "socialism" could be established only by the will of a majority, and denied intentions to import any social system from abroad.[5]

A subcommittee of the national committee wrote the draft program and sent it to the full committee for criticism. Five national committee members dissented in one way or another from the new program, and the fact that disagreement within the committee was made public indicated a slight departure from the postwar style of hard monolithic unity. Two national committeemen thought the draft program's new line on political action was too soft, two thought it was not soft enough, and one deplored the emphasis on immediate demands to the near exclusion of professions of socialism.[6]

The party, however, had not become democratic enough to allow these dissenters to publish their points of view in the regular party press. The whole "discussion" of the draft program was stacked in favor of the program as originally written. When the party's national election conference met in New York City in early August 1954—a substitute for a national convention—a worker in party headquarters could say that the discussion revealed "the unanimity of the Party." No one was surprised when the conference's 150 delegates unanimously ratified the program, which in its final form differed from the original draft only in some phrasing.[7]

The new Communist line, as it evolved from the draft resolution of December 1952 to the program adopted in the summer of 1954, as clarified and explained by other writings of party leaders, is best described by breaking it into various parts: policy toward political action, toward trade-unionism, and toward Negroes.

THE END OF THE AMERICAN LABOR PARTY

In the election of 1952, the national ticket of the Progressive Party, led by Vincent Hallinan, received under 150,000 votes and evoked none of the excitement, synthetic though it may have been, that had characterized Wallace's race in 1948. Organized labor supported Adlai Stevenson, whose campaign had the enthusiastic support of Democratic liberals. Plain to see, the Communists' support of the Progressives in 1952 had gained them nothing.

The Communists, consequently, reassessed their whole third-party line, which had been firm and unexamined since the formation of the Cominform in the fall of 1947. Their third-party ventures had cut their contact with the great mass of voters whom the Communists hoped to influence; labor, Negroes, and the liberals generally were obviously not going to bolt the Democratic Party in the near future. The problem for the Communists was how to go hunting for the big game within the vast coalition of political groups that constitute the Democratic Party without losing the smaller game they already had corralled within the American Labor and Progressive parties.

One method of actually abandoning third-party ventures without seeming to was to use double talk: to support Hallinan and Bass in 1952 "as the only clear voice for peace" had been "correct," but the third-party line had been too "rigid" and there had been a lamentable failure "to sufficiently unfold a policy of united front and of coalition approaches on issues and in congressional and senatorial races." [8] Another method was to reshape the A.L.P. into a combination independent party and Democratic Party pressure group by having it support some Democratic candidates and run some others under its own emblem, as it had before 1948. This tactic within the A.L.P. had something to be said for it because party Chairman Vito Marcantonio had a good organization, which in 1952 had been able to produce over 90,000 votes for Corliss Lamont in the Senatorial race.

Neither method worked. In the more than half-decade since the Communists abandoned third-party action, they have made no perceptible progress within the major parties and they have, ironically, alienated the fellow-traveling types who once followed the A.L.P. and the Progressive Party. These non-Communists, who like to call themselves "progressives" and who are sometimes referred to with some justification as "Stalinoids," can abide no alliance, even temporarily, with one of the major parties. They are too radical, too impatient, to accept the compromises inherent in working within the Democratic camp. Paradoxically, the progressives—in actuality, the *National Guardian* subscribers—are often to the "left" of the Communists, who, with their tighter organization, their discipline, and their messianic vision, are able to compromise, to accept as a temporary tactic working with groups they despise. Certainly the Communists never intended their turn toward the Democratic Party as anything more than a temporary tactic, a going back to get the "masses" within that camp and bring them out eventually into a real third party. The Communists admitted as much.[9] But the *National Guardian* crowd, a loose group of non-Communist but pro-Communist radical "socialists," centered in New York, refused even temporary alliance with the Democrats, and when the Communists scuttled the A.L.P. and the Progressive Party, the progressives wandered aimlessly in their own political never-never land, resentful of their treatment by the Communists but unable, given their firm popular-front belief that to criticize a Communist is to commit unpardonable Red baiting, to do anything to retaliate.

Both the Progressive Party and the A.L.P. collapsed quickly when the Communists changed their electoral tactics. The Progressives just quietly expired, failing to run candidates again. Hallinan displayed only minor resentment when he remarked that "the extreme left"—he could not bring himself to say "Communist Party"—"wanted the Progressive Party to lay down and die," which is what the Progressive Party did.[10]

Marcantonio's A.L.P. resisted a little more. Marcantonio and other non-Communists, who constituted a majority of the A.L.P., refused to follow the Communists' urging to support the Democratic candidate, Robert F. Wagner, Jr., in the 1953 New York City mayoralty campaign. The A.L.P. insisted upon running a candidate of its own, who, without Communist support, received only 54,372 votes. After the election, the A.L.P. disintegrated rather quickly. Marcantonio himself resigned from the A.L.P. two days after the election with a bitter and yet restrained statement. A "minority," he said—he could not bring himself to say the words "Communist Party" either—had sabotaged the A.L.P., which would have received twice the vote had the "minority" co-operated. But he "rejected the course of a purge of the minority [as] repugnant to the democratic principles to which I have subscribed throughout my political career." He predicted that the A.L.P. would become "more and more a mimeograph machine rather than a political party" and that the party would fail in the 1954 gubernatorial election to muster the 50,000 votes necessary to stay on the ballot.[11] Marcantonio's prediction was accurate: in 1954, the A.L.P. candidate for governor of New York, *National Guardian* publisher John McManus, fell short of the 50,000 minimum, and in October 1956, the A.L.P. officially folded.

After the demise of the A.L.P. and the Progressives, the *National Guardian* clientele, dimly aware that it had followed a political Pied Piper, had no electoral instrument. In the fall of 1955, the *National Guardian* urged its readers to withdraw from electoral activity altogether should they be unable to develop another independent party,[12] and in 1956, some of the progressives declared lukewarm support for Eisenhower as a "man of peace." In 1958, they organized in New York an Independent Socialist ticket with Corliss Lamont for United States senator and McManus for governor, getting on the ballot through nominating petitions. The Communists did not support them, and their ticket ran poorly.

TRADE-UNION "UNITY" AGAIN

By the time Stalin died, the Communists were as cut off from the main stream of the American labor movement as they were from the political activities of the "masses." Without influence in either the A.F. of L. or the C.I.O., the Communists and their sympathizers in the labor movement were reduced to defensive actions in the handful of Left-led unions against the membership raids conducted by competing unions in the main tents of organized labor. Defensive action against raids in the Left unions availed the Communist Party nothing, because the Communist leaders in these unions had to compromise with their anti-Communist rank and file by playing down their Communism and emphasizing their bread-and-butter unionism. At best, such methods could be only a holding action. But in fact, despite their lack of emphasis on political matters, the Communist union leaders saw their locals steadily deserting to their anti-Communist competitors.

At last, recognizing they were in a weak position which offered no prospect of improvement under their current line, the Communists changed their line on labor to one similar to their new line on political action. They slowly and awkwardly modified their position to play down their enmity to anti-Communist trade-union leaders, to make greater efforts to get within the main stream of labor, and to emphasize work within what they termed the "Right-led" unions rather than those expelled from the C.I.O. As in the political sphere, the Communists had got "too far ahead of the masses" in trade-unionism; now they determined to go back and pick up the "masses."

The party made its switch on political action more quickly and easily than its switch on trade-unionism. Indeed, the party embarrassed itself by inconsistently maintaining its old-fashioned strident leftism in the trade-union field after it had already abandoned these tactics in the political field.

In June 1953, three months after the beginning of the post-Stalin thaw in Russia and six months after the beginning of the new line on politics in the United States, there appeared in *Political Affairs* an article by Alex H. Kendrick and Jerome Golden entitled "Lessons of the Struggle Against Opportunism in District 65." Editors of the magazine indicated that the article was the first of two installments, the second of which would appear in the July issue. Kendrick and Golden blasted the leadership of District 65, the New York metropolitan area district of the Distributive, Processing, and Office Workers Union. The leaders of District 65 had once been very close to the party, if not actual members. In 1952, the top leaders of the union, David Livingston, president of District 65, and Arthur Osman, president of the International, left the comrades' cause and assumed a "third camp" position critical of both the Communists and Right Wing conservatives. Kendrick and Golden could think of nothing too harsh to say about the "renegades," who, they charged, lived a plush life on the rank and file's dues while they co-operated with the bosses against the membership, were aggressively "white chauvinist," and were guilty of "Zionism and Jewish bourgeois nationalism." Presumably, the choice vitriol was saved for the second and concluding installment.[13]

Part II of the Kendrick-Golden article never appeared. The line on trade-unionism changed between issues of the magazine. The July issue of *Political Affairs* contained a note that "pressure of space" prevented publication of Part II in that issue and that it would appear in August.[14] "Pressure of space," however, did not prevent publication of the first part of another two-part article on labor with quite a different line, one with a conciliatory tone that emphasized "unity." "There cannot be real labor unity which does not base itself on the principle of unity *despite* ideological differences and *inclusive* of these differences." There were, the author argued, "tiny, weak, young early buds of Spring" which "must be kept in mind by the Left in its work to win the Right-led unions for progressive policies and in its work to strengthen the role of the progressive Left-led unions in the struggle for a united labor movement." [15] The second installment advised against "name calling, re-raiding, and other forms of 'answering in kind' " because these tactics only solidified the "subjective reactions" of workers in non-Communist unions and made them feel their organizations were "under attack and that they must rise blindly to its defense." [16]

To buttress the new line on labor, party leaders soon found impeccable scriptural authority. They exhumed a preface written by Lenin to an edition of letters written by Marx and Engels that was beautifully appropriate to the new "unity" line, and thereby invoked three saints in one swoop: "And now we very clearly perceive the two lines of Engels' (and Marx's) recommendations, directives, corrections, threats, and exhortations. They most insistently called upon the British and American Socialists to merge with the labor movement and to eradicate the narrow and hidebound sectarian spirit from their organizations." [17] How could Kendrick and Golden, whoever they were, stand up to opposition like that?

To proclaim the new "unity" line and to apply it successfully were quite different matters. The Communists realized that the leaders of the C.I.O. and A.F. of L. unions were not eager to unite with leftist unions merely because the leftists wanted to unite and promised to behave. Non-Communist trade-union leaders would work with the Communists and their sympathizers only if they were pressured into working with them, and the way to bring the pressure, the Communists believed, was to build it from below, in the union rank and file. "The watchword for today must be *unity of struggle* . . . struggle to break through and defeat the divisive policies of the dominant labor leadership. . . . Through united front actions from below more and more advances can be made in this direction. Pressure *can* be exerted on the top leadership." [18]

The new tactic brought no results for the Communists. If there were "young early buds of Spring" for the Communists to nurture to maturity, they have not yet blossomed. There has developed within the main stream of American labor a greater degree of unity than there was in 1953. As the A.F. of L. and C.I.O. merged, along with several of their constituent international unions, the Communists became excitedly optimistic about the possibilities of new influence.[19] But the mergers have, if anything, shut the Communists out colder than ever. For example, when the Furriers merged with the A.F. of L. Meatcutters, led by Patrick Gorman, an old Socialist, the anti-Communists succeeded in keeping the old Communist furriers out of the leadership in the new organization. Merger in this case meant loss of power for the party.

In what little contact has developed between the Left unions and the central labor movement, the contact has come at the top, through the leadership, without pressure from below, and has involved some of the more disreputable trade unions. There have been "feelers" for co-operation between the Bridges union and the East Coast International Longshoremen's Association and between the I.L.W.U. and the Teamsters. These unions are natural allies economically, of course. But also involved is the ideology, or lack of it, of the I.L.A. and the Teamster leadership, which is more interested in power than politics and therefore might accept an alliance more ideological union leaders would reject. Should these "feelers" develop into an alliance between Reds and racketeers in the labor movement, the irony would be too much for the ghosts of Debs and Haywood to bear.

ANOTHER CHANGE IN THE NEGRO LINE

The Communist line on Negroes changed in the post-Stalin era in much the same direction as the change of line on political action and labor—and for the same reasons. The party's line on the Negro and its wild internal witch hunt against "white chauvinism" had thoroughly isolated the party from the movement for Negro equality. The general Negro liberation movement, led especially by the National Association for the Advancement of Colored People, enjoyed its greatest success since Reconstruction with such victories as the Supreme Court's decision against segregated schools. Communists were on the outside looking in.

Foster called a halt to the white-chauvinism spasm in July 1953, and later characterized the whole affair as "glaringly wrong policy." "The general idea that our Party was unable to fight for Negro rights until it first cleansed itself completely of all traces of white chauvinism . . . was a dangerously sectarian notion, which . . . [could] only lead our Party into distorted and fantastic conceptions of white chauvinism and undermine our fight against it, cripple the Party's mass struggle for Negro rights, and weaken its influence among the Negro masses—all of which this 'Leftist' mistake did in a very marked manner." [20]

The Communists were slower and more cautious in modifying their Negro line than in changing other aspects of their position. In the late fall of 1953, months after the Communists had decided to be conciliatory to the liberal wing of the Democratic Party and non-Communist labor leaders, a Negro Communist attacked Walter White and the N.A.A.C.P. with the old customary vehemence. White came in for criticism for an alleged "fawning attitude" toward the Eisenhower administration and for indulging in "an orgy of Red-baiting and anti-Communist slander" at the 1953 N.A.A.C.P. convention. The organization itself was guilty of "continuing subordination of the Negro workers to the bourgeoisie" and of being squeamishly superior in condeming the violence of the Mau Maus in Kenya. In December 1953, Communists organized the Third Annual Convention of the National Negro Labor Council, a party-front competitor to the N.A.A.C.P., and Pettis Perry's report of the convention was an attempt to justify the N.N.L.C.'s existence. [21]

Perry's sectarianism and his power within the party seem to have been the main obstacle to a change of line. In an article on the draft program of 1954, which on other matters was obviously inconsistent with the party line on the Negro, Perry attacked "Negro reformists" and continued to speak about the "right to self-determination in the Black Belt." [22] Indeed, the draft program itself, one white leader pointed out, only veiled the national-self-determination idea in new language.[23]

Perry went to prison in January 1955, after about two years of appeals, along with other "second-string" leaders, and the line changed almost immediately. The tactic now was a "mass policy" on the Negro question. The old policy of "dual unions," or "Left centers," as the Communists preferred to call them, was now dropped. The N.N.L.C. quietly expired as the Communists decided that the "central task is to influence . . . in a correct direction" such organizations as the N.A.A.C.P. and the Urban League. "The main thing to realize," wrote Foster, "is that we must work within the mass organizations and not isolate ourselves in separate movements." [24] Working within the N.A.A.C.P. meant, of course, a halt to vituperation against "Negro reformists." Doxey Wilkerson's report to his comrades on the 1955 N.A.A.C.P. convention contrasted sharply with the last Communist report on that organization. N.A.A.C.P. leaders were now "militant fighters," and the bourgeois group had somehow within two years become "highly conscious . . . of the decisive importance of trade union support." Only when the N.A.A.C.P. took a position diametrically opposed to the Communists did Wilkerson make any criticism, and then the criticism was mild. Wilkerson even optimistically interpreted a slight change in the wording of the N.A.A.C.P.'s traditional resolution against co-operation with Communist trade unions.[25]

Working "within the mass organizations" obviously meant that party members were to bury themselves within the N.A.A.C.P. and other Negro organizations in an attempt to mold their policies. How many Communists have infiltrated the N.A.A.C.P. is unknown, but obviously such buried Communists have been unable to influence the organization "in a correct direction." The national N.A.A.C.P. leaders have had sufficient experience with

Communists to be able to resist them effectively, and they know that to weaken their guard against the Communists is only to play into the hands of the Southern white supremacists, who would like nothing better than successfully to smear black with red.

As with the new positions on politics and trade unions, the new Negro policy of the party availed it nothing. Months after the decision to infiltrate the N.A.A.C.P., the Communists still complained of failure to make progress. During the party's internal crisis in 1956, Benjamin J. Davis, one of the hardest of the party's sectarians, had to note the "extreme isolation of our Party in the struggle for Negro rights." [26] And, for the Communists, failure in this field is particularly bitter. For if the Communists cannot capitalize on this spirited movement of America's most exploited and oppressed people, where can they expect success?

"THE AMERICAN WAY"

With such a new line of moderation and emphasis on contact with the masses in non-Communist groups, party members who remembered the Browder era and the fight against Browderism just after the war—and almost all remembered because there were so few new members—were bound eventually to ask an embarrassing question: Was not this new line "Browderism without Browder"? Party headquarters could not avoid the question. "Some comrades ask," said central office worker Betty Gannett in a 1954 pamphlet, "how does this type of democratic unity differ from what Browder advocated? Is there not a danger of once again becoming entrapped in revisionism?" She went on to explain that of course there was always a "right danger" to be avoided, but the new line was not Browderism at all. Of necessity, she emphasized the theoretical differences between the new line and Browderism because in their applications and, to a degree, in their style of action, they were similar. "Our party is the defender of the interests of *all* oppressed and exploited, the *whole* people. Browder had no faith in the people. On the contrary, he wanted the people to pin their faith on 'enlightened' monopoly capitalists." [27]

There were differences, important ones, between Browderism and the post-Stalin line. In their theories, the differences rested on quite contrasting expectations about Soviet-American relations. Browder had a "perspective" of harmony between the two nations, with the United States shipping to the Soviet Union a significant amount of its "surplus" industrial product, and at this time the Foster party expected nothing more harmonious than the "cold peace" line Stalin had laid down at the nineteenth congress. The main differences between the two flowed from the fact that Browder's party was considerably more successful. Browder's party had significant strength in the labor movement, a bridgehead into the Democratic Party's coalition through the A.L.P., and greater toleration if not strength in the Negro community; Foster's party was isolated and seeking the kind of alliances and influence that the Browder party had enjoyed.

Still, the similarities were sufficient to embarrass Foster and amuse Browder, now retired in Yonkers. There was, for example, the incident of the "outstretched hand" to the Catholics, a policy Browder had developed in the realization that a large part of the working class is in the traditionally anti-Communist Roman Catholic Church. The party's 1954 program declared for the same policy: "The Communist Party declares that it seeks no conflict with any church or any American's religious belief. On the contrary, we stretch out our hand in the fellowship of common struggle for our mutual goal of peace, democracy and security to all. . . ." [28] Foster hastened to qualify his personal position on the "outstretched hand" before anyone pointed out the origin of the idea. In July 1954, Foster explained, he had received a letter from an enterprising priest who proposed that Foster resume his affiliation with the Church, with which the Irishman had broken as a young man. Foster declined in a private letter quite promptly. But when the final version of the program appeared in the party's official theoretical journal in October, Foster published his letter in the same issue of the magazine. The letter reaffirmed his atheism, cited the Soviet Union as the shining example of what he meant by "freedom of religious beliefs," and criticized the conservative nature of the Church's politics. He then quoted the "outstretched hand" sentences of the party's program. The priest must have been bewildered indeed.[29]

Late in 1954, the party launched a new magazine for young people that smacked of a Browderite flavor. A pocket-sized product on slick paper with good photographs, *New Challenge: The Magazine for Young Americans* sold a lot of clever propaganda for fifteen cents. Tucked in among such articles as "How a Wonderful Day Got Started," on the origins of Mother's Day, "Duck, Men—Here Comes the Spitter," on baseball, and "Is the Mambo Here to Stay?" were party-line nuggets such as a denunciation of universal military training, "Why They March on May First," and "World Youth Set for Summer Meet." [30]

Another similarity in style between the post-Stalin and Browder periods was a revival of the "we-too-sing-America" theme, a rebirth of the peculiarly fuzzy, Whitmanesque, Popular Front "patriotism." The 1954 party program was entitled "The *American Way*" to jobs, peace, et cetera. The document emphasized that the party "has its roots deep in the history and struggles of the American people and its labor movement. . . . Its devotion to the true national interests of the American people is the source of its deep and abiding patriotism . . . sealed in the blood of hundreds of members of the Communist Party who have died in defense of our country and our people." [31]

No sooner had the party adopted this document than it embroiled itself in a humorous little public washing of dirty linen about what patriotism meant for a Communist. One Andrew Montgomery, probably a pen name, wrote an offbeat article for the summer issue of *Party Voice*. On Memorial Day, he wrote, in trying to get to the subway he was blocked by a parade. "As I stood and watched, numerous flags floated by. At first, hesitantly, and a little embarrassed, I started to salute each one. At times I looked up and down the street and hoped, inwardly, that none of my 'left' friends were looking." But then he decided that the party's new program was patriotic and that he need feel no embarrassment. "For if the Draft Program is anything it is a patriotic document. It is not, as some comrades think, a gimmick which assumes a patriotic coloration as a concession to national pride." He went on to say, "There exists in our party some trends of cultural and intellectual exclusiveness which border on snobbery and are a distinct liability to the progressive movement." Examples? "I have no doubt that there are comrades . . . who have not read a single American book outside of progressive literature in many moons but who can discuss in detail the latest Soviet book or periodical from China." Other comrades go only to foreign films, "see only the decline and fall of American culture," and have "a certain contempt for television . . . a mass media accepted by the workers." During the Olympic Games, too many Communists had rooted for the Soviet athletes rather than the American boys. And then "the question of coca-cola. It is one thing for the French people to wage a struggle against this drink which symbolized the role of Wall Street in their country. But it is an entirely different thing within the United States. Coca-cola is an accepted and popular drink here, and does not symbolize the policy of the government. Those comrades then who stop drinking it for political reasons demonstrate nothing but their own inability to understand that it is impossible to substitute internationalism for national pride at this stage of the struggle." [32] All in all, a refreshingly different article for a Communist magazine.

The candid but naïve Mr. Montgomery did not long go unanswered. The next issue of *Party Voice* carried a reply by Betty Gannett and V. J. Jerome, editor of the party's theoretical magazine. "We note with grave concern—indeed, with alarm—the distortions in the article . . . by Andrew Montgomery. . . . It is hard to understand how this article was printed in *Party Voice*—and without editorial comment." Patriotism, yes, but not the patriotism of the Montgomery article, "permeated with bourgeois-nationalism, with jingoism." "We are *of* the people, and no false charges from the enemy, or their echoings in our midst, can cut us off from our roots. The allegations and 'portrayals' in this article are figments; they reflect no reality in our Party. Dressed up as a 'critique' of sectarianism, they are utterly alien to Communist teaching and practice." The party is truly patriotic, engaged in "a struggle for a progressive concept of patriotism—*for patriotism on a higher level.*" As for American culture, Communists should not forget "there is an inherent relationship between an exploitive economic system in decay and its cultural superstructure. To work among the masses and to strengthen our ties with them, we cannot adopt uncritical attitudes or glorify cultural backwardness." The most serious error of the Montgomery article was its failure to understand that "True patriotism and proletarian internationalism cannot be counterposed to each other. . . . The whole article is a rejection of the Marxist-Leninist principle of the dialectical interconnection of that which is universal, or international, and that which is nationally unique." The reply ended on a somber note: "The article reflects a current danger of weakening before the ideological pressures of the war-inciting bourgeoisie. It reflects a certain capitulation to the propaganda barrage of chauvinist nationalism and to the Big Lie about the Communist Party. . . . The serious error of publishing this article should spur us all to deepen our concern with theory, to fortify ourselves with Marxist-Leninist understanding." [33]

The "patriotism" campaign proceeded without further errors such as Comrade Montgomery's. Party intellectuals began to write on the subject, and if they succeeded in fairly well obfuscating the subject with hairline distinctions and obscure references, a close reader still could draw the "correct" conclusion that the Communists were the true patriots and the anti-Communists were unpatriotic. After the Geneva Conference in the summer of 1955, one party intellectual, James S. Allen, had a vision of the Marxist conception of national interest coming closer to the popular understanding of that interest as Soviet-American relations continued to improve. "During the period of temporary isolation of the Left in American life, with the consequent encouragement of sectarian moods, [a] broad and dynamic vision of the national tradition was dimmed, at a time when reaction was glorifying everything that was backward in our history." But now "Marxists and progressives should revive and mature these concepts of the national interest and the national tradition as an inherent part of their outlook." [34]

Between the end of 1952 and the end of 1955, the party had come a long way ideologically. The process had been slow, uneven, and hesitant, but the party line had changed in some important particulars. At the very end of 1955, even the underground operation began to come out above ground. In September, Max Weiss, who had been underground for some time, openly visited party headquarters in Harlem in the company of his wife and daughter. The F.B.I. promptly arrested him, and soon he was indicted under the membership clause of the Smith Act. In late November and December, fugitives from indictment began to surrender voluntarily. Within a week, William Norman, Fred Fine, and James Jackson, all of them important leaders, turned themselves in.[35] The "first-string" fugitives, Green and Winston, who had disappeared after the Supreme Court's decision in the Dennis case in 1951, did not surrender until 1956.

In other and important respects, the party changed not at all. Communists still took on faith everything the Russian leaders said. The June 1953 East German working-class revolt seemed to Foster a "putsch . . . organized, financed, and led in the streets by tools of the Eisenhower Government." [36] When the Russians announced the execution of Beria and denounced him as an "agent of imperialism" and an enemy of peace and socialism, the *Daily Worker* duly accepted the same explanation, never acknowledging the significance of the affair.[37] When Khrushchev tried to make his peace with Tito, the Communists accepted without blinking the Russian story that Beria had been responsible for the whole difficulty.[38] And the party still suffered from literary filiopietism with each anniversary of the Bolshevik revolution, as in this full-page paean by Sean O'Casey in the *Daily People's World:*

Red Star shines over the Kremlin,
The Red soldiers with their Red cavalry are on the frontiers.
Star of Power.
Red mirror of wisdom.
Red health of the sick.
Red refuge of the afflicted.
Red course of our joy.
Red star shine on us all!

Still the party had changed some—the *People's World* published a letter of complaint about the poem from a party worker who sold the paper every weekend and found the poem a serious handicap to sales. "Go out some time if you doubt me and try and sell this kind of copy to the people." [39]

What changes there were added up only to changes in tactics. The more change, the more the same thing. The unchanging fundamental principle of the party, as well as its fundamental weakness, was that the party molded its aims and tactics in response to Soviet conditions and requirements rather than those of either the United States as a whole or of the American working class. Dedicated Communists believed, of course, that the interests of American workers were the same as the interests of the Soviet Union, and their belief was sincere. Sincere faith was, after all, what held the party together, to the degree that it was held together.

But the faith of the American Communists was soon to receive a jolt such as it had never encountered before. Nikita Khrushchev was preparing his speech for the twentieth congress of his party.

NINE: TARNISHED HEROES: STALIN AND FOSTER

When delegates to the Twentieth Congress of the Communist Party of the Soviet Union assembled in Moscow in early February 1956, no one in the United States, the Communists included, anticipated anything out of the ordinary. The congress surely would be another dull series of economic reports and abstract statements of party line, which Soviet experts in the Western world would inspect microscopically for significant clues. The twentieth congress, one of the most important meetings in communism's history, precipitated an unprecedented crisis in the Communist world and set in motion a chain of events that all but killed the Communist organization in the United States.

On February 14, Nikita Khrushchev delivered to the congress the report of the party's central committee. This report was not the famous "secret" Khrushchev speech, which came ten days later, but even this first speech was explosive. In an obvious but unexplicit reference to Stalin's regime, Khrushchev condemned the "cult of personality" or "cult of the individual" and announced a return to the Leninist principle of "collective leadership." In the speech he also declared that the Soviet Union's goal was "peaceful co-existence" with the West, asserted that each nation of the world would have to follow its own inevitable "path to socialism," and hailed united fronts of Communists with social democrats and other popular groups.[1] The *Daily Worker* revealed no excitement over this first Khrushchev speech. Sam Russell, correspondent in Russia for the London *Daily Worker,* had a story which featured the coexistence part of the report and the promise of a shorter working day for Russian labor. The editors of the New York *Daily Worker* published nearly two pages of excerpts from the speech but omitted the sections with the implied criticism of Stalin's leadership. Editorial writers and columnists ignored the criticism as well. They put their emphasis on Khrushchev's "various-paths-to-socialism" theme and on his disclaimer of intent to export revolution, each of which was consistent with the current American party line. The *Daily Worker* was caught without a good photographic cut of Khrushchev. The one it used was obviously outdated, showing a Khrushchev twenty years younger, with hair and a thinner face.[2] The first specific mention in the *Daily Worker* of Russian criticism of Stalin appeared in a news story about a speech by Anastas Mikoyan at the congress rather than the first Khrushchev speech, but there was no editorial comment and the story appeared under the innocuous headline "SOVIET LEADER CALLS FOR NEW STUDY OF CAPITALIST TRENDS." [3]

The first reports to reach the United States about Khrushchev's "secret" speech of February 24-25 came March 16. Even before Americans knew anything about the famous account of Stalin's paranoid misrule, a few American Communists publicly revealed their anxieties about the Russian congress. Others were unruffled. James S. Allen, a veteran Communist historian, declared in his regular column in the *Worker* of March 4 that he was not disturbed: "Marxists abroad are supposed to be embarrassed by the Party Congress just concluded in Moscow, according to what I read in the newspapers. I must confess that I have no sense of embarrassment." He went on to praise the Russians' "dynamic, bold, open-minded approach to all problems" and to condemn John Foster Dulles in routine fashion.[4] The first evidence of confusion and doubt among Communists in public prints appeared in a column by Alan Max, managing editor of the *Daily Worker,* on March 13. Max, once editor of Columbia University's humor magazine, had a reputation in the party as a writer of light satire, but now he was not trying to be funny. "Any Marxist who says he has not been jolted is either not being honest with himself . . . or minimizes the extent of the developments now in progress in the Soviet Union." So much for Mr. Allen. He went on to begin an examination of the errors of the American party, as thousands of others were soon to do: "We went overboard in defending things like the idea of Stalin as infallible, in opposing any suggestion that civil liberties were not being fully respected in the Soviet Union, in discouraging serious discussion and criticism of Soviet movies, books, etc." He ended the column by asking readers to write letters about their reactions to the twentieth Congress.[5]

Three days later, Communists realized there was a basic disagreement among the party's leaders. It seemed likely there would be a party disruption which would dwarf the upheaval of 1945 when Browder was downgraded. The Friday and Sunday editions always arrived in the same mail. Sunday's *Worker,* dated March 18 but actually received March 16, contained a letter from Ring Lardner, Jr., one of the "Hollywood Ten," which dared even to point out there was a cult of personality in the American party around William Z. Foster. "I wonder if some of the rather maudlin testaments to William Z. Foster on his recent birthday are really the most mature and effective way of acknowledging the respect due America's outstanding working-class leader." Lardner had a point there. The March issue of *Political Affairs* had combined the practice and the condemnation of the cult of personality in a novel manner. All but the last feature in the issue were eulogies to Foster, "Dear Comrade Bill," on his seventy-fifth birthday, February 25, 1956, the same day that Khrushchev finished his "secret" speech. The last item in the issue was Khrushchev's first report to the twentieth congress with its condemnation of the "cult of the individual as being alien to the spirit of Marxism-Leninism." That Lardner should write such a letter to the newspaper was not particularly surprising; what was startling to people who had read the *Daily Worker*'s dreary pages for years was that the editors should print it. All the more surprising was the editorial note following the letter: "Ring Lardner's letter raises a number of interesting and important questions of vital concern to the American Left. We are happy to have his views and by the same token invite our readers to submit theirs for publication." [6]

In the other issue of the paper which subscribers received that day was Foster's first comment. Foster conceded that Stalin had made "errors," but warned the membership that its "task is neither to rush indignantly to the defense of Stalin nor to tear him to political shreds, as some in our ranks seem inclined to do." There were, Foster argued, mitigating circumstances to be remembered in Stalin's defense. With the necessity of Russian industrialization, the hostility of other powers, the war with the Nazis, and then the cold war, "it was not difficult to fall into Stalin's command methods of leadership." Furthermore, American Communists should not forget "positive" features of Stalin's regime and "must be doubly vigilant not to fall into the bourgeois trap of making a negative and destructive sum-up of the whole situation." "The Stalin revaluation" is a problem for the Russians, not the American Communists, and "Of course, they will . . . master this problem, and in the doing . . . bring forth lessons of great value for the workers of all the world." [7]

No report of a secret speech appeared in American newspapers until March 16, after the Lardner letter and the Foster column were already in the mails. The first accounts were incomplete and undocumented. The speech was so sensational that even partial news about it threw the American party into an uproar. Khrushchev was reported by the newspapers as saying that Stalin had been a madman, acutely suspicious of his colleagues, personally abusive in his relations with subordinates, and ruthless in his persecutions. He had framed thousands of innocent Communist leaders and army officers, bungled the war with Germany, and created a feeling of terror among the top leadership of the Russian party.[8]

The American Communists obviously relied upon the "bourgeois press" for their information about what happened in the Soviet Union. There seems to be no reason to believe that the party had a "private line" open to Moscow in 1956 or since. Over and again during the party's upheaval, they reacted to the news from East Europe only as the news became available to readers of the New York *Times,* but surely many times American Communist Party leaders would have given a great deal for "inside information" from the Kremlin. In March 1956, the American Communists could not dismiss as capitalist lies the reports about the downgrading of Stalin.

There was too much evidence from the Soviet Union itself, and from Communist leaders elsewhere in Europe, that the charges had indeed been made. *New Times,* published by *Trud* in Moscow in ten languages and distributed in the United States by the Four Continents Book Company, had printed a special supplement on the twentieth congress containing the Russian central committee's resolution which had mentioned "re-establishing" inner-party democracy and former "violations of socialist law." [9] Nor did Russian criticism of Stalin cease with the end of the congress. On March 28, a *Pravda* article declared that under Stalin the "cult of the individual assumed ever more monstrous forms and did serious harm to the cause." [10] The next day, Hungarian Communist leader Matyas Rakosi announced that Laszlo Rajk had been convicted upon fabricated evidence, and a few days later, Polish Communists revealed that Wladyslaw Gomulka had been released from prison and "rehabilitated." [11]

Obviously, American Communists could not duck the anti-Stalinist controversy. Their public disagreement became intensified and, more importantly, quickly shifted from the question of Stalin to the matter of their own party's record in recent years. Ordinary rank-and-file members, repressed for years, found irresistible the *Daily Worker*'s invitation to express themselves. When George Blake Charney, New York State party chairman, promised in a public meeting that no member would be expelled or punished for expressing his own views, the audience, composed mostly of Manhattan active members, interrupted him with enthusiastic applause.[12] A *Daily Worker* letter from a Communist who called himself "Guido" was typical. The year before, "Guido" wrote, he and some Italian-American friends had written a series of letters to the editor which had been neither published nor discussed. Now he wanted to know what was being done to free the party of "dogmatism and bias" and wanted to ask the foreign editor, Joseph Clark, who had once been the paper's Moscow correspondent, why he had not reported the abuse of the Russians by the secret police.[13] (Clark replied that he had not been aware of the activities of the secret police when he was in Moscow but conceded, "I should have written how silly the glorification of Stalin appeared to me at that time." [14]) The energy and exhilaration of the Communists' long pent-up discussion and criticism was reminiscent of a group of children just released from the discipline of an authoritarian schoolmaster.

Before long, the letters to the editor and the writings and speeches of the leadership began to fall into a pattern. At one pole were those who were critical of Stalin and wanted a thorough revamping of the American party, and at the opposite pole were those who made only minor concessions on Stalin, opposed a full party discussion of its own problems, and wanted no essential changes in the party's program. The bulk of the membership was somewhere between these two extremes, but clearly a majority was for greater party democracy and for a flexible and moderate party line.[15] The staff of the *Daily Worker,* led by editor John Gates, came to symbolize the first tendency, while Foster symbolized the other extreme.

The extent of the division within the party was evident in any issue of the *Daily Worker.* One issue, for example, carried on opposite pages an editorial on the Rajk case, presumably written by Gates, and a column by Foster on "What Was Done to Check Stalin?" The editorial was strong. The Rajk case had been a "frame-up" and a "murder," and American Communists were entitled to know more than they had been told about the case. The editorial insisted that all connected with the frame-up be brought to justice. "We . . . demand that the investigations in Hungary and the Soviet Union shall be full and complete and shall bring to book those responsible for injustice, no matter how high their position was or is." But Foster, who would never "demand" anything of the Russians, dealt harshly with those who asked what Khrushchev and other Russian Communists did to try to prevent Stalin's tyranny. Foster absolved the Russian leaders of all responsibility on the grounds that any "organized movement against Stalin would have had to confront the prospect of a split in the Party." [16] Presumably, Foster regarded a monolithic party as more important than justice, which, of course, was good Leninist doctrine. Fear of a split in the American party troubled both the Foster "hards" and the Gates "softs," [17] although the softs wanted the kind of a party in which dissent did not imply party split.

THE TAX AFFAIR

Just when the disagreements among the Communists were getting sharp and outsiders were watching the spectacle with fascination, an agency of the United States Government intervened and nearly ended the fight. On March 27, 1956, four agents of the Federal Bureau of Internal Revenue walked unannounced into the *Daily Worker*'s offices on the eighth floor at 35 East Twelfth Street, told the newspaper staff to leave, and posted notices to the effect that all property in the office was seized as a lien against unpaid back taxes. The assets seized included, besides the battered office furniture and typewriters, the newspaper's records, morgue, and addressing machine. There were simultaneous raids at party headquarters on Sixth Avenue and at the *Worker* "offices" in Chicago, Philadelphia, and San Francisco, dingy little rooms in low-rent districts with almost no property in them, where local Communists received *Worker* mail and prepared copy for their regional section of the weekend *Worker*. The tax liens held that the *Daily Worker* owed a total of $46,049 in taxes and penalties for 1951 through 1953 and that the party owed $389,265 for 1951.[18]

Who in the federal government made the decision to make the tax raids is not clear. The Internal Revenue Office in Washington disclaimed all connection with the raids, saying that the district director for Lower Manhattan, Donald R. Moysey, had acted "entirely on his own, without realizing the implications." But *Time* observed that Moysey had been in his position for less than two months and that it appeared that the office of Attorney General Herbert Brownell had "planned . . . and directed" the raids.[19]

The *Daily Worker* staff refused to let the raid disrupt publication. The group moved downstairs one floor to the workshop of the F & D Publishing Company, an independent printing firm which printed the *Daily Worker,* and wrote their copy for the next day's issue with pencils. The issue appeared with the proud headline "OUR OFFICE SEIZED—HERE WE ARE." The next day, the staff moved into temporary offices with the *Morning Freiheit,* the Yiddish-language Communist paper on still another floor of the building. Each issue of the paper appeared on time during the several days the staff was out of its regular office.

Significantly for the battle within the party currently in progress, the *Daily Worker* kept the paper going without the help of the party's national officers. Eugene Dennis was at home writing a speech when the tax agents seized the office. Telephone calls from the *Daily Worker* to tell him what was happening only irritated him. Neither he nor Foster did anything to keep publication uninterrupted. The extent of Dennis's help was a sarcastic telegram to President Eisenhower designed for propaganda rather than for solving the immediate problem, the recovery of their offices and equipment. Whether Dennis and Foster were secretly hopeful that the federal government would unwittingly remove the Gates thorn from their sides, as many of Gates's followers believed, or whether they were so much in a mental rut of manifestoes, resolutions, and other party rituals that they were unable to act in a practical situation cannot be told. In any case, the federal government did not silence the *Daily Worker,* whether or not that was its intent, and the failure of the national office to help the paper intensified hard feelings between the two factions in the party.[20]

Notified that the Internal Revenue Bureau had assessed value of the seized office equipment in the newspaper offices and party headquarters at a total of $4,000, Communists borrowed the money, deposited it with Moysey's office, and moved back into their regular quarters in early April.[21] In order to prevent seizure for taxes on future income, the *Daily Worker* set up a special Emergency Committee for a Free Press, which received all payments for subscriptions and other income, in effect becoming the paper's financial office. Checks for subscriptions made out to the paper's publisher, Publisher's New Press, Inc., were returned with instructions to make payments to the Emergency Committee. In May, the *Daily Worker* and the party sought a federal injunction to prevent further seizure of income and property; their plea was denied.[22]

The whole tax affair was a fiasco. If the administration was seeking to shut down the paper, it failed; if someone thought the Communists could really produce over $400,000 for revenue, he was stupid. The affair served only to rally a great many anti-Communist organizations and individuals to the party's defense on civil-libertarian grounds. Several newspapers over the nation condemned the raids, giving the party the kind of favorable publicity it could not have bought at any price.[23] The American Civil Liberties Union defended the *Daily Worker* as did even the American Committee for Cultural Freedom, a group whose anti-Communism was almost unbounded.[24] All in all, the tax affair gained the federal government nothing and, by endangering the existence of the *Daily Worker,* came near to knocking out one side in the most important inner-party fight the Communists ever had.

JOHN GATES CRITICIZES

At public party meetings, it was plain that the fire of the dispute was hot indeed. The Jefferson School inaugurated a series of four meetings on the significance of the twentieth congress. At the last, John Gates, the main speaker, used blunter language than he did in his editorials; it was clear he was a Communist and a defender of the Soviet Union, but equally clear that he sought a thorough change in the American party's organization and line. Gates was obviously feeling his way, confused in his own mind about what the party should do.

John Gates, born Israel Regenstreif, grew up in the Bronx, did well in school, and went to City College. In early 1931, the Young Communist League at City College organized a campaign against the R.O.T.C. (Reserve Officers Training Corps), and several of the young Communists found themselves suspended. The seventeen-year-old Gates joined the Y.C.L., left college the next year, and went to work for the party trying to organize steel workers in Youngstown, Ohio. From the time he got off the train in Ohio until January 1958, except for his army service in World War II, Gates was a professional revolutionary, a "full-timer" for the Communist Party. He fought in Spain as a member of the Lincoln Brigade, rising to the rank of lieutenant colonel, the highest-ranking American officer in Spain. In World War II, he was a sergeant in a paratrooper division. After the war, he became editor of the *Daily Worker*. He was convicted at the first Communist Smith Act trial and spent his imprisonment in Atlanta Penitentiary, where for the first time since he left college, he read non-Communist, even anti-Communist books. Among the books he read was George Orwell's *1984,* but contrary to the stories in the party that his revolt from Communist orthodoxy dated from his reading of the book, he disliked it. He only wondered at the self-imposed censorship which had previously prevented him from even reading the works of an anti-Communist. The books that impressed him more, interestingly, were the historical volumes on the post-Civil War South by Professor C. Vann Woodward. He realized that the history of the Negro in the United States was somewhat more complicated than he had thought and that the pat Communist interpretation was inadequate. When Gates got out of prison in the spring of 1955, he was still a confirmed Communist. There were only seeds of doubt in his mind. After ten more months of imposed absence from party affairs, a condition of his parole, he went back to the *Daily Worker* as editor just before the twentieth congress convened.[25]

Gates said a great many things to his enthusiastic Jefferson School audience that would have been unthinkable at a Communist meeting only a few weeks earlier. He was strong for civil liberties, even for enemies of Communism. The party's approval of the prosecution of the Minnesota Trotskyists under the Smith Act had been "dead wrong," a position later endorsed by the *Worker*'s Virginia Gardner.[26] When "by peaceful means" a socialist government comes to power in the United States, there would be full civil liberties for all, "including those who advocate the return to capitalism." The Ford family, if it wished, would be allowed to "harangue the workers on the streets of Detroit for return of their factories." (The party's education director, Max Weiss, very cautiously and guardedly endorsed this position.[27]) But he spent most of his time arguing that the party's greatest emphasis should be "on the creation of greater democracy in the party" and on correcting "sectarian errors which resulted from self-imposed isolation from popular movements." "We stand isolated from the great popular movements, from the new merged labor movement, from the Negro movement, and absolutely isolated from the farm revolt." Just how the party could break out of its isolation, just what its program should be, Gates did not know. He knew only that Communists could not find the answers from Communists abroad. "We have to stand on our own feet, to learn to think through for ourselves, not to let others think for us, not to parrot what anybody says." Communists must study the works of non-Communists and reflect the desires of the working class. "We Marxists are not the best authorities on the United States within America. There are others more astute, more learned, have more facts. We have got to be modest, especially because we are so small, so unsuccessful, so isolated from the working class." Over and over again, he enjoined Communists to study, to think, to come up with new solutions. But he himself had no solutions to offer.[28]

Many Communists were in no emotional condition to think deeply in 1956. Some were thoroughly shaken, their faith of years shattered by the highest priests of their church. Samuel Sillen, editor of *Masses & Mainstream,* came near to an emotional collapse. One day he walked out of the *M & M* offices and never returned. A few months later, he was working as a salesman. The February issue of the magazine had to be skipped altogether.[29] Leaders of the New York State organization, mostly of the Gates tendency, were in such an emotional turmoil and fever of factional activity that their state magazine, *Party Voice,* failed to appear in March, April, and May. Many "progressive homes" were in retrogressive turmoil, husbands debating party policy with wives, sons in ideological conflict with parents. When the party tried to present a solid front to the general public for the 1956 May Day demonstrations, the results were feeble. A small and listless group assembled at the north end of the park in Union Square and listened to unknown third-rate speakers on such safe subjects as denunciations of Franco and Trujillo. Around the edge of the small crowd, a group of Trotskyists, far younger in years than those in the passive Communist audience, distributed copies of the *Militant.* The meeting was only a pallid parody of Communist May Day demonstrations of times past.[30]

SOVIET ANTI-SEMITISM

One special reason for anxiety among American Communists during the downgrading of Stalin was that the Soviets were revealed to be anti-Semitic and a large proportion of the American party was Jewish. In New York City, the party's center, perhaps one-half the members were Jewish. Many of them read Yiddish. Furthermore, even to non-Jewish Communists—and to non-Communists, too, for that matter—anti-Semitism was among the most heinous of sins. Had there been no Jewish questions involved in the international crisis of Communism after the twentieth congress, it is unlikely that the emotional impact upon the American party would have been as severe.

On April 4, 1956, *Folks-Shtimme,* a Yiddish Communist newspaper published in Warsaw, ran an article entitled *"Unzer Veitig un Unzer Treist"* ("Our Pain and Our Consolation"). One week later, *Freiheit* reprinted the article, again in Yiddish, and the *Daily Worker* very briefly summarized its contents in English. The full text of the article appeared in English for the first time in the American Communist magazine *Jewish Life,* along with a comment by the magazine's editors.[31] The Polish article praised Lenin's policy toward Soviet Jews and hailed the development of Jewish culture in the Soviet Union during the 1920's and early 1930's. But then had come the "social plague which is today known as infamous 'Beriaism' " and brought "tragic results" for Jewish culture "and for a number of [Jewish] community and cultural leaders." To put it bluntly, which the article did not do, the Soviet Communist leadership had killed them. Jewish life and culture survived the plague of the 1930's and fought against the Nazis during the war, only to be rewarded with the "destructive work of the Beria gang and the damaging effect of the cult of the individual." "How then did it happen that the spokesmen of the Jewish community . . . suddenly, and without a why or wherefore, were liquidated and its leaders condemned to death?" Now, however, everything has been set right once more. "The CPSU, with Leninist boldness, has penetrated to the very core of the terrible evil, in order to tear it out by the roots. . . . It is in this victory that we find our consolation, our hope and our certainty of the future." The comments of the editors of *Jewish Life* were stronger. They regarded the article "with profound sorrow and indignation" and used words like "murder," which the Poles had avoided. They called for more details. "Why were the crimes committed, who were responsible? The situation calls for a documented, detailed history of these crimes against the Jewish cultural and political figures." The guilty must be named and brought to justice. But to the American editors, too, there was "a beam of light" in contemporary Russia. The acknowledgment of the cult of personality "gives promise" of the end of Soviet anti-Semitism. "Steps are being taken in the Soviet Union to restore the rights of Jewish culture." The editors obviously expected more.

The *Daily Worker* staff, very largely Jewish but not so conscious of their Jewishness as the editors of *Jewish Life,* were more indignant. "We register our strong dissatisfaction that the Soviet leaders have not offered any explanation of what took place," said a Gates editorial. "What is being done to guarantee against repetition of these actions against any minorities in the Soviet Union?" The *Daily Worker* had been "too prone to accept the explanation of why Jewish culture had disappeared in the Soviet Union in the late 1940's." Now it demanded a full explanation—but it never received it.[32]

Instead, the Russian Communists consistently played down Communist anti-Semitism in the past and denied it in the present. Even when Ekaterina Furtseva, the only woman member of the Soviet party's central committee, in an interview with Tabitha Petran for the *National Guardian* tacitly admitted the existence of a quota system for Jews in the Soviet civil service—"the government had found in some of its departments a heavy concentration of Jewish people, upwards of 50% of the staff. Steps were taken to transfer them to other enterprises"—she denied anti-Semitism. "It is impossible," she said, "to speak of anti-Semitism in our country"—a sentence that admits of two interpretations.[33]

By no means were all Communists or all Jewish Communists in agreement with the *Daily Worker*'s indignant position. Many letters vigorously criticized the paper's "revisionism" and accused it of giving comfort to the enemies of communism. "The paper should not be so touchy." "It is regrettable that the paper [should be] so sensitive to wrongs committed by Parties elsewhere. . . ."[34]

The party itself, through its various resolutions and reports, took little notice of Soviet anti-Semitism. A statement of the national committee on the Khrushchev secret speech, issued in June after the full text of the speech was published in the United States, devoted three sentences to Soviet anti-Semitism.[35] By September, in its new draft resolution, the only reference was an indirect and obscure one to the effect that the American party had been "unprepared for and shocked by" the "mistreatment of certain national minorities."[36] In October, a group of twenty-six American Jewish Communists wrote a letter to Bulganin in which they cited evidence of Soviet anti-Semitism and requested a "public and authoritative statement" on Jews in the Soviet Union and expressed their "anxiety in respect to the reconstruction of Jewish communal and cultural life." No prominent party leader was among the signers.[37]

SHIFTING PARTY WINDS

The party's crusty cake of custom dictated the process by which it discussed and attempted to resolve its internal differences. The Communists had been through the process several times before, the last time in 1945. A series of reports, statements, and resolutions are always discussed at various party levels, culminating in the writing of a comprehensive statement of party principles called a draft resolution, always adopted in a routine manner at a national party convention. During performances of this ritual, outsiders who observe closely can learn a great many things about the party which have been hidden since the last such affair. The lid comes off for a while, only to be sealed firmly again when the national convention signals the end of the rites.

The upheaval after the twentieth congress lasted much longer than earlier performances of the ritual. In 1945, Jacques Duclos had published his article in April, the American party became aware of it in May, and the party convention was in late July. Actual sharp discussion did not last more than two or three weeks. But in the mid-1950's, the party crisis was protracted. Beginning in March 1956, it did not even get to the draft-resolution stage until September, and there was no convention until February 1957. And this time not even the national convention brought an absolute end to hostilities. The final blows were not struck until early 1958.

The party's national committee met from April 28 to May 1, 1956, in New York. This meeting was the first one the national committee had held since 1951 and was an "enlarged national committee meeting," meaning that important leaders who were not members of the committee were allowed to attend. The group debated vigorously and announced a party convention for December. Party secretary Dennis delivered the main report to the meeting, and Max Weiss and Claude Lightfoot submitted lesser reports on the significance of the twentieth congress and the 1956 American elections. The national committee also announced a "sixty-day pre-convention discussion," after which the committee expected intramural bickering to end. The leadership would then harmoniously write a draft resolution, to be mechanically ratified by the December convention.[38]

Dennis's report was, for him, a strong statement and indicated that a party majority had revised its thinking considerably in its first two months of turmoil. A cautious party bureaucrat with a damp finger always in the air to detect both rank-and-file and Kremlin breezes, Dennis had delayed any kind of a statement

until weeks after the twentieth congress adjourned. Not until
April 8 did he express himself publicly at all, and then his statement was so commonplace and equivocal that one could not be
sure what his position was or even if he had one.[39] After the publication of the *Folks-Shtimme* article, Dennis revealed a little
personal agony, but the most critical statement he made about the
Soviets was that Beria's treatment of the Jews was "a sad stain
upon, and wholly at variance with, the noble and inspiring record
of the Soviet Union." [40] Until the meeting of the national committee, Dennis's position clearly was in the middle, neither defending
Stalin nor criticizing him, neither defending the recent policies of
the American party nor defending them.

Dennis's national committee report, later published as a pamphlet, was a vigorous and comprehensive criticism of the party's
policies of the past few years. The party's isolation was partly its
own fault. Most of the party's errors had been "of a left sectarian
character." The party had been mistaken in thinking that total
war and fascism were almost a certainty and wrong in believing
that the United States was on the brink of a major economic depression. From these mistaken "perspectives," the party had been
wrong in not striving to prevent the C.I.O.'s expulsion of the Communist unions, had been "erroneous and harmful" in its third-
party policies, and had been in error in its Negro policy. He even
urged democracy within the party and "an end to dogmatism,"
although he did not explicitly concede that the party had been
undemocratic and dogmatic. For the future, Dennis advocated
"forging diverse labor-Negro-democratic front coalitions and alliances." [41]

Actually, Dennis had not gone far beyond the party program
adopted in 1954. He neither proposed any new policies nor criticized any past ones that had not already been tacitly dropped, but
he did criticize the party's postwar policies more explicitly and
much more vigorously than anyone in the 1954 discussions. His
report raised a great many eyebrows. Some national committee
members inferred that Dennis was critical of the party leadership

and that, since Dennis was himself number two man, he was criticizing Foster. Other national committee members thought Dennis was not far-reaching enough, was neither using a new broom nor sweeping hard enough with his old one.

Foster only "appeared briefly" at the meeting, because of his heart condition,[42] but he was there long enough to speak against the report and vote against it. He began his remarks by saying that he agreed with the report and then proceeded to tear it apart. Gates called Foster's position dishonest. If he was really against the report, as he seemed to be, he should say so. But the membership had to get the news that Foster had voted against Dennis's report from a story by Joseph Lash in the New York *Post,* which Foster later denied completely.[43] A report of the party's New York State organization stated that the national committee had debated the Dennis report for four acrimonious days, after which "most comrades came around to agree with the general direction the Dennis report was moving in, and the vote on his main line was unanimous." But, the report continued confusingly, Dennis's "hard-hitting summary which defended his main line was not unanimous. There was one against and three abstentations [*sic*], about 40 for." The report did not identify the dissenting voter. The vote against the report was Foster's; the three abstaining were Benjamin Davis, Ed Strong, and Carl Winter.[44]

Dennis had enumerated many of the party's errors and its mistaken assumptions from which the errors logically derived, but he did not even hint at the fountainhead of all the party's policies, which had isolated it: its slavish adherence to a line laid down in Moscow. Dennis did not say so, of course, but the Communists had made their decisions on the basis of the current line of the Soviet Union. And the Soviets never determined their line by any consideration of what was good or bad for the American party or for American workers.

There were Communists who dimly, but only dimly, perceived the real fountainhead of the party's isolation. To describe them as "national communists," as Yugoslavia's Tito, Poland's Gomulka, and Hungary's Nagy were national communists, is to exaggerate, but they tended in a national communist direction. That is, while remaining Communists, they wanted their party to make its decisions independently of Russian conditions. Gates was clearly thinking in a Titoist direction when he said the American party had to stand on its own feet and not "parrot what anybody says." This Titoist or national communist tendency dominated the leadership of the New York State organization in 1956.

Soon after the April-May meeting of the national committee, the New York State committee held a meeting and listened to a report by its organization secretary, Norman Schrank. Schrank's report went far beyond Dennis's in all respects, but its most significant aspect was its national communist tendency. "The influence of the international Marxist movement on our party is a source of much of our disorientation. The international Marxist movement weighed heavily on our past policies and estimates. In my opinion this influence cannot be exaggerated." He singled out Zhdanov's line at the 1947 meeting of the nine Communist parties. "We took this warning on the main danger of overestimating the strength of the bourgeoisie and underestimating the strength of the working class, and mechanically and in a doctrinaire way applied it to America—with the disastrous consequences which we are now examining in our work of the past decade. . . . What may be valid internationally, may not be valid in America, or fully valid." Schrank was close to accepting what had often been said of the Communists: they were not really Left; they were just East.

Schrank's report, actually a heretical document, became the basis of the party discussion in New York. At the state committee meeting, there was a vote on the proposal "That the State Committee approves the main line of the report by Norman Schrank as a basis for discussion." None opposed the motion, three abstained, and the rest voted in favor of it.[45] Surprisingly, much of the discussion in New York, the party's strongest state, was in fact based upon Schrank's report, and the subsequent issues of the state party magazine, *Party Voice,* were filled with the national communist heresy, vivid denunciations of the Foster-Dennis leadership, and an independence of thought extremely rare in Communist pages. Some of the statements in *Party Voice* were vigorous indeed: "I think that communist leaders are the worst snobs I have ever known." "I'm an American Communist. I don't want to be a Russian Communist." "The dictatorship of the Party and finally the dictatorship of a selected group within the Party is not and cannot become Socialism." [46]

Schrank's report even called for a reconsideration of "Browder's contribution," and this curious story justifies digression. The 1956 party crisis revived ghosts that the leadership assumed had long been exorcised. Browder, expelled from the party a decade before, received considerable attention. Even the party's ancient history produced a ghost when Charles Dirba, a leader of the "Left opposition" in 1921, which had advocated an entirely illegal Communist organization, wrote a letter to the *Daily Worker* that indicated his ideas had not changed much in the past quarter-century.[47]

In early July 1956, Earl Browder answered the door of the Yonkers apartment where he lived alone to find a man he did not recognize. The man introduced himself as Chick Mason and handed Browder a twenty-eight-page mimeographed booklet he had written entitled *Sources of our Dilemma: A Rejection of the "Right Opportunist-Left Sectarian" Explanation by our Leadership.* Browder took a quick look through the booklet and saw it was a defense of Browderism. He asked Mason if he represented an organized group or only himself, and Mason replied he was working alone. Browder asked Mason to bring him some more copies.

Mason had produced a rather confused piece of political analysis with unusually long quotations from the writings of Browder and Foster. His work certainly was not the product of an experienced Communist writer, but he managed to make his main point clear. "It is my contention that in order to understand our present isolation we will have to re-examine how we had once emerged from isolation, how we were beginning to learn to 'walk in the sun,' and what forces combined to stampede us back into the shell."

Mason returned to Browder's apartment in a few days with a few extra copies of his work. On the cover was the notation, "This article is being published serially in 'Party Voice.'" He drew a line through the announcement, apparently to indicate that *Party Voice* had reneged on a commitment. Parts of Mason's work were to appear, however, along with a disclaimer of endorsement, in the September and October issues of the New York party magazine.[48]

Mason did not succeed in his apparent objective. No organized group in the party wanted to revive Browder's ideas, and Browder himself was certainly in no mood to go back to the party wars. Yet the ghost of Browder hovered over the party during the tortured discussion of its difficulties; his name was frequently mentioned in party publications. Some Communists believed, as one member of the New York State committee put it, "It is undeniable that Browder made the first serious effort to apply Marxism to the American scene and to relate it to the American past and future," and this inevitably attracted those Communists who were groping their way toward the idea of an American party which shaped its policies without subservience to the exigencies of Soviet foreign policy.[49]

THE RUSSIANS AGAIN

In the middle of this hottest inner-party fight in Communist history, the United States Department of State released the text of Khrushchev's secret speech to the twentieth congress as it was edited for circulation among certain important Russian Communists. The Russians have never released the full text and never published any edition of it for general consumption.

American readers, though prepared by earlier reports from East Europe, found the fuller report in the New York *Times* of June 5 sickening. Khrushchev spoke of false confessions acquired "with the help of cruel and inhuman tortures." He cited chapter and verse from several cases, quoting letters from the victims of judicial murder. Stalin had been insanely ruthless. "Stalin . . . sanctioned . . . the most brutal violation of Socialist legality, torture and oppression, which led as we have seen to the slandering and self-accusation of innocent people." One of Stalin's most trusted political policemen, Rodos, responsible for the purging of several old Bolsheviks, was "a vile person, with the brain of a bird, and morally completely degenerate." Everything that capitalist critics had ever said about Stalin was now repeated by Khrushchev—and more.[50]

The Communists were jarred most severely. Many had joined the party because they sincerely saw communism as freedom, justice, and brotherhood; now they saw that Stalin's Russia was the negation of all these values. And for the party heretics, those who were struggling with Foster for a more liberal party, there was a particularly terrible realization. As *Daily Worker* columnist Howard Fast put it to a meeting of the paper's staff, "I wonder if there is any comrade here who can say now, out of what we know and have seen, that if our own Party leaders had the power of execution, he or she would be alive today." [51] They were alive because their party did not have power. To realize failure is a bitter experience; to realize that it is better to have failed is worse.

The only logical escape for the Communists was the argument that Stalinism was not socialism—the word Communists insist upon to the dismay of social democrats—but was an aberration from socialism. Many Communists wanted to believe in this escape, but they found it a little difficult. How, they kept asking themselves, if a socialist state is the best of all possible worlds, could such a fiend come to power? How could the proletariat, the theoretical womb of all economic and political virtue, bear such a monstrous travesty of "socialist justice"? Other Communists pursued less logical theories. Foster, for example, while not denying Stalin's "mistakes," a mild-enough word, emphasized the accomplishments of the Soviet Union even under Stalin. Still others hid their heads in the sand and continued to inveigh against "revisionism." And there were a few cranks, such as the woman who wrote the *National Guardian* that Bulganin and Khrushchev had "sold out to Wall Street" and would in time desert to Switzerland, where their reward, "a billion dollars apiece," had been "salted away" for them.[52]

The *Daily Worker* staff took the first of these rationalizations, embellished with a great deal of confession and breast-beating. Two editorials immediately after the publication of the speech summarized the position. "The State Department is dead wrong when it suggests that the evils of the Stalin era are inherent in socialism. . . . The exposure of Stalin's misrule, of his crimes against socialism and humanity is a measure of how much this was a departure from socialist ideas, and from what Lenin taught." But at the same time, "We were wrong, terribly wrong. We extended the proper and laudable sympathy for the world's first socialist state, and its defense against the monopolists and fascists who would destroy it, to a stupid and arrogant condemnation of those who told the truth about the violations of justice in the Soviet Union. We did not want to believe these crises could occur in a socialist state and so we refused to believe." No more such fawning approval and lack of a critical attitude toward the Russians. "We do not hesitate to state that we don't like the way Khrushchev's speech was made public. The leaders of the Soviet Union . . . should have published the speech immediately and made it available throughout the world." And why was there nothing in the speech about the "crimes . . . against Jewish culture and Jewish cultural leaders?" But still "socialism" is desirable for America. "We dedicate ourselves to helping the American working people find the American road to a complete reorganization of our society . . . a society of democratic socialism in which the civil and political rights of the individual and of groups will be guaranteed under the Constitution . . . a society in which the American people will own the resources and giant factories which they have built with their own hands and will at last, in friendship with the peoples of the whole world, determine their own destiny in their own way." [53]

Howard Fast was more eloquent. "I, for one, looked hopefully but vainly at the end of the document for a pledge that the last execution had taken place on Soviet soil. I looked for a pledge of civil rights, for the sacred right of habeas corpus, of public appeal to higher courts, of final judgment by one's peers rather than by professional judges. I looked for these things knowing full well how they have been mishandled and perverted in the courts of capitalism. . . . Instead, I learned that three more executions had been announced from the Soviet Union, and my stomach turned over with the blood-letting, with the madness of vengeance and counter-vengeance, of suspicion and counter-suspicion. . . . I think millions of human beings share my disgust at this idiotic behavior—wicked, uncivilized, but above all, idiotic." And then the *mea culpa:* "I knew that writers and artists were intimidated, but I accepted this as a necessity of socialism, even as I accepted all else that I have enumerated as a necessity of socialism." But Fast, too, remained steadfast for "socialism": "If of any value, [the Soviet Union] still has in me a friend—a man whose devotion to socialism and to social justice has not been shaken." [54]

The tide of the struggle within the party now clearly was with Gates and his supporters. Had there been a freely elected convention of the party in June, it surely would have reshaped the organization and adopted a line into some kind of "national communist" position closer to social democracy than the party had ever been. There even was some sentiment—how much will never be known—for dissolving the party altogether. Howard Fast wrote months after the fact that if there had been a party convention in June, the party would have been liquidated.[55] At the time, a party journalist, Sam Coleman, asserted in a letter to the *Daily Worker* that there were no national leaders for liquidation and few in the rank and file.[56] Obviously, hundreds of members quietly walked out on the party during the summer of 1956. To use an old radical party expression, they "voted with their feet." To these people, even Gates's national communism was a middle position.

Dennis's finger detected the stronger breeze. He wrote an article for the *Daily Worker* of June 18—the chronology becomes important here—in which he yielded a little more to that paper's position than he had before. He wrote that "The crimes and brutalities that sullied the latter period of Stalin's leadership are unforgivable" and deplored the "snuffing out the lives of more than a score of Jewish cultural figures." At the same time, Stalin's Russia had become an industrial power, had "wiped out illiteracy," and had given workers and farmers "status and dignity undreamed of under the Czars, and, in many ways, unmatched in the advanced capitalist nations." He disassociated himself from "ideas expressed in some of the letters, articles, and editorials appearing in the Daily Worker." He would not minimize the errors, but he could not "accept the viewpoint that wipes out and undermines pride and confidence in the Socialist countries." [57]

On June 24, the national committee of the party adopted and issued a statement a little stronger than earlier ones, although it had much of the on-the-one-hand-but-then-on-the-other-hand flavor that characterized the resolutions of the divided national committee. The "mistakes" in Russia "were primarily a result of wrong policies and concepts arising, in part, out of the fact that the Soviet Union was the pioneering land of socialism and was surrounded for decades by a hostile capitalist world." But on the other hand: "Khrushchev's contribution to the exposure of mistakes and to the process of correction . . . makes only a beginning in this direction. We cannot accept an analysis of such profound mistakes which attributes them solely to the capricious aberrations of a single individual, no matter how much arbitrary power he was wrongly permitted to usurp." The statement was also strong on the disclosures of Soviet anti-Semitism. "We are deeply disturbed by facts revealed in information coming from Poland that organs and media of Jewish culture were summarily dissolved and a number of Jewish leaders executed. This is contrary to the Soviet Union's historic contributions on the Jewish question. Khrushchev's failure to deal with these outrages, and the continuing silence of Soviet leaders, require an explanation." [58] The statement was a compromise between the Gates and Foster tendencies, yet it went farther in the direction of an independent attitude toward the Soviet party than any official statement ever had before.

The Communist parties of Western Europe began to kick up their heels a little, too. In an interview on June 16, Palmiro Togliatti, leader of the Italian party, went so far as to say that, although the twentieth congress "greatly aided the proper understanding and solution" of serious problems, "it is not possible . . . to consider satisfactory the position which was taken at the Congress and which today is being fully developed in the Soviet press regarding the errors of Stalin and the causes and conditions which made them possible." Quickly, the Danish, Norwegian, Finnish, and Belgian parties hailed the Togliatti interview.[59] By the end of June, the ferment of the Communist parties made itself felt in Poland. On June 28, the workers of Poznan rebelled, demanding "bread and freedom." In what was to become a pattern in East Europe, the object of the rioters' wrath was a building which housed the local state-security police. By June 30, artillery and tanks had crushed the revolt, leaving about five hundred dead in their wake.[60] The *Daily Worker* recognized the righteousness of the rebels' cause but argued that the American State Department had cynically exploited the Poles' just grievances and instigated the rebellion.[61]

At this point, the Russian party stopped short, surveyed the effects of the Khrushchev speech, and decided that matters had got too far out of hand. It had already, on June 27, in an effort to stop the heresy developing in the Western parties, published in *Pravda* a translation of Dennis's article of June 18, one of the least critical written by a Western Communist leader, deleting Dennis's adverse comments on Russian anti-Semitism.[62] (Publication in Moscow, despite the deletions, did wonders for Dennis's ego.) Now, on

June 30, as soldiers in Poznan were completing the quelling of the rebellion, the central committee of the Soviet party met and adopted a resolution "On Overcoming the Personality Cult and Its Consequences." *Pravda* published the resolution on July 2.

The central committee's resolution was remarkably like Foster's columns on the twentieth congress, although the resolution nowhere mentioned Foster and did mention and quote favorably from Dennis's article of June 18. The reactionary imperialists, said the resolution, were trying to exploit the revelations about Stalin "to undermine the trust of the working people in the first socialist country in the world." Washington had financed the "anti-people's demonstrations" in Poznan, but the Poznan "provocateurs and . . . diversionists" had lost their courage before the opposition of the Polish workers.

The main purpose of the resolution was to set aright "certain of our friends abroad" who did not fully understand the question of the cult of personality and "sometimes give incorrect interpretations of certain points." The central committee singled out Togliatti specifically for "incorrect tenets." The resolution dealt at some length with a question that had bothered many Communists: "How could the cult of the person of J. V. Stalin, with all its negative consequences, have arisen and become widespread under conditions of the Soviet socialist system?" The Russians really added nothing in reply to this question that Soviet apologists had not already written. A "besieged fortress encircled by capitalism," Russia had had to contend with enemy spies and diversionists as well as "Trotskyists, right-wing opportunists and bourgeois nationalists." In other words, Stalinism had not derived from socialism and was not the fault of the Russians; it was the result of capitalist opposition to socialism and the fault of the Western imperialists. And despite Stalin, the Soviets had performed miracles of production because they had a socialist state. Now that Stalin was dead—and it had been "impossible" to do anything about his mistakes before he died because any action against him "would not have been understood by the people"—the party was eliminating the results of the personality cult and "restoring Bolshevik norms of Party Life." Reports of a crisis of communism or confusion in communist ranks were only "fables" concocted by "bourgeois ideologists," only "malicious, slanderous attacks by our enemies." [63]

At any earlier time in the history of the American Communists, such Russian actions as the publication of Dennis's article with significant deletions and the resolution of the central committee would have brought capitulation to the Russians and an end to further dissent. But in 1956, the Russians could not silence the dissent from afar. The exhilarating effect of freer air and the fight between the hards and the softs had gone too far and too long to be stopped, despite the Soviets' obvious wishes. Foster, in an article with the significant title "Achievements as Well as Mistakes," went all the way in agreement with the Russians' resolution. He also warned the party that it was still "a worthy part of this great, constructive world movement." [64] Dennis was only slightly more reserved in his endorsement of the resolution. The central committee's action "is a most welcome development," and the resolution "goes a long way in explaining—while clearly not justifying—what has become known as the growth of the cult of the individual." [65]

The *Daily Worker* staff dissented. A Gates editorial interpreted the Russian resolution as another round in "a fraternal, critical discussion, conducted on an equal basis among Marxists," although clearly the central committee of the Soviet party had intended their statement to be the last word. "In the latest chapter of this discussion," the Soviet party "has now given its reply to some of these questions. Many Marxists will feel satisfied with the answers which the Soviet Communist Party now presents. Many will feel that the final answers still need to be found and that the discussion must continue." And to emphasize that they would continue the discussion, the *Daily Worker* staff published in the same issue a statement of the Canadian party's national committee which termed Khrushchev's explanations as "inadequate" and a column by the paper's foreign editor, Joseph Clark, which called the Russian deletion of Dennis's comment on anti-Semitism lacking in "full truth and candor." "It is a tragic fact, as Dennis put it, that 'the lives of more than a score of Jewish figures' were snuffed out. They can't be brought back to life by snuffing out a clause in an article." [66] Two days later, the *Daily Worker* printed the Togliatti interview of June 16, which the Soviet resolution had specifically indicted.[67] The paper continued to publish letters that were critical of the Russian silence on anti-Semitism and that were quite critical of Foster. One letter, from a party member of twenty-two years' standing, urged Foster to "stop parroting alibis." [68] Nevertheless, the *Daily Worker* calmed down after the publication of the Soviet resolution. It did not capitulate, and it did occasionally publish some dissenting thought; but it did not have the fire that it had in June.

The national committee of the American party met again on July 19 and adopted a statement on the Soviet resolution of June 30. The statement, not released to the press, not even to the *Daily Worker,* until July 25, represented still another compromise between the Foster "hards" and the Gates "softs"; the hards clearly had gained ground. Compared with the national committee's statement of the previous month, it was a pallid document indeed. The new statement called the Soviet resolution "a most valuable and important contribution." It denounced, as had the Russian resolution, the efforts of "certain monopolist circles" to use the discussion within international Communism for their own ends, and it declared that "nothing will ever shake [the Communist party's] firm adherence to the principle of international working class solidarity." The statement did make reservations about the central committee's resolution, although they were mildly stated: "We believe certain aspects of the origins and effects of past violations of socialist law and principle need, and will receive, further study and discussion. Among these are: the question of bureaucratic distortions in a Socialist society, as well as the happenings in the sphere of Jewish cultural institutions and their leadership."

"Bureaucratic distortions" replaced such words as "murder," and even Dennis's phrase "snuffing out" became only "happenings." Still, the statement was too strong for Foster, who would not consent to criticizing the Soviets for anything that they had not already criticized themselves. That was his consistent position throughout the crisis. He voted against the statement, but his sole negative vote was never publicly disclosed.[69]

When the New York *Times* reported, "The American Communist party, a bit grudgingly and somewhat later than its fellow parties, toed the Moscow line on post-Stalin policy yesterday," Gates took exception to its interpretation. He emphasized the "bureaucratic distortions" phrase and defended the national committee statement.[70] Not all Communists defended the statement. *Party Voice* published an anonymous criticism of the statement, presumably with the permission of the New York State organization.[71] Apparently, the statement was too strong for the Russians. *Pravda* published the statements of many of the Western parties on the June 30 resolution, but the Russians never mentioned the American party's statement.

If the Gates wing soft-pedaled on the matter of the party's relations with the Russians, it did not let up in its criticism of the hards on other matters. After the June meeting of the national committee, the party initiated a series of "discussion articles" in each Sunday's *Worker*. From this series were supposed to come the ideas upon which the draft resolution for the party convention would be written. Gates supporters, especially people in the leadership of the New York organization, dominated this discussion in every respect.

The Foster wing of the party expressed no new ideas—indeed, the hards scarcely bothered themselves at all. Benjamin J. Davis went along with Foster in a kind of "positive thinking" about the party's recent past. There had been some mistakes, yes, but these were being overemphasized and "we should not go overboard." [72] One old-timer who signed himself "Jarama" made it clear that he thought the Russians ought to do something about Gates and the *Daily Worker* staff. "It took the intercession of the Communist International to help us get rid of Lovestone & Company with his theory of exceptionalism. . . . It took the comradely advice of Jacques Duclos to break the hold that Browder . . . had on our Party." Now help was needed again. "Jarama" thought even Dennis was too unorthodox. Dennis's report in May had been called *The Communists Take a New Look,* and "Jarama" was satisfied there was nothing wrong with the old one.[73]

Week after week, the Gatesites or those who tended in his direction called for a thorough overhaul of the party. The party's organization, "borrowed hook, line, and sinker from the Communist Party of the Soviet Union" had to be replaced with a "structure conforming to a Party with a line of peaceful transition to socialism, a Party based on American democratic traditions of organization." The party must "boldly free itself from the fetters of dogmatic adherence to any political line which can be misconstrued as not reflecting the national interests of the American working class and people." New tactics, new line, new everything.[74]

The party softs, or "liberals," it was clear, had vigor and passion, and they knew precisely what they did not like about the party. But they never determined exactly what they were for. They were unable to formulate precisely what the new line and the new tactics should be. Just how and to just what purpose the party should break out of the isolation to which Foster's leadership had led it were questions they never answered.

FOSTER COUNTERATTACKS

Late in the summer of 1956, a special subcommittee of the party's national committee was busy writing a draft resolution. Party custom decreed there should be such a document, which would serve as a basis for further discussion and then be ratified at the national party convention, already postponed from December until February 9-12, 1957.

The national committee adopted a draft resolution on September 13 and released it for publication on September 23. A document of about 23,000 words, the draft resolution began with a relatively calm analysis of the problems confronting America. Prosperity was not stable, although the party did not expect an economic crisis soon. A socialist economy was "the only basic answer," but meanwhile the party endorsed and supported the "forward looking domestic and legislative proposals of the labor movement and other democratic organizations for economic betterment and social welfare." The party stated its support of peaceful coexistence with the Soviet Union and other communist countries but did not attack imperialism with its old-fashioned abandon. The document declared the party's support of the absolute abolition of Jim Crow and ended its first section with a defense of the Bill of Rights and civil liberties generally.

A section on political and economic reform did not differ substantially from what a group of militant New Dealers might have written. The party would limit the power of monopolies, cease tax favors to big business, strengthen the labor movement, and introduce such political reforms as abolition of the electoral college and gerrymandering. The party declared its faith that someday the working class would have its own political party, perhaps the Democratic Party, perhaps a farmer-labor party. Another section, on "The American Road to Socialism," had little to say about what that road was like beyond saying that socialism was not the immediate order of the day in America and that the party sought "the broadest possible unity of all socialist-minded elements," or, in other words, a united front.

The last section of the draft resolution, comprising about one-third of the total, had to do with the party's past errors and weaknesses. It contained nothing new to one who had followed the discussion. "Left sectarianism" had led the party to overestimate the danger of war and fascism and had led to its isolation from the labor and Negro movements. The party must stand with other Communist parties as brothers, mutually helpful and critical, rather than as father and son. In the past, the resolution confessed, the party had "tended to accept uncritically many views of Marxists of other countries . . . some [of which] did not correspond to American conditions." And the document urged some modifications of party structure and procedure, which if observed would reduce the party bureaucracy's power and lessen the separation between the leadership and the rank and file.[75]

The draft resolution obviously represented a repudiation of the kind of leadership Foster had given the party since 1945. On the other hand, it did not represent a total victory for Gates, the *Daily Worker* staff generally, and many of the New York party leaders, although it was closer to their position than to Foster's, because it in many places expressed the new ideas rocking the party in a compromising and weaseling way. The party only "tended" to follow the Russians. Although Left sectarianism was the "main danger," the party must "maintain its vigilance against right opportunist tendencies." The slogan of "self-determination for the Negro nation of the southern Black Belt" needed only reappraisal. Clearly, the national committee majority in September 1956, when it adopted the draft resolution, was between the Gates and Foster poles, although closer to Gates than it was to Foster.

Thirteen members of the national committee voted on the adoption of the draft resolution. Three others had been deported and six were in prison. Foster and Davis voted for the draft resolution only with qualifications, which they announced they would later publish. The others—Eugene Dennis, Fred Fine, John Gates, James Jackson, Claude Lightfoot, William Schneiderman, Jacob Stachel, Sidney Stein, Martha Stone, Ed Strong, and Carl Winter —voted yes without qualifications.[76] How the members who could not be at the meeting would have voted is a matter of conjecture. Williamson, deported to England, probably would have sided with Foster, and Green, then in a federal penitentiary, probably would have sided with Gates.

Foster voted his qualified yes only in the interests of party unity. He obviously could not have really endorsed the draft resolution; endorsement would have meant repudiating all he had written for months and admitting gross misleadership of the party. But the yes was only temporary.

On Sunday night, September 23, at about ten o'clock, the first edition of the next day's New York *Times* hit the streets. The edition carried a story by Harry Schwartz, one of the *Times*'s Soviet specialists, which was dropped from subsequent editions by space limitations imposed by later stories. Schwartz's article was about a review of Foster's *The Negro People in American History* that had just appeared in *Pravda*. The review was less of an examination of the book than a eulogy of its author. "Soviet people know Comrade Foster as a fighter for peace, democracy and socialism, as a noted figure in the international Communist and workers' movement . . . he well knows the needs and aspirations of the workers of his country. Thirty-five years of his life Comrade Foster has devoted to the struggle for the purity and unity of the Communist party of the U.S.A. against opportunists and diversionists . . . in the spirit of firm loyalty to the teachings of Marxism-Leninism." [77] Apparently, Foster first learned of his new accolade by reading the *Times* story. With this Russian feather in his party cap, Foster went back to fighting for "purity" and against "opportunists and diversionists." The next morning, he changed his vote on the draft resolution to a flat no.[78]

Foster hastened to the counterattack. The adoption of the draft resolution had been the nadir of Foster's power. After the *Pravda* review, he began a comeback. Within eight days, he had written a 15,000-word blast at the "opportunists and diversionists" for the October issue of *Political Affairs*. So eager was he to have his denunciation circulated that he released it on October 2, several days before the magazine appeared.[79] The main trouble with the draft resolution, Foster wrote, was that it "weakens seriously the Party's stand on Marxism-Leninism." It was for "firm loyalty to the teachings of Marxism-Leninism" that he had received *Pravda*'s blessing. Foster objected most strenuously to two sentences in the draft resolution: "Basing ourselves on these Marxist-

Leninist principles as *interpreted by the Communist Party of our country,* we must learn much better how to extract from the rich body of this theory that which is universally valid, combining it with the specific experiences of the American working class in the struggle for socialism in the United States. The Party must distinguish better between the additions to Marxist theory made by Lenin which are valid for all countries and those specific aspects of Lenin's writing which reflect exclusively certain unique features of the Russian revolution or Soviet society." [80] To Foster, the statement was nationalist heresy. The party should unqualifiedly endorse Marxism-Leninism; to do less would be to reduce Marxism-Leninism "to the status of a Russian Socialist philosophy, subject to a maze of national 'interpretations' before adoption." Then, in a nice revelation of his political ethics, he wrote, "If we were just forming our Party the questions of whether or not we should put the words 'Marxism-Leninism' into the Preamble would not be a too important tactical matter, but to take them out of that document . . . will be understood only as a major ideological retreat."

And the members' incessant talking about party errors irked Foster thoroughly. He conceded that the party had made some mistakes, but they had been only tactical in nature. The line had been "correct." The "Right tendency in the Party" "exaggerated," even "manufactured" alleged errors. Emphasis on errors "is . . . but a form of self destruction for the Party. It definitely originates in and feeds the plague of pessimism and liquidationism now afflicting the Party." Such emphasis must be erased from the draft resolution. The party was isolated, Foster admitted, but alleged errors had little or nothing to do with the isolation. The isolation was altogether the result of "objective conditions," pressures on the party from the outside during the cold war.

Foster injected a personal note into the party discussion. Before his article, the national party leaders had not singled out other party leaders for individual attack in their published writings, although some of the rank and file in the letters to the *Daily*

Worker pinpointed their criticisms by name. But now Foster minced no words. He was especially critical of Gates, Joseph Clark, and Joseph Starobin, a former party member and also once the *Daily Worker's* foreign editor. These people were guilty of inner-party "agitation" and "factionalism," he charged, as well as representatives of a dangerous "Right tendency." [81] Foster had taken off the gloves and put on brass knuckles. It was time for Gates and his followers to keep up their guard, for the old party chairman was a veteran at party infighting. He had won inner-party fights before Gates was out of grade school, and this experience was of considerable advantage over the party "liberals," none of whom had ever engaged in anything rougher than the relatively easy ousting of Browder in 1945. Gates was still in the army then and did not have even that experience.

Gates did not counterattack. No one fought back immediately. The *Daily Worker* concerned itself with the World Series—it was for the Dodgers, who had several Negro players and who lost— and the Presidential election—it mildly supported Stevenson and Kefauver, who ignored the Communists and who also lost. In a debate over the draft resolution at the Jefferson School on October 5, Sidney Stein, a national committee member who leaned in Gates's direction, did not even mention Foster's blast. (Incidentally, another speaker that evening, *National Guardian* publisher McManus, indicated that the fellow travelers were still to the "left" of the party; the draft resolution did not come out for socialism hard enough for McManus.[82]) There was nothing in the October issue of *Party Voice,* which, as the journal of the New York party, followed the Gates line, to indicate recognition that Foster had given the party battle a new character. Perhaps they were bemused by Decca Truehaft's recently published satire on Communist language, which applied her sister Nancy Mitford's method in her account of English upper-class and non-upper-class speech with sometimes humorous results. "Tell me not in mournful numbers / Life is but an empty dream" becomes in Communist language, wrote Mrs. Truehaft, "Do not project to me in moods of pessimism and despair / The perspective that no positive conclusions can be drawn from the present relationship of forces." [83] That Communists could laugh at satires of themselves indicated there was a new mood in the movement.

Foster, however, was not able to capitalize on the lethargy of his party enemies. Before everyone in the party could finish reading his long October 1956 article, events in Hungary and Poland were building up to a climax which would precipitate another party uproar. Communists in those countries were soon to come into open conflict with the Russians. The "fraternal" discussion was soon to become fratricidal.

TEN: HUNGARY AND FURTHER DISILLUSION

In the history books of another generation, the year 1956 will live as a year of revolution in some ways similar to 1848. Poland and then Hungary, each with a long history of nationalism, rebelled against Russian imperialism and yet remained Communist. These revolutions staggered the American Communist Party at least as much as Khrushchev's denunciation of Stalin a few months earlier.

In mid-October, the central committee of the Polish Communist Party named Wladyslaw Gomulka to join their body. Gomulka, only a few months before in a Stalinist prison, had come to symbolize the desire within Polish Communism for greater independence from Moscow. The term "national communist" is commonly applied to Gomulka, and it shall be used here in preference to coining a new term. The term is misleading in a sense, for it implies that the Russian Communists were internationalists and that the Poles, for example, were not. Surely the Russian Communists were at least as nationalistic as the Poles, and the Russians' "internationalism" was largely only a device for carrying Russian nationalism beyond its borders. After the Polish central committee appointed Gomulka, its members resigned in order to clear the way for Gomulka's election to party leadership. While the central committee deliberated, Khrushchev and other Soviet leaders arrived in Warsaw in an attempt to prevent Polish "liberalization." In a face-to-face showdown the Poles defied the Russians and elected Gomulka. When Russian troops started to enter Poland from the East German border, Polish troops fired at them and the Russian troops withdrew. Although the Russians had the power to crush any Polish rebellion, they realized that Gomulka had popular and well-disciplined support, especially among the workers and the students, and they restrained themselves rather than precipitate a bloody revolt. The Poles, knowing they would be crushed if they pushed the Russians too far, similarly restrained themselves. The Poles gained a measure of independence nevertheless.

Before the Polish crisis was over, on October 23, to be exact, the Hungarians tried to follow the Poles' example. Thousands of national communists demonstrated in Budapest, demanding that the Russians leave. When security police fired into the crowd, the demonstrators rioted and pulled down statues of Stalin. The next day, when ten thousand Russian troops entered Budapest, Erno Gero, who had called for the Russian military force, yielded the premiership to Imre Nagy. Fighting between the Hungarians and the Russians continued until October 29 during negotiations for Russian withdrawal. On October 30, the Russians began to withdraw from Budapest, leaving the rebels in control of the city. At the end of October, the rebel national committee in both Poland and Hungary seemed to have won.

American Communists, with only some Stalinist dissent, hailed the events in East Europe. The *Daily Worker* proclaimed in bold headlines "POLES CHEER MOVES TOWARD DEMOCRACY. DEMONSTRATE FOR INDEPENDENCE, FRIENDLY TIES WITH U.S.S.R." An editorial praised the Poles for "advancing the democratization and independence of their socialist regime" and Gomulka as "the champion of the independent Polish path to socialism." Gates had strong things to say about Washington. "We strongly condemn the efforts of the Eisenhower administration" to exploit the Polish situation for its own advantage. But he was also critical of Moscow. "We believe that Pravda had a right to discuss what it didn't approve of in Poland, just as the Polish press has the right to disagree with Pravda. We are dubious, however, of imputing on a blanket scale to sections of the Polish press, the desire to restore capitalism. This sounds too much like some of the unjustified criticism made of Yugoslavia in 1948." [1] Two days later, managing editor Max further criticized "the way Pravda unjustly (in our opinion) impugned the motive of the Polish press." [2]

The first events in Hungary likewise brought approval from American Communists. When Hungarian security police and national communist demonstrators clashed, the *Daily Worker* declared that "it is doubly a tragedy that it is in a country of socialism that this violent eruption occurs," but told its readers, "There is a forward movement in Hungary . . . symbolized by the restoration of Imre Nagy to the premiership." There was a danger from "Counter-revolutionaries and outright supporters of the former Horthy dictatorship," but the *Daily Worker* editors were confident that "out of these tragic events . . . socialism will be strengthened." [3] In a series of *Daily Worker* editorials from October 29 to November 1, Gates developed the thesis that the Hungarian and Polish revolutions proved that "Stalinist repression" was not in the best interests of communism. In Poland, Gomulka "acted in time to uproot the remnants of Stalinist repression," but in Hungary, Rakosi and Gero had "relied on force and repression instead of on the democratic aspirations of the people." Their Stalinist tactics, supported by the Soviet Union, had led to the growth of anti-Communist reaction, leaving Nagy not only the problem of the Stalinists, but a problem of rightist reaction. The Hungarian revolution, wrote Gates, was not "merely a plot planned from the outside." "To persist in the theory . . . is to fall into profound error." And Gates was explicit in his criticism of the *present* leadership in the Soviet Union. "Soviet delegate [to the U.N.] Sobolev . . . flew in the face of facts when he described the Hungarian upsurge as the work of a pro-fascist underground. It was the 20th Congress of the Soviet Communist Party which registered the need for ending with Stalinism. And the Soviet Union itself is making changes in the direction of democratization. However, this process is too slow and hesitant, as the Soviet actions in the Polish and Hungarian crises demonstrate." There were, wrote Gates, deep lessons for the American party in recent East European history: "Socialism will triumph if it proves its superiority to capitalism in every respect. It cannot triumph by repression or violations of democracy." [4]

This was strong language, even for a *Daily Worker* editorial. American Communists felt very strongly about Poland and Hungary, so strongly that on November 1 the New York City residents of the party's national committee met and adopted a statement that put the committee "fully in accord" with the *Daily Worker* editorials and did some criticizing of its own. The Soviet Government in a statement of October 30 had said it was "consistently putting into practice these historical decisions of the 20th Congress, which create conditions for the further strengthening of the friendship and cooperation between Socialist countries and the inviolable basis of maintaining the complete sovereignty of every Socialist state." The national committee denied the Soviet statement: "The events in Poland and Hungary show that despite the promises of the 20th Congress which aroused great expectations, these principles are yet to be fully applied in practice."

The national committee statement was, of course, too independent for some of its members. Foster did not attend the meeting. James Jackson, an alternate committee member, voted yes only with qualifications. Dennis and Davis abstained. Three dissenting members besides Foster indicated a gain for the Foster wing of the leadership. Dennis said he agreed "with many of the views set forth"; what his agreement was is difficult to ascertain in view of his stated disagreements. The statement, said Dennis, "minimized the primary responsibility" of the Polish and Hungarian parties "for the erroneous policies they pursued." The statement also failed to "appreciate the steps being taken to rectify the previous unequal and incorrect relationships" between the satellite and Russian parties. Dennis objected, too, that the statement did not adequately express "the vital principles of international working class and socialist solidarity," was wrong in saying the Nagy government was "oriented in a democratic socialist direction," and failed to analyze the effect upon Hungary of the State Department's "liberation" policy.[5]

The national committee adopted this statement on a Thursday. Over the weekend, before the statement was even published, the situation in Hungary changed tragically. On Sunday, November 4, hundreds of Russian tanks rolled back into Budapest to quell the rebellion with massive savagery. The Hungarians, armed only with light arms, hand grenades, and home-made gasoline bombs which had acquired, ironically, the name "Molotov cocktails," fought back as best they could, but their resistance was futile. Nagy took refuge in the Yugoslav Embassy, only to be kidnaped and taken to Romania a few days later when out of the embassy on a Communist-issued safe-conduct. About 80,000 Hungarians fled across the Austrian border while others staged a general strike against the Russians. The Russian-installed regime of Janos Kadar broke the strike. By the end of November, the revolution had been lost.

Most fortunately for Communist propagandists the world over, the Soviet military action in Hungary was not the only major military action of that last tense weekend before the American Presidential elections. Earlier in the week, the Israelis had invaded the Sinai Peninsula, and over the weekend British and French troops invaded Egypt to gain control of the Suez Canal, which the Egyptians promptly sabotaged. In the United Nations, the United States and Russia voted together for a cease-fire, which Britain, France, Israel, and Egypt accepted on November 6. The Egyptian invasion gave the Communists a chance to look the other way on Hungary and scream about what the "western imperialist warmongers" were doing. The party's national committee issued on November 5, the day before Election, a statement on the Egyptian crisis that bristled with words like "brutal aggression" and "flagrant violation," that congratulated Eisenhower for "belatedly" attempting to "extinguish the fires which Dulles' brinkmanship helped ignite," and that condemned Adlai Stevenson for his criticism of Eisenhower's policy in the U.N.[6]

Not all American Communists looked the other way. John Gates began his first editorial after the second Russian intervention "with a heavy heart in view of the weekend's renewed fighting in Hungary and the use of Soviet troops there." The Soviet intervention in Hungary "retards the development of socialism because socialism cannot be imposed on a country by force." Then Gates made a sweeping proposal: "We are for the withdrawal of all troops from all countries to their own borders. We are for the right of all people, the Hungarian people as well as those of Cyprus, of Egypt, of Israel, of Kenya, of Okinawa—the list could be greatly extended—to rule themselves in complete independence." He made it clear that he included the withdrawal of United States troops from West Germany and of Russian troops from East Germany.[7] Two days later, Max and Clark took similar positions. They conceded that reaction in Hungary had grown before the second Soviet intervention and that Nagy's decision to withdraw from the Warsaw Pact—the Communist N.A.T.O.—made the Russian decision to intervene again "probably inevitable." Here Max raised an embarrassing point. "To say that such a decision was inevitable only emphasizes the tragic errors of 11 years of Stalinist rule. Think of the implications," continued Max, "of the fact that Hungary, after eleven years of a certain kind of Communist rule, faced a fascist resurgence, while West Germany after 11 years of Adenauer faces a labor-backed Social-Democratic victory in the next election!" The Soviet intervention solved nothing; it "can only bring on new woes . . . socialism cannot be imported on bayonets." [8] The *Daily Worker* reprinted an editorial from the *Daily People's World* of San Francisco written by Al Richmond. The Soviet occupation of Hungary and its support of the puppet Kadar regime, wrote Richmond, "will only further discredit socialism in Hungary, and will greatly diminish its prestige on a world-wide scale." Richmond was particularly concerned about the conclusion that rebels in colonial areas could not help but make after the Soviets had quelled Hungarian independence.[9]

Such editorials as these sharply divided the party, divided it more than had the debate over the Khrushchev speech or the disagreement over how serious had been the errors of the American party of the past several years. The division was sharper because now some Communists were criticizing what the Russian Communists were doing currently rather than what the Russians admitted had been done in the past. The *Daily Worker* had actually published editorials critical of contemporary Russian Communist leaders, an unprecedented action. The party newspaper violated the actual but unadmitted Communist Party cardinal principle that American Communists must defend the Soviet Union and follow the Russian Communist example. To refuse to support and imitate the Russians was the ultimate Communist heresy. Such heresy in *Daily Worker* columns inevitably disturbed the faithful.

Letters from outraged readers poured in. A group of Michigan Communists wrote that they were "extremely disturbed" by the paper's "overwhelmingly negative approach." One old party member called the *Daily Worker* "anti-Marxist-Leninist and anti-workingclass," declaring that it and the New York State organization were full of "the right danger." Still another accused the *Daily Worker* staff of Red baiting.[10] Leaders as well as rank and filers were alarmed. Dennis wrote a letter to the paper in which he declared that the Soviet intervention was "anti-fascist and pro-peace," condemned one of Clark's columns as reaching "a new low," and charged that the editors were lacking in "Marxist, scientific, working class outlook."[11] James Allen blasted the *Daily Worker* editorial of November 5 in a long article.[12]

Yet the paper had its supporters. The Connecticut State organization declared that it "completely opposes and condemns the intervention of the Soviet army in the present Hungarian situation."[13] Enough Communist leaders agreed with Gates and his colleagues on the Hungarian question that the second national committee statement on Hungary, adopted November 18, was a compromise between the hard and soft tendencies.

The national committee met on Sunday, November 18, two weeks after the second Soviet intervention, determined to write a statement on Hungary that would minimize the differences between party factions. The result was one of the most obviously compromised national committee statements in party history. Neither Gates nor Foster and Dennis won the day. "We do not seek to justify the use of Soviet troops in Hungary's internal crisis on November 4. Neither do we join in the condemnation of these actions. . . . On this there are different viewpoints in the National Committee and the Party. With the unfolding of events further clarity on this point will be achieved." [14] Gates indicated what he thought of the statement by printing alongside it a long article by the paper's sports editor, Lester Rodney, who stated his views on the Soviet intervention in no uncertain terms. Rodney could "not understand how we can condone in any way the forcible imposition of an unwanted government on a people by the armed forces of another country and still speak to our fellow Americans about each nation's own path to socialism." As for alleged fascism developing in Nagy's Hungary: "I am afraid I no longer have confidence in the ability of the Soviet leaders to decide when a nation is fascist or going fascist. Eight years ago we were told that Yugoslavia was fascist." [15] Foster revealed what he thought of the statement when he announced he had voted against it.[16]

The national committee's effort to compromise differences was futile. Neither side would back down. In a *Daily Worker* article as long as the national committee statement, Dennis indicated that he could never condone the heresy of criticizing the Soviets. Those who condemned the Soviet actions in Hungary, Dennis wrote, "made the mistake of looking at [the Soviet Union] through the eyes of the American imperialists." [17] And Gates indicated he would not change his position even when he was criticized in Moscow. *Kommunist,* theoretical magazine of the Russian party, declared that the *Daily Worker* had been "babbling" and said it had "equated" Soviet actions in Hungary with the invasion of Egypt. Gates replied that "we do not 'equate' the events in Hungary with the imperialist invasion of Egypt. But neither do we condone Soviet policies in Hungary or those of the Hungarian Communist Party." He requested *Kommunist* to publish his reply and his other editorials on the subject.[18]

BOLTING THE PARTY

In the fall of 1956, the strife within the party was sharp enough to end in a party split, and at any earlier time in Communist history the party probably would have divided. But now it was clear that neither side stood to gain from a split. The party was small enough—and getting smaller every day—without splintering off into even smaller sects. Each side had seen enough Communist splinter groups to recognize the futility of that kind of activity. And although the Gates wing of the party talked about organizing a new, broadly based party of socialism, they really knew the idea was a pipe dream, that the record of the Communists prevented most non-Communists from participating in such an organization. Hundreds and hundreds of ordinary rank-and-file members saw the situation as hopeless and quit. But most officials were not yet ready to take the plunge into the cold, difficult world of the ex-Communist. Most of them decided to battle on until the convention in February and try to "win the franchise."

Several prominent Communists did leave the party after the Hungarian crisis. Howard Fast, still in the emotional turmoil that characterized his column on the Khrushchev speech, left quietly without announcement. His leaving made no stir until New York newspapers discovered his resignation in February 1957.[19] John Steuben, editor of *March of Labor,* left the party after the Kadar government threatened to execute strikers, making the eloquent request that he be allowed to live out his life "in agony and silence." [20] (Steuben, who had serious heart trouble, died only a few months later. Foster, Dennis, and Davis, who had once been close to him, did not attend the funeral.) Stetson Kennedy, who never admitted to being more than a fellow traveler but who nevertheless wrote for several party publications, had been in Budapest at the time of the revolt. He fled to Belgrade with his family and denounced Stalinism.[21] Another former American Communist, John Santo, formerly organization director of Mike Quill's Transport Workers Union, left Communism in a dramatic fashion. In 1949, Santo had been deported to Hungary, his country of birth. There he had become an important government official, in charge of the meat division of the Hungarian Ministry of Public Supply. In November 1956, he and his family fled to Austria, where he denounced the "dictatorship against the proletariat." He revealed that in Hungary he had always lived in fear, keeping a small traveling bag packed to take along if the secret police arrived at three o'clock in the morning, "their favorite hour." [22] The emotion of the factional fight was sharply revealed when Mrs. Santo, an American citizen by birth, arrived at New York's Idlewild Airport from Vienna. After she told newspapermen at the airport that Communist Hungary was "no place for an American woman," a woman relative there to meet her told her to say nothing more to the press. When she tried to go ahead in her talk with reporters, she and her relative engaged in a quarrel in which they slapped one another.[23] Ideological warfare infected even family homecomings.

How many members left the party in the fall of 1956 will never be known since the Communists did not conduct a party registration until the spring of 1958. Yet party officials knew that hundreds were quietly leaving.[24] No one will ever know with any certainty how many of the members who remained in the party leaned in the Gates direction and how many supported Foster and Dennis, although it is clear that until the convention in February 1957, the liberals, or softs, outnumbered the Fosterites. These softs by no means supported Gates completely. They represented quite a range on the party's political spectrum.

There was an interesting sociological pattern to the positions adopted by sections of the party membership. Age, length of party tenure, ethnic background, and the extent of experience outside the party's own little world often determined whether one supported Foster orthodoxy or advocated considerable change within the party, whether one stayed with the party until the bitter end or quit it altogether. There were many exceptions, of course, but the younger people, those who had come into the party during the Depression, those whose contacts with non-Communists had been wide, and those who were fairly well in the main stream of American culture tended in Gates's direction.

Almost all of the *Daily Worker* staff and the leaders of the organization in New York and California, the party's strongest states, were of the party's Depression generation. They were no longer youngsters, of course—the party's average age in 1956 was over forty—but they were younger in years than the hards and they had not been in the party as long. The symbols of the two extremes, Foster and Gates, indicated the difference. Foster was born in 1881, claimed to have first become associated with Marxist movements while still an adolescent in the 1890's, and joined the party in the early 1920's. Gates was born in 1914 and joined the party in 1931.

Foster had for years been an "inside" man in the party, and Gates had looked outward. Foster, of course, had wide trade-union experience as a young man, but in 1932 he had a serious heart attack which changed the direction of his life. For five years, he was in bed most of the time, seeing only other Communists, reading mostly party literature. When he recovered sufficiently to lead a fairly normal life, his political isolation remained. Gates, on the other hand, had tried to organize steelworkers in the 1930's, had seen a great deal of non-Communists in military service, and as *Daily Worker* editor had been obligated to look at the "outside" world and interpret it for his readers in terms of the party line. With fairly few exceptions, those who labored in the party's national headquarters administering the party's internal organization resisted change within the party. Those whose experience had been in trade unions or other "mass organizations" or in party journalism were for various degrees of change in the party's line and organization.

Those who were in one or another of America's subcultures also tended to support the Foster position. The party's Negroes and foreign-language groups, of which the largest was Yiddish speaking, were relatively isolated from the "outside" world. They lived in what amounted to ghettos and worked and associated with people much like themselves. Their contacts with the general American culture were few. Furthermore, except for the Negroes, these culturally isolated Communists were at least middle-aged and with long standing in the party. To them it did not make much difference personally if the party led a viable movement or not; they were old and tired, seeking more of an ideological old people's home than a vigorous political movement. They had fought their wars. They had been the backbone of the International Workers Order and still held that defunct organization's bargain insurance policies. They had seen their children grow up as Americans, reject their immigrant background and language, improve themselves economically, and move out of the lower-class ghetto. Now these old people read the *Freiheit*—whose circulation was greater than the *Daily Worker's*—and clucked disapproval of the storm that Gates, Fast, and the others created in the party. They wanted peace and stability in their party, not the disturbing editorials and resolutions demanding a thorough overhaul of their ideology and organization. Above all, they wanted the party to remain a party, and talk of dissolution particularly disturbed them; to dissolve the old people's home was out of the question. They were sorely troubled by the revelations of anti-Semitism in the Soviet Union, but they found some way to rationalize the uncomfortable fact. Some of them just refused to see. Others knew from first hand that, after all, the Russians had been anti-Semitic before the revolution too. You just could not expect much from the *goyem,* Communist or not.

THE 1957 CONVENTION

In the weeks immediately before the party's national convention, the question of whether to keep the party's name and form or to change it into some kind of political-action organization with a new name came to be the main issue between the orthodox and the unorthodox. The proposal for a new kind of organization, aside from its intrinsic merits or lack of them, symbolized other differences within the party, such as its relationship with other Communist parties of the world, its place in the tradition of American radicalism, its attitude toward Marxism-Leninism, and its views toward a monolithic party of the Lenin type with "democratic centralism."

In the first *Discussion Bulletin* before the convention, there appeared the first seriously stated proposal in print of the abandonment of the party and the establishment of a political-action association. The *Discussion Bulletins* were a residual piece of party ritual. Before earlier conventions, these *Bulletins* had been published for a few weeks, designed to offer members an opportunity for a little democracy before centralism became paramount again. In 1956-57, these special publications were superfluous since sharp discussion had been conducted for months in regular publications. Bernard Burton, of Los Angeles, once of the *Daily Worker* staff, argued that a political-action association would better enable Communists to work within trade unions and would avoid the "certain air of duplicity [that] is fostered when . . . workers learn that a fellow-worker is not only active in an organization of one of the major parties, but is also a member of another party, the C.P." Doxey Wilkerson endorsed the idea in the same *Bulletin,* but John Williamson, writing from England a defense of orthodoxy that was almost devoid of the ideas that had rocked communism internationally, assailed all such proposals as "liquidationist" and "revisionist," two choice party epithets.[25] John Gates, in a clear summary of his whole position, came out for a political-action association but was willing to postpone the change. He doubted that the question could receive enough serious and unemotional consideration before the party convention. His main contention on party organization was that democratic centralism had to be modified. "Our experience has been the tendency for this to become transformed into maximum centralization and minimum democracy. . . . Democratic centralism apparently results in a semi-military type of organization which is clearly not valid for our country in this period." [26] Foster retaliated. He called such proposals "a mess of Social-Democratic political and organizational pottage," and argued that "Our Party must be based upon democratic centralism." [27] He later wrote that "to defeat the project for a political action association is the life-and-death necessity now before the Party." [28]

Early in December, the state committee of the New York party debated a motion to put the organization on record favoring adoption of the political-association form. The committee members could not agree among themselves. A majority wrote a statement favoring such a change, and a minority prepared a dissenting statement.[29] The national committee, at its meeting in New York, December 17-19, amended the draft resolution and compromised the issue. The compromise was to the effect that the party convention would not "undertake to change the name and form of our Party," but that this action was not to "foreclose further consideration of these proposals." The new national committee should "explore" the idea further.[30] The majority in the New York State organization, the main center of sentiment for such a change, then agreed to the compromise.[31]

The compromise on a change in the party's name and form was the result of a larger spirit of compromise which permeated the party. Everyone was very much afraid of a split. During the national convention itself, speakers time and again unwittingly revealed that, although the factions had not been able to reconcile their differences, they had an implicit agreement not to push their view to the point that the other side would have no choice but to bolt.[32] Foster and his supporters were clearly a minority, although a sizable minority, so the compromise represented a greater yielding by the Gates wing than by the orthodox. Another piece of evidence to indicate the willingness of the Gates forces to compromise for the sake of unity was the conciliatory measures the New York organization took at its state convention, January 25-27, 1957, one of the series of local and state conventions that both preceded and followed the national convention.[33] This fear of a split gave Foster and his followers a great advantage. It enabled him to hang on until the tide eventually flowed strongly in his favor.

That the Foster wing of the party was not above a little skulduggery became apparent in the counting of the ballots cast in the New York State convention's election of delegates at large to the national convention. The state convention elected by secret ballot fourteen national convention delegates from a list of forty-six nominees. Tellers counted the ballots at the convention and disclosed that three of the fourteen elected were of the Foster faction and the other eleven were Gatesites, including Gates himself and state party chairman George Blake Charney. The *Daily Worker* four days later announced that the state convention had elected Foster, Dennis, Gates, and Charney, but did not list the others. The head teller, a supporter of Foster, took the ballots home with him and a few days later called the other tellers for a recount. The recount showed a change of party ballots, which if permitted to stand, would have made a majority of Foster supporters in the state delegation. The Gates wing learned of the change, accused the head teller of duplicity, and threatened to tell the whole story at the national convention if the original count were not certified. At an emergency meeting the weekend before the convention, the national committee decided to uphold the original count, destroy all the ballots, and keep the whole affair secret. The Gates faction agreed to keep still and not exploit the matter. But news of the affair leaked out, and although the party condemned "false press reports" as a "slander," the convention's credentials committee unwittingly confirmed the reports.[34]

No one doubted that the Russians supported Foster in the American party fight, and the Russians confirmed their backing of Foster just before the convention. Less than a week before the convention opened, American newspapers carried accounts of a story that had appeared in the Moscow newspaper *Sovetskaya Rossiya.* The Russian editors attacked "right wing elements" in the American party and singled out Joseph Clark for particular censure. Clark, the Russians charged, was as one with John Foster Dulles in support of "national communism" in an effort to "divide and conquer" the communist world.[35] The American battle, however, was beyond being stopped by the Russians. The "right wing elements" had rebuffed Moscow over Hungary and Russian anti-Semitism and were ready to do so again. Clark replied in his column of February 6. American Communists, he said, simply could not follow the Russian model: "Nothing can be more alien to Marxism than the view that all countries will come to socialism along the same path." [36] But Stalinists abroad—if they could still be called that after Khrushchev's speech—continued to try to shape the American party in their own image.

The sixteenth national convention of the Communist Party assembled on Saturday morning, February 9, 1957, in a ramshackle caterer's establishment called Chateau Gardens at Houston Street and Second Avenue in Manhattan's lower East Side. The building had once been a Russian Orthodox church, a fact that some observers found fraught with symbolism. The party had tried to rent better accommodations, but the proprietors of more than sixty New York hotels and halls had turned them down. Outside the door of Chateau Gardens stood a man with a camera who took photographs of all who entered. According to the report of an anti-Communist observer at the convention, "Uniformed and ununiformed cops swarmed all over the place." He was reminded of the *New Yorker* cartoon in which a Communist began his address, "Comrades and members of the F.B.I." [37]

The report of the convention's credentials committee was interesting for the evidence it contained about the party's national composition. There were 298 delegates, of whom seventy-eight were women. Fifty-four of them were Negro, two were Mexican, and one was Puerto Rican. Slightly more than half the delegates were over forty-five years old, and most of them had been in the party for a long time. For a party supposed to be rooted in the masses, a breakdown of the delegates' "mass organization" activities was discouraging. Only three were farmers, only eighty were trade-union members, and only thirty-four of the fifty-four Negroes were "in Negro work." [38]

At the convention's first afternoon session, the delegates listened to messages of greeting from foreign Communist parties and leaders. The most important of these was a message from Jacques Duclos, which Foster had received on January 21. Duclos tried to influence the Americans as he had in 1945. He warned them not to deviate from orthodoxy. The French party's central committee cabled reaffirmation of the Duclos communication the night before the convention opened.[39] After the reading of these messages from France, Eugene Dennis delivered the convention's keynote address. His speech—a rather routine one, typical of Dennis in that he qualified everything controversial—tried to make a show of independence. The "main line of our convention resolution is Marxist-Leninist in content and fully in accord with the interests and democratic traditions of our country, with proletarian solidarity and with the new and ever developing generalized experience of the international working class. In any case, our decisions will be our own, made by the collective judgment of this convention, and will be based on *our* Marxist understanding of American reality and the needs of our people and nation." [40] Just precisely what this statement meant was anyone's guess, but Dennis hoped the convention would understand the sentences as a declaration of independence. The *Daily Worker* so interpreted them.[41] A declaration of independence that failed to mention the Soviet Union was, at best, ambiguous.

Foster addressed the convention immediately after Dennis. Benjamin Davis read Foster's speech for him, although Foster was seated on the platform. His speech was certainly not even intended to be interpreted as a declaration of independence. Duclos, in fact, "is correct in warning us of revisionist tendencies in our Party." Foster's speech revealed his convention tactics. The Gates wing had committed itself to avoid a split and not to press too hard for its position. Foster took advantage of their concern for "unity" to attack with all the vigor he could muster, to claw away for all he could salvage. Those opposed to Foster had the votes to defeat him, but they were less concerned with defeating him than with preserving unity. Under the circumstances, Foster could not lose any more than he had lost already; he could only gain. The harder he fought, the better his chance to gain, because Gates would not fight back. And Foster understood the situation. In his speech, he identified Gates with the "Right danger," which "is now threatening the life of the Party." Gates and the *Daily Worker,* he declared, had in their editorials on the Polish and Hungarian crises been guilty of "impermissible yielding before aggressive American imperialism." [42]

Neither Gates nor his followers ever defended their position on Hungary and Poland at the convention. Indeed, they regarded the subject as a forbidden topic. The convention ignored Hungary. If it had not been for Foster's reference—and the futile shouts of rank and filers who wanted to speak on the subject but could not get the floor [43]—one would not have known that Hungary was any more pertinent to the convention than, say, real-estate taxes in Saskatchewan.

The morning after Foster's speech, the convention considered the report of a subcommittee that had to do with the party's name and form. This report could have been the convention's hottest subject if Gates had wanted to make it so. The subcommittee report itself was a compromise to which the national committee had agreed in December: the convention would "oppose" the change to a political-action committee but "it should not close the door to all constructive exploration and discussion of the subject as may be organized by the incoming National Committee." All the speakers on the question at the convention were for the compromising subcommittee report. Many delegates wanted to state their differing views on the question of a political-action association, but all the speakers, including Gates, supported the report. One hard group tried to amend the report to change the word "oppose" to "reject," but after its motion was defeated, only three opposed and seventeen abstained on the vote to accept the compromise report.[44]

The hottest debate at the convention had to do with the party's attitude toward Marxism-Leninism, and the debate became one that a medieval theologian would have appreciated. The draft resolution had stated that the party based itself on "Marxist-Leninist principles as interpreted by the Communist Party of our country." [45] Twelve of the twenty-six members of the convention subcommittee charged with presentation of that part of the main political resolution, a group led by Esther Cantor, of New York, wanted to strike the word "interpret" and have the party "creatively apply" Marxism-Leninism. The majority of the subcommittee refused the amendment, and the minority presented a dissenting report. The editors of the *Proceedings* cut their document extensively at this point, but it is clear that the convention got four and one-half hours behind schedule in its debate on which report to accept, in effect whether to "interpret" Marxism-Leninism or "creatively apply" it. By a narrow margin, the word "interpret" remained in the final document.[46] That a national convention of a political body as badly divided as the Communist Party would debate at length and with heat the difference between "interpret" and "creatively apply" reflects much about the irrelevance of Communist thinking and the unviability of the Communist movement. Nevertheless, the defeat of the "creatively apply" group constituted a victory for the Gates wing, if that wing can be said to have won any victories at all.

One curious decision of the convention was proposed by Sam

Kushner, secretary of the convention committee on miscellaneous resolutions. Kushner proposed that the convention move its national headquarters to his home city, Chicago, within one year. The party had been founded in Chicago in 1919, and Kushner argued that it was time to move back. The stated reasons were that the central location would be more convenient for the national membership, and that it would place the national leadership nearer the farmers, workers in basic industry, and Negro unionists. Except for the matter of central location, the arguments were dubious. It is probable that the main reason was not expressed: a move from New York would get the national office away from the center of party unorthodoxy. The delegates did not expect Kushner's proposal, but they passed it unanimously because those who were against it knew the move would not be made.[47] Despite the furor in the party about bureaucracy, party headquarters did not move to Chicago within a year. According to the party constitution, a national convention is the party's highest authority and a convention's decisions may be rescinded only by another convention. Party headquarters did move, but not to Chicago. A month after the convention, the party moved from 101 West Sixteenth Street, at the corner of Sixth Avenue, in New York City, just a few blocks away to 23 West Twenty-sixth Street. The Twenty-sixth Street house, a lovely three-story Georgian structure, has an interesting history. Vincent Astor used it for his office until 1942, when he sold it to Frederick Vanderbilt Field. Field sold it in early 1957 —he has lived in Mexico for several years—to a corporation which leased the place to Charles Dirba, the old 1921 "Left opposition" leader. Dirba subleased the house to the party.[48] The reader may ponder the symbolism. The house of a conservative American capitalist became the property of a communistic capitalist, then was leased to a ghost from the party's past and subleased to the party for national headquarters in violation of the national convention's unanimous vote.

The convention's election of twenty members of the new national committee represented a compromise, as did almost everything the convention did. The new national committee was to be composed of sixty persons, twenty elected by the convention and the remaining forty by the subsequent state and district conventions. The twenty elected, in the order of their vote, were as follows: Charlene Alexander, Claude Lightfoot, James Jackson, Dorothy Healey, Benjamin Davis, Eugene Dennis, William Z. Foster, Earl Durham, Doxey Wilkerson, Carl Winter, John Hellman, Fred Fine, Anna Correa, Carl Ross, Al Richmond, John Gates, Sidney Stein, David Davis, Charles Loman, and George Blake Charney.[49] The group represented the entire party spectrum from Stalinist orthodoxy (Foster, Davis, and Loman) to as unorthodox as one could be and yet remain in the party (Gates, Richmond, and Wilkerson). Miss Alexander, of Los Angeles, who received the most votes, was relatively unknown in the party outside California. But for a Communist convention, she had tremendous advantages: besides being young and personally attractive, she was a woman and a Negro. Four of the five candidates receiving the most votes were Negroes.

The convention had instructed the twenty elected national committee members to elect seven of their number to be a temporary secretariat until the state conventions finished electing the full national committee. The elected members made another compromise. The twenty suggested unanimously that all the New York residents among them be the temporary secretariat, and the convention accepted their recommendation. The New York residents —Charney, Davis, Dennis, Durham, Fine, Foster, Gates, Jackson, Loman, Stein, and Wilkerson—were of all varieties of Communist.[50]

The convention ended on a note of self-conscious unity. Gates told the convention, "Some of us have lost out on . . . [our] points of view, but no matter who lost, the Party has won." Foster became downright chummy in his reply. "The work of this convention, it seems to me we have got to understand it, as Johnny said, as a victory for the Party, and not a victory for any particular group or faction in the Party." [51]

Who did win the convention? Surely it was not the party as a whole, as Gates and Foster claimed. The party faded after the convention even faster than it had in 1956. Nor had unity really been achieved. As one disgruntled neighborhood party leader put it in his letter of resignation from the party, "When Foster, Dennis, Davis, and Gates were proclaiming the Party's great winning of unity, the fighting went on as murderously and vindictively as during the prior nine months . . . while Davis was proclaiming the end to factionalism, both factions were organizing their second state, pre-state convention factional caucuses." [52]

The Gates forces, or at least the opponents of Foster's orthodoxy, won some things. The "Main Political Resolution" adopted by the convention,[53] a slight modification of the draft resolution written the previous September, would have been completely beyond the pale in 1952. Foster had voted against the draft resolution, but now he voted for it in its slightly revised form. The Main Political Resolution was the end product of an evolution of the party line that had been under way since the nineteenth, not the twentieth, congress of the Soviet party, the last congress in which Stalin participated. The twentieth congress, however, certainly hastened the evolution. Gone now were all references to the Negro nation in the Black Belt and "national self-determination." The document exuded a sweet reasonableness toward social democrats and non-Communist labor and Negro leaders. And the document did contain some guarded statements on the independence of the American party. But it was by no means a Gatesian document. It said nothing about Hungary or Soviet anti-Semitism.

The convention seemed, on the face of it, to be a compromise and a standoff between the Foster and Gates factions. Actually, it was a victory for Foster. Foster had gained time from the convention. He had saved himself and his point of view from elimination by exploiting the general fear of a party split. The unorthodox had not been united, and they had failed to strike when their opportunity was best.

Apparently the Russian party exerted no more than a general influence on the convention. The Russians' endorsement of Foster certainly strengthened his position with some of the delegates and confirmed their approval of him, but it did not deter other delegates from their determination to shape the party in a fashion Moscow would not approve. Why the Soviets did not do more than they did to get the party to endorse their position is a matter for speculation. Perhaps they thought they had done all they could successfully to affect thinking in the American party. Perhaps they thought the game was not worth the candle. Perhaps they operated from the assumption that their position could not lose in the end because they could always grant "recognition," award the "franchise," to Foster and his supporters in the event that there was a split at the convention and the hards lost the fight. In any case, as matters in the American party actually developed in due time, it was not necessary for the Russians to exert great pressure. The Russians did not have to bend the American party to their will; the American party bent of its own volition.

The failure to bring together into one camp all those who were in disagreement with Foster's hard position was partly the result of considered judgment and conviction and partly the result of poor tactics. The California party, unorthodox enough to publish a biting satire on party orthodoxy in its state discussion bulletin,[54] refused as a matter of conviction to unite with Gates to drive out the hards and try to create a party truly independent of Moscow. Dorothy Healy, leader of the party in southern California, a month before the convention said privately that although she had no use whatsoever for Foster's kind of Communism, she thought Gates was as dogmatic in his position as Foster was in his. She wanted a party representing many kinds of opinions and hoped that both Gates and Foster would be elected to the new national committee. She also predicted that neither Foster nor Gates would win at the national convention.[55] Months after the convention, Gates thought his side had made a tactical blunder. He recognized that he had been unable to get any unity from the anti-Foster forces, but he thought that what strength he had should have been directed at Foster. His associates had persuaded him to level most of his criticism at Dennis, rather than Foster, and Gates thought the attack on Dennis had only driven Dennis and Foster closer together when Dennis might have been used by the unorthodox.[56]

To Gates's analysis of his failure at the convention must be added some other factors. First of all, Gates was never able to develop with clarity and exactitude just what he was for; he knew only what he was against. Without a clear positive program, he was at a disadvantage in rallying support. Second, old party habits of thought led Gates to overemphasize the consequences of a party split, compromise too much for his own tactical advantage, and, in effect, walk into Foster's trap.

The old fox had planned it well. To compromise in a party resolution, he well knew, meant nothing at all. But many of Gates's followers were disgusted with their leader's compromises, and, from the convention on, Foster won major victory after victory.

FOSTER GAINS THE UPPER HAND

A disgruntled Gates supporter made a prediction at the convention that turned out to be remarkably accurate. While the convention chairman was declaring him out of order and trying unsuccessfully to get him to sit down, William Mandel, of New York, told the delegates that the convention, "having patched up unity between two irreconcilable viewpoints, has failed in what appears to be its very success." The convention "has only advanced far enough toward independence to make the Party useful to the Voice of America as a stick with which to beat Communist Parties abroad. It has not advanced far enough to be acceptable to the American working class or to the American people at large." Then came his prediction: "The fully independent element will be the distinct minority in the full National Committee of the Party. This is because the most convinced adherents of the Gates viewpoint will not reappear at the reconvened State Conventions to vote for New York's eleven members of the National Committee, and the same thing will happen elsewhere." [57]

Many members had quit in the fall of 1956; others had set up conditions which the convention would have to meet. Now many of these members quietly left the organization. One member on his way out was quite explicit: "I have no desire to 'help' the Gates forces fight the Foster forces. I consider that too many leaders of the Gates forces gave up their fight in compromise after compromise, until they compromised themselves into Foster's outdated position; and these leaders will continue to do so, leaving rank and filers to break their backs, alone." [58] Precisely how many left just after the convention is an unanswerable question. A letter to the *Daily Worker* much later in the year said that "thousands" had left.[59] Many who did not officially resign just ceased their activity, much to the dismay of their section leaders.[60] As one local leader who quit the party told a writer for the *Nation,* "In my [New York] party section we have 160 on the books. Seventy pay dues, maybe a couple of dozen come to meetings; we sit around and argue about Hungary and Leninism. What the hell else is there to do?" [61] With such floundering about within the party and with Communist passion directed against other Communists rather than against the "outside" world, some members left on the grounds that the party was no longer an effective organization. They quit the party not so much because their political and moral ideals were outraged as because they belatedly recognized that the party was no longer an effective instrument of social change. The party had become a futile sect, and continued association with it was equally futile.

Even before state conventions had met to elect the rest of the members to the new national committee, Foster began to press his advantage against Gates. He was not altogether successful in this first attempt to purge his opposition. The eleven New York residents who together composed the temporary party secretariat met on March 14. The Fosterites rebuked Gates and *Masses & Mainstream* for not dealing roughly enough with Howard Fast, whose departure from the party had only recently become public and who had, at last, criticized the Communists. Foster also tried to push through a motion demanding Gates's resignation as editor of the *Daily Worker,* but those in the middle ground refused to go along with Foster and defeated the motion. Someone at the meeting "leaked" the news to the general press. A week later, the temporary secretariat met, confirmed the news, and blasted news "leaks." "Any unauthorized individual issuance of such information to the press is contrary to working class principles, a violation of Communist ethics and conduct and is to be categorically condemned." [62] Someone who called herself "Paula" wrote a letter to the *Daily Worker* which accurately described the situation in the party. "Many people I know have gotten so emotionally carried away by factionalism that they have forgotten the main purpose of the party. To them it seems the most important thing is to get rid of this or that leader 'who is throwing out Marxism.' " She warned pointedly, "There's more ways of 'liquidating the Party' than by holding a meeting and voting 'now it's liquidated.' Another way . . . would be to make it an organization no one wants to belong to." [63] Apparently, it was already an organization that many no longer wanted to belong to.

Enough Gates supporters had left the party in New York so that by the time the state convention met, March 30-31, 1957, the Foster forces were able to gain more from compromise than they had at the national convention. In the election of state committee members at large, the Gates forces held their own—most of the state committee members were yet to be elected by county and regional conventions. The resolution of the state convention "On the Jewish Question in the USSR," however, was a clear setback for the unorthodox. The national convention had ducked that issue as one too hot to handle when the theme song was "Unite for Unity." The convention, over the objections of several delegates, had only passed the problem on to the new national committee.[64] The New York convention's resolution on the matter was a puzzling bundle of internal contradictions. One paragraph noted that the Soviet Union had not yet "carried to fruition" any of its announced projects for the stimulation of Jewish culture, and the next declared, "We reject the slander of anti-Soviet elements accusing the Soviet Union of anti-Semitism. There is no official state policy of anti-Semitism." Any sentence in the resolution that could be interpreted as critical of the Soviets was followed by one that absolved them of any evil.[65]

Fortunately for Gates, the ground rules provided that the state conventions rather than the subsequent county conventions would elect members for the unfilled places on the national committee, for between the two local conventions even more Gatesites left the party. The newly elected national committee, composed of sixty-six members rather than the sixty prescribed by the convention, contained only a small scattering of members who supported Gates completely. Twelve members were fully as orthodox as Foster. The rest of them were in between the two positions. The middle group shifted from time to time in its position because, although it held some mildly unorthodox ideas on some points, it put unity and compromise above all else.[66]

The first time the new national committee met, the first week of May 1957, the center group almost slipped out of its compromise position. The full committee decided to elect by secret ballot a seventeen-member executive committee. When the ballots were counted, they discovered that Foster had not placed among the first seventeen. Gates was among the first seventeen. The committee then enlarged the size of the executive committee to twenty, thereby including Foster. Further to make amends, the committee granted Foster the position of chairman emeritus. The position entailed no special power or responsibilities. The national committee then rejected another motion asking for Gates's resignation as editor of the paper—this time the motion also wanted Joseph Clark's resignation—but it did adopt a report that criticized "certain inadequacies and shortcomings" in the Communist press. There was a need, the report said, "of improving the reportage of life and events in the Socialist lands, especially for providing a more thorough-going Marxist analysis of the foreign policy of these countries." [67]

At the county party conventions in New York City, where Gates had had his greatest strength, the Foster forces triumphed. At the Queens County convention, the hards were obviously going to be in control, and the Gates crowd did not even attend. In Manhattan, there had been so many Gatesite resignations that the only battle, over the post of county organizer, was between a Foster supporter and a Puerto Rican "ultra-leftist" who considered Foster too soft. In Kings County (Brooklyn), the Foster group accused the Gatesites of "white chauvinism" when they opposed the election of Charles Loman as county organizer. At the national convention, Loman had been harder than Foster on most matters. In the uproar over the "white chauvinism" charges, about thirty Gatesites walked out.[68]

Among those walking out of the Brooklyn convention was Joseph Clark. As he and five friends got in a car to start for home, they were completely angry about the turn of events in the party and ready to quit. As they drove down the Belt Parkway toward Coney Island, their comments on the party were bitter. Then the driver noticed a car with two men passengers that seemed to be following them. He turned off the highway. So did the following car. He drove down side streets, and the following car stayed with them. Now they forgot their anger at the party and began to swear at the F.B.I., the presumed affiliation of their followers. The driver let his five passengers out at various subway stations, and the pursuers gave up. Most of the six disgruntled Communists eventually quit the party, but they would have left it sooner had not the two F.B.I. men, if that is who they were, picked an in-opportune time to trail them.[69]

One of the functions of the county or regional conventions was to elect the rest of the members of the new state committee, some of which had already been elected at the state convention. Since Fosterites dominated most of the local conventions, they elected enough of their kind to dominate the state committee. The first meeting of the New York State committee, on May 25, elected Benjamin Davis the new state chairman, deposing George Blake Charney. Davis had been a consistent Foster supporter from the beginning. Charney remained in the New York organization as secretary, and party press releases asserted that "Davis and Charney will share equal responsibility." When one looked over the other state officers—Will Weinstone, who yielded to no one in his Marxist-Leninist purity, was education director—it was obvious that the Fosterites were in control.[70] Between the national convention and the county conventions, a matter of about ten weeks, enough Gatesites in New York, the seat of their greatest strength, had voted with their feet to create a Fosterite majority in the state organization.

Gates now had only a tenuous position in the party bureaucracy. Any time between June and the wild first weekend of November 1956, when the Russians moved back into Hungary and the French and English invaded Egypt, Gates would have emerged very strong from any kind of party elections. Had there been a party referendum—a fanciful supposition—any time during that period, it is altogether likely that Foster would have lost out completely. Foster was able to hang on because there were no elections then. Now the situation was reversed. As Gates himself put it, "My membership base is now on the outside." [71] And, ironically, what strength Gates had left in the party was due to the party's undemocratic structure, which prevented the rank and file from quickly and precisely expressing itself through the hierarchy. By the summer of 1957, Gates's greatest strength was at the top and his greatest weakness at the bottom. He had greater strength in the twenty-man executive committee of the national committee than in the full sixty-six-member body, and he had greater strength in the national committee than he had in the state and local organizations.

Before the national convention, it had been Gates's hope to transform the party within two or three years. If not much could be accomplished at the national convention, then much could be done, he thought, in the months and years to follow.[72] Gates's optimistic dream proved to be no more than a vision. His efforts after the spring of 1957 were necessarily defensive rather than designed to transform the party.

THE BICKERING FLICKERS ON

Much of the life disappeared from the *Daily Worker* after the national convention. Normally the dullest of newspapers, the *Daily Worker* acquired some sparkle after the twentieth congress. Although only a masochist could truly enjoy reading its files, the paper in 1956 and early 1957 did contain a great deal of conflict that lent it some interest. But in March 1957, the paper calmed down again and became almost, but not quite, its usual dreary self. Occasionally there was still something in its columns to indicate that Communists could break out of their intellectual dull gray mold.

For one thing, there was a dispute in the *Daily,* which must have been embarrassing for the staff, over what had actually happened at the recent national convention. Foreign Communist publications printed accounts of the convention that interpreted it as a victory for orthodox Marxism-Leninism. These accounts infuriated the *Daily* staff. Alan Max, the managing editor, tried to set the foreign comrades straight. When John Williamson wrote a story for *World News,* a British Communist weekly, that failed to mention that Foster and Dennis were no longer party chairman and secretary, respectively, Max took sharp issue with him. Williamson, as well as *Pravda* and *L'Humanité,* had written "accounts which completely missed the mark." [73] When Max discovered that a Soviet journal, *International Affairs,* had carried an article by T. Timofeyev which praised the convention for acknowledging "the vital force of proletarian internationalism," he could not restrain himself. It hurt that Timofeyev had written that the convention had "vigorously [opposed] revisionist and liquidationist tendencies," such as the idea of converting the party into a political-action association and organizing "a 'mass party of socialism,' into which the Communist party would dissolve itself." It hurt especially because Timofeyev had exaggerated only a little. Max replied with an open letter to *International Affairs.* The published *Proceedings,* he wrote, "read like an entirely different convention from the one discussed by your correspondent. . . . Such an account, especially if it remained uncorrected, could only tend to shake the confidence of your readers in the ability of your journal to give sound political estimates." [74]

Foster, naturally, could not let these words go unrebuked. Timofeyev was right, said Foster, Max was wrong. "The 16th Convention, while not without flaws [meaning he had not won entirely], was generally a constructive one [meaning he had won most issues]." The foreign journals were "correct," because the convention had rejected "revisionism" and "incorrect theoretical formulations" and made a "strong declaration for proletarian internationalism." "Thus the convention saved and reinforced the very spirit and structure of Communism in the United States." [75] It looked as if Foster intended to win by interpretation what little he had not been able to win in actuality.

The *Daily Worker* continued to criticize the Soviets occasionally, although usually in relatively mild language. In the spring of 1957, there was the complicated affair of Khrushchev and the Soviet bonds. The *Daily Worker* carried a paraphrased translation of Russian newspapers on the subject. For some years, Soviet citizens had been obligated to buy government bonds, which did not bear interest and were not negotiable, equivalent to from two weeks' to two months' earnings, depending upon the citizen's income. The Soviet Government ran a lottery for bondholders, and the lucky could hit a jackpot, but most bondholders received only their principal back in twenty years. Now Khrushchev proposed that the issuance of these bonds be stopped; the government, however, would not redeem any of the outstanding bonds at all until another twenty or twenty-five years. One sentence in the *Daily Worker*'s summary of the situation was entirely accurate: "Capitalists will never believe . . . that Soviet workers are accepting this voluntarily." [76]

Apparently not all Communists believed it either. George Morris, the *Daily*'s heavy-handed labor editor and a Fosterite, felt obligated to defend the Khrushchev action against criticism. The same thing happened in the United States, said Morris, except that the American Government accomplished its purpose by raising taxes. Furthermore, said Morris, all the Soviet people supported Khrushchev's action and not all Americans were for high taxes.[77] Joseph Clark could not agree with Morris, although the ghost of Robert A. Taft might have felt a certain sympathy for Morris's argument. To Clark, the whole affair of the bonds was undemocratic and indicated that the Soviet Union still had some distance to go in implementing the decisions of the twentieth congress.[78]

There was a far greater stir in the party and the *Daily Worker* when, in July 1957, Khrushchev ousted Molotov, Malenkov, Shepilov, and Kaganovich from power and banished them to obscure posts in the hinterland. Supposedly, the four had been removed from power because they resisted the growth of democracy in Russia. This was the emphasis Gates gave to his first editorial on the "recent historic Soviet events." The ousters were "a culmination of a series of sharp policy debates over questions of internal Soviet policy and foreign affairs." The four, under Molotov's leadership, had resisted the twentieth congress decisions for peaceful coexistence and "internal democratization." "We view with satisfaction . . . the rebuffing of a faction which opposed the steps to a new Geneva, to improved relations with all nations, to heighten the living standards and democratic rights of the Soviet peoples." Gates had one reservation: the debate on the issues within the Soviet party's central committee should have been public. In boldface type he declared, "The process of democratization requires such public debate." But Gates's editorial reservation was minor, "distinctly subordinate to the historic events themselves—events which will shape a peaceful world." [79]

Clark's column the next day was much more critical. He agreed with Gates that since the death of Stalin the Soviets had moved in the direction of relaxing international tension and of democracy, decentralization, and higher living standards internally. He had his doubts though about "the special demonology which says Malenkov was a foe of peaceful coexistence." "There was unquestionably an issue of policy behind every conflict in the Soviet party leadership. But this doesn't mean there wasn't also jockeying for leadership and power." Clark was more critical than Gates of the lack of public debate before the decision, although he conceded that "the fact that the Central Committee debated the issue is a far cry from the days when Stalin alone made decisions." If Malenkov was guilty, Clark wrote, "the Soviet people were entitled to evidence and a statement from both sides. They were never given the benefit of the public debate. . . . If anything, the methods used in the struggle against Stalinism show that it will take considerable time before democratic controls and procedures and direct working class control in all phases of Soviet life are established." He did not defend the four ousted Soviet officials. Quite the contrary. "It is fatuous to think that those ousted were not responsible for some of the achievements during the Stalin era as well as for the crimes. It would be just as fatuous to think that Khrushchev, Mikoyan, Bulganin and Voroshilov, [the] remaining collaborators of Stalin, were also not responsible for the Leningrad frameup and the repressions of the 30's, for which they now blame Molotov, Malenkov and Kaganovich." [80]

Clark was nothing but a "liberal bourgeois," raved one letter writer, who called himself "Red Gum." "Missouri Marxist" charged that Clark was "unscientific." [81] A considerable number of Foster-ite national leaders demanded that Clark be fired from the paper. Gates resisted the efforts to fire Clark, although he did not fully agree with him. When Gates threatened to resign if the national committee fired Clark, the Fosterites backed down. Unity was still the watchword for the party's public relations in the summer of 1957, and if Gates resigned, his action would be popularly in-terpreted—and rightly so—as the end of the party's "new look." [82] Then Gates wrote a long article which both differed with Clark on some aspects of his interpretation and agreed with him on other aspects, but which strongly defended Clark's right to interpret however he would for the *Daily Worker*.[83]

Interpretation of the Hungarian revolution continued to divide Communists and lend some life to the *Daily Worker*. In May 1957, Herbert Aptheker published a book entitled *The Truth about Hun-gary,* which he obviously considered a lasting contribution on the the subject if not the final word itself. Aptheker had some quali-fications for writing the book. A Ph.D. from Columbia University, he had specialized in American Negro history and clearly under-stood, even if he did not always practice, the canons of historical scholarship. *The Truth about Hungary* threatened to revive the whole controversy when Robert Friedman wrote a critical review of it for the *Daily Worker*. Uncritically favorable *Daily Worker* reviews for books by Communists who hewed to the party line had long been standard practice, but after the twentieth congress, the paper occasionally published intelligently critical essays. Fried-man's review was such an essay. He granted that Aptheker had performed a service in bringing together a great deal of scattered information. Aptheker had not interpreted his participants "either as all patriotic saints or all fascist sinners." Yet Friedman did not "believe that The Truth about Hungary is the full truth about Hungary." Its chief weakness, Friedman wrote, was that its con-clusions were not justified either by the events in Hungary or by Aptheker's description of them. Aptheker declared that Western imperialism was the underlying cause of the rebellion and saw in the Kadar postrevolution government hope for the future. Friedman could not accept either interpretation and said so, firmly but without malice.[84]

Again the Fosterites arose to swat down the heretics. "Faithful Reader" deplored Friedman's "obvious inadequacy in historical scholarship made all the more appalling by his dismissal of the book and his crude attack upon the Soviet Union which appears to have been his chief aim in the intellectually poverty-stricken review."[85] Then someone wrote an open letter to "Faithful Reader" which agreed that Friedman's review was poor but defended his right to publish such a review in the *Daily Worker*.[86] The discussion began to get a little silly when "Xaver" argued that Friedman's main difficulty was his failure to realize that the reason the Rakosi government had misruled was that there were so many imperialist warmongers elsewhere in the world; "if you expect people to behave normal under such conditions, you are asking too much."[87] Foster could not remain quiet in a squabble such as this one. He wrote another review of Aptheker's book, in which he praised the author's research and "well-organized and penetrating analysis." The book was a "very effective answer to this tissue of anti-Soviet vilification and warmongering."[88] Louis Weinstock, just out of prison, felt he had special qualifications for still another review. He and his wife had been born in Hungary, stayed there until after the overthrow of the Communist government in 1919, and then moved to the United States. He had visited Hungary during the Rakosi regime—and, he might have added, tried to get John Lautner to do likewise. Take it from one who was there, everything was fine in Communist Hungary. Everything was fine about Aptheker's book, too; it "is an outstanding Marxist contribution and deserves to be translated into many languages and circulated the world over."[89] After the Weinstock contribution, a reader begged Gates to call off the "symposium." "It is time to pause now, comrades, and ask—'Is the end in sight?'"[90]

THE END OF AN ERA

To many comrades, it seemed the end was indeed in sight. The party's new line was not breaking it out of its isolation any better than had its old one. The party, for example, had made a great deal of the Prayer Pilgrimage for Freedom, a big demonstration by non-Communist Negroes in Washington on the third anniversary of the Supreme Court's decision on school segregation. The *Daily Worker* gave the Pilgrimage consistent and favorable publicity, and some Negro Communists attended the Washington rally, but the Negro movement's leaders did not change their attitude toward Communists one bit. No matter that the party had changed its line, Communists were still anathema. A. Philip Randolph, co-chairman of the Pilgrimage, president of the Brotherhood of Sleeping Car Porters, and once a Norman Thomas Socialist, warned the Pilgrimage against accepting Communist help. The Communists, he said, "have no genuine interest in the solution of problems of racial discrimination, but seek only to use this issue to strengthen the foreign policy of the Soviet Union." [91] Nor did Communists make any advances in the labor movement. The national officers of the A.F. of L.-C.I.O. had too much experience with the Communists to submit themselves to any more. George Meany had his troubles with them back in the days when he was the A.F. of L.'s lobbyist at Albany, and Walter Reuther had not forgotten the attacks Communists had made upon him.

Some Communists, all of them unorthodox, were in the new and loosely organized American Forum for Socialist Education. This organization, founded in May 1957, was a curious collection of diverse political beliefs, Communist and non-Communist, from Stalinoid *National Guardian* followers at the most rigid left, through Gatesite Communists, Trotskyists of the various confessions, Dorothy Day *Catholic Worker* people, Musteite "reconcilers," philosophical anarchists, pacifists, and a sprinkling of Marxist professors. Fosterite Communists would have nothing to do with the American Forum, whose members were often as critical of the Soviet Union as they were of American policies.[92] Not many of the most optimistic radicals expected much from the American Forum, yet Gatesites were pathetically enthusiastic about the freedom of discussion and intellectual give-and-take of the Forum. If enthusiasm were a solution to the intellectual problems of radicalism and Marxism, the problems would have been solved long ago.

Several prominent Gatesites decided that trying to change the party was hopeless. Joseph Clark resigned from the party and from the *Daily Worker* in early September 1957.[93] Junius Scales, whose Smith Act "membership clause" conviction the Supreme Court had set aside in October, announced in December that he had quit.[94] Doxey Wilkerson, a national committee member, resigned November 26.[95]

Clark's resignation created quite a stir. In his letter of resignation he said that after twenty-eight years in the party—he had joined when he was only an adolescent—he found that "it is no longer possible to serve the cause of American socialism" within the organization. "Why didn't I resign at the time of the Khrushchev revelations on Stalin, or during the Hungarian uprising? The reason is that I had hopes for the cause of those opposing Stalinism within the party. . . . But . . . the hope I had for the party died." [96] According to Gates, Clark's hope had actually died sometime before he resigned, but Gates had been able to persuade him to stay on because his resignation would appear to be a major victory for Foster.[97] Gates replied to Clark's letter. He thought there still was hope for the party, but wrote that Clark and the *Daily Worker* staff "parted in sorrow and not in anger, as friends, not enemies." [98] A majority of the party's national administrative committee, a smaller unit of the national executive committee composed of Dennis, Benjamin Davis, Jackson, and Lumer for the "hards" and Gates, Fine, and Stein for the dissenters, issued a statement that was not so kind. Clark, the statement said, had "lost all conception of a sound working-class attitude toward the Soviet Union" and had abused the freedom of expression which the party had granted him.[99]

Many were to follow Clark's trail within a few months because Foster and his wing of the party, obviously with the support of the Russians, were attacking with all the force they could muster, in effect demanding that the Gatesites surrender or get out. Foster's energy in the attack was amazing, especially for a seventy-six-year-old man with a heart condition. His frantic attack ended on October 16 with a serious cerebral hemorrhage, which for weeks paralyzed his right side and impaired his speech.[100] His writing production was prodigious in the last weeks before the stroke. He wrote a blast of the Gatesites and a personal statement of dedication to Moscow for the Russian magazine *Kommunist*. (*Kommunist* later came to his aid and condemned Gates for "bourgeois nationalism." [101]) He engaged in a bitter exchange of letters with one "M.G." in the *Daily Worker* in which he pulled all the stops; "M.G." was "outlandish," guilty of "bourgeois national chauvinism," and a "crackpot," besides.[102] When another old man, Alexander Bittelman, wrote a long, tedious, and confused series of articles for the *Daily Worker* entitled "I Take a Fresh Look"—a grossly exaggerated title—that did not measure up on Foster's orthodox yardstick, he wrote a blistering reply for *Political Affairs* so long that the editors had to divide it into two installments.[103] And he took time out from the party wars to glory in the Russians' success with Sputnik I. "Triumphing over all the capitalist enemies and the croakers and knockers in the labor movement, the USSR . . . is now travelling ever faster along the road to the eventual realization of the greatest social system of well-being, democracy and mass happiness that the world has ever seen or that man has ever dreamed of. The earth satellite is the harbinger of still greater things to come; achievements which . . . had to await the coming of Socialism upon the world scene." [104]

The battle between the Gatesites and the Fosterites came to a head in December, and when the crisis was over, the Communist

Party had turned the corner from one era into another. Immediately following the giant celebrations in Moscow for the fortieth anniversary of the Bolshevik revolution, twelve Communist parties, each of them in power in its country, met and issued a declaration. The twelve parties were from Russia, China, Albania, Hungary, northern Vietnam, East Germany, Bulgaria, North Korea, Mongolia, Poland, Romania, and Czechoslovakia. The Yugoslavian party refused to participate. The meeting seemed to be 1948 all over again. The declaration hailed the Soviet Union as "the first and mightiest Socialist power" and contended that "the vital interests of the working people of all countries call for their support of the Soviet Union." The twelve parties did not revive the Cominform, defunct since Khrushchev and Tito kissed and made up temporarily, but they did discuss launching a new periodical to take the place of the Cominform's old *For a Lasting Peace, For a People's Democracy!* [105]

The *Daily Worker* ran a brief news story about the twelve-party declaration, shorter than those in the general press,[106] and said nothing editorially. Not until a month after the declaration did it print anything more about the Moscow meeting, and then it published only the text of the declaration.[107] There was a struggle going on behind the scenes in the party. On December 2, the national administrative committee of seven convened. The four Fosterites on the committee (Davis, Dennis, Jackson, and Lumer) had prepared a statement hailing the declaration. The three Gatesites (Stein, Fine, and Gates himself) tried to dissuade them, but they were outvoted. On such a major matter, they argued, any statement would have to come from a party echelon closer to the membership than the administrative committee, which was only part of the executive committee, which in turn was only part of the full national committee. The four Fosterites mailed their statement to the full national committee; the statement was not published.

The larger executive committee met for three days, beginning December 20, to consider the twelve-party declaration and the future of the *Daily Worker*. The Fosterites did not have a majority with Foster himself incapacitated. Robert Thompson, who had a few months before been released from prison, read a report on the twelve-party declaration. The return of Thompson, who had gained infighting experience as the chief hatchet man against Browder, was of great value to the Foster wing. But now the executive committee prepared a statement on the declaration that was at odds with Thompson's views. The statement declared, "We American Communists should not repeat the mistake we often made in the past, of accepting the views of brother parties regarding their own problems as necessarily applying in the same way to the problems our Party faces, or of accepting a generalized estimate of the world situation without our own critical appraisal as to whether it is fully correct, or applicable to our own country." To do anything else, the statement continued, would be contrary to the decisions made at the sixteenth national convention of the party. The statement also noted that the twelve-party declaration had said that Right opportunism was the "main danger at present," but that the American party had gone on record at the last convention to the effect that "left sectarianism" was the main danger. The executive committee approved the statement by a vote of eleven to seven, with two abstaining and two absent. Those voting for the statement were Charney, David Davis, Fine, Gates, Dorothy Healy, Lightfoot, Lima, Ross, Russo, Stein, and Martha Stone. Those voting against were Benjamin Davis, Dennis, Durham, Elizabeth Gurley Flynn, Jackson, Lumer, and Thompson. Carl Winter and Jack Stachel abstained, and Foster and George Myers were absent.[108] This vote was the last victory for the unorthodox.

At the same meeting, the executive committee began the complicated decision to cease publication of the *Daily Worker,* which was disastrous for the Gates faction. With only Gates voting no, the executive committee voted to recommend "to the owners and publishers of the Daily Worker that they consider suspending the Daily and make an all-out effort to preserve the Worker." Actually, the recommendation to the party's official publishers, a small group of relatively wealthy and aged party nonentities, was only a technicality. But the executive committee "also decided to poll the 60 members of the National Committee on this proposition, with the understanding that the NEC [national executive committee] proposal would not be final or operative until the full National Committee had made a collective decision." [109] Thus, on December 22, when the executive committee adjourned, the decision to cease publication of the *Daily* was not final, although it probably would be before long.

Those who voted for this recommendation to "consider" closing the *Daily* had two quite different motives. Those who agreed with Gates or were nearer agreement with him than they were with Foster wanted the *Daily* to continue but did not see how continued publication was financially possible. The Fosterites wanted the *Daily* to close shop to silence Gates.

The *Daily Worker* had been in a desperate financial condition for a long time. It had lost money for years—if it ever broke even —but special fund drives by the party and direct subsidies from the party treasury kept it going. In 1956 and 1957, the paper was in worse financial condition than ever because many in the Foster faction would not donate money and often would not renew their subscriptions. There is an abundance of evidence to indicate that Fosterites deliberately sabotaged the *Daily*. Back at the time of the sharp conflict in the party over Hungary, Foster, Dennis, and Davis had joined Gates in a desperate appeal for funds "regardless of . . . differences" within the party. "Any withholding of support to it would be disastrous to our entire movement." [110] There must have been cause for their concern about party "differences" affecting support for the paper. At the national convention, a Fosterite delegate had declared, "The *Daily Worker* has lost readers, and the support of many good old-timers. . . . They have stopped buying the *Daily Worker,* reading the *Daily Worker,* or supporting the *Daily Worker.* If we want to do work for the upkeep of our paper, of the saving of our paper, I think the first thing would be that the *Daily Worker* should change" its position on Hungary. The speech evoked applause.[111] When Clark resigned from the party, one O. H. Leeds, of Brooklyn, wrote, "Well, it's one gone and one to go. . . . A group of us in Brooklyn have pledged a week's pay for the paper, payable on the day Johnny Gates . . . is either dumped or quits." [112] The departure of many members from the party in 1956 and 1957 also seriously hurt the paper's finances. Some Gates supporters believed the rumor, which may have been true, that the party had $250,000 cached away, originally intended for the underground, which the Fosterites refused to use to keep the *Daily* going.

In October 1957, the paper cut down its size. It had been eight pages and five days a week, Monday through Friday. The *Worker* on Sunday ran sixteen pages. Beginning October 22, the *Daily* reduced itself to four pages and dropped the Friday edition altogether. The *Worker* dropped to twelve pages. The cutback reduced the number of pages a week by exactly one-half. The retrenchment did not save enough to make the paper solvent. Steve Nelson in early December announced there was a deficit of $175,000, which the staff hoped to pare down to $150,000 by further economies. National party officials, he said, had often discussed suspending the *Daily* to save the Sunday edition but had calculated that it cost only $50,000 a year more to publish both.

After the executive committee meeting adjourned on December 22, but before the poll of the full national committee had been completed, the Fosterite majority of four on the administrative committee double-crossed their parent body and released a statement to the press to the effect that the executive committee had voted to discontinue the *Daily*. Harry Schwartz, of the New York *Times,* telephoned Gates on Christmas Day to confirm the press release. Gates refused to comment, and Schwartz said the *Times* would print the story anyway. Gates then told Schwartz that the decision to cease publication was not yet final, that he wanted to see the paper continued, and that if there were any announcement to be made, the *Daily Worker* itself, not any party committee, would make it. Schwartz included Gates's statement in his story.[113]

The four Fosterites on the administrative committee then accused Gates of "leaking" to the press, in "violation of the most elementary organizational principles common to all working-class organizations." This accusation was too much for seven *Daily* staff members, who wrote a letter to the four saying their statement about Gates was "groundless, uncalled for, and too reminiscent of previous harmful practices which the Communist movement has criticized itself for and which it is trying to shed." The signers of the letter were Abner Berry (Negro affairs), Jesus Colon (Puerto Rican affairs), Max Gordon (politics), Ben Levine (television column), Alan Max (managing editor), David Platt (movies and plays), and Lester Rodney (sports).[114] A. B. Magil, Simon Gerson, George Morris, and Virginia Gardner did not sign the letter.

Gates and the *Daily Worker* were almost, but not quite finished. The national committee completed its poll on the question of whether or not to suspend publication of the *Daily* between Christmas, 1957, and New Year's, and the national committee voted to suspend. At a New Year's Eve party, Gates told Elizabeth Gurley Flynn and Jack Stachel that he probably was going to resign from the party soon. He had earlier told many people that if the *Daily* had to cease publication because of the pressure of the Foster group he would leave the party. On Monday, January 6, Dennis called a meeting of the administrative committee. All but Fine were present. Dennis began the meeting by saying that he understood "on good authority" that Gates was going to leave the party. Was that right? Gates replied that he probably would leave. Dennis wanted to know when he was going to quit. Gates replied he did not know yet, but that he would tell the administrative committee when he had made up his mind. Then Dennis introduced a resolution, already prepared, that would have removed Gates from all party offices because he was going to resign, and asked Gates what he thought of that. Gates replied that Dennis's motion was not in accordance with the procedures for suspension from office as provided in the party constitution adopted at the last convention.

Gates's constitutional objection jarred Dennis, who recessed the meeting and caucused with Davis, Thompson, and Lumer. They did not ask Stein and Gates to stay. When Dennis called for the meeting to resume, Stein refused to attend. Gates returned. Dennis read a modified resolution which had the same effect, and the committee passed it. Gates said they had held the party's constitution and convention in contempt but that their contempt was not as great as that which he held for them. Gates left the room and never saw Dennis again. Stein telephoned other members of the national executive committee, of which the administrative committee was a part, and the larger body reversed the administrative committee's resolution.[115]

On Thursday, January 9, the *Daily* announced that its last issue would appear the following Monday. On Friday, January 10, John Gates called a press conference in the little Albert Hotel on East Tenth Street, named for Albert Pinkham Ryder and built by the painter's brother. While press cameras flashed and television cameras whirred, Gates announced that after twenty-seven years in the party, he was resigning "to rejoin the American people and find out what Americans are thinking about." The party, he said, had "ceased to be an effective force for democracy, peace and socialism in the United States." Although the ideals that attracted him to the party still motivated him, he did "not believe it is possible any longer to serve those ideals within the Communist party." [116]

The *Daily Worker*'s last issue, thirty-four years to the day after its first issue in Chicago in 1924, was a curious document. The fight between the Gatesites and the Fosterites continued to the very end. Alan Max wrote, "Our tragedy was that we were unable to change ourselves. We could not keep up with the vast changes in the country. . . . Each attempt to change ourselves succeeded only briefly—then it foundered on the rocks of dogmatism." The administrative committee ran a statement on Gates's resignation that in effect said "good riddance." "For some time Gates has been politically disoriented and has been challenging many of the basic principles of scientific socialism, Marxism." And Will Weinstone, typical of the old-timers who now would dominate the party, had one final letter, which could just as well have been written ten or twelve years earlier: "In my opinion . . . the main attack must today be made against revisionism and liquidationism which undermine the very foundations of the party and its principles . . . and hinder the mobilization of the party and brass for their tasks in relation to the mass struggles of labor and the people." [117]

The same old words, the same old incantations, but an era in Communist history had passed.

CONCLUSION: AN IMPOTENT PARTY

The *Daily Worker* was dead. John Gates, the chief spokesman for the unorthodox Communists, had resigned, and those of his party supporters who had not already quit the party were in the process of leaving. The party settled down to its unexciting, orthodox, pre-Khrushchev style. The Sunday *Worker,* now officially edited by William L. Patterson but actually directed by Benjamin Davis, became a dull gray caricature of a newspaper. No more did it print angry letters to the editor on matters that made any difference. One letter denounced boxing as "the cruelest form of capitalist exploitation." The only controversy in the letters column was over the question of whether or not opera singer Maria Callas could "carry a tune." [1] The question of whether or not the staff members who had departed with the demise of the *Daily* would get the full severance pay required by the American Newspaper Guild contract received not one word of comment in the paper. The party itself was becoming the ideological home for aged and isolated Reds that some members really wanted.

The Fosterites demonstrated that they exercised effective control of the party at the national committee meeting of February 14-16, 1958, the first after Gates's resignation. Jack Stachel came armed with a resolution condemning Gates's ideas as "but the most extreme expression of a revisionist ideology . . . a product of the pressure of bourgeois ideology within the working-class and its organizations, including the Party, and an expression of accommodation to this ideology." Stachel called for members to demonstrate their "devotion and love for the Party" with a campaign to rout Gatesism from the organization. "There is no place in the Party for a Gates or his ideology. The departure of such individuals will not injure but strengthen the Party. The answer to his resignation must be a determination to reveal and defeat all alien ideology in our ranks." Sidney Stein, a middle-of-the-road party leader, offered the national committee a milder resolution. By a vote of 36 to 12 with seven abstaining, the national committee adopted Stachel's resolution.[2]

Another matter of business was a general resolution on the party's role, organization, and ideology. Carl Winter and Claude Lightfoot, who were not as rigid as Foster but were die-hards nevertheless, presented a compromise resolution with which they hoped all could agree. Their resolution was an amended version of one originally drafted by the northern California party. Stein gave the resolution qualified support. Dennis saw that there was no need for compromise since he and the other Fosterite hards had the votes. Dennis offered a resolution of his own, an affirmation of Communist orthodoxy. The party must be, he insisted, "a working class vanguard party guided by the science of Marxism-Leninism. It must not be confused with other types of political parties of a united front character, or with an idea of a so-called united socialist party in which adherents of Marxism-Leninism would be only one among a number of other ideological currents." After a sideswipe at Gates's "anti-Marxist views and actions," Dennis went on to the November 1957 declaration of the twelve Communist parties in Moscow, about which there had been "controversy in the national leadership." The declaration was "a document of far-reaching, historic importance. . . . It reinforces the unity both of the socialist countries and of the international working-class and Marxist movements. It is a major Marxist-Leninist contribution to the fight for world peace, democracy, national freedom and socialism." American Communists "should study it and learn from it." Dennis rejected "the erroneous and harmful views of those who regard the Declaration as a 'reversal' or a 'retreat' from the position of the 20th Congress of the CPSU." He urged the national executive committee to prepare a "definitive statement on the Declaration, to issue outlines and otherwise do everything possible to stimulate its widest study." Finally, Dennis, too, called for a party purge: "To defend and reinforce unity, it is necessary at all costs to eradicate all factional activities and groupings in our ranks." After considerable discussion, the national committee accepted Dennis's resolution by a vote of 32 to 20, with three abstaining.[3] A new national executive committee subsequently declared its full approval of the twelve-party declaration, thus reversing the statement on the declaration that the old executive committee had adopted December 22, 1957.[4]

Twenty dissenting votes on such a resolution were too many for the hards' comfort. These dissenting national committee members had been elected by the national and state conventions, and thus were not to be removed easily or constitutionally. The hards circumvented the problem by calling for a new national executive committee, one which they could pack with officers who had demonstrated "devotion and love for the Party" to their satisfaction. Outvoted on the proposal in the full national committee, the dissenters refused to accept nomination to the new executive body. One of the dissenters, Albert J. ("Mickie") Lima, of California, accepted nomination because he wanted to maintain a connection between the top leadership and the *People's World*. The hards' resolution called for fifteen members on the new executive committee (five less than the old one), and the national committee chose nine at the February meeting. The other six were to be elected later. The nine were Lima, Dennis, Benjamin Davis, Elizabeth Gurley Flynn, James Jackson, Hyman Lumer, George Myers, Jack Stachel, and Robert Thompson.[5] Foster, still incapacitated from his stroke, was unable to serve on the executive committee, but he later rallied enough to write for *Political Affairs* again.

Still elated by the sputniks—and gratified that the United States space satellite was smaller—Foster demonstrated that his stroke had not changed his views: despite "the mistakes of the 'cult of the individual' period under Stalin . . . Socialist democracy in the Soviet Union has achieved the greatest level of freedom for the working classes in the history of mankind." [6]

The Fosterites, now in complete control of the party organization, did not have to stage a full-scale purge. Most Gatesites simply quit. Alan Max, Lester Rodney, Abner Berry, and Max Gordon, all of the old *Daily Worker* staff and all bitter about their lack of severance pay, departed in February. George Blake Charney and two less important New York officials resigned their party positions but not their membership in March. So did Carl Ross, secretary of the Minnesota organization. On April 1, twenty-six state and local leaders of the California organization resigned from the party and declared their intention to organize a new group free of Moscow domination. Hundreds of rank and filers departed as quietly as possible, knowing that to resign noisily was only to identify oneself as having once been a member and thereby to jeopardize one's economic welfare and risk unpleasant social pressures. Thompson, back from prison and again the unofficial defender of the faith, lashed out at those who had resigned, charging that they were "an anti-party conspiracy." To Thompson, the answer to those who were disaffected by the drive for purity was to drive for even more purity. He seemed as disturbed by those who remained in the party and shrugged off the resignations as by those who quit altogether. "Unquestioned loyalty to the party and a readiness to fight for it against its attackers must be established as fundamental criteria for Communists. . . . The party cannot tolerate its continued belittling at the hands of people holding party membership; nor can it tolerate failure to defend it against slanders and attacks." [7]

Thompson's campaign for party purity succeeded in bringing about the departure of two more unorthodox leaders. Later in the spring of 1958, George Blake Charney resigned from the party altogether, as did Sidney Stein, who had helped Thompson hide out in the Sierras when Thompson was a fugitive from justice. The Fosterites now had almost the kind of party they wanted. The only significant center of opposition was in California, where Dorothy Healy refused either to resign or to capitulate. By June, the party was again quickly responsive to the desires of international Communism. Early in that month, the Soviets announced the execution of Imre Nagy and two of his associates in the Hungarian revolt. Almost at once, the *Worker* approved editorially of the execution. At a national committee meeting later in the month, a resolution criticizing the editorial failed of passage by a 3-to-1 vote.[8] Although Thompson continued to rail against factionalism, the party was almost as close to monolithic unity as is possible without the use of legalized terror. The party demonstrated again in the summer of 1958 that it was entirely serious about purity and unity when it expelled a curious little group of "ultra-leftist" sectarians.

After there has been a purge of the "right" in the Communist Party, it is usual for a small group of disgruntled "ultra-leftists" to charge that the purgers are as guilty of "revisionism" as the recently purged. The Left sectarians made such charges in 1946 and 1947. In the summer of 1958, this happened again. A small group from the New York waterfront and Harlem, with a few followers in Pennsylvania and Ohio, led by Harry Haywood, a hard champion of Negro nationalism, asserted that Dennis and Thompson were as contaminated with wrongheaded theories as Gates had ever been. Thompson promptly had them expelled. Eighty-three of the expelled "ultras" held a conference in New York in mid-August and organized themselves into the Provisional Organizing Committee for a Marxist-Leninist Communist Party. They had sufficient strength, most of it among Negroes and Puerto Ricans, to publish a four-page printed monthly newspaper, the *Marxist-Leninist Vanguard,* very much like the fugitive publications of earlier groups but slicker in its form than the usual mimeographed Left-sectarian publications.[9] The new group's chances of survival are remote. Even Haywood gave them up as hopeless before the year was over.

The party's crisis was over by the summer of 1958. The Fosterites had won everything: control of the party machinery, control of its press, control of its policies. Yet their victory was hollow. They had won little more than the "franchise" over a nearly dead party.

The weekly *Worker,* besides being lifeless and sterile, was in dangerous financial condition. After weeks of a drive to gain 9,000 subscriptions, it had sold only one-fourth that many.[10] At the end of May 1958, the staff did not see how it could afford to get out the June 1 issue, due to go in the mails on May 30. The staff raised some money from sympathizers in a desperate struggle for survival, got a priority on party funds, and persuaded the printer to postpone his bill twenty-four hours. Still the *Worker* could afford only four, rather than the usual sixteen, pages.[11] The situation was similar on the West Coast, where the *People's World* was down to one edition a week.

The party's schools, which had enrolled thousands of students, were all closed. The Jefferson School of New York, once the biggest, had had trouble finding enough students to make the operation pay since about 1953. The 1956 crisis finished off the already moribund institution. In November 1956, its board of trustees announced that the school would close at the end of the term.[12] In San Francisco, the California Labor School, which once had an "extension division" with classes throughout the Bay area as well as southern California, closed its doors a few months later.[13] In a desperate effort to eke out a Marxist living, a group of New York party intellectuals in the fall of 1957 tried renting a hall and selling courses themselves—$6.00 for seven lectures or $3.50 for four.[14] The tuition was cheap enough, but few took advantage of the bargain offer.

As an electoral group, the Communists showed how feeble was their power in the 1957 New York City elections, conducted while the *Daily Worker* was still publishing and before all the Gatesites departed. Elizabeth Gurley Flynn, as good a candidate as the party had, ran for the city council from the Twenty-fourth District, a lower East Side area. Under the label of the People's Rights Party, where she had polled 1,437 Bronx votes for the city council in 1954, she could in 1957 gather only 710 votes from a total of 70,168. The contrast to the elections twelve years earlier, when the Communists elected two city councilmen, was striking. The dismal showing was not due to lack of effort. Her campaign manager, Arnold Johnson, a faithful Fosterite, a graduate of Union Theological Seminary, revealed that the party had distributed 100,000 leaflets, conducted thirty outdoor meetings, and made three radio broadcasts.[15]

At no time during the party's crisis did even the top party leaders have better than a rough estimate of how many members had quit and how many remained. Just before the twentieth congress convened in Moscow, the party had conducted a membership registration, which showed there were over 20,000 members, 8,800 of them in New York City. In the summer of 1957, months after the party's convention, the national committee estimated the total membership at about 10,000, 3,500 of them in New York.[16] New York losses were proportionately greater because it was a center of party discontent. When Gates resigned from the party in January 1958, he estimated the national membership at less than 7,000.[17] Late in the winter of 1957-58, the party registered its members again, the first accurate count in slightly over two years, and the registration indicated that the estimates had been too high. More members had quit than national headquarters knew. The registration showed that there were slightly under 3,000 members of the Communist Party. In a little over two years, there had been a membership drop of over 85 per cent, the greatest decline in percentages (though not in total numbers) in the party's history. Robert Thompson, the party's new executive secretary, subsequently announced that his administration was "increasing and stabilizing" the membership, but it is not likely that the membership total today is much over 3,000.[18]

More members might have quit if the economic prospects of the former Communist had been better. The more prominent in the party a man had been, the more difficult it was for him to find steady employment. One former member was hired and fired from fourteen mediocre jobs in a six-month period in 1957. Every time his new employer discovered his Communist background, he was on the street again.[19] For a former Communist organizer or journalist to find a job suited to his training and experience is especially difficult; he is sure to be known as a former Communist, and employers are sensitive to the possibility of adverse public reaction. By the spring of 1958, few of the prominent former Communists had found the jobs they wanted; some were unemployed. John Gates had just written a book, published late in the year. Max Gordon was a part-time graduate student in history at Columbia University. Doxey Wilkerson had enrolled as a graduate student in the School of Education at New York University. Many of them were salesmen. Former Communists also face at least a brief period of difficult social and psychological adjustment. The former Communist needs something to fill the void the party had once occupied, something else to which to dedicate himself.

One sometimes hears stories of "professional ex-Communists" who reap large incomes as anti-Communist experts. Some of these people have done rather well financially; others have not. Most former Communists reject that kind of career, preferring, to use John Steuben's phrase when he quit the party, to live out their lives "in agony and silence." Actually, there are former Communists of both kinds at almost all income levels. The most curious former Communists, perhaps, are the few who have done well financially in Wall Street. A few are former members; more are former fellow travelers. To some observers, their Wall Street careers indicate that they never were good Communists; other observers argue that their success in capitalist speculation indicates the value of a Marxist economic education. To generalize even about the economic status of former Communists is impossible because there are so many of them—perhaps a quarter-million in the United States.

There are more former Communists in America than ever before because the party has never been smaller. The two Communist groups that split from the Debs Socialists in 1919 claimed a total of 70,000 members. Two years later, when they merged to form the present Communist Party, they claimed 10,000 to 12,000, and even this was three to four times their size in 1958. No longer does the Communist Party tower over the other Left Wing American parties. In January 1957, the Socialist Party of Norman Thomas merged with the Social Democratic Federation, which had split from the Socialists in the mid-1930's. The new combined organization is as large as the Communist Party, and, furthermore, it is growing slowly.[20]

The number of dues-paying Communists, of course, is not a fully satisfactory measure of the party's strength, for it continues to have sympathizers who support the movement financially and otherwise, and there may be a number of hidden members. In the summer of 1958, Thompson boasted that the party had recently raised $20,000 for the *Worker* in three weeks.[21] Thompson's boast revealed more than he realized. In 1947, the San Francisco Communists had collected one-third that amount at one mass meeting, and the national organization had raised $250,000 in twenty days.[22] As the membership has declined, so has the number of fellow travelers. The increasing futility of party action and the events of 1956 in East Europe disillusioned the fellow travelers as well as party members. The Communist Party today is almost dead as a political force. The American Communists' threat, or potential threat, to national security is another matter—a police and military matter—but as a political movement the Communists are impotent.

Those who are left in the party can be described as a "hard core," a phrase with chilling connotations. Certainly most of the Communists left are hard, and together they constitute only a core of what the party once was. But even some of the champions of hardness do not seem to have as much steel in their conviction as they once had. Foster, the old man himself, was not able fully to rally his old-fashioned vocabulary of contempt when he blasted Theodore Draper's coldly objective history of the party's origins and earliest years.[23] And Elizabeth Gurley Flynn was milder in her denunciation of Gates when he quit the party than she had been in her comments on Anna Louise Strong when Stalin exiled her from Russia in 1949.[24] Among the top leaders, only Robert Thompson, the soldier, seemed as ruthless in 1957-58 as he had been in exterminating Browderism in 1945-46.

It does not seem likely today that the Communist Party will revive, but such a prediction cannot be made with assurance. Communist parties elsewhere in the world have grown from nearly nothing into a formidable political force within a brief period when the conditions for their growth were right and when they developed a line with popular appeal. The conditions necessary for the growth of the American party certainly are not present today, and the party has not had a line attractive to Americans since the end of the war in Europe. Even if there were the necessary conditions —an end of American-Russian tensions, a major economic depression on the scale of the 1930's, widespread social discontent, and a consequent pervasive demand for far-reaching political and economic change—it could well be that the Communist Party's record of tailoring its policies to the zigzagging exigencies of Soviet foreign policy and its history of vituperative attacks on respected working-class leaders and of internal repression of freedom would badly inhibit really important growth of the party. This speculation, however, assumes that the American general public knows the history of the Communist Party; and the general public, even the usually informed public, knows relatively little of Communist history despite the flood of anti-Communist literature America has produced.

It is not likely that the Communist Party will die out completely. If it were going to dissolve, it would probably have done so during the Hungarian crisis. Such groups seldom sign their own death certificates. Even the Industrial Workers of the World still maintain an office, and the Greenback Party occasionally runs a candidate. It is not probable that the Communists will decline to the levels of the I.W.W. and the Greenback Party, relics of the pre-Communist era, because they will continue, we may assume, to stay abreast of current world problems, and the Communists have the U.S.S.R. to look to and to serve. Yet the party has done very little recruiting for some years now, and its average member is already middle-aged. The time may have already come when more Communists die annually than are recruited.

At this moment, the Communist Party seems destined to join a collection of other sects as an exhibit in the museum of American Left Wing politics. It is a nice irony that it was Leon Trotsky, the antichrist of Communism, who years ago and in another context coined the phrase that today fits the American Communist Party: "swept into the dust bin of history."

SUICIDE AND INFANTICIDE

How does one explain this decline of the Communist movement in the United States?

The Communist Party, in the first place, was never strong. The explanation of this failure involves the totality of American political, cultural, and economic history, especially the relative lack of class consciousness in the United States. Here, however, we are primarily concerned with why the Communists declined from their 1947 peak.

William Z. Foster and his hard followers—to the extent that they were concerned with the party's viability at all—held that the answer to the question lay in an analysis of conditions and forces outside the party, in what they called the "objective condition" or the "objective situation." They also used the term "life itself," an interesting choice of words. John Gates and his sympathizers held that the answer to the question lay in an exploration of the party's "errors," the mistakes of judgment it had made during the years it was in decline. Both Foster and Gates were right; but neither was completely right.

One important external condition that hurt the Communist Party was American postwar prosperity, the longest and most vigorous prosperity the United States has ever enjoyed. Postwar America has had economic recessions—in 1949, in 1953-54, and again in 1957-58—which brought hardship to large numbers of people, but these recessions were nothing comparable to the calamity of the Great Depression of the 1930's. During periods of prosperity, social discontent does not disappear entirely, but it is not as intense as it is during serious depressions. The average American worker who has been steadily employed since the war, who has bought a home, a car, and a television set, is not likely to be stirred by Communist denunciations of capitalism and imperialism even if he is behind on his installment payments. The era of the picture window and the tail-finned automobile has produced its own dissatisfactions and frustrations but not the kind that leads one to seek salvation in Left Wing politics. Postwar prosperity has tended to make American labor even more middle class than it was under the leadership of Gompers and Green and consequently less inclined than ever to pursue revolutionary purposes. Prosperity has affected youth as well as labor. Good times have sluiced off the natural revolt of young people into nonpolitical activities—beards and Zen Buddhism, for example—and the Communists' efforts to build a youth movement have failed conspicuously. All in all, prosperity's effects have been pervasive—the Communists would say "insidious."

A more important external condition hampering the Communists was the cold war and its many ramifications within American society. The American public, quite properly, identifies the Communist Party with the Soviet Union, which has never been more unpopular in the United States. Opposition to domestic Communism is nearly universal and more intense than ever before in America's long tradition of hostility toward that particular "foreign ideology." During the war, the fact that Russia and the United States were allies against the Nazis had brought a rather spectacular reversal of American opposition to Communism. At the end of the war, public-opinion polls indicated that Americans had less resentment against Communists than they had had before Pearl Harbor. But the public's tolerance of Communists, or at least its indifference toward them, quickly disappeared as tensions between America and Russia became severe. By the early 1950's, the American Communists had become community outcasts— and nearly outlaws.

This popular anti-Communism expressed itself partly in anti-Communist legislation and prosecutions. From 1949 on, the American Communists were forced to spend a large part of their time, energy, and money trying to stay out of prison and trying to maintain the legality of their organization. The party necessarily went on the defensive, and imprisonment deprived it of some of its abler leaders.

But another, and probably more important, aspect of postwar anti-Communism was the development of labor and non-Communist left-of-center groups into strong centers of anti-Communism. Before 1945, patriotic and business organizations had the field of anti-Communism almost to themselves, and although they certainly helped to condition the American population against Communist ideas, they had little influence in labor circles and among non-Communist critics of the *status quo*. The most important addition to the ranks of anti-Communism came in the early postwar years when the C.I.O. declared war on the Communists, and non-Communist liberals organized Americans for Democratic Action. The Communists had to "reach" the worker in basic industry and the political rebel, but the development of labor and liberal anti-Communism not only deprived the Communists of an audience, but developed hostility toward the Communists precisely where the Communists most wanted power. The decline of the American Communist Party can be told largely in terms of the conversion of the non-Communist Left into the anti-Communist Left.

The party would have had a difficult time confronting these external conditions even if it had adopted the wisest of policies. The Communists, however, were not wise, even in their choice of tactics. With postwar international relations and the conditions of American society in the late 1940's what they were, the Communists could hardly have selected a less propitious time to adopt a hard line.

At a time when most of organized labor was tying its political fortunes to the Democratic Party, the Communists embarked upon third-party adventures. The Communists so flagrantly dominated the Progressive Party that they thoroughly alienated many non-Communist critics of the *status quo,* and for years to come, many American political rebels who cannot feel altogether comfortable within the major political parties will resent the way that the Communists discredited the tradition of third-party revolt. At a time when American Negroes were beginning to make progress in their program for first-class citizenship and integration into the fabric of American life, the Communists returned to their old "self-determination for the Negro people in the Black Belt" position, which smacked too much of segregation, of "Red Crow," to attract Negro militants. When American writers were increasingly moving away from the social themes which permeated their product in the 1930's, the Communists insisted that literature be a "weapon" in the class struggle. When Americans were "returning to religion," the Communists went back to their old line that religion was an opium, a kind of superstition foisted upon a gullible public by self-serving economic interests. At a time when relations between the Soviet Union and the United States were dangerously strained, American Communists insisted that the Soviet position was entirely right and the American position entirely wrong. The Communists' "errors" made the "objective situation" worse.

The party's obeisance to Moscow was the source of its "errors" and the root cause of its unhappy "objective situation." If Foster ever perceived this fundamental fact about his party, he never expressed himself. And Gates, at least while he was still in the party, perceived it only dimly and without seeing all its ramifications, even though he favored loosening the Communists' tie to the Soviets.

The Communists made all their important "errors" either in direct response to obvious Soviet desires or in response to their habit of aping the Soviets and other foreign Communist parties. The Communist Party's 1948 electoral policy was a direct result of Zhdanov's speech in Poland and the organization of the Cominform in September 1947. Until news of the speech and the establishment of the new Communist international organization reached the United States, American Communists were still talking about a third party as a lever within the Democratic coalition rather than as an independent, competitive ticket. The Communists' other disastrous mistakes had their root cause in Russian policy. Their line on the American Negro derived directly from Stalin's theory—but not his actual policy—about the several nationality groups within the Soviet empire. The American party's wild estimate of the danger of total war and domestic fascism was the same as that of Communist parties everywhere. In their underground of 1949 and after, the Communists copied the tactics of European Communists with dire results. Indeed, their whole shift in policy from an accommodating line to a hard line in 1945 was dictated by their conformity to the zigzagging direction of Russian foreign policy.

The "objective situation" itself was not a result of the American party's connection to foreign Communism, but the party's reaction to the "objective situation" was. No one compelled the Communists to follow the Soviets' foreign policy against United States policy when relations between the two nations deteriorated. It would have been possible for the Communists to have criticized both American and Russian policy. A few genuine rebels did. Of course, the Communists would have no longer been Communists if they had done so, because compliance with Russian foreign policy has been the one constant, unvarying characteristic of Communist parties the world over. Nevertheless, the Communists could have decided to be American radicals rather than Russian weather vanes. They could have decided to be Left rather than East. And surely the attitude of the American public toward the Communists would have been different if the Communists had applied the same standards of criticism toward Russia as they did toward the United States.

Nothing but their own habits of mind compelled American Communists to defend themselves against anti-Communist attacks with a repression within their party at least as hysterical as that with which they were confronted; they reacted to McCarthyism with Stalinism. The closeness of the American Communists to the Soviet Union and other foreign Communist organizations—a tie unique in American politics—was their basic weakness.

And yet, paradoxically, their identification with the Soviets was, if one considers their whole history, a source of strength as well as a root of weakness. Their birth during and immediately after World War I was a result of the Bolshevik revolution. They survived the 1920's because the Bolsheviks survived the decade, and at that time the Russians subsidized them directly with "Moscow gold." In the 1930's, the American Communists profited from the fact that American capitalism was depressed and the Russian economy was expanding. Many Americans, thinking mistakenly that the Russian economy was truly socialist because the Russians despised capitalism, admired the Soviets for their material advancement—although even during the American depression, the American living standard was far higher than the Russian— and ignored the Russian totalitarian denial of individual liberty and dignity. The American Communists reaped advantage from their Russian connection in those days, as they did again during World War II, when the Soviet Union was an American military ally and its armies were slaughtering—and being slaughtered by— the Nazi *Wehrmacht*. Even today, the party finds some advantage in its Eastern bonds. The American Communists are relieved of the burden of having to think for themselves. That chore is performed by their abler European and Asian comrades; the American Communists have only to translate to the American scene. In addition, the party, to a slight degree even today, basks in the reflection of Soviet achievements, as it did to a greater extent from 1930 to 1945. The Soviet Union is a going concern, whether one approves of where it is going or not. Lincoln Steffens, after a trip to Russia when the Communist regime there was young, said he had been "over into the future, and it works." He was partly right. Whether or not it is the future still remains to be seen, but it does "work" if one applies the materialist value standard of industrial expansion, of tons of steel produced, kilowatt hours of electric power generated, or sputniks put into orbit, and does not apply the Western values of democracy, of diversity, and of individual liberty and due process of law. Whether the Russian economy "works" better than the American economy in the long run also remains to be seen. To the degree that Americans do admire the Soviet Union, the American Communist Party derives some reflected advantage from their Russian identification.

It is probable that the American Communist Party will continue to exist in some feeble form or other until the Soviet party finds it no longer useful. At the moment, at least, the Russians find the American party too useful to let it disappear entirely, though they think more highly of the French and Italian parties, which are of greater value to them. The Russians do not have any apparent hope for the success of their American comrades. Nor have the Russians pursued policies calculated to strengthen the American branch. The coup in Czechoslovakia and the Berlin blockade during the 1948 election campaign are cases in point. The Soviets find the American Communists useful primarily for propaganda purposes elsewhere in the world. Russia can maintain that the American Communists are the "vanguard" of the American working class and that the American people do not really support their "imperialist warmonger" rulers. Foreign Communists, especially the French, capitalized on the Rosenberg case to heighten anti-American sentiment and used *We Charge Genocide,* the American party's outrageous book on the treatment of the American Negro, for the same purpose. Some of the material on the United States in the Cominform's shrill newspaper, *For a Lasting Peace, For a People's Democracy!*, was only a paraphrased version of *Daily Worker* stories.

But such is the irony of history and life that, despite the degree of utility the American branch has for the Soviet party, the Soviet administered to the American Communists their last crushing blow. The disadvantages under which the American party labored had been becoming less severe before the twentieth congress and continued to ameliorate thereafter. McCarthyism clearly was in decline after the fall of 1954. The Supreme Court, in a series of important decisions—the Jencks case, the Yates case, and the Scales-Lightfoot case—removed some of the legal blocks that put the party at serious disadvantage. Before the twentieth congress of the Communist Party of the Soviet Union and Khrushchev's secret speech, the American party was ineffective; after the twentieth congress, it was impotent. The party's final crisis was not the result of either "error" or the "objective situation." It was precipitated entirely by the Russian denunciation of Stalin and the crushing of the Hungarian revolution.

To add to the irony, it was John Gates who, among the top leaders of the party, was most forcefully affected by these foreign events, and it was Gates who most wanted to loosen or sever the connection with the Soviet Union and to build an independent Communist Party which would look toward America rather than Moscow.

Of all the generalizations about the Communist Party of the United States and its history that might be made from the evidence, the most important and most nearly universally valid one is this: the American Communist Party was and is the willing instrument of the Soviet Union. The revolution does indeed devour the children it has borne and nursed and never weaned.

BIBLIOGRAPHICAL ESSAY / NOTES / INDEX

BIBLIOGRAPHICAL ESSAY

There are not available today the kind of manuscript sources on the Communist Party's history since 1945 that the historian likes to have. If the party itself has correspondence, unpublished reports, and membership records, it does not make them available. There is undoubtedly a rich store of materials on the party in the files of the Federal Bureau of Investigation, but their records are also unavailable. I have, therefore, been forced to rely primarily upon the party press, upon personal interviews, and upon what information I could glean from nonparty sources.

The party press is a much richer storehouse of information than one would expect. The press was the party's primary means of communication to the membership, and it necessarily revealed a great deal. Its press did not print its innermost secrets, but a great many matters that one would not expect to be printed did appear. Especially after the party crisis broke in 1956 did long-hidden incidents, plans, and conditions come to light.

I have been through the files of the *Daily Worker* and its Sunday edition, the *Worker,* throughout the period, as well as the *Daily People's World* of the West Coast. The Cominform newspaper, *For a Lasting Peace, For a People's Democracy!,* which I trust had a somewhat more abbreviated title in at least some of the several languages in which it was published from 1947 to 1956, was useful for the international Communist line. The best single source for the American party's line was *Political Affairs,* the monthly published by the party, until 1944 called the *Communist.* Communist pamphlets, most of them published by New Century, were also useful. One cannot ignore the "inner-party" press, the magazines intended only for party eyes. The publications of this type that I was able to unearth were *Contact,* published by national party headquarters in 1947, *Party Voice,* a monthly published by the New York organization from 1953, and the preconvention *Discussion Bulletins* published in 1945 and again in late 1956 and early 1957.

One has to learn to read Communist publications. First of all, one has to learn party jargon, or Communese, which differs from English in several important respects. In Communese, for example, the word "correct" means in harmony with the international line of the moment rather than "true." In fact, many things that were "correct" were demonstrably untrue. But even after mastering Communese, there is the problem of learning what is significant in party publications. Frequently, what a Communist left unsaid was as important as what he did say. Sometimes the mere fact that some subject or other received a considerable amount of attention in the press—for example, denunciations of Keynesianism in 1948—was more revealing than what was actually said. The reader of this book will be able to see the problems of interpretation involved in some of the quoted Communist writings. And in using the Communist press, one must exercise more than the usual scholarly caution about veracity.

Communist publications, especially pamphlets and inner-party publications, are not easy to find. I was fortunate in having available the small but invaluable collection of party materials that William Goldsmith gathered for the "Communism in American Life" project. This excellent collection should someday be made available to all scholars. Among the better public libraries on this subject are the New York Public Library and the Wisconsin Historical Society, at Madison, but I found two private libraries of great utility: the library of the now defunct Jefferson School of Social Science in New York and the personal library of Philip Jaffe, an assiduous collector of such materials, in Stamford, Connecticut. The librarian of the Jefferson School was most co-operative. He sometimes sold me duplicate copies of pamphlets and magazines. What has happened to the Jefferson School collections since the place closed late in 1956, I do not know, but those materials should be preserved. Finally, anyone working in this field of historical research must haunt party bookstores, which are never identified as such and have innocuous names. They are easily identified by the publications they sell. For some reason, most of these bookstores are presided over by rather vague old ladies who seldom have the right change.

Among the nonparty sources that were useful were the mimeo-

graphed minutes of the national committee of the Progressive Party
and the many press releases of that organization in Philip Jaffe's collection. I also found extremely revealing the testimony, cited in Chapter IV, that was taken by a C.I.O. committee in its hearings on
charges against the International Longshoremen's and Warehousemen's
Union. And then there is the testimony to be found in the published
hearings and reports of various Congressional committees investigating
Communism. On the whole, Congressional sources are a disappoint-
ment, although I sometimes found them useful. Both committee members and counsel were interested in names to be investigated further.
They frequently cut off a witness who seemed about on the point
of revealing something significant about the party's operations with
an exasperating request for more names. The most useful reports of
these committees were the result of traditional library research methods rather than of interrogation of witnesses.

I was able to get more interviews than a historian customarily can.
Earl Browder was helpful on the backgrounds of certain party leaders
and party problems. He also lent me some of the Left-deviationist
publications he had collected, as did Philip Jaffe. After the party
became engaged in a sharp internal struggle in 1956, I was able to
get information through interviews with party leaders and journalists,
primarily John Gates. Much that I learned in these interviews only
confirmed what I had already surmised, some of the information led
me to pursue new avenues of conventional research, and some of the
information I could have learned only through such interviews. Perhaps this book should be dedicated to Nikita Khrushchev, whose secret
speech on Stalin's crimes in February 1956 created conditions in the
American party which considerably facilitated my research.

Secondary sources useful in the writing of this book were dis-
tressingly few. Irving Howe and Lewis Coser in *The American Communist Party: A Critical History* (*1919-1957*) (Boston: Beacon,
1957) devote only sixty-three pages to the period after 1945, and
their volume is easily the most comprehensive history of the party
in this period heretofore published. John Gates, *The Story of an
American Communist* (New York: Nelson, 1958) is a useful autobiography. Its tenth chapter, pp. 157-191, is an account of the party's
crisis after the 1956 Khrushchev speech. The book appeared after I
had completed this volume, but it does not conflict with my account.
Through the party press and interviews with Gates and others in 1956
and 1957, I had been able to gather more details than Gates could
include in one chapter of an autobiography. J. Edgar Hoover's *Masters*

of Deceit: The Story of Communism in America and How to Fight It (New York: Doubleday, 1958) is rather superficial as a history of the party, although it is occasionally useful for the party's organization and methods. Actually, the F.B.I. director's book is a better primary source about anti-Communist activities. Quite useful to me were Max M. Kampelman, *The Communist Party vs. the C.I.O.: A Study in Power Politics* (New York: Praeger, 1957), Philip Selznick, *The Organizational Weapon* (New York: McGraw-Hill, 1952), Wilson Record, *The Negro and the Communist Party* (Chapel Hill: University of North Carolina Press, 1951), and the unpublished University of Chicago dissertation on the Progressive Party by John Cotton Brown, which I used extensively in Chapter V. William Z. Foster's *History of the Communist Party of the United States* (New York: International, 1952) is, for the postwar period, primarily a defense of the party's line and a denunciation of Browderism. Whatever value it has is as a primary source for the party line in the late Stalin period, and it is not as useful in this sense as the files of *Political Affairs*.

In 1955, the Fund for the Republic, Inc., published a large volume entitled *Bibliography of the Communist Problem in the United States*. Professor Joel Seidman, of the University of Chicago, is now engaged in enlarging and bringing that bibliography up to date. In view of these works, each of them far more comprehensive than anything I could append to this volume, it seems unwise to present the usual list of sources. For the materials I have used, the reader is referred to the notes.

NOTES

Abbreviations: *PA* for *Political Affairs*
DW for *Daily Worker*
Wkr for *The Worker*

CHAPTER ONE: NEW LEADER AND NEW LINE

1. Interview with Earl Browder, March 6, 1956.
2. Earl Browder, "Teheran—History's Greatest Turning Point," *The Communist*, XXIII (Jan. 1944), p. 8.
3. Wilson Record, *The Negro and the Communist Party* (Chapel Hill: University of North Carolina Press, 1951), pp. 203-5, 213-14.
4. Roy Hudson, "Labor's Victory Wage Policies," *PA*, XXIV (April 1945), p. 311; Irving Howe and B. J. Widick, *The UAW and Walter Reuther* (New York: Random House, 1949), pp. 114 ff.; Sidney Lens, *Left, Right and Center: Conflicting Forces in American Labor* (Hinsdale, Ill.: Regnery, 1949), pp. 343-5.
5. "Browder Answers Some Questions," *New Masses*, Jan. 2, 1945, p. 17; A. B. Magil, "Letter to a Liberal," *ibid.*, Jan. 9, 1945, pp. 7-8; "The Irresponsibles," *ibid.*, Jan. 2, 1945, p. 8; Magil, "Where Do the Liberals Go from Here?," *ibid.*, Jan. 23, 1945, pp. 9-12; Virginia Gardner, "Copperhead Field Day," *ibid.*, Jan. 2, 1945, pp. 13-14; Earl Browder, "Browder on National Service," *PA*, XXIV (Feb. 1945), pp. 115-16.
6. Earl Browder, "After V-E Day—What Next?," *PA*, XXIV (June 1945), p. 485.
7. Carl Ross, "Universal Military Training," *ibid.*, XXIV (Jan. 1945), pp. 60, 64; Roy Hudson, *op. cit.*, pp. 311-12; John Williamson, "The CPA —Our Most Indispensable Weapon," *PA*, XXIV (Jan. 1945), p. 46.
8. Earl Browder, "A Political Program of American Fascism," *ibid.*, XXIV (Feb. 1945), p. 107; Browder, "The Study of Lenin's Teachings," *ibid.*, XXIV (Jan. 1945), p. 4.
9. The January 1944 letter was published in *ibid.*, XXIV (July 1945), pp. 640-55; Foster quotation from "The Danger of American Imperialism in the Postwar Period," *ibid.*, XXIV (June 1945), pp. 494-5.

10. Eugene Dennis, *The People Against the Trusts* (New York: New Century, Dec. 1946), p. 4; interview with Earl Browder, May 14, 1956.
11. *Wkr*, March 4, 11, 1956; *DW*, June 22, 1956; interview with Earl Browder, March 6, 1956.
12. Eugene Dennis, "Yalta and America's •National Unity," *PA*, XXIV (April 1945), pp. 302-10; Dennis, "Postwar Labor-Capital Cooperation," *ibid.*, XXIV (May 1945), pp. 415-22; *DW*, June 16, 1945.
13. "The Present Situation and the Next Tasks" as it was adopted by the national board, June 2, 1945, appears in *DW*, June 4, 1945, and *Wkr*, June 10, 1945; the text as it was approved by the national committee and then further edited is in *DW*, July 2, 1945, and *PA*, XXIV (July 1945), pp. 579-90; the resolution as finally adopted by the convention is in *Wkr*, Aug. 12, 1945.
14. Earl Browder, "On the Question of Revisionism," *DW*, July 24, 1945; W. Z. Foster, "Browder on Revisionism," *ibid.*, July 25, 1945.
15. *Ibid.*, July 3, 1945.
16. *Ibid.*, Jan. 28, 29, Feb. 14, 1946; "On the Expulsion of Earl Browder," *PA*, XXV (March 1946), pp. 215-17.
17. Interview with Earl Browder, May 14, 1956; *Distributors Guide*, Jan. 4–April 27, 1946. The newsletter had sixteen issues. William Browder formally announced the publication's demise in a mimeographed letter to the subscribers, July 8, 1946, over two months after the last issue appeared.
18. Interviews with Earl Browder, March 6, May 14, 1956.
19. *DW*, April 27, 30, 1946; *Wkr*, April 28, 1946.
20. Interviews with Earl Browder, March 6, May 14, 1956.
21. *DW*, April 14, May 24, 1946; "Statement of Comrade Heller to the Executive Committee of his Club," March 25, 1946, mimeographed document in the possession of Philip Jaffe, Stamford, Conn. Heller remained loyal to the party and the U.S.S.R. despite his expulsion. See his letters to the editors of the *DW*, June 25, 1956, and the *National Guardian*, June 4, 1956.
22. See, for example, W. Z. Foster, "On the Expulsion of Browder," *PA*, XXV (April 1946), pp. 339-48; Foster, "One Year of Struggle against Browderism," *ibid.*, XXV (Sept. 1946), pp. 771-7; Alexander Bittelman, "Problems of Peace, Democracy, and National Independence. On Earl Browder's book, 'War or Peace with Russia,'" *ibid.*, XXVI (June 1947), pp. 508-19; Howard Jennings, "Revisionism and American History," *ibid.*, XXV (Aug. 1946), pp. 742-62; Gilbert Green, "The Browderite Conception of History," *ibid.*, XXVIII (Oct. 1949), pp. 65-84; Robert Thompson, *The Path of a Renegade. Why Earl Browder Was Expelled from the Communist Party* (New York: New Century, April 1946).
23. "American Labor Faces May Day," *PA*, XXVII (May 1948), p. 394.
24. "The Convention Unanimously Rejects Browder's Appeal," *ibid.*, XXVII (Sept. 1948), pp. 935-6.
25. *DW*, Sept. 12, 1946; "The Minton-McKenney Flight," *New Masses*, Sept. 24, 1946, pp. 5-8.
26. "Statement of the National Board of the Communist Party on the Recent Expulsions of Vern Smith, Ruth McKenney, Bruce Minton and

William F. Dunne," *PA*, XXV (Nov. 1946), pp. 1011-15, and *DW*, Sept. 30, 1946. See also Jim Allan and George Morris in *DW*, July 7-9, 1947; Oleta O'Conner Yates, "The Struggle against Deviations and Factionalism in San Francisco," *PA*, XXV (Dec. 1946), pp. 1092-1103; and William Weinstone, "The Tactics of the Party in the New York State Elections," *ibid.* (Oct. 1946), pp. 911-13.

27. Interview with Earl Browder, May 14, 1956; *DW*, March 24, 1948; *Towards Socialism*, May 1, 1948, Oct. 10, 1949; *Turning Point*, Nov. 1949, p. 11.

28. Harrison George, *The Crisis in the C.P.U.S.A.* (Los Angeles: privately printed, 1947), p. 14.

29. *Towards Socialism*, May 1, 1949; interview with Earl Browder, May 14, 1956.

30. William Z. Foster, *The Twilight of World Capitalism* (New York: International, 1949), pp. 31-2; see also Foster, "American Imperialism, Leader of World Reaction," *PA*, XXV (Aug. 1946), pp. 686-95; and Foster, "American Imperialism and the War Danger," *ibid.*, XXVI (Aug. 1947), pp. 675-87.

31. Eugene Dennis, *Peace or War: The People against the Warmakers!* (New York: New Century, May 1946), p. 7, a speech delivered at a May Day rally in Cleveland, 1946; *DW*, Aug. 8, 1946; W. Z. Foster, "American Imperialism and the War Danger," *loc. cit.*, pp. 675-6; James S. Allen, "The Policy of Anti-Soviet Encirclement," *PA*, XXV (Oct. 1946), pp. 879-92; Alexander Bittelman, "The Anglo-American Bloc," *ibid.*, XXV (July 1946), pp. 588-96.

32. William Z. Foster, *The New Europe* (New York: International, 1947), p. 89; see also John Stuart, "The Aim of Soviet Policy," *New Masses*, April 16, 1946, pp. 10-13; Joseph Starobin in *DW*, Feb. 16, 1946; Max Weiss, "Oust the Trotskyites from the Labor and Progressive Movement," *PA*, XXV (Feb. 1946), p. 132; and Weiss, "The Struggle on the Ideological Front," *ibid.*, XXV (Sept. 1946), p. 842.

33. William Z. Foster, *The New Europe*, p. 89; see also Joseph Clark in *DW*, Feb. 23, 1947.

34. *DW*, Aug. 7, 1947; also in *PA*, XXVI (May 1947), pp. 391-4.

35. The quotation is from Adam Lapin in *DW*, Nov. 24, 1945.

36. *Ibid.*, Feb. 13, 1946.

37. *Wkr*, Dec. 18, 1949; "Greetings to Joseph Vissarionovich Stalin on His Seventieth Birthday (December 21, 1949)," *PA*, XXIX (Jan. 1950), pp. 1-3; Alexander Bittelman, "Stalin: On His Seventieth Birthday," *ibid.*, XXVIII (Dec. 1949), p. 1.

38. Eugene Dennis, "The London Conference," *ibid.*, XXIV (Nov. 1945), pp. 965-6.

39. *DW*, March 30, 1946; see also Allen, "The Policy of Anti-Soviet Encirclement," *loc. cit.*, p. 879.

40. "Washington-London Axis," *New Masses*, March 19, 1946, p. 4.

41. *DW*, Oct. 14, 1946.

42. *Ibid.*, Feb. 5, 6, 8, 1947.

43. Joseph Starobin in *ibid.*, July 20, 1946.

44. Joseph Starobin, "The Truman Doctrine," *PA*, XXVI (May 1947), p. 403.

45. William Z. Foster, "Organized Labor and the Marshall Plan," *ibid.,* XXVII (Feb. 1948), p. 99.
46. Milton Howard, "The Ruhr—Can Liberals Support Revival of Reich Trusts?," *DW,* July 18, 1947, reprinted in *Fighting Words: Selections from Twenty-five Years of the Daily Worker* (New York: International Publishers, 1949), pp. 59-61; see also Joseph Clark, "American Labor and the German Working Class," *PA,* XXVII (April 1948), pp. 337-43.
47. James S. Allen, *Marshall Plan—Recovery or War?* (New York: New Century, 1948), p. 51.
48. *Ibid.,* pp. 48-9, 55, 62.
49. Arnold Johnson, "The North Atlantic Pact for Aggression," *PA,* XXVIII (May 1949), p. 16.
50. W. Z. Foster, *Twilight,* pp. 34-5.
51. Rob Fowler Hall, "Stop American Intervention in China!," *PA,* XXIV (Dec. 1945), p. 1065; James S. Allen, "The Policy of Anti-Soviet Encirclement," *loc. cit.,* p. 883; Frederick Vanderbilt Field, "Get Out of China," *New Masses,* Aug. 13, 1946, p. 11; Field, "Doublecross in China," *ibid.,* Sept. 10, 1946, pp. 8-11.
52. *DW,* Nov. 3, 1947.
53. Statement by the party secretariat, "Trieste and the Right of Self-Determination," *ibid.,* May 28, 1946; W. Z. Foster, *The New Europe,* pp. 18, 25-7, 77, 87.
54. *For a Lasting Peace, For a People's Democracy!* (Bucharest), July 15, 1948. This official Cominform newspaper, published in several languages, had appeared from Belgrade until the Tito schism.

CHAPTER TWO: THE PARTY LINE FOR AMERICA

1. Max Weiss, "The Struggle on the Ideological Front," *PA,* XXV (Sept. 1946), pp. 838, 847.
2. Jack Stachel, "Highlights of the Recent Labor Developments," *ibid.,* XXV (July 1946), p. 579.
3. Statement by the party's national board, "The People's Fight for Wages, Jobs, and Security," *ibid.,* XXIV (Nov. 1945), p. 1001; see also Eugene Dennis, "The Progressives Can and Must Unite," *ibid.,* XXVI (March 1947), pp. 195-203, and Hal Simon, "Some Lessons of the Recent Strike Struggle," *ibid.,* XXV (June 1946), pp. 499-500.
4. The editors, "Hit and Run," *New Masses,* Oct. 16, 1945, p. 8; Lewis Merrill, "Memo to Professionals," *ibid.,* Jan. 8, 1946, p. 15; J. B. S. Haldane, "The Party for Professionals," *ibid.,* March 12, 1946, p. 12.
5. Lillian Gates, "The People Fight Back for Rent and Housing," *PA,* XXVI (April 1947), pp. 316-27; Henry Schubart, "The Housing Crisis," *ibid.,* XXV (March 1946), pp. 240-53; Virginia Gardner, "Why You Can't Get a House," *New Masses,* Jan. 15, 1946, pp. 3-5; George Bernstein, "The People's Fight for Progressive Taxation," *PA,* XXIV (Dec. 1945), p. 1108.
6. Jacob Mindel, "Benjamin Franklin," *PA,* XXVI (May 1947), pp. 471-

80; see also Abner Berry, "The Fourth of July, 1947," *ibid.*, XXVI (July 1947), pp. 571-5.
7. Interview with Earl Browder, July 31, 1956.
8. Peter Seeger, "People's Songs and Singers," *New Masses,* July 16, 1947, pp. 7-8.
9. William Z. Foster, "Leninism and Some Practical Problems of the Postwar Period," *PA,* XXV (Feb. 1946), p. 106; Eugene Dennis, *What America Faces* (New York: New Century, 1946), pp. 58-9; Gilbert Green in "Speeches in Discussion on the Draft Resolution of the National Board at the Plenary Meeting of National Committee, C.P.A., June 18-20, 1945," *PA,* XXIV (July 1945), p. 596.
10. Foster, *op. cit.,* p. 106; Henry Winston, "Not Against but with the Stream," *PA,* XXVI (Aug. 1947), p. 737.
11. Eugene Dennis, "Postwar Labor-Capital Cooperation," *PA,* XXIV (May 1945), p. 415.
12. *DW,* Sept. 4, 1946.
13. *Wkr,* April 21, June 2, 1946.
14. *DW,* June 11, 1946.
15. James S. Allen, *Who Owns America?* (New York: New Century, June 1946), pp. 29, 6; Alexander Bittelman, "The Beginning of the Economic Crisis in the United States," *PA,* XXVIII (July 1949), pp. 22-32; Gil Green, "A Few Thoughts on Our Perspectives," *ibid.,* XXVIII (Aug. 1949), pp. 731-8.
16. Arnold Berman, "On Method in Political Economy," *PA,* XXXV (June 1956), pp. 44-57.
17. *Izmenenija vekonomike kapitalizma v itoge vtoroj mirovoj vojny* (Moscow, 1946).
18. *Commercial and Financial Chronicle* (New York), March 2, 1944. The biographical material here is from the introduction to this article.
19. Eugene Varga, "Toward a New Crash?," *New Masses,* Jan. 29, 1946, pp. 3-5, 15.
20. The present writer has based his account of Varga's book upon a manuscript translation by the Russian-born Irene Browder (Mrs. Earl Browder), in the library of Philip Jaffe, Stamford, Conn., and the excellent article by Frederick C. Barghoorn, "The Varga Discussion and Its Significance," *The American Slavic and East European Review,* VII (Oct. 1948), pp. 214-36.
21. Barghoorn, *op. cit.,* pp. 227-31; Leo Gruliow, translator, *Soviet Views on the Post-war World Economy* (Washington: Public Affairs Press, 1948); Joseph P. Lash, "Iron Curtain for the Mind," *The New Republic,* Dec. 27, 1948, pp. 13-15; New York *Times,* Sept. 8, Nov. 28, 30, 1946.
22. A translation of this article appears in *Communist* (Bombay), II (June-July 1949), pp. 108-22, along with another attack on Varga by his chief critic, K. V. Ostrovitjanov.
23. I. Kuzminov, "The Crisis Character of the Economic Development of the U.S. in the Postwar Period," *PA,* XXVIII (May 1949), pp. 54-70, translated from *Bolshevik* (Moscow), Dec. 15, 1948; Eugene Varga, "Against Reformist Tendencies in Works on Imperialism," *PA,* XXVIII (Dec. 1949), pp. 74-86.

24. James S. Allen and Doxey Wilkerson, eds., with an introductory essay by William Z. Foster, *The Economic Crisis and the Cold War* (New York: New Century, 1949). Foster's communication appears on pp. 1-10.
25. Bernard Karsh and Phillips L. Garman, "The Impact of the Political Left," in Milton Derber and Edwin Young, eds., *Labor and the New Deal* (Madison: University of Wisconsin Press, 1947), pp. 103-8.
26. William Z. Foster, "The Wage and Strike Movement," *PA*, XXV (Feb. 1946), pp. 121-9; Alexander Bittelman, "Wages and Prices under Monopoly Capitalism," *ibid.*, XXV (May 1946), pp. 434-6.
27. John Williamson, "For a Mass Party of the Working Class," *ibid.*, XXV (March 1946), p. 227.
28. *Final Proceedings* of the Eighth Constitutional Convention of the Congress of Industrial Organizations, 1946, pp. 111-14.
29. *Time*, Nov. 25, 1946; New York *Times*, Nov. 17, 24, 1946.
30. *DW*, Nov. 19, 29, 1946.
31. William Weinstone, *The Case against David Dubinsky* (New York: New Century, 1946), p. 5; *DW*, April 16, 19, 1946.
32. Carl Winter, "The Face of a Social-Democrat—Walter P. Reuther," *PA*, XXV (May 1946), p. 410.
33. See Max Weiss, "Oust the Trotskyites from the Labor and Progressive Movement," *ibid.*, XXV (Feb. 1946), pp. 130-148.
34. V. J. Jerome, "The Vatican's War on Peace," *ibid.*, XXV (April 1946), p. 325.
35. *Ibid.*, p. 311.
36. (New York: International, 1949), p. 94.
37. Jerome, *op. cit.*, p. 325.
38. W. Z. Foster, *The Twilight of World Capitalism* (New York: International, 1949), pp. 98, 92, 99.
39. William H. Melish, "The Church and Fascism," *New Masses*, March 12, 1946, p. 14.
40. Granville Hicks, *Where We Came Out* (New York: Viking, 1954), pp. 51-8.
41. New York *Times*, Feb. 28, 1943; *The New Yorker*, Feb. 27, 1943; interview with Earl Browder, March 6, 1956.
42. William Z. Foster, "Elements of a People's Cultural Policy," *New Masses*, April 23, 1946, p. 9; see also Foster, *Twilight*, pp. 145-6.
43. Albert Maltz, "What Shall We Ask of Writers?," *New Masses*, Feb. 12, 1946, pp. 19-22.
44. Eugene Dennis, *What America Faces*, p. 61.
45. Howard Fast, "Art and Politics," *New Masses*, Feb. 26, 1946, pp. 6-8; Joseph North, "No Retreat for the Writer," *ibid.*, Feb. 26, 1946, pp. 8-10; Alvah Bessie, "What Is Freedom for Writers," *ibid.*, March 12, 1946, pp. 8-10; John Howard Lawson, "Art Is a Weapon," *ibid.*, March 19, 1946, pp. 18-20.
46. *Wkr*, April 7, 1946; *DW*, April 8, 1946.
47. *DW*, Sept. 11, 1946.
48. Herb Tank, "A Christmas Story," *Fighting Words: Selections from Twenty-five Years of the Daily Worker* (New York: International Publishers, 1949), pp. 225-6.

49. Earl Browder, "On the Negroes and the Right of Self-Determination," *The Communist*, XXIII (Jan. 1944), pp. 83-4.
50. James W. Ford in *DW*, June 25, 1945; Benjamin J. Davis, Jr., in *Wkr*, July 22, 1945; see also letter from Edna Lewis, *DW*, June 29, 1945, and article by William Harrison, *Wkr*, July 15, 1945.
51. *Wkr*, Aug. 12, 1945.
52. Claudia Jones, "On the Right to Self-Determination for the Negro People in the Black Belt," *PA*, XXV (Jan. 1946), pp. 67-77.
53. Max Weiss, *ibid.*, XXV (May 1946), pp. 457-78.
54. Francis Franklin, "The Status of the Negro People in the Black Belt and How to Fight for the Right of Self-Determination," *ibid.*, XXV (May 1946), pp. 438-56.
55. Testimony of Wilkerson in Hearings before the Subcommittee To Investigate the Administration of the Internal Security Act . . . of the Committee on the Judiciary, United States Senate, 83d Cong., 1st sess., March 1953, pp. 637-43. This committee was popularly known at the time as the Jenner Committee.
56. Doxey Wilkerson, "The Negro and the American Nation," *PA*, XXV (July 1946), pp. 652-68.
57. James S. Allen, "The Negro Question," *ibid.*, XXV (Nov. 1946), pp. 1046-56; Allen, "The Negro People As a Nation," *ibid.*, XXV (Dec. 1946), pp. 1132-50; William Z. Foster, "On Self-Determination for the Negro People," *ibid.*, XXV (June 1946), pp. 549-54.
58. "Resolution on the Question of Negro Rights and Self-Determination Adopted by the National Committee, CPUSA, at Its December 3-5, 1946, Meeting," *ibid.*, XXVI (Feb. 1947), pp. 155-8. The resolution appears also in William Z. Foster and others, *The Communist Position on the Negro Question* (New York: New Century, Feb. 1947), pp. 9-13. For another account of the party line on the Negro immediately after the war, see Wilson Record, *The Negro and the Communist Party* (Chapel Hill: University of North Carolina Press, 1951), pp. 235-43.
59. Foster and others, *op. cit.*, p. 14.
60. William Z. Foster, "On the Question of Negro Self-Determination," *PA*, XXVI (Jan. 1947), p. 56.
61. *DW*, Feb. 23, Oct. 22, 1946, May 31, 1948, Oct. 2, 1950; *Wkr*, Feb. 10, 1946.
62. Henry Winston, "Party Tasks among the Negro People," *PA*, XXV (April 1946), pp. 358-9.
63. *Wkr*, July 22, 1945.
64. *Ibid.*, Aug. 12, 1945; Eugene Dennis, *What America Faces*, p. 55; Foster and others, *op. cit.*, p. 13.
65. Henry Winston, "Not Against the Stream," *op. cit.*, p. 734.

CHAPTER THREE: PARTY ORGANIZATION, PARTY STRENGTH, AND PARTY LIFE

1. *DW*, Aug. 24, Sept. 6, 1956.
2. The party constitution appeared in *Wkr*, Aug. 12, 1945.

3. Testimony of Barbara Hartle in Hearings before the Committee on Un-American Activities, House of Representatives, 83d Cong., 2d sess., June 15, 1954, p. 6111; Herbert A. Philbrick, *I Led 3 Lives, Citizen, "Communist," Counterspy* (New York: McGraw-Hill, 1952), p. 227.

4. *Theory and Practice of the Communist Party. First Course. Marxist Study Series #1* (New York: Communist Party, National Education Department, March 1948), pp. 44-5. The first printing of this pamphlet was June 1947.

5. *Ibid.*, pp. 44-5.

6. John Williamson, "New Organizational Problems of the Communist Party," *PA*, XXIV (Dec. 1945), p. 1119; Williamson, "For a Mass Marxist Party of the Working Class!," *ibid.*, XXV (March 1946), p. 224.

7. *DW*, May 22, 1947.

8. "National Committee Names Officers," *PA*, XXV (Sept. 1946), p. 770.

9. *Theory and Practice of the Communist Party*, p. 45.

10. A Bronx Negro Woman Comrade, "Social Relations among Communists," *Party Voice*, IV (June 1956), p. 22.

11. For further discussion of the military aspects of the party's organization see Philip Selznick, *The Organizational Weapon: A Study of Bolshevik Strategy and Tactics* (New York: McGraw-Hill, 1952).

12. New York *Times*, May 16, 1956; interview with Max Gordon, Aug. 29, 1958.

13. See House Committee on Un-American Activities, *The Communist Party of the United States as an Agent of a Foreign Power*, House Report No. 209, 80th Cong., 1st sess., 1947, pp. 32-4, for a list of Comintern representatives in the 1920's and 1930's.

14. *Ibid.*, pp. 33, 55-6.

15. For example, *New Times*, published in English by *Trud* in Moscow and available on some newsstands in the United States, the Cominform newspaper, *For a Lasting Peace, For a People's Democracy!*, the press of the European Communist parties, and reports by foreign correspondents in the general American press.

16. For the Coplon case, see David Dallin, *Soviet Espionage* (New Haven: Yale University Press, 1955), pp. 478-92; for the other cases, see New York *Times*, April 11, 27, Aug. 8, 10, Nov. 16, 1957.

17. Dallin, *op. cit.*, pp. 477-8.

18. J. Edgar Hoover, *Masters of Deceit: The Story of Communism in America and How to Fight It* (New York: Holt, 1958), pp. 293-5.

19. Claire Neikind, "U.S. Communism: Its Underground Plans and Its Secret Business Empire," *The Reporter*, IV (Jan. 23, 1951), p. 5; Bella Dodd, *School of Darkness* (New York: Kenedy, 1954), pp. 209-11. Weiner died in 1954. See Lem Harris, "William Weiner: An American Communist," *PA*, XXXIII (Nov. 1954), pp. 50-5.

20. Interview with Earl Browder, March 6, 1956; New York *Times*, Jan. 9, 1959.

21. *Proceedings*, Seventh General Convention, International Workers Order, June 16-18, 1947 (New York City), pp. 99-100; *Wkr*, June 29, 1947.

22. See speech by Sam Milgrom, I.W.O. general director, in *Proceedings, op. cit.*, pp. 12-51, and the speech by Benjamin Davis, *ibid.*, pp. 52-4.

23. James B. Haley, "Report on Examination of the International Workers Order, Inc., New York, N. Y., by the Insurance Department of the State of New York," mimeographed document in the files of the New York State Insurance Department, New York City, dated Jan. 15, 1950, p. 31.
24. *DW*, April 19, 1946, Jan. 8, 1948.
25. Carl Dorfman, "Training Good Leaders in Harlem," *Contact*, I (Feb. 1947), p. 10. *Contact* was an inner-party monthly magazine published by the party's National Organization and Education Commission in 1947.
26. John Williamson, "Improve and Build Our Communist Press—The Next Step in Party Building," *PA*, XXV (Sept. 1946), p. 826.
27. *DW*, Oct. 1, 1945, Oct. 4, 1949; *Wkr*, Oct. 6, 1946, Oct. 5, 1947, Oct. 10, 1948.
28. Morris Childs, "The Daily Worker—Problems and Prospects," *PA*, XXV (Sept. 1946), p. 834.
29. Interview with Joseph Starobin, Oct. 1, 1956. The emphasis in this account differs from that of Bella Dodd, *op. cit.*, p. 201, but it does not differ as to facts. Miss Dodd was a member of the national commitee and abstained, but did not vote against the Gates appointment. Stachel's role in the direction of the paper is indirectly confirmed in Louis Budenz, *This Is My Story* (New York: Whittlesey House, 1947), pp. 216-17, 342.
30. Paul Morrow of the John Brown Club, Harlem, "Rest Day, Press Day," *Contact*, I (Aug. 1947), p. 12; see also *ibid.*, I (June 1947), p. 10.
31. John Williamson, "Improve and Build Our Communist Press," *loc. cit.*, p. 821; "The Plan That Gets the Subs," *Contact*, I (March 1947), p. 4. The *World*'s circulation was as follows: 1946, 14,573; 1947, 15,411; 1948, 13,747—*Daily People's World*, Oct. 1, 1946, Oct. 2, 1947, Oct. 4, 1948.
32. *Wkr*, Oct. 13, 1946; Byron Edwards, "Detroit Shop Clubs Come Back to Life," *Contact*, I (Feb. 1947), p. 8.
33. *Wkr*, Feb. 10, 1946.
34. "Give It to 'Em—But Good!," *Contact*, I (July 1947), p. 1.
35. Interview with Earl Browder, March 6, 1956; John Williamson in *Wkr*, July 1, 1945.
36. *Wkr*, July 1, 1945.
37. John Williamson, "The C.P.A.—Our Most Indispensable Weapon," *PA*, XXIV (Jan. 1945), pp. 49, 54.
38. Interview with Earl Browder, March 6, 1956; John Williamson, "New Organizational Problems of the Communist Party," *PA*, XXIV (Dec. 1945), p. 1122.
39. Henry Winston, "Toward a Party of 100,000," *PA*, XXVI (Jan. 1947), p. 67; Winston, "For a Fighting Party Rooted among the Industrial Workers!," *ibid.*, XXVII (Sept. 1948), p. 838.
40. *Wkr*, Jan. 12, 1947; "Give It to 'Em —But Good!," *loc. cit.*, p. 11.
41. *DW*, March 24, 1947; *Wkr*, April 6, 1947.
42. Dorothy Jones, "Money Is Everybody's Job in San Francisco," *Contact*, I (June 1947), p. 14.
43. *DW*, April 18, 20, 1946.

44. John Lavin, "Harlem's Fighting Tenants' Group Gets Results," *Contact*, I (June 1947), p. 1; *DW*, June 2, July 1, 1947; Henry Davis, "God Must Have Sent You," *Contact*, I (April 1947), p. 4.
45. Joe Weiss, "Ulcers for Jim Crow," *Contact*, I (Nov. 1947), p. 3; John Williamson, "What Every Communist Should Do Now," *Wkr*, Jan. 20, 1946, and his article in *ibid.*, Jan. 27, 1946; *DW*, Jan. 31, 1946.
46. *New York County Control Bulletin*, June 1947, as cited in *Digest of the Public Record of Communism in the United States* (New York: Fund for the Republic, 1955), p. 553.
47. *Wkr*, June 23, 1946.
48. John Williamson in *ibid.*, March 24, June 23, 1946.
49. *DW*, Feb. 15, July 16, 1946.
50. An organizational study by the New York State party, dated Nov. 1952, cited in *Handbook on Puerto Rican Work* (New York: Communist Party of New York, 1954), pp. 64, 70.
51. Henry Winston, "Not Against but with the Stream!," *PA*, XXVI (Aug. 1947), p. 735; Winston, "Some Aspects of Party Work," *ibid.*, XXVII (March 1948), p. 247.
52. Jack Kling, at that time the party treasurer, "Dues, Dollars, Drives," *Contact*, I (Sept. 1947), p. 11.
53. Henry Winston, "For a Fighting Party Rooted among the Industrial Workers!," *PA*, XXVII (Sept. 1948), p. 838.
54. *DW*, Nov. 6, 1947; *Daily People's World*, April 17, 1947; *Labor Fact Book 10* (New York: Labor Research Association, 1951), p. 137.
55. New York *Times*, Nov. 18, 1945, Nov. 7, 1947, Nov. 22, 1949; New York *Herald Tribune*, Nov. 14, 1941, Nov. 9, 1943, Nov. 9, 1947; *DW*, Oct. 8, Nov. 5, 7, Dec. 2, 1947, May 19, 1948; *Wkr*, Sept. 7, 1947.
56. All returns are from *DW*, Nov. 7, 1946; *Wkr*, Dec. 15, 1946.
57. Commonwealth of Massachusetts, *Election Statistics, 1946* (Boston, 1947), p. 311; *Wkr*, Nov. 9, 1947.
58. State of California, *Statement of Vote, General Election, November 5, 1946* (Sacramento, 1946), p. 4.
59. State of New Jersey, *Result of the General Election Held November 5th, 1946* (Trenton, 1946); Robert M. Montgomery, Michigan Director of Elections, to the present writer, Lansing, March 23, 1956; *Annual Election Report of the Secretary of State of the State of Indiana, 1946* (Indianapolis, 1946), pp. 1032-5, 1040-1; State of Colorado, *Abstract of Votes Cast, 1946* (Denver, 1946), pp. 11, 16; Arthur Bary, "The Denver Elections," *PA*, XXVI (Jan. 1947), p. 52. Bary grossly exaggerated the Communist vote in this article. Then the Colorado State chairman and later the party's Rocky Mountain district organizer, Bary was expelled from the party in 1956 on a nonideological charge—*DW*, April 20, 1956.
60. Max Kampelman, *The Communist Party vs. the C.I.O.: A Study in Power Politics* (New York: Praeger, 1957); *Communist Domination of Certain Unions*, Report of the Subcommittee on Labor and Labor-Management Relations of the Committee on Labor and Public Welfare, U.S. Senate, 82d Cong., 1st sess., Senate Doc. No. 89, 1951. This important document is a reprint of the reports of the various C.I.O. committees that sat in judgment on the Left unions in 1950.

)46, July 22, 29, 1947.
le's World, May 23, 1956.
of Industrial Organizations,
gate Charges against Inter-
n's Union," May 17, 1950,
a verbatim transcription of
headquarters, Washington,

and the Third-Party Move-
see also his "New Organi-
;" ibid., XXIV (Dec. 1945),
Action Can Defeat the Drive
1948), pp. 866-7.
w York: National Veterans
. 1946); DW, Jan. 15, 17,
17; Carl Reinstein, "New D-
17), p. 11; John Williamson,
immunist Party," PA, XXIV
npson, "Party Policy in the
, pp. 42-9.

d "GETTING ON WITH NORMAL

E OF COLUMN ON COMMUNIST

ARMY—THE PROGRESSIVE

1. Adam Lapin, _____ :ans," PA, XXIV (Oct. 1945),
   pp. 876-81.
2. Eugene Dennis, America at the Crossroads: Postwar Problems and
   Communist Policy (New York: New Century, Dec. 1945), pp. 7-33.
   Foster's opening remarks appear on pp. 3-6.
3. V. J. Jerome, "Lenin's Method—Guide to the Grasp of Reality," PA,
   XXV (Jan. 1946), p. 16.
4. DW, Jan. 16, 1946.
5. Eugene Dennis, What America Faces: The New War Danger and the
   Struggle for Peace, Democracy and Economic Security (New York:
   New Century, March 1946), pp. 36-8; see also Wkr, Feb. 24, 1946.
6. George Blake Charney, "Lessons of the Congressional By-Election in
   N. Y.," PA, XXV (April 1946), p. 363. This account of the election
   is based on the Charney article and DW, Jan. 29, 30, Feb. 1, 3, 5, 7,
   16, 19, 20, 1946, and Wkr, Feb. 3, 24, 1946.
7. Proceedings, Seventh General Convention, International Workers Order,
   June 16-18, 1947, New York City, pp. 113-15.
8. Dwight Macdonald, Henry Wallace: The Man and the Myth (New
   York: Vanguard, 1948), p. 101.

9. See, for example, Henry A. Wallace, "How To Guarantee the Peace," *New Masses,* June 19, 1945, pp. 6-7; Wallace, *Soviet Asia Mission* (New York: Reynal and Hitchcock, 1946).
10. Interview with Earl Browder, May 14, 1956.
11. Jacques Duclos, "On the Dissolution of the Communist Party of the United States," *PA,* XXIV (July 1945), pp. 670-1, 672.
12. Alexander Bittelman, "How Shall We Fight for Full Employment?," *ibid.,* XXV (Jan. 1946), p. 66; *DW,* May 27, June 12, 13, 1946.
13. New York *Times,* Oct. 28, 1955.
14. Account of the speech is based upon Russell Lord, *The Wallaces of Iowa* (Boston: Houghton Mifflin, 1947), pp. 577-8; Macdonald, *op. cit.,* pp. 107-9; New York *Times,* Sept. 13, 1946.
15. *DW,* Sept. 13, 14, 1946.
16. New York *Times,* Sept. 15, 19, 21, 1946, Oct. 28, 1955; Macdonald, *op. cit.,* p. 111.
17. Eugene Dennis, "Concluding Remarks on the Plenum Discussion," *PA,* XXVI (Jan. 1947), p. 15.
18. *DW,* July 25, 26, 1946.
19. Eugene Dennis, "Defeat the Imperialist Drive toward Fascism and War," *PA,* XXV (Sept. 1946), p. 802; *Wkr,* July 28, 1946.
20. William Z. Foster, "On Building a People's Party," *PA,* XXVI (Feb 1947), pp. 119-20.
21. Eugene Dennis, "Concluding Remarks on the Plenum Discussion," *PA,* XXVI (Aug. 1947), p. 696. Dennis had two speeches published under this title in *PA* in 1947, one in January and one in August.
22. Eugene Dennis, *The People Against the Trusts* (New York: New Century, Dec. 1946), p. 43.
23. For further criticism of "shotgun" anti-Communism see J. Edgar Hoover, "How To Fight Communism," *Newsweek,* June 9, 1947, pp. 30-2; Herbert A. Philbrick, *I Led 3 Lives: Citizen, "Communist," Counterspy* (New York: McGraw-Hill, 1952), pp. 249, 299-301.
24. Interview with Earl Browder, May 14, 1956.
25. *Time,* Sept. 9, 1946, pp. 22-3. Louis F. Budenz has asserted that the idea for I.C.C.A.S.P. was worked out in his office while he was on the *Daily Worker* and that the party assigned Alexander Trachtenberg and Lionel Berman to get the organization formed. Budenz, *Men Without Faces: The Communist Conspiracy in the U.S.A.* (New York: Harper, 1950), pp. 220-1; Budenz, *The Techniques of Communism* (Chicago: Regnery, 1954), pp. 33-4.
26. *DW,* March 11, Nov. 12, 1946; James A. Wechsler, *The Age of Suspicion* (New York: Random House, 1953), pp. 208-9.
27. Quotations from A. B. Magil, "Reveille for Progressives," *New Masses,* Jan. 14, 1947, pp. 3-6, and the preamble text reprinted on p. 6; *DW,* Dec. 30, 1946; New York *Times,* Dec. 30, 1946; New York *Herald Tribune,* Dec. 30, 1946; Harvey V. Brandt, "The Ideological Function of the Progressive Party of 1948," master's thesis in the library of Columbia University, dated 1949; Karl Marx Schmidt, Jr., "The Wallace Progressive Party," doctoral dissertation in Johns Hopkins University Library, dated 1951; Matthew Josephson, *Sidney Hillman:*

Statesman of American Labor (New York: Doubleday, 1952), p. 662n.
28. *DW,* Dec. 9, 1946, Jan. 6, 1947.
29. Wechsler, *op. cit.,* pp. 211-17; New York *Times,* Jan. 5, 1947; Arthur M. Schlesinger, Jr., "The Third Force in America," *ADA World,* Feb. 19, 1948; Robert Bendiner, "Revolt of the Middle," *The Nation,* Jan. 18, 1947; Wechsler, "Liberals without Reds," *The Progressive* (Madison, Wis.), Jan. 13, 1947. The U.D.A. turned over its treasury of $2,200 to A.D.A. See financial report attached to "Minutes of Joint Meeting of Executive and National Political Committees, ADA, July 16, 1947," a mimeographed document lent to me by Professor William E. Leuchtenburg of Columbia University.
30. A. B. Magil, "Progressive Unity or Division," *New Masses,* Jan. 28, 1947, pp. 6-9; see also editorials and columns by Max Gordon in *DW,* Jan. 7, 25, March 3, April 2, 1947.
31. William Z. Foster, "On Building a People's Party," *PA,* XXVI (Feb. 1947), p. 120.
32. *DW,* Aug. 14, 1947.
33. Simon W. Gerson, "Electoral Coalition Problems in New York," *PA,* XXVI (Oct. 1947), pp. 897-8.
34. Merrill Raymond Moremen, "The Independent Progressive Party of California, 1948," master's essay in the library of Stanford University, dated 1950; *Daily People's World,* July 26, 28, Aug. 25, 1947.
35. William Z. Foster, "Concluding Remarks at the Convention," *PA,* XXVII (Sept. 1948), p. 827; see *Daily People's World,* July 26, 29, 30, 1947; *DW,* Aug. 25, 26, 27, Sept. 7, 25, 26, 1947.
36. See Peter Cacchione in *DW,* Aug. 26, 1947, and the account of Marcantonio's speech to the Mine, Mill convention at St. Paul, *ibid.,* Sept. 7, 1947.
37. *Wkr,* Sept. 28, 1947.
38. Eugene Dennis, *The Communists Take a New Look* (New York: New Century, May 1956), pp. 20-1, 31.
39. This account is based upon New York *Times,* Oct. 6, 23, 1947; the resolutions appeared in *ibid.,* Oct. 6, 1947, *DW,* Oct. 7, 1947, and *PA,* XXVI (Nov. 1947), pp. 1051-1056. Two English translations of the Zhdanov speech are in *PA,* XXVI (Dec. 1947), pp. 1090-1111, and in the first issue of *For a Lasting Peace, For a People's Democracy!,* Nov. 10, 1947. I use the *PA* translation, which is much the more literate.
40. *L'Humanité,* Oct. 6-23, 1947.
41. The Communists determined on the third ticket a few days before the Zhdanov speech was published on Oct. 22, but after the publication of the resolutions on Oct. 5. The resolutions were a sufficient basis for action, but it is possible that the American party leadership knew of the Zhdanov speech before its publication.
42. *DW,* Oct. 7, 1947.
43. *Final Proceedings,* Ninth Constitutional Convention of the Congress of Industrial Organizations, Boston, Mass., Oct. 13-17, 1947, pp. 274-93. For the story of how the foreign-policy resolution was written, see Philip Murray's speech, pp. 290-1.

44. "Congress of Industrial Organizations, Hearings before the Committee to Investigate Charges against International Longshoremen's and Warehousemen's Union," May 17, 1950, pp. 66-7, 98-101, 141-6, a typescript verbatim transcription of the hearings, A.F. of L.-C.I.O. headquarters, Washington, D. C.
45. *DW,* Oct. 20, 1947.
46. *Ibid.,* Oct. 21, 1947.
47. Interview with Henry Wallace, Nov. 10, 1956.
48. Interview with Michael Straight, Nov. 14, 1956.
49. *DW,* March 27, May 26, 1947.
50. Interview with Michael Straight, Nov. 14, 1956. Straight was with Wallace on much of this trip.
51. *DW,* Sept. 21, 1947.
52. Michael Straight to the present writer, Washington, D. C., Oct. 10, 1956; interview with Straight, Nov. 14, 1956.
53. Interview with Henry Wallace, Nov. 10, 1956.
54. James A. Wechsler, "My Ten Months with Wallace," *The Progressive,* Nov. 1948, p. 5. *The Progressive,* founded by Robert M. La Follette, Sr., before World War I, is not to be confused with the Progressive Party. The magazine opposed Wallace in 1948.
55. Interview with Michael Straight, Nov. 14, 1956.
56. *DW,* May 26, Sept. 23, 1947; *Wkr,* Dec. 14, 1947.
57. New York *Times,* April 18, 1947; *Proceedings,* I.W.O. convention, *op. cit.,* pp. 23, 52-4, 113-5.
58. William H. Miller to Michael Straight, Chicago, June 9, 1947, in files of *The New Republic* correspondence, Washington, D. C. Miller was a New York lawyer and a twice-defeated A.L.P. state assembly candidate whom P.C.A. sent to Chicago to be state executive director.
59. "Minutes of the Joint Meeting of Executive and National Political Committees," A.D.A., July 16, 1947.
60. *DW,* Jan. 14, April 19, 1946; interview with Norman Thomas, Aug. 2, 1956.
61. *DW,* June 7, 1947.
62. *The Progressive,* April 1948, pp. 36-7.
63. *DW,* Sept. 3, Oct. 16, 1947.
64. *Ibid.,* Nov. 3, Dec. 11, 1947; *Wkr,* Dec. 14, 1947.
65. Michael Straight to the present writer, Washington, D. C., Oct. 10, 1956; interview with a former *The New Republic* editor who prefers to remain anonymous, June 1957. Wallace confirmed the stories of the delegations in an interview, Nov. 10, 1956, but it had not occurred to him before that the visits came at opportune times, such as after a Murray denunciation of a new party.
66. *Wkr,* Dec. 21, 1947; interview with Henry Wallace, Nov. 10, 1956.
67. *Wkr,* Oct. 5, 1947; *DW,* Nov. 6, 1947; Gil Green, "The Chicago Elections," *PA,* XXVI (Dec. 1947), pp. 1112-19.
68. Albert E. Kahn to Louis Adamic, Croton-on-Hudson, N.Y., Dec. 12, 1947, carbon copy in files of the N. Y. Insurance Commission, New York City. Kahn used his home address in the letter but it was typed by an I.W.O. stenographer and bore the legend "uopwa #16," the union "bug" of the United Office and Professional Workers of America, Local

16. This "bug" appeared also on mimeographed material from the Communist and Progressive parties. The U.O.P.W.A. was expelled from the C.I.O. in 1950.
69. *DW*, Dec. 19, 29, 1947; *Wkr*, Dec. 28, 1947.
70. P.C.A. press release, dated Dec. 29, 1947, in library of Philip Jaffe, Stamford, Conn.

CHAPTER FIVE: PROFESSIONAL SOLDIERS IN A CAMPAIGN THAT FAILED

1. Editorial and Max Gordon column, *DW*, Dec. 30, 31, 1947.
2. *Wkr*, Jan. 4, 1948.
3. William Z. Foster, "The Political Significance of Keynesism," *PA*, XXVII (Jan. 1948), p. 43; Jacob Mindel, "The Economic Theories of John Maynard Keynes," *ibid.*, XXVII (Feb. 1948), pp. 156-66; Joseph Roland, "The Question of the National Debt," *ibid.*, XXVII (March 1948), pp. 266-78; Albert Prago, "Notes on Keynes' Concepts of Saving and Investment," *ibid.*, XXVII (April 1948), pp. 367-75; Max Weiss, "Wallace's 'Toward World Peace,'" *ibid.*, XXVII (May 1948), pp. 400-11; James S. Allen, "A Comment on State Capitalism and Socialism," *ibid.*, XXVII (May 1948), pp. 426-39; Celeste Strack, "The Keynesian Palace Revolution," *ibid.*, XXVII (May 1948), pp. 448-59; I. G. Bliumin, "The Economic Teachings of Keynes," *ibid.*, XXVII (July 1948), pp. 638-61, translated from a Russian journal; Milton Howard in *DW*, April 7, 1948.
4. (New York: Reynal and Hitchcock.)
5. Weiss, *op. cit.*, pp. 407, 410.
6. New York *Times*, Jan. 2, 1948.
7. "Congress of Industrial Organizations, Hearings before the Committee to Investigate Charges against International Longshoremen's and Warehousemen's Union," May 17, 1950, pp. 72-3, 104-11, A.F. of L.-C.I.O. headquarters, Washington, D. C.
8. *Ibid.*, pp. 71-2.
9. William Z. Foster, "Organized Labor and the Marshall Plan," *PA*, XXVII (Feb. 1948), p. 106; John Williamson, "Trade Union Problems and the Third-Party Movement," *ibid.*, XXVII (March 1948), p. 233. John Gates, then editor of *DW*, told me in an interview, Dec. 6, 1956, that although he never heard Foster express himself in the words Quill quoted, he had heard Foster express himself to the same effect, and Gates did not doubt the truth of Quill's testimony.
10. Eugene Dennis, "The Role of the Communist Party in the Present Situation," *PA*, XXVII (March 1948), p. 213; also see his published pamphlet, *The Third Party and the 1948 Elections* (New York: New Century, March 1948), p. 46.
11. C.I.O., Hearings . . . to Investigate I.L.W.U., *loc. cit.*, p. 72.
12. *DW*, Feb. 18, 1948.
13. Samuel Lubell, *The Future of American Politics* (New York: Anchor, rev. ed., 1956), pp. 91-3.
14. *DW*, April 28, 1947.

15. Alexander Bittelman, "New Tasks and Realignments in the Struggle for the Jewish State in Palestine," *PA*, XXVII (Feb. 1948), pp. 146-55.
16. Michael Straight, "What Happened in the Bronx," *The New Republic*, March 1, 1948, pp. 7-8.
17. Lubell, *op. cit.*, p. 93.
18. *DW*, Feb. 18, 1948; Straight, *op. cit.*, pp. 7-8.
19. *DW*, Feb. 16, 1948.
20. New York *Times*, Feb. 19, 1948.
21. *National Guardian*, Nov. 12, 1956, described Miss Petran as one of the Wallace movement's "chief advisers in foreign affairs." For her ideology, see her article in *ibid.*, June 25, 1956.
22. Frederick Vanderbilt Field, "American Imperialist Policy in the Far East," *PA*, XXV (Nov. 1946), pp. 988-1000.
23. New York *Herald Tribune*, March 22, 1948; for further information about the group, I am indebted to a person who was briefly one of the "researchers" and who prefers to remain anonymous. This informant is not the person who gave the Alsops their story.
24. Hearings before the Committee on Foreign Affairs, House of Representatives, 80th Cong., 2d sess., pp. 1581-1625, quotations from pp. 1582, 1593, 1613-14; Victor Perlo and David Ramsey, "Europe and American Aid," *The New Republic*, Jan. 12, 1948, pp. 15-20; Michael Straight repudiated Perlo and Ramsey in "ERP: Aid to Peace or Road to War?," *ibid.*, March 15, 1948, pp. 11-12; Jennie Lee in London *Tribune*, reprinted in *ADA World*, Aug. 7, 1948.
25. Henry A. Wallace, "Where I Was Wrong," *This Week*, Sept. 7, 1952, p. 7.
26. *Henry A. Wallace: The First Three Months* (Washington: A.D.A. Publicity Department, 1948).
27. Milton Howard in *DW*, March 7, 1948.
28. *Wallace: The First Three Months.*
29. New York *Times*, March 18, 1948; "The People's Victory in Czechoslovakia: An Editorial," *PA*, XXVII (April 1948), p. 296.
30. Interview with Henry Wallace, Nov. 10, 1956.
31. Quoted in Matthew Spinka, *Church in Communist Society: A Study of J. L. Hromádka's Theological Politics* (*Hartford Seminary Foundation Bulletin, No. 17*) (Hartford, Conn.: Hartford Seminary Foundation, 1954), pp. 28, 30.
32. Spinka, *op. cit.*, p. 21; Joseph L. Hromádka, *Doom and Resurrection* (Richmond, Va.: Madrus House, 1945); New York *Times*, May 30, 1958.
33. Dorothy Thompson, "How I Was Duped by a Communist," *The Saturday Evening Post*, April 16, 1949, pp. 19, 75-85; Hermann Budzislawski, *"Ich war Amerikas berühmteste Frau," Die Weltbühne* (East Berlin), III (Dec. 7, 1948), pp. 1531-4; interview with Mrs. Ida Landau, widow of Overseas News Agency Manager Jacob Landau, Dec. 10, 1956.
34. Interview with Henry Wallace, Nov. 10, 1956; Henry Wallace to the present writer, South Salem, N. Y., Nov. 20, 1956.
35. *Wkr*, May 30, 1948; also in *PA*, XXVII (June 1948), p. 506.

36. William Z. Foster, "The 1948 Elections and the Struggle for Peace," *PA*, XXVII (Sept. 1948), p. 775. This entire issue was devoted to speeches and documents of the 1948 Communist convention. There was no October 1948 issue of *PA*.

37. William E. Leuchtenburg, "Wallace in the Rockies," *The New Leader*, Sept. 25, 1948, p. 5; Merrill Raymond Moremen, "The Independent Progressive Party of California, 1948," master's essay in the library of Stanford University, dated 1950, pp. 110-12.

38. *DW*, July 23, 1948.

39. *ADA World*, Aug. 7, 1948.

40. John Cotton Brown, "The 1948 Progressive Campaign: A Scientific Approach," unpublished doctoral dissertation in the library of the University of Chicago, dated 1949, pp. 122-4, 140-2, 145. This dissertation is important. It is the best account available, since the press was excluded, of the platform committee's deliberations. Brown was one of Tugwell's graduate students. Tugwell arranged for Brown to sit in on the platform committee meetings, technically as his assistant, but actually to take notes for his dissertation. Interview with Rexford Tugwell, April 17, 1956.

41. Brown, *op. cit.*, pp. 156-7; interview with Rexford Tugwell, April 17, 1956.

42. Brown, *op. cit.*, pp. 161-5.

43. *Ibid.*, pp. 168-79.

44. *DW*, March 15, 1948.

45. Interview with Rexford Tugwell, April 17, 1956; Brown, *op. cit.*, pp. 180-7; *Labor Action*, Aug. 2, 1948. *Labor Action*, a Shachtmanite weekly, is a useful source. It is special in its slant, but the Shachtmanites were well informed on Communist tactics.

46. Brown, *op. cit.*, pp. 187-90.

47. Hearings before the Committee on Un-American Activities, House of Representatives, 83d Cong., 2d sess., Jan. 13 and 18, 1954, pp. 3869-70.

48. James A. Wechsler, "The Philadelphia Pay-Off," *The Progressive*, Sept. 1948, p. 9; *Labor Action*, Aug. 2, 1948.

49. Wechsler, *op. cit.*, pp. 9-10; *Labor Action*, Aug. 2, 1948; James A. Wechsler, *The Age of Suspicion* (New York: Random House, 1953), p. 231.

50. Brown, *op. cit.*, pp. 194-5; *Labor Action*, Aug. 2, 1948; Wechsler, *Age of Suspicion*, p. 232; *Daily People's World*, July 26, 1948; interview with C. B. Baldwin, Nov. 15, 1955.

51. Brown, *op. cit.*, pp. 239-40; *Labor Action*, Aug. 2, 1948; "Report by Steve Muller of Students for Democratic Action on the Founding Convention of the Young Progressives of America," appendix I of *Henry A. Wallace: The Last Seven Months of his Presidential Campaign* (Washington: ADA Publicity Department, 1948). Quotations from this appendix.

52. Interview with Rexford Tugwell, April 17, 1956; *Wallace: The Last Seven Months;* Henry A. Wallace to Herbert A. Philbrick, South Salem, N. Y., Feb. 1, 1952, printed in New York *Herald Tribune*, Feb. 4, 1952.

53. Leuchtenburg, *op. cit.;* Moremen, *op. cit.*, pp. 133-4; Baltimore *Sun*

story as quoted in New York *Herald Tribune* editorial, Aug. 23, 1948; interview with Rexford Tugwell, April 17, 1956.

54. John Williamson, "Only Militant, United Action Can Defeat the Drive against the Unions!," *PA,* XXVII (Sept. 1948), p. 864; William Z. Foster, "Concluding Remarks at the Convention," *ibid.,* XXVII (Sept. 1948), pp. 824-5.

55. *DW,* Oct. 20, 1948; I. F. Stone, "Confessions of a Dupe: Why I Was for Wallace," *The Truman Era* (New York: Monthly Review Press, 1953), pp. 67-8. The column originally appeared Aug. 25, 1948.

56. Interview with Henry Wallace, Nov. 10, 1956; Henry Wallace to the present writer, South Salem, N. Y., Nov. 20, 1956.

57. Joseph and Stewart Alsop in New York *Herald Tribune,* March 22, 1948; A.D.A., *Bat Boy for Reaction,* a small pamphlet, 1948; Moremen, *op. cit.,* pp. 187, 216-17, 242.

58. Rexford G. Tugwell, "Progressives and the Presidency," *The Progressive,* April 1949, pp. 5-6; New York *Times,* Sept. 7, 1948.

59. *Statistical Abstract of the United States* (Washington: Government Printing Office, 74th ed., 1953), p. 321. The *World Almanac* for 1953 gave Wallace 1,137,992 votes. State figures cited here are from the *World Almanac* unless otherwise indicated.

60. Mimeographed text of Wallace's address at a dinner of the National Wallace for President Committee, New York City, April 19, 1948, in library of Philip Jaffe, Stamford, Conn.

61. State of California, *Statement of Vote, General Election, Nov. 2, 1948* (Sacramento, 1948), p. 5.

62. Lubell, *op. cit.,* p. 219. Lubell estimated (p. 220) that three-fourths of the Wallace voters were Negro or Jewish.

63. Max Gordon in *DW,* Nov. 10, 1948; George Blake [Charney] and Al Terestman, "The People Win with Marcantonio," *PA,* XXVIII (Jan. 1949), pp. 85-94; James W. Ford, "The 1948 Elections in Bedford-Stuyvesant," *ibid.,* XXVIII (Feb. 1949), pp. 70-81.

64. See, for example, M. Marinen, "Election Struggle and Onslaught of Reaction in U.S.," *For a Lasting Peace, For a People's Democracy!,* Sept. 1, 1948; and Jan Marek, "Political Notes," *ibid.,* Nov. 15, 1948.

65. *DW,* April 14, 1948.

66. New York State Committee, "The Election Results in New York," *PA,* XXVII (Dec. 1948), p. 1082.

67. William Z. Foster, *The Twilight of World Capitalism* (New York: International, 1949), pp. 124-6.

CHAPTER SIX: THE PARTY AND ANTI-COMMUNISM

1. Eric F. Goldman, *The Crucial Decade: America, 1945-1955* (New York: Knopf, 1956), pp. 116-17.

2. For further details see Hadley Cantril, ed., *Public Opinion, 1935-1946* (Princeton: Princeton University Press, 1951), pp. 130-1; Samuel A. Stouffer, *Communism, Conformity and Civil Liberties: A Cross-Section of the Nation Speaks Its Mind* (Garden City: Doubleday, 1955), pp. 43-4.

3. William Z. Foster, "Keynote Message of Greetings to the Plenum," *PA*, XXIX (May 1950), p. 11; Michael Bianca, "How To Fight Mc-Carthyism," *ibid.*, XXX (Oct. 1951), p. 23.
4. William Weinstone, "The Fight to Repeal the Legislative Blueprint for Fascism," *ibid.*, XXIX (Oct. 1950), pp. 35, 43; see also Alexander Bittelman, "Who Are the Conspirators?," *ibid.*, XXX (July 1951), p. 21; Gus Hall, "The Present Situation and the Next Tasks," *ibid.*, XXIX (Oct. 1950), p. 7; William Z. Foster, in "Is the United States in the Early Stages of Fascism?," *ibid.*, XXXIII (Nov. 1954), pp. 4-21, concluded that at that time, while the Senate was in the process of censuring McCarthy, fascism was a growing danger.
5. Foster in *Wkr*, Jan. 15, 1950; Weinstone, *op. cit.*, p. 38.
6. Abner Berry in *DW*, Oct. 2, 1950; James W. Ford, "The Communist Party: Champion Fighter for Negro Rights," *PA*, XXVIII (June 1949), p. 48.
7. Weinstone, *op. cit.*, p. 40.
8. James Rorty and Moshe Decter, *McCarthy and the Communists* (Boston: Beacon, 1954), p. 150; *DW*, Aug. 15, 1946, and Rob F. Hall, "The People Won't Mourn La Follette," *ibid.*, Aug. 19, 1946.
9. "America's Hour of Peril—Unite! Save Democracy and Peace!," *PA*, XXX (July 1951), pp. 1-8.
10. Editorial, "The Trap against Unity," *DW*, July 14, 1949.
11. *DW*, Jan. 12, 1946.
12. *Ibid.*, Feb. 1, 1946.
13. *Ibid.*, Aug. 5, 1946.
14. *Digest of the Public Record of Communism in the United States* (New York: Fund for the Republic, 1955), pp. 194-6.
15. New York *Times*, Jan. 18, 19, 1949.
16. C. Herman Pritchett, *Civil Liberties and the Vinson Court* (Chicago: University of Chicago Press, 1954), p. 233.
17. *Ibid.*, pp. 233-6, 280 note 7
18. *DW*, Feb. 25, 1949.
19. *Wkr*, Jan. 30, 1949; *DW*, March 22, 1949.
20. *Wkr*, Sept. 19, 1948; Elizabeth Gurley Flynn in *ibid.*, April 3, 1949.
21. See his introduction to George Marion, *The Communist Trial: An American Crossroads* (New York: Fairplay Publishers, 2d ed., 1950).
22. For a critical discussion of the constitutional issues involved in the decision see Pritchett, *op. cit.*, pp. 71-7.
23. *DW*, March 7, 1952.
24. Subcommittee . . . of the Committee on the Judiciary, United States Senate, 84th Cong., 1st sess., Committee Print, *The Communist Party of the United States of America . . . A Handbook for Americans* (Washington, D. C., 1955), p. 34.
25. Foster, "Keynote Message of Greetings to the Plenum," *PA*, XXIX (May 1950), pp. 10-11; see also *DW*, March 21, 1950.
26. Committee on Un-American Activities, House of Representatives, 81st Cong., 2d sess., House Report No. 1954, *Review of the Scientific and Cultural Conference for World Peace Arranged by the National Council of the Arts, Sciences, and Professions and Held in New York City, March 25, 26, and 27, 1949.* This report has utility, but it is a typical

report of this committee in that its emphasis was on lists of names rather than analysis.

27. *DW,* Oct. 3, Dec. 5, 6, 1949.
28. *Ibid.,* Nov. 21, 1950, Nov. 14, 15, 1951; *Wkr,* Sept. 11, 1949; *For a Lasting Peace, For a People's Democracy!,* March 31, Nov. 24, 1950.
29. *DW,* May 18, 21, 23, June 14, 1950; *Wkr,* June 11, Oct. 1, 1950; *Labor Fact Book 10* (New York: Labor Research Association, 1951), p. 26.
30. *Wkr,* May 18, 1947, March 28, 1948; *DW,* Sept. 29, Oct. 11, 14, 19, 30, 1947.
31. Dyson Carter, "New Ways of Killing," *New Masses,* Sept. 3, 1946; *DW,* March 19, 20, April 9, 1952
32. Frederick Vanderbilt Field, "Wall Street's Aggression in Korea and the Struggle for Peace," *PA,* XXIX (Sept. 1950), p. 15; for secretariat statement, "Halt Wall Street Aggression in Asia!," *ibid.,* XXIX (Aug. 1950), p. 2; *For a Lasting Peace, For a People's Democracy!,* Sept. 22, 1950.
33. *DW,* June 26, 1950.
34. Betty Gannett, "Wall Street's War against the Korean People," *PA,* XXIX (Aug. 1950), p. 7; Field, *op. cit.,* p. 26.
35. Interview with Joseph Starobin, Oct. 1, 1956; Joseph Starobin, "A Communication," *PA,* XXXVI (Jan. 1957), pp. 60-2.
36. Eugene Dennis, "The MacArthur Ouster: A Letter to the Members of the Communist Party, U.S.A.," *PA,* XXX (May 1951), pp. 3, 6. Italics in original.
37. *Wkr,* July 13, 1952.
38. *DW,* July 28, 30, 1953.
39. John Swift, "Some Problems of Work in Right-Led Unions, II," *PA,* XXXI (May 1952), p. 32. Not to be confused with the "John Swift" articles of 1953. "John Swift" was clearly a pen name.
40. *DW,* June 29, 1950.
41. Joseph Rockman, "Tasks in Broadening the Fight for Peace," *PA,* XXXI (June 1952), pp. 15-29. "Rockman"—another obvious pen name —pointed out that sectarianism hurt the party cause in the peace movement. In his sharpest sentence he wrote that "We place an impossible task for ourselves if we . . . insist that the Negro people fight for peace under the leadership of the Left or not at all" (p. 29).
42. Gus Hall, "Through United Front Struggle to Peace," *ibid.,* XXIX (May 1950), p. 37; Hall, "The Present Situation and Next Tasks," *ibid.,* XXIX (Oct. 1950), p. 21. Each of these articles was a report to the national committee.
43. Wallace speech at second national convention of Progressive Party, Ashland Auditorium, Chicago, Feb. 24, 1950, Progressive Party press release in library of Philip Jaffe, Stamford, Conn.
44. *DW,* March 30, 1950; see also William Z. Foster in *ibid.,* March 3, 1950.
45. *Ibid.,* July 30, 1957, for denunciation of Walter Wallace.
46. "Minutes of the Meetings of the Executive Committee of the Progressive Party on the Situation in Korea and China, July 6, 8, 9, 10, 11, 1950," mimeographed documents in library of Philip Jaffe, Stamford, Conn.

47. New York *Times,* April 26, Aug. 18, 19, 21, 1957, Jan. 3, March 16, 1958.
48. "Minutes," July 10, 11, 1950. See note 46.
49. "Minutes of Special Meeting of National Committee, Progressive Party, 13 Astor Place, New York City, July 15, 1950"; Wallace's press release of same date. Both in library of Philip Jaffe, Stamford, Conn. See also Wallace's brief account of his leaving the Progressives in "Henry Wallace Tells of His Political Odyssey," *Life,* May 14, 1956, pp. 183-4.
50. *Daily People's World,* Oct. 10, 1950.
51. In January 1952, for example, she appeared on a program with *DW* staff writers Joseph North and John Pittman to increase the paper's circulation—*DW,* Jan. 18, 1952.
52. Richard M. Scammon, comp. and ed., *America Votes: A Handbook of Contemporary Election Statistics* (New York: Macmillan, 1956), pp. 33, 259, 421-2.
53. Max M. Kampelman, *The Communist Party vs. the C.I.O.: A Study in Power Politics* (New York: Praeger, 1957), pp. 157-8.
54. *Wkr,* Dec. 19, 1948.
55. John Williamson, "Two Conventions of Labor: The Situation in the Trade Union Movement," *PA,* XXVIII (Jan. 1949), p. 35.
56. *Proceedings,* Tenth Constitutional Convention, Congress of Industrial Organizations, 1948, pp. 281-2.
57. *Wkr,* Jan. 9, 1949.
58. *Proceedings,* Eleventh Constitutional Convention, Congress of Industrial Organizations, 1949, pp. 272-3. For background on the Quill union and its peculiar combination of Irish Catholic membership and Left leadership, see James J. McGinley, S.J., *Labor Relations in the New York Rapid Transit Systems, 1904-1944* (New York: King's Crown, 1949), pp. 316-25.
59. *DW,* May 20, 1949. For background on W.F.T.U., see Kampelman, *op. cit.,* pp. 233-45.
60. *Proceedings,* Fourteenth Convention, United Electrical, Radio, and Machine Workers of America (U.E.), Cleveland, 1949, pp. 205-25.
61. *Proceedings,* Eleventh Constitutional Convention, C.I.O., 1949, pp. 240, 281, 288, 302, 305.
62. Kampelman, *op. cit.,* pp. 167-222.
63. Even the *DW*'s labor columnist, George Morris, saw U.E.'s situation as hopeless. See *DW,* Sept. 28, 1956.
64. Vernon Jensen, *Nonferrous Metal Industry Unionism, 1932-1954* (Ithaca: Cornell University Press, 1954), p. 305.
65. *Testimony of the Director on February 3 and February 7, 1950 . . . on the 1951 Appropriation Estimates for the Federal Bureau of Investigation,* Department of Justice, 1950; *Digest of the Public Record,* p. 550.
66. *DW,* Oct. 4, 1950, Oct. 2, 1953; *Wkr,* Oct. 8, 1950, Oct. 11, 1953.
67. *DW,* May 25, 1950.
68. *Ibid.,* April 6, 9, 1951.
69. *National Guardian,* Aug. 15, 1951.
70. Committee on Un-American Activities, House of Representatives,

Trial by Treason: The National Committee to Secure Justice for the Rosenbergs and Morton Sobell (Washington: Government Printing Office, 1956), pp. 13, 15-24.

71. For Communist denials of anti-Semitism, see Klement Gottwald, "The Prague Treason Trials," *PA,* XXXII (Feb. 1953), pp. 46-50; and Samuel Rosen, "Zionism and Bourgeois Nationalism," *ibid.,* XXXII (June 1953), pp. 38-48, and (July 1953), pp. 57-65; Jacques Duclos quotation from Robert B. Glynn, *"L'Affaire Rosenberg* in France," *Political Science Quarterly,* LXX (Sept. 1955), p. 509.

72. Glynn, *op. cit.,* pp. 514-15.

73. Irwin Edelman, "An Open Letter to the Rosenberg and Sobell Friends," undated one-page mimeographed flier. Internal evidence indicates the "letter" was written between June 19 and July 16, 1953. For this document I am indebted to Mr. Edelman.

74. Edelman, "The Rosenberg Case: Some Observations," *Contemporary Issues* (London), V (Oct.-Nov. 1954), p. 319. This article indicates that Edelman had some highly unusual ideas, to say the least. In the article, he argued that Bloch, the Communists, and the F.B.I. conspired to execute the Rosenbergs. Nevertheless, he did suggest a legal argument which a Supreme Court justice thought warranted consideration.

75. S. Andhil Fineberg, *The Rosenberg Case: Fact and Fiction* (New York: Oceana, 1953), pp. 110-13; Edelman, "The Rosenberg Case," *loc. cit.,* p. 319.

76. Communist Party national committee, "The Rosenbergs: Heroes of Democracy," *PA,* XXXII (July 1953), pp. 2-3.

77. *DW,* Feb. 16, 25, June 22, 1953; Edith Segal, *Give Us Your Hand! Poems and Songs for Ethel and Julius Rosenberg in the Death House at Sing Sing* (New York: National Committee to Secure Justice in the Rosenberg Case, 1953).

CHAPTER SEVEN: THE PARTY'S INTERNAL SECURITY

1. Edmund Wilson, *The American Earthquake: A Documentary of the Twenties and Thirties* (New York: Doubleday, 1958), p. 212.

2. *Testimony of the Director on February 3 and February 7, 1950 . . . on the 1951 Appropriation Estimates for the Federal Bureau of Investigation,* Department of Justice, 1950, pp. 142, 145. How many F.B.I. agents were in the party and how highly they were placed is a matter known only to the F.B.I. Earl Browder said in an interview, May 14, 1956, that he had always operated on the assumption there was at least one agent in the national office, but that he never suspected any of the leaders who were prominent after the war. John Gates in an interview, Dec. 6, 1956, said he did not suspect any of the top leaders of the party.

3. Interview with John Gates, Dec. 6, 1956; for verification of the small club organization, see Lee Amistad, "For a Marxist-Leninist Policy on Party Organization," *Party Voice,* I (March 1953), supplement, pp. 8, 12.

4. Amistad, *op. cit.,* p. 8.
5. Testimony of John Lautner in *United States* v. *Kuzma,* #11,655 (3d Circuit, 1954), Record on Appeal, transcript, pp. 1689-1701.
6. "The Status of Our Party," *Party Voice,* IV (July 1956), p. 4.
7. *DW,* Aug. 31, 1950; interview with Joseph Starobin, Oct. 1, 1956; interview with John Gates, Dec. 6, 1956.
8. See J. Edgar Hoover, *Masters of Deceit: The Story of Communism in America and How To Fight It* (New York: Holt, 1958), pp. 273-89. This account emphasizes underground methods and the difficulty of "shadowing" people using such methods.
9. Alex Parker, *Organizing the Party for Victory over Reaction. Report Delivered at the National Conference of the Communist Party* (New York: New Century, Dec. 1953), pp. 11-12.
10. *Ibid.,* pp. 15-17; interview with Max Gordon, Aug. 29, 1958.
11. Peggy Dennis, "Comradely Yours," *Wkr,* June 11, 1950.
12. See "The Status of Our Party," *loc. cit.,* p. 4.
13. A letter to the editor of *DW,* June 11, 1956, asserted that "thousands" were expelled, including whole clubs in some cases.
14. B. S., "Party Democracy and Dissent," *Party Voice,* IV (June 1956), p. 3.
15. *D.W.,* Feb. 23, 24, March 30, April 8, 1949.
16. *Ibid.,* June 8, 1956.
17. *U.S.* v. *Kuzma,* transcript, pp. 1398-1408.
18. Zoltan Deak, "The Tito-Rajk Conspiracy against the Camp of Peace and Democracy," *PA,* XXVIII (Dec. 1949), pp. 87-94.
19. This account is based upon Lautner's testimony in *Brownell* v. *Communist Party of the United States,* Subversive Activities Control Board Hearings, 1952, pp. 9259-61, 9294-9309; *DW,* Jan. 17, 1950; and *U.S.* v. *Kuzma,* transcript, p. 1749. Professor Herbert Packer of Stanford University Law School, who is making a study of government witnesses and counsel in Communist cases, reports that Lautner was one of the most consistent of government witnesses in his testimony.
20. B. S., *op. cit.,* p. 3.
21. William Z. Foster, "Keynote Message of Greetings to the Plenum," *PA,* XXIX (May 1950), p. 13.
22. *DW,* April 3, 1950.
23. Eugene Dennis, "Let Us March Forward with Supreme Confidence," *PA,* XXIX (July 1950), p. 14.
24. Interview with Max Gordon, Aug. 29, 1958.
25. Henry Winston, "Building the Party—Key to Building the United Front of Struggle," *ibid.,* XXIX (May 1950), p. 80; *Wkr,* June 11, 1950.
26. George Siskind and Harry Martel, "Psychoanalysis: Ideological Instrument of Imperialism," *PA,* XXIX (Dec. 1950), pp. 61-74, quotations from 61-2, 73-4.
27. *Scientific Session on the Physiological Teachings of Academician I. P. Pavlov* (Moscow, 1951).
28. Alvin S. Herwitz, "Pavlov's Teachings in Psychology and Physiology," *PA,* XXXI (Sept. 1952), pp. 57-64; see also Joseph C. Clayton, "Some Problems in the Struggle Against Psychoanalysis," *ibid.,* XXXIII (April 1954), pp. 40-52.

29. Howard Fast, *The Naked God: The Writer and the Communist Party* (New York: Praeger, 1957), pp. 148-53.
30. See *We Charge Genocide: The Historic Petition to the United Nations for Relief from a Crime of the United States Government against the Negro People* (New York: Civil Rights Congress, 1951).
31. Richard O. Boyer, *Pettis Perry: The Story of a Working Class Leader* (New York: Self Defense Committee of the 17 Smith Act Victims, April 1952).
32. *Brownell* v. *Communist Party,* S.A.C.B. Hearings, p. 9314.
33. Robert Thompson, "Strengthen the Struggle against White Chauvinism," *PA,* XXVIII (June 1949), p. 18
34. *DW,* May 25, 1949, April 24, 1950; I. C., "Left Errors in Trade Union and Negro Work," *Party Voice,* IV (June 1956), p. 6.
35. *DW,* July 7, 1949; I. C., *op. cit.,* p. 6.
36. Pettis Perry, "Press Forward the Struggle against White Chauvinism," *PA,* XXIX (May 1950), p. 144; "A Statement on Florida Vacations," *DW,* April 19, 1951; interview with John Gates, Dec. 6, 1956.
37. *DW,* Aug. 27, 1951. Party headquarters subsequently moved to the Jefferson School building at Sixth Avenue and Sixteenth Street.
38. *Wkr,* June 18, 1950.
39. Fast, *op. cit.,* pp. 144-5; William Z. Foster, "Left Sectarianism in the Fight for Negro Rights and Against White Chauvinism," *PA,* XXXII (July 1953), p. 28.
40. Foster, "Left Sectarianism," *loc. cit.,* pp. 17-32, quotation from p. 24.
41. Amistad, *op. cit.,* p. 2.
42. "The Status of Our Party," *loc. cit.,* p. 4.
43. Amistad, *op. cit.,* pp. 2-3; see also Parker, *op. cit.,* pp. 31-42.

CHAPTER EIGHT: SLOW THAW IN THE COLD WAR

1. The draft resolution, under the stated authorship of the party's national committee but obviously the work of a smaller body, appeared in *PA,* XXXI (Dec. 1952), pp. 4-13; John Swift, "The Struggle for a Mass Policy," *ibid.,* XXXII (Feb. 1953), p. 17; "Readers Guide to Economic Problems of Socialism in the U.S.S.R.* by Joseph Stalin," *ibid.,* XXXII (June 1953), pp. 66-96.
2. Draft resolution, *loc. cit.,* pp. 10-11; National Committee, C.P.U.S.A., "Resolution on the Situation Growing out of the Presidential Elections (Final Text)," *PA,* XXXII (July 1953), p. 12.
3. William Z. Foster, "Left Sectarianism in the Fight for Negro Rights and Against White Chauvinism," *ibid.,* XXXII (July 1953), pp. 17-32; Foster, "The 34th Anniversary of the Communist Party," *ibid.,* XXXII (Sept. 1953), p. 8.
4. As an article in *ibid.,* XXXIII (April 1954), pp. 4-19; as a pamphlet, with the same title, published by New Century the same month. The party hoped the pamphlet would have a circulation of a million, but it achieved only 650,000.
5. *Draft Program of the Communist Party, loc. cit.,* pp. 17-18.

6. Committee on Program Drafting, "A Letter on the Draft Program," *ibid.,* XXXIII (April 1954), pp. 20-7.
7. Betty Gannett, "The Communist Program—A Vital Document," *ibid.,* XXXIII (Sept. 1954), p. 48; for the final version see *ibid.,* XXXIII (Oct. 1954), pp. 1-20, and *DW,* Aug. 9, 1954.
8. Draft resolution, *loc. cit.,* p. 11.
9. See, for example, "A Letter on the Draft Program," *op. cit.,* p. 21; Pettis Perry, "The November Elections and the Struggle for Jobs, Peace, Equal Rights, and Democracy," *PA,* XXXIII (Sept. 1954), p. 15; Andrew Stevens, "Perspectives for Political Action," *ibid.,* XXXII Oct. 1953), p. 5; William Z. Foster, "Perspectives for a Labor-Farmer Party in the U.S.," *ibid.,* XXXIV (Feb. 1955), p. 15.
10. *DW,* April 22, 1955.
11. A.L.P. news release, Nov. 4, 1953, in library of Philip Jaffe, Stamford, Conn.
12. *National Guardian,* Nov. 7, 1955.
13. Alex H. Kendrick and Jerome Golden, "Lessons of the Struggle Against Opportunism in District 65," *PA,* XXXII (June 1953), pp. 26-37.
14. *Ibid.,* XXXII (July 1953), p. 4.
15. John Swift, "The Left and the Struggle for Labor Unity, I," *ibid.,* XXXII (July 1953), pp. 33-42, quotations from pp. 36, 41, 42. Italics in original.
16. John Swift, "The Left-Led Unions and Labor Unity, II," *ibid.,* XXXII (Nov. 1953), p. 64.
17. V. I. Lenin, "Preface to 'Letters to Sorge,'" *ibid.,* XXXII (Nov. 1953), p. 64.
18. V. J. Jerome, "May Day—1954; What Faces Us?," *ibid.,* XXXIII (May 1954), p. 7. Italics in original.
19. See George Morris, "The AFL-CIO Merger," *ibid.,* XXXIV (March 1955), pp. 30-40, and his columns in *DW,* Jan. 19, 21, 1955; see also editorial in *DW,* Dec. 29, 1954, and William Z. Foster in *ibid.,* Dec. 31, 1954, Dec. 1, 1955.
20. William Z. Foster, "Notes on the Struggle for Negro Rights," *PA,* XXXIV (May 1955), p. 31.
21. Hugh Bradley, "The N.A.A.C.P. Convention," *ibid.,* XXXII (Nov. 1953), pp. 57-9; Pettis Perry, "The Third Annual Convention of the National Negro Labor Council," *ibid.,* XXXIII (Feb. 1954), pp. 1-8.
22. Pettis Perry, "The Negro People in the Struggle Against McCarthyism (Draft-Program Discussion)," *ibid.,* XXXIII (May 1954), pp. 40-2.
23. Gannett, *op. cit.,* p. 59.
24. Frederick C. Hastings and Charles P. Mann, "For a Mass Policy in Negro Freedom's Cause," *PA,* XXXIV (March 1955), pp. 11-12; William Z. Foster, "Notes on the Struggle for Negro Rights," *loc. cit.,* pp. 40-41.
25. Doxey Wilkerson, "The 46th Annual Convention of the NAACP," *ibid.,* XXXIV (Aug. 1955), pp. 7-10.
26. Benjamin J. Davis, *The Negro People on the March* (New York: New Century, Aug. 1956), p. 30.
27. Betty Gannett, *The Communist Program and the Struggle for Jobs,*

Peace, Equal Rights, and Democracy (New York: New Century, 1954), pp. 29-30. Italics in original.

28. "The American Way to Jobs, Peace, Equal Rights and Democracy: Program of the Communist Party," *PA*, XXXIII (Oct. 1954), p. 20.
29. William Z. Foster, "Reply to a Priest's Letter," *ibid.*, XXXIII (Oct. 1954), pp. 45-8.
30. All from the May 1955 issue.
31. "The American Way," *loc. cit.*, p. 19.
32. Andrew Montgomery, "Our National Pride," *Party Voice*, II (July-Aug. 1954), pp. 8-9.
33. V. J. Jerome and Betty Gannett, "Patriotism and National Pride," *ibid.*, II (Sept.-Oct. 1954), pp. 21-7; published also in *PA*, XXXIII (Oct. 1954), pp. 28-35. Italics in original.
34. James S. Allen, "Democratic Revival and the Marxists," *Masses & Mainstream*, Oct. 1955, pp. 1-11, quotations from pp. 9, 11; see also Herbert Aptheker, "Patriotism and the Nation," *PA*, XXXIV (July 1955), pp. 22-33.
35. *DW*, Sept. 20, Dec. 1, 7, 8, 1955.
36. *Ibid.*, June 29, 1953.
37. *Ibid.*, July 13, 1953.
38. Nemmy Sparks, "The Yugoslav-Soviet Rapprochement," *PA*, XXXIV (Dec. 1955), pp. 27-34.
39. *Daily People's World*, Nov. 4, 16, 1955.

CHAPTER NINE: TARNISHED HEROES: STALIN AND FOSTER

1. New York *Times*, Feb. 15, 1956; *For a Lasting Peace, For a People's Democracy!*, Feb. 17, 1956; N. S. Khrushchev, "Report to the XXth Congress, CPSU," *PA*, XXXV (March 1956), pp. 51-64.
2. *DW*, Feb. 16, 17, 1956; *Wkr*, Feb. 19, 1956.
3. *DW*, Feb. 20, 1956.
4. *Wkr*, March 4, 1956.
5. *DW*, March 13, 1956.
6. *Wkr*, March 18, 1956.
7. *DW*, March 16, 1956.
8. New York *Times*, March 16, 1956; New York *Post*, March 16, 1956.
9. *New Times* (Moscow), March 1, 1956, special supplement, pp. 10-11.
10. As quoted in New York *Times*, March 28, 1956.
11. *Ibid.*, March 30, April 7, 1956.
12. *Ibid.*, March 24, 1956; see also account in *DW*, March 26, 1956.
13. *DW*, March 27, 1956.
14. *Ibid.*, March 26, 1956.
15. Important Communists admitted there were these divisions in the party. See Charney speech cited in note 12.
16. *Ibid.*, April 2, 1956.
17. See editorial in *ibid.*, March 19, 1956, and story under headline "WHAT WILL THE WORKER SAY?," *Wkr*, March 25, 1956.
18. *DW*, March 28, 1956; New York *Times*, March 28, 1956.
19. New York *Post*, March 28, 1956; *Time*, April 9, 1956, p. 35.

20. Howard Fast, *The Naked God: The Writer and the Communist Party* (New York: Praeger, 1957), pp. 50-1; interview with John Gates, Dec. 6, 1956.
21. New York *Times,* March 30, April 3, 1956.
22. *DW,* May 25, 1956.
23. *Time,* April 9, 1956, pp. 98, 100.
24. New York *Post,* March 28, 1956; New York *Times,* March 31, 1956.
25. John Gates, *Evolution of an American Communist* (New York: privately printed, 1958); interviews with Gates, Dec. 6, 1956, July 30, 1957. *Evolution* is a pamphlet version of the articles Gates wrote for the New York *Post,* Jan. 20-26, 1958. See also Gates, *The Story of an American Communist* (New York: Nelson, 1958).
26. *DW,* April 11, 1956.
27. *Ibid.,* April 5, 6, 1956; see also the cautious statement on civil liberties in a communist state in Editors of *PA,* "Socialism—USA and USSR," *Monthly Review,* VII (April 1956), pp. 497-500. The cover of this issue mistakenly says April 1955.
28. From notes made by the present writer at the meeting, April 4, 1956.
29. The March issue explained that "circumstances beyond our control" prevented publication of the February issue.
30. From personal observations of the meeting, April 30, 1956. A letter in the *DW,* May 4, 1956, complained about the meeting.
31. *DW,* April 11, 12, 1956; "What Happened to Soviet Jewish Culture? The First Authentic Statement and Our Comments," *Jewish Life: A Progressive Monthly,* X (May 1956), pp. 3-7, 27, 40. The present account is based on the *Jewish Life* translation.
32. *DW,* April 13, 1956.
33. *National Guardian,* June 25, 1956.
34. Letter from "A. F.," *DW,* April 24, 1956; letter from A. Unger, *ibid.,* April 25, 1956; see also Dora Teitelboim, *"We* Will Mourn Our Dead," *Masses & Mainstream,* IX (June 1956), pp. 1-7.
35. *DW,* June 25, 1956.
36. *Draft Resolution for the 16th National Convention of the Communist Party, U.S.A. Adopted Sept. 13, 1956* (New York: New Century, Sept. 1956), p. 58.
37. *DW,* Oct. 29, 1956.
38. *Ibid.,* May 3, 1956.
39. *Wkr,* April 8, 1956.
40. *DW,* April 16, 1956.
41. Eugene Dennis, *The Communists Take a New Look: Report to the National Committee of the Communist Party, U.S.A.* (New York: New Century, May 1956).
42. *DW,* May 3, 1956.
43. New York *Post,* July 22, 1956; *DW,* July 25, 1956. Subsequently, letters in the *DW* complained that party members had to rely on the "capitalist press" for full information about national committee affairs. See issue of Aug. 2, 1956, for example.
44. *Party Voice Discussion Supplement.* This four-page report by Norman Schrank was undated, but it appeared some time in May 1956. It discussed the national committee meeting that ended May 1, and the pres-

ent writer obtained a copy of it on May 31. Hereafter cited as Schrank report. For the votes on the report, John Gates to the present writer, Brooklyn, July 8, 1958.

45. Schrank report.
46. A Bronx Negro Woman Comrade, "Social Relations among Communists," *Party Voice,* IV (June 1956), p. 22; Food Worker, "A Rank and Filer Speaks his Piece," *ibid.* (July 1956), p. 9; D. V., "A Letter," *ibid.,* p. 23.
47. *DW,* July 25, 1956; for background of Dirba see Theodore Draper, *The Roots of American Communism* (New York: Viking, 1957), pp. 335, 339-40.
48. Interview with Earl Browder, July 31, 1956; *Party Voice,* IV (Sept. 1956), pp. 27-32; (Oct. 1956), pp. 21-5.
49. Don Lester, "One Essential in the Fight Against Left Sectarianism (From the discussion at the State Committee Meeting)," *ibid.,* IV (July 1956), p. 14.
50. These quotations are from the text as published in New York *Times,* June 5, 1956. A more convenient and better-edited version is in Russian Institute, Columbia University, ed., *The Anti-Stalin Campaign and International Communism* (New York: Columbia University Press, 1956), pp. 2-89, hereafter cited as *Anti-Stalin Campaign.* Another edition of the text of the speech, with annotations by Boris I. Nicolaevsky, was published in the *New Leader* under the title *The Crimes of the Stalin Era* (New York, 1956). Bertram D. Wolfe in *Khrushchev and Stalin's Ghost* (New York: Praeger, 1957), pp. 88-253, reproduces the speech and provides a thoughtful commentary on it.
51. Fast, *op. cit.,* p. 51.
52. *National Guardian,* May 14, 1956.
53. *DW,* June 6, 7, 1956.
54. *Ibid.,* June 12, 1956.
55. Fast, *op. cit.,* p. 27.
56. *DW,* Aug. 23, 1956.
57. Reprinted in *Anti-Stalin Campaign,* pp. 148-65.
58. *DW,* June 25, 1956; also in *Anti-Stalin Campaign,* pp. 269-73, and *PA,* XXXV (July 1956), pp. 34-6.
59. *Anti-Stalin Campaign,* p. 148.
60. New York *Times,* June 29, 30, July 1, 1956.
61. *DW,* July 2, 1956.
62. *Anti-Stalin Campaign,* p. 148.
63. Text of the resolution is in *ibid.,* pp. 276-306; *DW,* July 3, 1956; and *PA,* XXXV (Aug. 1956), pp. 32-47.
64. *DW,* July 5, 1956.
65. *Ibid.,* July 4, 1956; also in *Anti-Stalin Campaign,* pp. 326-7.
66. *DW,* July 3, 1956, incorrectly dated June 3 on front page but correctly dated on other pages; editorial also is in *Anti-Stalin Campaign,* pp. 323-4.
67. *DW,* July 5, 6, 1956.
68. *Ibid.,* July 9, 1956; see also July 10, 23, 1956.
69. *Ibid.,* July 26, 1956; also in *PA,* XXXV (Aug. 1956), pp. 48-9; John Gates, Brooklyn, to the present writer, July 8, 1958.

70. New York *Times*, July 26, 1956; *DW*, July 27, 1956.
71. "On the National Committee Statement," *Party Voice*, IV (Sept. 1956), pp. 8-10.
72. For Davis, *Wkr*, Sept. 2, 1956; for Foster, *ibid.*, Aug. 26, 1956.
73. *Ibid.*, Aug. 12, 1956.
74. Quotations from Bill Norman in *ibid.*, Aug. 19, 1956, but see also, all in *ibid.*, "B. S.," July 8, 1956; Albert Blumberg, July 15, 22, 1956; Fred Blair, July 29, 1956; Lillian Gates (Mrs. John Gates), Carl Hirsch, and "C. E. W.," Aug. 5, 1956; William Albertson, Aug. 12, 1956; Frank Carlson, Aug. 19, 1956; and "A Party Member," Sept. 3, 1956.
75. *Draft Resolution . . . 1956;* published also in *Wkr*, Sept. 23, 1956; New York *Post*, Sept. 22, 1956.
76. *Wkr*, Sept. 23, 1956; New York *Times*, Sept. 23, 1956; New York *Post*, Sept. 22, 1956.
77. New York *Times*, Sept. 24, 1956.
78. *DW*, Sept. 27, 1956.
79. *DW*, Oct. 3, 1956.
80. *Draft Resolution . . . 1956*, p. 56. Italics added.
81. William Z. Foster, "On the Party Situation," *PA*, XXXV (Oct. 1956), pp. 15-45, quotations from pp. 15, 20, 34.
82. From notes of the present writer at the meeting, Oct. 5, 1956; *Wkr*, Oct. 21, 1956.
83. Decca Truehaft, *Lifeitselfmanship, Or How To Become a Precisely-Because Man: An Investigation into Current L (or Left-Wing) Usage* (Oakland, Calif.: privately published, 1956), p. 11. Also published in *Mainstream*, IX (Oct. 1956), pp. 36-45.

CHAPTER TEN: HUNGARY AND FURTHER DISILLUSION

1. *DW*, Oct. 22, 1956. This editorial evoked criticism. See letters in *ibid.*, Oct. 25, 26, 1956.
2. *Ibid.*, Oct. 24, 1956.
3. *Ibid.*, Oct. 25, 1956.
4. *Ibid.*, Oct. 29, 30, Nov. 1, 1956.
5. *Ibid.*, Nov. 5, 1956. For Soviet statement of Oct. 30, see *ibid.*, Nov. 1, 1956, and Paul E. Zinner, ed., *National Communism and Popular Revolt in Eastern Europe: A Selection of Documents on Events in Poland and Hungary, February-November, 1956* (New York: Columbia University Press, 1956), pp. 485-9. The two translations differ slightly.
6. *DW*, Nov. 6, 1956.
7. *Ibid.*, Nov. 5, 1956.
8. *Ibid.*, Nov. 7, 1956.
9. Quoted in *ibid.*, Nov. 8, 1956.
10. *Ibid.*, Nov. 13, 21, 1956. See also letters from Helen Turner and "Constant Reader," Nov. 19, 1956.
11. *Ibid.*, Nov. 12, 1956.
12. *Ibid.*, Nov. 15, 1956.

13. See letter of Jack Goldring, in *ibid.,* Nov. 15, 1956. Goldring disassociated himself from the Connecticut party statement.

14. Appears in *ibid.,* Nov. 20, 1956, under title "An Open Letter to the Membership," and in *PA,* XXXV (Dec. 1956), pp. 1-5, under title, "On the Events in Hungary."

15. *DW,* Nov. 20, 1956.

16. *Ibid.,* Nov. 21, 1956.

17. *Ibid.,* Nov. 29, 30, 1956.

18. *Ibid.,* Nov. 26, 1956.

19. New York *Times,* Feb. 1, 1957. Fast told the present writer in an interview, in Dec. 1956, that he had left the party some weeks before.

20. New York *Times,* Jan. 19, 1957.

21. *Ibid.,* Dec. 18, 1956.

22. New York *Herald Tribune,* Nov. 24, 1956.

23. New York *Times,* Dec. 16, 1956.

24. Interview with John Gates, Dec. 6, 1956.

25. *16th National Convention Discussion Bulletin, No. 1,* Nov. 1, 1956. There were five of these *Bulletins,* all published by party headquarters in New York. Their dates were No. 2, Nov. 27, 1956; No. 3, Dec. 10, 1956; No. 4, Jan. 1, 1957; and No. 5, Jan. 15, 1957.

26. John Gates, "Time for a Change," *PA,* XXXV (Nov. 1956), pp. 53-5.

27. Foster, "Marxism-Leninism in a Changing World (Part II)," *ibid.,* XXXV (Dec. 1956), p. 62.

28. Foster, "Origins of the Crisis in the CPUSA," *Party Voice,* V (Jan. 1957), p. 25.

29. *DW,* Jan. 2, 1957.

30. *Discussion Bulletin, No. 5,* Jan. 15, 1957.

31. George Blake Charney and Bill Norman, "A Letter to the Readers," *Party Voice,* V (Jan. 1957), p. 2.

32. *Proceedings* (abridged) of the sixteenth national convention of the Communist Party, U.S.A. (New York: Communist Party, 1957), pp. 17, 46, 72. Hereafter cited as *Proceedings.*

33. New York *Herald Tribune,* Jan. 31, 1957; New York *Times,* Jan. 31, 1957.

34. New York *World-Telegram and Sun,* Feb. 7, 1957; *Proceedings,* p. 174; *DW,* Feb. 8, 1956.

35. New York *Times,* Feb. 4, 1957.

36. *DW,* Feb. 6, 1957.

37. Notes by Bernard Rosenberg on the Communist Party convention, typescript report prepared by Mr. Rosenberg, a lecturer at the New School for Social Research, for the Fund for the Republic, Inc. A briefer version of Rosenberg's report is in *Dissent* (New York), IV (Spring 1957), pp. 152-6. Subsequent citations to Rosenberg are to the unpublished report. The convention admitted thirteen non-Communist observers to its meetings.

38. *Proceedings,* pp. 173-4.

39. *Ibid.,* pp. 42-5.

40. *Ibid.,* pp. 45-7, quotation from pp. 51-2.

41. *DW,* Feb. 11, 1957.

42. *Proceedings,* pp. 37-67, quotations from pp. 63-6.

43. Rosenberg, *op. cit.*
44. *Proceedings,* pp. 70-85.
45. *Draft Resolution for the 16th National Convention of the Communist Party, U.S.A., Adopted Sept. 13, 1956* (New York: New Century, Sept. 1956), p. 56.
46. *Proceedings,* pp. 164-73, 318; Rosenberg, *op. cit.*
47. *Proceedings,* p. 175; Rosenberg, *op. cit.*
48. New York *Times,* May 3, 1957.
49. *Proceedings,* p. 195.
50. *Ibid.,* pp. 232-3, 239.
51. *Ibid.,* pp. 235-6.
52. Letter of James McCluskey to the Inwood Section, C.P.U.S.A., February 1957, copy in the author's possession.
53. The document appears in *Proceedings,* pp. 253-328.
54. C. L. of Los Angeles, "The 'Main Task'—or Candide Revisited," *The Party Forum* (San Francisco), Nov. 1, 1956.
55. Interview with Dorothy Healy, Jan. 16, 1957.
56. Interview with John Gates, July 30, 1957.
57. *Proceedings,* p. 237.
58. Letter of McCluskey to Inwood Section.
59. *DW,* Oct. 11, 1957.
60. Interview with Merle Brodsky, a leader in the California East Bay area, March 28, 1957.
61. Robert Claiborne, "Twilight on the Left," *The Nation,* May 11, 1957, p. 414.
62. New York *Times,* March 18, 23, 1957; *DW,* March 22, 1957.
63. *DW,* April 3, 1957.
64. *Proceedings,* p. 247.
65. *DW,* April 3, 4, 1957.
66. Interview with John Gates, July 30, 1957.
67. New York *Times,* May 6, 11, 1957; *Wkr,* May 12, 1957. Gates said in an interview, July 30, 1957, that he had a higher percentage of supporters in the executive committee of twenty than in the full national committee. The executive committee members were: George Blake Charney, Benjamin Davis, Eugene Dennis, Earl Durham, Fred Fine, Elizabeth Gurley Flynn, William Z. Foster, John Gates, James Jackson, and Sidney Stein, of New York; David Davis, Philadelphia; Claude Lightfoot, Chicago; Hy Lumer, Cleveland; George Myers, Baltimore; Carl Ross, Minneapolis; Michael Russo, Boston; Martha Stone, Newark; Carl Winter, Detroit; Dorothy Healy, Los Angeles; and Albert J. ("Mickie") Lima, San Francisco.
68. New York *Times,* May 11, 1957.
69. Interview with Joseph Clark, Dec. 30, 1957.
70. New York *Times,* June 7, 1957; *DW,* June 7, 1957.
71. Interview with John Gates, July 30, 1956.
72. Interview with John Gates, Dec. 6, 1956.
73. *DW,* April 4, 1957.
74. *Ibid.,* June 4, 1957.
75. *Ibid.,* June 12, 1957.
76. *Ibid.,* April 19, 1957.

77. *Wkr,* May 5, 1957.
78. *Ibid.,* May 19, 1957.
79. *DW,* July 9, 1957.
80. *Ibid.,* July 10, 1957.
81. *Ibid.,* July 17, 18, 1957.
82. Interview with John Gates, July 30, 1957.
83. *DW,* July 24, 1957.
84. *Ibid.,* June 19, 1957.
85. *Ibid.,* June 26, 1957.
86. *Ibid.,* July 2, 1957.
87. *Ibid.,* July 19, 1957.
88. *Ibid.,* July 9, 1957.
89. *Ibid.,* July 23, 1957.
90. *Ibid.,* July 26, 1957.
91. New York *Times,* May 18, 1957.
92. See letters from Harold Collins, *DW,* Dec. 17, 26, 1957.
93. *Ibid.,* Sept. 9, 1957.
94. *Ibid.,* Dec. 19, 1957.
95. *Wkr,* Dec. 15, 1957.
96. *DW,* Sept. 9, 1957.
97. Interview with John Gates, July 30, 1957.
98. *DW,* Sept. 10, 1957.
99. Ibid., Sept. 12, 1957.
100. *Ibid.,* Oct. 21, Nov. 20, 1957.
101. New York *Times,* Dec. 9, 1957, Jan. 12, 1958.
102. *DW,* Oct. 2, 8, 11, 1957.
103. The Bittelman series was in *ibid.,* Oct. 1 to 16, 1957; William Z. Foster, "The Party Crisis and the Way Out," *PA,* XXXVI (Dec. 1957), pp. 47-61, and *ibid.,* XXXVII (Jan. 1958), pp. 49-65. Foster obviously had a copy of the Bittelman articles before they were published entirely. The last appeared on the day of Foster's stroke.
104. *DW,* Oct. 9, 1957.
105. New York *Times,* Nov. 22, Dec. 3, 1957.
106. *DW,* Nov. 25, 1957.
107. *Wkr,* Dec. 15, 22, 1957.
108. *DW,* Dec. 31, 1957; the executive committee's statement appears in *PA,* XXXVII (Jan. 1958), pp. 1-4; Robert Thompson's report appears in *ibid.,* XXXVII (Feb. 1958), pp. 26-35. An editorial footnote on p. 30 of the Thompson report repeats the gist of the *DW*'s Dec. 31 account of the administrative committee's actions.
109. *DW,* Dec. 31, 1957; New York *Times,* Dec. 26, 1957.
110. *DW,* Nov. 13, 1956.
111. *Proceedings,* pp. 242-3.
112. *DW,* Sept. 13, 1957.
113. New York *Times,* Dec. 26, 1957; see also *DW,* Dec. 30, 31, 1957.
114. *DW,* Dec. 30, 1957.
115. Interview with John Gates, Feb. 23, 1958.
116. New York *Times,* Jan. 11, 1958.
117. *DW,* Jan. 13, 1958.

CONCLUSION: AN IMPOTENT PARTY

1. *Wkr,* March 16, Jan. 26, Feb. 16, 1958.
2. *Ibid.,* March 9, 1958; "On the Resignation of John Gates," *PA,* XXVII (March 1958), pp. 7-9; interview with John Gates, Feb. 23, 1958.
3. *Wkr,* March 9, 1958; "On Uniting and Strengthening the Party and Its Mass Base," *PA,* XXVII (March 1958), pp. 1-6; New York *Times,* Feb. 22, 1958.
4. "On the Peace Manifesto and the 12-Party Declaration," *PA,* XXXVII (June 1958), pp. 22-6; the older statement appeared in *ibid.,* XXXVII (Jan. 1958), pp. 1-4.
5. *Wkr,* March 9, 1958; New York *Times,* Feb. 22, 1958; interview with John Gates, Feb. 23, 1958. At a national committee meeting in June 1958, four more members—Andrew Krchmarek, Claude Lightfoot, Burt Nelson, and Carl Winter—were elected to the executive committee—New York *Times,* July 12, 1958.
6. William Z. Foster, "The Superiority of World Socialism Over World Capitalism," *PA,* XXXVII (May 1958), pp. 19-28, quotation from p. 26.
7. New York *Times,* March 8, 28, May 3, 1958; New York *Post,* April 16, 1958; *Wkr,* May 4, 1958.
8. New York *Times,* July 12, 1958.
9. *The Marxist-Leninist Vanguard* (New York), Sept.-Nov. 1958. The first issue appeared in Sept. 1958.
10. New York *Times,* May 3, 1958.
11. *Ibid.,* May 31, 1958; *Wkr,* June 1, 1958.
12. New York *Times,* Nov. 28, 1956; *DW,* Nov. 28, 1956.
13. San Francisco *Chronicle,* May 3, 1957.
14. Original announcement in *DW,* Oct. 11, 1957.
15. New York *Times,* Nov. 7, 1957.
16. Interview with John Gates, July 30, 1957.
17. New York *Times,* Jan. 11, 1958.
18. New York *Post,* April 16, 1958; New York *Times,* May 3, July 12, 1958.
19. Interview with Joseph Clark, Dec. 30, 1957.
20. Theodore Draper, *The Roots of American Communism* (New York: Viking, 1957), p. 272; Irwin Suall, national secretary of the combined socialist organization, to the present writer, New York, March 6, 1958.
21. Bob Thompson, "On the Work and Consolidation of the Party," *PA,* XXXVII (Aug. 1958), p. 46.
22. Dorothy Jones, "Money Is Everybody's Job in San Francisco," *Contact,* I (June 1957), p. 1; *DW,* March 24, 1947; *Wkr,* April 6, 1947.
23. William Z. Foster, "Draper's 'Roots of American Communism,'" *PA,* XXXVI (May 1957), pp. 34-40.
24. Elizabeth Gurley Flynn in *DW,* April 8, 1949, and in *Wkr,* Jan. 26, 1958.

INDEX

The Ball Red Book

Produced by Geo. J. Ball, Inc.

Vic Ball, Editor
Frank Batson, Azaleas
Bob Danielson, Roses

Jim Ferguson, Bedding Plant Sales
William Hamilton, Mums
Ian Mackay, Garden Roses

Robert Rieman, Snapdragons

Special Guest Contributors

Dr. A. A. DeHertogh: Bulb Forcing
Paul Ecke, Jr.: Poinsettias
Robert Hastings: Lilies
Prof. W. D. Holley: Carnations, CO_2
Dr. Kenneth Horst: Chemical Sterilizing
Robert McColley: Foliage Plants
Dr. Marlin Rogers: Pollution Problems
Dr. James Shanks: Hydrangeas
Dr. Herbert Streu: Insect Control

Third Printing, Thirteenth Edition

Table of Contents

Part I—General Greenhouse Subjects

1. All About GROWING BEDDING PLANTS

Bedding plants, the world over, are big—and getting bigger fast!

Best intelligent estimates say, "At least $53 million per year wholesale value." Probably $60 million plus. Except for mums and foliage plants, bedding plants are the No. 1 floriculture crop in dollar value. Next to foliage plants the fastest growing. (No real hard census figures on bedding plants since 1970.)

Last figures, 1970, bedding-plant sales, on wholesale, were $44.8 million—up 37% over 1959.

Several reasons, as we see them:

1. Unlike roses, for example (special occasions, expensive), spring plants are not costly, can be and are enjoyed by the working man. Almost anyone can afford a touch of color in his garden. Annuals are truly "flowers for the masses," and bedding-plant growers are doing a rather effective job of selling this facet of the mass market.

2. The development of container growing and plant materials suitable for this purpose. A variety of patio pots, tubs and hanging baskets are opening up a whole new market for bedding plants. More than 25,000,000 apartment and condominium balconies and patios are potential planting sites!

3. Another reason we see for the boom in flower gardening: It's just getting to be a lot easier and less costly to have a few annuals in your front yard. Example: Plant pot 'n all (Jiffy-Pot) annuals versus the old dug-up, replanted way.

Plus—far better small garden plows and tools, automatic watering equipment, bug sprays, etc.

Plus—what a lot breeding has done to give the gardener more show for his money and effort. The dramatic improvement, for example, in impatiens, where we've gone from the tall, sparse flowering varieties to the *Elfins*, which are dwarf and free-flowering.

Perhaps most of all, more people are turning to gardening as one answer to the ever-increasing pressures of our modern way of living.

Whatever the reasons, the bedding-plant business outlook is good—and getting better.

MAKE A PLAN—AND A BUDGET

Both are terribly important to profitable production of spring plants.

First, the plan. Take your season a week at a time! Why not do like mum propagators—number the weeks of the year from 1 through 52. Example: May 28 to June 3 (1972) will be week no. 22.

The job of planning is to decide months ahead just how many flats of each variety of everything you grow must be ready to deliver—on week 22,

Bedding-plant production at the Sedan Floral range, Sedan, Kansas—one of the largest. Note, by the way, everything up off the floor (disease prevention), and every pack includes a Tag-Along plastic label.

for example. Then you count back from May 28 and put down the correct date to sow seed—and to transplant—to deliver the goods on May 28. And so on through the entire season. Perhaps you will only plan a fresh lot of most varieties to be available every second week.

Of course, the guts of a good plan is good records from previous seasons. So, the good planner notes each week through his selling season what he has too much of, what he is short of, so he can adjust for next year. Easy to say, hard to do (so little time in May), but vital to profit. You don't ring the cash register for plants you throw out; the same for the ones you could have sold but didn't have.

If interested, write for Bedding Plant Record Book, Seed Department, Geo. J. Ball, Inc., West Chicago, Illinois 60185.

A word on budgeting. Really, a well-run business should lay out the whole season's expense and revenue in detail—again well in advance of the season. Based on your general production plan (above), list all the expenses you can anticipate for the coming season. Again, base it on last year's cost—adjusted where needed.

Such a record should *include* all costs—taxes, insurance, labor, cost for flats, seed, soil, labels, etc. Include your own salary!

Budget your sales, too, and forecast your profit. A really sharp business-man predicts his profit rather closely.

If you do the budgeting job seriously, it will sometimes put real pressure on your price decision. Are we not going to make a fair return for the coming season? If not, should we raise our prices? Or, shall we reconsider the size of pack we grow in?

Good, honest, budget-minded management often anticipates a loss—and does something about it before the season even starts.

ON GOOD SEED GERMINATION

There are several rules that simply must be followed:

1. **Sow good seed.** Remember, seeds are living things! No one can guarantee a perfect stand—but reputable seedsmen through dry storage, regular germination testing, etc., come close to it. There are low-priced flower seeds—but the occasional problems that result more than wipe out the savings.

2. **Germination medium.** The majority of bedding plants today are sown in Jiffy-Mix—or a material close to it. Mainly peat, fine vermiculite and a touch of fertilizer. It's uniform, always the same, holds moisture well, allows for easy removal of seedlings, and it's sterile—free of disease. Just be sure the flats used are well drained and, of course, sterilized. Various mixes of peat, vermiculite, soil, perlite, etc. can be used—must be sterile, free of salts, fine-textured.

3. **Uniform moisture—always!** An absolute must for successful germination is uniform moisture. Once sprouted, if seedlings dry out, they will die. Several ways to do the job. As good as any is an electric mist system until seeds sprout. The normal rate is six seconds of mist every ten minutes, sunup to sunset. Some growers with forced-air heating leave the mist on twenty-four hours a day. Another practical answer is to simply soak the flats thoroughly before sowing, mist them well after seeding, then either wrap the flats in a sheet of poly or cover the entire bench over with polyethylene to retain moisture. Leave the poly on until the seeds sprout, then it must come off promptly.

One way to insure 75° soil temperature for prompt germination of annuals. There is a 1-inch pipe every 12 inches across the bench—running the length of the bench—plus two 2½-inch lines below the bench—one with fins. It's hot water—supplied by a small used residential hot-water heater, gas-fired. The grower: Bert Bosgraaf; son Tom in the photo. Tom says soil temperature actually runs near 80°—germination is prompt and lovely.

4. **Must be warm!** Here's probably the No. 1 reason for irregular, slow, and poor germination. So often the greenhouse temperature is, in fact, 65, even 70°—but the soil temperature in the seed flats can be as much as 10° lower. Reasons for this:

A. Moisture evaporating from the surface of the seed flat cools the soil—certainly 5 to 10° or more.

Ken Reeves, bedding-plant grower of Toronto, Ontario, finds frequently that the soil temperature in his germination flats will run 10° or more lower than the house temperature. By the way, a glass-rod thermometer for checking actual soil temperature can be obtained from local horticultural supply houses for about $4.00.

B. Quite often, water applied through misting is as low as 50° or in the mid-40's. Tests at Michigan State prove that this cooled the soil sharply —and took around 8 hours for the temperature to come up again to the 70's. Adequate soil temperature can be insured by hot-bed cables installed below the flats. Propagating mats will do this job very nicely —cost about $3.95 per square foot covered. See the interesting plan worked out by Bert Bosgraaf, Grand Rapids grower, photo page 5.

We have discussed this matter of soil temperature for germination with dozens of successful growers. Without exception, they maintain a soil temperature of at least 72-74° and, in some cases, 78° or even 80°. The only exceptions are snapdragon, larkspur, stock, and verbena, which are better at around 65°.

5. **Cool back promptly!** This high-moisture/75-78° germination chamber will normally sprout good seed in 3-5 days. As soon as the seed is well-sprouted, it must be moved out to full sun, fresh air, better a 50 to 60° night temperature. Keep the flats watered, but on the dry side. The object is to harden seedlings, prevent damp-off.

6. **To cover or not?** Almost uniformly, successful growers do not cover fine seed such as petunia, begonia, etc. The seed washes down into the Jiffy-Mix particles shortly after sowing. However, nearly all growers do cover coarser seed, such as salvia, zinnia, tomato, etc. Some seeds (USDA tests) do require a three-day period of darkness for germination, therefore, must be covered. Examples: verbena, dusty miller, larkspur, pansy, phlox, portulaca, vinca.

Growers using Jiffy-Mix almost never feed flats; there is enough nutrient material in the mix. However, growers using other mixes may want to apply a supplemental feeding—one ounce of 20-20-20 to 3 gallons of water applied with a Hozon.

Some growers, to be extra careful, apply Dexon, Terraclor, Truban or Benlate to flats of Jiffy-Mix as a preventive against damp-off. Its a good idea to wait a full 24 hours after application.

Paul Peterson of Delray Beach, Florida, grows several million vegetable plants in Jiffy Mix. It is a blend of peat moss and vermiculite with some nutrients added. Prepared mixes, such as Jiffy-Mix, provide good air-water relationships that promote uniform growth. They also save mixing and steaming labor.

SOIL MIXES FOR BEDDING PLANTS

Clearly, the majority of bedding plants today are grown in mixes with little or often no soil. And the trend is toward completely soilless mixes. The same, by the way, for much of pot-plant production in the U.S. Interesting note: The good European growers, particularly of pot plants, are further down this road of soilless mixes than we in the U.S.

Back to bedding plants, the actual mixes used by growers across the U.S. vary endlessly. Peat is nearly always a major component. Most often, we also hear vermiculite, perlite, hypnum peat, wood-bark shavings (or sawdust), etc.—occasionally some sand. Commercial Jiffy-Mix (peat, vermiculite, plus fertilizer) is used widely by U.S. growers. A heavy majority use it for seed germination and an increasing number are using straight "J-Mix" for growing-on bedding plants.

Typically, it takes a little study and experience to grow good annuals with these artificial mixes—but once you have it, you *know* every crop will be a good one from there on out. Often noticeably better than soil crops.

STEAMED
PEAT-No.4 VERMICULITE
MIX without 5-10-5
LIQUID FEED

NOT STEAMED
PEAT-No.4 VERMICULITE
MIX without 5-10-5
LIQUID FEED

Steaming is simply not necessary with Jiffy-Mix (peat-lite mix)—in fact, more often than not, the plants grow better without it, especially when other conditions are not right. Example: The plants above were given liquid feed with their watering, but no dry feed with the original mix. Under these conditions, the unsteamed box proved number-one quality.

Why the trend away from soil—toward these mixes? Some key reasons, as we see it:

1. Finding good, uniform soil, free of weed-killer, chemicals, etc., is getting tougher, more costly each year.

2. Adding peat, other additives, fertilizer, etc., is costly. Equipment, labor needed for large soil sheds, etc. "It would cost me $10,000 for sheds and equipment," says one grower—now using Jiffy-Mix.

3. Bedding plants grown in peat mixes are *consistently* good—and generally some better than the same plants in soil.

4. Peat-vermiculite—Jiffy-Mix, for example, is far lighter weight than soil—about half as heavy as a soil-peat-sand (4-2-1) mix per Connecticut Greenhouse News Letter #34, May 1970 (Univ. of Conn.). Far easier to handle flats during transplanting, etc. Example: California law prohibits women lifting over twenty-five-pound loads—often exceeded by a flat of wet soil. Also, a big point in truck delivering of bedding plants—by weight, you can carry twice as many soilless flats per truck as with soil.

5. Jiffy-Mix growers say their women transplant 30 per cent more flats per hour in Jiffy-Mix as compared to soil—"Just press seedlings into the mix." Less shock after transplanting.

6. Watering frequency cut about one-half, says one grower using peat-lite.

7. Far better shelf-life at point-of-sale—plants in peat-lite can survive far longer without water.

GROWING IN PEAT MIXES IS DIFFERENT!

There are some very important points to be observed in growing in mixes of peat-vermiculite, etc. Let's call them precautions.

1. Critically important in preparing the soilless mixes that the mix be thoroughly and completely mixed! A poor mixing job can bring on big problems

—small lots of soil which have excessive fertilizer, etc. Especially critical when we consider the very small quantities, especially of minor elements, which must be mixed with these soilless mixes—unless the mixing is 100 per cent thorough, these small quantities simply will not be distributed through the mass—with obvious perils. Probably one key reason why quite a few growers buy commercial mixes rather than mix their own. Cement mixers tend to be unreliable in getting a thorough blend of small amounts of fertilizer, etc.

2. Before setting plants into these peat-lite mixes, it is critically important that the mix be thoroughly watered. Many growers repeat three times to be sure that not only is the entire container thoroughly wet—but that any tendency for salt build-up to accumulate has been leached out.

3. Several growers commented that they prefer to let the plants start making new roots before they start feeding. Again, a precaution against any possibility of salt build-up.

4. Never use ammonia nitrogen when growing in such soilless mixes—always use the nitrate form.

5. An interesting point: One reason almost everyone includes some additive along with peat—if a pack of annuals in clear peat dries out, it is not

S. S. Couch, Rogersville, Tennessee. Everything grown here in 2¼-inch Jiffy-Strips. The strip of 12 is torn into 2 units of 6 each, grown and sold in a poly tray. Note the spic-and-span cleanliness of the operation, beautiful uniformity of plants. And, by the way, Spray-Stick irrigation! Well done!

likely that especially the point-of-sale retailer will ever get it wet again. Dry peat is just tough to get to take water.

TEMPERATURE-WATERING-FEEDING

Feeding-watering-temperature can be played many ways in growing a bedding plant!

Let's start with the objectives. Certainly, any good bedding-plant grower wants to produce a top-quality plant in the shortest time possible from sowing to sale. He should make all feeding-watering-temperature decisions with this goal in mind! But how many different ways you see it done!

First decision: Should annual plants—petunias, for example—really be sold in flower? Is a petunia plant in flower really a better-quality plant than a sturdy, vigorous, well-branched plant not yet in color? Unfortunately, the majority of bedding-plant growers will tell you that especially with non-florist outlets (food chains, K-Mart, etc.), a flat of petunias simply must show some color—the more, the better.

What a real shame this is!

The fact is that the bushy, well-branched, still-succulent, somewhat-soft petunia plant will just grow circles around the plant that was sold in flower. If you doubt this, try it. We have—repeatedly. And, always, the answer is the same. A month after setting the two lots of plants out in the field, the soft, not-yet-in-flower petunia has produced perhaps twice the amount of growth, and now produces twice as much color as the plant that was allowed to come into flower—and to harden somewhat—before it was sold to the home gardener and planted outdoors. A few really top-quality retail growers—especially those who have built a backlog of customer confidence—do sell the softer "no-flower" plants. Example: Dick Chamberlain, Carlisle, Pennsylvania. We wish there were more like him—and hope that this message will go over as the years go by.

So, reluctantly, and against our convictions, we proceed with all the tricks to make a petunia plant flower in the least time from sowing.

WHAT ARE THE RULES?

The rules for making particularly petunias flower earlier in the flats and packs are simple:

A. Warmer temperature means earlier flowering. Sixty-degree night temperature flowers earlier than 50°. See table on page 11.

B. Warmer temperature plus regular and heavier feeding means earlier flowering. See chart, page 11.

C. More water and warmer temperature again mean earlier-blooming petunias. See chart, page 11.

And the same thing no doubt would apply to the great majority of other annuals—grown as bedding plants.

First, a little comment on the above three points. Speaking temperature, almost any grower knows that petunias at 40° nights will produce short, stocky, free-branching plants—but will take a long time from sowing to flowering. Sixty-degree night temperature, on the other hand, still produces a good quality plant—and in a lot fewer weeks than 40°. Seventy-degree nights certainly would flower still earlier, but almost surely a soft, poor-quality plant.

Let's talk feeding a bit. A plant clearly on the hungry side will be inferior in quality and certainly later in flowering. Heavy and frequent feeding does tend to soften such plants as petunias. Coupled with high moisture and high temperature, lots of feed can over-soften petunias. The typical grower,

HIGHER TEMPERATURE MEANS EARLIER BLOOM
Tests by Ball staff at West Chicago

VARIETY	Sown	Pricked off	% in bloom May 21		% in bloom June 1	
			50°	60°	50°	60°
Petunia Allegro	3/9/62	3/27/62	0	5	10	75
Petunia Pink Magic	3/9/62	3/27/62	4	96*	100	100
Marigold Spry	3/9/62	3/14/62	100	100	100	100
Snap Sequoia	3/9/62	3/27/62	0	15*	0	50

REMARKS- the 60° lot was saleable and flowered 2 weeks earlier.

*60° plants, some taller but very saleable.

especially in soilless mixes, will certainly not feed along with every watering. Ken Reeves of Toronto says, "Apply fertilizer with judgment. Too much too often means too lush, too soft a plant."

The last, and toughest one, is watering. Again, more watering means earlier bloom—but it is so easy to overwater, run plants up ruinously soft and tall. Certainly including petunias. Again, Ken Reeves of Toronto tells it well. "We water freely for the first week or so to get the plants started,

WARM TEMPERATURE PLUS MORE FEED MEANS EARLIER BLOOM
Tests by Dr. John Seeley, Penn State

PETUNIA ALLEGRO
SOWN MARCH 2 – POTTED APRIL 1
WATERED WEEKLY

	50° % in flower May 21	60° % in flower May 21
Fed once	0%	33%
Fed every 3 wks.	0%	86%
Fed weekly	7%	90%

NOTE: 60° plants were not too tall.

MORE WATER WARM TEMPERATURE MEANS EARLIER BLOOM
Tests by Dr. John Seeley, Penn State

PETUNIA COMANCHE
SOWN: MARCH 2 – POTTED: APRIL 1
FED WEEKLY

	50° % in flower May 21	60° % in flower May 21
Run Dry	7%	60%
Watered Daily	53%	96%
Watered Daily-Plunged	70%*	93%*

*Plunged plants (real wet) flowered earliest – but were too tall.

11

then begin to hold back—depending on growth and also demand for plants. We really sort of dole out water. We have fine automatic equipment to do it—but better done by hand; then, you won't overdo."

In other words, the grower simply has to watch the plants, use judgment. Know that keeping them very much on the dry side will delay flowering, will produce a harder, shorter plant.

A bit on slow-release fertilizers. Many very good growers rely heavily on such materials as MagAmp—in some cases alone, sometimes combined with liquid feeding. Bud Spurgeon of Maryville, Tennessee uses MagAmp on all bedding plant soils—plus a 20-20-20 liquid feed. But, "Depending on how anxious we are to push along a lot of plants, we may liquid-feed several times a week, or maybe not for weeks in a row. You've got to watch the plants."

Harold Ahrens, very large bedding-plant specialist at Osseo, Minnesota, includes some dry fertilizer with his original mix—but after that, relies entirely on MagAmp. Three pounds per cubic yard of medium-grade in all bedding-plant soils.

Harry Tayama, Ohio State Department of Floriculture, supports slow-release fertilizers. "Good bedding plants can be grown with MagAmp or Osmocote—but strikingly good plants can be grown in a combination of both slow-release fertilizer and liquid feed. Almost a sort of synergistic effect." He recommends using half the recommended rate of the slowly available materials.

A fair conclusion on the whole question of feed, water, temperature: Most good growers do start plants at 60° nights (some even at 70°) for the first 3 to 5 weeks after transplanting. Then, as plants become established, most growers drop them to 45° or 40° nights to get some hardening effect. Watering and feeding more heavily at first, and less during the cool-temperature phase—again to somewhat harden-back the growth.

One more very interesting point on the feed-water-temperature controversy: Assuming that everybody wants short plants—and most growers do want flowers as soon as possible—then by all means, use retardants. For example, B-Nine. Its better to control height with retardants than with cold temperature. Cool temperatures will keep the plants from getting too tall, but also will delay flowering. Retardants keep the plant short, but flowers develop just as fast as without B-Nine.

WHEN TO SOW?

Assuming normal handling of watering and feeding, and assuming a 60° start for 4 to 5 weeks, then a cool-temperature finish, here would be a fairly close idea of when to sow for different sale dates:

1. For the average grower, again 60° to start, cool finish, allow 2¾ to 3 months from sowing of seed until petunias, for example, are ready for sale. This seems to work out fairly well at different latitudes. Vandon Knight in Memphis sows January 2 for sale April 1. George Lucht (Malmborg's) in Minneapolis, sows February 15 for first substantial sales May

1. 5. His main sowing: March 1, for sale June 1. Florida/California growers would cut this time somewhat due to more favorable growing conditions in midwinter.

2. Later sowing for June sale of petunia plants: Allow 1¾ to 2 months from sowing of seed to sale of plants—again depending on how warm, how much water, how much light. John DeWinter, Grandville, Michigan, sows mid-March for late May-early June—a little over 2 months sowing to sale. Some Minnesota growers sow April 1 for sale June 1—a warm 60° all the way, for a total of under 2 months sowing to sale. Another northern grower sows May 1 for sale June 25—about 1.9 months sowing to sale.

3. The slower, cooler grower: There are still substantial growers who start sowing in January, even as early as mid-December, carry petunias anywhere from 45° down to freezing. Such growers will take as much as 4.5 months sowing to flowering. More typically, 4 months or a little under. Again, their goal: tough, high-quality plants, everything in color and also saving of fuel. Making some sowings quite early this way does spread the transplanting labor. And sometimes, allows double-cropping. See below.

DOUBLE-CROPPING

There's another little trick in bedding-plant growing that we hear more about each year. Example: Some of the northern growers are making sowings of such things as petunias around the first of the year, pushing them along at 60° for a month or so, then perhaps closer to 50°—to produce saleable plants around late March or April 1. Such crops are planned frankly for the near-South market—Missouri, Tennessee, Kentucky, West Virginia, etc. The objective is that as soon as this "southern crop" is off the benches, around April 1, the grower transplants a second batch to replace them—thus getting two bedding crops a year from the same bench. Some northern growers, by working hard to develop this southern market, get this all-important double crop from as much as half of their total bedding-plant bench area each year; all of which, of course, means more dollars per square foot from the bedding-plant operation.

These same growers do push the other way—to develop late-June sales, even up through July 4—especially for the northern resort areas. Again to increase the amount of double-cropping on their range.

USE RETARDANTS

The majority of good commercial bedding-plant producers do use retardants on most annuals—generally, B-Nine. The main reason is simply that plants treated with a retardant three or four weeks after transplanting will stay shorter longer. Especially when a couple of weeks of wet weather slows demand down in late May, this çan prevent many thousands of flats from overgrowing and becoming worthless. Put it a different way—rarely are petunias or other plants too short; often, they are too tall. So, in a way, you can hardly help but improve the quality—at no more penalty than a single application of retardant.

Then you can hold plants back either by cooling them down or using retardants. Very low night temperatures delay height *and flowering;* retardants delay only height—no delay in flowering.

Procedure is simply to apply one spray—normally at 2,500 ppm (0.25%)—or 5 teaspoons of B-Nine in 1 gallon of water.

Application should be made 3 to 4 weeks after transplanting of annuals. B-Nine should always be applied when the plant foliage is dry—and do not water for 24 hours or more after application, or the material will be washed off.

Just for the record, B-Nine does not keep plants short after they are planted out in the customer's garden. Actually, it seems to have no effect after a month or so.

Some growers use continuous applications (weekly) which are started shortly after transplanting of annuals with no damage. However, if plants which have not previously had retardant are given a spray of this material after buds are showing, it can damage flowers—mainly, it causes flowers of red varieties to bleach nearly white."

Of the dozen or so bedding-plant growers across the country studied in connection with this chapter, virtually all are using B-Nine. Some use one application, some use several. A few on petunias only, but most growers apply it to all bedding annuals.

GROWING CONTAINERS, PRICES

Here, we will tackle the question of growing containers—and along with it, prices. Reason: the two seem to revolve around each other.

Up until 10 or 15 years ago, the U.S. bedding-plant business was done in a

Janoski's Greenhouse, Clinton, Pennsylvania, either sows seed or dibbles transplants in Jiffy-7 peat pellets. Jiffy-grown plants can be handled easily and transplanted with virtually no plant stress. Holding Jiffy-7 transplants is Mrs. Janoski.

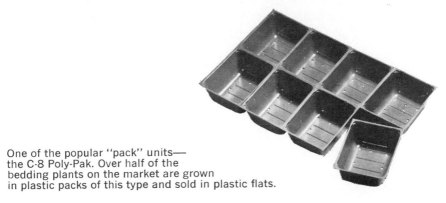

One of the popular "pack" units—
the C-8 Poly-Pak. Over half of the
bedding plants on the market are grown
in plastic packs of this type and sold in plastic flats.

22 to 24-inch wooden flat—some in pots, majority in flats. Plants were dug and wrapped by the dozens for the waiting customer. Then came the first packs (Pony-Pack, Carl Tasche, Los Angeles) and the lid was off. The one rule since then (and still today) has been constant rapid change. And certainly, more changes ahead. The purpose of this chapter is to cover briefly how the job is done as of today 1975. What we see:

1. There is very substantial production of bedding plants in pots—Jiffy-Pots, plastic, etc. Probably the heavy half, though, is in "Paks"—6, 10, perhaps 12 packs in a flat—often the flat is plastic—and often, you see the Handi-Flat. Of this pack part of the picture, plastic clearly dominates. The majority of plants are grown in "Poly-Pak" types of vacuum-formed trays (see photo, above) From 3½ by 3½ inches, lots of 4 by 5-inch, some as large as 10 by 10 inches. These "Paks" are grown and sold mainly in plastic flats. Heavier, thicker, now molded—but nearly all are plastic.

Zinnia Mini-Pink, ready for sale in Cell-Pak/Handi-Flat combination.

Jiffy-Potted annuals at McMullen's, Lexington, Kentucky. The McMullens grow and sell bedding annuals—everything is in a 2½-inch Jiffy-Pot. They use the No. 425 —extra-deep nursery pot.

The great majority of growers today even use a standardized flat size. Example: the ubiquitous Handi-Flat (11½ by 21¼ inches). This flat—or something very close to it in size—is used by a substantial majority of bedding-plant growers all over the U. S. This fact, by the way, has been a major help in mechanizing such operations as filling flats, etc.—the simple fact that one machine can serve most of the industry.

2. Cell-Paks—really very similar to the plastic Handi-Paks described above— but this time, each pack is divided into four or eight or more individual squares or cells. The effect is that for a really negligible increase in cost, the customer can get individually "potted" plants—instead of an open pack. See photo bottom of page 15. Understandably, the trend is rather steadily toward Cell-Paks and away from the old open pack. Cell-Pak plants are grown and sold in a Handi-Flat or equivalent—a roughly 11 by 21-inch plastic flat.

3. A third contender—not as big as plastic, but still important, is the molded or fiber pack. Example: The Garden-Pak. A big convenience to the housewife—the sides can be torn away easily at planting time. For the grower, molded packs of this type are a little better draining than plastic. Perhaps a bit more forgiving of overwatering. Put a different way, the grower in plastic is under some more pressure to be sure his soil is loose and well drained. The fiber Market-Pak-type container has a pleasing and earthy cocoa-brown color. Also, by the way, such materials are biodegradable—more of a consideration each year with the rising pressure on pollution. They will finally rot away. Plastic won't.

4. Peat pots—steadily increasing in popularity among bedding-plant growers for many years, they have found a place, especially where the grower is aiming for more of a quality market. Somehow, we see more of such as the ever-present Jiffy-Pot being used for vegetables, especially the 2½ and

3-inch sizes for tomatoes. The Jiffy-Strips have also become very popular in bedding-plant production—much faster spreading them out on a bench, etc. Other peat pots available: the Erin Pot and Pullen Pot.

5. Jiffy-7—a unique development mainly of peat encased in a plastic netting —and ingeniously compressed to one-seventh of its volume for shipping. The grower just spreads the little "wafers" out over the bench, expands them with mist, and plants. Again, very popular in certain bedding-plant markets.

6. Other individual containers. Other interesting contenders for the bedding-plant trade include cellulose propagation blocks, foam-plastic blocks and Kys-Kubes; again, mainly peat put up in block form (not compressed).

7. Plastic pots! Also available to the bedding plant grower, a wide variety of sizes and shapes of both thin vacuum-formed and the heavier molded types of plastic pots. Example: the square Poly-Pot, generally from 2¼-inch to 4-inch sizes. For such purposes as *Patio* Tomatoes, etc., there are larger Poly-Tainer-type materials from a one-pint size up to 4 and 6-quart, and larger.

8. Clay pots. Still very much a part of the spring-plant business in certain areas.

9. Molded fiber pots. Made of the same material as the Garden-Pak, available from 2¼-inch up to a 6½-inch size, used for such spring crops as geraniums.

ABOUT CELL-PAKS

The name coding is important. Example: "AC9-8." The "AC" designates a Cell-Pak. The "9" means 9 cells per pack (3 by 3). The "8" denotes 8 packs per Handi-Flat, (see photo of an AC9-8, bottom of page 19). The individual cells of an AC9-8 Handi-Pak, for example, are roughly 1¾ inches square.

Jiffy-7 pellets in a 10-pack for growing/selling. Pellets in the foreground have not been expanded. Geraniums at the left are growing in expanded pellets.

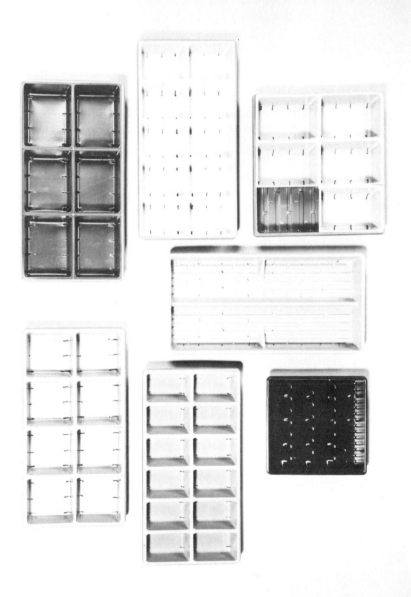

Plastic flats accommodate a variety of cropping programs. The Handi-Flats shown above can be used with Handi-Paks, Cell-Paks and Handi-Pots. Standard Handi-Flat size is $2\frac{1}{4}$ x 21 x $11\frac{1}{2}$ inches. Half-flats also are available.

18

Promising approach to spring-plant containers: Jiffy-Strips. "Strip" annuals give the home gardener all the advantages of an individual Jiffy-Potted plant—but cost the grower less to produce. Key reason: he now handles a dozen plants at once instead of one. The Jiffy-Tray (J-225) on the left is designed to hold a dozen 2¼-inch square Jiffys in a strip. Six 2¼'s can be grown and sold in a Jiffy-Tray (J-26).

TRENDS—CONTAINERS

Several things seem to be happening.

1. Certainly, there is a clear trend, especially through non-florist outlets, toward smaller packs, lower unit cost, but higher return to the grower per square foot. The "discounts" or "supers" found that the housewife buys plants *by the price per pack,* not by how many plants it holds or how large it is. So they pressure the grower for smaller packs—at a lower cost per pack.

2. On the surface, contradictory to the above, there seems to be a definite increase in production of various individually potted annuals. A good example is the clear increase in the use of Jiffy-7s—the same for others of the new individual-pot containers (BR-8, Oasis, etc.). We wonder if perhaps this isn't partly supported by the frankly better trade which many

Well-done production of spring annuals in Cell-Paks—at Delhi Hills Flower and Garden Center, Cincinnati, Ohio—Bill Krueger in the photo. All annuals here are grown in Cell-Paks—and Tag-Alongs in every pack. Pack illustrated is AC-9/8 Cell-Pak.

Here's a bedding-plant structure designed and used at Powell's, Troup, Texas. Fiberglass over the roof, down to about the 5-foot level on both sides. They can enclose the sides with a sort of plastic muslin material—rolled up on warm days. In the photo, Billy Powell.

good retail growers cater to. Or rather, perhaps in the long run, the supers and discount houses, too, will move in this direction. In potted plants generally (pot mums, etc.), the supermarkets particularly are clearly buying good merchandise, moving away from cheap inferior quality.

STRUCTURES FOR BEDDING PLANTS

Certainly, the heavy majority of bedding plants in the U.S. are grown under polyethylene—supported by an endless variety of structures. Poly, of course, is short-lived—usually good through May if applied in late fall or the February before. Some of the newer materials often go through two years—example: Monsanto "602." The cost is somewhat higher—almost 2.1¢ against about 1.4¢ per square foot for regular poly. The great virtue of poly, of course, is that it is cheap—and if properly put up, ventilated and heated, will grow every bit as good a bedding plant as the best greenhouse built. The very large bedding-plant area around Kalamazoo is mainly polyethylene—a substantial amount of fiberglass is beginning to show up. The 6-acre Ahrens range at Osseo (Minneapolis) is nearly all poly. There are large areas of bedding plants still under glass—example: Toledo, where large blocks of old tomato glass are used for this purpose. The very large Sedan Floral range in Sedan, Kansas, mostly bedding plants, is mainly fiberglass—built for bedding-plant production.

The structure illustrated above is a very practical answer to the bedding-plant problem—certainly modest in cost, yet gets away from the

S. S.. Couch & Sons, Rogersville, Tennessee. A very neat and well-done retail-growing spring-plant operation. We thought the display area was particularly innovative here. They have built three rather large Quonset houses and tied them together with a sort of marquee running across the end of the three houses. The area under the marquee is enclosed with a wire fence. Customers can move from one house to another protected from rain (under the marquee). Also, you can't leave the area without going by the cash register.

odious task of removing and recovering poly each year. The structure, built by Billy Powell at Troup, Texas, starts with a one-inch pipe driven into the ground 2½ feet deep—which, of course, supports the structure. The roof "hoops" are made of ¾-inch solid steel rods—welded, by the way, to the driven stakes. The rods are spaced every 4 feet down the length of the house. The Powells fasten a wooden 2 x 6 the length of the house and about 5 feet above the ground—one on each side of the house. Fiberglass is then spread across the roof from one 2 x 6 over the top of the roof, and down to the other 2 x 6, where it is secured. Also, there is a 2 x 4 sort of "purlin" at the top of the house—end to end—and one more on either side between the ridge and the side 2 x 6. This makes a total of 5 purlins—3 are 2 x 4's and 2 are 2 x 6's—on a 20-foot Quonset structure.

The 4 or 5 feet from the 2 x 6 to the ground on each side is covered at Powell's with a sheet of plastic muslin which can be rolled down at night and rolled up on warm days, allowing free air passage across the plants. No fans. For more northerly areas, a sheet of poly could be rolled down over

21

this 5-foot "sidewall"—rolled up on a pipe or piece of 2 x 2 on warm days.

Just a brief word on venting of open-flame heaters—so often a part of bedding-plant structures. It is so critically important that there be provision to carry the "smoke" or hot gases from the flame out the roof—and not discharge them into the house. Also, it's equally important that there be ample fresh-air inlets to provide oxygen to burn the fuel. Partial combustion can make "big problems" in a bedding-plant house—plants that just slowly stop growing—and so often, the grower never really knows why. See page 68.

Beware of open-flame heaters!

MECHANIZING THE JOB

Several things conspire to put real pressure on especially larger bedding-plant growers to mechanize. First, of course, the ever-increasing scarcity of good help—and with it, the ever-increasing cost of such people. The problem is compounded in bedding-plant production by highly seasonal demand for help. So, aggressive growers everywhere are looking for ways. Suggestions:

1. *Flat-Filling.* There is equipment available today which will fill a typical 21-inch Handi-Flat full of plastic packs or Cell-Paks, level them off, and firm the soil. A good example: the Famco Flat-Filler, which will fill roughly 800 to 900 flats per hour, requires 2-3 men. Cost is nearly $2,300. Flat-fillers are widely used among commercial bedding-plant people today.

2. *Dibblers.* Simply a series of wooden or plastic pointed "fingers" which will punch holes in a flat of soil where plants are to be transplanted. Some of them are designed so that the dibble board lowers over the flat and makes the holes in response to foot pressure—leaving the hands free to move the flats in place.

Many growers speed the transplanting job by some sort of dibble board, such as the one pictured above.

3. *Watering-Feeding.* More and more, growers are turning to automatic irrigation—and with it, where wanted, fertilizer injection. There are several ways to go: The "Rainbird"-type nozzle (about a 12-foot circle), nozzle set 6 feet above the ground is widely used. The Hieberts of Sioux Falls, South Dakota, operate several acres of bedding plants—all irrigated with overhead nozzles—rather high water pressure. Even geraniums are watered this way. The large Powell spring-plant operation at Troup, Texas, is all mechanically irrigated. Billy Powell uses a nozzle similar to the Spray-Stick nozzle. They are located about 5 feet above the ground—3 rows

Bedding-plant production at Harold Ahrens' greenhouses, Osseo, Minnesota. It is a highly mechanized and a remarkably large operation—around 300,000 square feet. A typical growing house (pictured), 30 by 6-800 feet long, poly roof. Everything so very clean! In the photo: G. Carl Ball (left), and Harold Ahrens.

of nozzles down a 20-foot Quonset house. Fifty pounds pressure. Harold Ahrens of Osseo, Minnesota, irrigates his 6 acres of greenhouse bedding plants with 20 Ever-Rain machines. It's a device which propels a nozzle down the walk, using hydraulic pressure to wind the hose, thus moving the nozzle. Sort of a Hoseboye—but lightweight! Roughly 100 feet of ⅝-inch hose is used with each unit. One trip down the 30-foot-wide house does the job very nicely.

4. *Soil Mixing.* You see a wide variety of cement mixers, front-end loaders, tractors, conveyors—large cement-floor soil sheds in which to do the job. All expensive—another reason more growers each year go to such commercial mixes as Jiffy-Mix.

5. *Transplanting.* See page 24 for comments on direct-seeding equipment for bedding plants—objective: to get away from all that transplanting.

6. *Moving Materials.* Again, there is a wide range of conveyor tracks, pallets, lifting equipment, farm wagons, conveyor belts used by bedding-plant growers. Perhaps that most efficiently mechanized production of bedding plants we have seen would be the Ahrens' operation at Osseo, Minnesota. First, there are wide blacktop "roads" on either side of each greenhouse— and throughout the entire work area. Mr. Ahrens and his sons use a wide variety of farm tractors with four-wheel farm wagons, pallets with good modern fork lift equipment, Taylor-type carts with endless trailers. Especially interesting is a new Lindig unit (Lindig Manufacturing Corporation, St. Paul, Minnesota) which will fill larger-size flower pots—used for shifting 2¼-inch material to 5 and 6-inch pots, also for potting rose plants, etc. It can keep 6 men busy potting—average output reported at about 250 six-inch pots per man per hour. That's one every 15 seconds. Cost approximately $5,000.

DIRECT SEEDING

Difficult to cover such a matter in a RED BOOK—The picture changes, certainly at least yearly. However, there is strong interest across the U. S. in various approaches to direct-seeding annuals. Quite a few growers in recent years have been direct seeding, by hand, some of the less-expensive and easy-to-handle seed items such as alyssum, celosia, portulaca, etc. Typically, the grower does not thin, and they produce just as good a plant as transplanted ones.

The most serious bid for commercial equipment to seed mechanically is the Fricke Seeder. A number of growers across the U. S. have tried Fricke seeding for spring production. Certainly, it is not perfect—but many growers feel that this will be the way of the future. One of the big questions is, of course, petunia seed—just a bit too small to handle with the present Fricke equipment, but improvements of the machine might help that. There is also some in pelleting small seed to enable them to be handled more efficiently through such equipment as Fricke.

One of the problems of direct seeding is, of course, the need for fairly

A Fricke-Jiffy Seeder used on a test basis at Ahrens', Osseo, Minnesota. See notes below. Note, by the way, the little 2-inch rollers just ahead of the seeder—to provide a small indentation for the seed—plus a light covering of sand, which is applied over the seed. All done mechanically.

large bench areas which will provide the very critical 70°, or better yet, 75° *soil* temperature for prompt germination of such items as petunias. Some growers consider moving portable heaters into houses during this germination period—only 5 or 6 days. Other growers have tried setting up warm-temperature chambers until seeds sprout—then move them to a cooler house. Petunias germinate slowly and irregularly at much below 70-75° *soil* temperature.

The Fricke Seeder Model 100 efficiently places seeds in preset positions, and can sow seed in as many as 96 positions in a flat within seconds, with 97% accuracy when properly operated. The vacuum head

One of the many mechanical devices available to move bedding plants—the Taylor cart. The one shown here in use at Powell's, Troup, Texas—hauls 60 flats at a lick.

swings back and forth, picks up single seeds, and deposits them into the distribution tubes. The seeder can easily be placed over a conveyor track, becoming part of an automated production system.

This adjustable model permits easy positioning of seed drops over any configuration of pots or packs. This makes the seeder completely flexible for conversion from one pot or pack to another. The seeder can accommodate flats up to 15 by 22½ inches.

It is further improved by a vibrator that shakes any surplus seed off the needles, thus minimizing the number of doubles in any position.

The seeder comes with seed dryer and vacuum motor (110 volt, 60 cycle), and four suction plates designed for specific seeds: extra-small (petunias and tobacco); small (alyssum, impatiens, pansies, portulaca, snapdragons, celery, lettuce); medium (salvia, zinnias, peppers, tomatoes, some varieties of cucumbers and melons); and large (pelleted seed). A dimpled insert is placed in the extra-small plate to reduce the amount of small seed, such as petunia, needed to operate effectively.

INSECTS—DISEASES

Bedding plants are generally not a big problem on either score. Normally, any regularly followed preventive-spray program, along with normal sterilizing of soil, etc., controls virtually all insect-disease problems.

Phytophthora, or crown rot, should be mentioned. It is a problem mainly on petunias and exclusively in the Southeast, Southwest and up into Colorado. Typically affected petunia plants will develop a rot at the crown of the plant a few weeks after being planted in the customer's garden. Soon, the plants just rot away. The disease can be carried in the soil and, of course, can be brought into customers' gardens with plants. Several comments:

1. Certainly, all commercial bedding-plant growers should practice rigid steam or thorough chemical sterilizing of soil, flats, all material which comes in contact with plants. Also, it is critically important that plants be either grown up off the ground or on a sheet of polyethylene; or if on gravel, sand, etc., that the surface be either chemically or steam-sterilized in some way. A flat of petunias can very easily pick up phytophthora from unclean lower soil.

2. The home gardener can clean up a flower bed which has grown infected petunias by application of Truban at the rate of 6.5 ounces 30% wettable powder in 100 gallons of water. This will cover 400 square feet of area. Treat before planting and repeat at nine-week intervals.

All of which points up the possibility of making this material available through garden centers, etc., wherever petunias are grown.

VEGETABLE VARIETIES FOR BEDDING-PLANT SALES

Vegetables have become an increasingly important part of the total inventory of a bedding-plant establishment. Certainly, the owner/operator of the establishment has to keep up with the new varieties, and the ones that will give his customers optimum performance and keep them coming back to his place of business.

The following is a listing of varieties that are relatively new and have proved popular and successful with growers in all areas of the country.

Here's Better Boy Tomato at Herman Wallitsch Nurseries, Louisville, Kentucky. Vegetables are coming up here, led by tomatoes (No. 1), peppers, cabbages and eggplants.

TOMATOES

In bedding-plant sales, tomato seedlings rank right at the top with petunias, marigolds, and impatiens. However, the wholesale or retail grower should use discrimination in the varieties he offers to his customers. If a tomato plant fails during the season, it's generally due in some way to one of the following: verticillium wilt, fusarium wilt, or nematodes. Therefore, it would certainly behoove the bedding-plant establishment to offer those varieties that carry VFN resistance.

One thing should be made clear when discussing varieties with VFN resistance. Just because a variety carries VFN resistance doesn't mean that it's immune to these diseases and organisms. It simply means that it's resistant to the organisms that cause verticillium and fusarium wilts and certain strains of nematodes. Certainly, any plant in a weakened condition can fall prey to these wilts and nematodes. However, a hybrid plant with VFN resistance is a stronger plant than one without VFN resistance, and is less likely to fall prey to these wilts and nematodes. In addition, 9 times out of 10, a plant with VFN resistance will produce fruit longer into the season than a plant without VFN resistance.

The large majority of tomato seedlings sold through a bedding-plant establishment end up in a homeowner's garden. Some homeowners like to stake their plants, others let them grow sprawling on the ground in a bush-type manner. The following hybrid varieties perform well when staked: *Better Boy* is a midseason variety maturing in about 70 days. It carries VFN resistance, and produces continuously throughout the season. Fruit will average in the 14 to 16-ounce range and is relatively crack-free. It has an excellent meaty interior with a deep red color. *Super Fantastic* is very similar to *Better Boy* except the fruit is a little smaller, and the vine is not quite as vigorous. However, it does carry VF resistance. *Early Girl* is a 45-50-day tomato, one of the earliest. The fruit is in the 6 oz. range, uniform throughout the entire growing season. It also carries VF resistance.

The following varieties perform best when allowed to grow on the ground in a bush-type manner: *Bonus* is a 75-day tomato with smooth, crack-free fruit that will weigh in the 10 to 12-ounce range. It has a good, vigorous vine which provides shade for the fruit. This variety carries VFN resistance. *Spring Set* is an early variety, maturing in 60 to 65 days. It's a very prolific producer of fruit in the 8-ounce range. After the first heavy fruit set, production starts to taper off as the season wears on. This variety carries VF resistance.

In recent years, tomato varieties have become available which could be put in a novelty classification: *Beefmaster* is a large *Beefsteak*-type tomato, except this is a hybrid variety with VFN resistance. The problem with this variety is its lateness (80 days), and the large indented calyx area. However, one shouldn't be fooled by the rough exterior of this variety; what it lacks in appearance, it makes up in flavor and interior quality. Generally, a *Beefsteak*-type tomato is pink, but this variety is a deep red, and maintains a mild flavor. *Patio* is a variety that has become increasingly popular over

Pepper plants in Cell-Pak/Handi-Flat combination—an attractive package for sale to the home gardener.

the years. It has been bred specifically for growing in tubs and containers. It's excellent for the homeowner or apartment-dweller who wants to grow a vegetable on his patio. The fruit is in the 4 to 6-ounce range in tight clusters. In addition to the fruit, the homeowner will find that the dark, crinkled leaves will make an attractive foliage plant for his patio. *Small Fry* is a cherry-type tomato, producing fruit approximately 1 inch in diameter. Production is very prolific and fruit is usually in clusters of 7 or 8. This variety can also be grown in a container, like *Patio*, or outside in the homeowner's garden. The sweet fruit is excellent for salads or light snacks. This variety also carries VFN resistance.

PEPPERS

Pepper varieties are usually chosen for a specific use, such as frying, stuffing, canning, etc. Many people seem to have their favorite varieties, depending on the area of the country they live in.

Listed below are pepper varieties that have proven to be popular with all areas of the country. *Cubanelle* is a frying-type pepper that matures in approximately 65 days. The fruit is slightly tapered and has a blunt end. This variety is excellent for home and market gardens. *Bell Boy* is an F_1 hybrid variety that is classified as a "bell" or "block"-type pepper. It is a sweet pepper maturing in approximately 70 days. It has very prolific production of mostly 4-lobed fruit with good foliage cover. *Midway* and *California Wonder* are both sweet, block-type peppers producing large, 4-lobed fruits, excellent for stuffing. Both varieties carry resistance to tobacco mosaic virus. *Midway* is an improvement over the old *Staddon's Select* variety. *Hungarian Yellow Wax* is a hot variety good for processing and pickling. The fruit shape is long and tapers to a point. Fruits are yellow and mature to a deep red. *Long Red Cayenne* is another hot variety which can be used for processing, drying, or sauce. The fruit is long, slim, and wrinkled, and the tapered point sometimes curls back towards the upper portion of the pepper. The fruits come in green, but mature to a bright red.

MUSKMELON

Classic is an oval-shaped variety. It is tolerant to fusarium wilt and powdery mildew, and will provide the grower with fruit in the 4 to 4½-pound range. The thin rind, small seed cavity, and salmon-colored flesh make an excellent fruit for the local market and home gardener. *Burpee Hybrid* is one of those multiple-use varieties. Its round shape with thick rind makes it excellent for shipping, but it also makes a good home-garden variety. Fruit will weigh in the 4 to 4½-pound range.

EGGPLANT

Royal Knight is an F_1 hybrid variety producing elongated fruit 7 to 9 inches long. *Beauty Hybrid*, also a hybrid variety, produces fruit that has more of an oval shape. Both varieties produce glossy, purple-colored fruit of high quality.

CABBAGE

Flat Top is a hybrid variety maturing in approximately 85 days. The heads are in the 9-pound range, very uniform. *Emerald Cross* is also a hybrid variety. It is not resistant to yellows; however, it has proven to be a very popular variety. The heads of this variety are globe shaped and average 6 to 7 inches in diameter.

GVB

Oman's Flower Farm at Prairie View, Illinois is a striking example of a well-planned retail-sales area. Everything up on benches, well displayed, with informative signs on each bench for each variety. Signs list variety name, hybrid, colors, spacing, height and price. Note the attractive wood sign suspended from the roof for quick identification of each variety group. Bill Dodd and his wife operate this fine retail operation.

2. INCREASE YOUR BEDDING-PLANT SALES

The selling-and-distribution end of your bedding plant business is of great importance. When we consider the fact that over one-half the money spent on business in this country is spent on distributing and selling the product, and less than one-half spent for producing, the full realization of the importance of selling is more forcibly brought to mind. We feel that the above ratio has a definite bearing on the bedding-plant business as well.

The bedding-plant business is good and is getting better. No other segment of the floral industry has come close to approaching the terrific increase in growth that bedding plants have shown during recent years. New homes and condominiums are being built continuously. Both are sources of potential business. The continuing trend of population movement from crowded city quarters to homes in suburban and rural areas with larger lots—and more space for gardening—is also potential business. The development of industrial complexes, with manufacturing firms constructing new buildings of modern architectural design with considerable thought being given to outside appearance and landscape design, represents still another potential market.

Another sector, growing at an even more rapid rate, is vegetable gardening. At this writing, the sale of tomato plants for the home garden has skyrocketed. Along with tomatoes, cabbage, peppers, cucumbers and melons have increased in sales with the return to home gardening. The high cost of store produce has had a large bearing on this, but other factors enter in, including the constant rise in the cost of living and the fresher taste of home-grown vegetables.

Just about anyone in bedding plant production wants his business to *grow* and to *make money.*

And the No. 1 way to do just that is to develop, let's say, "sales muscle."

Strength in sales brings in more customers, more volume. If you have ample *demand* for your plants, you can get the extra dime for a pack of petunias. And, that's more profit! After all, one important reason growers don't raise prices is simply that they are afraid of losing sales.

So, sales muscle *is it.*

Let's take a look at some of the tangible things you can do in your own bedding-plant operation to generate this all-important sales horsepower.

ADVERTISE!

Surely, a key part of building sales muscle.

The mission of an ad is to get people to come to your place—and to bring them to you in a buying mood.

A good ad—with some originality, some of you in it—is best.

Go to it, if you have a knack for such. Some of us do, some don't.

But whatever you do, advertise.

A friendly contact with your local newspaper may benefit you immensely, from free publicity to help in designing a trademark, printing a sales brochure, or your letterheads.

Just as with producing plants, the job gets done right if it's planned carefully and well in advance. Sit down with your local newspaperman several months in advance of the sales season, when you have the time, decide what is the right date for insertion of your series of ads in the local paper, and most important of all, actually lay the ads out so the job is done ahead of time.

Perhaps one other constructive thought on ads: when the first warm days of spring come along and people get the gardening itch, they will be heading for a greenhouse or garden center. Chances are a lot better they will head for *your* place if you've been hitting the newspapers steadily with ads the few weeks before.

Another certainly important way to advertise is by radio—or TV. Many successful garden centers do either one—or both. Most successful "audio" promotion projects the personality of the proprietor. A 10-minute Saturday morning chatty talk on what to do in the garden this week.

Example: The Zoerbs, prominent retail growers of La Crosse, Wisconsin, have a radio question-answer show every Wednesday morning. Very popular.

OPEN HOUSES BUILD SALES

A well-done open house held a month or 6 weeks before your bedding-plant season can be another major factor in building spring plant sales. We've known of lots of them held by retail growers in all parts of the country. They are usually held on Sunday and often, they feature a spectacular display of plants. The classic for midwestern and eastern growers is a house or 2, or 3, filled with really well-done geraniums—all in flower. It *can* be a spectacular sight! Zoerbs of La Crosse Floral, La Crosse, Wisconsin, have held such affairs and they feel it does help sales. Coffee or light refreshments are often offered. Some give the ladies a rose or carnation as a gift. Some open houses are held on the first good Sunday of the season, with local garden-clubbers there to help out and answer questions. Almost always, sales are played down—no effort made to sell plants and flowers—unless someone really wants something. Incidentally, many growers ask people to register their name and address when they attend an open house so they can be included on their mailing list.

Deutschmann's in St. Louis held an open house with their poinsettias at Christmas time. Very effective!

Speaking of Deutschmann's, this brings up another aspect of open houses. The Deutschmanns got their suburban newspaper to run a 4-color picture of the poinsettia display—together with a couple of local junior citizens—on the front cover of their magazine section that Sunday. We have seen other cases where geranium displays have also been featured in color—really in some fairly small-town newspapers. This brings up the point that a good open house can also be a springboard for some valuable free publicity. Newspaper editors are generally looking hard for interesting and unusual displays of plants—things that people want to read about, especially when they find such a thing at the establishment of a good advertiser—you won't have much trouble getting them to spend the money for color printing.

One progressive grower, Glenn Gross of Ashcombe Vegetable Farm at Mechanicsburg, Pa., runs 26 ads per year. He sells other items in addition to bedding plants, such as home-grown tomatoes, melons, berries, jams, etc. In return, the local paper, and it's a large-city one, runs articles on his place, including pictures. Plus, he likes to write, and he writes stories on how to care for annuals, tomatoes, etc., and they print them on the business page. Great public relations!

Another one, Oman's Flower Farm—Bill Dodd and his wife run the show at Prairie View, Ill.—was written up in one of the Chicago papers. The women swarmed out to his place the following day.

GOOD HIGHWAY SIGNS

Have you looked at your highway sign lately? Of course, we know that you have one—but the point is, have you taken a critical look? You can put an awful lot of style into a highway sign and tie it in very well with your ads, stuffers, etc. Of course, you can also put a lot of money into it, but certainly, the more aggressive and successful retailers in all fields give attention to this focal point of their advertising program. Actually, a good highway sign is a key link between your efforts to advertise and get the customers into your place of business and your proper organization to sell them once they have driven in. A sign is literally in between the two jobs. Notice how lavishly such places as motels, restaurants and even chain food stores spend on signs.

Having a good, bright, fresh modern one, well-lighted at night, can also help build sales strength.

Holub's, Oskaloosa, Iowa. New retail display area here. Neat and inviting-looking peninsular benches. Everything up at eye level, wide aisles, cement walks. Convenient shopping.

A good sign can go a long way to set the atmosphere of a garden center—and we thought this was a good example.

ADVERTISE BY MAIL

Good, colorful, direct-mail "propaganda" sent out a month or so ahead of the planting season can be another effective means of building your sales

Point-of-sale booklets and invoice stuffers like those pictured below help get your message across—tell your customers what you have for sale.

muscle. It is a task to get out stuffers or mailing pieces to a long mailing list, but most successful bedding-plant people do this.

Typically, retail bedding-plant growers print up at least a small leaflet and sometimes 4 to 6 pages, listing the spring plant material they will have available, all varieties and prices. This is sent off to their mailing list well in advance of the selling season. We have seen occasionally such lists which have gotten to be rather elaborate, well-done, and colorful. But, at least something to hit your customers a few weeks before planting time —to again remind them of you.

Along with your own list, Ball has available a number of colorful booklets on the growing of annuals from started plants. We have, in all cases, left

Herman Wallitsch, H. R. Wallitsch Nurseries, Louisville, Kentucky, substantial pot-plant and bedding-plant grower—plus an interestingly done garden-center retail outlet. Herman did an exceptionally good job of designing this retail display rack. It's built of just hardware-store aluminum channels. Lightweight, attractive —and gets the plants up at eye level.

the back page blank for you to imprint your own sales message. These are colorful, with good colored pictures of annuals in use in various home settings. Ideal to hand out at garden-club meetings, or to hand out right by the cash register at your checkout counter.

KEEP A "WELL-DRESSED" DISPLAY

First, the importance of keeping your display well stocked: this is an axiom of merchandising—you don't have to take our word for it. You can study any supermarket display, and they are, of course, the fellows who wrote the book on merchandising. They are death on half-full or disorderly displays of merchandise. Restocking and straightening your sales area should

John's Fruit Stand, a major Dallas, Texas outlet for fruits and vegetables, also handles a variety of nursery items including bedding plants. Price and item signage is at eye level. Plants are in standard 21-inch flats merchandised on a 3-tier rack. Flats are displayed with the ends out when the rack is full. A half-filled, rack can be kept looking full by turning the flats lengthwise.

be given top priority and the time of someone who really understands the importance of this job. Eric Schaefer, bedding-plant grower and retailer of Montgomery, Illinois, put it this way: "The more you have on display, the more you will sell."

Second, try to keep the plants up close to eye level. Generally, plants should be up off the ground where they are easy and convenient for customers to examine—and to buy. One of the most successful bedding-plant growers in the Chicago area sells from pack-filled flats laid out in sections near his frame *on the ground*. But, in our observation, he is the exception to the rule—his merchandise is so good that it would sell under any circumstances. But it would sell even better if it were up on a level where it could be examined closely, as people simply do not like to stoop over to look at plants. They don't have to do this for other merchandise, so why should they have to do it for yours?

Many growers use colored picture labels such as Tag-Alongs. They are a great help to self-service. They have helpful information on them— sun or shade, how far apart to plant, etc. Some retail growers report their customers come back the next spring with the Tag-Along and ask for the same variety again. One in each pack is the best way to go; and most growers can easily get 5¢ more a pack with a colorful label in it.

SELF-SERVICE

There are two solid reasons for this. One is, it saves you money—1 clerk under properly-organized self-service can wait on 5 times as many customers as he can without self-service. The other reason is that it increases sales. People don't want to be waited on anymore—they want to wait on themselves—and when they are allowed to do this in a suitable environment, they buy more. Without attempting to go into great detail, we do urge most strongly that you give attention to this matter if you have not already done so—a carefully laid-out sales area, with elevated display racks and benches, properly engineered for smooth flow of traffic, with push-carts for use by the customers and material clearly marked as to price, use, specifications, etc. Art Bezdek, successful retail grower of Marion, Iowa, says that in his experience, if he can get a shopper to get hold of a pushcart, she will buy several times as much material as when she goes through without one. So, of course, she should be encouraged in every way to take a push-cart through your shopping area—or even a little red wagon.

There is one other very important point in connection with self-service —simply that self-service really gives you an opportunity to make your place of business an information center on home planting with annuals. It gives you a chance to service your customers personally in a way that your chain-store competitors can never do. The chains have self-service, but they have no one around who knows a petunia from a pansy. You can,

Interesting point at Ashcombe Vegetable Farm, Mechanicsburg, Pennsylvania: Space is allotted to each bedding-plant item according to sales. If petunias account for 50% of total sales, they get 50% of the space. If Cascade Petunias are 12% of sales, they get 12% of the available display area. Also note the attractive signs.

either by yourself, or have your help spend time around the sales area helping customers with their problems, making planting suggestions—just simply being friendly. It is so important that someone acknowledge the presence of your customers—especially the preferred ones. Just a personal remark or two, letting them know you are interested in having them visit you, pays off in big dividends. People love to be recognized—and especially by name.

Glenn Gross, operator of Ashcombe Vegetable Farm, Mechanicsburg, Pa., is a real merchandiser. He hires a local garden-club member who is a retired dentist, to be readily available on weekends to answer questions and help in selections. He also hires a local policeman to help direct traffic. Customer relations of the highest order!

Women garden-plant buyers are really hungry for this special attention. Of course, it becomes something of a job to not get "in a corner", so to speak, and have to spend 20 minutes talking for a 75¢ sale. But there are little techniques for working this out, too—like leading a customer to the tell-all sign—a well-organized table of bedding-plant information.

USE CONTAINERS SUITABLE FOR YOUR MARKET

Of primary importance here is the fact that people want variety. If plants are not offered in a choice of containers, chances are that they might do their buying where this choice is offered. While we realize that less efficiency from a production standpoint is involved with the use of various types of containers, we must keep in mind our customers' needs and desires.

During the course of the past several years, we have seen the sale of bedding plants go from digging from a bed or flat, to flat sales, to packs, and individual pots.

Devol's, Marietta, Ohio. This operation is all Cell-Paks. Mr. Russell Devol, shown at left, likes them. There are four Carefree Geraniums in an AC-4, retail $1.00. Mr. Devol reports good, steady demand for Carefrees, by the way, over the past several years. So often, we get the feeling that such growers as Mr. Devol sort of developed a clientele for Carefrees— some gardeners who have had them for several years are pleased with the showing they make, especially in mid-to-late summer—and they come back for more.

Pepper in Jiffy-7.   Petunia in Jiffy-Pot.

A departure from the pack-type selling unit is the Cell-Pak. This is a plastic pack that has been vacuum-formed to provide individual cells within the pack. This permits each plant to have an individual soil ball. A push on the bottom "pops" the plant out, ready to plant in the garden. They are available in various sizes, from 4 cells to a pack to 12 to a pack. The larger cells are used mainly for begonias, tomatoes and *Carefree* Geraniums; the "6's," "9's," and "12's" for other annuals.

As the trend in plant containers has advanced from flat sales to packs, even now it seems to be moving toward individual pot sales. While many growers have used Jiffy-Pots for specialty items such as hybrid tomatoes and double petunias in addition to their flat and pack line, more of them report consistent demand for wider variety of plants in Jiffy-Pots. People are willing to pay a premium price for a Jiffy-Potted plant which, together with other advantages, gives them a most convenient plant to handle with a great livability. Since Jiffy-Potted plants represent better value, many retail growers have gone over to selling bedding plants in Jiffys only, especially where they are competing strongly with mass outlets that sell lesser-quality merchandise at a low price.

The Jiffy-Strip, consisting of individual square Jiffys molded together in strip form, and the plastic Jiffy-Tray to hold the Strip, a suitable merchandising unit for Jiffy-Potted plants. The use of the Strip affords the grower the convenience of pack-type culture, yet allows him to sell the plants in individual Jiffy-Pots.

Jiffy-7 peat pellet is a proven product. It combines the function of a pot and potting soil into one unit, compressed to one-seventh its ultimate size for easy storage and handling. The Jiffy-7 comes in a small wafer of compressed peat encased in net, with fertilizer added. When water is applied, it expands 7 times to form a pot approximately 1¾ inches in diameter by 2 inches high. Seeds may be started directly in it, or seedlings or cuttings transplanted into it.

They save time, all handling of soil, peat and fertilizers, plus the fact that, until expanded, they occupy very little space. Available as single pots, on tapes, or prepacked in units of 6 or 10 in plastic trays, ready to expand.

New are the Jiffy-9 peat pellets. They incorporate a binder in the peat to hold the expanded pellet together without the need for a plastic netting. Although they're not as durable as the Jiffy-7, they do have the advantage of a flat bottom. Two sizes are available—the 135 spacesaver for plants that will be grown for 3-4 weeks—and the 150, which expands to 2-inches and used for plants that are to be held longer and for larger cuttings. Both have preformed holes for direct seeding, transplanting and sticking cuttings. Both are ideal for most bedding, foliage and vegetable plants, providing handling is kept to a minimum.

PRICE

In our observation—for what this is worth to growers—there are a lot of plants being sold which could ring the cash register a little louder—say by 5 or 10 per cent—than it is now ringing. This 5 or 10 per cent would double the profit of many growers—if profit is reckoned realistically to include such expenses as the proprietor's own salary. We know a lot of growers more or less kid themselves about this point, taking money in one pocket and spending it out of the other, and if they have any left at the end of the year after they have paid their grocery bills, they have made some money accordingly without giving regard to depreciation of their physical plant, etc.

Here are a couple of tip-offs on this all-important question of charging a bit more:

1. Your price structure is far more important to you than it is to your customers. When we get a good advertisement going in the trade papers, we run it in several different papers for several issues; we begin to get complaints around the office—even from the Advertising Department. "Oh, that old ad. Let's change it. We are getting tired of looking at it." We have to say in response to this, "It's no matter that you are tired of looking at it, but are the consumers? If it is still pulling, why abandon it? *It's what the customers think that counts.*"

Art Bezdek of Marion, Iowa quoted a survey that he made of the importance of price to retail buyers of bedding plants. Not one person who was asked could remember exactly what price she had paid for the plants she had bought except for geraniums—they all seemed to remember geraniums. The fact is, this question of price causes you a lot more worry than it does your customers. Remember, you are thinking about your price all day long, your customers only for a moment, once.

2. Here is a little subtle psychological twister: Price, in most people's minds, is a direct reflection of quality. Most buyers will look for quality—unconsciously assume that there is more quality there if the price is higher.

Think of the implications of this fact. You are actually downgrading the quality of your product in your customer's mind when you charge a price lower than the next fellow's.

3. Another interesting point: If you can introduce into your line of merchandising a new feature—a step-up of quality or a convenience factor—you have the possibility of importantly raising your price. Not to say that you must, or that you should; we must all consider competitive situations, but certainly, such a step-up in quality or convenience opens up to you the possibility of increasing your price.

It does seem strange that in one town, a wholesale grower can ask for and get 65¢ a pack at wholesale (retail at $1.25 to $1.39), while less than 40 miles away, other growers are selling at 60¢ a pack retail. Why can a wholesale grower receive more than a retail grower? He has to value his time, work and plants more. Just think what would happen to your income if you raised your price (retail) from 65¢ or 75¢ a pack to $1.00 or $1.25 per pack!

The cost of shoes, gasoline (ever see the oil companies *not* raise their prices to the same level when one of their competitors does?), bread, shirts, everything, jumps every year or two—and sales continue to go up.

EXTEND YOUR SEASON OF SALE

Each year, the bedding-plant business seems to move more and more into June and even well into July. The way to cultivate this late-season business is not by offering leftovers in late June, or later. Rather, the correct way is to plan for sowings and transplantings for the late-June-and-July market. Have fresh, saleable merchandise timed for these periods. People, especially at resorts and lake cottages, seem to be ready to plant right straight through July now, where it used to be strictly a May or early-June activity.

GROW AND SELL QUALITY

As we said in our opening paragraph, quality is certainly a factor in sales. To give an idea of the importance with which we regard this matter of quality, we would even say that you can perhaps pay less attention to all the sales and distribution techniques and advertising points we have been talking about if you have outstanding quality. Your plants will sell themselves by word-of-mouth advertising which is, by far, the most effective form of advertising. When you have a satisfied customer who will tell her friend or friends where they should buy their plants, you will be crowded in the spring—no matter if you advertise or not, or if you make your plants easy to buy, or label them and put them up at eye-level, or what have you. If you have quality, customers will seek you out. Of course, if your quality is only average, these sales techniques become more important; and if your quality is below average, the question of sales techniques can spell life or death to your business. Extra quality will get you talked about, and this is the best type of advertising you can get. Extra quality, combined with good advertising and a sales program, is an unbeatable combination.

It's a way of boosting *your* bedding plant sales for the future.

SALES NOTES FOR WHOLESALE GROWERS

A substantial part of today's bedding plants are produced by wholesale growers—and retailed through various non-florist outlets.

Food chains, "supers," discount houses—and a major part of it through garden centers, various roadside outlets.

This wholesale grower really faces the same challenge as the retail grower —to develop sales strength. He, too, wants to build sales and profits. But the tools and techniques to build this sales muscle are quite different from those used by the retail grower. We'd like to offer a few suggestions.

PERSONAL SOLICITATION

First, we must point out the obvious fact—wholesale-bedding-plant growers are not all of a cut. They vary from quite small to the very large growers—up to a half-million flats a year and more. Also, their markets vary.

One way or another, though, a key factor in sales of bedding plants at the wholesale level is effective personal solicitation. In the case of a smaller grower supplying several local outlets, this would probably be the proprietor or owner calling directly on the store buyers. In a larger operation, it might be either the proprietor or a member of his staff whose express reason for being there is to do this very job. Mose Frink, Cedar Falls, Iowa wholesale grower, is a good example—selling to perhaps 200 customers. Frink's has a man out doing this selling job starting a month or two before the active season.

A wholesale grower who sells to a chain with 10 stores in an area keeps a running count on each store. He then makes up a bar chart on each store, showing the number of packs each has moved. This is shown to the head buyer in charge of all 10 stores. If 2 stores are in new neighborhoods and one is moving 10,000 packs and the other 2,000, someone hears about it from the district manager. If there is an obvious disparity in sales due to lower incomes, that can be understood; but not where all things are equal. The store manager is not doing a job of moving the plants. His drivers also report by phone to him any store that isn't taking care of the plants, such as not watering them. He gets on the phone and calls the store and tells them to get out and water them. So far, it has worked out well for him—sales are up.

PRESEASON CATALOG PRICE LIST

It surely is important for a wholesale grower to publish some sort of a good, complete listing of what he has to offer—and get in the hands of the trade well in advance of the selling season. At a minimum, it should be a list of all material available, full description as regards plants per pack, packs per flat, etc. Also prices.

Again, talked with Mose Frink recently; we saw the "catalog and order form" published by Frink's, pictured at right. It is a large, 12-by-15-inch affair. By the way, Frink's put a bright, four-colored cover featuring petunias on this catalog.

Mostly, though, it is in fact a complete list of all varieties of everything they have to offer in the way of spring plants.

One sheet in this price offering that especially appealed to us was a "suggested retail price schedule." Here, Frink's is proposing specific retail prices for the things they offer (example: suggested 1971 retail price for 9 petunias in a pack: 79¢). And even more, we like the little comments that Frink's puts ahead of this suggested retail price schedule. It sounded constructive to us, and like good business, so we would like to pass it on to our readers. Remember, this is a wholesale grower talking to his retail dealers who will sell to the public. We quote:

"A critically important question, in terms of profit, is proper pricing of your product. We offer the following thoughts on the subject and also a chart listing our suggested retail prices for your consideration and guidance.

"Top-quality merchandise should bring a premium price and the public is willing to pay a premium price for high quality. The dealer, however, must have the courage to ask a price which allows for a fair profit.

"As your supplier, it is our purpose to assist the dealer in every way possible to make the margin of profit to which he is entitled, so that when the bedding-plant season is finished, there have not been just endless weeks of labor and risk, but a rewarding profit figure that will encourage even greater enthusiasm for seasons to come.

"Remember that you are handling a perishable product and throughout the season, you are certain to have some quality depreciation. If the correct initial price structure is used, it will allow you to 'special' this depreciated merchandise at reduced prices and still show a profit.

"Don't be afraid of competition—*be the competitor*. Your cheap competitor knows only too well what his products and labor are worth."

Then follows a list of specific proposed prices. Incidentally, a 4-inch clay-potted geranium's cost to the dealer is 65¢; suggested retail price for the same plants: 98¢

WORK THE PHONE

The other obvious and important tool in wholesale sales, especially as the season progresses, is to keep in close contact with buyers by phone. Regular calls to all important buyers. Orders come in for half a load to a point a hundred miles away. Get busy on the phone and sell enough material to fill the truck.

PICTURE LABELS

In many ways, much of what we have to say about sales-building by retail growers has application to the wholesale grower's situation, too. Tag-Along labels have become standard practice among many wholesale growers—particularly since so much of their retail sales are on a self-service basis—no knowledgeable clerks.

In certain situations, a colorful booklet, such as "Where and How to Use Annuals," could be a real help.

And, certainly, the suggestion on correct selection of varieties and "using the right container" is every bit as important here. It's so very important for a wholesale grower to keep his finger on the pulse of demand for both varieties and containers.

JCF

Lyndale Fruit and Vegetable Market, Minneapolis, Minnesota. Palmer Siegel is the "mover." Very large retail display—part of it shown below. Everything is clearly marked, varietywise and pricewise. Big and busy. On the left, Bob Whitman, G.J.B., Inc. One type of outlet for a wholesale grower to cater to.

Here are Jiffy-7 Trays—at Bodie's Greenhouse, Ridge Springs, South Carolina. Kester Bodie in the photo.

3. GROWING CONTAINER ROUNDUP

Certainly a key decision for most growers today is—"Which container?" Your choice of containers is really that important because:

1. Certain crops just plain grow better in container "A" than in container "B." Really! Geraniums in a Jiffy-7 *will* outgrow clay-pot/soil plants.

2. Choice of containers is often an integral part of your overall marketing plan. Bedding-plant growers appeal to the discount outlet with container "A" (small pack, fewer plants, lower unit price), or to the prestigious garden center with container "B" (larger pack, more space per plant, higher price per pack). And so on.

3. Price—cost. Some containers cost more—but may well be worth the difference—for *your* crop.

And to make the whole container question even a bit more complex: The array of available pots, packs, etc. changes so very much. Every year, new products appear, old ones die.

So—the purpose of this chapter is to offer a brief objective appraisal of the most important growing containers on the market today. What's good (and not so good, perhaps) about each. Roughly, their cost.

Are you sure that there isn't something new here that might do *your* growing job better than the container you have been using?

Read on:

JIFFY-7

First offered in 1967, the "7" has risen fast, and today, challenges the old favorite, the Jiffy-Pot.

The grower gets a pellet about 1¾ inches in diameter by ¼ inch thick. It is peat (and fertilizer) compressed to 1/7 its original volume and wrapped in a plastic mesh. You set them out on a bench or in a flat, apply mist or just water. In 4 or 5 minutes, they expand to a "pot" full of peat—about 1¾ inches in diameter by 2 inches high. Ready to plant—seeds, seedlings or cuttings.

There are several types:

No. 700—the original—pH 5.5-6.0 plus normal nutrients.

No. 703—pH 6.0-6.3 with reduced nutrients, recommended for flower cuttings (poinsettias, geraniums). Has a predrilled hole.

Especially for bedding-plant growers, Jiffy-7s are available in plastic trays (No. 726 with 6 pellets, No. 720 for 10 pellets). The trays come with the Jiffy-7s already in place on the bottom, ready to water, plant, grow and sell in the packs.

PRO-CON-COST—JIFFY-7:

Briefly:

Pro

1. The grower gets pot, soil and all, sterile, ready to plant. No problem of getting soil, additives, mixing it, steaming it. No "soil shed"—very small storage area required to keep a supply on hand. What does it *really* cost you to turn out a cubic yard of your present mix—plus pot cost?

2. Plants—almost all kinds—do grow so very well in the Jiffy-7! Really remarkable. It's good peat, well aerated (through the net container), just the right amount of nutrients. Earlier-blooming petunias, earlier, better tomatoes. U. S. growers are learning what our German friends learned years ago about how well things do grow in peat.

Con

1. At first, it is slower transplanting things into Jiffy-7s, but somehow, women seem to get the hang of it after awhile. Most growers finally end up with no more transplanting cost than with soil.

2. Must be wet—but really, any peat must be thoroughly wet before planting. At least you know that once it is expanded, the Jiffy-7 Peat Pellet is really wet.

3. Used individually, they can tip over. One obvious answer: The tray application.

Cost. The Jiffy-7 costs 3.6¢. This price and all others to follow will be approximate average prices—midway between the small-volume and large-volume buyer.

MAIN USES—JIFFY-7:

1. Bedding plants—probably the biggest single use today. Used for all annuals, perennials, vegetable plants for home gardeners. (Also, by the way, for market gardeners—by the millions!) Growing and selling plants in trays of 6 and 10 have helped here—with bedding-plant applications.

2. Poinsettias—another big use. Hundreds of growers across the U. S. stick unrooted cuttings into the type 703, then weeks later, shift to the flowering pots.

3. Geraniums—another big use for Jiffy-7s. Again hundred of geranium growers across the U.S. just stick unrooted cuttings directly into the expanded 7s . . . geraniums generally seem to do very well in them. Kester Bodie of Ridge Springs, South Carolina, roots all his geranium cuttings in Jiffy-7s. He says his "Jiffy-7 geraniums are ready for sale in less than three weeks." Mr. Bodie finds the Jiffy-7 prepackaged Trays of ten work best for him. "Customers tend to take all ten, instead of 4 or 5, just great!"

4. Started plants for the market-vegetable grower. Commercial vegetable growers like Jiffy-7s for started plants for uniform crops, earlier maturity. No mixing of soil, sterilizing, etc.—enables the vegetable grower to produce good plants without all the equipment necessary to run a flower greenhouse.

5. Nursery production—both soft and hard wood cuttings are easier to root in Jiffy-7s. Transplanting is easier, too—less risk of setback due to root loss. Andy Braumbaugh, of Springhill Nursery in Tipp City, Ohio, finds his Japanese Red Maples root best in Jiffy-7s. He says, "Twenty-one days after planting, roots are showing . . . Jiffy-7s save storage space and labor, and those twenty-one day roots are the real icing on the cake."

Trends. Jiffy-7s have been on the market nearly ten years and they're holding their own. Every year growers try new crops—and Jiffy-7s always seem to fit right in. And, consumer awareness seems to be setting trends. As home gardeners use Jiffy-7s and see the results, they're more apt to request transplants in Jiffy-7s the next season. Jiffy-7 Trays seem to be the best way to market transplants—they ship well and are easy to handle.

Newest addition to the expanding line of Jiffy peat products, the Jiffy-9 is like the Jiffy-7 in principle and use—except there is no net and a binding gel has been added to hold the pellet together. For best results expand Jiffy-9s under mist and allow about 4 hours for the binding gel to activate before planting. pH is 5.5 to 6.0, nutrients are added to assure good initial growth. Jiffy-9s have a predrilled hole, making insertion of unrooted cuttings easy; also, they are excellent for germinating and transplanting all greenhouse and nursery crops.

There are two types:

No. 135—expand to 1½″ by 1½″.
No. 150—expand to 1¾″ by 2⅛″.

No. 135's are available prepacked in green plastic trays, twelve to a tray. The trays have drainage holes. This is an ideal package for shipping and marketing plants started in Jiffy-9s.

PRO-CON-COST—JIFFY-9:

Briefly:

Pro

1. As with the Jiffy-7, Jiffy-9 users get the pot, soil, starter nutrients, completely sterile and ready to plant. Even less storage space required for the Jiffy-9s than with Jiffy-7s. Once again, consider costs to mix your own soil, plus costs of pots and labor to fill them.

2. Just about every type of plant grows well in Jiffy-9s. Germinate seeds, transplant, root cuttings in them. Jiffy-9s have good water holding capacity, good aeration, and nutrients for fast take-off. When root development is well underway you transplant Jiffy-9 and all.

Con

1. If you try Jiffy-9s but have never used Jiffy-7's, the same initial problem will crop up—at first transplanting is slower until the help gets used to them.

2. If you're switching to Jiffy-9s from Jiffy-7s, you'll find you can't handle the 9s in the same way. Without the net, when handled individually, Jiffy-9s may crumble apart. There's easy ways to overcome this, of course; when wetting up allow time for the binding gel to activate. And, transport Jiffy-9s in their trays or in flats rather than one by one. Once roots are established they'll help hold the 9s together, then they can be handled individually for transplanting.
   Cost. The Jiffy-9 costs about 1.1¢, less than the Jiffy-7. This is an average price.

MAIN USES—JIFFY-9

1. Bedding plants—Combine inexpensive Jiffy-9s with their attractive trays and you've got a great package deal for shipping and marketing bedding plants.

2. Pot plants—Growers are using Jiffy-9s for all types of flowering pot plants—points, pot mums, and geraniums. Peter Sacco of F & F Greenhouse, Wood Cliff Lake, New Jersey, starts all his geraniums in Jiffy-9 #150's. He says he prefers Jiffy-9s "because they're really a true soil block, absolutely no root restriction. . . There seems to be such an ideal peat, air, water relationship that they even forgive a little forgetfulness on our part, whether we overwater or forget to water."

Trends. When first put on the market, Jiffy-9s moved slowly for various reasons, including the fact that growers handled them as they would Jiffy-7s and were disappointed. Now, after additional research and information are made available to growers, the Jiffy-9 should take its place in greenhouse and nursery operations. The best way to use Jiffy-9s is in the trays. This makes the best package for production, handling, shipping, and marketing. The #135 is best for short-term production, for longer crops, such as nursery stock, you may prefer the #150.

THE JIFFY-POT

Jiffy-Pots were first offered in 1954, and have proven to be the most important innovation by far in growing containers since World War II. They are used today by the hundreds of millions by growers all over the world—for a wide variety of crops. The final mark of approval: Competitive peat pots have become a part of the market. Examples: Erin Pots, Planco Peat Pots, Pullen Pots.

Jiffys (and other peat pots) are simply flower pots made of a mixture of 70 per cent good European peat, 30 per cent virgin wood fiber, plus soluble fertilizer. They are made today, both round and square, in a range of sizes from 1½ inches up to 4 inches in diameter. "Jiffy-Strips" have been on the market for some years—Jiffy-Pots molded together in strips 2 pots wide in either 6's or 12's per strip. Plastic trays are offered to accommodate the

The full range of Jiffy-Pots—from 1½-inch (in strips) up to 4-inch. Why Jiffys? First, plants just grow better in them, plus the "plant pot 'n all" appeal—big to everyone from home gardener to the "million-a-year" market grower. Used by the hundreds of millions the world over.

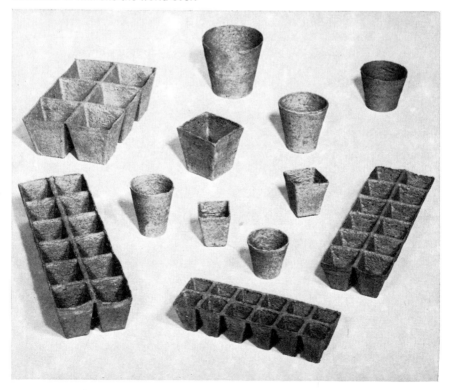

Three-inch Jiffy Pots are used to produce annuals in flower for borders, beds, window boxes and urns by E. J. Seve, Kansas City, Kansas. The flowering annuals bring three to four times the price of 1¾-inch pack-grown material.

various sizes of Jiffy-Strips, permitting growing and selling of especially bedding annuals in packs rather than handling them individually.

PRO-CON-COST—JIFFY-POT:

Pro

1. Most important "pro": Again, plants just grow better—earlier petunia flowers, earlier tomatoes compared to the same plants grown in clay or plastic pots. Somehow, plants seem to grow better with aeration and moisture-holding qualities of the peat pot.

2. You plant pot and all—the other really major point that has made the Jiffy-Pot big throughout the world. No labor to knock out or remove plants, no transplanting shock. Equally important for the home gardener and for the greenhouse or market grower.

3. Biodegradable—fancy new word that says, in a couple of years, the Jiffy-Pot will disintegrate in your garden soil. We expect to hear this word a lot more from here on out! Jiffys are biodegradable.

Con

1. We see the "wicking-action" problem in field plantings. Especially if plants are set a bit high with ½ inch or so of the Jiffy-Pot sticking out in the air, there is a tendency for the pot wall to act as a wick, drawing moisture out of the soil ball. Also, generous irrigation and deeper planting help. Incidentally, the Jiffy-7, by nature, won't "wick."

2. Handled individually, Jiffys tend to tip over. Again, a problem on retail display of individual plants. The answer: Jiffy-Strips.

3. Some problem again at the retail point of sale, especially bedding plants, and especially if pots are damp. The customer may break off a piece of the rim as he tries to pick up a plant. Again, the answer: Offer Jiffy-grown plants in plastic packs of 6 or 12.

Cost. The 2¼-inch round Jiffy will average around 1.7¢—the 4-inch, around 6.9¢.

USES

1. Bedding plants are probably the No. 1 use of Jiffy-Pots across the U. S., especially in strips—in trays. The 2¼-inch are big in annuals; 3-inch for tomatoes, geraniums, tuberous begonias, caladiums.

2. Geraniums—another major use of Jiffys. Unrooted cuttings stuck directly into Jiffy-Pots with Jiffy-Mix, peat-lite, sometimes a 1-1-1 soil mix. Mr. Louis Fox of Manetto Hill Greenhouses, Patchogue, New York, has been using Jiffy-Pots since they were first introduced, 1954-55. He says, "We root our geranium cuttings directly into them and get excellent root penetration. They ship well to customers where we do not deliver by our own truck. Twenty years is a long time to stick with one product, but nothing we've tried has improved on them."

3. Poinsettias—again a major use of Jiffy-Pots—often with Jiffy-Mix or peat-lite mix.

4. Substantial use made of Jiffys for various cut-flower crops. Carnations, snapdragons, asters—to get plants established before benching.

5. Nursery stock—The "plant pot 'n all" feature of Jiffy-Pots makes them a natural for nursery stock production. Growers can root hard-or softwood cuttings in them when roots are established—line them out with no setback. Kenneth Taylor, nurseryman in Neosho, Missouri, found he could save a whole year on nursery stock liners with Jiffy-Pots. He says, "We're now growing liners in three years rather than with four with 2½-inch extra-deep Jiffy-Pots. . . . There is quick and steady growth after lining out because of outstanding root penetration through Jiffy-Pot walls. Shock-free transplanting and less labor have meant great cost savings."

Trends. Hard to tell accurately, but you get the feeling that Jiffy-Pots and peat pots generally in the U. S. are holding about steady; the substantial increase is going into Jiffy-9s. Perhaps some increase in nursery-trade use of Jiffy-Pots—especially with the extra-deep (2½ by 3⅛-inch) nursery pot. Heavily used for conifers, deciduous trees, shrubs, etc., also ground covers. Nurserymen find they can set Jiffy plants out in the field in midsummer heat—not possible with even clay-pot plants.

OTHER POTS, BLOCKS, CUBES

Under this heading comes a most interesting array of new candidates for this market. Several represent attempts by research people to upstage soil and peat as growing media (examples: BR-8 Blocks, Oasis Blocks).

Will technology finally win out over soil?

Anyway, here is a brief rundown on some of the contenders:

BR-8 BLOCK

A treated cellulose-fiber material which, in its several years' career, has won some friends, such as the geranium and poinsettia market, and has encountered some problems. The problems in many cases call for better understanding by growers of how to use this particular fiber block for growing. The monumental effort to launch this one has enjoyed only modest success so far —but we understand the BR-8 is scheduled for continued production. Only time and experience will give the final verdict on BR-8!

OASIS BLOCK

This one is an expanded plastic-foam block (close kin to the oasis block used by retail shops)—not too much experience has been logged with either this or the BR-8—but again, there is the possibility that some adaptation of these ideas might really become important. Both this and the BR-8 carry the important disadvantage of great bulk for storage and shipping.

KYS-KUBE

This is simply a block of peat with some vermiculite, some fertilizer, pressed together firmly, but not at all compressed. You might almost say it is molded— enough to hold together during storage and shipping. Like the Jiffy-7, it must be wet very thoroughly before planting. Again, not enough industry experience to really make a firm judgment—certainly interesting. It is basically a peat block!

The Kys-Kube again is bulky to warehouse and ship—underscoring the genius of the Norwegians who compressed the Jiffy-7 to 1/7 its original volume.

Perhaps it is a fair statement to say that greater exchange capacity for one thing gives an edge to both the Kys-Kube and the Jiffy-7—simply because of the peat. The Kys-Kube looks best so far in rooting application rather than for bedding plants for retail sales.

SMALL PLASTIC POTS

There is an array of vacuum-formed, thin-walled plastic pots. Low in cost, readily available and easy to handle. But generally having hard competition with the array of peat containers. These pots also compete with the Cell-Pak, which is also low in cost per plant.

MOLDED POTS

Again, another group of the brown molded-fiber pots (Garden Pots), which are somewhat more forgiving of overwatering as compared to plastic pots; they also offer biodegradability (that important word again), but they have a hard time competing with plastics in this market.

PAKS—PLASTIC

Here comes a whole array of vacuum-formed (thin-walled) "packs." Plastic trays in such sizes as 3 by 3, 4 by 6, etc. (See photo, page 54.) They are very heavily used for bedding-plant production. Generally low-cost, strong enough to grow and sell—annuals.

The point here: Somehow, growers (especially bedding-plant) have finally standardized rather well on a "flat" size—most major production of bedding plants is done in a flat about 11 by 21 inches. Example: Handi-Flat 6-10 (see picture, page 53) is 11½ by 21¼ inches outside. Advantages of this standardization:

1. There is a major payoff in the several mechanization trends coming up in bedding plants—mostly flat-filling equipment and now more recently, direct-seeding machines. Such equipment just costs a lot more if it must accommodate various-sized flats.
2. Standardizing flat size permits designing a whole series of plastic packs, also Cell-Paks (see page 20)—all of which will fit the basic "Handi-Flat"—not possible if the industry operated on a series of different-sized flats.
3. Pricing—at least everyone is selling the same number of square inches of plants per flat under today's system. It offers some basis for comparison of prices.

PRO AND CON

On the "pro" side

1. Thin-walled plastic packs are again low-cost—and adequately do the job.
2. Many such packs come lightly joined in groups of 6, 10, 12, etc., enabling the grower to fill a standard flat with packs in one operation.

Now, problems

1. Plastic simply is not quite as forgiving of the grower who tends to overwater. Especially a problem where the soil mix is a bit heavy—but millions of fine bedding plants are grown in plastic packs!
2. Plastic packs are not biodegradable.

Here are the Handi-Paks—very widely used, especially for growing spring annuals. The Handi-Pak is supplied to the grower in multiples, each of which fits into a Handi-Flat (11½ x 21¼ inches). Individual flats are easily separated at point of sale. The lower center unit is the A-12—12 packs, each 4¾ by 3 inches.

Cost. Examples of cost of thin-walled plastic packs: The A-8 Handi-Pak, 4¾ by 4¾ inches (eight packs per Handi-Flat) costs about 2.7¢ each. Same size Cell-Pak (AC6-8) costs about 2.9¢ per pack. Six "cells" per pack, 8 packs per flat.

MOLDED PACKS—GARDEN-PAKS

The Garden-Pak, for example, is again a pack mainly for growing annuals, competing directly with the plastic packs described above. They are made of molded fiber impregnated with some asphalt to give them longer life. They are offered in a fair variety of shapes and sizes (photo, page 54).

Garden-Paks not long ago were the real backbone of the "pack" bedding-plant business. Plastics have made heavy inroads—but still, many thousands of growers stick tight with their molded-fiber containers. Some of the reasons are: First, that molded fiber is a bit surer to turn out a good plant—a little more forgiving of overwatering than plastic; molded fiber is porous—plus ample drain holes. No doubt, another major point is the rather pleasant and "earthy" brown color of the molded-fiber packs. Add to this the ease for

Here is the Garden-Pak—molded-fiber pack, used widely, again for bedding-plant production, in a variety of sizes. Easy for the home gardener to tear the pack apart and to remove plants—and, incidentally, molded fiber is a bit more forgiving of overwatering by the grower—as compared to plastics.

the home gardener to simply tear the pack apart when plants are to be set out.

And, the final plus: They are biodegradable. Certainly, several years exposure will rot them away—unlike the plastic pack. Pricewise, they run 3 to 7¢ each, depending on size. Main limitations of molded fiber: Somewhat higher cost, a little bulkier for shipping—then there is a point that the whole series of plastic packs are designed to fit so neatly into a uniform "Handi-Flat" type of growing flat.

Trend on molded fiber—probably steady.

CELL-PAKS

The Cell-Pak is finding increased usage by the bedding-plant trade. The Cell-Pak is sort of a happy halfway ground between the open plastic pack and, on the other hand, individually potted plants. You might say they are a series of plastic trays roughly in the same size range as the plastic pack—but in this case, each plastic pack is divided into a series of cells (see photo, page 18). Each cell, of course, produces an individually potted plant. Cell-Pak container cost to the grower is only a very little bit higher than growing in straight plastic packs.

This interesting grower experience highlights the case for Cell-Paks. The grower had been growing in an A-8 plastic pack; this meant 8 packs per

11½ by 21¼-inch Handi-Flat, 12 petunia plants per flat. Last year, this grower switched over to a Cell-Pak, the same 8 packs per 11½ by 21¼-inch Handi-Flat, but now, he is planting only 9 plants per pack instead of 12. In other words, the same 8 packs per 21-inch flat, but now only 72 plants per flat instead of 96, and *he received the same dollars per flat for the Cell-Paks.* Customers were willing to pay that much more per plant in order to get individual potted plants—plus the advantage of easy "pop-out" removal.

An interesting comment on size trends in Cell-Paks—again, comments from our container people. First, Cell-Paks are available in a range from a minimum 32 cells per Handi-Flat to a maximum 96. The 96 is, of course, a very small "cell"—interesting mainly to bargain-discount stores. The trend the past year or so is away from the 96-cell flat; the most popular size is 72 cells per flat; a close second is the 48-cell flat. This reflects somewhat more emphasis on quality in bedding plants. The better garden-store and food-chain outlets like the 48-plant size better than the 72.

Costwise, Cell-Paks are inexpensive—and just a bit higher than a comparable-sized open-plastic pot. The AC6-8 Cell-Pak (4¾ by 4¾ inches, 6 cells per pack) costs 3¢ per pack vs. comparable-sized Handi-Paks at 3.8¢.

Trends: Clearly, the trend on Cell-Paks is upward. More Cell-Paks last year, less of the old open pack, but still, in the overall, more open packs than Cell-Paks.

HANGING BASKETS

Perhaps the largest increase in the whole world of containers the past year or two has been in the use of hanging baskets. Somehow, they seem to have hit the public's fancy. Perhaps they are tying in effectively with the move toward patio gardening. For whatever reason, hanging baskets are still moving up.

There are many types available such as Lockwood, Ball, Hefty, T.O., and Cherokee.

> *Hanging basket.* This is, in fact, a large, shapely, injection-molded container in which plants are grown. There is a built-in saucer below to catch drainage from the pot—which makes it usable within porches, homes, etc. No water on the floor. They are made in green, white or terracotta, and a wire hanger is included. Most growers fill them with a light peat-perlite material, such as Jiffy-Mix, or at least with a soil with a lot of peat in it. Costs somewhat more than other types of baskets—but very popular—coming up strongly in sales.

> Cost is roughly 85¢ for the 10-inch-diameter

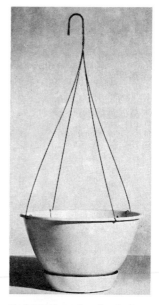

Today's hanging baskets—in several ways an improvement over old hanging baskets. First, no liner required, and second, a built-in saucer permits hanging these pots overhead in the home. No drip.

Here is an example of the so-called "nursery pot"—lower cost, less rigid. Container is used for growing and selling rose plants, evergreens and nursery stock, garden mums, etc.

hanging basket with wire hanger and saucer below.

What are the main plants used in hanging baskets? Certainly many *Cascade Petunias* and ivy geraniums. Other popular items include impatiens, begonias, coleus, browallia and even tomatoes.

As we have said so often—what a shame there isn't some sort of low-cost automatic irrigation system to keep these hanging baskets watered. So often, they just don't get regular attention. Big advantage to hanging baskets is they need not take up valuable bench space. They can be hung between benches or above. Watering can be done with Chapin equipment.

NURSERY POTS

These are the larger, thin-walled plastic containers used for growing/selling a variety of evergreens, azaleas, foliage plants, and certainly garden mums for fall sales. These are containers that are competing directly with, and moving importantly into the so-called "gallon-can" market.

Several important nursery cans:

1. The 6-quart Poly-Tainer—ornate, somewhat less costly compared to GPS, widely used. It costs roughly 20¢.

2. GPS No. 89—another widely used nursery pot. It does have a nice rim—easy to pick them up! The cost, roughly, for an 8-inch diameter, 9-inch deep pot, is about 23¢.

3. Herculite—Lowest cost of the nursery cans (costs roughly, for an 8-inch diameter, 9-inch deep, about 16¢). Herculites seem generally good for the several months required for most crops, if handled with reasonable care.

FLOWER POTS—4-6-inch

This is the main market for holiday pot-plant growing—lilies, poinsettias, pot mums, mainly 5 and 6-inch, an important market in 4-inch for spring geraniums, as well as year-round demand for mass market 4-inch flowering and foliage material. Like the rest of the container world, again, important changes are going on here!

The big controversy, of course, is the gradual switch from clay over to rigid (injection) plastics. No doubt, there is a strong trend toward plastics. They are lighter-weight, by far, and not nearly as breakable. However, a couple of points are working hard for the clay pot. For one thing, clay is porous and always a little more forgiving from the grower's point of view. Less prone to overwatering problems. Len Holmberg, large pot-plant specialist of Fairhope, Alabama, made an interesting comment on this. Says Len: "Pot mums in clay—same-size plants, same soil mix, need watering 1½ to 2 times as often as the same size plastic pot. We know this. Get used to it. Feel that over the years, our quality is about the same in clay or plastic. Another point: We don't have to include gravel or broken pot chips in the bottom of plastic pots. Drain holes up the sides of the pots take care of this."

Lastly, there is a certain prejudice that has developed about plastic pots— a sort of mental tie in the mind of the public that plastic-grown pot plants came from a low-price outlet. Sort of subconsciously, this says "really good plants in good flower shops are grown in clay," but this feeling is gradually eroding, and certainly, plastics are coming up.

Here are several of the most important lines offered today:

1. *Lockwood*—A leading manufacturer of plastic pots for growers. Pots are made of a high quality poly and come in a wide variety of sizes in standards, azaleas, squares, geraniums and bulb pans. They also come with side and bottom drainage.

2. *Ball Pots*—A good growing container made of semi-rigid polyethylene. Pots have a raised inside bottom so water can run off to drainage holes. Sizes over 3 inches come with side and bottom holes.

3. *Hefty Pots*—High quality injected molded plastic is blended to make a strong and flexible pot. Choice of white, green and terra cotta colors available in round and square pots.

4. *T.O.*—Fine quality pots with side

Here is a 6-inch azalea injection-molded, plastic flower pot—steadily replacing clay, especially for the 4-inch, 5-inch, and 6-inch market. Lighter, less breakable.

and bottom holes. Pots come in a wide variety of sizes and colors.

5. *Cherokee*—One of our newest suppliers in the southern market. Generally competitive in all sizes. Pots are made of a high quality plastic. Sizes and colors vary.

6. *Packer*—A new line of decorative pots in 4-inch foliage and 6½-inch azalea sizes. Pots are 20 sided and have a polished finish. These two sizes have detachable saucers, which are sold separately. Pots are both attractive and durable.

Costs are roughly 1 to 1½¢ more for a 6-inch clay pot than for the same size in plastic—about 10¢ for a 6-inch plastic, roughly 11¢ for a 6-inch clay. These prices do vary!

LONG-RANGE TRENDS IN CONTAINERS

Where are we going in 5 or 10 years in containers?

1. Clearly, there seems to be a move toward more of individually grown pot plants, especially in bedding plants—toward the Jiffy-7 and Cell-Pak idea and away from the open pack. Looking back 10 years, we have come from open flats (dig and wrap plants) to substantial use of individual potted plants—our feeling is that we will move more this way in the future.

2. Peat will probably be evermore a factor in this world of growing containers—more of the Jiffy-7 idea, Jiffy-Pots, Kys-Kubes and certainly, newer adaptations of these ideas. Plants do grow well in peat!

3. More designing and manufacturing of containers for specific markets and specific crops.

4. Biodegradability will become evermore important. The public just won't sit still for horticulture littering the landscape with old plastic growing containers.

4. GREENHOUSES, PLASTIC AND OTHER

What changes more or faster than the greenhouses we build? And the roofs on them? Yet, what is more important to the grower than to make the correct decision here? Structures *are* his capital investment.

Over the past several years, the field has narrowed. Today most growing structures are either glass, fiberglass, or polyethylene. A little of PVC and vinyl. So, here is a brief look at this new "big three."

A good example of low-cost poly structure for year-round growing in the Midwest. The house is a National, 30 feet wide. No accurate cost figures, but the grower quotes approximately $1.50 per square foot for material.

GLASS

Glass has always been a good way to go—if the grower:

A. Is likely to be there twenty or thirty years from now—not likely to be be moved out by expressways, subdivisions, etc.

B. Is well capitalized—to handle the original investment, plus cost to maintain (10 to 14 cents per square foot per year).

To put this in a different way: If the objective in business is to get *started* in flower growing with a bare minimum of available capital, good plastic is the best bet. If the grower's goal is to make the most per cent of dollar profit on his invested capital on a three-to-five year haul, then plastic is hard to beat. But if an operator is well capitalized, dug in for the long haul, no immediate prospect of moving, then our thought is: build glass.

RIGID PLASTICS

Two different approaches here. First, the top-quality rigid materials on a good steel frame. A good, permanent, low-maintenance greenhouse. Competing, frankly, with glass. IBG, for an example, reports that their sales today

Fire has consumed many acres of rigid-plastic greenhouses—tests at Colorado State University (Ken Goldsberry) show that the principal culprits are grass fires—aspen excelsior pads used for cooling create enough heat for ignition, sometimes electric system problems, sometimes weeds around the greenhouses. Welding has been known to start such fires—even fireworks.

(1975) are around 85 per cent fiberglass—and the heavy half of that is acrylic-modified, Tedlar-coated—their top grade. Gary Schultz of IBG says that they are building such a house for a minimum 15 per cent less cost than the same structure with glass. So much less labor compared to glazing a roof! The "acrylic-modified," by the way, means that a per cent of acrylic resin is included. Plexiglas is an example of a pure acrylic resin. This acrylic resin in its pure form is water-clear and permanent, but too costly and not strong enough to be used by itself on the greenhouse roof. However, mixed with the original "fiberglass"-type materials—and coated with Tedlar—it seems to be the Cadillac of plastic roofing materials, circa 1975. What its light transmission qualities will be after 20 years exposure, only time will tell. Tests and actual experience so far (10 years) have been encouraging. The odds should be far better than the materials of 6 or 8 years ago—because of both the acrylic modification—and the Tedlar, which gets away from the dust-holding fuzz. We occasionally see rigid plastic roofs of 6 or 8 years ago which have lost a third or more of their light-transmission quality already—with ruinous results on winter crops in the North. All we can add here is that big, established growers, particularly on the West Coast, are building acres of greenhouse area covered with these new high-grade fiberglass materials.

Another reputable greenhouse builder questioned on this point was far

Here's a structure put up several years ago by Lowell Hall, azalea grower, Hubbard, Oregon. Lowell figured a top of $2.00 per square foot for labor and material—including heat, pad-and-fan cooling, and overhead irrigation. The roof is 20-year, 4-ounce fiberglass with Tedlar. All home-designed and home-built.

less optimistic about rigid plastic in general. Reasons: serious loss of light transmission after a few years, also the fire hazard.

Speaking of fire hazard, IBG has a neat trick of including a 10-foot strip of fire-resistant material at regular intervals down the roof—a sort of fire-break. This flame-retardent material could be used all the way through, but would be expensive.

We said there were 2 basic approaches to rigid plastics. The first, the top-quality greenhouse. The other approach worth commenting on is use of often the less-costly and less-permanent grades of fiberglass on less-permanent structures. To go to the other extreme, there is a good bit of building of single 100 to 150-foot houses, often wood structures, and sometimes even arch-roof Quonset houses—covered with these lower-cost rigid plastics. Big problem is the uncertainty of light penetration. Some kinds darken badly after as little as several years. You get the feeling that the top grade —acrylic/Tedlar—is the cheapest, even from a 15-year point of view.

Modern fiberglass structure—IBG Arch II.

The Van Wingerden "Do Mor" polyethylene structure—shown at their Oberlin, Ohio range. Note the workers unrolling polyethylene down over the roof of the structure. The strip of poly being unrolled is actually a cylinder, or tube—laid flat, it makes the double-layer polyethylene.

Another look at the Van Wingerden "Do Mor" structure—note the device used to fasten the poly roof to the gutter—reported to be fast, and a secure fastening.

Several other comments about rigid plastics in general:

A. Properly installed, a fiberglass roof is a near-zero maintenance matter. Except only for the deterioration and light transmission—and the accompanying need for refinishing, etc., on the older materials.

B. Fiberglass is easily the best bet of all in case of hail. Not hailproof, but the odds are very good.

C. Crop growth under fiberglass—excellent at first, but dropping severely on some of the older materials as light transmission decreases.

POLYETHYLENE—A NUMBER OF WAYS TO GO

Polyethylene use in horticulture today is big! Probably well over 200 million square feet is used today (1975).

Poly is a one-year or less roof. The new 602 material may go up to two years, but cost is more. Against this one big limitation, though, it has some big advantages:

1. Growers agree that poly always grows as good a crop as any other roof—and often better. Perhaps the tightness helps keep humidity up—to the liking of many crops.

2. Low initial cost. Even an all-metal, metal-gutter, permanent poly structure, such as the Van Wingerden design, can be put up for as low as 70¢ per square foot, just material—the greenhouse only, no benches, heating, fans, etc. This, by the way, is in multiples of an acre or more.

3. The labor cost of annual removal and re-covering is coming down. Again the Van Wingerden "Do Mor" house, with a clever arrangement for clamping poly to the gutter, permits a crew of 7 men to recover an acre of greenhouse in one day. Double layer, by the way. Cost to re-cover, material only, around $2,000—again for the double-layer material. This is about 5 cents per square foot.

Northern growers are taking a fresh look at what can be done with these new polyethylene structures. From a hard business point of view, they offer an interesting possibility of producing just as good, perhaps even a bit better, a crop as compared to glass or grade A fiberglass. And, most important of all—at one-third or less initial investment—for the structure alone. Remember, the business is finally judged on what per cent it returns after taxes on its invested capital. Certainly the total package of heating, fans, benches will cost more than the 70¢-a-foot figure above for the structure. But still the difference in structure cost of less than 75¢, compared to more than $2.50 for good glass, is compelling.

Lloyd Bachman of Bachman's, Inc., Minneapolis, has built about three acres of this Van Wingerden house. Lloyd's reasoning is simple—plants grow so well under poly, the clamping device permits simple and fast re-covering of the roof and, lastly, the structure is all galvanized—zero maintenance. Lloyd is using these structures for straight 60° cut-flower and pot-plant crops—just like his glass houses—year round.

By the way, Lloyd has also built several acres of Lord and Burnham's very best grade glass—it will provide a most interesting comparison.

Rosacker's, also Minneapolis, has been operating a several-acre area of polyethylene Quonset-style houses, photo page 64, for about 10 years. It's a year-round deal—again a full range of cut-flower and pot-plant crops. Don Rosacker reports quality "equally as good—at times, better." Such experiences make one wonder whether a new trend may be shaping up in northern cut and pot production. Built around these low-cost, new-type poly structures.

Once again, here are four ways to go—different approaches to poly structures:

1. *The Van Wingerden House.* An interesting new design—evidently a modification of a 12-foot-wide Dutchlite structure. Gutter posts are 1¼-inch galvanized pipe set in concrete. They support a rather wide galvanized metal gutter, which in turn supports a metal bow—from gutter to gutter. A system of braces steadies the house, both lengthwise and crosswise. A

Here are the Rosacker-style poly greenhouses—a few miles north of Minneapolis—used for a variety of year-round cut-flower and pot-plant crops. In the photo: Dick Chamberlain (Ledge Hill Gardens, Carlisle, Penn.), visiting during a Bedding Plants, Inc. meeting.

At left: An interesting piece of equipment for application of poly over Quonset houses. Actually, it's a little homemade bit of welding—which permits moving a large, heavy roll of polyethylene over the roof of a greenhouse, unrolling the poly as you go down the length of the house. Built and used by Rosacker's, Minneapolis.

principal advantage of the house is a clever clamping device for securing the plastic to the gutters. The grower buys poly in a giant tube—14 feet, 4 inches in diameter. The tube is laid out flat on the roof. It is rolled to a stick parallel to each gutter. The clever clamping device fastens this roll of plastic securely to the gutter—almost airtight—quickly and easily. Seven men apply one acre of polyethylene in a day. Small, 1/32 hp squirrel-cage fans are installed, one per house, to inflate the area between the two layers of plastic—about $16 each. Cost for all materials, less polyethylene, from the ground up, about $26,000 per acre, greenhouse only. Available only in acre blocks, by the way. Write Van Wingerden Plastic Greenhouse, Inc., Horseshoe, NC 28742.

2. *Rosacker's—Minneapolis.* These structures are designed for year-round use in Minnesota and are basically 20 by 80 feet. Believe it or not, a 3 by 12-inch timber is used around the base of the house. Holes are drilled into it. The overhead arches are 1-inch outside diameters, 16-gauge tubing —like conduit, but heavier. They are simply inserted into the heavy timber at the baseboard. Don uses double-thick poly, 4 mil., and again the squirrel-cage fan to inflate the area between the sheets of poly. Open-flame heaters are used here, Resner XA-150—a 150,000 BTU unit. Two of them will keep a 20 by 80-foot house at 60° except on most severe nights. The material, by the way, is available from J. R. Johnson, Johnson Wholesale Floral, 3333 Edward Avenue, N.E., Minneapolis, Minnesota.

Again, Don Rosacker reports, "Every bit as good crops here as under good glass houses."

3. *The Criterion House.* X.S. Smith Co. of Red Bank, N.J. (Distributed by Geo. J. Ball, Inc.). We've seen many of these being erected in recent years throughout the country. They are of metal pipe rigid frame construction, offered in either freestanding or gutter-connected form. Available in five different widths of 14, 22, 25, 28 and 30 feet, the freestanding house can be built to any length in four-foot increments. A house 22 feet by 96 feet can be erected by two men in just several hours. No concrete footing is required. Basic greenhouse cost, materials only, is 75¢ per square foot.

The gutter connected type is available in 17 foot wide bays and in lengths of 96, 144 and 192 feet. Height at the gutters is 8 feet. Basic cost for greenhouse material begins at less than $1.00 per square foot.

4. *The Powell House*—designed and built by Billy Powell of Powell's Plant Farm, Troup, Texas. This is an interesting combination of Quonset and fiberglass (photo, page 20). It's the usual steel-rod Quonset structure, except that the roof, from about the five-foot level up, is covered with ten-year fiberglass. From the five-foot level down, the side can be enclosed in cold weather with a sheet of plastic muslin. On warm days this is rolled up and there is ample ventilation. No fans. Still a fairly low-cost house—and no annual removal and recovery with poly!

POLY-TUBE VENTILATION

More and more greenhouses are built without top or side vents. Growers rely mainly on the large 3 to 3½-foot fans at the end or sides of the houses —used also as a part of fan-pad cooling in summer. But in cold weather, such fans draw in a blast of very cold air, force it onto the plants. The answer: install overhead Poly Tubing (photo, page 66), turn large fans on low speed. Pad areas and any existing ventilators are closed up tight. With the fans on, a slight vacuum is created in the greenhouse. The overhead Poly Tubes sort of "inflate." Being open to the outside air on both ends, they draw in fresh outside air and the Poly Tube, having small holes at regular intervals, dispenses this outside air into the greenhouse. No draft, just a

Poly Tube ventilation installation.

steady movement of cool, fresh outside air.

First worked out by the University of Colorado Floriculture Department (Bob Holley), the system today is widely used on all types of structures, all growing areas.

"Poly Tube" is a trade name for the large polyethylene tube which is available from greenhouse suppliers generally. A system of louvers to shut off the flow of outside air into the tube is available from Acme Engineering Corporation, Muskogee, Oklahoma—trade name: Flo-Master® wall shutters.

Operation of the Poly Tube is often tied in to a thermostat—set to operate the large cooling fans and draw air in through the tubes only as temperature in the house exceeds the temperature called for.

Note in the photo, above, that the Poly Tubes are vented to outside air through a large galvanized stovepipe—and that the stovepipe turns down as it leaves the greenhouse—to keep rain and snow from entering the greenhouse.

You will notice in the picture that we used a ¾-inch piece of plywood to hold the galvanized stovepipe. Two halves of plywood were cut to make a half circle large enough to accommodate the 20-inch diameter pipe joints. The plywood was securely fastened on 2 x 4 studs on the gable ends of the greenhouse. The 2-foot lengths of pipe joints were secured to the ¾-inch plywood and the elbows were then joined to the pipe-joint extension outside the house with the elbows turned downward to prevent rain and snow from flowing in. A hole was punched through the 2-foot pipe joints at the top where it contacts the ¾-inch plywood and a screw-eye was screwed into position. One end of an insulated wire was securely fastened to the screw-eye and the wire was then run through the plastic tubing, making sure that no tear or hole was made in the plastic during the process. The other end of the wire was fastened to a turnbuckle which had been inserted at the opposite end of the house. Insulated staples were used through the wire and plastic to hold the tube up at about five different places on the roof bars. Masking tape was put around the sharp edges of the pipe, before drawing the plastic over the pipes at both ends, as a precaution against cutting the plastic. Masking tape was also used to secure and hold the plastic onto the galvanized pipe.

We recommend using 4-mil Poly Tubing. This comes prepunched with 3-inch-diameter holes in both sides of the tubing at 30-inch intervals.

In figuring just how much Poly Tubing it will take to ventilate a house properly, remember that the sum of the areas of all the holes in the tube cannot be larger than the area of the fan.

Also we would suggest that if the length of the house is 100 feet or more, the Poly Tubing should be attached to a vent pipe at each end.

5. BEWARE UNVENTED HEATERS!!

Every so often we come across a crop of bedding annuals or mums or something that is just plain unhappy. In obvious trouble. The grower doesn't really know why. But, there is a problem.

All too often, the culprit is an open-flame heater.

Each winter we come upon clear examples of gas damage from poorly vented unit heaters, or heaters with no provision for air inlet to the burner. In some cases, the damage is minor, just close to the heater. In others, it is devastating. One whole crop of bedding plants—40,000 square feet or so of poly greenhouses—perhaps a 60 per cent loss. A pot-mum grower who lost 8,000 pots of mums—really a total loss. In another case, 35,000 square feet of cut mums—total loss.

Most of these problems occur in polyethylene greenhouses—probably because the poly houses are so airtight. But, one of the serious losses described above was in a glass greenhouse. So, it can happen under glass, too!

When you see these major losses, you wonder how many other crops are just not quite what they should be—again because of poorly vented heaters. And the grower never knows the difference.

So, we're taking a little space to describe the problem in some detail—and the remedy.

THE TYPICAL PROBLEM

Most cases of injury from heaters look about like this: First, it is usually a polyethylene structure and usually almost airtight, which is easy to do with poly. The problem, of course, occurs only with open-flame unit heaters installed right in the greenhouse. Steam-unit heaters are never a problem,

A good example of good venting of open-flame greenhouse heaters. The grower (in the photo) is Jim Harris of Palmetto Greenhouses, Simpsonville, South Carolina. Note the duct carrying the flue gases away from the heater. In this case, the duct extends on down and under the ridge of the greenhouse to the end. Furthermore, Jim has installed a fan at the end of each duct to be sure that the gases are moved on out of the greenhouse. In other words, it's kind of like a forced-draft chimney.

simply because there is no open flame.

The problem occurs where such open-flame gas or oil-fired heaters are either vented poorly or not at all, or where there is no provision for air inlet to the burner. By venting, we mean that there is simply no provision for the "smoke" from the fire to get out of the greenhouse. Also very important is the matter of provision for bringing fresh air in to provide oxygen for the fire to burn. We have seen severe damage to bedding annuals in such a house, drum-tight, where there was a small vent provided to allow the gases to escape—but evidently not large enough—and, in this particular case, no provision for fresh air to get in to provide oxygen for the fire. A couple of 12-inch holes punched in the poly wall down near the ground greatly relieved the problem.

To be sure we understand, the problem we are talking about might be related to what would happen if you tried to operate a regular coal boiler without a chimney. There would be no place for the smoke and gases from the fire to escape to—so they just all pour into the greenhouse. Some growers who have had severe damage have reported that the gases from the fire were so severe that they would make your eyes burn on cold nights. Obviously, there should not be noticeable smoke and gases from the fire in a greenhouse where the heaters are properly vented, even on a cold night.

SYMPTOMS

The several crops we have seen:

A. *Bedding annuals*—Serious injury from heaters will actually curl the leaves of such plants as tomatoes and petunias. Soon, the top growth is deformed and stunted and obviously "unhappy." Impatiens seem to be very susceptible. Tomatoes are especially unhappy in these fumes—again, leaves curl badly and the plants just stop growing. Actually, all plants seem to be more or less affected by it—perhaps tomatoes are particularly sensitive.

B. *Mums*—Response of mums to fumes from heaters is very typical, really very easy to spot, once you get to know what to look for. Let's take a typical pot mum. As each stem of the plant comes up and starts to form its bud, the gas injury seems first to simply delay the development of the bud. The bud will grow to perhaps a ⅛ or 3/16-inch size, then it will stop developing. Soon vigorous side buds will start to grow on out past the center bud. They will be typically halfhearted, semivegetative shoots. There is a bud in the tip of each of them, but something is holding the buds back from normal development. By the time all this has happened, the plant is weeks past its normal flowering date—and we still only have these halfhearted little ¼-inch-or-less buds. It's a little like heat delay in midsummer. As the problem develops further, more and more of these semivegetative side shoots keep developing. Perhaps if the problem is caught in its early stages, and if the side buds are quickly removed, and the problem of the heater corrected, the buds might go on and develop. Once it gets out of hand, and once the side buds have passed the original center bud by an inch or two, probably the best thing is to discard the crop and start over.

Typically, on the mum problem, by the time the crop should be in full flower and ready for market, we have only the aborted center bud and several 2 or 3-inch, half-vegetative side shoots to show for our effort. No color.

C. *Other Crops*—We just don't have experience with other crops—but certainly, you would expect more or less the same type of damage from any greenhouse crops.

REMEDY

We do not have detailed engineering specifications for different-sized heaters; however, it would be a fair bet that any unit heaters installed by a reputable firm would have built into them an adequate-sized vent to allow for escape of smoke and gases from the fire. The only problem is to be sure that this vent is carried on out through the roof so that the gas can escape. Again, we have seen cases of very tight polyethylene greenhouses with no provision for fresh-air inlet. How big an inlet is required for a given heater? Nothing definite on this, but we have seen a hole 6 to 8 inches in diameter near the ground near the heater, and it seems to do the job.

Evidently, the flue-gas impurities are mainly sulfur dioxide. Reports from other workers indicate that lack of fresh air being supplied to the burner results in typical ethylene injury.

6. GROWING IN SOILLESS MIXES
By W. D. Holley (Ret'd)
Colorado State University

Have you ever really thought about how many problems, failures or near failures are directly related to the soils we grow in? Whether these problems stem from disease organisms or from lack of air for healthy root growth, they cost the producer money and they can be prevented.

There are two separate and distinct types of media required for greenhouse growing. For container use, the medium is used for a short time and is sold with the plant, so we need a temporary substrate that has specific characteristics. Above all, it should be reproducible. Once it has been perfected for a given system of growing, the identical mix can be made year after year. The mix for container soils should have excellent air-supplying power, but should hold lots of water. To get these two factors together requires copious amounts of organic matter. Container mixes must also have good capillary water movement so they can be watered with modern automatic irrigation systems. Container mixes in general should be light in weight. Where there are exceptions, some sand may be added.

Ideal media for cut flowers, on the other hand, should be as permanent as we can get. Physical change from year to year should be minimum. Cut-flower substrates should not hold a lot of water, for we can set the watering frequency to fit the growing plants and the light energy available. This means that we do not need organic matter in media for cut flowers. In fact, any organic matter will change with time, so what is good this year will not work as well next year. We also do not need capillarity. Watering systems today are available that will place the water uniformly over the surface so it only has to move downward. Our main concern, then, with media for growing cut flowers is air supply, watering frequency and nutrition control. These can be done best in gravels that hold very little water.

We now have the equipment and the technical competence to grow in inert media. We have been watering with a nutrient solution for years. All that remains is to make this nutrient solution more complete. We irrigate our soils with bench-spray systems. To convert to inert media, we must water much more frequently. This requires an automatic system that waters at the right pressures on a predetermined frequency for an exact time. The nutrient solution is not reused, so water-tight benches and pumps are not needed. Disease spread, if low pressures are used, is no worse than it is in soil. One major source for error *is that an inert medium is not as forgiving of mistakes as soil.* Feeding and watering must be done exactly, but production can be 15 to 20% greater when culture is done properly in inert media.

MEDIA

The ideal medium should change little, if any, over many years of usage. This in itself eliminates the use of organic matter, if we seek permanency in a medium. A balance between water-holding capacity and air-supplying power should be sought. Of the two aeration is more important. With automation, irrigation frequency is not a real problem. The ideal medium should have enough weight to give firm support for the plants; but the lighter-weight material we can use, the cheaper it can be handled.

Volcanic scoria has been used for at least 10 years in growing some of our carnations at Colorado State University. Nucleus stock plants have been grown in 10-inch pots of scoria since the inception of the shoot-tip program. One bench of roses has been grown 8 years and it's one of the most productive benches we have had. We have also used coarse sands, mixtures of gravel, manufactured lightweight aggregates, and mixtures of these along with various arcillated clays.

Table 1 shows several measurements and particle size analyses on a number of inert media. If the water-holding capacity is too great, one has no advantage over soil. The free-water-holding capacity of a given medium should determine the watering frequency. Free-water-holding capacity is regulated primarily by the percent of particles with smaller diameters. A medium should have a number of particle sizes rather than be screened to a definite size.

Table 1. Particle size distribution of various inert media and their moisture-holding capacities.

Medium	Remarks	Percent of particles with diameters larger than[1]:				Percent of particles with diameters smaller than 0.02"	Bench capacity[1] (qt./ft.[2])
		0.20"	0.12"	0.04"	0.02"		
A.	Granitic sand and gravel	7.1	25.7	75.6	98.2	1.8	3.3
B.	Large idealite	100.0					1.5
		(Particles ranging from 5/16" to 3/4")					
C.	River sand and gravel (squee-gee)	23.7	83.0	95.5	98.8	1.4	2.0
D.	Fine idealite	00.0	00.0	53.9	94.9	5.0	4.5
E.	Regular idealite	42.3	76.7	98.9	99.4	0.5	1.8
F.	Scoria (volcanic ash)	46.7	62.0	79.1	92.0	7.1	5.8[3]

[1] Percentages are by weight.
[2] Bench capacity: Maximum moisture-holding capacity of a medium 7 inches in depth, quarts per square foot.
[3] Approaches and exceeds maximum moisture capacity of good greenhouse soils.

It is our belief that moisture content of inert media at bench capacity should not exceed 3 to 3½ quarts per square foot or about 1½ pounds of water per gallon of medium 7 inches deep. If the water-holding capacity is too great, the air-supplying power is reduced and one loses some of the advantages of the system. We have grown in a medium that held only 1½ quarts per square foot with good success if the medium was watered frequently.

Dr. Joe Hanan has defined a desirable medium as one that has at least 80% of the particles larger than 0.12 inches, 95% larger than 0.04 inches and not more than 2% smaller than 0.02 inches. As the percentage of particles smaller than 0.02 inches increases, the moisture content increases rapidly. The air supply is reduced in direct relation to increased moisture-holding capacity. We have been successful at CSU with ordinary gravel screened to ⅛-¼-inch sizes.

WATERING FREQUENCY

The most important advantage in the use of inert media is that water can be applied freely without danger from overwatering, and that moisture stress can be minimized. In a medium that holds 3 quarts per square foot, less than 1 quart should be removed between irrigations if moisture stress is kept at a minimum. If more is removed, the suction required on the part of the plant to extract moisture probably increases very rapidly. If inert media are allowed to get too dry between irrigations, the effect on plant growth will be even more marked than if plants were growing in soil. As water is removed from an inert medium, the suction curve rises more steeply than it does for soil.

We know from previous work that a mature carnation plant uses approximately 1 quart per square foot per day, with a maximum usage at noon at the rate of possibly as much as 2 quarts per square foot per day. Under these conditions, from 1 to 2 irrigations per day are required if each irrigation applies 1 quart per square foot or slightly less. We have programmed our irrigation on a maximum of 4 waterings per day in the middle of the summer to as little as 1 watering per day in the middle of the winter with a gradual change-over from summer to winter and from winter to summer. Roses have been handled pretty much in this same manner. We set the irrigation system to operate just enough to barely "drip the bench." *A lot of water can be wasted* if the irrigation remains on for too long a time.

The system lends itself to integration with accumulated solar radiation for controlling the number of irrigation cycles, or a commercial timing system can be used with hydraulic or solenoid valves that will enable the watering to be done a preset number of times per day for a set interval of time.

ADVANTAGES AND PROBLEMS

Advantages

The major advantages of the system are: (1) reproducible results without constantly having to amend the medium, (2) removing water stress as a limiting factor in greenhouse culture, (3) better results with saline or high-sodium water supplies, (4) more easily steamed with less chance of "steaming injury," (5) cannot be over-watered and, (6) permits more exact nutrition control. Yield and grade of carnations, roses, snapdragons and chrysanthemums have been excellent by this method. The yield, especially in the top grades, has been much greater than in our best soils.

Carnations were planted in side-by-side plots of a good soil and a lightweight manufactured aggregate and grown for 3 years. Differences in yield and grade were up to 30% better in the inert substrate during the first year and decreased with successive years. During the second and third years, growth was equal in the 2 substrates during winter when water stress was minimum even in soil. The differences favoring the inert medium occurred from April to October each of the latter 2 years.

Problems

There are some problems that must be avoided. With frequent watering, the lower foliage is wet most of the time. This problem can be minimized by carefully adjusting the angle of the irrigation spray so that it wets a minimum of foliage. Pressure should be adjusted carefully on each bench so that the spray barely covers the bench area at the point farthest from the inlet. High pressure (above 4 psi) causes fogging and undue spread of foliage diseases in the middle of the bench. Minimum pressure to cover a 42-inch bench with the Gates system is about 2½ psi. Spacing of the nozzles is critical. Plants should not be set directly in front of a nozzle, as this blocks flow of the spray to the middle portion of the bench. There is little lateral movement of water in a good medium, so the water must be put on where it sinks and drains through. Growth is not necessarily soft with frequent irrigation in inert media, but it certainly is heavy and good. Proper nutrition and proper aerial environment are extremely important with this system. Attempting to control growth by withholding water from inert media is a negative approach that should not be used.

The recently developed Chapin twin-tube irrigation system promises to eliminate foliage wetting. Tubes with 4-inch hole spacing arranged along the outer edges and between linear rows of plants have watered carnations in gravel more satisfactorily than the Gates system. Absolutely no foliage loss resulted in one year of watering by this method and the surface of the gravel remained so dry that oxalis seed did not germinate. The twin-tube system involves very low volumes and pressures so large areas can be watered from one automatic valve. Time to water a bed 6 inches deep is around 5 to 6 minutes.

Some nutritional problems have been experienced by several commercial growers in changing to inert substrates. Phosphorus and/or calcium hunger are most common. When starting with new gravel, the application of some superphosphate and limestone to the surface prior to planting helps to avoid this. Usually, applications of one half the rate applied to soil are adequate. Calcium and phosphorus should also be supplied regularly in the nutrient solution. Unless the nutrient solution is acidified, salts of magnesium, calcium and phosphorus interact in the concentrate tank to form precipitates. Any appreciable sludge in the tank must be avoided or phosphate and calcium hunger may result. There are several alternate solutions to the precipitate problem. The addition of up to 1 lb. of crude nitric acid per barrel of concentrate will usually prevent the calcium phosphate precipitate. The use of 2-head injectors, where calcium nitrate is added to one tank and the phosphate and magnesium sulfate are in another tank, prevents interactions, as they are not mixed until diluted. Finally, if all else fails, solutions can be alternated; potassium nitrate, ammonium nitrate and borax form the base solution used continuously. Calcium nitrate is doubled in one tank and magnesium sulfate and phosphoric acid are doubled in the next.

NUTRIENT SOLUTION

After a series of experiments at Colorado State University, we recommend the following nutrient solutions after irrigating carnations, chrysanthemums and snapdragons growing in inert media in Colorado. This solution results from some compromises, but is developed for ionic balance and should result in optimum tissue levels of the major nutrients. We recommend the following weights of chemicals per 1000 gallons of irrigation water when used on a continuous basis:

5 lbs. potassium nitrate
3 lbs. calcium nitrate
1 lb. ammonium nitrate
2 lbs. magnesium sulfate
1 lb. phosphoric acid
½ ounce borax

These recommendations are for Colorado mountain water that contains almost no dissolved salts. Growers who use other water supplies should know what the water contains and make allowances for the dissolved salts. Calcium, magnesium and sulfates may be present in adequate to excess quantities. Unfortunately, sodium and chlorides are often present in undesirable levels also. Where calcium is present at 60 ppm or higher, substitute one pound of ammonium nitrate for each two pounds of calcium nitrate. If magnesium is present at 25 ppm or more, and sulfate in the water supply exceeds 25 pph, add no magnesium sulfate to the nutrient solution.

Editor's note: For other discussions on growing floriculture crops in inert mixes, see page 7, a discussion on bedding-plant production in either totally or partly-soilless mixes. Also, see notes on pot mum production in soilless mixes.

7. PEAT-LITE MIXES—COMING UP FAST

Each year we see more and more of them!

Already the majority of seed germination is done in peat-vermiculite mixes. Mum propagating is done mainly in mixes of peat and perlite. A fair number of commercial pot-plant growers have gone over to such soilless mixes as peat, vermiculite, perlite, bark, etc. Many large bedding plant growers today use mixes with no soil, most of the rest grow in two-thirds inert materials and one-third soil.

Most used of these inert mixes is some combination of peat and vermiculite or perlite—plus fertilizer. Trainloads of such mixes are produced and sold by "mix specialists." Example, the widely used Jiffy-Mix, available from horticultural dealers, generally. Also Redi-Earth and Pro-Mix. And a variety of other mixes, several of which contain some soil, although nearly all are soilless or predominantly inert materials.

Some growers mix their own. Several problems: First, the critical importance of getting a really uniform mix. Especially with small quantities

STEAMED
PEAT-No 4 VERMICULITE
MIX with 5-10-5
LIQUID FEED

STEAMED
PEAT-No 4 VERMICULITE
MIX with 5-10-5
NO LIQUID FEED

STEAMED
PEAT-No 4 VERMICULITE
MIX without 5-10-5
NO LIQUID FEED

These flats do dramatize the point about feeding in mixes. The above three flats, grown in Jiffy-Mix-type materials, were fed as follows: left flat, dry with the original mix, plus liquid feeding each watering; center flat, dry feed with original mix, no liquid feed; right flat, no liquid or dry feed. There's something about the combination of both forms of feed that really wins!

STEAMED
PEAT-No 4 VERMICULITE
MIX with 5-10-5
LIQUID FEED

STEAMED
PEAT-No 4 VERMICULITE
MIX with 5-10-5
LIQUID FEED

STEAMED
PEAT-No 4 VERMICULITE
MIX without 5-10
NO LIQUID FEED

The same story as the photo above—this time the other way around. The left flat, both dry feed with the original mix and liquid feeding; center flat, no dry feed with the original mix, but, yes, liquid feed each watering; right flat, no feed.

of fertilizer, a poor job of mixing can be disastrous. Then, too, the specialist has important advantages of buying power. The big peat buyer (boatloads) buys better peat for less. He can afford better mixing equipment. The trend, in balance, seems toward specialist mixes.

And we haven't mentioned the very real problem of getting good, uniform, reliable soil. So often we hear of major crop disasters resulting from weed killers (Atrazine, for example) used by farmers, or high salt content in a lot of soil. Once you get settled down to growing in a peat-lite mix, you can reasonably count on getting the same result every time. There is also the matter of weight. Plants in peat mixes, such as Jiffy-Mix, will weigh

Excellent cut flowers can be grown in Jiffy-Mix-type materials. Both the right and left trays above were filled 3½ inches deep, dry feed in the original mix, plus liquid feed with each watering. Photo early February in West Chicago. Variety: Indianapolis. Quality was **fine.**

conservatively half as much per tray of bedding plants, or per 6-inch pot plant, as will the same plant in soil. It depends some on moisture but it surely is a factor.

These are some of the reasons why more growers each year turn to specialist-produced inert mixes.

These specialist mixes, by the way, are already very big in Europe. Surely a predominance of pot and spring plant growers and seedling producers over there use such mixes. Always predominantly peat.

RULES FOR GROWING IN MIXES

A rather thorough series of tests has been run at West Chicago on growing crops in peat-vermiculite mixes such as Jiffy-Mix. The tests extended over several years, on eight different crops. Based on this, here would be our recommended rules for success with such materials as Jiffy-Mix:

1. It is important with these peat-vermiculite mixes to be sure that the mix is wet all the way through before planting. This often requires repeated soaking. Dry peat is hard to wet! Drying spots in a pack of annuals, or a pot plant, will mean a poor plant.

2. Once Jiffy-Mix is wet, it should be used. Mostly, fertilizer tends to dissolve, salt builds up. Don't wet the mix until you are ready to use it.

3. Don't really know why—but we surely do know that you will get a lot more growth in Jiffy-Mix using both a slow-release fertilizer in the original mix—and liquid fertilizer with every application of water throughout the crop. It's really a striking difference! Tests on pot mums developed 3½-inch flowers with regular liquid feeding only, 5½-inch flowers under the same conditions with liquid plus MagAmp in the original mix. You

get somewhat the same response by including regular dry balanced fertilizer in the original mix—but slow-release materials, of course, last longer. Note photos, page 75. Jiffy-Mix, with MagAmp added, as marketed under the trade name **Jiffy-Mix Plus.**

4. When you water these mixes, water them well. Leach so that water runs through the pot or flat. Avoid salt buildup! Some growers make a heavy application of clear water one day a week to be sure that no salts are accumulating.
5. Steaming is not necessary with peat-vermiculite mixes.
6. Avoid ammonia nitrate feeding in these mixes.

A WORD ABOUT BARK-LITE MIXES

Ground bark is proving useful as a constituent of growing media for pot plants and container grown nursery stock. The possibility of bark replacing peat does exist simply because the supply of peat is more finite. Currently (1975) there are about six different bark-lite mixes being produced and sold by mix specialists. Compared to peat, bark has a faster decomposition rate, releases its minerals faster, but requires much higher rates of nitrogen application.

8. AIR POLLUTION PROBLEMS AFFECT BEDDING PLANT PRODUCERS

Marlin N. Rogers
University of Missouri

In today's world, pollution of our environment is a matter of concern to all thinking citizens. It is a topic having many political, economic, and social implications. We are concerned about the pollution of our water supplies, solid-waste disposal problems, excessive noise levels around us, radioactive fallout, the destruction of spots of natural beauty by our advancing urbanization, and the contamination of the very air which we breathe and in which we must carry out our vital activities.

It is not surprising that plants, among the various types of living organisms, are considered to be the most sensitive biological indicators of the presence of trace quantities of aerial pollutants when we stop to consider how a plant is constructed and how it operates. To synthesize the carbohydrate supplies needed for normal growth, plants must "mine" vast quantities of air to collect the carbon dioxide, a gaseous raw material, needed to support photosynthesis. To grow a crop of corn yielding 100 bushels per acre requires ten tons of carbon dioxide gas. To secure this quantity, the corn plants growing on that acre of land must process 33,500 *tons* of air. A plant whose anatomy is organized to "strain" such vast quantities of air to secure its basic building blocks for growth is, at the same time, vulnerably exposed to the damaging effects of

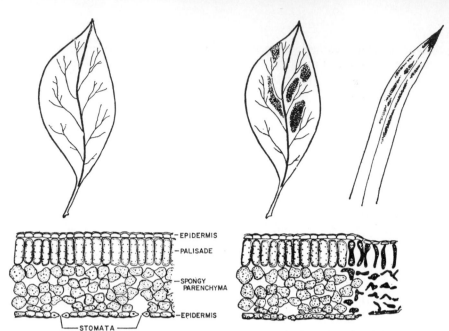

Fig. 1*. Normal dicotyledon leaf and cross section.

Fig. 2. Sulfur dioxide injury. Note blotchy interveinal areas on dicotyledon leaf and streaked areas on monocotyledon leaf (grass type).

trace quantities of other phytotoxic gases which might be present in the air it is processing.

Although their relative importance may vary from place to place, it now appears that damaging air pollutants may be ranked in the following descending order of importance nationally on the basis of their measured economic effects on all economic plants: sulfur oxides, ozone, fluorides, peroxyacyl nitrates, ethylene, chlorine, and nitrogen dioxide (Middleton, 1967). Estimates of the total monetary damage to agricultural crops amounts to about $100 million annually in California, and to more than $500 million for the U. S. as a whole.

GENERAL SYMPTOMS OF AIR-POLLUTANT INJURY

The most common symptoms of air pollution injury to plants are caused by loss of water (plasmolysis) from cells in the leaf and their subsequent death. This water loss appears to result from changes in the permeability of the membranes surrounding each cell, which permit the water contained inside the cell to "leak out." Cells in different parts of the leaf appear to be affected differentially by each specific toxicant. In some cases, only cells in the upper palisade layer may be affected; in others, only cells adjacent to the stomatal pores collapse; while in still other instances, groups of cells extending completely through the leaf may be killed. These differences help identify

*Figures 1 through 5 reprinted by permission from *Air Pollution*, Vol. 1, First Edition, pages 258, 260, 262 and 263, and Vol. 1, Second Edition, page 405, by Brandt.

which specific pollutant material may be causing a particular phytotoxic effect (Brandt, 1962.)

SULFUR DIOXIDE

SOURCES

The principal sources of sulfur dioxide in the air are electrical generating plants using low-quality, high-sulfur-content soft coal, the smelting or refining of sulfur-containing copper, lead, zinc, and nickel ores, and the production, refining and use of high-sulfur petroleum and natural gas (Wood, 1968). Power generation by coal-burning plants is the most important single source of trouble. Since more and more of these large plants are being set up at mine-mouth locations, sulfur dioxide problems in the future will not necessarily be confined to metropolitan areas. Calvert (1967) has calculated, for example, that when three such plants are completed and in operation near mines in western Pennsylvania, about one-third of the southwestern part of the entire state will theoretically be subjected to ground-level concentrations of sulfur dioxide of 0.15 ppm, which is approaching the threshold point for injury—particularly if ozone is also present at low concentrations (Menser and Heggestad, 1966).

NECROTIC SYMPTOMS

On broad-leaved plants, sulfur dioxide causes formation of necrotic (dead) spots in the parts of the leaf between the major veins. Both palisade and spongy parenchyma cells die, and the affected areas become papery in texture and usually ivory or light tan in color. The area immediately adjacent to the main veins usually remains green in color. Older florists, who, in their earlier days, burned poor-quality soft coal in boilers located in the end of their greenhouses, will remember this kind of injury which used to occur, at some time or other, nearly every winter. On grasses and other plants having parallel veins, injury is likewise pretty much confined to the interveinal areas, with the final bleached pattern giving a streaked effect. Chronic injury appears only as a generalized chlorosis (lightening of color between the veins) with the death of a few isolated cells being shown by white or brownish flecks.

As long as aerial concentrations of sulfur dioxide are low, the gas dissolves in the moisture present inside the leaf, forming sulfites, which are gradually changed into relatively harmless sulfates. However, if sulfites accumulate faster than this conversion can occur, cell permeability is affected and the cells begin to lose their water (Brandt, 1962).

Plants having succulent leaves of high physiological activity are most likely to be injured. The plants highly susceptible to injury may be damaged after exposure to 0.48 ppm for four hours or 0.28 ppm for 24 hours (Thomas, 1961).

Table 1. Bedding plants susceptible to sulfur dioxide injury.

Aster	Cornflower	Rose
Begonia	Cosmos	Sweet William
Canna	Geranium	Tomato
China Aster	Lettuce	Verbena
Chrysanthemum	Marigold	Viola
Coleus	Morning Glory	Zinnia

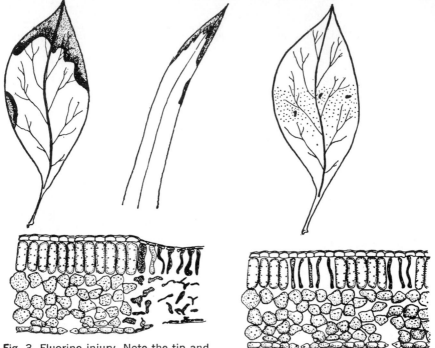

Fig. 3. Fluorine injury. Note the tip and edge necrosis on both the dicotyledon leaf and the monocotyledon (grass-type) leaf with sharp line of demarcation. Section shows severe collapse and shrinking of internal structure.

Fig. 4. Ozone injury. Note flecking or stippled effect on leaf. On sectioning, only the palisade layer is affected.

OZONE

First discovered as a cause of trouble in 1956 in California, and now a major problem for the Connecticut Valley shade-grown tobacco producers, it has been claimed that, "In New Jersey, ozone is our most important single phytotoxic air pollutant, affecting, as it does, many plant species within our state" (Daines, *et al.,* 1960).

SOURCES

While there are sizeable quantities of ozone in the higher atmosphere that may occasionally be brought to the surface of the earth during violent weather disturbances, such as hurricanes and thunderstorms, the main source of this pollutant is photochemical reactions in polluted atmospheres. Oxides of nitrogen emitted into the air by any kind of combustion occurring at high temperatures (e.g., boilers, incinerators, automobile carburetors) react, in the presence of sunlight, with oxygen, to produce ozone, O_3, an extremely active chemical substance. If hydrocarbons are also present, ozone tends to accumulate to higher levels than it would otherwise.

Since motor vehicles are major sources of both hydrocarbons and nitrogen oxides, we would expect relatively high levels of ozone to build up daily in sunny climates in metropolitan areas with high traffic density—and such is the case (California Bureau of Air Sanitation, 1966). Although it is difficult to make specific measurements of ozone concentration with currently available instrumentation, it has been found that naturally occurring levels range from zero up to about 0.50 ppm. Sensitive tobacco varieties may be injured by one-tenth this level for eight hours (Heggestad, 1969). Plant injury from ozone has been reported from most of the states along the eastern and western sea coasts, Utah, Wisconsin, and from most of the larger metropolitan areas of the country (Taylor, 1968).

SYMPTOMS

The most common type of symptom resulting from exposure to ozone consists of tiny, discrete, usually light-colored spots, flecks, or stipples over part or most of the upper surfaces of the affected leaves of broad-leaved plants, which are caused by

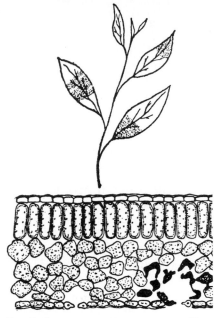

Fig. 5. Smog-type injury. Note position effect with age of leaf. On sectioning, initial collapse is in the region of a stomate.

the collapse of the upper palisade cells just under the upper epidermis of the leaf. (The ordinary florist's first impression might be that a sudden and massive invasion of red spiders had attacked his plants—but he would be unable to find any mites upon close examination of the leaves.) In plants without an upper palisade layer, the spots may go completely through the leaf and be visible on both surfaces. In grape, the stippled spots are pigmented and dark brown in color rather than the lighter colors typical of most other plants. In some other plant species, a more general necrotic bleaching of the upper surface of the leaf appears (Heggestad, 1968). Leaf age may affect the severity of symptom expression in many plants, with the more mature leaves being more susceptible than very young leaf tissue.

Ozone injury to onions causes a tip burn of leaves which may gradually increase in size and extent. In this plant, however, there are resistant varieties in which the stomata close quickly after the pollutant contacts the guard cells. This prevents further entry of the ozone into the leaf and offers considerable protection. It has now been ascertained that this resistance mechanism is controlled by a single dominant gene pair, so with this crop, it should be relatively easy to develop ozone-resistant varieties by plant breeding (Engle and Gableman, 1966).

Similarly, tobacco breeders have been able to produce ozone-resistant varieties of cigar-wrapper tobacco which can continue to be grown profitably in the Connecticut Valley, where this crop has long been of great commercial importance, even in the presence of ozone concentrations that would be disastrous to most of the older cultivated varieties. It appears, in fact, that the plant breeder may possess one of the important keys of the future to practical control of ozone injury to these and many of our other cultivated crops, including the different kinds of bedding plants susceptible to injury by this pollutant (Gableman, 1970).

Even though necrotic symptoms might not be apparent, long-continued exposure of plants to sublethal concentrations of ozone may result in reduced growth rates and the development of chlorotic symptoms indistinguishable from those typical of old age or iron, manganese or nitrogen deficiency. Premature defoliation and abscission of blooms and young fruits of crops such as tomato, pepper and citrus may also occur (Taylor, 1968).

SYNERGISM BETWEEN OZONE AND SULFUR DIOXIDE

Single air-pollutant gases are rarely present around plants in a natural growing situation, as would be true in controlled experiments. Does the presence of mixtures of air pollutants cause different plant responses than the presence of individual toxicants?

At one time, researchers had evidence which they interpreted as showing an actual interference between materials. Sulfur dioxide was thought to interfere with the damaging effects of other air pollutants, such as the mixtures of oxidants present in Los Angeles air and the reaction products of ozone and gasoline. However, more recent work has shown quite clearly that at very low concentrations, sulfur dioxide and ozone have synergistic effects, i.e., cause plant damage at levels which would not be damaging if the gases were present singly (Menser and Heggestad, 1966). Tobacco varieties, which normally require exposures of about eight hours at 0.1 ppm of ozone alone to cause symptoms, were injured and showed typical ozone-injury symptoms after two hours exposure to 0.03 ppm of ozone, if sulfur dioxide was also present simultaneously at about 0.25 ppm. Such findings only serve to point out some of the new subtle and potential dangers we face as we continue to add new gaseous components to our atmosphere.

Table 2. Bedding plants susceptible to ozone injury.

Sensitive	Intermediate Sensitivity
Begonia sp.	Abutilon
Chrysanthemum	Carnation
Fuchsia	Coleus
Geranium	Impatiens
Onion	Lettuce
Petunia	Mimosa pudica—Sensitive Plant
Tomato	Verbena

FLUORIDES

Although fluorides are high on the list of important pollutants in relation to injury to *all* crops, it appears that few of the commonly grown bedding plants are highly sensitive to this product. Fluorides are highly toxic at exceedingly low levels of concentration for the plants they do affect, however. For example, gladiolus may be adversely affected by exposure to concentrations as low as 0.1 ppb (parts per billion) for five weeks. This is because plants act as accumulators or biological concentrators of these sub-

Tomato test plants showing typical ethylene-injury symptoms. Left, untreated control plant; center, plant exposed to 1-2 ppm ethylene for 24 hours; right, plant exposed to 1-2 ppm ethylene for 1 week. A few tomato test plants in active growth should be maintained at all times by a grower who suspects that he might be experiencing ethylene problems. Then, if the plants begin to show these epinastic symptoms, he will be aware of his problem, and may be able to correct it before it causes trouble to his other less-sensitive plants.

stances, and are able to accumulate high levels in the upper tips and outer margins of the leaves. However, since they are not of any particular concern to bedding-plant producers, they will not be discussed further here.

PAN—Peroxyacetyl Nitrate

During the mid-1940's, another type of plant injury began to be indentified in southern California as being associated with "smog" (Middleton, et al., 1950). In this case, the injury consisted of silvering, glazing, bronzing, and sometimes death of the lower leaf surfaces of sensitive plants. More recently, this type of injury has been ascribed to "oxidants." Haagen-Smith, et al. (1952) was later able to show that these symptoms could be produced artificially by exposing plants to the reaction products resulting from a mixture of ozone and vapors of certain unsaturated hydrocarbons, or by the photochemical reaction of nitrogen dioxide and hydrocarbons. Stephens, et al. (1961) later showed that these "silver-leaf" symptoms were due to peroxyacetyl nitrate (PAN) present in the air at very low concentrations. PAN concentrations of 20 to 30 ppb are common at Riverside, California, with peaks of 54 to 58 ppb having been reported there, and in Salt Lake City. Peaks as high as 210 ppb have been reported from Los Angeles, California (Taylor, 1969).

SOURCES

This material is produced in the atmosphere as a secondary product from air-pollutant substances already present, and results from a photochemical reaction between nitrogen dioxide and simple olefins. The concentration of this and other closely related compounds has a diurnal fluctuation, essentially disappearing during the hours of darkness, but building up to, and remaining at, maximum levels from shortly after sunrise until sunset (Jaffe, 1967). The most serious and widespread plant injury has been reported from around Los Angeles, California, even though occasional damage has been reported from at least 18 other states and several foreign countries (Middleton and Haagen-Smith, 1961; Taylor, 1969).

3 IND. WHITE
CONTROL
5 WEEKS UNDER S.D

3 IND. WHITE
C₂H₄ ATM
5 WEEKS UNDER SD

Typical ethylene-injury symptoms on chrysanthemum. Left, control plant given 5 weeks of short-day treatment in an ethylene-free atmosphere. Right, plant of same age given same amount of short-day treatment in an atmosphere containing 1-2 ppm ethylene. Note the closely-spaced leaves, failure to initiate a flower bud, and loss of apical dominance, as indicated by the breaking into growth of the axillary side shoots. Similar symptoms developed on plants grown in tightly constructed plastic houses heated by gas-fired unit heaters lacking any special provision for air intake to supply the needs of the combustion.

SYMPTOMS

Symptoms usually appear first on the lower surfaces of young, recently expanded leaves as a glazing or bronzing. At higher concentrations and longer exposures, more severe symptoms occur—complete collapse of transverse bands of tissue across individual leaves. Leaf susceptibility is closely correlated with age and maturity of the cells. As a leaf expands, it matures first near the apex and finally near the base. For this reason, then, it is common to find bands of collapsed tissue near the tip of the upper leaves injured on the plant, in the middle of leaves further down, and near the base of the lower leaves affected, particularly if the plant had been subjected to a single exposure to the pollutant. This type injury is typical in the case of petunia and tobacco. Repeated exposures, of course, would affect different areas of tissue each day and would eventually result in overall injury to leaves extending over much of the stem of the plant (Taylor, 1969).

Since the injured tissue of the leaf usually stops expanding, a pinched or distorted leaf margin may result as the rest of the uninjured leaf tissue continues to expand. The glazing or silvering symptom has been found (Borbrov, 1965) due to drying and desiccation of cells just under the epidermis and the separation of the two cellular layers. Cellular death and injury began first in cells adjacent to the substomatal cavity.

Repeated exposure of plants to PAN and other forms of oxidant air pollution often results in accelerated senescence of leaf tissue, chlorosis, leaf abscission, etc. It has been suggested (Rich, 1964) that these effects may be caused by endogenous ethylene production within the plant, triggered by continuous or successive exposures to low concentrations of oxidants in the atmosphere.

RELATION BETWEEN LIGHT AND PAN INJURY

High light intensity greatly increases the severity of plant injury from PAN, and minimum exposures to light before, during and after exposure of the plants to the toxicant are necessary for the development of visible symptoms (Dugger, et al., 1963; Taylor, et al., 1961; Taylor, 1969). Early in the morning, it was necessary for the plants to receive about three hours of light before they became susceptible to injury. If as little as a 15-minute-long period of darkness was given during the middle of the day preceding exposure of the plants to PAN, a full hour of sunlight was required to restore sensitivity. Likewise, almost three hours of light following exposure of plants was necessary to secure symptom development.

Recent work by Dugger and Ting (1968) has shown a good correlation between a decreased sulfhydryl content in plants brought about by irradiation with far-red light and increased resistance to injury by PAN. Perhaps it may be possible in the future to protect some of our greenhouse plants by simply flicking on a source of far-red irradiation during smog periods of high PAN concentrations.

Table 3. Bedding plants susceptible to PAN injury.

Sensitive		Resistant		
Aster	Petunia	Azalea	Touch-Me-Not	Onion
African Violet	Tomato	Begonia	Coleus	Ivy
Fuchsia	Sweet Basil	Chrysanthemum	Cabbage	Calendula
Impatiens	Celery	Periwinkle	Cauliflower	

Another look at typical symptoms of ethylene injury to Indianapolis chrysanthemum. Plant at right grown in ethylene-free atmosphere. Left, plant given about 8 weeks of short-day treatment in an atmosphere containing 1-2 ppm ethylene. Note the closely spaced leaves; decreased amount of leaf blade expansion, senescence; yellowing and browning of older, lower leaves on plant; and failure of plant to initiate any flower bud.

Two plants of #3 Indianapolis White chrysanthemums that have received 10 weeks of short-day treatment. Plant on the left, which is in full bloom, was grown normally in an ethylene-free atmosphere. Plant on the right was grown in a tightly constructed plastic greenhouse covered with rigid PVC, and the house was heated with an open-flame propane burner. This plant is still completely vegetative, has a thick, heavy stem with closely spaced leaves, and most of the vegetative side shoots (in the axils of each leaf) have started into growth (another symptom typical of ethylene-damaged plants).

ETHYLENE

Forty or 50 years ago, ethylene injury was common to greenhouse plants due to leaks in gas mains carrying the manufactured or "illuminating gas" in use at that time, which normally contained two to eight percent ethylene. However, with the gradual replacement of manufactured gas by natural gas, which has a much lower level of ethylene (usually none), many plants known to be especially sensitive to ethylene are not damaged by prolonged exposures to gas mixtures containing as much as one or two percent natural gas (Gustafson, 1944). Hasek, *et al.* (1969) have recently published an excellent and comprehensive review of the effects of ethylene on flower crops.

SOURCES OF ETHYLENE

The principal sources of ethylene gas now are (a) a product of combustion, particularly exhaust fumes from motor vehicles, and from dirty or improperly adjusted greenhouse heating devices; (b) losses from industrial plants, such as polyethylene-manufacturing establishments (Hall, *et al.*, 1957); and (c) the natural by-products of plant respiration, particularly those from diseased or damaged plant tissue. Ethylene from the latter source is particularly important as a cause of plant injury in flower-storage rooms and refrigerators.

SYMPTOMS

Probably no other air pollutant causes as great a variety of symptom expression as does ethylene gas. In some cases, growth-regulator types of injury occur, with the appearance of epinasty (bending down of petioles even though the plant is turgid) of foliage (Crocker and Zimmerman, 1932; Denny and Miller, 1935). In other cases, ethylene causes premature senescence, which shows up as yellowing and dropping of lower foliage, early ripening and dropping of florets in snapdragons, calceolarias, larkspur (Fischer, 1950) and roses (Shull, 1930), or "going to sleep" in carnation flowers (Crocker and Knight, 1908). Orchid flowers are very sensitive indicators of ethylene, with "dry-sepal" injury showing up on Cattleya after exposure to concentrations as low as 0.1 ppm for eight hours (Davidson, 1949).

Plant stems and roots have been reported in other cases as losing their normal orientation to gravity. Cotton plants growing downwind from a polyethylene plant in Texas in fields where ethylene levels varied from 0.04 to 3.0 ppm lost apical dominance and became prostrate and vine-like in growth (Hall, et al., 1957). Plant roots have also lost their sense of direction and have actually grown up out of the ground instead of in the normal downward direction (Michner, 1938).

Gas-fired unit heaters, used for heating tightly constructed plastic houses, should have both air-exhaust pipes to vent out the exhaust fumes from the burner and air-intake pipes to bring in fresh, outside air to support the combustion of the fuel being burned. Burners without air intake can, in severely cold weather, when a great deal of fuel is being burned to maintain house temperatures, exhaust the oxygen content of the air in the greenhouse to the point that incomplete combustion occurs, resulting in the release of ethylene and other damaging air pollutants inside the house that cause plant injury.

Ethylene, arising from incomplete fuel combustion in gas-fired unit heaters in tightly constructed plastic houses, has caused the production of thickened stems with short internodes and prolific development of side branches on carnations and chrysanthemums (Holley, 1960; Rogers, *et al.*, 1969). In addition, the latter workers were able to show that ethylene concentrations of one to two ppm in the air prevented or delayed flower-bud initiation in short-day plants, such as chrysanthemums and poinsettias, even though the plants were being subjected to flower-inducing day-length treatments. Similar results have also been reported as being true for cocklebur, the classic "guinea-pig" plant for photoperiodic studies (Abeles, 1967). Thus, it would appear that this phenomenon could be true for short-day plants in general.

One of the best ways for bedding-plant producers to monitor their greenhouses for the possible presence of ethylene gas is to grow a few indicator plants along with their crops. Tomatoes, exposed to one ppm ethylene for three hours, show epinasty, and African marigolds and sunflowers are even more sensitive, responding to 0.005 ppm ethylene. However, since tomato plants are usually easier to grow on a year-round basis, they are probably the most logical and reliable indicator plant to use to warn flower growers of the presence of possibly harmful ethylene levels in their various growing areas.

Table 4. Plants affected by ethylene.

Sensitive	Intermediate	Resistant
Marigold	Azalea	Cabbage
Cattleya Orchid	Gardenia	Onion
Philodendron sp.		
Rose		
Tomato		
Sweet Potato		

EFFECTS OF ENVIRONMENT ON TOXICITY BY AIR POLLUTANTS

We have already seen that age and succulence of leaf tissue are often important factors in determining relative susceptibility of different parts of plants, and that different pollutants act differently. Ozone, for example, affects the more mature tissue, while PAN causes more damage on the younger leaves.

In addition to age of tissue, the environmental conditions under which the plants are grown are often of great importance in determining the extent and seriousness of damage. Here again, we see variations from plant to plant and from pollutant to pollutant but, in general, it appears that those environmental conditions which favor the development of the most prolific and healthy plant growth result in the most severe air-pollution injury. This is a particularly difficult problem because if we are to attempt to reduce damage from air pollutants by controlling the growing environment around the plants, it means that we will have to grow the plants under less than ideal conditions and be satisfied with slow, poor-quality plant growth in order to secure *any* growth. For the practicing florist, this is not a very satisfactory alternative.

Temperature has important effects on the response of plants to the photochemical oxidants, ozone and PAN-type substances. It has been shown that plants such as spinach, romaine lettuce and endive may be as much as eight times more resistant to injury if, before exposure, they are given a week at 55° following an earlier growth period at 75° (Kendrick, *et al.,* 1956). These authors suggest growing the more susceptible plants during the cool parts of the growing season and restricting the kinds of plants being grown during the warm months to those known to have a high degree of resistance—particularly in outdoor growing areas such as California, where many plants can be grown on a year-round basis.

Relative-humidity levels can also be of importance. It has been shown, for example, that tobacco plants may be more severely injured in the humid growing areas of the East than in the more arid growing areas of the West by similar levels of air pollutants (Heggestad, *et al.,* 1963; Taylor, 1968).

Experiments with light intensity have yielded conflicting results. Dugger, *et al.* (1963) found that bean plants grown under 900 foot-candles of light were more sensitive to injury from ozone than similar plants grown under 2,200 foot-candles. Menser, *et al.* (1963) and Darley and Middleton (1966), on the other hand, found that a dark period prior to fumigation reduced the injury on tobacco.

Increased carbon dioxide levels have reduced ozone injury to tobacco, but not to bean (Heck and Dunning, 1967). The explanation proposed was that the elevated carbon dioxide levels caused a partial closing of the stomata in the leaf which reduced entry of the pollutant. If this is actually true, this could be another potential benefit from carbon dioxide enrichment of greenhouse atmospheres by florists.

Today, many florists are moving away from soil mixtures for growing their plants and are using lightweight artificial mixes more and more. These result in excellent plant growth with a minimum of problems, but the improved plant growth may become a partial liability in smoggy growing areas. Heck and Dunning (1967) found that bean plants grown in a mix consisting of either peat-perlite or vermiculite were more severely damaged by ozone than were plants of the same age grown in a soil mixture.

PLANT PROTECTION AGAINST AIR POLLUTION

Research has suggested many measures that might be taken at specific times to protect individual kinds of plants from particular air-pollutant substances. Due to the great diversity of toxicants and the great variability in the kinds of plants florists grow, however, there is not likely to be any one kind of treatment that will give perfect control of all problems for all kinds of plants, except complete eradication of air pollutants from our plant-growing atmospheres. Government-instituted and enforced air-quality standards are now beginning to appear in more and more areas. This represents a progressive step, but it is not likely that our overall air-pollution problems will show much improvement within the next couple of decades. In fact, the problems will more likely be worse before they are better. Therefore, we need to see what kinds of things can be done to afford interim protection.

In a few cases, plant growers may have some choice of the kinds of plants they could grow in a particular growing situation. Generally, we have only one or two specific air-pollutant problems to contend with at any given spot, so it may be possible to simply select plants resistant to our local problem and no longer attempt to grow susceptible items. Or, as the tobacco growers in the Connecticut Valley have been able to do, it may be possible to replace our currently susceptible varieties with new ones developed specifically with resistance to air pollutants as one of their important characteristics.

Filtration of all incoming air into our plant-growing greenhouse to remove toxic gases is possible, and has long been practiced by research scientists studying air-pollution problems in highly polluted atmospheres (Darley and Middleton, 1961). Such a system costs money, of course, and adds to production costs, but in the more severe situations, it may be the only alternative available if a grower is to continue in business. Florists have used air-filtration units, such as the Dorex air filter, in their refrigerators and flower-storage rooms for years to absorb harmful levels of ethylene and prevent injury to their cut flowers.

Various kinds of chemicals that can be applied to plants which either absorb or destroy air-pollutant chemicals have been shown able to afford a degree of protection, but generally, the protection is minimal and usually not economically feasible as a practical control measure. Numerous kinds of anti-oxidants, anti-ozonants, and fungicidal materials have been shown to have effectiveness against the oxidant-type air pollutants. Of these materials, the dithiocarbamate fungicides, such as zineb, have probably shown about as great effectiveness as any other materials and, since this is a chemical already frequently used around greenhouses, might be considered for this additional new purpose. If it is to be used successfully, however, it must be applied evenly to the stomate-bearing surfaces of the leaves, and it must be replenished periodically to provide continuous protection. Even so, if the concentration of ozone or PAN becomes too great, the protection will fail and plant injury will still occur. The undesirable appearance of the residues is also a very practical disadvantage, as well.

Application of chemical growth retardants such as B-Nine and Quel has also recently been shown by Marc Cathey to render treated plants much more resistant than normal to air-pollution injury. Since these chemicals also make most of our bedding plants more drought-resistant and improve their general appearance at the same time, bedding-plant producers should be planning to include treatment with such materials as a routine part of their culture in the future.

Bibliography

A complete bibliography on which the above story is based, may be found in the Proceedings for the Third National Bedding Plant Conference, 1970, pp. 35-38. If anyone is interested in specific material, please contact Dr. Marlin Rogers, Department of Horticulture, University of Missouri, Columbia, Missouri.

A good example of a package steam generator—truck-mounted. This is a 100 hp. high pressure Cyclotherm generator. The framework above it supports a canvas cover used to protect the steamer when not in use. This unit is designed to work with a steam rake (see page 105). The boiler is moved right to the job. The winch used to draw the rake is mounted below the boiler. This unit was designed by Jerry Knouse, grower, Stuart, Fla.

9. SOIL STERILIZING—STEAM

Soil sterilizing (more correctly, *"pasteurizing"*) is done both with steam and with various chemicals. Since the great majority of sterilizing by commercial flower growers is done with steam, we will cover that first.

WHY STEAM?

To put it simply, it's vastly less work than the old-fashioned alternative, changing soil. Very few growers still actually wheel their soil out and in annually (hard to see why anyone should). Steaming of soils annually is now common practice; the purpose of this story is to point out the most efficient and easiest ways to do the job.

What does steaming accomplish? Properly done, it should kill weeds practically 100%, kill all soil-borne insects (on raised benches), and in general all of the bacteria and fungi and virus organisms that are harmful to commercial crops. In addition, it makes heavy soils more granular, greatly improving drainage and aeration. This granulation often brings the greatest growth improvement of all!

SOURCES OF STEAM

There is so much equipment available today that will provide steam for greenhouse sterilizing that lack of steam-generating equipment is no longer the problem that it was. Suggestions:

1. *Use Existing Boilers.* Many places have steam boilers already installed and in use for heating. A boiler capable of heating a range of glass is always

Here's a package steam generator that serves both for heating and soil sterilizing. It's at Jacobson Greenhouses, Spokane, Washington. Mr. Jacobson, Sr. is on the left; son Don on the right. It's a York-Shipley boiler, burns #6 oil or gas, 200 hp. Cost around $12,000 (burner and boiler).

adequate for sterilizing. Low-pressure boilers are entirely adequate—just be sure the mains are amply large all the way to the bench being steamed.

Some ranges have hot-water boilers. In nearly all cases, such boilers can be easily converted into steam generators. Best procedure is to contact the manufacturer of the boiler, to be sure. Among boilers that *cannot* be converted: Lord & Burnham Heavy-Duty hot water boilers W36, W30, W24, and W18, also Kroeschell hot water boilers of the old type. Reason: these boilers are so designed that there is not enough room in the top of the boiler to collect and separate the steam from hot water without running the water level dangerously low.

Conversion of most hot-water boilers to steam consists of valving off the flow and return lines, installing a water bottle with tri-cocks and gauge glass, and a safety valve set to blow steam at 15 lbs. Also, automatic water feed, and low-water alarm are usually installed. For full details see your local boiler dealer.

2. *Rough Steam Generators* (Rough, pronounced *"row"*). Oil-fired, com-

The Rough Bros. steam generator—about 15 hp capable of steaming 250 sq. ft. of bench area in 2-3 hours. Cost—$2,300.00 to $2,500.00. Source: Geo. J. Ball, Inc.

pletely portable, capable of generating at 8 psi-425,000 btu per hour output (maximum pressure 15 lbs.). They burn #1 fuel oil. Outlet size on the Rough Steamer is 1¼ inches. Cost is in the $2,300-$2,500 bracket for these units. Many have been bought by greenhouse operators, mainly for smaller places. In general, they are capable of steaming 250 to 300 sq. ft. of raised bench area at a time—within about 2 hours. They are low-priced, rugged, and practical. Main limitation is capacity.

Interesting fact: 2 of these steamers combined will yield 30 hp capacity—at not much over half the cost of a 30 hp package steamer. They would be more cumbersome, used in this way, than the package steamer.

3. *Package Steamers.* The grower who wants more steam-generating capacity than the above units will produce will soon be talking either package steamers—or else bricked-in boilers. In most cases, such equipment will be bought for the dual purpose of heating the greenhouses and sterilizing soils. Probably the minimum size we are talking about here would be a 25 hp boiler which would be capable of steaming a 500 sq. ft. bench in 2 or 3 hours.

An increasing number of package steamers are going into greenhouses both for steaming and for general heating (even up to 300-400 hp). All costs considered, they tend to be cheaper. A big advantage, especially in the larger sizes, is that the package-steamer deal includes both boiler and burner—designed by the factory to work properly *together*. The buyer doesn't have to work the "bugs" out of the job after it's installed. By the way, there's much less installation involved, too.

The package steamers are generally rated at their full capacity—no overload factor as is usually figured in a regular boiler. Bricked-in permanent boilers have been considered a little more rugged, simple, easier to keep clean. Generally they are "fire tube" while the package steamers are "water tube." The latter work on much less volume of water. However, growers who have the package steamers are generally quite satisfied with them.

Among the more generally used makes are:

Lord & Burnham. Source: Lord & Burnham, Irvington, New York.

Cleaver-Brooks. Source: Fred W. Kramer & Associates, 5314 W. Harrison, Chicago, Illinois.

York. Source: York-Shipley Inc., York, Pennsylvania.

Sellers. Source: Sellers Engineering Company, 4874 N. Clark Street, Chicago, Illinois 60640.

To get a rough idea of cost on package steamers, here are f.o.b. factory prices on one of the popular makes (low pressure). This price includes boiler and oil burner all put together ready to hook up and turn on, but remember this is only a rough figure. Prices can vary $2,000 to $3,000 because of the many combinations of pressures, fuels, and electrical characteristics. Therefore, in quoting prices, manufacturers will want to know what particular unit is involved and the auxiliary equipment required.

30 hp costs $ 5,420, burns #3 oil or gas in areas where available.

50 hp costs $ 6,500, burns #3 oil or gas in areas where available.
100 hp costs $ 9,200, burns #3 oil or gas in areas where available.
250 hp costs $17,300, burns #3 oil or gas in areas where available.
500 hp costs $27,500, burns #6 oil or gas in areas where available.

4. *The bricked-in, permanent-type boilers.* The comparisons in the preceding paragraphs outline their strong points and weaknesses. Sources:

Lord & Burnham Company, Irvington, New York.

Kewanee Boiler Company, Kewanee, Illinois.

HIGH PRESSURE—OR LOW?

A few years ago, it was generally believed that 75 or 100 lbs. of steam pressure was needed to do a real job of steaming. Gradually, experience has shown that a large enough boiler with adequate main sizes can do the job just as well for practical purposes with 10 or 12 lbs. pressure—or even with 5.

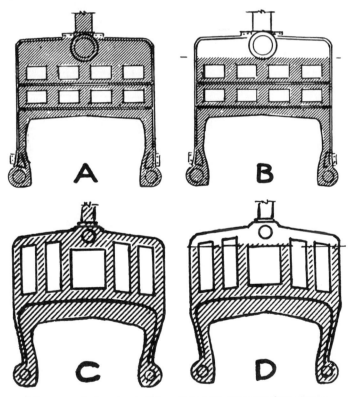

Why some hot-water boilers cannot be converted to steam.
A—Shows a section of an L & B Master boiler filled with water for hot-water heat.
B—The same section with the water line lowered to leave a steam dome for steam sterilization of soil.
C—Section of a boiler designed only for hot water, such as the L & B Heavy Duty.
D—It cannot be used for steam sterilization because when the water line is lowered the tops of the flue ways are exposed to the direct heat of the fire without water protection.

The important fact to remember is that, as the steam enters the bench, it immediately drops down to perhaps 1 lb. per square inch anyway. Much more than that would promptly blow the cover off! The only advantage of high-pressure steam is that smaller mains can be used.

Main sizes are critically important. Where low pressure (less than 15 lbs. per square inch by definition) is used, the main should be no smaller than 2 inches inside diameter anywhere between boiler and bench where a 500-sq.-ft. bench is being steamed at once. If 2 beds are to done simultaneously, a 2½ or 3-inch main would be needed. In most cases, mains for carrying steam to the heating system are already there—and are amply large. Main problem is to get steam from the mains to the benches. Rubber hose for this purpose can be had in any of these sizes—details later.

HOW BIG A BOILER?

For various reasons, growers split up areas to be steamed small enough so they can handle each individual patch in not over 2½ to 3 hours. It simply isn't economical to keep working away all day on a bench. Growers usually figure how much area they must be able to handle in a week or a month—depending on the crop they grow, etc. A carnation grower generally should be able to steam his entire range in not over a month. If he had 90 benches, that would be 3 benches a day.

The general rule is that, for each horsepower of boiler capacity, 20 sq. ft. of bench area can be steamed at once. A 30 hp boiler would handle 600 sq. ft. at once. If a carnation grower had 90 benches, each not over 600 sq. ft., a 30 hp boiler would do the job in 30 days—3 benches a day.

GETTING THE STEAM TO THE BENCH

There should be very little pipe fitting and hard work in this end of the job, if the grower is properly set up for it.

Let's take a house 300 x 30 ft.—with a center walk and six 150-foot benches going each way from the center. Normally, there will be a steam main overhead going down the center walk—the heating main. First step is to weld a 2-inch nipple into this main about in the center of the house. Now, it will be about 18 to 20 feet from the nipple to the end of the farthest bench in the house—and less to the center benches. To conduct the steam from the nipple to the ends of the benches, a steam hose should be purchased —probably 25 feet long to be on the safe side, and a full 2 inches inside diameter—including couplings. Cost—around $3.60 per foot, plus $6.00 for full-flow couplings. Such a hose can be obtained from the Abbott Rubber Co., 311 N. Des Plaines St., Chicago, Illinois. The hose we use is a 2-inch wire-braid steam hose. It is designed to stand up to 25 lbs. pressure (not high pressure), and temperatures up to 250° F.

The big point: steam can be delivered to the end of any of the 6 benches in the house without any pipe fitting once the steam hose is fastened to the nipple.

Shows the collapsible canvas hose used to carry steam down the bench and distribute it. Steam escapes through the sidewalls of the hose. Cost about 52¢ per foot. Lightweight, easy to handle. Will rot after a year or so, especially if not dried between uses. Source: Jednak Floral, Box 1917, Columbus, Ohio 43216. In the photo: Lou Kovarik of Geo. J. Ball, Inc.

How we tie the canvas hose over the 2-inch-inside-diameter rubber hose.

Thin plastic covers are available at a lower cost. Will not last as long as the heavier grade and must be handled more carefully.

A little different approach to holding the covers down for sterilizing—simply a heavy iron chain laid down just inside the bench boards. Works out very well.

The rest of the problem is to find a conductor that will carry the steam on down the bench—with holes or pores of some kind that will release it a little at a time as it travels down the bench. Many growers use boiler flues with holes drilled in them. Others have used ordinary gutter-type down-spouting —again with holes. We find the thin-wall, collapsible, 5-inch canvas hose by far the best here. It is porous enough so that steam just leaks out through the walls of the hose very evenly and nicely down the bench. Actually we get better, more-even distribution of the steam with this hose than with down-spouting. Best of all, it is easy to handle. A 150-foot roll of it can be carried under one arm—and can be unrolled down the bench by one man in a minute or two. So much less work than handling big, clumsy tubes.

Source: Jednak Floral, Box 1917, Columbus, Ohio 43216.

We find that if the hose is wet before use, the steam will escape more rapidly and evenly than if it is dry. Also, after each use, we hang the hose out over some support wires or whatever is handy to dry it out.

"Coupling" the porous canvas hose to the steam hose is no trick at all. Just stick the steam hose into the end of the porous canvas hose—in a foot or so. Then run a couple of loops of binder twine or wire tight around the "joint." The far end of the porous canvas hose is shut by simply tying it up with heavy cord—just like the end of a sausage.

COVERS

There are various sterilizing covers available from greenhouse suppliers from 3 mil to 8 mil in thickness. The 8 mil sterilizing cover, 6 feet by 100 feet costs about $35. The heavier covers seem to last longer and handle more easily. We use the heavier cover (8 mil) with very good results. For a source of supply, try Jednak Floral, Box 1917, Columbus, Ohio 43216.

PREPARING THE SOIL

First, the humus is added—usually peat moss. More and more growers are getting away from manures. We have entirely because of the "after-steaming" troubles we ran into. If the soil is very dry, we give it a light watering. Quite-dry soil will heat up slowly because the heat will not distribute well through the soil. Incidentally, if soil is wetter than normal (wetter than normal for planting), it will also heat up slowly. Reason here: it takes a lot of heat to warm up all that water.

Fundamentally, the application of heat to a soil raises the temperature of the moisture in that soil. This moisture in turn conducts the heat to everything that it contacts. However, if a soil is saturated with water, a tremendous amount of heat is required to heat the excess water, and consequently, the temperature rise is slow. Conversely, if a soil is extremely dry, heat is not conducted through the soil mass because the large amount of dead-air space acts as an excellent insulator.

If weeds are a serious problem, it's a good idea to keep the bed moist for a week or so prior to steaming. This will soften or sprout the weed seeds, making them much easier to kill during steaming.

The bench is next rototilled or plowed, being sure to loosen the soil clear down to the bottom board. Most growers turn the soil away from the sideboard to be sure the soil caked against the side is removed and loosened. Also, this exposes the sideboard, insuring that it will get steamed. All lumps must be broken up; steam won't penetrate to the center of large lumps.

The porous canvas hose is next unrolled down the center of the bench on

The bench being steamed. Cover can be held down with pipe laid just inside the bench board as shown at left. If outside of sideboard is smooth, the plastic sheet will sort of seal itself against the wood or cement— without any pipe (see right side of bed farther down). "C" clamps and 1 x 2 used to fasten cover up at this end.

98

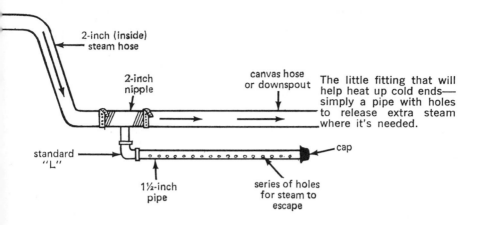

2-inch (inside) steam hose

2-inch nipple

canvas hose or downspout

The little fitting that will help heat up cold ends— simply a pipe with holes to release extra steam where it's needed.

standard "L"

cap

1½-inch pipe

series of holes for steam to escape

top of the soil—not buried! The bench is covered, and away we go. It should take less than half an hour to prepare a bed for steaming, once it is plowed.

Incidentally, we make a practice of adding 4 lbs. of 40% superphosphate per 100 sq. ft. to all beds before steaming once a year.

TRICKS IN FASTENING COVERS

The only other problem is fastening the plastic covers down so the steam won't blow them off. Several methods are commonly used:

1. Quite often, it is possible just to drape the covers over the beds and down the sideboards, with no mechanical fastener. As steam is turned into the bed, a good bit of moisture condenses on the inside of the cold cover. This will run down toward the edges. Very quickly, it will form a sort of seal between the cover and the sideboard of the bench. It's the same idea as when a wet handkerchief is smoothed out against a window—it just sticks! Wherever this will work, it is by far the easiest and best. Limitations: some benches have side supports fastened to the outside of the bench sideboard; in other cases, the outside of the board is just too rough or uneven to hold the plastic. Incidentally, only the thinner (3 mil or less) plastics will adhere in this way. The other problem is that once in a long while, particularly if a little too much steam gets turned into such a bench, these covers will blow off. Steam escapes to the sides, and if there is a crop on the next bench, it will be damaged.

2. If the above won't work, the next easiest and most practical method is to weight the plastic down with a pipe just inside the sideboard. We usually turn the soil away from the sideboard entirely before plowing the bed—to be sure there is no soil caked against the sideboard. This soil is well pulverized, then pushed back against the sideboard—enough so that the top inch or two of the *inside* of the sideboard is still exposed. The cover is spread across the bench, so that it overlaps a foot or so on either side. Then, pieces of 1-inch or ¾-inch pipe are laid on top of the cover just inside of the sideboard. True, there's an inch or two of the inside of the sideboard

that doesn't get steamed, except what steam leaks up through. From a practical point of view, this doesn't seem to matter. The strip could be painted with a formaldehyde solution.

This method is fast, simple, and very generally used. Some growers use heavy link chain in place of pipes with good results. See photo page 98.

3. Two other alternatives, neither too good. First, the bench can be prepared as described above. Instead of laying a strip of pipe on top of the cover just inside the sideboard, a piece of 1 x 2 is set in. Another strip of 1 x 2 is held in place just opposite the first piece—on the outside of the sideboard flush with the top of the board. The two are held together with a common hardware store "C" clamp. It works fine—except that it takes a good bit of time to fasten a bed down. Also, there is still that 2-inch strip inside the sideboard that doesn't get steamed. We often use these hardware clamps around ends and other hard-to-fasten places—holding the rest of the cover down with just pieces of pipe.

The other alternative is to nail the cover down to the outside of the sideboard with strips of lath or 1 x 2. Trouble: it takes a lot of time, and worst of all, the nail holes will start tears in the plastic.

Incidentally, where a row of purlin posts falls in the center of a bench, 2 strips of plastic can be laid down—one on either side of the row of posts. The 2 strips can be joined with clothespins, one snugly on either side of each purlin post.

Note, also (page 99) the sketch of the gadget to heat up cold ends. Sometimes its seems that the first 5 feet are hard to get warm—the cover won't rise. The little gadget in the sketch releases extra steam at this point to help the job along.

Speaking of cold ends, it's important, before hooking up a bench to the steam line, to run the cold water out of the mains. If this isn't done, several gallons of water will be dumped onto the soil at the inlet end. Muddy, wet soil probably won't heat up enough to get sterilized.

WHEN TO STEAM, HOW OFTEN, HOW LONG?

The general practice among miscellaneous growers is to steam all benches once a year—most generally in the summer. It's done then partly because most growers are discarding their spring crops, getting ready for the next season. There's more help available then (schoolboys). Also, where direct-benching of seedlings and cuttings is done in midsummer, growers like to steam immediately before doing this planting. Hot weather is the hardest time to make direct planting work, and steaming eliminates surface rots.

However, there are several very good reasons for *not* steaming in the summer. Mainly, wherever "after-steaming" troubles occur, steaming should not be done in hot weather. For a variety of reasons, these build-ups of ammonia, nitrite nitrogen, etc. after steaming nearly always occur in hot weather. In such cases, it would seem much better to do the steaming during winter-spring. Then too, it's often extremely hot in the greenhouses in midsummer. It seems unfortunate to aggravate this problem by introducing raw steam!

More and more cut-flower growers steam before every crop. They find the increased growth of mums, snaps, and other crops more than pays for the cost of steaming. After-steaming troubles are kept in check by running the fertility way down as the previous crop is flowered and cut, and by using only peat or other long-lasting organic matter—no manure or compost.

How long to steam? Almost everyone agrees on the rule of heating the coolest point in the bench to 180° for 30 minutes. Why? Nematodes and most soil insects are killed instantly by exposure to 140°. Ten minutes at 140 to 160° will kill most fungi and bacteria—and weed seeds. The difference between 160° for 10 minutes and 180° for 30 minutes is a safety margin—and is generally considered a practical requirement. Virus organisms such as mum stunt seem to be controlled satisfactorily by this 180° for 30 minutes.

It is of obvious importance that soil temperature be *measured*—by an accurate thermometer. Best for this job, in our experience, is the Taylor thermometer that comes in a metal jacket. It can be rammed down into a bench of soil without fear of breaking a delicate glass instrument. Source: Taylor Instrument Company, 95 Ames Street, Rochester, New York. Ask for their 2-inch dial Bi-Therm with 8-inch stem, range 0 to 220° F. Cost: around $11.00 each. On raised benches, a few holes are drilled up from beneath for taking readings. On ground beds with sideboards, holes can be made in the sides near the ground. On flat ground beds, small holes must be made in the cover.

AFTER-STEAMING TROUBLES

Some soils, some areas, and certain seasons will make trouble in this respect. Sometimes the plants will take off in grand style, grow for 3 to 4 weeks, then quite suddenly lose their roots, wilt, sometimes even die. Often, they will recover soon enough, go on and make a crop. In other cases, the plants or seedlings will never really start to grow. Snap seedlings will be yellow, roots poor. Almost all of this sort of trouble occurs during warm weather. Almost always it happens within the first 30 days after steaming. It is generally worse in areas where soils are heavy.

Probably the most common direct cause is build-up of ammonia (not nitrate) nitrogen—both will be very evident in soil tests. Reason behind this is worth understanding:

Peat, manure, and other forms of organic matter in soils contain nitrogen. Before this nitrogen can be used by plants, it must be converted to the *nitrate* form. This is done by several types of bacteria. Ammonifying bacteria convert the organic nitrogen to ammonia. Nitrifying bacteria convert it in turn to the nitrate nitrogen that plants can use (actually, some is used by plants as ammonia).

Now, what happens when we heat soil to 180°? Unfortunately, we very often kill most of the *nitrifying bacteria*—but the ammonifying bacteria are hardier and often survive. Therefore, several weeks after steaming a bench, it is not unusual that large quantities of ammonia nitrogen should be found in the soil—often enough to burn roots. Some growers attempt to get rid of this ammonia by heavy leaching. Others cultivate deep, run the soil dry, attempting to let the ammonia "air out." Neither method is too dependable. It's a tough problem.

Why does the problem come up mainly in hot weather? That one's worth understanding, too. All soils contain organic matter (more or less!). This material is constantly decomposing. This decomposition requires bacteria and oxygen. It occurs more rapidly at higher (summer) temperatures. Therefore, during hot weather, the decomposition of organic matter is occurring at a rapid rate, and is accordingly *using up much of the available oxygen in the soil.*

This is important because the bacteria that are busy trying to convert that excess of ammonia to nitrate nitrogen *also need oxygen to do their job.* It seems to work out in practice that, in hot weather, the "decomposition team" of bacteria gets first call on the available oxygen, therefore slowing up the important work of those nitrifying bacteria just when we need them the most—to convert that excess ammonia to *nitrate* nitrogen.

There is also reason to believe that the ammonifying bacteria themselves are stimulated by high temperatures. This would, of course, mean more ammonia.

What To Do About It

Now that we understand the problem, what can be done to solve it?

1. For soil organic matter, use high-quality, long-lasting kinds of peat such as German or Canadian sphagnum peats, or other forms of organic matter that break down slowly. Sphagnum peat will not normally release enough ammonia after steaming to cause damage. It also makes for good aeration, letting the nitrifying bacteria do their work. Manure or compost should be avoided, since they break down rapidly after steaming, releasing toxic quantities of ammonia and making the soil soggy.

2. Avoid sterilizing in hot weather.

3. Don't feed the previous crop after it shows color, and leach it during the last waterings. If the nitrogen is low, there's more room for build-up after steaming without reaching the danger point.

4. Keep soils cultivated during critical periods—to encourage air to enter the lower soil.

5. Keep soils medium-dry when steaming—sterilizing wet soils encourages build-up of ammonia.

6. Addition of 4 lbs. of gypsum or 4 lbs. of 40% superphosphate per 100 sq. ft. immediately after steaming seems to help tie up some of that free ammonia (the superphosphate will, of course, add phosphorus, too). The calcium teams up with the ammonia to form a water-soluble salt that will leach out. It also encourages the nitrifying bacteria.

7. Some growers leach heavily after steaming.

Two other indirect approaches to the problem that we are considering: One is the possibility of chemical sterilizing during hot weather. Main problem: at least 2-3 weeks for complete airing-out of soil after treatment.

Even then there is an element of hazard to the new crop.

More recently, growers have been reporting good control of rot organisms on direct-benched cuttings, seedlings, etc., with Terraclor. In some cases it was worked into the soil dry before benching. Others applied it as a drench. Still other growers dipped the cuttings or seedlings in a dilute solution just before planting.

General result: much less rotting of plants after benching.

Second, the possibility of using one of the various artificial mixtures (such as peat-sand, peat-vermiculite) as a growing medium in place of our conventional soils. These artificial mixtures are often finding their way into commercial practice. Where growers learn to handle them, good results are obtained. The "after-steaming" troubles are not a problem where these mixtures are used.

STEAMING OUTDOOR AREAS

Outdoor beds for asters, mums, young carnation stock, etc. can be sterilized by various means. Actually, sterilizing of such beds is becoming general practice. Methods:

1. *Conventional Thomas-method covers.* Plastic covers are laid over the area to be steamed just as is described in the preceding pages.

Steam raking at Jerry Knouse's, Stuart, Florida. Jerry on right. The rake (13 ft. wide) is just behind the tractor—teeth buried, of course. The rake is pulled here by the tractor which is equipped with special gears to slow it down to 20 inches per minute or less. He has an electric motor in place of the original gasoline tractor motor. As the tractor moves forward, it pulls the rake with it.
Note the long "skirt" dragging out behind the rake—chap on the left is holding a corner of it up to be seen. This holds the steam down in the soil. This equipment will do an acre of ground (sandy) in about 4 days.

2. *Steam rake.* In effect, a large (12-foot-wide) rake is pulled through the soil. "Teeth" are 10-15 inches long. The rake is so designed that a jet of steam escapes from the tip of each of the "teeth." A large sheet of canvas is attached to the rake, trailing 20-30 feet behind the rake as it is dragged through the soil. Since the rake moves very slowly, this "skirt" acts as a cover, holds the steam down in the soil (for about an hour). Thus, a given point, as the rake and trailing skirt pass by, is heated to 180° or better for almost an hour. The steam can be introduced as much as 12-14 inches below the surface in soft and sandy soils, thus catching nematodes from below (so they can't dig deeper to escape the heat).

A 12-foot-wide rake teamed up with an adequate boiler can do an acre in about 4 to 5 days. Cost for the rake (as made by a local machinist for a Florida grower) around $1,500—including a winch to pull it, not including boiler cost.

Similar devices are used in injecting chemicals for sterilizing soils. Out West they are known as "chisels." The teeth are, in effect, a chisel with the sharp blade on the front edge.

3. Outdoor growers, in the West and Northwest and in Florida, are showing increasing interest in various chemicals for sterilizing soils. They are generally less expensive and less trouble to apply. Up to now, the big problem has been that they tended to fall short of desired results in controlling disease organisms. Also, great care must be used to insure that all the gas is aired out of a soil before planting. However, newer materials are coming onto the market which are making a better showing than the older materials. The Florida mum growers are following these materials quite closely. Several recent cases have shown much of the same remarkable "boost" in growth following chemical sterilizing that has been experienced with steam—no explanation, but impressive results.

Three rather serious crop losses have come to our attention in the past year or two where crops were planted on land sterilized with chemicals— evidently, before the material had been entirely leached or aerated out of the soil. There was one major crop loss of this type on mums. Various smaller losses have occurred to greenhouse crops. Carnations are reported to be very susceptible to injury from traces of some of these materials. This "after-sterilizing-injury" problem is one that must certainly be watched closely where chemicals are used on growing soils.

STEAMING BULK SOILS

It is quite a simple matter to rig up a box that will handle anywhere from a small quantity of soil for germinating a few flats of seed on up to equipment that will handle hundreds of yards. However, we have found the portable wagon idea very useful (See illustration of portable wagon, page 107). It saves shoveling the soil down into and up out of a box, and of course, the wagon goes to the soil pile, then to the steam source, and finally to where we use the soil. By thus reducing handling, we also reduce the chances of re-

A steam rake on the ground all ready to dig in. Note canvas "skirt" off to right, also the steam hose.

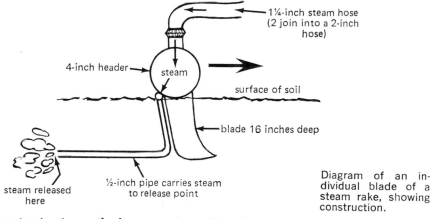

1¼-inch steam hose (2 join into a 2-inch hose)

4-inch header

steam

surface of soil

blade 16 inches deep

½-inch pipe carries steam to release point

steam released here

Diagram of an individual blade of a steam rake, showing construction.

contaminating soil after steaming. (Shovels, tools, etc., are steamed right along with the soil—a good idea with bench steaming, too.)

A Converted Truck Body

We are indebted to Paul Ecke, Encinitas, California, for the following details on a well worked out converted truck body (pictured on page 106) for sterilizing bulk soils. (This appeared in the Ohio Florists Bulletin No. 276.) We quote:

"The dump truck used had a body 12 feet long and 7 feet 4 inches wide inside. The 4 lines extending the length of the body are 1½-inch galvanized pipe, and holes ¼ inch in diameter are drilled on each side and the bottom (none on top) every 4 inches the entire length of each pipe. These

Shows the dump truck fitted by Paul Ecke for sterilizing bulk soil. Note that the header at the top of the body is 2 inch.

Here is the same truck filled with soil and with the canvas cover roped down securely, and steam main hooked on.

holes are for the escape of the steam into the soil. The 4 pipes connect by means of a bushing into a 2-inch galvanized pipe header and standard tees and ells are used. A 1½-inch galvanized pipe extends up from the header and then to the right-hand side of the headboard. The 4 pipes are capped at the rear end of the truck with standard 1½-inch pipe caps.

"The header pipe is fastened to the headboard with steel pipestrap. The supports at the rear of the truck for the 4 lines of 1½-inch pipe are made of 3/16 x 1½-inch steel, with a round loop of the same material holding the pipe in place. This loop should be large enough so the pipe will turn easily, without binding when the setup is dismantled.

"The 4 lines of pipe are 22 inches apart and the outer lines are approximately 11 inches from the side of the truck. The pipes arc supported 8 to 9 inches above the floor of the truck body. To make it easier for the soil to slide out, the floor of the body should be covered with light-gauge galvanized sheet iron.

"Figure 2 shows the truck with the sides and end installed. These are made of wood and are 2 feet high, making it possible to steam approximately 6½ cubic yards of soil."

The soil used was loaded onto the truck by means of a Fordson tractor with a shovel. Once filled and covered with a heavy canvas, the truck is driven up to the boiler room where a 2-inch line is hooked onto the 2-inch header. Two hours of steaming at 10 pounds pressure are required to do a truck-load. Thermometers are used to check the temperature of each load. Once

An interesting way of sterilizing soil for pot crops. The grower uses a peat-sand mix that can be used immediately after steaming without risk. The mix is steamed right in the trailer (perforated pipes are set in the bed). The trailer is wheeled right into the head house and is used as a potting bench.

the soil is steamed, of course, it can be hauled off and dumped wherever it is wanted.

Lindig steam-sterilizing wagons are available. They are capable of sterilizing 12-140 cu. ft. of soil.

LK

Showing the remarkable growth "stimulation" that results from sterilizing soils— apparently either with steam or with chemicals. The right bench of mums shown below was treated with a bromide material (MC2) before the mums were benched, the left bench was left untreated. Same planting date, etc. Mums were grown on both beds last year.

Grower Lawrence Kendall (left), and son, Howard (right) of Vero Beach, Florida. We have noted this same difference in beds steamed compared to non-steamed checks.

10. CHEMICALS FOR STERILIZING

By Dr. Kenneth Horst
Cornell University

In recent years, a number of chemicals have been formulated as liquids to be applied in the soil for killing nematodes, certain insects, weeds, and more recently, fungi. Most of these chemicals become gases and diffuse in the soil to bring about the kill. The soil temperature must be 50° F. or above at the 6-inch level to permit good gas dispersion. Soil must be tilled to reduce or bury crop debris and be in good planting condition when treated.

One of the problems arising from the sterilization or near sterilization of soil with materials such as chloropicrin, methyl bromide, or steam is that such treatment removes most organisms—beneficial as well as disease-producing—from the soil. Under such conditions, the first organisms to be introduced have very little competition and can develop very rapidly. If a disease-producing organism is introduced first, serious problems may result. For this reason, when using soil treated this way, it is imperative to use clean planting containers, tools, and other equipment, and especially clean or pathogen-free planting stock. Because of the difficulty of doing this under most nursery conditions, other approaches to the problem need to be found.

Of course, nearly all steaming of soils in the U.S. is done to the 180° F, 30-minute standard. However, where less than a complete kill of soil life is wanted, one approach is to *pasteurize* the soil at temperatures of 160° F for 30 minutes—the so-called aerated-steam method. Another approach is through the use of fungicides, applied either as drenches or as additives to the soil. These may either prevent the re-entry of disease-producing organisms or prevent their development in the soil, should they become introduced.

CHEMICALS—PRO AND CON

While steam sterilization is the most popular, the most reliable, and generally the most economical method of soil sterilization, many occasions arise where steam is not available and chemicals would be less expensive than setting up a steam system. Certainly, over the last few years, progress has been made in the field of chemicals.

Dr. Donald E. Munnecke, Plant Pathologist, U.C.L.A., says, "An ideal chemical for treating soil is one that kills a variety of fungi, bacteria, insects and weeds; is inexpensive and harmless to the operator and equipment; is quick-acting and effective deep in the soil as well as on the surface; is harmless to nearby plants, and is not toxic to subsequent plantings in the soil."

As yet, the above-described chemical has not been developed. Therefore, there are three general types of material available: those which will control diseases, those that will control insects and nematodes, and herbicides which will control weeds. Of the classes of organisms to be controlled, the diseases are the most difficult. If a chemical will control the soil-borne fungi, chances are it will control the other organisms as well.

One major drawback of chemicals for treatment of greenhouse soils is the time required for complete aeration of the chemicals after treatment. Planting too soon will result in loss of roots—or even the crop. Waiting two weeks for soil aeration is an expensive process where the grower must "harvest" 25¢ to 29¢ per square foot of bench area per month just to break even. This period for aeration is much less critical in terms of outdoor areas that are cropped only once a year. Also, great care must be used in working with chemicals under glass to insure that gas escaping from a bed doesn't get to other plants in the house.

There are several materials available now that can be used safely in the greenhouse with no damage to the crops. These will be discussed separately.

WHICH CHEMICAL?

There are dozens of materials sold for this purpose. We don't claim to have carefully analyzed the performance of them. The charts on pages 113-117 reflect mostly the experience of commercial growers and pathologists around the country as we have observed them. They have been prepared by the Department of Plant Pathology at Cornell University.

Before discussing individual materials, it should be pointed out that the results of chemical treatment may vary widely according to soil texture, moisture, and temperature. Dosage should vary accordingly. Heavy, dry, cold soils generally require more chemical to get the same results.

TERRACLOR (PCNB)

This material, though commonly grouped with the fungicides, is not really a fungicide, but a fungistat. This means that it does not kill most of the organisms against which it is effective, but prevents their development. However, it is extremely good for controlling certain soil-borne disease-producing organisms such as rhizoctonia and various species of sclerotinia. In addition to this, it has the advantage that it has a relatively long residual action and is practically insoluble in water. Thus, once it has been added to the soil, it will remain effective for periods as long as six months to a year.

Terraclor is best applied to the soil prior to planting. One to two pounds of the 75% wettable powder per 1000 sq. ft. should be worked into the top 2 to 4 inches of soil. If a rhizoctonia problem should break out after the plants have been started, Terraclor can be drenched on at the rate of 1 to 1½ lbs. of 75% wettable powder per 100 gals. water and applied at the rate of 1 pt. per sq. ft. or 100 gals. applied to 400 sq. ft. of bed. Most plants are not injured at this concentration, but try it on a few plants first to make sure injury does not occur. Terraclor is not effective against pythium. Do not make repeated applications of Terraclor.

Results of Vapam soil sterilizing at Rinker's, Stuart, Florida. Lane Rinker (left) and Allan Weise (of Rinker's). The bed (lower right corner) shown here was given one quart of Vapam per 100 sq. ft., allowed 13 days to aerate, the picture taken 15 days after benching of cuttings.

Rinkers reported good control of weeds that were a tough problem. The rotting of cuttings after benching has been no problem. The Vapam was applied by a man with a hose (with "rose" nozzle) —and a second man coming along behind, spraying the surface to create a water seal. They like the Vapam deal.

DEXON

The water molds, pythium and phytophthora, are found occurring naturally in most soils, and in addition, they are rapid invaders of sterilized soil. Dexon is a fungicide which has been found to give excellent control against water mold root rots of many plants including gloxinias, African violets, chrysanthemums, poinsettias, azaleas, snapdragons, and geraniums. Recommendations regarding application rates vary between 100 and 200 parts per million. This is equivalent to 4 to 8 ozs. of the 35% wettable powder per 100 gals. of water to be applied at ½ pt. per 6-inch pot. For bench and field plants, apply 1½ lbs. 35% wettable powder per 100 gals. water to 400 sq. ft. of bed. A second application may be made 2 to 4 weeks later if necessary, since Dexon does not have a long residual effect. The frequency of application depends partly on the crop and the disease severity, but with most susceptible crops, it is recommended that Dexon be put on every 7 to 10 days.

Cover pail with black cloth, as Dexon deteriorates upon standing in solution and exposure to light.

DEXON-TERRACLOR MIXTURES

A 35-35% mixture of Dexon-Terraclor is available which is effective against water molds and rhizoctonia. A first drench of 4 to 8 ozs. per 100 gals. of this material can be used, but repeat drenches should be of just

Dexon alone, since Terraclor does not break down in the soil and may build up to a toxic level.

BANROT

Banrot is a newer broad spectrum fungicide made up of 15% wettable powder Ethazol plus 25% Thiophanate-m. Use as soil drench at 8 ounces per 100 gallons for control of root rots caused by pythium, rhizoctonia, sclorotinia, sclorotium, fusarium and thielaviopsis. Use 100 gallons over 200 square feet of bed, or 1600 six-inch pots. Drench every 4-6 weeks. Be sure to check label before using.

BENLATE

Benlate, a new systemic fungicide, has given excellent control of a number of soil pathogens including rhizoctonia, sclerotinia, sclerotium, fusarium, thielaviopsis, verticillium and cylindrocladium. The 50% wettable powder is available as Benlate for ornamentals and Tersan 1991 for turf. The rate of application is ½ to 1½ lbs. per 100 gals. of water applied at 1 pt. per sq. ft. Most plants are not injured at this concentration, but try it on a few plants first to make sure injury does not occur. Plant roots must be confined to the treated area as "container plantings." Results of field tests have been erratic, but not inconsistent with the postulation that a large percentage of the root system is required to take up the fungicide.

CHLOROPICRIN AND METHYL BROMIDE

Combinations of chloropicrin and methyl bromide, either 55-45% mixture or 66-34% mixtures, are more effective against fungi than the materials used alone. The combination must, of course, be covered with polyethylene sheeting. Some authorities state that, using chloropicrin sealed in with plastic, the control of verticillium approaches the results obtained with steam. However, chloropicrin applied under glass is apt to cause injury to other crops in the same house. Methyl bromide is less dangerous, but has been known (along with other chemicals containing bromine) to be toxic to some crops, especially carnations. Therefore, it is not wise to use methyl bromide on carnation soil. A good precaution, where chemicals are considered, is to try them on a small scale first to see how they affect specific plants grown under your conditions.

TRUBAN (ETHAZOL)

Specifically for water mold control, Truban is often combined with other materials in a soil drench program. Use 8 ounces per 100 gallons of water. Apply 100 gallons to 200 square feet of bed, or 1 cup per 6 inch pot. Follow the application with an additional watering to improve the penetrability of the material into the soil drench every 6 to 8 weeks as necessary.

COST

Ease and cost of doing the job vary greatly, depending upon which type of chemical is being used. For instance, applying such chemicals as methyl bromide is far from an agreeable task—and it is dangerous if not handled properly. Vapam is much easier to handle—but probably less effective. Approximate cost of using each of the various methods is indicated on the chart.

We may conclude from the above discussion that chemicals might be most profitably and effectively used under the following conditions:

1. Where overhead costs are low, so that time for aeration is not expensive. In general, this means outdoor areas that are cropped only once or twice a year.

2. Where weeds and perhaps soil-borne insects are the main reasons for sterilizing. Chemicals are generally not dependable for control of certain hard-to-kill disease organisms.

3. Chemicals are used more generally on less valuable crops—outdoor flower and vegetable crops—where the cost and potential return are lower than for more intensive forms of culture.

4. Chemicals tend to be used where steam boilers are not available. Boilers cost money! Rental of a portable boiler may be the best solution for some growers.

SAFETY PRECAUTIONS

1. Always read the label before using pesticides. Note warnings and cautions each time before opening a container. *Read and follow directions for use.*

2. Keep pesticides away from children, pets and irresponsible people. Store pesticides in a secure place away from food and feed.

3. Do not smoke while using pesticides and avoid inhalation.

4. Do not spill pesticides on skin or clothing. If they are spilled, remove contaminated clothing and wash exposed skin areas thoroughly.

5. Dispose of empty containers so that they pose no hazard to humans, animals or valuable plants.

6. If symptoms of illness occur during or shortly after using pesticides, call a physician or get the patient to a hospital immediately. Physicians now have available information for the quick and effective treatment of accidental overexposure to pesticides. If possible, take along a label from the pesticide container.

7. You may obtain prompt, up-to-date information on the symptoms and treatment of cases resulting from exposure to toxic agricultural chemicals by calling your "Poison Control Center."

FUNGICIDE TABLES
Soil Fumigants

Accepted Common Name	Some Trade Names	Application Rate	Effective Against	Min. Soil Temp.	Cost (Approx.) $/100 sq. ft. ($/unit)	Comments
chloropicrin*	Larvacide Picfume	3 cc on 12-in. centers or per cu. ft. of soil (480 lbs./acre)	Weeds, most fungi, nematodes, soil insects. Controls *Verticillium*.	60°F.	$1.38 $1.22/ lb.	Soil must be covered with gas-proof cover for at least 24 hrs. It is most effective at soil temperatures from 60°F. to 90°F. Soil must be well aerated for 10-21 days before planting. Fumes are toxic to living plants.
98%* methyl bromide 2% chloropicrin. Under pressure in 1-lb. cans and 30-lb. cylinders	MC-2 Pestmaster Soil Fumigant-1	4 lbs. per 100 sq. ft. or 100 cu. ft. of soil applied under tarp.	Weeds and insects at lower rates; bacteria and most fungi at higher rates. Inadequate *Verticillium* control.	50°F.	$6.12 $1.53/ lb.	It can be used in houses where plants are growing, although slight leaf injury has been observed on carnations, mums, geraniums, and lilies. In clear, warm weather, sandy, arid and other light soils, air soil for 3-4 days, heavier soils, air for 7-12 days. Fumes slightly toxic to plants. Do not use for treating soils to be planted to carnations, salvia, and snapdragons.

*Indicates that the usage of the material is restricted and can be used by permit only in certain states.

FUNGICIDE TABLES—Cont.

Accepted Common Name	Some Trade Names	Application Rate	Effective Against	Min. Soil Temp.	Cost (Approx.) $/100 sq. ft. ($/unit)	Comments
67%* methyl bromide 33% chloropicrin	Dowfume MC-33	½ lb. per 100 sq. ft. or 250 lbs. per acre.	Weeds, insects, bacteria, fungi, including *Verticillium*.	50°F.	73¢ $1.45/ lb.	Same as above.
Technical grade dichloropropene-dichloropropane mixtures	D-D Vidden D Telone (100% dichloropropene, $2.40/gal.)	20-40 gals. per acre.	*Nematodes* and insects.	50°F.	27¢ $3.00/ gal.	Apply with hand injector or tractor-mounted equipment. Wait 14-28 days before planting. Fumes toxic to living plants.
liquid carbamate SMDC	Vapam VPM	Drench in 1 qt. /100 sq. ft. Use at least 15 gals. water. Injected—1 pt. per 100 sq. ft. (50 gals./acre).	*Nematodes*, most weeds, and insects.	50°F.	$2.57 $4.85/ gal.	Do not plant for 2 to 3 weeks after treatment, then make test plantings of seedlings or cuttings and wait a few days before planting entire crop. If soil is cold or excessively wet, wait 3 to 4 weeks. Fumes toxic to living plants.

Material	Active ingredient	Rate	Controls	Temp.	Cost	Remarks
Vorlex	Mixture of 80% dichloropropene-dichloropropane, 20% methyl isothiocyanate	25-40 gals. per acre.	Nematodes, weeds, and fungi.	50°F.	93¢ $13.50/gal.	Apply with hand injector or tractor-mounted equipment. Wait 14-28 days before planting. Fumes toxic to living plants.
Pestmaster Fumigant EDB-85 Dowfume W-85	ethylene dibromide	3-6 gals. actual chemical per acre.	Nematodes and insects.	50°F.	01¾¢ $10.20/gal.	Apply with hand injector or tractor-mounted equipment. Wait 14-21 days before planting. Fumes slightly to moderately toxic to living plants.
Nemagon 12.1EC	12.1%	3 to 4½ oz./1000 sq. ft.	Nematodes.	60°F.	06¢ $17.15/gal.	Can be used with living plants.
Formalin	40% formaldehyde	1 pt. in 6¼ gals. water applied at ½ gal. per sq. ft.	Fungi and bacteria.	60°F.	$2.25 $2.25/gal.	Soil should be moist before treatment, tarp-covered for first 24 hrs. Aerate for 14 days. Treated soil may be used for potting if aired until all odor of formaldehyde has gone. Fumes toxic to living plants.

*Indicates that the usage of the material is restricted and can be used by permit only in certain states.

SOIL DRENCHES

Accepted Common Name	Some Trade Names	Application Rate	Effective Against	Min. Soil Temp.	Cost (Approx.) $/100 sq. ft. ($/unit)	Comments
PCNB	Brassiocol Terraclor	1½ lbs. (75%)/ 1,000 sq. ft. mixed with top 1-2 inches of soil, or drenched on living plants at the rate of 1 to 1½ lbs. per 100 gals. water. Drenched at 1 pt. per sq. ft. or 100 gals. applied to 400 sq. ft. of bench.	Rhizoctonia, Sclerotinia.	—	29¢ $1.90/ lb.	Specific for Rhizoctonia, Sclerotinia spp., and Sclerotium spp. Not effective against water molds. Good residual action.
Thiram	Arasan (42S)	1 fl. oz. (42%)/ 6 gals. water Higher dosages may cause injury. Use 1-2 pts./ sq. ft.	Fungi.	—	55¢ $16.45/ gal.	Effective in preventing root-and-stem rot of poinsettias.
Nabam	Dithane D-14 Parzate liquid	1 fl. oz. (22%)/ 4 gals. water. Use 1-2 pts./sq. ft.	Fungi.	—	10¢ $2.65/ gal.	Spot treatments to prevent disease spread. Little residual effect.

Product	Rate	Diseases		Price	Remarks
50% benomyl Benlate (for turf—Tersan 1991, same % active & same price)	½-1½ lbs./100 gals. water; apply ½ pt./6" pot.	Cylindrocladium, Thielaviopsis, Sclerotinia, Fusarium, Verticillium and Rhizoctonia.	—	$2.35 $9.30/lb.	Plant roots must be confined to the treated area as "container plantings." Results of field tests have been erratic but not inconsistent with the postulation that a large percentage of the root system is required to take up the fungicide.
Truban	3-10 ozs./100 gals. of water applied to 400 sq. ft. of bench area or ½ pt./6 in. pot.	Pythium and Phytophthora.	—	84¢ $9.00/lb.	Good residual qualities —treat at 4 to 12-week intervals, if necessary.
Dexon-Terraclor	8 ozs. 35% WP Dexon plus 4 ozs. 75% WP Terraclor per 100 gals. water applied to 400 sq. ft. or ½ pt./6 in. pot.	Rhizoctonia and Pythium.	—	54¢ Dexon—$3.80/lb. Terraclor—$1.90/lb.	Cover container with black cloth and apply immediately upon mixing, as Dexon deteriorates upon standing in solution and exposure to light.
Dexon	8 ozs. 35% WP per 100 gals. water applied to 400 sq. ft. or ½ pt. per 6 in. pot.	Water molds (Pythium, etc.).	—	48¢ $3.80/lb.	Cover container with black cloth and apply immediately upon mixing as Dexon deteriorates upon standing in solution and exposure to light.

11. MITE AND INSECT CONTROL

Dr. Herbert T. Streu

Rutgers University

PREVENTION—THE EASIEST WAY

Control of greenhouse insects and mites is usually practiced only when a particular pest problem is severe—and the extent of losses which result is dependent upon the ability of the grower to "put out the fire." At these times, control is most difficult and plant injury, resistance problems and control failure are most often experienced. The value of a preventative program cannot be overemphasized. Exclusion of pests from a greenhouse is virtually impossible, and a regular program which will prevent their establishment provides the insurance necessary for the production of a high-quality crop. The cost of such a program will more than pay for itself in the long run. Pest control, through prevention, like disease prevention, fertilizer application, pinching on certain dates or any of the other accepted cultural practices should be built into the production schedule of every floricultural crop.

METHODS OF APPLICATION

The practices of greenhouse-pest control include application of miticides and/or insecticides in any of a variety of ways:

SPRAYS

Spraying is generally the most effective of all the methods—but sprays are also the most expensive to apply. When applied with good equipment by a careful worker, sprays give excellent kill and residual protection—especially when plants are young, or before the foliage becomes too dense for good spray penetration. Adequate pressure should be maintained and good nozzles used to deliver the spray to both upper and lower leaf surfaces.

When mixing sprays, either liquid concentrates or wettable powders are most often used. Choice of formulation will depend upon the stage of plant growth, plant sensitivity and formulation availability. In general, wettable powders leave visible residues on the foliage whereas liquid concentrates virtually leave none. The liquid concentrates, however, do contain organic solvents which may injure sensitive plants and soft-growing terminals.

Most insecticide manufacturers incorporate sufficient wetting agents in concentrates to adequately wet "average" types of foliage. Some plants, like carnations, roses, and others which have particularly waxy foliage, are hard to wet and a wetting-agent spreader should be added. Remember that too much wetting agent will result in excessive spray run-off and inadequate insecticide residues, whereas too little wetting agent will result in poor wetting and spotty residues. A little experimentation is usually necessary to determine the right amount. Start with small amounts and increase gradually to the point of good wetting.

Sprays are only as effective as the coverage. Dense foliage, compact growth habit, and tight-growing terminals limit the penetration and contact of insecticides with the target organisms. Rapidly growing plants quickly produce unprotected foliage, and sprays must be repeated accordingly.

AEROSOLS

Aerosols are literally very small droplets "in solution" in air! A sufficiently small droplet (50-150μ) for suspension in air may be produced in a variety of ways, the most familiar being the aerosol "bomb" in which a pesticide is contained under pressure in a metal cylinder using Freon as a propellant. Technically, smokes, fogs and some mists also produce aerosols and all have similar effectiveness properties. Some insecticides with high-vapor pressures, when used as aerosols, will quickly form a true gas, and the propellant, then, simply becomes a convenient vehicle to quickly dispense the gas. Vapona, for example, is equally as effective whether applied from a "bomb," or as a smoke, fog, or mist. The choice of the vehicle or device to apply Vapona and similar materials, is largely one of economics and/or personal preference.

Chemicals which do not completely volatilize tend to settle very slowly from the air and deposit on upper leaf surfaces only. Aerosols of all types, therefore, offer no, or only slight residual effectiveness. They must be repeated regularly and proper timing of applications to coincide with pest life cycles and critical developmental stages is necessary for effective control. Ease of use, resulting in quick applications with savings of labor, combined with no visible chemical residues, make aerosol application a popular method.

Remember that correct calculation of dosage is a vital part of aerosol effectiveness. Space treatment is dependent upon dosage calculated per unit volume per length of time! A leaky greenhouse, incorrect greenhouse volume calculation, the presence of fans, pads, etc., together with a windy day, all quickly dilute the dosage resulting in control failure.

THERMAL FOGGERS

. . . are efficient devices for dispensing many insecticides in aerosol form. The materials are usually formulated as 10% actual insecticide in an oil-solvent mixture which, when delivered into a hot-air column in the machine's exhaust, is sheared and heated to form tiny "fog" droplets (10-60μ). Fogs exhibit characteristics very similar to other aerosols with the distinct advantage of forming an easily visible cloud of fog, which facilitates dosage/time observation. Leaky houses, uneven distribution due to wind or other air movements, or other factors responsible for poor control, are easily detected.

Remember that fogging-oil formulations are especially vulnerable to oxidation and sludge and tar formation. Keep the machinery clean and in good operating condition by following directions carefully. Wood alcohol is valuable for cleaning clogged insecticide lines, and should be used regularly. Store fogging oils in cool, dry conditions to prevent oxidation.

MISTING DEVICES

Misting devices, using formulations which form fine droplets when mixed with an air blast from a blower, depend upon a highly volatile solvent as an insecticide carrier. The solvent evaporates almost immediately, leaving the insecticide droplets suspended in air. Some misting devices can be used to blow an insecticide up into a jet fan which, in turn, blows the insecticides through the poly tube. Excellent distribution is obtained by this convenient method—especially in large houses.

SMOKES

Smokes employ only insecticides which are stable under the relatively high heats necessary to volatilize the compound as a "smoke." Formulations tend to be somewhat limited, but offer a quick, simple way of applying certain materials. Small growers find these devices particularly useful.

Remember that all aerosols produced with any of the above methods exhibit similar characteristics, and the choice of any one will depend upon individual preference and growing conditions.

VAPORIZATION

Some materials, like Vapona and Dibrom, exhibit high vapor pressures and readily form gases under sufficient heat. Hot plates or heat pipes can be used to vaporize these compounds quickly and efficiently. The gases, however, have no residual effects, but because they leave no residues, can be used effectively on crops nearing harvest. Regular usage necessitates continued application, the timing depending upon the crop, the temperature and pest development. Remember to keep the foliage dry, and to distribute the materials uniformly throughout a house. One Vapona generator, for example, for a large house, will produce a "cloud" of highly concentrated gas near the generator and may cause a burn on sensitive plants nearby. Vapona is particularly useful at low temperatures (60-70 degrees F), whereas many other materials are effective only at temperatures above 70 degrees F.

DUSTS

Dusts leave a heavy residue on plant surfaces and are not commonly used. On some plants with dense growth habits, compact foliage, and hard-to-wet surfaces, dusts may provide a very efficient vehicle for pesticides. Mites infesting 1 or 2-year carnations are more easily controlled with dusts of Pentac than with sprays.

SOME IMPORTANT GREENHOUSE PESTS

The number of insects, mites, slugs, snails and other pests infesting greenhouse crops is quite large, and treatment of each in detail would occupy a book in itself. There are, however, several which are common to the most important crops and warrant individual discussion.

MITES

The two-spotted spider mite (*Tetranychus urticae* Koch), also called "red spider," "spider mite," "spider" and various other names, ranks as one of the most important pests of greenhouse crops. It attacks a wide variety of plants, causing severe damage. Infestations usually result in crop losses— both in quality and quantity. Carnations, for example, may never recover completely from a heavy mite infestation.

One of the problems in dealing with mites is their small size. Fully developed females are only 1/50 of an inch long, and infestations are usually noticed only when plant damage becomes evident. At that time, the population of mites is generally large and more difficult to control.

A second problem is the complex life cycle, which involves a number of inactive, nonfeeding stages which are unaffected by many commonly used miticides. Eggs, laid at the rate of about 10 to 12 a day at 70 degrees F, hatch i· · 6-legged larvae which feed for only a short time. This stage is followed b.. an inactive "resting" stage, or chrysalis, from which emerges another active feeding stage after about a day and a half.

This sequence of active stage-resting stage continues until adults appear from the last resting stage. There is a total of 3 resting stages, together with the egg, which are, in many cases, unaffected by aerosols, gases, or even non-residual sprays of many compounds. As a result, since feeding stages emerge from nonfeeding ones, applications of most pesticides must be repeated.

Mites feed and develop mostly on the undersides of leaves. They spin protective webbing and infest leaf axils, opening flowers and growing terminals. Sprays, aerosols and fumigant gases are often ineffective in reaching these mites, and again, repeat applications are a must.

Since the rate of mite (and insect) development is dependent upon temperature, the frequency of application to control infestations will depend upon the season, night temperatures, the amount of shading and other variations in individual greenhouses. The warmer the temperatures, the more frequent the application—sometimes as often as every second or third day! During winter months, every 10 days to 2 weeks may be sufficient. A grower must, therefore, develop his own schedule of application by watching for the appearance of active mites.

The type of chemical compound being used and its formulation will also influence the application schedule. For example, most of the organophosphate-type miticides kill quickly, and if active mites are observed within a day or two, applications should be repeated. Pentac, on the other hand, kills slowly and up to 3 full days are necessary for complete kill of active stages. A spray or dust of Pentac will give long residual control of mites and only the rate of plant growth will determine when sprays must be repeated. Aerosols of Pentac, however, either as smokes or fogs, will give no residual protection and applications will have to be repeated, as in the case of the organophosphates. Remember that Pentac can only be used indoors! Ultraviolet light renders it ineffective.

Resistance is a common problem also, and the *kind* of resistance which develops within a mite population will depend upon the *kind* of chemical (or chemicals) a grower has been using. Organophosphate resistance is the most common type, and use of any of the many organophosphates will generally result in control failure following development of resistance to any one of the many a grower may have been using. For example, if parathion has been used for a long time and resistance to it has developed, a similar miticide such as Malathion, Dithio, Vapona, or others, will generally also be ineffective within a short period of time. Selection of a different type of compound, however, is recommended *after* resistance has been noticed.

A guide for chemical selection based upon similar chemical and miticidal properties of the most commonly used miticides is as follows:

ALDICARB (TEMIK 10G)

A granular systemic insecticide effective against aphids, leafminers, thrips, whiteflies, mites and nematodes. This material can be broadcast at the rate of 20-40 ounces per 1,000 square feet, or applied to individual pots. Generally 1/10th to 1/8th teaspoon per 6 inch pot has been satisfactory. However, certain cultivars may be damaged. Read the label for registered uses and safety precautions. Repeat at 3-6 week intervals.

Organophosphorus compounds include such materials as TEPP, Dithio, Dibrom, Vapona, Systox, Meta Systox-R, Malathion, Ethion, parathion, Trithion, Diazinon and several others.

Carbamates like Zectran may show some cross resistance to organophosphate resistance. Do not follow with these materials if a high level of phosphate resistance is present.

Chlorinated Hydrocarbons include Dimite, Kelthane Chlorobenzilate, Acaralate.

Morestan also differs from the others.

Pentac is unique and although a highly chlorinated material, differs from all others.

Sulfites—Aramite and Omite.

Sulfones and Sulfonates include Tedion, Ovex, Mitox, and Genite.

To utilize the guide, keep accurate records of chemical usage. Most important, note the effectiveness. If mite control begins to fail, select another miticide from any of the other groups. Do not select one from the same group. Continue to use the material until it appears to be losing its effectiveness then begin to use another from a still-unused group. However, remember to check all possibilities for mite-control failure. Check label directions for dosage, recommended temperatures during application, as well as for spray coverage and penetration, etc.

Resistance may not be the problem and improper or haphazard and careless usage will result in consistent control failures despite switching from group to group. Keep careful spray records and record the observed results.

A regular treatment schedule will usually prevent populations from building up. Resistance, however, can develop with such a program of regular usage of one type of compound. Occasional rotation with a miticide from another class will insure effectiveness.

Remember that mites infest and thrive on many types of weeds in and around greenhouses. Cleanliness is as necessary to a successful program of mite control as any of the other components. And, finally, in the case of mites especially, the preventative approach is most important—an ounce of prevention is worth many, many pounds of cure!

Cylamen mites (*Tarsonemus pallidus* Banks) often infest a number of greenhouse crops including African violets, begonias, cyclamen, gloxinia, impatiens and others. The mites live in unopened buds and in developing foliage in growing terminals. Their feeding produces twisted, hardened and distorted foliage and flowers. Heavy infestations may cause browning and death of growing tips and flowers. Sprays or dips of Kelthane, Endrin, or Thiodan are usually effective.

GREENHOUSE WHITEFLY

(*Trialeurodes vaporarium* Westwood). Whitefly is commonly found infesting many greenhouse crops, but it develops more rapidly on some than on others. Poinsettias, tomatoes, fuchsia, salvia and ageratum are particularly favorable, and chickweed is an especially good host. Weeds must be removed if whitefly is to be controlled!

Most growers know only the adult whitefly, which is conspicuous when it flies about the foliage of infested plants. Whitefly adults are not strong fliers and generally are not noticed until disturbed. The adults, however, are only one stage in a complex life cycle, and killing adults at infrequent intervals will not control the populations of immature individuals which live on the undersides of leaves. Nymphs and larvae resemble scale insects and exude honeydew while feeding. Sticky foliage, blackened with sooty mold which grows on the honeydew, are indicators of heavy infestations.

Growers who rely on fumigants like Vapona or Dibrom for control kill only adults. Within a few days after treatment, more adult flies emerge from the scalelike immature stages, mate and lay eggs, thereby continuing the infestation. Applications must, therefore, be repeated at intervals sufficiently frequent to prevent more egg-laying. Since whitefly development is dependent upon temperature, reapplication must be made when adults are observed. In warmer weather, 3 applications per week may be necessary. As many as 10 or 15 applications in carefully timed sequence are usually necessary! Miss the correct timing, and females will have a chance to lay more eggs and the problem will go on and on!

Remember that sprays are more effective than fumigants, but good coverage of the undersides of leaves is absolutely necessary. Malathion is effective if the spray concentrate is used. Repeat applications, however, are necessary.

APHIDS

(*Aphididae*, several spp.). Aphids, sometimes called "greenfly," "aphis," or "plant lice," are common to most greenhouse crops. The most common species is the green peach aphid (*Myzus persicae* Sulzer). It ranges in color from pink to orangish, to yellow or gray-green, and is the most important aphid on carnations and chrysanthemums. When chrysanthemums begin to flower, this aphid will congregate in the blooms where control is almost impossible. Normally, the insects tend to be dispersed throughout the plant, not congregating on growing tips like other species.

Aphids do not overwinter in the greenhouse, but continue to reproduce—

females giving birth to living females. Occasionally, winged individuals are produced which fly to other plants, thereby spreading the infestation. In the fall, winged aphids move into the greenhouse from out-of-doors, and spray programs during this time of year must be designed for aphid control.

Sprays of Meta Systox-R, Phosdrin, Malathion or Lindane are all effective. Vapona is highly effective. Control failures are commonly encountered, however, because of failure to kill insects protected in growing plant terminals, leaf axils or in developing flowers. Sprays must be applied carefully and thoroughly. Because green peach aphids do not congregate in the upper parts of the plant, a light going-over with spray equipment will not do the job.

Resistance to organophosphorus compounds does occur and Lindane, nicotine or Baytex should be tried. Reinfestation from outdoors, however, often accounts for control problems and repeated treatments are necessary.

Aphids are controlled with systemic insecticides on some crops, such as lilies and chrysanthemums. Soil drenches when the plants are young will give good protection for as long as 6 weeks in chrysanthemums and for the total growing period in the case of lilies. Exercise care in handling the spray concentrate.

"WORMS"

"Worms" are the larvae of various species of moths (Lepidoptera). Adult moths fly into greenhouses, attracted by lights at night, or gain entry as pupae in soil, or are introduced as eggs and young larvae in and on cuttings and plants brought in from the field or from other sources. Many species infest greenhouses, including the cutworms, army worms, and corn earworms, the loopers, the leaf rollers, and the plume moths, among others.

Treatment tends to be similar for most, however, although borers and worms which infest blooms present individual problems. In general, preventative sprays with long-lasting residues are the best. Many of the organophosphate materials kill only on contact and are less effective. Aerosols, smokes, and fumigant gases kill only adults and are ineffective on most larvae—especially those which are protected in flower buds, developing terminals and inside stems.

Sprays of *Bacillus thuringiensis* Berliner (Biotrol BTB, Dipel or Thuricide 90TS), Sevin, Zectran and Lannate (when available) are all effective and offer good residual protection. Lindane, Dieldrin and Methoxychlor give excellent protection, but tend to be less effective against certain species. If a particular species seems to be establishing, switch to an alternative material.

Remember to keep foliage well protected. Stomach poisons are the most effective, but are difficult to administer when the worms are protected in growing terminals. Rapidly growing plants must be sprayed often.

LEAF MINERS

Leaf miners of several sorts are encountered on many crops. The chrysanthemum leaf miner (*Phytomyza syngenesiae* (Hardy)) is one of the more important pests on mums, and once established, becomes somewhat difficult to control. The leaf miner adult is a small gray-to-black fly, which is colored yellow on the lower portion of the head and abdomen. Females lay eggs in leaves, and the tiny white maggots which hatch, mine and burrow within the leaf tissue, cause considerable damage.

Fumigations with Vapona or parathion kill only adults, and applications must be repeated. The maggots can be killed with sprays of parathion or Meta Systox-R, but thorough coverage is a must. Protection is important, and Lindane will give good kill of adults.

GENERAL RECOMMENDATIONS

There are many good, general-purpose spray mixtures which can be used in preventative programs. In general, the organophosphorus compounds will kill both mites and insects and can be used with a good, general-purpose fungicide. Some materials, however, are miticides only, and must be combined with a good, general-purpose insecticide and fungicide. Remember that too much wetting agent is as bad as too little; so when using a wetting agent/spreader, add small amounts until satisfactory coverage is attained.

When using pesticides, be careful! All insecticides and miticides are poisonous and must be used with care. Many are readily absorbed through the skin, and should be handled with protective clothing. Remember that liquid concentrates and wettable powders are particularly hazardous—*handle with care*, avoid spilling and breathing the dusts. Dispose of unused sprays and empty containers in a safe way.

PREVENTATIVE SPRAYS

The following general spray mixtures are suggested for preventative programs. They may not work for all growers, and use of recommended materials for specific pests may be necessary if an infestation becomes established.

SPRAY NO. 1

24 ozs. Omite 30% WP
8 ozs. Lindane 25% WP
8 ozs. Benlate 50% WP
24 ozs. Zineb, Ferbam or Maneb
plus spreader-sticker, if necessary

SPRAY NO. 2

16 ozs. Diazinon (AG500) 50% EC
8 ozs. Pentac 50% WP
8 ozs. Benlate 50% WP
24 ozs. Zineb, Ferbam or Maneb
plus spreader-sticker, if necessary

SPRAY NO. 3

Meta Systox-R (see label for directions)
24 ozs. Kelthane 50% WP
8 ozs. Benlate 50% WP
24 ozs. Zineb, Ferbam or Maneb
plus spreader-sticker, if necessary

SOME COMMON PESTS AND CONTROL RECOMMENDATIONS

Aphids—Baytex, Cygon or Defend, Diazinon, Dithio, Lindane, Malathion, Meta Systox-R, OMPA, parathion, Phosdrin, Thiodan, Vapona, Temik.

Cyclamen mites—Diazinon, Endrin, Kelthane, Thiodan.

Leaf miners—Cygon or Defend, Diazinon, Meta Systox-R, Malathion, parathion, Vapona, Zectran.

Mealybugs—Cygon or Defend, Dithio, Diazinon, Meta Systox-R, Malathion, parathion, Temik. (Use liquid concentrates.)

Thrips—Dieldrin, Dithio, Malathion, parathion, Vapona, Temik.

Whitefly—Cygon or Defend, Dithio, Thiodan, Vapona, Temik.

Fungus gnats—root drenches of Lindane, Diazinon, or Systox.

Leaf rollers—Dylox, parathion, Sevin

Army worms, loopers, corn earworms—*Bacillus thuringensis,* Lannate, Zectran.

Some crops may be injured by certain of the above chemicals. If in doubt, try the treatment on a few plants first.

12. ABOUT UNCHECKED GROWTH

The most exciting discovery in flower growing the past 20 years, we feel, is the phenomenally rapid growth our ordinary mums, snaps, carnations, etc., are capable of making *if given unchecked growing conditions.* Using this principle of *rapid, unchecked growth,* we are able to flower crops in less time, with less labor, with heavier production, and good quality. For a good example, we cite the modern mum crop that is flowered in as little as 3 months (from a direct-benched cutting) compared to nearly twice that length of time for a bench of fall mums years ago. The purpose of this chapter is to point out some of the reasons why some crops *don't* always achieve this full, rapid growth of which they are capable.

A MEASURING STICK

To provide some definite standard for comparison, here are growth rates that should be realized on several typical crops—if ideal conditions are provided:

a. Mums: a good cutting benched directly to good soil should make 10-15 inches of new growth within 30 days (grown no-pinch).

b. Snaps: a good seedling benched directly should be at least 6-8 inches high within 30 days.

c. Carnations: a good cutting in good soil should make 8 inches or more of new growth in 30 days.

These figures are based on spring-summer-fall growth; something less than this should be expected during the dark winter period.

SEVEN WAYS PLANTS ARE CHECKED

Where rapid unchecked growth is not being achieved, the reason will fall under one of these headings, in most cases:

1. *Poor Physical Condition of Soil*—A very common growth "inhibitor." A soil which is poorly aerated, poorly drained, tight, waxy, and hard will surely cause a stunted, slow, uneven growth, yellowish foliage. Root development, upon examination, will be poor and not white. Mildew will often take hold of a plant which has been checked by poor soil conditions.

In some cases, some relief can be achieved by a thorough, deep cultivation followed by withholding of water till the soil has dried reasonably. However, the trouble is in the soil itself, and the real cure is to replace it. A soil in good physical condition is one which has large particle sizes. Clay is the extreme of a tight soil with too-small particles. A soil of good structure will, when watered, soak up water—not shed it.

How to obtain good porous soil for greenhouse use? Most growers start out with a good piece of farm land—a field which has been producing better-than-average field crops, and which seems, by feel, to have good loose structure. Such soil can be improved still further by planting it down to bluegrass for at least one year, and manuring it heavily and frequently. Also, it should be limed if it shows an acid test. Many growers like to dig the soil as a sod, pile it up and let the sod clumps rot over a winter.

In bringing such a soil into the greenhouse, we often add 10-15%-by-volume peat moss to it—plus a good dose of acid phosphate. Either good rotted manures, peats, or leaf mold will provide the needed loosening up of the soil and organic matter. Our experience with sand as a soil "opener" has not been good.

If real care is used in selection of the original soil, such a program of preparation should produce a fine, loose, porous soil that will grow any crop well.

2. *Seedling or Cutting Was Hardened—Poor at Time of Benching*—Certainly, rapid growth cannot be realized if a hardened, poor plant is benched. In the case of snaps, we like to bench a well-rooted seedling when the first pair of true leaves has just developed. Potting or transplanting must be done with caution—rarely over 3-4 weeks before final benching, if optimum results are to be obtained.

In the case of mums, we are, in most cases, benching cuttings directly. A soft, well-rooted, but not over-rooted cutting will make truly surprising growth in good soil. Roots should be 1 to 1½ inches long, and the entire cutting should be brittle, easily broken, not hard and woody.

Especially where cuttings are used (mums and carnations) it is vitally important that they be free of diseases. Cuttings from the large propagating specialists are generally dependable in this respect.

Above all, the plant must never be allowed to harden in a pot or shallow flat. If you have any doubt on this point, try direct-benching as compared to potting with the same sowing to see whether the potting is checking the plants.

3. *Nutrients—Too Low or Too High*—A surprisingly common cause of "slow-down" in growth of greenhouse crops. Most usual cause—lack of nitrates or potash. Symptoms of nitrate deficiency on snaps and mums: yellowing of foliage and hardening of growth. On carnations: short internodes, retarded growth, lack of bloom on foliage. An excess of ammonia is not uncommon, especially during the first 3-5 weeks after sterilizing. On newly planted material, this will cause a yellowing of new growth, hardening and "slowdown" of growth, or even complete loss of roots.

Obviously, soil testing is the only reliable way to definitely identify such troubles as these.

4. *Disease Troubles*—This one, in some cases at least, is not easy to recognize, and yet can cause plenty of "slowdown." The various stem and root rots, such as those that attack carnations, stocks, peas, and asters, are quite evident. Mum stunt is not hard to identify as the plant develops, but can't be spotted easily in the early stages. Carnation virus diseases as a group are very difficult to spot except under certain conditions, yet can cause great loss of vigor.

5. *Bugs*—In most cases easy to identify, yet it's surprising how far a spot of spider can spread unless the grower is watching closely. No plant can achieve its full potential if it is being robbed of its strength by insects. Symphilids are a very common reason for "slowdown" of greenhouse crops.

6. *Lack of Water*—Generalizations on watering are dangerous, but we will go far enough to say that the great majority of greenhouse crops would be making better, more rapid growth during the summer if they were watered more often and more thoroughly. Lack of water is, no doubt, a common cause of "slowdown" of greenhouse crops. Watering must be slowed down drastically in winter.

7. *Too cold*—Winter and spring mums, for example, will make less than half the headway at 45° than they will at 60° minimum. Snaps will grow much faster at 50° than at 40°. Correct temperatures depend on the crop, period of year, etc. Unnecessarily low temperatures, though, are a common cause of "slowdown."

13. GREENHOUSE COOLING

Evaporative type cooling of greenhouses is certainly among the 2 or 3 major developments of our generation in the field of greenhouse production. The majority of ranges in the Midwest and East are now pad-cooled. Nearly all glass in the Southwest and Colorado is cooled.

HOW IT WORKS

Evaporative cooling of greenhouses as practiced today is simply an application of the old idea of cooling air by drawing it through a wet pad. The cooling effect is, of course, achieved through *evaporation of water—not* by drawing warm air over cold water. As each gallon of water is evaporated, 8,100 BTU's of heat energy are absorbed. Actually, temperature of the water running over the pads is not particularly critical.

In greenhouse work, the wet pads consist of large pads of excelsior erected along the entire side or end of the greenhouse (photo below). They are kept wet by a constant flow of water from water troughs installed above them—with holes every few inches which drop water onto the pads.

Air is drawn through these pads by installing large fans on the opposite side or end of the greenhouse. All vents are closed, holes plugged, etc., so that when the fans are turned on, air is drawn through the pads, across the house, and out through the fans.

HOW COOL?

Results from cooling systems vary endlessly—depending on humidity in the outdoor air, how hot it is, efficiency of the cooling system, etc. Obviously, more degrees of cooling can be achieved where outdoor air is hot—95 or 100°—to start with. *Dry* air cools better under this system. Applying partial shade to the roof of the greenhouse helps.

To strike some sort of a reasonable average result that should be accom-

Aspen excelsior padding as installed at West Chicago for greenhouse cooling.

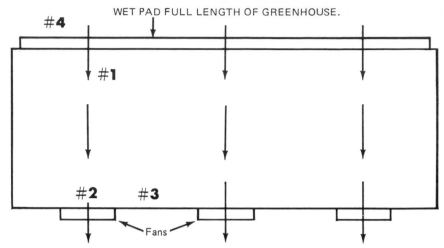

AIR IS DRAWN THROUGH WET PADS BY FANS.

plished, under moderately dry, midwestern-summer conditions, let's set up an example (based on tests with this type of equipment at our own range). Refer to sketch above. Air at #4 (outdoors) is 94° (dry thermometer). Wet-bulb reading outdoors: 74°. At point #1, the air has just been drawn through the wet pad from outdoors and is, of course, coolest in the house—79° in this case. At point #2, the air has been drawn across the width of the greenhouse, has naturally heated up some in the minute or so required to cross the house. Reading at #2 was 82°. Point #3 is midway between the 2 fans—tends to be a sort of hot pocket if fans are too far apart. Even with about 35-foot spacing of fans, this point tends to be several degrees warmer than #2. In this case, it read 85°.

Reading (dry thermometer) in an adjoining similar house with double top vents and continuous side vents all open was 95°. Shade was applied to both houses to allow about 5,500 foot-candles of light through on a clear afternoon.

In general, this relation between temperatures in various parts of the house follows the above trends. The temperature at point #1 can be computed for your own temperature-humidity conditions with fair accuracy. Select a typical "hot" summer afternoon. Take dry and wet-bulb readings outdoors (a sling psychrometer should be used). Let's assume dry bulb reads 100°, wet bulb 75°. Subtract 75 from 100—a difference of 25°. Eighty percent of this difference (80% of 25) or 20° is the amount that air should be cooled as it passes through the pad. In this case, temperature at point #1 in our sketch should be 80°—if pads are properly installed, etc.

From this method of figuring, it is easy to see why evaporative cooling is so popular and effective in the Southwest and Colorado. However, the experience thus far shows that the amount of cooling that can be achieved in the Midwest and East is enough to be extremely helpful on summer crops.

EFFECT ON CROPS

Again, it will take more experience to write the full story. So far, though, indications by crops as we see them:

a. *Mums:* Troublesome "heat delay" is mostly eliminated, and quality of flowers (size, depth of color) very noticeably better. Pot mums tend to stay shorter when delay is eliminated. Locate pink and bronze varieties nearest the pad—at the coolest point—to gain maximum color intensity. Also, most heat-sensitive varieties should be near the pad.

b. *Carnations:* Nearly all Denver carnations are now cooled. In the East and in California, some are and some are not. Depends partly on the local weather.

c. *Roses:* Less actual experience here. There are many test installations. It would seem that much of the quality of Northwest summer roses should be within the reach of midwestern and eastern growers with cooling.

COST

Again, many figures are heard. Some growers quote as low as 35¢ per square foot of ground covered—labor and materials. Where all work is paid for, and costs kept accurately, a figure of 40 to 50¢ is about average—depending on wage levels, efficiency, etc. Larger jobs are cheaper, of course.

Speaking of costs, a study of comparisons between cost of vents and cost of pad-fan installations would lead to the conclusion that vents are on the way out. For example, a house 25 by 96 feet can be equipped with complete fans and pads for about $1300. To install top vents on both sides and 2 rows of side vents in such a house would cost 2 to 3 times as much—and would do a much less effective job of ventilating in hot weather. Perhaps greenhouses of the future will have only a few top vents to provide that "crack of air" so important in winter. Another solution to the problem is the use of poly tubing for ventilating. See page 66 for further details. With such tubing, no vents are required. Actually, many ranges are being built today with no conventional ventilators!

Typical fan used for pad-fan cooling of our houses at West Chicago. Rapid air movement adjacent to the fan doesn't seem to harm the crop.

14. ARE *YOU* MECHANIZED?

If you really want to be objective about your own operation, this chapter can be a sort of score board on how well you are doing. How much available equipment are you using—today?

WHY MECHANIZE?

Mechanizing is so deadly important for even survival of U. S. flower production! The reasons:

Imported Flowers. We are seeing more flowers, especially cut flowers coming into U.S. markets from South America and Europe each year. Face it; the U.S. is committed to free-world trade. If some other country can, for one example, produce carnations for half of the U. S. cost, our carnation producers had better develop mechanized production fast—to offset the cheap labor advantage of these challengers, and we had best do an efficient job of marketing our products—taking full advantage of better availability of the domestic crop—the obvious advantage the local producer has of servicing the local market better. And U. S. producers had best encourage breeding—under controls—so that low-cost-producing areas are not allowed to hit U. S. markets with our own better varieties—without paying their share of breeding costs.

Pot plants and bedding plants are under less pressure by foreign competition, but they are far from immune. We recall so well a northern European pot-plant grower who recently went to New York, determined to open a substantial market for 4-inch pot mums in the eastern U. S. He didn't make it—but he will keep trying.

And, to be sure, the new, huge jet air-freighters, with low-cost, fast trans-Atlantic service, are going to encourage this invasion of our U. S. flower market from all over the world.

One thing is certain: The only real way to keep cut-flower, pot-plant production strong in the U. S. is to be so efficient that no other country can do the job better! If U. S. growers become most efficient, they can really become a nation of flower *exporters,* not importers. After all, the U. S. sells wheat to China.

But, U. S. wheat growing is 99.4% mechanized!

Perhaps a bit shorter-ranged, but again, an important reason for mechanizing, is simply to reduce costs, make your own operation more profitable, less dependent on hard-to-find, good hand labor. A well-mechanized range of pot plants or cut flowers or bedding plants is just about easiest to live with, and apt to be a lot more profitable.

So, here come 12 ways you can mechanize your operations—today!

AUTOMATIC WATERING

WATERING—CUT FLOWERS

Watering of greenhouse cut-flower crops by mechanical means is a well-established, proven practice. Certainly, all greenhouse benches of roses,

Ooze Headers provide a no-splash method for watering cut flower crops. These headers are placed across the bench, 8 inches apart and connected to a ½-inch main running down one side of the bench.

mums, carnations, snapdragons, etc., should be watered mechanically. Widely used for this purpose is Chapin equipment. Called Ooze products, there are 2 basically different systems used.

Number 1, and most widely used, is the Twin-Wall Hose which is a double-walled plastic tube arrangement which has the important advantage of delivering a uniform rate of application up and down the bench. These tubes are spaced about every 8 inches across a typical bench of cut flowers. A bench 250 feet long can be serviced satisfactorily from the center point. Cost for a 3½ by 100 foot bench; including headers, etc., would be roughly 15¢ per lineal foot.

Many rose growers have simply installed a ¾-inch steel pipe down the center of the bench with a row of 360° nozzles. In many cases, the grower has installed a sort of wall, 6 or 8 inches high, above the sideboard of the bench, to prevent this water from spraying out into the walks.

Number 2 is the Ooze-Header System. The Ooze Headers are made of 8 mil plastic material and sewn with a plastic thread. The openings around the thread provide a continuous row of water outlets. These headers are placed across the bench, about 8 inches apart and connected to a ½ inch plastic main running down one side of the bench. A ¾ inch water supply will usually handle 1200 to 1600 square feet of bench.

Suitable for the same type of bench watering is a more recently introduced product called DuPont Viaflo Tubing. It is a porous plastic tubing which inflates with the application of a few pounds per-square-inch water pressure from within and allows the passage of water through pores in the

Because of their popularity in Europe, American growers are trying capillary mats in ever growing numbers. Shown above is the Troy capillary mat, available in three and four foot widths. Plants automatically take up water through the root zone if the mat is kept wet. DuPont Viaflo tubing can be used to wet the mat.

wall. Available in 1000 foot rolls. Price per lineal foot is about 3.1¢.

Lastly, a variety of overhead irrigation devices are used on cut flower crops. Rainbird nozzles, Skinner nozzles or the Chapin Spray Hanger will do the job.

WATERING—POT PLANTS

Here again, equipment is available and well proved to the point where virtually all commercial pot-plant crops should be watered mechanically. The most common equipment is the Chapin tubes. A very small diameter (.036 inch, inside diameter) tube is installed in each flower pot. They do the job very well. It is possible to buy the main tubes and also the smaller tubing, leading to the individual plants, and assemble this equipment on a "home-made" basis. However, the apparent conclusion of most major pot-plant growers is that it is actually economical in the long run to buy it ready to use.

It should be pointed out that it is possible and, in fact, quite practical to regulate watering of plants through Chapin tubes with a system of ordinary time clocks and electric (solenoid) valves so regulated as to provide a given volume of water to each plant each day. It works! Actually, the same thing can, of course, be done with bench crops.

More recently, a larger-diameter tube has been provided by Chapin— roughly .060 inch, inside diameter, compared to .036 inch of the regular tube. The larger tube, of course, delivers a larger volume of water faster, and therefore tends to flood the surface of the pot momentarily. This tends to send water more evenly over the entire surface of the pot; the smaller tubes, especially in the case of a very sandy soil, have a tendency to let the water simply go down a rather narrow corridor, out the drain hole—leaving the outer edge of the pot dry. To put it a different way, the larger tube would come nearer doing a good job of leaching in case of a marginal salt problem.

A critical question by many smaller retail growers: Does it pay to obtain and install this type of equipment for spring geraniums? The cost per plant, to install Chapin watering, on the basis of 1,000 plants, would be roughly 10½¢ per plant—material, plus a small amount of labor cost. What does it cost to hand-water these 1,000 plants for several months in the spring when you are busy? Cost, by the way, for a time clock, and electric-valve installation to make it completely automatic, would be about $50.00 more (the same whether it served 1,000 or 50,000 plants).

CAPILLARY WATERING

Capillary watering, or mat irrigation, has rather suddenly become important in this country. While various forms of it have been used in this country and particularly in Europe for many years, it is just in the past 18 months or so that pot plant growers have started to move from the tube system to mats.

Sand was originally used as the sub-irrigating "mat," but its use is declining because it requires an accurately level bench with pots set on it accurately to a uniform depth—more difficult to set or relocate.

Advantages of the mat system of irrigation are:
1. You can grow any combination of pot sizes on the same bench with each getting their proper amount of water.
2. No splashing of water on the foliage.

Chapin watering system on a crop of pot mums. Reduced watering costs soon pay for a system such as this.

Here's a major bedding plant production, all watered mechanically. This is part of the Sedan Floral operation at Sedan, Kansas, operated by Mrs. Eileen Focht, and Mr. W. R. Novotny. The above panels control the watering of between 5 and 6 acres of greenhouse area, all in bedding plants! Each bed is watered on a pre-determined time sequence set up on the above control panel.

3. Better uniformity in water supply.
4. Much easier to move and respace pots on a bench without changing, switching or adding more tubes on.

Disadvantages:

1. Algae growth on mats and pots.
2. Rooting through into the mat.
3. Initial cost somewhat higher than tube system at present time.
4. Keeping the mat at the proper moisture level especially at time of maturity when the grower is attempting to harden-off or tone-up his crop.

Many different soil mixtures have been used for pot trials across the country—each one apparently quite successful. Capilarity must be maintained at all times between the mat and soil. If pot drainage holes are blocked, even partially, the pot will stay dry.

New mat materials are appearing on the market at a very rapid rate. Most prominent include Troy Felt, Vattex P, Pellon and Dorix.

There are any number of ways of keeping the mat wet. They include Viaflo plastic tubes, Chapin Ooze Tubes and Chapin Leader Tubes.

For detailed information on mat irrigation see the November 1974 issue of GROWER TALKS.

WATERING—BEDDING PLANTS

Many progressive bedding plant growers all over the U.S. have already mechanized watering—and feeding—of bedding plants. It can be done—and should be. Examples:

A. Sedan Floral Company, Sedan, Kansas. Five acres plus, all bedding plants, modern greenhouses—and all mechanically watered. Water application done with a Skinner nozzle system. Actual application of water to bedding plants here, by the way, is done by one electronically controlled panel (see photo, page 136).

B. Perry's Plants, Inc., LaPuente, California. Again, a large, wholesale bedding plant operation—premises cover 30 acres—watering again mostly automated. They use a Rain Jet sprinkler head, capable of throwing a square pattern, 36 feet by 36 feet, maximum. Mostly, it is done with 10-foot by 10-foot nozzles. The nozzles sit on the riser about 24 inches above the flat. Application, it is reported, is fairly even, but it does require some spot watering every few days. They water everything well at night, so plants going out on delivery the next morning will be well watered.

C. Spurgeon's Plant Farm, Maryville, Tennessee. Again, a large, wholesale bedding plant specialist, and again, mainly automated watering. Here they use the overhead Rainbird nozzle which will cover about a 12-foot circle. The nozzles are set about 6 feet above the ground. Feed is also supplied through the nozzles.

D. Ken Reeves, Toronto. A large, modern, wholesale bedding plant range—and again, fully equipped for automatic watering. Application again is overhead (Dutch nozzles). Ken has an electronic control which permits automatic watering of 40 different areas in the range—anywhere from 2 to 30 minutes per station. It can all be preset to run in sequence, by itself. However, Ken feels that it is important not to turn on the automatic gadget and let it go. Actually, they sort of dole out water. The object is to keep the plants growing—but not too fast or too lush. Water freely the first week or so, and then begin to hold back.

E. S. S. Couch, Rogersville, Tennessee. Another large, wholesale bedding plant operation that is at this time all irrigated with Spraystick.

WATERING—FIELD CROPS

A wide range of crops is grown either as cut flowers in the open field or, in other cases (hydrangeas, for example), set out as pot plants in the field by commercial growers. Watering of such crops can be done with so-called Rainbird-type nozzles. This equipment mechanically rotates itself around a continuous 360° circle—so that each nozzle, with fair pressure, will adequately cover an area with a diameter of roughly 20 feet. These nozzles can be set up with the use of portable aluminum tubing.

There are, of course, various other automatic-irrigation devices available for open-field use—example, the well-known Skinner irrigation systems— a long line of pipes with nozzles drilled at regular intervals. The pipe rotates from right to left and back to right again, thus covering an area the length of the pipe and a width of 15 to 25 feet or so, depending on pressure, etc. They also work very well.

FERTILIZING

Here again is a job which can, and really should be done mechanically on practically any crop of any size, in the greenhouse or outdoors.

There have been several commercial units available on the market which will inject a liquid fertilizer concentrate, normally at the rate of 1 to 100, into the water as it is being applied to the crop. More each year, both bench crops and pot-plant crops are being fed along with the irrigation water. Each time the crop is watered, it is fed. The system works wonderfully—somehow, plants do seem to grow better with this system of feeding than they do with intermittent-dry or other applications. Of course, it is self-regulating in the sense that in the winter, when light intensity is very low and growth is slow, the water requirement is greatly reduced—and along with it, the fertilizer need. In summer, when light intensity and temperatures are high, much more water is needed—and again, more fertilizer.

For a grower of perhaps ½ acre or so, probably a commercial injector, such as the Smith's injector (Smith Precision Products Co., 1299 Lawrence Drive, Newbury Park, Calif. 91320), or the Ferto-ject equipment (Ferto-ject, 4701 Old San Jose Road, Santa Cruz, California) would be best. Cost for a Smith unit, which will inject water into a ¾-inch main, is roughly $520.00. The larger unit, manufactured by Smith, which will handle a 2-inch main, costs about $1,200.00.

For the smaller grower, there are several smaller, less-expensive types of injectors available. Examples:

A. *Gewa.* Three models with variable or preset proportions ranging in price from approximately $370 to $572. A portable unit on a wheeled cart with a fertilizer-tank capacity of 4 to 26 gallons.

B. *M-P Mixer Proportioner.* Moderately priced, preset or variable-proportion unit with water-flow rate capacity of 3 to 40 gallons per minute. Four models priced from approximately $18 to $275.

The above units are available from most greenhouse-supply distributors.

HEATING—TEMPERATURE CONTROL

Here again, boiler and temperature-control devices can be fully automated —and should be—on any size commercial-growing operation today. We know of several places of 75,000 to 100,000 square feet (including our own) where there is no fireman or temperature man on duty at all, except for the most severe 3 or 4 months of the winter. Even on these nights, the so-called fireman actually does other work. He is there really as a safeguard against the possibility of failure of equipment, which does happen. Often, the owner-manager has alarm equipment in his home so that he can be on guard in case of such failure.

Thermostats (one installed in each greenhouse), if properly adjusted, should maintain temperatures within 2 degrees of a predetermined point. They do work—and the days of the nightman, continually walking houses to check temperatures and turn pipe lines off or on, should be no more.

It should be added here, though, that where such fully automatic heating systems are in use, it is critically important that there be well-designed low-temperature alarms installed around the greenhouses. If any thermostats should fail, or if an end door should blow open, or if any other malfunction occurs, as soon as the temperature drops perhaps below 40°, an alarm should quickly bring someone to the problem. Our own range has such an alarm installation. The alarm will also sound here if boiler pressure falls below a given point, or if the water level goes below a set point. Similar alarms can be installed in refrigerators, by the way, to guard against the possibility of thermostats sticking and freezing a box full of flowers. Incidentally, in selecting the equipment for thermostatic control of greenhouses, it is important that all electric valves be of a fail-safe type—valves that will open when the power shuts off rather than the type which closes when anything goes wrong.

Like all other automatic equipment, such boilers and thermostatic-temperature systems will work fine—but they must be maintained properly, and constantly watched. We run one temperature check of all of our houses every night—in writing—to guard against the possibility of a thermostat suddenly going 5° or 10° off one way or the other. In severe weather, it is just good business to have a competent person on the premises at night.

INSECT CONTROL

Insect-control procedures are the business of a qualified entomologist and we do not propose to go into them in detail here. We would like to point out, though, that from a labor-saving point of view, the procedure of having

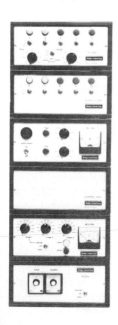

The Phillips Series 100 solid state system can provide automatic control over lighting, watering and heating functions in the greenhouse. Growers can decide how extensive they need to automate by adding or subtracting components from the system. The basic cost is $350.

Mechanized spray application. This equipment will cover the equivalent of about one million square feet of glass in one day—one man. And thorough covering, too. Could be done under glass if the house was designed for it. Photo at Pan-American Plant Co., Bradenton, Florida. Crop: mum stock.

a rather highly paid grower walking up and down benches, a bench at a time with a spray hose, is at best expensive. Of course, much of the burden of insect-control work is now taken over by aerosols, which are a great deal less time-consuming—but expensive in themselves, really. Fogging systems are being used somewhat by greenhouse growers, but for some reason, don't seem to be the final answer. Somehow, a liquid spray with plenty of pressure still seems to be the most effective way to kill the bugs. Just to think ahead a little bit, notice the spray procedure used on the large mum-growing areas in Florida. For example, our own Pan-American Plant Company sprayer (photo above), could cover the equivalent of about one million square feet of greenhouse area in one day—one man. This is, of course, a field procedure. However, if a new greenhouse area was being laid out, it could be specifically designed to permit the use of this type of equipment—with the attendant great saving in labor. An example of what can be done—at Sunnyside Nurseries, Hayward, California, one spray rig, one trip down the house, covers a 36-foot-wide house. The greenhouse is sprayed in 10 minutes. Again—it can be done!

HARVESTING—GRADING CUT FLOWERS

As we mentioned before, the task of picking, bunching, grading, wrapping, etc., of cut flowers is, today, at least two-thirds, or perhaps three-quarters of the work on a typical cut-flower-producing range. Certainly, the majority

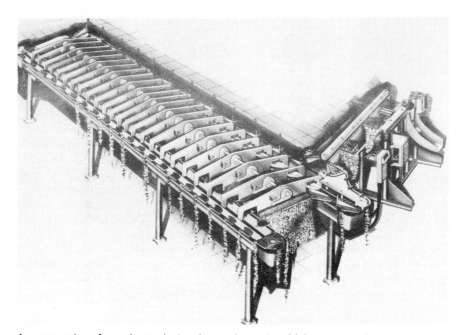

An example of modern electronic equipment which can grade roses—and, potentially, other crops. This equipment is designed and manufactured by Floral Grading, 1105 N. Fairoaks Ave., Sunnyvale, California 94086. It is designed to grade out according to stem length, bunch into 25, tie and wrap about 35,000 roses in an 8-hour day. It operates at full speed with 2 people feeding roses into it, and eliminates better than two-thirds of the hand labor involved in grading and tying roses. Costs in the neighborhood of $35,000. By the way, less-sophisticated equipment for this job was seen recently at the Frank J. Baker Company, Utica, New York—doing a practical job of grading with much-reduced hand labor.

of this work can be automated. Obviously, not much has been accomplished along this line—but let's think about it for a minute.

One time-consuming task is simply moving flowers from the bench to the packing room. There is, of course, a wide range of equipment which could take this task over. If stems were cut to a uniform length, then mechanical weight-grading, in many cases, would sort out the different sizes or grades of flowers. Stem-stripping is, of course, already mechanized. Flowers can be assembled into bunches by hand, then wrapped and tied with string mechanically. Granted, it would take a lot of work to achieve all this— yet again, this is the principal labor cost on the typical cut-flower range. Certainly, there are possibilities here.

One interesting point in connection with automated harvesting of flowers is the idea of growing crops that can be harvested all at one time. Pompons, for example, could be handled this way. Main problem here is that most beds of pomps simply do not mature uniformly enough to permit such a semi-automated approach to harvesting. So here is a job for the breeder—to develop strains that will mature uniformly. Actually, this has been done in other crops—tomatoes for example.

APPLICATION OF BLACK CLOTH

"Pulling" black sateen on hot summer evenings is laborious, uninteresting —and particularly difficult to do at the correct time. Result: Many mum crops are shaded several hours too early with resulting real damage to the crop, to say nothing of the real benefit derived by being able to remove the cloth after dark to keep plants cool at night.

So growers have approached the problem with their typical mechanical bents. Result: Dozens of larger growers across the country have designed their own mechanical equipment to pull the cloth on their own ranges. GROWER TALKS, over the past 5 years, has described many of these installations in some detail. Some have used "off-the-shelf" equipment, such as garage-door openers, etc. Others have been built from the ground up by the grower. Many of them have worked very well. An especially good example of a well-designed sateen operation would be the one done by Will Weatherford, Southern Floral, Houston, Texas, page 258.

More recently, a serious new piece of equipment has come on the market-named "Simtrac," produced by Simtrac, 8243 Christiana, Skokie, IL. Mr. Harold Grossman seems to be the prime mover of the project. From our limited exposure to it, it seems to be well designed. It will apply cloth over large areas in just seconds. Cost for everything but the cloth, on fairly large areas, gets down to about 75 to 80 cents per square foot of ground covered. Add to this the cost for the black sateen—or black poly. To apply to a single bench, cost for equipment goes up to $1.00 to $1.25 per square foot—again, plus cloth. See photo below, of the installation at Schaefer's range, Montgomery, Illinois. Ed Schaefer reports that though

"Simtrac" system of applying black cloth, installed at Schaefer's, Montgomery, Illinois.

expensive, the installation will probably pay for itself in 7 to 8 years, just from plants saved from damage through improperly pulled black cloth. Increased production and further improved quality could bring the amortization period to 3 to 5 years.

MACHINE PLANTERS

Much work has been done in this area over a period of many years. There are, of course, field planters which will handle larger plants such as tree seedlings, nursery stock, etc.—just planting them out in rows in the open field.

In recent years, the Europeans, particularly the Germans, have been very active in trying to develop machines which will pot fairly small seedlings, such as lettuce, cabbage, etc. One example was the Erdprinz. They are used considerably over there, but still, in spite of quite a bit of testing over here, have not become at all a part of American horticulture. Perhaps someone will pick up these devices and put some more effort into them, ironing out the bugs, etc.—and make them work, for example, on transplanting bedding plants.

There is equipment available today (Holland Transplanter Company) which will set Jiffy-Potted plants out into the field, firm them in, give them a bit of water. It's practical!

SUPPORTING CUT-FLOWER CROPS

Not many years ago, the standard practice was to string wires down a bench, "cross-string" the wires, making squares to support cut-flower crops. Now, wire and plastic mesh is available to do this job—and should certainly be used in all cases.

POTTING TABLES

Large, efficient pot-plant growers have learned that much of the "moving" work connected with pot plants can be eliminated by efficient management. Typically, a 4-wheel wagon is devised which will hold perhaps several yards of soil. Steam pipes with perforations are installed in the bed of the wagon in such a way that the wagon can be filled, the soil in it steam-sterilized, the steam line disconnected, and the wagon wheeled right out to the greenhouse where the potting is to be done. The same wagon serves as a potting bench, and since the job is done right out in the greenhouse, there is a very short move of potted plants from the potting bench to the greenhouse bench, where they are to be grown. This can be done with conveyor tracks.

A good example of such a combined steaming and potting table is available from the Lindig Manufacturing Corporation, 1875 W. County Rd. C, St. Paul, Minnesota 55113. Cost for a wagon, roughly 9 feet long by 4 feet wide, equipped for steaming, is about $1,750.

AUTOMATED POTTING

Equipment is available today which will go a long way towards automating

A new U.S.-built potting machine from Soil Systems, Inc., P.O. Box 1148, Apopka, Florida. It handles a maximum of 7,200 5-inch mum pots per hour (5 people). Fills pots or flats, firms the soil; can punch a hole for a 2¼-inch pot ball, or 5 smaller holes for 5 mum cuttings in a 6-inch pot. On the left, Bill Gunesch, Park Floral Company, Englewood, Colorado. The other gentleman is Bill Meadows.

the potting operation. Example: The Bruno Krause potting machine called the Plantorex is available from Timm Enterprises, 5204 Trafalgar Rd., Oakville, Ontario, Canada. This machine is capable of taking about 2,000 4-to-6-inch pots per hour off a stack, placing them on a belt, filling them with soil, leveling them, punching the correct-size hole for a 2¼-inch plant to be shifted or, in case of pot mums, it will punch 5 smaller holes to accommodate the 5 cuttings. Girls then insert the cuttings or 2¼-inch plant (or whatever) into the pots as they go by on the endless belt (see photo, page 274).

SHADE THE GLASS—AND WASH IT

California growers are finding ways to apply shade to their large areas of glass—and remove it—mechanically. Example: One man with a helicopter can shade 500,000 feet of glass in 45 minutes (see photo, page 145). The whirly bird, operating about 4 feet above the roof, does the job at a lower unit cost than by hand application.

Then again, in California, there's equipment to wash the roof—German-made. Rotating brushes, with a strong stream of water applied through the core of the brushes, are moved up and down the roof by a mechanical device. They operate from ridge to gutter, then move over and do another strip. They

Here's a different way to mechanize flower production! This fellow shades 500,000 square feet in 45 minutes.

will wash one span, 260 feet, in 40 minutes. Ray Hasek of the University of California floriculture staff would have details for anyone interested.

BEDDING PLANT AUTOMATION

Actually, a whole subject by itself—covered in some detail under Bedding Plants; see page 22.

German-made greenhouse roof-washing machine.

15. LOW-TEMPERATURE STORAGE

For as long as we have had refrigeration, growers have traditionally cut their crops the day before shipping and stored the flowers in a cool room in cans of water. This practice was based on the sound, basic fact that cut flowers last longer in a cool temperature than they do in a higher one. In the late 1940's, research work was done (principally at Cornell University, Ithaca, New York) on tolerance of flowers to temperatures with a view toward longer-term storage. The obvious and common problem of a surplus of carnations, for instance, a week or two before Mother's Day, and then not enough to go around for the holiday itself, was the practical application of a longer-term storage project. Flowers have traditionally been an extremely perishable product; if they aren't used within a few days of cutting, they rapidly become worthless. Wouldn't it be profitable to the grower to be able to store his surplus cut for a later, better market period?

Research workers developed a technique of "dry storage." Flowers were cut and immediately placed in large containers without water. The cans were sealed and placed in a 31° chamber. Thirty-one degrees was determined to be the lowest temperature at which flowers could be stored with no ill effect. When the flowers were removed from storage, an inch or two of their stems were cut and then they were placed in containers of warm water. Within a few hours, the flowers were taking on water and were in an excellent, turgid condition. It was claimed that some flowers (pompon chrysanthemums, for instance) could be stored as long as a month and, at the end of their storage period, last as long as freshly cut flowers.

Research workers found that different kinds of flowers varied widely in their reaction to this 31° storage treatment. In general, the tropical flowers, such as orchids or gardenias, couldn't be successfully stored at such low temperatures. Some varieties of roses took on a bluish cast as a result of long-term 31° storage. Some carnation varieties were subject to "sleepiness." Pompon chrysanthemums apparently stored excellently. What is the present status of this new technique?

There seem to be widely divergent opinions among those growers who have tried dry 31° storage. Almost all of them agree that the picture isn't as rosy as it looked when the research reports were released. Almost everyone who has done a good job of storing pompon chrysanthemums agrees that they can be kept for at least 3 weeks with no apparent bad effects. Beyond this, opinions vary. Some growers have been successful with carnations; some complain about "sleepiness" or "scalding" of outer petals—particularly on certain varieties. Rose growers aren't too enthusiastic. They say that their roses dry-stored for 2 or 3 weeks look perfect when they first come out of storage, but open much more quickly than freshly cut flowers and don't last as long. Rose growers generally agree that floribundas (*Garnette,* for instance) store much better than hybrid teas. Also, some varieties" blue" considerably during storage. Some of the large reputable rose producers do store cut roses up to 4 and 5 *days* for the several big holidays. It must be done under precise conditions, and only top-quality flowers may be stored;

but if the rules are followed, experience is that these stored flowers have virtually the same life as fresh ones.

Wholesalers and retailers are generally suspicious of "stored" cut flowers. True, their suspicions are sometimes based on flowers that haven't been properly stored. Growers who are doing a good job of dry-storage of flowers generally don't talk about it for fear of prejudicing the salability of their flowers.

Several facts are emerging as a result of growers' attempts at 31° dry storage. The research work pointed out that flowers actually keep better in low temperatures—and the lower the better. Flowers stored in open conditions in vases of water at 40° kept better than those similarly stored at 45°. In other words, the colder the better, down to 31°. Many growers are reducing the temperature of their refrigerated chambers down to 32° or 33°, even though they store their flowers in vases of water. Rose growers say that *Garnette* will successfully store under these conditions a good 3 weeks. Most hybrid tea varieties will store well under these conditions for as long as 2 weeks.

Some growers are storing very successfully using the "dry" or "canned" method. They say the reason for so many failures is lack of attention to the important requirements of successful storage. They agree that the following factors are all important:

1. Store only TOP-QUALITY flowers. Poor flowers to begin with will be worse when they come out of storage.

2. Flowers to be stored should definitely be cut tighter than normally. How tight to cut is a fine line that must be learned from experience. A rose, for instance, cut too tight, never will open completely. Yet, a rose must be cut tighter than normal for successful long-term storage. Flowers cut too far open are apt to shatter when taken out of storage.

3. Do a good job of air-tight storage. Good, heavy, wax-lined cardboard containers are available. Much work has been done in large cardboard containers about 24 inches in diameter and 3 feet long. Best if the top is sealed with some sort of airtight device. Also good in placing flowers in such containers to be careful to cushion the flower heads so they won't bruise by touching each other. Fill each container to its maximum capacity.

4. Flowers placed in storage should be freshly cut (preferably cut in the morning while they are fresh and turgid) and put into sealed containers immediately. Do not put flowers in water before storing.

5. When flowers are removed from storage, cut an inch or two of their stems off and place them in warm water (about as warm as your hands can comfortably stand) in room temperature. They should take water almost immediately and will be in good shape in a few hours.

6. Some flowers and varieties will not store successfully and some will store better than others. In general, cool-temperature crops will store better than warm-temperature crops. Orchids and gardenias definitely will not

stand 31° storage. Experiment with varieties under your own conditions. Some varieties store better than others. Large standard mums, for instance, are apt to bruise and aren't too successful in 31° storage.

7. Keep the temperature of your refrigerator as close to 31° as possible. Every degree above that point means poorer storage.

Everyone who has tried low-temperature storage of cut flowers agrees that, whether or not you pack in dry, sealed containers, cut-flower storage should be done as close to 31° as possible. The old idea of 40° or 45° storage has definitely not proved as effective as lower temperatures.

Mum and carnation growers have learned that they can store unrooted cuttings in sealed cellophane bags for up to several weeks in a 31° chamber with very little deterioration. Budded rose plants are stored best as near to 31° as possible—with high humidity.

16. GREENHOUSE COST ACCOUNTING

What crops make the most money? What should selling prices be? Are costs excessive in some areas?

These are the questions which greenhouse cost accounting should answer —answers which should enable you to direct your business to more profitable results. Following is a description of a simplified system which our experience indicates should be most helpful to you if you do not have an established system now:

The main idea is to sort out (for all important crops) all expenses and all income—by crops. You should know just what it costs you to produce those 5,000 poinsettias—and just how many dollars net after selling cost you got for them. And. of course, how much net profit for the crop?

Where possible, it is desirable to group related products, such as Christmas plants or Easter bulbs, into single crops, to avoid voluminous record keeping. Having listed all the "crops" on which it will be desirable to determine profitability, assign crop numbers to them. Example: (1) *Bedding Plants,* (2) *Roses,* (3) *Mums,* (4) *Christmas Plants,* etc. Obtain a common 8½ by 11-inch ring binder and rule sheets into 5 vertical columns, headed: *Receipts, Labor, Material, Overhead* and *Number of Units of Sale.* Enter crop names and numbers in the upper right hand corners of the sheets, and you are ready to start (see illustration of crop-record form, page 151).

CROP COST RECORD

RECEIPTS

Determine the best method of recording receipts by crop or crop number. This might be by cash-register coding, sales-slip copies or, in a small operation, by entry on a work sheet prepared for this purpose. If wholesale, commission-house statements may be used to enter receipts. In this case, commissions and the Allied Florist percentage should be deducted prior to entry. Accumulate receipts on a weekly or monthly basis, and enter on the crop records.

LABOR

The form shown below, which we use in one of our operations, may be helpful to you. This form may be printed on the backs of timecards or used as a separate reporting form in conjunction with pay periods. Employees enter the number of hours spent on individual crops each day. At the time pay checks are prepared, the time spent on crops is totaled and converted to labor cost. Total labor cost by crops may now be totaled and balanced with the dollar total being paid to the employee. Labor cost is then entered on the individual crop records. If there are several employees, their records should be totaled to permit just one entry per pay period on the crop-record sheets.

Name		Clock No.		Hourly Rate			Date		
Crop No.	1 2 3 4 5 6 7 8 9 10 11 12 13 14 15 16 17 0 Total								
Wed.									
Thur.									
Fri.									
Sat.									
Sun.									
Mon.									
Tues.									
Total Hrs.									
Total $									

Lists of crop numbers are posted at the time clock and bulletin board and in other locations for employees' convenience. Note that one column, designated "0" for overhead, is provided for recording time spent on general labor and maintenance. Amounts for these items are charged to a general overhead account which may later be distributed to crops.

MATERIALS

Invoices for such things as seeds, cuttings, plants and bulbs should be entered directly on the crop records. Estimates should be made of the cost of fertilizer and insecticides used at the time of application and entered on the records. All materials used should be charged directly to the crops to the greatest possible extent. General supplies should be charged to the general overhead account.

OVERHEAD

In addition to the items mentioned above, overhead includes expenses for heat, electricity, water, tax depreciation, etc.—all expenses which cannot be charged directly to crops.

Totals may be obtained for overhead expenses monthly by totaling the entries for such items in your regular profit-and-loss accounting system or by charging all such items to a general overhead account as mentioned above.

Generally speaking, overhead is chargeable to individual crops on the basis of their use of bench space in the greenhouse. Thus, each crop should be charged with the same proportion of total overhead expense as its proportion of total bench space used.

Bench-space usage is obtained by measuring the space occupied by each crop at the end of each month. The measurement can usually be obtained by sight estimate or by pacing distances. If bench widths are fairly uniform, the measurements need be made in linear feet only, and need not be converted to square feet. The allocation of overhead expense to individual crops can now be made by making the calculations illustrated on the work sheet shown below:

Crop No.	Bench Space Used	%* to Total		Total Overhead Expense		Crop Overhead Expense
1	200 ft.	20	×	$5,000	=	$1,000
2	100 ft.	10	×	5,000	=	500
3	400 ft.	40	×	5,000	=	2,000
4	300 ft.	30	×	5,000	=	1,500
	1,000 ft.	100		$5,000		$5,000

* % to total is obtained by dividing total bench space into space used by each crop.

Overhead expenses for each crop are, of course, entered on the crop-record sheets.

NUMBER OF UNITS OF SALE

Units of sale may be in terms of flats, pots, packs, dozens, etc. Where practical, enter the estimated number of units which will be available to sell at the time the crop is planted, and the number of units actually produced at the time the crop is completed. When related to total cost, these entries provide cost per unit for pricing purposes.

CROP PROFIT

<table>
<tr><td colspan="6" align="center">CROP COST RECORD</td></tr>
<tr><td colspan="6">Crop _Roses_</td></tr>
<tr><td colspan="6">Crop No. _2_</td></tr>
</table>

When each crop is completed, the figures for labor, materials and overhead are totaled and subtracted from receipts to show the total profit derived from the crop. Where units of sale are available for the crop, this figure is divided into total expenses to show cost per units of sale.

In some cases, it may be desirable to estimate cost per unit of sale just prior to the selling season for a crop as a guide in establishing selling prices. This can be done by totaling the expense items, estimating additional expenses for remainder of growing period, and relating to estimated number of units of sale.

Month	Receipts	Labor	Material	Overhead	Units of Sale
Jan.	$850.00	$97.00 61.00 83.00 102.00	$35.00 35.00 11.90 35.00 5.50 35.00	$400.50	608 dz.
Feb.	1,200.00	78.00 107.00 81.00 98.00	20.00 20.00 12.00 20.00 15.00 20.00	450.00	873
Mar.	1,100.00	90.00 110.00 85.00 78.00	20.00 25.00 9.00 20.00 15.00	525.00	758
Total	3,150.00 2,798.90 351.10 net profit	1,070.00	353.40	1,375.50 353.40 1,070.00 2,798.90	2239 2239 / 2,798.90 $1.25 dozen

It is usually desirable to check a cost-accounting system against the regular profit-and-loss accounting system at the end of the year. This is done by totaling receipts for all crops and comparing with sales on the profit-and-loss statement. Expenses for all crops are then totaled and compared with total expenses on the profit-and-loss statement. If the cost-accounting figures are within 3 to 4 per cent of profit-and-loss figures, the result can be considered quite satisfactory. If not, the cost-accounting system needs to be tightened up.

ALTERNATE PLANS

Some even simpler plan may fit your individual requirements, and if it follows the principles outlined above, should prove quite satisfactory. For example, you might have just 2 columns on your cost records, one for receipts and one for expenses. Direct labor and material items would be entered in the expense column as described above, but overhead would be entered on an experience formula basis as follows:

6 cents per square foot of bench space in months
when no heat is required.

8 cents per month when average outdoor daily
temperatures are 50° to 65°.

10 cents per month when average outdoor daily
temperatures are under 50°.

If such a system is used, it would be realistic on most ranges to boost this overhead cost at least 35% to 50% from January 1 till July 1, lower it accordingly the rest of the year. Space is in demand in the spring, so a crop must pay more for it!

Seed can be germinated in many different materials! The 16 trays above show 4 different flats germinated in each of 4 different mixes. Left to right: 4 trays of Dwarf French marigolds; snapdragon Torch, petunia White Magic, and salvia St. John's Fire. Each of the 4 varieties of annuals was germinated in 4 different soil mixes. For example, the 4 front trays in the photo were filled with half each peat and No. 2 vermiculite (a bit coarser); the next 4 to the rear, half each peat and perlite; and the last 4 to the rear, 2/3 soil and 1/3 peat. We examined them carefully and saw no important difference between any of the mixes—really.

17. SEED GERMINATION

The plant industry today is based on fast-crop techniques of production. This requires production of good seedlings that can be transplanted at the proper time to fit the schedule for the crop being handled. In order to do this, we must have an organized, standardized system for the reliable production of seedlings for any operation. The schedule should be coordinated with the normal daily workload, which can be accomplished with help and space available. If more plants are seeded than can normally be handled over a given period of time, the quality of the seedlings and efficiency of transplanting will deteriorate and result in overgrown seedlings that cannot respond to fast-growth requirements.

To make your production profitable, you must standardize the controlled condition for seedlings and transplants, and produce quality seedlings at the time which the schedule requires.

Have on hand, well in advance of the sowing date, good viable seed which will respond if given the proper conditions. Seed is no place to cut corners in production. Sow the varieties which have been promoted and sell the best. Since much of our seed is sown in late winter or early spring, we have to create an artificial atmosphere for seedling growth.

The elements necessary for seed germination and seedling growth are a loose, porous medium for root development and growth, temperature, light or dark reaction, and, of course, nutrients and an ever-present moisture supply. The addition of CO_2 under certain conditions can greatly aid seedling development. Many growers are developing a specialized area for germination along the following lines:

1. Use a peat-lite mixture for germination in a well-drained flat or plastic tray—always remember the seedling container must drain out excess moisture. Jiffy-Mix is becoming universally accepted as the seedling medium. Some growers add fine sterilized sand to the Jiffy Mix—up to 33%. The addition of sand makes the seedling roots come apart easier in transplanting. Never sow your seed too thickly; sow thinly for good seedling development. We recommend that you sow seed in evenly spaced rows for both good growth and prevention of spread of disease organisms.

2. Bottom heat or soil temperature should never go below the 70-72°F range. Bottom heat is a must for most seed germination (one exception: pansy—germinate warm, then cool immediately). See table, page 155. The night greenhouse temperature should be in the 65°F range, to insure even bottom heat. Once the seedlings are established, they can be removed from bottom heat.

3. The soil should have uniform free moisture present at all times to insure germination. The simplest way to provide this is with an automatic mist system on a time clock. This would be approximately 6 seconds of mist every 10 minutes, 7:00 a.m.-5:00 p.m., extended as the day lengthens. If you are using a forced hot-air system, you had better leave it on 24 hours a day to insure proper moisture.

4. Light requirement. You can definitely improve your seedlings by supplementing artificial light 24 hours a day. A very good way to do this is to have a double line of tubes approximately every 18 inches across the bench. The natural sunlight is not blocked by the fixtures if they are spaced properly. The light supplied by one cool white tube alongside a

A very practical method of watering seed flats, in our experience. Simply install a mist irrigation line over the flats and set it on a time-clock—in warm summer weather during the day we mist these flats 7 seconds every 10 minutes. Much less than this in the winter, and, of course, none at night. Also, cut down on the mist after germination occurs. Works fine.

natural daylight tube will give a stockier, stronger seedling in less time, especially early in the season. Move seedlings to lights after germination for growing-on. Lights and mist are difficult accomplishments; however, they can be done. Most seedlings germinate well, without being covered, in full sunlight, while other seedlings need a 3-day period of darkness for germination. Some of the latter are verbena, dusty miller, larkspur, pansy, phlox, portulaca, sweet pea, vinca rosea. This is accomplished by using a black poly bag to cover the flat during germination. The flats should be kept warm during this period.

5. Your seedling medium should be low in fertilizer elements, and because of this, you should feed your seedlings weekly with a diluted fertilizer solution, as soon as established. An example would be 1 ounce of 20-20-20 to 3 gallons of water, applied with a Hozon and watering hose or sprinkling can. Begonias can be very difficult plants to germinate and grow at times; however, by giving a weak feeding of 9-45-15 plant starter at regular intervals, development will be quite fast. They are very shallow-rooted in the seed flats, and consequently, need the extra fertilizer at regular intervals to improve their vigor. (The constant mist tends to leach the soil surface.) Impatiens is another plant that requires extra care in germination. Germinate the seeds under mist with no soil cover. They are easily germinated over a wide range of temperature when exposed to light and mist.

6. The next step is to subject your seedlings to cooler temperatures (55-60°F) for a period of several days prior to transplanting. This "tones" your seedling, makes it more acclimated for transplanting. Actually, a seedling should be large enough to handle with several pairs of well-defined leaves. However, if you sow too thickly, you cannot have proper seedling development. The proper amount of seed per flat varies with variety. If you

CHECK LIST FOR GERMINATION TROUBLES

SUFFICIENT MOISTURE? ABSOLUTE NECESSITY — UNIFORM – NOT EXCESSIVE.

CORRECT TEMPERATURE? — USUALLY 65-70° — SOME PLANTS COOLER.

SEEDS COVERED TOO DEEP? AIR IS AS ESSENTIAL AS HEAT AND MOISTURE!!! FINE SEEDS REQUIRE LITTLE OR NO COVER — WILL "WASH" INTO SOIL.

ANTS-MICE — MORE OFTEN RESPONSIBLE THAN PEOPLE GENERALLY REALIZE – EVEN FLORISTS!

CLEAN, DISEASE - FREE STERILIZED MEDIUM?

YOUR SEEDSMAN IS ONLY HUMAN -- DOES HIS BEST. IF YOU THINK HE IS AT FAULT, WRITE AND GIVE HIM A CHANCE TO HELP!

ABOVE ALL, REMOVE SEEDLINGS TO COOL AIR AND PLENTY OF LIGHT AS SOON AS SPROUTED - - BEST DAMP-OFF PREVENTATIVE!

;ow more than 1,400 petunia seeds per flat, you will probably have to ransplant some prematurely, or some seedlings will become overgrown. Fourteen hundred seeds should give you 1,000 seedlings to a standard flat.

COMMON PROBLEMS WITH GERMINATION:

1. A combination of lack of drainage and temperature too low during germination.
2. Seed flats drying out during germination. *Very important.* Once dried out—germination will go down.
3. Disease organisms present in flat or growing medium because of insufficient sterilization, or contamination.
4. Overtreatment with methyl bromide or other drench materials (mercury compounds).

GUIDELINES FOR GERMINATION OF ANNUALS.

	Optimum °F temperature for best germination	Continuous light or dark	Usual number of days required for uniform germination
Begonia	70	Light	15
Browallia	70	Light	15
Carnation	70	Dark/Light	20
Calceolaria	70	Light	15
Celosia	70	Dark/Light	10
Centaurea	65	Dark	10
Cineraria	70	Light	10
Coleus	65	Light	10
Cyclamen	60	Dark	50
Dahlia	70	Dark/Light	5
Dianthus	70	Dark/Light	5
Gloxinia	70	Light	15
Impatiens	70	Light	15
Kalanchoe	70	Light	15
*Lobelia	70	Dark/Light	20
Marigold	70	Dark/Light	5
Pansy	65	Dark	10
Petunia	70	Light	10
Phlox	65	Dark	10
Salvia	70	Light	15
Snapdragon	65	Light	10
Vinca	70	Dark	15
Zinnia	70	Dark/Light	5

*Except variety Heavenly which requires 50°F for best results.

RD

18. THE CO₂ STORY

by W. D. Holley (Ret'd)
Colorado State University

Carbon dioxide assimilation is the basic process in nature carried on by all green plants in the presence of light. The rate of this process is affected primarily by light, temperature and the CO_2 concentration around and inside the leaves. The use of CO_2 to increase plant growth has been known by researchers for 75 years. Many publications appeared in Europe on this subject from 1920 to 1930. Major reasons why the addition of CO_2 to greenhouse crops was not adopted at the time were: (1) no cheap sources of pure CO_2, and (2) depression prices, especially on tomato and cucumber, discouraged growers from increasing production.

Normally, plants get CO_2 from the air around them. Average CO_2 content of the air is approximately 300 parts per million, or 0.03 of 1%. This CO_2 content in the outside air varies with weather, proximity to large bodies of water and to industrial areas. Inside a greenhouse, the CO_2 content is much more variable. A closed house may have 400 ppm or more during the night. Mulches and rotting soil materials release small amounts of CO_2 constantly. Plants also give off CO_2 in respiration and during the night when they do not use it, there is an accumulation in the greenhouse. As soon as day begins, plants start using CO_2. If the house remains closed, the CO_2 concentration often drops quickly below the level outside. Some CO_2 continues to filter in through cracks at an estimated average rate of 2 air changes per hour during relatively still weather. CO_2 levels often drop to 200 ppm, and even to 125 ppm, in closed houses during winter days. As plants continue to respire during daytime, 125 ppm is at or near the point where they are able to assimilate only that given off; growth stops. In practice, plants probably continue to grow at such a reduced rate that for all practical purposes, they are standing still.

When these facts were brought to light at Colorado State University in late 1958, it became evident that CO_2 was actually limiting the winter growth of roses and carnations, and probably most other plants. Logic told us that growers in climates where greenhouses remained closed much of the winter could probably benefit most from adding CO_2 to their houses. They would have a deficiency of CO_2 more of the time and they would have more closed-system time in which CO_2 could be added without wasting it. Logic also pointed to Colorado and similar climates where CO_2 might be used to advantage.

SUPPLEMENTAL CO₂

In the 10 years since the 11th Edition of the *Red Book* (1965), the use of supplemental CO_2 in greenhouses has been considerably better understood. One only needs an elemental understanding of how plants grow to appreciate the potential value of adding CO_2 to his crops. During the 10 years, crop responses have been researched. All of them respond to higher CO_2

At right, tomato and cucumber plants maintained for three weeks in growth chambers, at top, 1000 ppm carbon dioxide, and bottom, 400 ppm carbon dioxide. Plants exposed to 1500 foot-candles of fluorescent (cool white) light.

levels, but some responses are either not economical, or in some situations the plants are too tall or become hungry for major nutrients. In other words, high CO_2 levels may require altering other factors if the grower is to maximize his benefits.

Most of the controversy over use of CO_2 is tied in with climate. In the South or Far West, greenhouse construction may not be tight, or most winter days require considerable ventilation, especially with cool crops. Under such conditions, adding CO_2 may afford little benefit to plants. Under tight greenhouse conditions across the northern half of the country (from November to March), supplemental CO_2 is standard practice among progressive growers. Most crop manuals and current instructions for growing crops include recommendations of CO_2 levels from 1000 to 1500 ppm. Efficient use of higher levels by most crops is questionable due to lack of energy in winter.

Each winter, one or more carnation growers in Colorado decide not to use CO_2. By late January or February, they begin trying to blame poor feeding or poor temperature control for the weak stems they are producing.

CROP RESPONSES

Some crops respond better to high CO_2 levels than others. Even some varieties of roses and chrysanthemums are more responsive. Other crops have specific responses that can be of value to the producer. Snapdragons produce a lot more weight in winter when CO_2 is added, while spring crops have less weight, but are faster. Carnation grade and quality improve within 3 weeks of the start of CO_2 additions; yield increases 4 to 5 months later. Blindness in iris has been virtually eliminated by some growers. Cattleya and cymbidium orchids are reported to have more flowers per cluster or stem. Higher CO_2 concentration and higher temperatures have improved rooting, increased flowering, height and branching of geraniums. Production increases of 10 to 35% have been reported on foliage plants in

157

Florida. CO_2 and increased temperatures have improved stem length and weight of chrysanthemums. The winter chrysanthemum schedules may be cut by as much as 2 weeks when CO_2 is added.

A commercial test by Pierce Bros., Waltham, Massachusetts, compared *Yuletide* Roses treated with 1000 ppm CO_2 with a similar untreated house. The treated house produced 53% more weight of total roses, made up by increased numbers and improved grade. There are some other rose growers in the country who question a need for supplemental CO_2. Probably most U.S. growers now consider adding CO_2 in winter just as essential as feeding or watering. While much has been learned about the use of CO_2 in greenhouse growing, there is more to come. The application of CO_2 to closed greenhouses in winter is practical for growers of most flower and vegetable crops. We need to know what crops respond economically and what varieties in each crop respond best. Different levels will eventually be worked out for each crop. Even the breeder may supply us with more responsive varieties.

SOURCES

There are several types of CO_2 burners offered to the trade, principally those using propane or natural gas as fuel. Among these is the Johnson CO_2 producer. This generator produces CO_2 by an efficient, low-cost method, the oxidation of propane or natural gas. This unit will produce 8.25 pounds of CO_2 per hour using LP gas, based on one air change per hour to furnish 1500 ppm CO_2. Natural gas will yield a slightly less amount. The Johnson CO_2 Producer is designed to cover 4,800 sq. ft. and ranges in price up to about $150.00, depending upon the model, automatic or manually operated.

The fuel used in a CO_2 burner must be relatively pure or toxicants such as sulfur dioxide and ethylene may damage the crop. The burner must produce perfect combustion and be absolutely safe. These features increase the cost of even the simplest type of burner. The Johnson units are safe from the standpoint of both human and plant injury. When using propane, H.D. 5 is to be used exclusively, and when natural gas is used, the grower should check with the gas company to be sure the gas has a low sulfur content— not to exceed 1 gram per 100 cubic feet of gas.

Many ordinary gas burners have been adapted to greenhouses for CO_2 production. All open-flame burners used in the greenhouse should be checked regularly to be certain that they are not unduly polluting the air for workers and plants. Clean accumulated dust and dirt from around the burner. Adjust the flame to a clear blue color. Clear all gas-jet holes for maximum burning. Check all pipe connections for gas leaks. And above all, be sure there is enough air available to the burner for complete combustion, even when the greenhouses are tightly closed and iced-over. Fourteen cubic feet of air are needed to burn one cubic foot of gas. Incomplete combustion causes the release of ethylene, carbon monoxide and other toxicants into the greenhouse atmosphere. Chronic exposure to low levels of these toxicants causes shortened internodes, increased branching and crippled flowers. Don't guess with CO_2 burners. Be certain they are safe.

MEASURING CONCENTRATION

We still do not have an inexpensive method for monitoring CO_2 levels. Spot measurements can be made with portable apparatus costing less than $100.00. These spot measurements can be used to determine the range of levels produced by a new burner installation. By measuring on bright and on dark days, the outer limits of levels being maintained can be estimated. A ball-park figure for burners manufactured for CO_2 production should be available from the supplier. The highest level (2,000) occurs on cloudy days when less CO_2 is consumed by the plants.

Carbon dioxide levels should be regulated according to light energy for most efficient use. A basic low rate is used on a dark day, 1½ to 2 times this rate on a lighter day, with a further increase on a sunny day so long as the house remains closed.

19. ON SOIL TESTING

Soil testing, properly done, is an aid to flower growing that we feel no modern range can afford to do without. There is much question as to how to test, how often to do it, etc., but the grower who does no testing is passing up a good practical guide in his feeding and growing program. A real help in case of trouble, and incidentally, a means of cutting fertilizer bills.

WHEN TO TEST?

Ideally, we would like to run nitrate, potash, phosphates, and acidity on all our benches once a month throughout the year—but that would be a lot of testing, and expense. We've tried many different schedules, and on our own range have settled down to this: once-a-month tests are made on all benches where crops are in active growth, or where we feel excesses (from sterilizing, etc.) might be present. We watch carefully. all beds that have been steamed in the past month or two—for excess nitrates (also for ammonia and nitrites). We watch out for deficiencies of nitrates and potash where there is a heavy lot of rapidly growing material on a shallow raised bench—especially in spring or summer. Watch this, too: a shallow bench during spring or summer

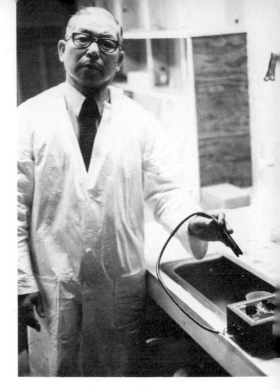

Here's the Solu Bridge instrument described in the text. The main purpose is to check total soluble salts in the soil. Simple to operate and recommended where any considerable amount of soil testing is done. Source: Beckman Instruments, Inc., Cedar Grove, New Jersey.

with a heavy, rapidly growing crop will need heavy and frequent watering—which means rapid leaching of nutrients. Then, too, light green or yellowish-colored foliage and retarded growth are sometimes tip-offs of a lack of nutrients.

On the other extreme, small seedlings or young (3-4-inch) plants on a ground bed during the winter months will have very modest nutrient requirements. We go over such crops lightly on our monthly tests.

In addition to these monthly tests, we welcome samples of soil from our section men at any time. If a bench or a crop doesn't seem to be taking off well, or if for any reason a nutrient shortage or excess is suspected, we run a test on it immediately.

About excess soluble salts: we have a Solu Bridge unit (RD-B15-VS2) with which we can very easily run a test for excess total soluble-salt content in the soil. It is made by the Beckman Instrument Inc., 89 Commerce Rd., Cedar Grove, Essex County, New Jersey. (See photo above.)

While this instrument is no longer being made, the current model S.D. B-15 will do the same job at a cost of approximately $172.00. Many cases of excess salts have been spotted with this unit. As for frequency of soluble-salt tests, it is run only if we have some reason to suspect an excess of salts in the soil.

Will one test taken from a house reflect the true nutrient picture over 6 or 8 benches? We think definitely not. There is too much chance for error. First, that little spoonful of soil that is selected for the test might have a particle from a recent fertilizer application—that would throw the test off completely. The tests themselves are really only qualitative—not designed to give really accurate readings of parts per million. We believe they would be better calibrated to read "low, medium, high" rather than parts per million.

To offset this problem, we take at least 6 cores per bench. In other words, if we sample from one bench, we take 6 cores from different locations in the bench; if we want to group 4 benches together, we would take 6 from each bench for a total of 24 cores. These are well-mixed, and then the sample for testing is selected from this mixture.

WHAT TEST TO USE?

There are several reliable systems of soil testing offered to greenhouse men (Sudbury, LaMotte, Spurway). We have always used the Spurway system, are used to it, and feel it is as good as any. One big advantage of Spurway tests: most of the floriculture schools and floriculture extension men over the country, as well as most large commercial growers, use Spurway tests. This means that by using Spurway tests, a grower will be able to talk in common terms with schools and most other growers. The other tests vary too much in procedure to permit comparing results in parts per million. One of the discouraging things about this whole greenhouse soil-testing picture is that the same sample of soil from the same bench, tested 3 different places under different systems, will give widely varying answers.

Whatever system is selected, it is important that the grower stick with it, and develop, as soon as possible, a feel for the relationship between the test results and his growing crops. That's what really counts. One other important point here is that the same person should do all the testing and reading, since a number of different people reading the same test will invariably come up with different results.

TESTING PROCEDURE

We follow the procedure outlined in the Spurway System. Equipment, reagents and instructions for these tests can be purchased from the Edwards Laboratory, P. O. Box 318, 202 Milan Ave., Norwalk, Ohio 44857. The average grower will have need only for the equipment and reagents for tests for nitrates, potash, phosphates, and soil acidity—with the possible addition of several bottles of reagents for the nitrite and ammonia tests. Renewals of the reagents can be purchased from the Edwards Laboratory.

Growers interested in setting up better, more complete laboratory facilities can obtain all sorts of laboratory supplies and reagents from Central Scientific Co., 1700 Irving Park Blvd., Chicago, Illinois.

Testing may be done on a packing-room table, in your kitchen (some reagents are poisons and strong acids), or better yet, build a small table and a sink in a corner of your office or service building for this purpose—where equipment can be kept clean and ready without wasting time laying it out.

SOME SUGGESTIONS ON THE TESTS

All glassware and testing equipment must be kept absolutely clean at all times. The tests are very sensitive to begin with, and if equipment is not strictly clean, tests will mean little. Glassware must be rinsed in distilled water after washing; otherwise, with hard waters, a lime crust will form. Be sure to use distilled water and not tap water for the tests.

We use a full level teaspoonful rather than half a spoonful for the test. The amount of distilled water and No. 1 reagent added to the soil must be doubled, too. We feel this lessens the chance of error through some impurity getting into the soil sample.

In taking samples, scrape off the top ½ inch of soil, then take your sample as a core from there down to the bottom of the bench (6-8 inches down).

Reagent No. 2 is highly perishable. As soon as the least discoloration is noted, it should be discarded. Since it is made up almost entirely of sulfuric acid, it must be handled with care.

SCHOOL TESTING

In some states, state-college floriculture departments run tests at cost as a service to growers. This type of service is on the increase, and is quite popular where offered. Undoubtedly, the quality of testing under such supervision is excellent. There are some disadvantages: first, the time lag in getting reports back. If a crop is in trouble, the grower who can test a sample himself, and has a result in an hour, will be able to take corrective action the same day. Also, soil samples can change a little during the several days in the mail—especially in nitrates—due to bacterial action in the soil.

PROPER NUTRIENT LEVELS

Although these tests should not be expected to be scientifically accurate, some limits in terms of parts per million of the various nutrients must be set down. Here is our experience using Spurway tests:

Nitrates: most greenhouse crops should be somewhere between 30 and 50 ppm. Anything from 75 to 100 ppm is in the danger zone.

Potash: we like our soils to run between 20 and 40 ppm.

Phosphate: 5 ppm is normal, 10 ppm is high; you rarely get any excess.

Calcium: 150 ppm.

Acidity: soil pH is a number used to describe degree of acidity or alkalinity in soils: pH 5 is strongly acid (good for azaleas), pH 6 is moderately acid, pH 7 is neutral, pH 7.5 is definitely alkaline. Most of our cold-house crops prefer soils neutral or slightly acid.

PLANT-TISSUE TESTING (Foliar Analysis)

Foliar analysis is a detailed laboratory procedure used to determine the amounts and levels of nutrients in the plant. While in use for many years as a research tool, techniques have been, and are now being developed and improved to such an extent that it is becoming a valuable tool in the diagnosis of plant ills as well as helping to determine what kind of and the amount of minerals to be supplied to a plant. Application of this method to commercial flower crops has increased considerably in recent years, and although a great deal of information yet remains to be gathered, it shows promise of becoming a very valuable asset to the commercial flower grower.

While actual testing procedures may vary from one station to another, generally, the plant sample is taken from young, mature leaves near the top of the plant. The sample is dried and analyzed with the mineral content being reported in percentage of dry matter or parts per million, dependent upon the element. The interpretation or reading of the test will vary with sampling procedure, crop, and the individual analyzing the results. However, by the use of a series of continued tests on a single crop, a set of values can be established to use as a basis for determining whether the plants contain either a deficiency or excess of a given element. The values are relatively stable when compared with the values received from soil testing in which there can be many sudden temporary changes.

To be effective, tissue-testing must be used in conjunction with a regular soil-testing program. In itself, it does not give us the complete picture of a nutrient problem, since it does not take into consideration the soil pH or salt reading which can affect the movement of a mineral into the plant tissue. These two factors can only be determined by soil tests. At the present time, it is quite valuable in determining deficiencies or excesses in a plant of the minor or trace elements which can cause trouble to some major crops in certain parts of the country. In connection with this use, it has proven to be a valuable tool, especially for rose and carnation growers.

Plant-tissue testing is a scientific, detailed laboratory process. Directions for sampling and handling of plant materials by the testing agency must be strictly adhered to. Otherwise, the analysis will be of very limited value. This service is available from the horticulture department of many universities, as well as from certain commercial plant laboratories.

EH

20. FERTILIZER APPLICATIONS

It's clearly impossible to give any specific directions for applying fertilizers that will fit the needs of each of the dozens of greenhouse crops. However, we present the following, based on our experience with these materials, as at least reasonable rates of application where tests, growth, or your judgment have indicated the need.

NITROGEN

Ammonium sulfate, sulfate of ammonia (21% nitrogen). 1 pound per 100 square feet, or in solution, 1 ounce to 2 gallons of water.

Sodium nitrate, nitrate of soda (16% nitrogen). Use same as ammonium sulfate.

Dried blood (about 10% nitrogen—not quite so quickly available as above). Usual application 2 to 3 pounds per 100 square feet.

Ammonium nitrate (34% nitrogen). ½ pound per 100 square feet, or in solution, 1 ounce to 5 gallons of water.

Urea (46% nitrogen). ½ pound per 100 square feet. In solution, 1 ounce to 7 gallons of water.

Calcium nitrate (15% nitrogen). Use same as ammonium sulfate.

Ammonium phosphate (di-ammonium phosphate contains 21% nitrogen, 53% phosphoric acid). Use ½ pound per 100 square feet, or 1 ounce to 5 gallons liquid.

PHOSPHORUS

Superphosphate, acid phosphate. Usually 20% phosphoric acid, sometimes 45%. The 20% material is usually used at 5 to 10 pounds per 100 square feet; 45% is used about half this strong.

Bone meal. 20% phosphoric acid, but very slowly available. Superphosphate much better. Raw bone meal contains about 4% nitrogen, steamed bone meal half as much.

POTASSIUM (POTASH)

Potassium chloride (muriate of potash). Contains about 50% potash and is used at about 1 pound per 100 square feet, or 1 ounce to 2 gallons of water.

Potassium sulfate (sulfate of potash). Contains about 48% potash and is used at the same rate as the muriate.

MagAmp (7-40-6). Use at 15 pounds per 100 square feet of bench space, or 10 pounds per cubic yard of potting soil.

Osmocote (14-14-14). Use at 18 pounds per 600 square feet of bench area.

Osmocote (18-9-9). Use at 14 pounds per 600 square feet of bench area.

FOR LOWERING pH

Aluminum or iron sulfate. Try 1 to 2 pounds per 100 square feet; more if needed. In solution, 1 ounce to 2 gallons of water.

Sulfur (finely ground). 1 to 3 pounds per 100 square feet.

FOR RAISING pH

Ground limestone (calcium carbonate, lime, calcium hydroxide) or *dolomite* (calcium—magnesium carbonate). Application of 5 pounds per 100 square feet will raise pH from ½ to 1 unit. The finer the grind of the limestone, the more quickly it will react.

MECHANICAL LIQUID FERTILIZATION

With the development and refinement of fertilizer injectors or proportioners, a grower is now able to more fully automate his plant-production operation. These proportioners are simply mechanical devices which inject concentrated fertilizer stock solutions into the pipelines used for watering. Thus, it is possible to supply the plants with dilute amounts of fertilizer at

The Smith injector, a unit for injecting liquid concentrates into the watering system. It does the job well for us. In the photo: Gottfried Pendzialek, G.J.B., Inc.

each watering. The basic concept here is that feeding with each watering is correlated with the rate of growth. Under conditions of high temperatures and bright light, the plant grows faster and requires more fertilizer. Under these same conditions, the soil dries out faster, necessitating more frequent watering, at which time fertilizer is automatically applied. Under darker conditions with lower temperatures such as we have in the wintertime, growth is slower, and drying out is reduced, which lessens the need for water; thus, less fertilizer is applied. It is important to remember that when fertilizer is applied with each watering, it must be done thoroughly. If the watering is light, soluble salts can quickly accumulate, causing severe checks in growth. Many growers find it advisable to alternate between clear-water applications and dilute fertilizer solutions.

For a number of years now, we have been applying nearly all of the fertilizer to our greenhouse crops in liquid form through a mechanical injector. It has worked out from many points of view.

First, the injector. There are 2 basic types available today. One type uses the "venturi" principle to create a pressure difference between the container holding the fertilizer stock solution and the water line, so as to cause a flow of stock solution into the water. The other system involves a positive displacement pump which injects the stock solution into the water. Generally, we prefer the latter type. One of our machines, for example, is set to deliver 1 gallon of liquid concentrate to each 100 gallons of water used. When watering, whether we are using 4 gallons per minute or 10 gallons per minute, the concentration rate will always be the same. Therefore, we add 1 pound of 25-10-20 to 1 gallon of water to make the stock solution, and this delivers to the plants 1 ounce to 6 gallons of water. When we turn the hose off, the machine turns itself off—automatically. It is not necessary to turn the machine on when you start to feed—just turn the water on anywhere on your range, and the injector starts to work.

EQUIPMENT USED

We have been using the unit manufactured by Smith Precision Products Company, 1299 Lawrence Drive, Newbury Park, California 91320. Present list price for the units we use is around $1,200.00. Roughly, one of these units will inject water (at 1 to 200) enough to supply a 2-inch main. Smith makes a smaller unit—capable of treating a ¾-inch water main—for around $520. We have one of each size installed on our range—of a little over 100,000 square feet. The manufacturer recommends mixing the fertilizer in one barrel, then siphoning it to a clean barrel before using. This helps prevent sucking up residue that can clog the machine. We add dye to each barrel—one ounce of Pontacyl Carmine 2 G. This dye comes from E. I. DuPont de Nemours, Dyes and Chemicals Division, 7 South Dearborn St., Chicago, Illinois. The men can see by the color of the water they are applying whether or not they are getting fertilizer.

We have had no trouble applying this liquid concentrate at 1 to 100 or 1 to 200 through the various automatic watering systems currently available.

PRACTICAL APPLICATION

As you get to using this proportioning type of feeding equipment, certain practical advantages begin to appear:

1. It is vastly less work to feed this way than to apply it in dry form—or even using a central tank that must be refilled often. Actually, feeding with proportioning equipment is little extra work. You feed as you water.

2. Somehow, plants seem to respond better to liquid feeding than to dry applications. There is no good scientific reason for this, but many growers confirm the fact. Perhaps part of it is the regularity—we feed (very dilute) every time we water, the year around, except for one or two crops in winter, such as carnations. Plants are always getting a little readily available fertilizer.

3. Maintaining nutrient levels at desired points is simplified. For several years, we have been working on a fixed rate of fertilizer application. This has kept our nitrogen levels in the 35-50 ppm range, and potash about the same. Rate of application: per 50 gallons of *concentrate:*

    50 pounds ammonium nitrate

    20 pounds potassium chloride

This concentrate is injected into our water at the rate of 1 gallon per 100 gallons of water. That's quite dilute! It's interesting to note that a bench may be watered 6 times as often in August as it will be January—and under this system, will get 6 times as much nitrogen. This assumes that you always feed as you water. Generally, a crop's need for nitrogen and potash varies from season to season, roughly in proportion to its need for water. Actually, some crops seem to be overfed if fed with all waterings through dark weather—even though waterings might be weeks apart. Carnations in our dark midwestern winters are one example.

4. It shouldn't be a factor, but often is—simply that a job that is troublesome tends not to get done. If feeding means assembling equipment, filling large tanks, or perhaps applying it dry—a laborious task—then it is just a little less apt to get done on time. That's especially true in the spring when everyone is busy—and when fertilizer is needed.

If, on the other hand, applying liquid fertilizer is simply a matter of fastening the hose to the fertilizer line, there's no reason for not getting it done.

The system seems to work out well on all the crops we grow here—mums, pot mums, spring bedding material, calceolarias, stocks, asters, etc.

OTHER TYPES OF INJECTORS

There are a number of other types of injectors available and being used effectively by growers today. These include:

The *Commander*, a positive-displacement type that dilutes at 1:128, available from Merit Industries, Inc., P.O. Box 8075, Cranston, R.I. 02920.

The *Fert-O-Ject*, a positive-displacement type available in various dilution ratios from the L. D. Funk Co., 4701 Old San Jose Rd., Santa Cruz, Calif. 95060.

The *Gewa*, a pressurized stock-solution tank-type venturi injection with variable dilution ratios. Imported from Germany and distributed by H. A. Wirth, P.O. Box 25, Sayville, N.Y. 11782.

In determining which type or model to use, a grower must take into consideration the following factors:

1. Capacity of the watering-injector system.
2. Dilution ratios required.
3. Mobility.
4. Service available.

Where injectors are semipermanent or permanent installations, it is

Thousands of growers the world over liquid-feed plants with each irrigation (below-right plant). Here's a significant way to grow bigger flowers, better plants: Combine controlled-release fertilizer (MagAmp) with liquid feed. Result: The left plant below. Flowers 57% larger. You can see the difference. See text.

recommended that a water bypass line be installed to permit clear water only to be supplied to an area where fertilizer is not needed.

Injectors or proportioners are subject to mechanical difficulties and should be checked periodically. Usually when a malfunction occurs, it results in a weaker dilution being applied to the plants, causing them to be under-fertilized. To check the dilution ratio of an injector that is set up to deliver at 1:100, place the intake-suction tube into a quart bottle filled with water. Run 100 quarts (25 gallons) through the unit. If the unit is proportioning accurately, the 1-quart stock solution should be emptied. If it isn't, the dilution ratio is weaker than intended, and the machine should be repaired.

SOLUBLE FERTILIZERS

Soluble fertilizers are readily available today in a wide range of analyses, all rather high in fertilizer. Examples of some of these are 20-5-30, 20-20-20, 15-30-15, etc. Two of the major manufacturers of these commercially prepared mixes are the Robert B. Peters Co., Allentown, Pa., and Plant Marvel Laboratories, Chicago, Ill. Many others are available and will do the job of supplying the necessary elements needed when used according to the manufacturer's directions. The advantages of commercially prepared mixes are: The better ones are usually very soluble and easy to mix. Also, many of them already contain small percentages of the trace elements together with an indicator dye.

Mixing your own, especially for the larger grower, affords an opportunity to save some money. Also, if you really study your fertilizing procedures closely, you may want to decide for yourself what form of nitrogen you want to use (ammonium or nitrate).

Sources for these materials: most growers have established local sources for common fertilizer materials.

Directions for mixing: First, let's put down some simple "rule-of-thumb" dilutions for the most common nitrogen and potash carriers (from *Ohio State Bulletin #272*):

Ammonium sulfate .... 1 oz. per 2 gals. or 3 lbs. per 100 gals.
Ammonium nitrate .... 1 oz. per 5 gals. or 1¼ lbs. per 100 gals.
Urea .... 1 oz. per 7 gals. or ⅞ lb. per 100 gals.
Potassium chloride .... 1 oz. per 2 gals. or 3 lbs. per 100 gals.
Potassium nitrate .... 1 oz. per 2 gals.
20-20-20..2 lbs. per 100 gals
15-30-15..3 lbs. per 100 gals.
10-10-10..4 lbs. per 100 gals.

The preceding dilutions are suitable for an average feeding of flower crops, not for the feed-with-every-watering system.

Now are you interested in making up your own 25-0-25, or possibly a 15-30-15? Here is an excellent table giving ounces of fertilizer per 50 gallons of water for various formulas. It's by James Shanks and from the *Maryland Florist Bulletin #5*: This formula roughly equals 3 pounds of fertilizer per 100 gallons.

This table gives the number of ounces of material to add to 50 gallons of water to produce the equivalent of having added a complete fertilizer with a given analysis.

OUNCES OF MATERIAL PER 50 GALLONS

| | Equivalent Fertilizer Analysis in % | | | | |
	5	10	15	20	25
Nitrogen Carriers					
Ammonium nitrate 33% N	3.6	7.3	10.9	14.5	18.2
Ammonium sulfate 20.5% N	5.8	11.7	17.5	23.4	No
Sodium nitrate 16% N	7.5	15.0	22.5	No	No
Urea 42% N	2.9	5.7	8.6	11.4	14.3
Ammonium phosphate (mono) 11% N	10.9	21.8	No	No	No
Potassium nitrate 13% N	9.2	18.5	27.6	No	No
Phosphorus Carriers					
Calcium phosphate (mono) 55% P_2O_5	2.2	4.4	6.6	8.7	10.9
Ammonium phosphate (mono) 48% P_2O_5	2.5	5.0	7.5	10.0	12.5
Potassium phosphate (mono) 50% P_2O_5	2.4	4.8	7.2	9.6	12.0
Potassium Carriers					
Potassium sulfate 50% K_2O	2.4	4.8	7.2	9.6	12.0
Potassium chloride 50-60% K_2O	2.4	4.8	7.2	9.6	12.0
Potassium nitrate 44% K_2O	2.7	5.5	8.2	10.9	13.6
Potassium phosphate 34% K_2O	3.5	7.0	10.6	14.1	17.6
Magnesium Carriers					
Magnesium sulfate 15% MgO (epsom salts)	8.0	16.0	No	No	No

Do not use more than a total of 30 ounces of all materials in 50 gallons. Note that some materials contain more than one element (as ammonium phosphate, which contains both nitrogen and phosphorus). To get the equivalent of 10% phosphorus, we could use 5 ounces of ammonium phosphate, which can be seen by the table to also supply about 2.5% nitrogen to the solution. Thus, if we are aiming at a 25 percent nitrogen fertilizer, we need only to supply 22.5% from some other source. To produce the equivalent of a 25-10-10 fertilizer in 50 gallons of water, add as follows:

16.3 ounces of ammonium nitrate

5.0 ounces of mono-ammonium phosphate

4.8 ounces of potassium sulfate

For 15-15-15 fertilizer with calcium and magnesium, add:

8.6 ounces of urea

6.6 ounces of mono-calcium phosphate

7.2 ounces of potassium sulfate or potassium chloride

8.0 ounces of epsom salts

Every greenhouse establishment should have adequate scales or balances for weighing fertilizer materials. Never guess the amount—it can be dangerous! The rate of application is important. For pot plants, use the amount of a normal watering, but make the application while the soil is moist. For bench crops, use a quart per square foot, or 1 gallon per lineal foot for the usual 4-foot-wide bed or bench, being sure the soil is already in a moist condition.

ABOUT PPM

This term is being widely used today in connection with greenhouse-fertilizer programs. The majority of soil-test reports and fertilizer recommendations are made in terms of "parts per million," which simply refers to a concentration of material. Thus, a fertilizer concentration of 200 ppm nitrogen means that for each million parts of water going on the bench, there are 200 parts of nitrogen contained in the water. Following is a simple formula for determining ppm that is accurate enough for most greenhouse-crop fertilizations.

Multiply the % of any element in any given fertilizer by 75. This will give you the ppm of 1 ounce of fertilizer in 100 gallons of water.

For example: On page 169 we see that sodium nitrate contains about 16% nitrogen. Therefore, .16 x 75 = 12 ppm nitrogen in a solution of 1 ounce of sodium nitrate in 100 gallons of water. To determine the number of ounces required to make up a 100 ppm solution, divide 100 by 12. 100 ÷ 12 = 8½ ounces.

ABOUT PHOSPHORUS FEEDING

You may have noticed through this story the emphasis on liquid feeding of nitrates and potash—but not phosphates. The point is this: The commercial grades of nitrate and potash fertilizers are quite water-soluble. They tend to be leached out of the soil rapidly—and are also used in considerable quantities by plants. Phosphate—20 or 45% commercial grades—on the other hand, dissolves much more slowly and is less called for by plants. Because of this, you can apply 5 pounds of 20% superphosphate to 100 square feet of soil yearly —and ordinarily you'll have enough phosphate in the soil to carry the crops through. It's good to watch this with occasional soil tests, but in our experience, one good application a year is enough.

But, because the nitrate and potash fertilizers dissolve out and are used so rapidly, we must keep adding them—through a liquid-feeding program described here—or through dry feeding.

Many of the so-called "balanced" formulas that are offered include 20 or 30% phosphate. Especially in the case of soluble fertilizers, this phosphate is quite expensive—and for the reasons outlined above, is normally not needed. Therefore, almost all of our liquid feeding has been with 25-0-25—meaning, of course, 25% each nitrates and potash, and no phosphates.

Calcium is much the same story: 2 pounds of gypsum (calcium sulfate) per 100 square feet yearly will insure adequate calcium under most circumstances.

WHEN NOT TO FERTILIZE!

Especially when you get into fully automatic and easy-to-use equipment such as a proportioner, it's an easy matter to overdo on feeding. So, let's wind up with a couple of paragraphs on when *not* to feed.

Mums, especially on well-drained, open, porous, peaty soil on raised benches, like fairly heavy feeding. You have to go a bit light till they get established—then heavier as the crop develops. A heavy, bushy growth, 2 or

3 feet tall, on a shallow raised bench in midsummer, can use ½ pound of 25-0-25 per 100 square feet applied weekly along with the normal 2 or 3 waterings per week. Mums to flower from late December through March, especially on ground beds, must be fed quite sparingly or they will run into wild, soft growth and stems, and it will be difficult to get proper set, etc. The above ½ pound per 100 feet every *month* would be more like it—maybe even less, depending on the soil test. Then, toward spring, as growth is more rapid, feeding must increase.

Incidentally, it is good general practice to be sure soil is normally moist before applying liquid fertilizers. Many growers water one day, feed the next.

In the last 3 weeks or so of any crop, it's a good idea to stick to clear water. This reduces fertility to a safe level before steaming and rebenching, and helps avoid toxic effects on tender cuttings or seedlings.

SLOW-RELEASE FERTILIZERS

In recent years, the use of these materials has become rather widespread and they can substitute for the use of injectors with liquid feeding. One of the materials that has been very successfully used now for a number of years over a wide range of crops is MagAmp. Pelletized into 2 grade sizes, the material will last up to 3 or 4 months in soils where heavy watering is practiced, such as in the greenhouse. MagAmp (7-40-6), when thoroughly and uniformly mixed with soil, will supply a constant source of nutrients to the plant, and yet its release can be controlled to a certain extent by withholding water. MagAmp can be added to the soil prior to sterilizing without having any effect on the nutrient release. The main advantages of slow-release fertilizers such as MagAmp can be briefly summarized as follows:

1. They supply the plant with a constant source of nutrients.
2. They can save the labor of numerous applications of water-soluble materials, thus making it necessary only to water, rather than periodically apply additional dry or liquid fertilizer.
3. During the wintertime when water is not applied at frequent intervals, nutrients will still be available.

Growers have obtained good results over a wide range of greenhouse crops simply through the addition of MagAmp at planting or potting time without additional fertilizer being supplied during the crop duration. Listed below are some of the crops and recommended rates of application.

Crop	*Recommended Rate*
Pot plants (lilies, poinsettias, geraniums, pot mums)	15 to 20 pounds/cubic yard
Bedding plants	8 to 10 pounds/cubic yard
Cut mums and carnations	15 pounds/100 square feet
Roses	15 to 18 pounds/100 square feet (coarse)

COMBINATION FEEDING (Constant liquid plus MagAmp)

While the use of either constant liquid feeding or one-shot, slow-release fertilizer in itself has proved able to produce a top-quality crop, rather startling, impressive results have been obtained when these 2 methods have

Another striking example of the effect of combining slow-release fertilizers with regular liquid applications. Plants to the right of the man with the camera were liquid-fed regularly—normal application. From the camera to the left, plants received liquid plus half-rate MagAmp at time of planting. Not too clear in the photo, but the plants that received both MagAmp and liquid fertilizer are an average 6 inches taller than those which received liquid only.

been used in combination. At this writing, some growers have already adapted this combination feeding program to a wide variety of crops and are achieving improved plant growth with resultant higher quality and increased returns on the crop.

A series of comparative trials here at West Chicago displayed almost amazing results. Two groups of pot mums (variety *Bright Golden Anne*) were grown on the same schedule under identical conditions, except that "Group A" was liquid fed *only,* receiving 200 ppm of a complete liquid fertilizer with minor elements at each watering. "Group B" received the same liquid fertilizer application as "Group A." In addition, MagAmp was incorporated into the original potting soil at the rate of 18 pounds per cubic yard. The results showed plants from "Group B" to be far superior to those in "Group A." Plants receiving the combined-fertilizer treatment ("Group B") were much larger-flowered, freer-flowering and much heavier in overall quality. Comparable results have been obtained by growers using this combination feeding method on a number of major greenhouse crops such as poinsettias, hydrangeas, Easter lilies, bedding plants, cut flowers (including roses). General recommendations call for using MagAmp at ½ the rates listed above if combining its use with periodic liquid feedings. At the present time, we can only theorize on possible reasons for the greatly improved quality as seen in the combination (liquid and slow-release) fed plants. Nevertheless, it would merit trialing by growers today who presently are using either the liquid feed or slow-release fertilizing program. *EH*

21. WHEN WILL THEY BLOOM?

There are a number of factors involved in the growth of a plant that will influence its flowering time. Some of the factors involved include temperature, moisture, light intensity, day length and fertility. Some plants such as chrysanthemums and poinsettias will flower only when exposed to the proper day length. Other plants will flower when they reach a certain stage of maturity, regardless of the day length or photoperiod. The amount of water given to a particular bedding-plant crop can greatly affect its flowering time. Many bedding-plant growers regulate the timing of their crops chiefly through watering practices and temperature.

Since the above-mentioned factors vary greatly from one greenhouse to another and from one geographic area to another, a grower's most accurate timing information would be found in accurately kept records from previous years' production.

Keeping in mind the extreme variations involved in the factors affecting the flowering time of a given plant, the following will serve as a general guide in crop planning and timing. The data presented is based on our many years of experience here in the Chicago area, at temperatures generally considered optimum for a given crop. For every 200 miles south of here, figure the season being advanced by one week. For detailed information on the crops listed, please consult the index.

Crop	Sow	To Flower
AGERATUM	Jan. 15	3-inch pots in April.
	Feb. 15–Mar. 1	For 2¼-inch and pack sales in May. F_1 hybrids can be sown 10 days later to flower at same time.
ALYSSUM	Mar. 10	For pack sales in mid-May.
ASTERS Cloth House (no lights)	Apr. 15	Transplant to Jiffy-7s or Jiffy-Pots on May 5. Plant out in late May. *Ball* or *Perfection* varieties best; flower late August.
ASTERS Cloth House (lighted)	Mar. 1	Transplant March 20, light from germination till early May. Plant out mid-May; will flower early July.
	Mar. 20	Transplant to Jiffy-7s or Jiffy-Pots. Light from germination till early May. Plant out in late May. *Ball* or *Perfection* varieties best; flower late July.

Crop	Sow	To Flower
ASTERS Greenhouse (lighted)	Sept. 10 Oct. 20 Dec. 20 Feb. 1	March April May June Above 4 sowings must be lighted continuously from germination until plants are 20-24 inches tall. Use 60-watt bulbs 5 feet apart. Lights on sunset till 10 p.m. nightly, or 4 hours in the middle of the night.
BEGONIAS Fibrous- rooted	Aug. 1	For Christmas and January sales in 3-inch pots if grown at 60°, given high humidity and regular feeding.
	Sept. 1	Will make heavy 4's by Valentine's Day.
	Nov. 1	Will make 3-inch for Easter.
	Dec. 1	For 4's or heavy 3's for bedding sales or Mother's Day.
	Jan. 1	Will make nice 3's for bedding in May if kept at 60°.
	Feb. 1	Nice 2½ to 3-inch flowering pot plants for late May and early June.
	Late May	Will make nice 4 or 5-inch by Thanksgiving if kept heavily shaded, cool and humid over the summer, then 60° through the fall.
	Early July	Heavy 4's for Christmas.
BEGONIAS Tuberous- rooted	Dec. 1	For 4's or heavy 3's for bedding sales in May. Absolute 65° minimum temperature for this and later sowings.
	Jan. 1	For good 2¼'s by early May—3-inch for late-May bedding sales. Will bloom easily by July 1 outdoors; fine flowers.
	Feb. 1	3-inch by early June and flower outdoors early July.
CALCEOLARIA (Pocketbook plant)	July 15 (lighted)	Start lights November 1. Will flower for Valentine's Day and into early March. Five hours light per night. Lights off December 10.
	Sept. 1	To flower 5-inch plants for Easter (early April). Carry them steady 50° nights. Must be shaded from sun after mid-February.
	Sept. 15	Will flower some in 5's for Easter, balance through April.

Crop	Sow	To Flower
CALENDULA (Greenhouse-cut)	Aug. 10	To flower from Christmas through early March—at not over 45° from October on, if you can possibly keep them that cool.
	Sept. 1	Will bring in a few for Christmas, especially if on raised benches; heavy crop January, February, early March. Keep at 45° nights for quality.
CALENDULA (Bedding)	Apr. 1	June, for bedding sales in May.
CANDYTUFT Hyacinth-flowered	Oct. 15	Late February, raised benches.
	Nov. 20	April, better quality than the February crop.
	Jan. 1	May, best if grown 45°, space 6 x 6 inches.
	Jan. 15	Memorial Day; if grown cool, very nice.
CELOSIA	Early April	Will make good flatted transplants for late May sales. Earlier sowings may flower prematurely, ruining plants.
CENTAUREA Cyanus	Jan. 15	Greenhouse cut flowers in May.
CHERRY, CHRISTMAS	Early Feb.	For 6-inch plants at Christmas.
	Mar. 1	For 4-inch fruited plants for Christmas. For maximum fruit set, plunge pots in ground outdoors during the summer. Last pinch July 1.
CHRYSANTHEMUM	See page 246.	
CINERARIA	Early Sept.	Late February-March at 50°. Figure about 6 weeks between final shift and flowering date.
	Oct. 1	March-April.

Crop	Sow	To Flower
COLEUS	Feb. 15	For 3-inch pots for Mother's Day and May combinations. Grow at 60°.
	Mar. 15	For 2¼-inch pots and pack sales in May. Grow at 60°.
CYCLAMEN	Oct. 1	6's for Christmas a year later.
	Nov. 1	Finish as 5's for January a year later.
	Feb. 1	Finish as nice 4's for January-February a year later.
DAHLIA	Dec. 15	For 4-inch pots for Mother's Day.
	Mar. 1	May pack sales.
DELPHINIUM (and most perennials)	Aug. 1	Will make well-established plants for sale the next spring. Will flower in June.
	(greenhouse crop)	Transplant to frame September 1. Keep from freezing until December 1, then move to 40° greenhouse. Late March, raise to 45-50° to flower late April and May. *Giant Pacific* strains best.
	Sept. 1	Transplant to frame late September. Will normally root enough to stand the winter. Will flower the next summer.
	Jan. 1	Transplant to packs or Jiffy-Pots and move to 45° house, plant outdoors or sell early April. Will flower first summer.
DUSTY MILLER	Feb. 15	For sales in early May in packs.
FEVERFEW	see Matricaria	
GERANIUM F₁ hybrid *Carefree*	Mar. 1	Mid-May for green-pack sales.
	Jan. 1-15	Memorial Day in 4-inch pots, in bud and bloom.
GERBERA	Jan. 15	To have established 3 to 4-inch pot plants for June benching. Crop will flower the following winter and spring.

Crop	Sow	To Flower
GLOXINIA	Dec. 15	For nice blooming 5 or 6-inch plants in June. For Christmas, sow June 1, and for Valentine's Day, a July 15 sowing is right. Minimum growing temperature 65°. Crop time can be reduced by use of supplementary light for 4 hours per night.
GYPSOPHILA (Annual)	Dec. 15 and on; sow outdoors Apr. 20	Flower March 15. Successive sowings take about 3 months to flower from seed.
IMPATIENS	Jan. 20	3 and 4-inch pots for May sales. Grow at 60°.
	Feb. 15	For May sales in 2¼-inch pots and packs. Grow at 60°.
KALANCHOE	Mar. 1	Variety *Vulcan* in 4-inch pots for Christmas at 60°. Shade with black cloth from September 1 to October 5, 5 p.m. to 7 a.m. To flower December 1, shade from August 1 to September 1.
	Apr.	3-inch pots for January.
LARKSPUR (Outdoors, direct-sown)	8 weeks prior to first hard freeze in fall.	June. Midwestern and eastern growers sow late August, early September.
LARKSPUR (Late sowing)	Late Nov.	June-early July. Sow late enough so that seed will not germinate before spring.
LARKSPUR (Outdoors, spring sowing)	Apr. 1	Sow as soon as ground thaws. Will flower late July.
LARKSPUR (Greenhouse)	Early Sept.	February, 50°, raised benches.
	Oct.	April—better quality than above. 45° and raised benches.

Crop	Sow	To Flower
LARKSPUR (Greenhouse)	Early Dec. Late Jan.	Early May. Mid-June.
LOBELIA	Feb. 15	Mid-May in 2¼-inch pots and packs.
MARIGOLD (Greenhouse-cut) F₁ hybrid tall	Jan. 15	May. Space 4x 5 inches. Grow single-stem. Disbud to one flower.
MARIGOLD Tall for bedding	Mar. 15– Apr. 1	For pack sales in May.
MARIGOLD Dwarf for pot and bedding sales	Feb. 1 Mar. 15	Nice 3-inch pots in flower in April. For flowering 2¼-inch pots and pack sales—May 15.
MATRICARIA (Feverfew)	Oct. 1	Early May. If lighted starting December 15, they will flower early April.
Greenhouse-cut *Ball Dbl.*	Nov. 1	Late May-early June.
White from seed.	Feb. 1	Planted outdoors, flowered mid-July, good quality.
MYOSOTIS *Ball Early*	Aug.	November. Later sowings up to January will flower through to spring.
PANSY (For bedding East and Midwest)	Late July through Aug.	Transplant to frames or beds early enough so they will become well established before winter. Southern growers sow 2½ months prior to first killing frost.
PANSY (Bedding)	Nov. 1	Transplant to flats as ready. Winter-over in a cold frame for fine, heavy plants for bedding by April 15.

Crop	Sow	To Flower
PANSY (Bedding)	Dec.	Transplant to flats as ready, carry in 45° house, dry, low nitrates. Will flower in April.
PANSY (Winter cut flowers)	Aug. 1	12 x 12 inches in ground beds for long-stemmed flowers from late January on.
PEPPER, CHRISTMAS	Apr. 15	Christmas in 4-inch pots.
	June 1	Christmas—panned 2 or 3 2¼-inch pots to a 5 or 6-inch pot and given single pinch.
PETUNIA	Nov. 15	April 1 and through the month as heavy 4-inch pots.
Doubles, Giants,	Dec. 20	Mother's Day as heavy 3-inch pots for combinations.
F₁ hybrid	Jan. 1	As heavy 3-inch pots for Decoration Day.
Grandi-	Feb. 15	Mid-May for 2¼-inch pot and pack sales.
floras	Mar. 15	Memorial Day—small pots, packs or flat sales.
(Above most suitable for 3 and 4-inch pot sales.)	Apr. 15	Will still make good plants for early-June sales.
PHLOX (Annual)	Mar. 1	For May bedding sales.
PRIMULA Malacoides	July 15	For nice 5 or 6-inch plants in February.
	Aug. 10	For nice 5 or 6-inch plants in April.
	Early Sept.	Will make nice 4's for February.
PRIMULA Obconica	Jan.	Make heavy 6's for December flowering.
	July 1	Good 4-inch in flower by February.
	Oct.	April, 4's. Need shady, cool, humid house over the summer.
SALVIA	Feb. 15	For May sales in 3-inch pots.
	Mar. 1-15	For 2¼-inch pots.
	Mar. 15-Apr. 1	For pack and flat sales in May.

Crop	Sow	To Flower
SCABIOSA		Handle same as salvia (page 179).
SCHIZANTHUS	Oct. 1	For spring pot plants.
SHAMROCK	Jan. 1	To finish one plant in a 1-inch pot.
	Dec. 1	To make a 2-inch plant for St. Patrick's Day.
SNAPDRAGON Single-stem)	Aug. 16	December 16-January 1.
	Aug. 28	January 20-February 10.
	Sept. 17	February 23-March 15.
	Oct. 6	March 16-March 31.
	Oct. 25	April 5-April 20.
	Nov. 14	April 25-May 5.
	Dec. 11	May 10-May 15.
	Jan. 2	May 19-May 24.
	Jan. 20	May 26-May 31.
	Feb. 9	June 3-June 8.
	Feb. 25	June 10-June 15.
	Mar. 10	June 18-June 23.
	Mar. 31	July 3-July 8.
	Apr. 20	July 18-July 23.
	May 5	July 31-August 5.
	May 25	August 20-August 25.
	June 10	September 5-September 10.
	July 3	September 24-September 29.
	July 17	October 16-October 26.
	Aug. 1	November 10-November 19.
SNAPDRAGON (Pinched)	July 20	Mid-December.
	Aug. 1	Mid-January.
	Aug. 20	Mid-February.
	Sept. 5	Early March.
	Sept. 20	April 15.
	Nov. 15	Mid-May.

All above dates based on 50°, raised benches.

Crop	Sow	To Flower
SNAPDRAGON (Outdoor bedding)	Feb. 15	For spring bedding sales in pots or packs. Grown cool with single pinch.
STATICE Sinuata	Jan. 10	Will flower in May in greenhouse; ground beds.
	Apr. 1	Will flower in August, planted outdoors.

Crop	Sow	To Flower
STOCK	Aug. 1	January 15 (see below).
	Sept. 15	March 1.
	Oct. 20	April 1.
	Jan. 5	May 1.
	Feb. 10	June 1.

Above schedules based on direct sowing on raised benches, 50°. If ground beds are used, if seedlings are transplanted, or if 45° temperature is carried, allow an extra month on winter crops and 2 weeks more on May crops. Sowings made prior to July 10 or after February 15 may go blind.

On Easter crop, buds should show 9 weeks before cutting date. For South and near-South, less time will be needed for above crops.

Tennessee and Oklahoma latitude requires only 4 months, even for an early-spring crop.

Crop	Sow	To Flower
SWEET PEA (Winter flowering)	July 15	Will flower November through Valentine's Day.
	Sept. 1	Flower from Christmas through March.
	Oct. 1	Mid-February through Mother's Day.
	Nov. 1	April 1 through Memorial Day.
	Dec. 1	Mid-April through May.
SWEET PEA (Spring flowering)	Oct. 1	Mid-April through June.
	Nov. 1	Late April through June.
	Dec. 1	Mid-May through June.
VERBENA	Feb. 10	For flowering 3-inch pot sales in May.
	Mar. 1	For flat or pack sales.
VINCA ROSEA	Feb. 1	2¼-inch pots for May sales. Sow 2 weeks later for packs—grow at 60°.
	Mar. 15	For pack sales in late May.
VIOLA	Same as for pansy.	
ZINNIA	Mid-Apr.	Grow at 60°. For May bedding sales. Will flower July and August.
Dwarf *Thumbelina*	Mar. 15	Blooming plants for pack sales in mid-May.

Part II—Cultural Notes by Crops

For convenience, the material on specific crops is arranged here alphabetically. Crops are listed under their common names—Antirrhinum as snapdragons, Mathiola as stocks, Rhododendron as azaleas, etc.

Germination information listed under each crop heading is largely based on the work done by Dr. Henry M. Cathey of the U.S.D.A. at Beltsville, Md. "Light" simply refers to the fact that maximum germination is obtained when the seeds are exposed to light. Conversely, "dark" indicates that for top germination, the seed should *not* be exposed to light. If neither "light" nor "dark" appears, it indicates that the seed will germinate well under either condition, or a combination of the two. "Alt. 70-85°" indicates that this crop should be grown at an alternating temperature of 70° nights and 85° days.

AGERATUM

ANNUAL *(A. mexicanum) 200,000 seeds per oz. Germinates in 8 days at 70°. Light.*

The development of uniform F₁ hybrids from seed has been responsible for the big switch-over from cutting-propagated varieties to those grown from seed.

Uniform and free-flowering, they grow to a height of about 6 inches.

AGERATUM BLUE BLAZER
One of the widely-used F₁ hybrids. Vigorous, free-flowering mid-blue, about 6 inches high. In the background, Zinnia Pink Buttons.

Other recently introduced F₁ ageratum hybrids are *Royal Blazer, Summer Snow* and *Blue Angel.*

Royal Blazer is a deeper blue, grows about 8 inches high and flowers a little later than *Blue Blazer.* The buds are of a reddish-purple color.

Summer Snow is a pure white that grows 6 inches high and has similar plant habit and flower to that of *Blue Blazer.*

Blue Angel, a mid blue, has a uniform habit and blooms continuously throughout the season.

In the inbred class, *Blue Mink,* a tetraploid, is still being widely used. Growing 12 inches high, it has large powder-blue flowers freely borne on shapely plants. For use in May combination pots, we suggest sowing around February 1.

ALYSSUM

ANNUAL *(Lobularia maritima)*

90,000 seeds per oz. Germinates in 8 days at 70°. Light.

The most widely used plant for edging purposes (known botanically as *Lobularia*). Alyssum holds up quite well through our hot, dry summers. The most popular variety, *Carpet of Snow,* stays quite uniformly down to a height of 3 to 4 inches and withstands the heat quite well. This strain is sometimes known as *Snow Cloth.* It makes a spread of 10-15 inches, and good plants that are produced by sowing around March 1 should be spaced out about 8 inches.

New Carpet of Snow and *Tiny Tim* are more recent introductions that maintain a more compact, uniform habit than the regular widely used strains. The variety *Tiny Tim* will, in most areas, flower several weeks earlier than other varieties. In addition to these white forms, a number of purple varieties are available. *Oriental Night* is a compact type. *Royal*

ALYSSUM CARPET OF SNOW
Sometimes called "Snow Cloth," this is the most popular variety of this fragrant, low-growing border plant.

183

Carpet, low and spreading in growth, produces violet-purple flowers on plants 4 inches high. *Rosie O'Day* is a lavender-rose shade, low and spreading in habit. All are at their best in cool temperatures.

All annual alyssums have the same rich, honey-like odor. The perennial forms that are without this rich fragrance are balanced by more color. *A. Saxatile Compactum (Gold Dust)* is a dwarf-growing variety which forms greyish-green leaves covered by masses of golden-yellow flowers. Flowers in early May.

This variety is very hardy here, and is excellent for edging and rock gardens.

AMARANTHUS

ANNUAL *(A. tricolor) 44,000 seeds per oz. Germinates in 8-10 days at 70-75°.*

Related to celosia, producing the same colorful but rather coarse effects. Varieties vary in height from 2 to 5 feet. In our trial grounds, we frequently find it difficult to get a stand of them when transplanted. This is partly overcome by sowing direct after the soil becomes well warmed, for they are natives of hot, moderately dry climates. Too much moisture usually is disastrous for them.

Early Splendor gets up to about 3 feet and has brilliant red coloring with many base branches. Another variety commonly grown is *Tricolor Splendens Perfecta (Joseph's Coat),* which reaches a height of 3 feet and has beautiful green, red and yellow foliage. At times, especially in the South, these varieties are referred to as "summer poinsettias."

AMARYLLIS (Hippeastrum)

One of our most brilliantly colored indoor spring bulbs, amaryllis is easily forced for flowering from Christmas (using prepared bulbs) throughout the spring. Bulbs should be received from suppliers from November on. They should be potted immediately upon receipt. Do not expose the bulbs to excessively low or high temperatures before potting.

Pot amaryllis in a large enough pot so as to leave an inch of soil around the bulb—a 5 to 7-inch pot is usually adequate. Potting soil should be of a loose consistency, with either peat moss or well-rotted manure mixed with a good soil. The bulb should be potted so as to leave its upper third exposed above the soil line.

Water amaryllis well when potted and then water sparingly until root growth has started (lukewarm water helps). Temperatures of 60-70° are suitable for forcing. However, lower temperatures may be used to delay flowering—down to 45-50°.

AMARYLLIS
One of our most brilliant colored
indoor spring bulbs.

Special heat-treated "prepared" bulbs may be obtained from Holland that will flower for Christmas from a November 1 potting. For flowering after Christmas, bulbs should be potted about 8 weeks before flowering.

When amaryllis are in full growth, they should be watered frequently and fed a balanced fertilizer once a month. They enjoy full sunlight during growing season. However, when coming into flower, partial shade helps to bring out their brilliant colors. Reducing temperatures to 60° at this time helps to keep the flowers in good shape longer.

After an amaryllis has flowered, it should be kept in a growing condition throughout the summer as long as its leaves remain green. During this period, the plant is building up its bulb for next season's flower. When leaves dry out, the plants should be kept in a cool, dry, and dark location until they begin to show signs of growing in the late fall or winter. At this time, plants should be kept in the same pots and given a top dressing of some type of compost.

After flowering in the spring, bulbs may be plunged outdoors in a shady location for their summer growth. They should be lifted and brought inside before frost. A minimum of 2 months dormancy is usually required before repotting and forcing.

Amaryllis are usually propagated by bulbs, but may also be raised from seed that flowers the third year from sowing. After flowering, bulbs normally produce smaller bulbs or "offsets" during their summer-growing season. These may be removed at potting time in the fall (be sure each bulblet has roots) and will flower the second year. This is the only way of perpetuating particularly desirable individual specimens. In starting seedlings, or offsets, be particularly careful not to disturb roots. Use Jiffy-(peat) Pots for growing small plants.

Bulbs are normally sold by sizes that designate the bulb's diameter in inches. Usual sizes range from 2½ to 4 inches. The larger the bulb, generally speaking, the more and larger the flowers that result.

Amaryllis are usually bought in mixtures of "hybrid" strains, although they are also available in separate colors. The superior strains contain a complete color mixture ranging from pure white through rose, red, carmine, scarlet, crimson, and variegated or striped flowers.

ANTIRRHINUM

See snapdragons.

AQUILEGIA (Columbine)

PERENNIAL *(A. species)   15,500 seeds per oz. Germinates in 3-4 wks. at 70-85°*
Chill at 40° for 4 or 5 days before sowing.

Under some coarse protection, columbines are dependably hardy with us
and rather attractive. They are among the most colorful and easily grown
perennials. We have noted them doing fairly well in slightly shaded garden
locations, but generally speaking, they enjoy a fully exposed location and
rather light or sandy soil. To work up an outdoor supply, sow about February
1 and plant out after hard frosts are over. They will not flower much the
first season, but will flower freely the following. For some reason, they drop
out after 3 or 4 years with us, so keep additional sowings coming on. While
in many areas they are sold as field-grown plants, many bedding-plant
growers offer them in packs or Jiffy-Pots right along with their bedding
annuals.

An F_1 hybrid, *Spring Song* is being widely used today along with
McKana's Giant, which is an excellent strain that has been popular for
many years. *Spring Song* grows to a height of about 2½ feet. It is earlier,
produces more flowers per stem, as well as more stems per plant. Colors
range from bright reds through blue shades to yellows and bronzes.

Dragonfly Mixture is a dwarf strain in a bright range of colors that attains
a height of nearly 18 inches and is useful toward the front of a perennial
border.

AQUILEGIA McKANA'S GIANTS
Extra long-spurred favorite.

ARABIS (Rock Cress)

PERENNIAL *(A. species)*   *120,000 seeds per oz. Germinates in 3-4 wks. at 65-75°*

The standard variety is *Alpina Snowcap,* popular for rock-garden work. It is dwarf in habit (6 to 8 inches) and produces dense masses of shining, snow-white flowers in very early spring. In full flower, it might be mistaken for a cap of snow. *Alpina Pink* is a delicate pale-pink color. Both are easily grown from seed.

ASPARAGUS

ANNUAL *(A. species)*   *400-900 seeds per oz. Germinates in 4-6 wks. at 70-85°*

Both *Plumosus* and *Sprengeri* are extensively grown for green material. *Plumosus* is the most popular, and is widely grown under lath structures in Florida. The main requirements of both are heat, lots of water, and partial shade. In the greenhouse, its growing season seems to spread over all but 2 or 3 midsummer months, during which it is partially dried off. Germination of the seed barely holds for a year, so should be sown as soon after it is harvested as possible. New-crop seed is usually harvested in January or February. Sow either kind in a 70° temperature.

These plants are widely used in hanging baskets, urns and window boxes, and are also sold as specimen plants. A growing temperature of 60° is satisfactory. To produce a good 2¼-inch pot requires about 10 months time. A heavy 3 or 4-inch pot will require about 15 months growing time.

Asparagus Falcatus is a slow-growing foliage plant with dark green, wide leaves, useful for hanging baskets and pot-plant sales as a house plant. The fronds can be used for arrangements.

A recent addition to the asparagus-fern line is *Asparagus Meyerii.* Producing gracefully tapered spikes of a bright green color which tend to cascade as they elongate, this variety maintains a neat, unique habit that makes it very attractive as a pot plant. About 14 months is required from seed sowing to a finished 4-inch pot.

ASPARAGUS MEYERII
An interesting different form addition in an old established line.

A fine crop of Ball's florist strain cloth-house asters. Seed sown April 27, Jiffied, benched to cloth house June 11, spaced 10 x 12 inches. Photographed on August 16. Nice crop!

ASTERS

ANNUAL (*Callistephus chinensis*)

12,000 seeds per oz. Germinates in 8-10 days at 70°

This versatile flower was one of the favorites of the late Geo. J. Ball, who, over 60 years ago, developed the forebears of some of today's finest varieties. Probably no one series in history has become so well known, or has been grown by as many florists as the Ball Florist strain, available as a mix. Despite the inroads of diseases like "fusarium wilt" and the "yellows," they are still grown profitably in some areas, chiefly by specialists.

Certainly, no flower in substantial commercial use today approaches the keeping quality of chrysanthemums as well as asters do.

Additional knowledge concerning off-season culture, based largely on work done at Ohio State University, has also aided growers in producing good greenhouse crops in late winter and early spring—or in any of the 12 months. As a result, many growers are finding off-season asters a welcome relief from too many mums or snaps at glut periods. Details concerning off-season culture will be discussed later in this article.

CLOTH-HOUSE CULTURE

The usual handling by retail growers calls for sowing April 15, transplanting to Jiffy-7s or Jiffy-Pots 2-3 weeks later, and planting out to the cloth house about May 20-25, depending on the weather. It's very important that the plants not be allowed to "draw up," either in the seed flats or in the pots. In the hot greenhouse in late May, one week's delay in setting the plants out-doors can very easily stretch them ruinously. Actually, the plants would be better off in a frame—and kept a bit on the dry side, but not wilting, either.

Above all, have things planned enough ahead so that the Jiffy-7s or Jiffy-Pots will be ready for the seedlings in ample time—and the cloth house up and ready not later than May 15. Then, as soon as you get a break in the weather, you can get them out. This is based on a May 10, "last-frost" date —adjust accordingly if you are farther north or south. Space 12 x 12 inches in beds.

FOR AN EARLIER CROP

By sowing a bit earlier and lighting part of your crop, you can start cutting a month earlier, and keep in production till frost. For this early crop, sow March 20, plant to Jiffy-7s or Jiffy-Pots on April 15, plant outdoors May 15-20. Plants must be lighted 4 hours per night from the time they germinate till May 15. Use 60-watt bulbs, spaced 5 feet apart and 2½ feet above plant tops.

A few growers still plant seedlings directly to the cloth house. We find that every 2 or 3 years, a spell of really hot weather follows the planting of these tiny seedlings to the open ground, and they either die out or are badly checked. Potting in Jiffy-Pots, we feel, is well worth the trouble and cost. Most growers do.

ABOUT DISEASES

There are two principal offenders; both can be definitely controlled.
1. *Stem rot (fusarium wilt):* This is a rotting of the plant at the surface of the soil, usually with dark brown lesions extending up the stem. Steaming soil to 180° for ½ hour, 8 inches deep, will, according to our experience, reduce loss to almost nothing. Next to that, planting asters to soil not used for that crop before usually prevents any serious loss. We find that after 3 years of continuous asters, we must move our house to get away from the rot. Third choice is use of chemical soil fumigants—MC2 and others. Frankly, we haven't had much experience with these materials. One grower from Ohio said that he had greatly reduced his rot loss on asters with use of MC2. Where land is available, we would be inclined to move to a new plot.

Much work had been done toward breeding of strains resistant to wilt. The big joker seems to be that "wilt" virulence may vary from place to place so that the "potency" of the organism which causes it may be greater in one area than in another. In general, however, we find the Perfection type reasonably resistant to wilt if the cloth house is moved to fresh soil every 2 years (or if the soil is steamed). Also, benching Jiffied plants generally seems to help reduce rot loss compared to planting of bare-root plants.

2. *Yellows:* Part or all of the plant just turns a sickly yellow and stops growing. Flowers on affected plants are also more or less yellowed and do not open properly. Plants are normally a foot or more high before the injury appears. Often, one side of a plant is affected first. Infected plants should be destroyed at first signs of infection.

It's a virus that affects many weeds and common garden annuals. The only way an aster can get yellows is via the aster leafhopper. This little fellow (¼ inch) looks like a small grasshopper. He picks up the yellow virus from weeds, etc. outside the house; then as he feeds on the aster foliage, he infects the clean plant. Aster yellows can be eliminated if plants are grown in a cloth enclosure kept tight enough to exclude the hopper. This calls for cloth that runs 22 threads per inch.

How about growing them outside a cloth house and controlling the hoppers by spraying? Well, spraying with Malathion does help, but of all the crops of asters we have seen not under cloth, many of them have had more or less yellows. Of course, eliminating weeds and wild vegetation from the land around your aster planting helps, either with or without the cloth.

CARE OF THE CROP

A regular spraying program is essential. For any cloth house crop (asters, pomps, snaps, etc.) we depend on weekly spraying with Malathion using 2 lbs. of 25% wettable powder to 100 gallons of water. Other materials do a good job also, but manufacturers' recommendations should be followed closely. Aster foliage is touchy. Most brands include their own spreader. This kept our cloth house quite free of aphis, spider, thrip, and leafhopper—all of which are quite fond of asters. If aphis aren't kept under strict control early in the summer, they will surely get into the opening blooms—and there's no cure for that. To prevent rust and botrytis, spray every 10 days with Zineb wettable powder at rate of 1½ lbs. per 100 gallons of spray.

We usually feed our asters once—several weeks after they are planted out. Any balanced fertilizer, or one of the liquid feedings, is all right.

A word about watering. If June is a dry month, a thorough soaking once a week will be essential—and throughout the summer, too. If it's one of those "rain-all-the-time" seasons, then you'll wonder why you put a water line out there. In fact, we had one June so wet that we took a severe stem-rot loss as a result of it.

Disbudding of the side shoots or "suckers" from the 8-10 lateral stems on each plant is essential to quality flowers. We hit the crop twice during the season for disbudding.

GREENHOUSE ASTERS—WINTER AND SPRING

Many growers have written us to say that their spring greenhouse aster crops were the best-paying crops that they had on their place. While asters can be flowered any month of the year, the spring and early-summer months seem to be the most profitable. The only important requirements are: 50°

night temperature, and additional lighting, which must be supplied continuously from the seedling stage until plants are 20 to 24 inches tall. The only exception is the period from May 15 to August 1, during which day length is long enough. 60-watt bulbs with reflectors, spaced 5 feet apart, or the lighting setup you use for mums is satisfactory. Lights must be turned on from sundown to 10 p.m. daily, or for 2 hours in the middle of the night. Spacing is usually 8 x 8 inches. *Perfection White, Pink,* and *Rose* are especially fine for off-season culture. *Azure Blue* and *Purple* do equally well, but these colors will be wanted in lesser quantity. Use sterilized soil for best results. The *Perfection* series is very similar to the Ball Florist strain.

Single-stem cropping under lights could be useful to a grower in a scheduled rotation with mums and snaps. Space 4 x 4 inches. Cut-off time could be reduced by about 20 days.

The following schedule worked out at Ohio State checks closely with our own experience where a 55° night temperature was used.

OFF-SEASON ASTERS (UNDER GLASS)

Sow Seed	Pot Seedlings	Bench Plants	Approx. Flwg. Date
July 15	Aug. 10	Sept. 15	January
Aug. 15	Sept. 10	Nov. 1	February
Sept. 10	Oct. 1	Dec. 1	March
Oct. 20	Nov. 15	Jan. 1	April
Dec. 20	Jan. 10	Mar. 1	May
Feb. 1	Feb. 20	Apr. 1	June
Mar. 15	Apr. 1	May 15	July
Apr. 20	May 10	June 15	August
May 20	June 10	July 15	September
June 10	July 1	Aug. 1	October
June 20	July 15	Aug. 20	November
July 10	Aug. 1	Sept. 1	December

As in summer, avoid deep planting. Set plants as shallow as possible without exposing roots. Steam sterilizing is very effective in controlling stem rot. Not only the final bench, but also potting soil, germination flats, labels, etc., must all be carefully steamed.

Late-spring and early-summer greenhouse conditions favor rapid development of spider and aphis. We have had excellent success in controlling these pests with Malathion.

ASTER VARIETIES

As with so many flowers, there are dozens of varieties of asters. However, for the florist cut-flower trade, we strongly advise staying close to the *Perfection* which have been developed especially for commercial cut-flower growers rather than for the home-garden "retail-packet" trade. They are large-flowered, and fully double, without objectionable open centers; they have long, firm stems and require a minimum of disbudding. They bloom naturally around August 20-25, but are equally satisfactory for off-season lighted culture.

There are several other classes worth pointing out. The so-called "shaggy types" are a very distinctive class. They are flat flowers having shaggy, interlaced petals. The *Cregos* are good examples. They are attractive, true to type in general, and available in a complete range of colors. They would provide a pleasing variation for the retail grower, but being flat, they would not likely ship well. The *Powder Puff* asters are of a bouquet type, quite hard-flowered, maturing in mid-August. They are not large but have several fully double flowers on each stem.

POT-PLANT ASTERS

An item that may be due more consideration by the pot-plant grower who is supplying the mass-market outlet. In addition to their lasting qualities—often as long as 3 weeks in the average home—they offer a variety of colors which can't be had in pot mums. Bright, true rose-pinks, lavenders and purples are available, in addition to pure whites and red shades. Our current recommendations are as follows:

1. Grow at 60° during the months of October through April.

2. Light (we have found interrupted schedules most satisfactory, same setup as for mums) up to time terminal bud is the size of a nickel. Only exception is the period from May 5 to August 20. Plants may be shaded (between April 1 and September 15) from "lights-off" date until full bloom in order to bring laterals into flower near same time as terminal.

3. Grow in 2¼-inch Jiffy-Pots and shift, especially if panning-up 2 or more plants per pot. Permits selecting uniform plants. Use sterilized soil only.

Dwarf pot asters provide long-lasting plants for home use, in colors not available in mums.

4. The most widely used varieties are the *Dwarf Queens*. However, from our own trials, we have observed that no one strain produces the best pot plants in all colors, and therefore we have selected the best in each color from various strains and listed them as "Ball Best of All."
5. Sales are exceptionally good at Easter and Mother's Day.
6. Make nice plants singly in 3 or 4-inch pots, or panned in 5's and 6's.

AUBRIETIA

PERENNIAL *(A. deltoidea graeca)*

80,000 seeds per oz. Germinates in 2-3 wks. at 60°

Excellent perennial for rock garden and edging where sandy soil and a well-drained location are available. Cultivated varieties nearly all fall into the species *deltoidea*.

Aubrietia resembles some of the dwarf "cushion"-type dianthus in general habit of growth. They form dense mats of foliage that are covered with small bluish-lavender or purple flowers during the spring and summer. Foliage remains green throughout the season. Most kinds prefer a well-drained location and slightly sandy, light soil for best growth and maximum hardiness; a light shade is also desirable. Seed sown during the summer will flower the following spring.

Propagation is customarily by seed or division of clumps. Seed strains vary somewhat in color. *Manon* is an improvement over other existing strains. It contains bright lavender, purple, red and carmine colors on large rounded blooms. They are about 4 inches high.

A house of dormant azaleas in August, just potted from the flats on shelves into gallon cans. At this stage, the plant is 15 months from an unrooted cutting. This crop will be ready in October of the next year. Note use of tobacco cloth overhead as shading. In the photo: Frank Batson, Salem Nursery, Inc.

AZALEA

Revised by Frank Batson, Salem Nursery, Inc., Salem, Oregon.

Azaleas are surely one of our major greenhouse pot plants today. The notes that follow describe modern cultural practices of this greenhouse pot azalea—including comments on year-round flowering.

THE MAIN CLASSES

One of the more confusing aspects of azaleas is the nomenclature of types and varieties. Greenhouse-forcing azaleas generally fall into 4 main groups.

1. The *Indica* varieties are usually the larger-flowered and come in single, but mostly double flowered types in a wide range of colors. Our present *Indica* varieties are thought to have originated from species native to India. These were brought to Europe during the past century where considerable hybridizing produced many varieties in use today. The Belgians did a lot of this earlier breeding, and for this reason, the *Indica* varieties are sometimes known as Belgian azaleas. Such excellent varieties as *Albert and Elizabeth, Jean Haerens, Mme. Petrick, Triomphe,* and *Paul Schame* come under this *Indica* group.

2. *Kurume* Azaleas originally were found in and about the city of Kurume in Japan. This type includes most of the small-flowered single varieties that have small, numerous leaves and dense, shapely plants. Such varieties as *Coral Bells, Hexe, Snow, Hinodegiri* and *Salmon Beauty* are of the *Kurume* group. Incidentally, the *Kurume* class is probably the hardiest for outdoor garden purposes of any of the forcing azaleas. They live over winter with protection along our coast lines beginning with Long Island, down the southern coast, and throughout the West Coast to Seattle.

3. The *Pericat* group originated in this country in the late 1920's. It is midway between the large-flowered *Indicas* and the small-flowered *Kurumes* in flower size and general habit. The *Pericats* are generally late-flowering and find their best use for Easter forcing. Such varieties as *Marjory Ann, Rival, Sweetheart Supreme* (an excellent early-forcing *Pericat*), *Pericat, Rose Pericat,* and *Pink Pericat* belong in this group.

4. The *Rutherfordianas* were introduced in this country about 1935 and are the most recent group. They resulted from crosses between *Indica* and *Kurume* varieties. *Rutherfordiana* flowers are midway between the two parents in size and are known for their keeping quality. Such varieties as *Dorothy Gish, Rose Queen, Constance, Alaska,* and *Snow Queen* belong in this group.

Many of the above-named varieties are no longer generally available, but have been included here as a matter of historic reference.

Azaleas are produced either by cuttings or by grafting; however, due to the high labor cost involved in grafting, only a few highly specialized growers are now using this method.

In the past, it was generally observed that own-root plants were the less expensive and were produced in only the smaller sizes, while the grafted plants were the ones that were made up into the larger finishing sizes and specimen plants. Today, with the many new, fast-growing, vigorous varieties, this is no longer true, and almost all azaleas produced are on their own roots.

The only real need for grafting today is to produce the so-called "standard" or tree-form specimen plant.

The general question of varieties, classes, and grafted vs. own-root varies considerably in different sections of the country according to climates and demands.

Propagation of azaleas is better left to specialists. Cuttings or small grafted plants may be purchased during the winter or spring months. Liners are cuttings that have been grown-on a few months from their cutting stage. Plants larger than liners are usually sold by grades expressed in the inches of diameter of the plant. Thus, a plant with a head between 3 and 5 inches across is known as a 3/5 size. Generally speaking, a flowering azalea, particularly in sizes 6/8 and larger, is the result of a minimum of 2 years of growing. Rooted cuttings are normally taken during early spring and are rooted by fall. They become liners by spring and perhaps 3/5's or 4/6's by the following fall. These same plants planted indoors during the winter and outdoors during the following summer become flowering plants of at least a size 6/8 by the second fall. Very large plants (12-inch or larger) require a third year to reach their size.

The forcer who buys plants during the winter or spring for flowering the following fall should buy at least a 3/5-size plant (growing-on stock, 3-to-5-inch top diameter of the plant). These might mature into a 6/8 plant by fall. Liners purchased during the winter or spring should normally be grown over the second winter for forcing purposes.

A point worth noting here is that along with the many new varieties has also come a new terminology in regard to sizes. Today, a liner does not necessarily mean a very small plant. The terms "2-pinch" and "3-pinch" liners indicate a plant that has had that number of pinches and will be six or 10 months old.

The Yoder line of growing-on stock is sold as a number, such as "No. 722," which means a head size of 7 inches with an average of 22 shoots. Other firms may market their liners that are pot-grown as a 3-inch or 4-inch-pot-size liner.

The trend today is away from the smaller sizes of growing-on plants or liners. It is usually more economical, in both time and space, to purchase a larger-size plant in the spring that can be potted, given one more pinch, and flowered that winter.

The late '60's and early '70's seem to be the years of the florist azalea. There has been more breeding and introduction of new varieties suitable for greenhouse forcing done in the last 5 years than has been done since the late '20's when the *Pericats* came out, and into the mid-'30's when the *Rutherfordianas* were introduced.

Many of the old familiar names, such as mentioned at the beginning of this article, are now gone from the lists of available varieties and whole new groups are on the market.

Of course, there are a few of the old-timers still being grown and these few, having stood the test of time, have been the backbone of the azalea market up to the present time.

These few are: *Chimes, Hexe, Lentengroot, Erie, Alaska, Sweetheart Supreme, Red-Wing* and *Dorothy Gish,* along with its sports *Gloria* and *White Gish.* These last 4, especially, because of their adaptability to year-round flowering. A few others could be added to this list, depending upon what local-market demands are.

Some of the new varieties out are the *Whitewater* Series and the *"Bird"* Series: *Skylark, Warbler,* etc., introduced by Yoder Brothers, and the recently-introduced varieties of Geo. J. Ball, Inc., such as *Dogwood, Satellite* and *Red Hot* as well as several other *Yuge* varieties.

One of the most promising new seedlings is a deep red of exceptional lasting qualities, developed by San Gabriel Nursery, called *Mission Bells.* This variety stands a good chance of replacing *Chimes* as the No. 1 red for Christmas. Available through Geo. J. Ball, Inc.

Those growers buying rooted cuttings or small liners for growing-on over a 2-year period will usually plant them in flats or benches for the first year, and then transplant them to the finishing-size pot in the spring, moving them outdoors for the summer under either lath or saran, and then moving them back into a frost-free holding area in the late fall.

If one buys a larger-size liner, it can be potted direct and placed under the same environment as described above.

GROWING MEDIA:

Azaleas should be planted in a straight coarse grade of either German or Canadian peat moss having a pH of between 4.0 to 5.5. Such peat will actually contain chunks or lumps of peat up to the size of a golf ball mixed in it along with finer material. These lumps will guarantee that you have well-aerated medium and will insure a rapid take-off of the roots. This grade of peat is sometimes sold as "chicken litter peat."

There are 3 common disorders of azalea plants that should be watched for during their growing season. The first and most important is the plant's root system. Well-grown azaleas should have an extensive ball of glistening-white roots. Azalea roots are prevented from growing or are injured for 3 chief reasons: (1) too high soluble-salt content, which can be cured by leaching; (2) lack of oxygen in the growing medium, which means too much water and/or insufficient drainage—a reason for growing in straight peat moss; or (3) too little water. Assuming a well-drained medium like peat moss is used, azaleas should be watered heavily and should not be allowed to dry out.

The second symptom is chlorotic foliage. Yellowish or light green foliage WITH DARKER GREEN VEINS indicates a lack of iron. Applications of iron sulfate at the rate of 1 pound per 100 gallons will correct this. Other light, yellowish foliage symptoms are usually associated with alkaline soil,

Use of a large rotating drum to mix coarse peat moss and fir-bark. Lime and fertilizer are also added, and water is injected as drum rotates to help moisten the peat moss. Note large-size chunks of peat moss.

overwatering, and/or poor drainage or root injury. Chlorotic foliage on azalea plants is a sure sign of trouble and will ultimately lead to loss of leaves and plants. It is unwise to use application of iron as a panacea for all chlorotic azalea troubles. Try to find out first what is causing the chlorosis and then take appropriate remedial action.

Leaf-drop is the third symptom of azalea trouble. Once more, this is indicative of improper growing. Underwatering, overwatering, and/or poor drainage, nitrogen, or general nutrient deficiency, or poor root action will cause leaf-drop. Root injury of bed-grown plants may easily occur during the fall-digging process unless plants are lifted and handled carefully. Azaleas will drop their leaves in cold-temperature storage (temperatures above 40°) unless lighted. Look under "Forcing" for lighting and storage directions.

Azaleas that are grown in greenhouses during the winter or early spring can be planted outdoors as soon as danger of frost has subsided. Outdoor beds should be well-drained and should have ample facilities for watering and overhead syringing. Particularly in our hot, dry, midwestern locations, azalea beds should be shaded with either lath or cloth shading. In some of our coastal regions where summers aren't excessively hot or dry, this shading is not necessary. It is good practice to erect sideboard beds for azaleas outdoors to provide adequate drainage, and these beds should be filled with straight German peat moss.

Spacing is important in growing azaleas. At no time should plants be allowed to much more than touch each other. This is particularly important during their summer growing season prior to winter forcing. A crowded plant will not develop into a desirable, bushy-shaped plant.

Properly timed pruning or pinching is necessary to assure a well-shaped plant with a uniform setting of buds. Plants should be pruned during their earlier stages of growth, not only to assure well-shaped plants, but to remove any early-formed flower buds, and to keep the plant in soft, vegetative growth. The final pruning of azaleas should be done not later than July 1

197

in latitudes north of Memphis and earlier for plants and varieties destined for early forcing. Any of the *Indica* varieties for Christmas flowering should be pruned last by late May; *Kurume* varieties for Christmas forcing should be pruned last in early June. All pinching at this time should be "soft" pinching—pinching down into hardwood will not result in shoots that will make buds. Too-late pinching often results in late flowering as well as only one bud to a stem, whereas earlier pinching results in laterals producing buds that will flower along with the central flower.

Bud initiation and development in azaleas are strictly temperature relationships. Generally speaking, buds are initiated in approximately 8 weeks of temperatures above 65° for eight hours per day. Temperatures below this will continue the plants in vegetative growth. Plants should be well-budded under these conditions by late August or early September. At this time, all shade should be removed from the beds. If grown outdoors, remember that plants are very susceptible to frost damage—they must be dug and/or moved indoors before frost.

FERTILIZING

Because azaleas have a rather fine root system, they are subject to root injury if too high a concentration of fertilizer is applied.

There are probably more azaleas lost to overfertilizing (allowing high soluble salts to build up) than to any other single cause. This does not mean, however, that fertilizers should be withheld. A light feed at least once a week, or even twice a week during the period of active growth in the summer, should be the rule. Just prior to feeding, the plants should be given a thorough watering to flush out any salts that might be left over from the preceding feed.

Applying B-Nine in the early summer to help set the flower bud as well as to develop a more compact plant. Note use of portable sprayer tank that can be set on the electric cart. Much easier and faster than a wheel-mounted type. Tank holds 30 gallons. In the photo: Don Gower, Salem Nursery, Inc.

The old method of feeding only 2 to 3 times during a growing season will just not make a plant when using the newer varieties. But, by the same token, a grower must use more care in feeding and, if at all possible, a soluble salt test as well as a pH reading should be made just prior to feeding. (For suggested rates, see the year-round section.)

GROWTH RETARDANTS ON AZALEAS

It has been found that B-Nine growth retardant produces more compact plants and additional buds when applied to azaleas.

Each variety reacts differently; some respond better than others.

To produce additional flower buds, spray to run-off condition with a 0.25% concentration approximately 1 month after the final pinch. New growth should be started before application and should be out 1 inch in length.

To produce compact plants, spray to run-off condition with a concentration of 0.37% in early July. The final pinch should be made in sufficient time so that new growth has started before applying the B-Nine.

B-Nine should not be applied with any other spray materials and at the time of spraying, the plants must be in a fully turgid condition, as a wilted plant just will not absorb the B-Nine into the foliage. For this reason, it is best to apply B-Nine late in the afternoon so that maximum absorption can occur during the night. The plants should not be syringed for at least 24 hours after applying.

Spraying should be done to just before the point of run-off and need be applied to the upper leaf surface only.

Add 1 teaspoon of Dreft to each gallon of spray to insure uniform spreading and coverage.

Azaleas that have been treated with B-Nine seem to be more tolerant of early-fall frost than those not treated; B-Nine produces a tougher plant.

It has been observed by some growers that treated plants may be slightly delayed in flowering. This delay may actually be beneficial when landscape plants are involved, as it allows the nurseryman additional selling time. Other than slight delay and increased flower buds, normal flowering can be expected; however, on some varieties, a slight decrease in flower size may occur.

CHEMICAL PINCHING

Today, it is possible to reduce the amount of hand labor involved in the manual pinching of all stages of azalea production.

By using the chemical pinching agent, "Off-Shoot-O," and following the manufacturer's directions to the letter, it is usually possible to produce a larger plant simply because less of the new growth is removed and also, if properly applied, all of the small, shorter shoots in the middle of the plant will be pinched. Often, these shoots are missed if the plant is only given a straight-across shearing-type pinch. It may also allow one to get in an extra pinch during the same growing period by permitting pinching of new shoots

Four-gallon hand sprayer with pressure gauge and cone nozzle added. Used only for chemical pinching. Plastic trigger-type test bottles, each contains a different strength of Off-Shoot-O.

after only 8 weeks of growth. This could not be done by hand pruning, as it would mean removing most of the new growth and therefore, no additional size would be gained.

Chemical pinching will not work if a flower bud is present; therefore, it is necessary to start any chemical pinching program from a known vegetative point. This means the grower must manually prune and shape the plant the first time by hand. Thereafter, plants may be chemically pruned at 8-10 week intervals. This does not mean, however, that all hand pruning can be eliminated. Depending upon varieties and amount of growth obtained between pinches, some additional shaping of long shoots must be done. Also, it should be remembered that any plant that is straggly or misshapen to start with MUST first be shaped by hand. Treating poorly shaped plants will definitely not improve their form, it will only exaggerate it. Without uniformity, the results will not be uniform.

Treatment should be made after, not before the shaping is done. This allows more direct and better coverage of the lower shoots and requires less of the chemical to do the job.

The sooner after hand shaping the chemical is applied, the better. However, in no case let more than one week elapse, for to do so would mean that any new breaks just starting to swell and push out of the pruned stem would be killed just as the tips of the unpruned shoot are; because a chemical-pinching agent is simply a type of contact chemical which kills the tender terminal growing points without injuring the more-mature plant growth beneath it.

It is usually safer to treat plants that are outside under lath or saran than in the greenhouse or plastic house. This is because it is absolutely necessary to have some movement of air around the plants that will aid in the rapid drying of the spray material upon the plant foliage. Should the foliage remain wet for more than 15 minutes, excessive foliage damage may occur. The use of fans within the greenhouse is highly recommended.

Under no circumstance should an attempt be made to chemically pinch when a rapid drying of the foliage is not possible such as during a rainy, dark period.

The chemical-pinching process is subject to any number of uncontrollable variables. Each and every variety responds differently depending upon the following conditions:

1. Tightness of spacing.
2. Time of day.
3. Season of the year.
4. Temperature.
5. Humidity.
6. Light intensity.
7. Wind velocity.
8. Configuration of the tip of the plants. Example: The variety *Red Wing* tends to form a natural cup of its uppermost leaves surrounding the tip. This cup will hold the pinching agent in close contact with the tip; therefore, a much lower concentration is needed. The variety *Gloria* does not form this special "cup" and will require a higher amount of the chemical to get the same tip kill.

Spraying in still air at high temperatures (above 85°) and high humidity (over 70 per cent) is not recommended, as incidence of foliar burn is increased.

Trial sprayings of at least 3 concentrations on 10 plants each of every variety to be sprayed THAT day is recommended. A small, plastic trigger-type sprayer (such as a housewife uses to dampen clothes with) is an ideal test sprayer for this purpose. Fill them with a 3, 4 and 5-ounce-per-quart rate and treat 10 plants with each. This way, one can "bracket-in" on the proper amount to use on any given variety FOR THAT GIVEN DAY and HOUR.

Tip kill will occur within 15 to 30 minutes, but foliage damage, if any, may not show until several hours later; therefore, select the lowest possible rate that shows a definite blackening of *all* of the tips and begin spraying within the hour. If you cannot complete the job within 4 hours, or if the natural conditions show any marked changes, *stop* and retrial again. This may seem like a lot of unnecessary work, but if you've ever seen an entire bed of plants literally "cremated" because of using too high a rate, or not drying off fast enough, you will probably agree that it is time well spent.

However, in order to not paint too black a picture, it is possible that many of these "cremated" plants will actually come back out of it; that is, new shoots will appear from the old leaf axils below the dead branches, etc., but there will be a loss of growing time and size that cannot be made up.

When applying the spray for smaller lots, a 3-gallon hand sprayer may be used to which has been attached a Type TG 0.5 solid-cone-spray nozzle. If much spraying is to be done, a small pressure gauge should be soldered or brazed onto the top of the can so that the recommended pressure of 20-40 pounds may be maintained. The adjustable nozzle commonly found on this

Use of a hand-held boom sprayer (left) and a tractor-mounted boom for covering larger areas.

type of sprayer should not be used, as it produces too large a droplet size even at its finest setting.

To apply to large areas, a motorized sprayer should be used in connection with a spray boom, either hand-held or tractor-mounted.

One large southern grower has been said to apply his material through a mist blower.

In general, chemical pinching is an absolute must for the large azalea growers who can take the time to check each variety each day, and can even afford to lose a few plants now and then. For the small retail grower who only produces a limited number of plants each year, it would seem that chemical pinching may be a luxury that he may well not be able to afford, at least at this date.

INSECTS AND DISEASE

Spider mite, aphids and worms (leaf rollers and leaf miners) are the main pests of azaleas. These can be controlled in the greenhouse by using a Dithio aerosol bomb alternated every third time with an Aramite bomb. To kill the moth stage of leaf rollers, a DDD spray should be used.

Outside, any of the available insecticides that are now legal to use in your particular state may be used; however, it is always best to use the wettable-powder form rather than the emulsion.

By using the new systemic fungicide, "Benlate," the most serious disease problem of azaleas has at last been brought under control. Cylindrocladium has caused wilting, defoliation and death of plants, attacking foliage, stems and roots alike, and has caused widespread loss at all stages of growth in all parts of the country.

Apply Benlate as either a spray or a soil drench. Other watermold types of fungus can be controlled by drenching with Dexon.

A good sanitation program and cleanliness of operation will aid greatly in reducing loss by disease. Prevention is far better than cure.

FORCING

Most azalea forcers buy plants in the fall, either when they are dug or after a required cool-temperature treatment. Plants fully budded and ready for forcing can be purchased anytime from early September on. If you buy plants in the fall for forcing, be sure to ascertain whether or not the plants purchased have been "precooled." Azaleas need a ripening or conditioning period at lower temperatures—40 to 50°—after which they are placed in higher temperatures for forcing. Plants grown in certain sections of our country with cool fall weather are naturally precooled. The state of Oregon and Washington have such conditions. October 1 shipment of certain varieties will bloom in December. Plants from other sections where temperatures do not get as low as 40 to 50° at night must be artificially precooled for proper forcing. A minimum of 4 weeks of this cold storage is required for *Kurume* varieties and 6 weeks for *Indica* varieties. Many forcers place their plants in refrigerated storage chambers to assure uniform temperatures during this cold-storage period. To keep leaves from dropping, artificial lighting (at least 10 foot-candles intensity) for 12 hours each day is required.

During this precooling treatment, uniform temperatures are very necessary. For instance, if plants are stored in a cool greenhouse and temperatures get up to 60° during warm, bright days, the plants will not force uniformly. Plants during this cold-storage treatment should be kept only moderately wet. Excessive watering or excessive dryness of the roots will cause leaf-drop. If you buy plants already budded, their care upon arrival is most important. Plants should be immediately unpacked, unless frost damage en route is suspected. Azaleas that arrive in a partially frozen condition stand an excellent chance of recovering by storing the unopened cases in a cool temperature—35 to 40°—for several days, to effect a gradual thawing out. Be sure to notify the transportation company immediately if frost damage is suspected, so you will have the basis of a claim if the plants do not recover.

Plants upon receipt should be watered thoroughly by immersing root balls in water until soil is saturated. Place in a shaded house at forcing temperature—60 to 65°. They can be potted immediately or heeled-in on benches of peat moss. Potting should be done in straight peat moss. Be sure to keep plants amply watered during their first 2 weeks, particularly. Frequent syringing to maintain atmospheric moisture is important, also.

Two-thirds of all Pacific Northwest-produced azaleas are forced for the Christmas holiday. The forcer should obtain only early-blooming varieties if he expects to make Christmas. Some of the better early forcers are *Chimes, Dorothy Gish, Gloria, White Gish, Mission Bells*, Erie, Dogwood** and *Red-Wing.*

Forcing should begin by the first week of November at a night temperature of 60°-65°F.

In the North, no shade of any kind should be used over the plants. Southern growers may need a light shade, such as a single layer of tobacco cloth.

Overhead syringing usually hastens flowering, but only up to when color begins to show.

Lighting the plants at night the same as for mums will also help flowering and will tend to even out the flowering.

Watch for aphids, red spider and whiteflies during this period.

*Denotes patented varieties.

AZALEA DOGWOOD (Pat.)
The 5-petaled pure white florets contrast brilliantly with the glossy deep green foliage. Dogwood is an early variety; responds well to year-around schedules.

As forcing proceeds, shoot-bypassing of the flower bud may be noticed. These should be removed before they are one-half-inch long, or "blasting" of the bud may occur. Do not pinch them off, but remove the entire shoot, using a quick sideways movement, right down to the base of the bud. On some varieties, it is best to hold onto the bud with one hand as you strip off the bypassing shoots with the other. This is especially true if there are several shoots and they have grown out 1-2 inches or more and have hardened up at the base; otherwise, the bud may be ripped off along with the shoots.

As the forcing continues, the temperature may be raised or lowered to time the flowering. A plant that is in the "candle" stage, or is just showing color the full length of the bud, may be stored in a 42°-to-48°F cooler, using 12 hours of light, for a period of 2 weeks, without detrimental effects.

Plants that are going out to a shop or to a customer should be slightly beyond the "candle" stage if they are to open up properly. A plant that is still in tight bud, but showing some color, if placed in a low-light-intensity area, may "stick" and never open as it should.

Again, we stress that to make Christmas, order only early-forcing varieties that have been adequately cooled. To try and force later types, such as *Lentengroot,* will often mean missing the holiday completely. Such varieties, it seems, must go through a longer cold precooling and ripening period or "gestation period," as one broker calls it, and no matter how hard they are forced, they will not flower until this ripening requirement is satisfied.

Valentine's Day. Any of the previously named varieties, as well as *Jean Haerens, Sweetheart Supreme, Hexe,* or *Lentengroot,* may be used. At this time of the year, usually 4 to 6 weeks at 60°F will force most varieties quite easily.

Easter. Easter is the most difficult holiday to force for, due to the variability of the date, but material obtained anywhere in the country will force readily for it. In fact, if Easter is late, the biggest problem is to hold plants back from flowering prematurely. If one has a cooler, the plants may be held back much better than if only a cool, shaded greenhouse or storage shed is used.

For an early Easter, 2 to 3 weeks at 60°F is all that is required. If it is late, 1 to 2 weeks will be sufficient.

Mother's Day. The only way to hold plants for this holiday is by storing them in a cooler. They should flower 1 to 2 weeks after being removed from cold storage. The extra work and effort of storing is usually well worth it, for after all is said and done, the azalea is still "the aristocrat of pot plants."

Azalea plants unsold at the end of the forcing season can be kept for forcing the following year. They should be repotted with fresh peat moss and trimmed. Trimming should be confined to soft top growth. Beginning in March or April, they should be grown at least 60°F so as to start new growth. Thereafter, they are treated the same as younger plants.

YEAR-AROUND PRODUCTION AND FLOWERING

There has been much interest in year-around production of azaleas. However, the growing of year-around plants, while not difficult or complicated, requires close adherence to a tight monthly schedule. To deviate from the schedule will defeat the whole purpose of having it, and the net results will be to *not* have blooming azaleas available every week of the year.

A brief discussion of the steps required to produce a true year-around azalea program is outlined below.

PROPAGATION:

The cuttings are stuck in a sterilized propagation bed having bottom heat using a medium of half peat and half sand or perlite.

Mist is maintained 24 hours for the first 3 to 4 days after sticking, and is used only during the day from then on. The cuttings are in the propagator for 12 weeks, with the first pinch being made while still in the propagation bed seven weeks after sticking. This is just a tip roll-out, taking as little as possible. At the end of 12 weeks from stick date, there should be 2 to 5 shoots 1 to 1½ inches long coming from this pinch.

These rooted cuttings are then lined out in a bed of straight coarse peat moss into which 10 pounds of fine dolomitic limestone and 5 pounds of a 10-6-4 fertilizer per 100 square feet has been incorporated and steam-sterilized.

An over-stick of 20 to 25 percent should be made so that only those rooted cuttings showing at least 2 good, strong breaks are transplanted.

The liners are spaced 3 by 4 inches, and immediately after transplanting, and following the initial watering-in, they are watered with a Benlate-Dexon drench.

The second pinch is given 2 weeks after benching and is again just a roll-out of the tips.

Eight weeks after the second pinch, the liners are potted into 6-inch

AZALEA SATELLITE (Pat.) A freckled, variegated rose and white with large flowers. Blooms naturally Valentine's Day to Mother's Day.

clay pots and set pot-to-pot. Liners with 4 or more good breaks are potted alone. Those with only 2 to 3 breaks are combined with another 2 to 3-break plant. At 4 weeks from potting, the plants are given their third pinch. This time, a harder pinch is used so as to start to shape the plant. One to 2 sets of good, large leaves should be left on each stem.

Eight weeks after the third pinch, the fourth pinch is given; again, a harder pinch so as to shape and build the plants. The plants are also final-spaced at this time to about 10 by 10 inches or more.

The fifth and final pinch is given 8 weeks after the final spacing.

Once the rotation is in order, the third, fourth and fifth pinches of different lots will all be done at the same time.

Chemical pinching may be used on the fifth pinch because the plants are then at final space, and there is air circulation around them. Take your cutting first, finish shaping any long shoots not needed for propagation, and then apply the chemical pinch. (See directions under "Chemical Pinching" section.)

VARIETIES FOR YEAR-ROUND FLOWERING

Not all varieties are suitable for year-round forcing; many of the new, fast-growing types are.

Those that have worked the best in our program are listed below.

Dorothy Gish	*Red-Wing*
Gloria	*Mission Bells*
White Gish	*Dogwood*

INDUCING BUD SET

Five weeks after completion of the fifth pinch, the plants are sprayed with B-Nine at the rate of 0.25% (5 tsps. of B-Nine to 1 gal. of water). It is recommended that 15 drops of a spreader such as "Slick," "Tween-20," or "X-77," etc., be added to each gallon to insure even coverage of B-Nine on the foliage. The spray should be applied to the point of run-off on the upper-leaf surface only.

It is very important to get total plant coverage—all leaves. Often, the lower foliage is hard to get at because of the density of the foliage; therefore, it may be necessary to spray from both sides of the bench.

The plants must be well watered before spraying and should not be rewatered or syringed for 24 hours following treatment.

Besides helping to set buds, a B-Nine treatment will usually bring about an increase in root growth as well as a darker-green foliage color. The plants also tend to hold their roots better while in the cooler and to resume active root growth more quickly after coming out of the cooler.

Lights are turned off and no longer used the *same day that B-Nine is applied*.

The plants that are *treated* in September, October, November and December need to receive 2 sprayings spaced a week apart. Those plants which initiate buds during late fall (previously mentioned months) need the additional spraying of B-Nine to "push" the bud initiation. B-Nine should be applied as near to the scheduled date as possible; however, if dark, cloudy weather has prevailed prior to the spray date, a delay of 3 to 4 days may be in order.

Bud-setting period. Following the B-Nine treatment, the plants are no longer lighted; therefore, if they are in the same house, a black cloth or black plastic drop is used to separate the treated from the nontreated plants.

The bud-setting phase extends over a period of 12 to 15 weeks. The sunny-day temperature is between 80° to 85° with night temperature set at 65°.

The regular fertilizing program is continued right up to the time the plants are taken to the cooler.

Toward the end of the bud-setting period, "wild growth" may start to appear around and below the bud. This growth should be removed from the plants before they go into the cooler.

TO COOLER

As each lot completes the bud-setting phase, the plants are taken to the cooler for a 6-week period. If weekly flowering is wanted, the lot is divided into 4 smaller groups and one group per week is taken to the cooler and one group per week is taken *from* the cooler. With the first 2 groups, it is advisable to pick out those plants showing a better bud development to go into the cooler first. This allows 2 more weeks of development for any plants that might be delayed.

While the plants are in the cooler, lights are maintained for 12 hours each day. Space in cooler is 8 by 8 inches. If possible, the cooler should be divided with different circuits so that half of it is lighted from 12 a.m. to 12 p.m. and the other half from 12 p.m. to 12 a.m.; therefore, there will be light on at all times and the cooler will never be totally dark. The lights are 100 watts, spaced 4 feet apart and 2 feet above the top of the plant. Temperature in the cooler should be maintained at 47° to 50° F.

Plants going to the cooler should be watered just before going in. While in the cooler, watering once a week is a must. Upper shelves may be covered with a heavy, asphalt-type roofing paper to prevent water from dripping through onto the electric light bulbs and plants below.

A "Chapin" type of automatic watering system may be used to advantage in the cooler, as it prevents any foliage wetting and may be automated still further by using a time clock that adjusts to the days of the week as well as hours per day.

Any leaves that drop while in the cooler should be cleaned up as each group is moved out and before the next group is moved in. The cooler used for azaleas should not be used for hydrangeas or bulbs, as both of these will give off ethylene gas which will cause leaf-drop of the azaleas.

FORCING

The conditioned plants are taken from the cooler at the end of 6 weeks and moved to a 65° night-temperature forcing house. Once in the forcing house, the plants should be heavily watered and then covered by a single layer of cheesecloth *directly on the plants*. This cover is kept wet during the day and should remain on for 2 days to prevent sunburning of the foliage which often occurs after removal from the cooler. This is more important in the summer than at other times of the year. Also, location will play a part in this. Northern growers may not need to do this, while deep-southern growers most certainly will.

Syringe plants at regular intervals (once a day minimum) for the forcing period prior to color show. More frequent syringing is in order if light and temperatures are high.

Lights should be used during the forcing period to help speed up the forcing and to even out the flowering. (See "Lights".)

As the plants begin to force, "wild growth" will also start to appear around and below the buds; this growth must be removed as it will cause the buds to "blast."

The plants should be fertilized one week after coming out of the cooler and fertilization continued once a week until the buds begin to show color.

Once the plants are forced to the point where the buds are about two-thirds open, they should be removed from the forcing house and taken to a 45° to 50° cooler or cold house to hold until sold. These plants will hold very well in this stage for 7 to 10 days. Light should be used in this cooler for 12 hours each day. While in the cooler, they should be watered once a week. Before selling or shipping, each plant should be rewatered. If you happen to be in an area where the water contains a high percentage of calcium or other minerals that might have left a residue on the plant foliage, these plants can be made more attractive by spraying the foliage with "Green-Glo" at half strength. This spray must be applied before the buds start to show color. Often, the only variety that will need this treatment will be *Red-Wing,* as *Gish* and its sports usually retain a naturally shiny foliage.

Forcing time will vary greatly around the country; however, if lights are used and temperature is held at 65° nights, the forcing time should take only 5 weeks.

FERTILIZING OF AZALEAS

No plant should be fertilized during the 7 days preceding a pinch and no feed should be applied until the new growth is at least ½-inch in length. This is to prevent tip burn of the new breaks. If soil tests show a high soluble-salts level during a pinch period (60 soluble salts or above, 5-1 dilution Solu Bridge), a good, heavy leaching is in order. Salts must be kept below 60 soluble salts or less during a pinch period. Salts will tend to build up more during the winter months because of less watering.

There is no hard-and-fast rule to follow in what or how much to feed azaleas. Past experience will be your best guide; however, a rule of thumb is, nitrogen levels should be maintained between 15-25 ppm (Spurway), phosphorus 3-5 ppm; potash 15-20 ppm; calcium 100-150 ppm. One teaspoon peat media—26 cc water (Spurway, 2 drops reagent #1). Any of the commercial azalea formulas (21-7-7) should be satisfactory, or you may prefer to mix your own. The pH of the plants should be maintained about 5.0.

Below are several different fertilizer formulas. All rates are per 100 gallons of water.

Fertilizer "A"—23-10-12.
  10½ ozs. ammonium nitrate
   6   ozs. diammonium phosphate
   6   ozs. potassium nitrate

General azalea feed is used when pH is in the range of 4.9 to 5.4. Weekly soil tests for pH and soluble salts are highly recommended. Soil tests for nutrients should be made monthly. Application of fertilizer weekly pays dividends.

Fertilizer "B"—21-0-0.
  1½ lbs. ammonium sulfate
   1   lb. iron sulfate

Used to lower the pH anytime it rises above 5.5. Also, generally used after the plants have set bud, for this is the time the pH usually begins to rise. Iron sulfate will correct any iron chlorosis that may develop.

Fertilizer "C"—15-3-3.
  42 ozs. calcium nitrate
   3 ozs. monocalcium phosphate
   4 ozs. potassium nitrate

Used to raise the pH anytime it drops below 4.8. Also used to supply calcium to plants. A regular watering should take place between "C" feedings; otherwise a rapid buildup of soluble salts may occur. "C" feed 15-3-3 should not be used just before a pinch if the salts are already high.

Since azalea plants are extremely salt-sensitive, fertilizers should be applied cautiously, preferably in frequent small doses with an injector.

To correct iron chlorosis without lowering the pH, either Sequestrene Fe 330, made by the Geigy Chemical Co., or Nu-Iron, made by the Tennessee Corp., may be applied by adding these to the regular feed at 4 ozs. per 100 gallons for the Sequestrene and 6 ozs. per 100 gallons for the Nu-Iron. One of these materials should be used in the *FIRST FEED FOLLOWING EACH*

PINCH, and every 4 to 5 weeks throughout the entire program.

Because of the different water sources and conditions found in various parts of the country, it would be advisable to add a chelated concentrate containing all the various trace elements to the feed at least once a month to prevent any deficiency from occurring. Should physical observation indicate excesses or deficiencies, check the trace elements—magnesium (Mg), iron (Fe), boron (Bo), copper (Cu), sulfur (S), plus others if the problem is not determined.

High soluble salts affect the tips of the younger leaves first. A visual indication of high salts is a yellowish-brown color, starting at the leaf tips and proceeding gradually over the entire leaf, and can result in leaf-drop if the salts are not reduced by a good leaching as soon as this color appears. Roots that turn brown may also indicate high salts, although overwatering or lack of drainage can also turn the roots brown.

SOIL TESTING

It is recommended that a weekly soil test of each potting be made.

A teaspoon of peat should be taken from 10 to 15 different pots and composited to get an average sample. From this sample, the following amounts are used to make the Solu Bridge and pH test.

Solu Bridge—There are two types of instruments available with which to check the actual sample although the same Solu Bridge machine is used for either.

Type 1—*Glass electrode,* in which a small amount of the liquid is drawn up into it by means of a rubber bulb. Use 10 grams of peat and 50 cc of distilled water.

Type 2—*Plastic dip tube,* in which the whole tube is plunged into the sample. This type requires a larger sample in order to cover the dip tube. Use 40 grams of peat and 200 cc of distilled water.

pH—Use 1 tablespoon of peat and 30 cc of distilled water.

It is realized that many growers do not do their own testing; however, anyone can run his own soluble salts or pH test using one of the newer-type Solu Bridge and analytical pocket pH meters as sold by the Edwards Laboratory, Norwalk, Ohio. Cost for both machines should not exceed $225.00. The tests are very easy to run and the few minutes a week that it takes can make the difference between a good crop and a poor crop.

A once-a-month sample can then be sent off to be tested by a soil-testing laboratory for nutrients as nitrogen (N), phosphorus (P), potassium (K) and calcium (Ca).

The knowledge gained by knowing weekly the pH and salt levels can be invaluable in the production of year-around azaleas, for it has been observed that the pH and salts change rapidly following each feeding. By applying the proper feed or by leaching, the levels can be held to a rather close range, thereby achieving the rapid uptake of nutrients that is necessary for fast, lush growth.

The pH should be held between 4.9 and 5.5. Soluble-salt levels must not exceed 85 to 90 during normal growing periods. Anything above 90 should be leached before the next weekly feed is applied.

TEMPERATURE

Night temperatures must be maintained at a minimum of 65°F. Day temperatures should be about 70-75°, cloudy; and sunny-day temperature, 80-85°F. These growing temperatures are maintained from potting to refrigeration.

WATERING

Azalea plants should be kept moist at all times, not allowed to dry out, as it is hard to rewet dry peat. When watering, water thoroughly. Whenever a soil test shows high soluble salts (above 60 during pinch period or above 90 during normal growing period), a heavy leaching is in order. This is done by watering each pot 3 times in the same day. When feeding, be sure the medium is moist. If it is on the dry side, it should be watered first and then the feed applied. This can be done the same day.

LIGHT INTENSITY

For optimum growing of azaleas, a maximum of 4,000 foot-candles and minimum of 2,000 is sought. In high-light-intensity areas and during the summer, a shading of glass or cheesecloth, or a combination of both, can be used to keep foot-candles below 4,000. During the fall and winter months, it is seldom that the intensity is in excess. Very likely, more light is needed. At such times, the shade should be removed from the glass to allow as much light as possible.

LIGHTS

The effect of using lights to maintain a 16-hour day the year around becomes evident in the soft, "lush" growth. Lighting increases stem length and leaf size, a necessity for year-around azalea production. In effect, it produces more growth in a shorter period of time.

In all instances when a reference is made to lights or lighting, it refers to extending the total number of hours that the plants are receiving either natural daylight or artificial light to 16 hours in one 24-hour period. Lights are turned on at 10 p.m. each night and are turned off when the accumulative number of hours of daylight and artificial light reach 16. See Table 1 for specific amount of supplemental light required.

The equipment used to light azaleas is similar to that used on chrysanthemums. One-hundred-watt, clear bulbs are spaced 4 feet apart and hung about 30 inches above the top of the plants.

A reflector is a must, as it directs the light more evenly over the bench and increases the total foot-candles of light that the plants receive. Using the described equipment, the plants will receive between 25 and 40 foot-candles; the higher the foot-candle, the better.

Lights are used over the plants from the time of transplanting into the 3 x 4-inch bed until the day the B-Nine is applied.

Lights should not be used over the cutting beds, as this tends to produce too much top growth before rooting takes place.

Table 1—LIGHT SCHEDULE

To determine correct light zone, refer to the map and use the appropriate chart below.
Light from 10 p.m. for number of hours indicated.

ZONE 1			ZONE 2		
Date		**Hours Extra Light**	**Date**		**Hours Extra Light**
Nov. 15—Feb. 1		8	Dec. 1—Jan. 15		8
Feb. 1—Feb. 15		7	Jan. 15—Feb. 1		7
Feb. 15—Mar. 1		6	Feb. 1—Mar. 1		6
Mar. 1—Apr. 1		5	Mar. 1—Mar. 15		5
Apr. 1—Apr. 15		4	Mar. 15—Apr. 1		4
Apr. 15—May 1		3	Apr. 1—May 1		3
May 1—May 15		2	May 1—June 1		2
May 15—Aug. 1		1	June 1—July 1		1
Aug. 1—Aug. 15		2	July 1—Aug. 1		2
Aug. 15—Sept. 1		3	Aug. 1—Sept. 1		3
Sept. 1—Sept. 15		4	Sept. 1—Oct. 1		4
Sept. 15—Oct. 15		5	Oct. 1—Oct. 15		5
Oct. 15—Nov.1		6	Oct. 15—Nov. 1		6
Nov. 1—Nov. 15		7	Nov. 1—Dec. 1		7
ZONE 3			**ZONE 4**		
Nov. 15—Feb. 1		7	Dec. 1—Jan. 15		7
Feb. 1—Mar. 1		6	Jan. 15—Feb. 15		6
Mar. 1—Mar. 15		5	Feb. 15—Mar. 15		5
Mar. 15—Apr. 15		4	Mar. 15—Apr. 15		4
Apr. 15—May 15		3	Apr. 15—June 1		3
May 15—Aug. 1		2	June 1—July 15		2
Aug. 1—Sept. 1		3	July 15—Sept. 1		3
Sept. 1—Oct. 1		4	Sept. 1—Oct. 1		4
Oct. 1—Oct. 15		5	Oct. 1—Nov. 1		5
Oct. 15—Nov. 15		6	Nov. 1—Dec. 1		6
ZONE 5					
Nov. 15—Feb. 15		6	May 1—Aug. 15		3
Feb. 15—Mar. 15		5	Aug. 15—Oct. 1		4
Mar. 15—May 1		4	Oct. 1—Nov. 1		5

212

TABLE 2
SUGGESTED SCHEDULE FOR A YEAR-ROUND PROGRAM

Lot No.	1	2	3	4	5	6	7	8	9	10	11	12
Propagation	Jan. 1	Feb. 1	Mar. 1	Apr. 1	May 1	June 1	July 1	Aug. 1	Sept. 1	Oct. 1	Nov. 1	Dec. 1
First Pinch	Feb. 20	Mar. 20	Apr. 20	May 20	June 20	July 20	Aug. 20	Sept. 20	Oct. 20	Nov. 20	Dec. 20	Jan. 20
3 by 4-inch Transplant	Mar. 25	Apr. 25	May 25	June 25	July 25	Aug. 25	Sept. 25	Oct. 25	Nov. 25	Dec. 25	Jan. 25	Feb. 25
Second Pinch	Apr. 10	May 10	June 10	July 10	Aug. 10	Sept. 10	Oct. 10	Nov. 10	Dec. 10	Jan. 10	Feb. 10	Mar. 10
Pot	June 1	July 1	Aug. 1	Sept. 1	Oct. 1	Nov. 1	Dec. 1	Jan. 1	Feb. 1	Mar. 1	Apr. 1	May 1
Third Pinch	July 1	Aug. 1	Sept. 1	Oct. 1	Nov. 1	Dec. 1	Jan. 1	Feb. 1	Mar. 1	Apr. 1	May 1	June 1
Fourth Pinch and Final Space	Sept. 1	Oct. 1	Nov. 1	Dec. 1	Jan. 1	Feb. 1	Mar. 1	Apr. 1	May 1	June 1	July 1	Aug. 1
Fifth Pinch	Nov. 1	Dec. 1	Jan. 1	Feb. 1	Mar. 1	Apr. 1	May 1	June 1	July 1	Aug. 1	Sept. 1	Oct. 1
B-Nine	Dec. 5	Jan. 5	Feb. 5	Mar. 5	Apr. 5	May 5	June 5	July 5	Aug. 5	Sept. 5	Oct. 5	Nov. 5
To Cooler	Mar. 15	Apr. 15	May 15	June 15	July 15	Aug. 15	Sept. 15	Oct. 15	Nov. 15	Dec. 15	Jan. 15	Feb. 15
From Cooler	Apr. 25	May 25	June 25	July 25	Aug. 25	Sept. 25	Oct. 25	Nov. 25	Dec. 25	Jan. 25	Feb. 25	Mar. 25
Flower	June 1	July 1	Aug. 1	Sept. 1	Oct. 1	Nov. 1	Dec. 1	Jan. 1	Feb. 1	Mar. 1	Apr. 1	May 1

The dates shown are not exact to the time intervals listed at the beginning of this section, but are close enough to form a type of monthly pattern that is much easier to follow. Once a program is established, the dates can be adjusted to fit one's own area and climate.

BALSAM

ANNUAL *(Impatiens balsamina)* *3,300 seeds per oz. Germinates in 8 days at 70°*

Quite-tender, summer-flowering annuals that belong to the impatiens family of plants, producing the same soft, sappy growth that calls for plenty of uniform moisture. Most popular class is the Dwarf-Bush Type. Flowers of this type overcome the shortcomings of the old strains, in that the flowers stand out above the foliage. The *Color Parade Mix* is most widely used.

With an enriched soil and plenty of moisture, they are colorful border plants throughout the summer. The double-bush types grow somewhat taller than the dwarf-bush-flowered, are of good size, and are most commonly used as a color mix.

For bedding-plant sales, they should be handled the same as impatiens.

BEGONIA

ANNUAL *(B. semperflorens)* *Approx. 2,000,000 seeds per oz. Germinates in 2-3 wks. at 65° (tuberous) or 70° (fibrous). Light.*

An almost endless range of beautiful pot and bedding plants comprise the popular begonia clan. From the huge, showy, double tuberous types to the widely used fibrous group, they embrace many desirable forms. The last-named class is a most popular one for combinations, pots and bedding plants, economically grown from seed. Their value as a bedding plant for shady locations, and even in full sun with the new F_1 hybrids, can't be emphasized too strongly.

FIBROUS-ROOTED

Very few spring bedding annuals have achieved such a rapid rise in popularity in recent years as the perpetually flowering, fibrous-rooted begonia. For many years, they have been grown as pot plants or as specialty items for bedding. Today, with the availability of many excellent F_1 hybrid varieties, most growers offer them in packs just like petunias, marigolds, etc.

They are free-flowering with excellent habit. They are adaptable to a wide range of planting areas. Most important of all, they are "low-care" items, which makes them so well adapted to the American homeowner's yard today.

In sowing, use very light, sandy material with some sifted peat to help maintain uniform moisture without the need of frequent watering. Sow the seed thinly and carefully in shallow rows, and on a well-watered, smooth surface. If gone over with a misty spray, the seed will be washed in enough to make further covering unnecessary, except for a piece of slightly tilted glass, which will maintain moisture without frequent waterings. At 70° media temperature, germination should take place in 10 to 14 days. Because of their extremely fine root system, dilute liquid feedings should be started as soon as the seedlings emerge to prevent post-germination stall. When large enough to handle, the seedlings can be potted directly from the seed flat to a

VIVA ▲

▲ SCARLETTA

F₁ hybrids, Scarletta, Linda, and Viva. Three good reasons why wax begonias have achieved great popularity as a bedding annual.

◄ LINDA

2¼ or 2½-inch pot. Nice flowering 2½'s can be produced in 4-6 months from sowing, which indicates sowing early January for the main spring supply. While all begonias enjoy a fair amount of heat, some growers, with the coming of warm spring temperatures, run begonias out into frames. Full air and some cool temperature bring out the rich, natural colorings of the foliage, many being rich red, others with red edges and several with dark, metallic-bronze foliage that contrasts strikingly with the flowers. Botanically speaking, the *gracilis* type is a tuberous species, but the term has been applied to several varieties in the semperflorens group by German growers, and usually refers to those with finely fringed leaves.

While fibrous-rooted begonias, by the nature of their growth, divide themselves readily into 3 groups, tall, intermediate and dwarf, the dwarf class is by far the most popular and widely used. These three groups can be further divided into green-leaved and bronze-leaved varieties. In most areas, the green-leaved will retain a better foliage appearance when planted in full sun (F₁'s).

In the dwarf class, such inbred varieties as *Adeline, Snowbank, Ball Dwarf Carmen* and *Dwarf Indian Maid* are still being used by some growers, but these are rapidly giving way to such new improved **F₁'s** as:

    Scarletta. Bright scarlet.   *Linda.* Rich rose.

215

Derby. White/salmon bicolor.

Viva. Pure white.

White Tausendschon.

The dwarf class will average 3-5 inches in height when grown in pots; 6-8 inches in outdoor beds.

Topnotch varieties in the intermediate class with a height of 5-6 inches in pots, and 8-10 inches in beds, include the following F₁'s: *Matador, Pink* and *Red Tausendschon, Othello* and *White Comet.*

FORTUNA BEGONIA

RIEGER BEGONIAS

To meet increased interest in large flowered single begonias, plant breeders have intensified their efforts. New and improved strains are being introduced each year. Currently, the Fortuna and Caravelle Series are most popular in green foliage strains, while the Danica Series is becoming more popular in the bronze leaved class. Separate colors are rose, pink and scarlet. They all reach a height of 12-14 inches in outdoor beds.

The fibrous-rooted double strain is somewhat of a novelty, producing about 50% doubles. They make a neat, showy pot plant. *Christmas Candle, White Christmas* and *Jewelite* are 3 varieties available in this class.

TUBEROUS BEGONIAS

Strong, 4-inch flowering plants of both double and single camellia-flowered tuberous-rooted begonias can be grown from seed in 6 months, or an early-December sowing will flower from June on, if grown uniformly warm with a light shade after February, with plenty of humidity. We have repeatedly produced nice summer pot plants in this way, the resultant blooms being fully equal to the finest tuber-grown plants. Night temperature of 65° is an absolute necessity, however, for successful results. Separate colors as well as mixtures are available.

Two recent hybrid introductions to this class are Nonstop Orange and Nonstop Red. Eight inches tall with compact plant habit, they produce medium size double and semi-double flowers.

Because of their genetic background, the tuberous types have a tendency to stall or simply stop growing under conditions of extremely low light, such as we might encounter during the winter months. If a grower has encountered this problem, we suggest that supplemental light for 4 or 5 hours per night be given the plants from germination till about the first of March.

Another valuable tuberous-rooted class is known as *Lloydi.* This type is dropping or pendulant in habit, which fits it perfectly for use in hanging baskets or porch boxes. The same plant produces double and single flowers. This strain is offered in a mixture of good colors.

Tuberous begonias 6 months from seed! Sow early January in a minimum temperature of 60° for blooming 4-inch plants by early summer.

Also popular with retail growers is the ornamental-leaved strain known as *Rex*. The Changeant strain makes especially attractive pot plants, and is easily produced from seed.

For Christmas-flowering varieties, the semituberous class is used. While for years the American varieties *Melior, Lady Mac,* and *Marjorie Gibbs* have been used extensively for this purpose, the Norwegian or Scandinavian varieties now are rapidly taking over because of their sturdiness, flower-holding ability and better keeping quality in the home. Some of the more popularly grown Norwegian varieties are *Tove, Karolina, Red Solfheim* and *Compacta*. Since this type is difficult to propagate, in most cases, it is more profitable to buy 2¼-inch pots in June, shift them to 4-inch pots, and then move them to 5 or 6-inch pots when well-rooted. This final shift should be made by September 10. Grow them at 60° nights till first flowers appear, then drop temperature to 55°. They do require staking, and although they are self-branching, some pinching should be done to shape them up.

RIEGER® BEGONIAS

Developed by Otto Rieger of Germany and introduced to America by Mikkelsen's Inc. of Ashtabula, Ohio, owners of plant patent rights, the Riegers represent a valuable addition to the wholesale pot plant growers' listing.

Available as 2 inch started plants through distributors, including Geo. Ball, from licensed propagators, these colorful begonias can be flowered on a year/round basis. Flowering schedules are available. Only slightly photoperiodic, the use of lights in the winter stimulates vegetative growth while 3 weeks of black clothing in the summer shorten plant growth. Crop time runs from 10 to 16 weeks.

The Riegers consist of two series: Schwabenland and Aphrodite. The former is available in 15 separate colors ranging from reds through oranges and pinks to shades of yellow and gold. Most popular is Schwabenland Red. The Aphrodites in seven separate colors are fully double and well suited for hanging baskets.

Important cultural requirements include:
Soil mix high in peat (50-75%) and perlite.

Keep plants slightly on hungry side. They are not heavy feeders.
Keep water off foliage—they are susceptible to certain foliar diseases.
Shade glass during periods of high light intensity.
Temperature—60-65°.

BELLIS (English Daisy)

PERENNIAL *(B. perennis var. monstrosa)*
135,000 seeds per oz. Germinates in 8 days at alt. 70-85°. Light.

Though a true perennial, this is commonly grown in America as an annual or biennial. They enjoy cool, moist conditions, such as those which prevail in England, where they are at their best. However, they are much used by our florists because of the attractive way they flower during the cool spring months. They are much like pansies in this respect, the seed being sown in August and the young stock wintered as recommended for that crop. Their compact growth fits them especially for edging as well as bedding and spring plant combinations. They are especially susceptible to aphids, and this pest must be anticipated. While improved varieties are regularly being offered, the *Super Enorma* strain is generally considered the standard variety. They are easily propagated by divisions made when the plants are semi-dormant, but they can only be summered to advantage where summers are comparatively cool.

BELLS of IRELAND

ANNUAL *(Molucella laevis) 4,200 seeds per oz. Germinates in 3 wks. at alt.*
50-85°. Light. Prechill at 50° for 5 days.

Undoubtedly the greatest difficulty involved with growing a crop of *Bells of Ireland* is germinating the seed. However, consistent, reliable results have been obtained by using the above-listed directions.

This rather unique cut-flower item has gained increased popularity in the last few years, not only as material for bouquets, but for its usefulness in unusual and striking floral arrangements. The plants are base-branching with stems 2 feet or more in length, closely set with large bell-like sheaths of translucent green surrounding a tiny white flower. The overall impression is that of a flower spike with green florets. It may be used in the fresh or dried state, and is easily grown in greenhouse benches, in pots or outdoors in summer. Best results are usually had if seed is sown outdoors after danger of frost is past. Germination in hot weather is difficult. If you do sow inside, late March and early April are the best times. If grown single-stem, plants should be spaced 3 x 6 inches. Seedlings benched around the first of April will begin to flower in late May grown at 50°.

BROWALLIA

ANNUAL *(B. species)*
108,000-240,000 seeds per oz. Germinates in 15 days at 70°. Light.

This native of tropical America is a half-hardy annual that will provide an abundance of bright flowers through the summer when grown in the shade. For sales in 3 to 4-inch pots for May, they should be sown in early December; 2¼-inch pots can be had from a February 1 sowing. They should be grown at 60°. To get the growth compact and shapely, grow near the glass and do some pinching as needed. Overenriched soil encourages growth at the cost of flowers, just as it does with most plants. They are also excellent for hanging baskets to be placed in a sheltered area. They must be carefully hardened-off before planting outdoors. Most popular variety is *Speciosa Major Blue Bells Improved,* with 1 to 2-inch, violet-blue flowers. Also available are the varieties *Silver Bells,* a clear, glistening-white, and *Sky Bells,* a bright powder blue.

CALADIUM

Caladiums are widely grown decorative foliage plants sold mostly as pot plants and, in warmer climates, for outdoor bedding. In recent years, caladiums have found wider use in the central and northern sections of the U.S.

BROWALLIA
BLUE BELLS & SILVER BELLS
Excellent for hanging baskets in shaded areas.

Caladiums make a striking display against the deep green of evergreens. One of the few really satisfactory shade subjects.

for outdoor planting. In these climates where warm weather isn't dependable until mid-June, caladiums must be started in greenhouses.

Plants are grown from tubers produced in Florida. Tubers are sold in grades expressed in inches of diameter. A No. 2 tuber should measure between 1 and 1½ inches across; a No. 1 should measure between 1½ and 2½ inches; a Jumbo should measure 2½ to 3½ inches and a Mammoth should measure 3½ inches or more. A No. 3 size, measuring ¾ to 1 inch across, is also available for special purposes. New-crop tubers are generally available in mid-December. Some specialists, however, store bulbs under controlled conditions and can ship at any time during the year.

The caladium is a tropical plant native to the Amazon River district of Brazil. The important environmental conditions that produce fine caladiums are: high temperatures (this includes bulb-storage conditions), ample water and feed, combined with loose, well-drained soil and high humidity.

If tubers cannot be planted as soon as received, they should be unpacked and stored in dry air at 70° temperature with ample air circulation.

There are several ways of starting caladium tubers. They may be planted directly out-of-doors where temperatures don't go below 65° at night; they may be started in flowering-sized pots, or they may be started in Jiffy-(peat) Pots for later transplanting. Most growers start tubers in peat moss beds and transplant either into Jiffy-Pots or other containers as soon as roots are started. From the standpoint of the caladium itself, probably the best way is to plant the tuber in straight peat moss in an 80-85° temperature with high humidity. Bulbs should be planted approximately 1 inch deep. The peat should be kept not too wet until root action has started; thereafter, the more water, the better. If the peat moss used is a comparatively rough grade, drainage will not be a problem. For small retail growers who don't have 80 or 85° space in which to start caladiums, electric heating cable may be used in a section of bench to provide the necessary temperature. Install the heating cable in a layer of sand or gravel over the necessary bench area, pot tubers in Jiffy-Pots and place the pots on the gravel over the cable. Set the cable thermostat

CANDIDUM

The most popular variety. White with green veins.

at 80 or 85°, and the caladiums will start to leaf in 4 or 5 weeks. A plastic cover over the caladiums helps to maintain the necessary high humidity and temperature. However, this cover should be removed occasionally to permit air circulation.

Caladium growers are divided over the question of whether to plant the tubers upside-down or right-side-up. The tuber is not unlike a potato tuber in that its growth begins from eyes. If the tuber is planted with eyes on the bottom, generally speaking, more eyes will develop and they will develop more uniformly. However, more time is required for the plant to start. If the eyes are faced up, the plant will emerge and start growth more quickly.

Tubers usually have one main eye that is larger than the others. This main eye will produce the largest branch on the finished plant. Many growers ream out this main eye, thus forcing the plant's energy into the other side eyes; this procedure produces a bushier, more-branched plant.

If caladium tubers are started in Jiffy-Pots, a No. 2 tuber will fit easily into a 3-inch pot or a No. 1 tuber will be accommodated in a 3½-inch pot. The advantage of using Jiffy-Pots is lack of transplanting shock when the plants are moved.

The size tuber to use depends on the size wanted in the finished plant. The larger the tuber, the larger the finished plant. Mammoth-grade tubers produce the large, exhibition plants, whereas No. 2's produce good 4 or 5-inch pot specimens. Some growers use the No. 3-size tuber for small, 4-inch pot plants. For most purposes, a No. 1 or Jumbo-size tuber will produce a very satisfactory plant. Some specialist growers even go so far as to cut their tubers into pieces, each piece having at least 2, but perhaps 3 or 4 eyes. This procedure makes for more uniform-sized finished plants. Generally speaking, each eye produces one branch on the finished plant.

If the plant is ultimately to be sold as a pot plant, as soon as root action is well started (usually 2 or 3 weeks), it should be planted into its final-size pot. One plant will fill a 4 to 5-inch pot and several may be planted in a 6 or 7-inch pot. A good potting-soil mixture consists of ⅓ each peat moss, soil and sand. Caladiums grow best in temperatures between 70 and 75°.

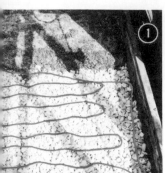

Here is one way to start caladiums in Jiffy-Pots for bedding-plant sales. (1) Place heating cable on top of 1 inch of gravel and cover with peat and sand mixture. (2) Plant caladiums in Jiffy-Pots, set firmly on the sand-peat mixture, and cover with plastic cover. (3) Caladiums are ready for sale in 5 weeks from the planting date.

They should be kept well watered and fed with a balanced fertilizer (not too much nitrogen) every 4 weeks. A cheesecloth shade over the plants as their leaves mature will brighten colors.

Caladiums destined for sale as bedding plants are best started directly in Jiffy-Pots and sold in these pots as soon as top growth is well started— 4 to 5 weeks. Some retail growers plant 6 tubers in a Market-Pak (or a similar container used for bedding plants) and sell them "by the container."

Caladiums should not be planted outdoors until night temperatures stay above 65°. If you or your customers use caladiums for outdoor planting, remember that they do best in partial shade, although some varieties perform well in open sun, and they should be planted in a well-drained location and kept watered and fed. Caladium troubles are usually caused by a too-dry soil and/or too much bright sun (foliage has a burned look), or too-low temperature (tubers fail to grow or grow slowly and eratically).

VARIETIES

There are hundreds. Probably ¼ to ⅓ of all caladiums used are of the variety *Candidum*—white with green veins. The following list includes only a few of the many fine varieties available, but is representative of the biggest-selling colors.

Candidum. White with green veins.

White Christmas. Another excellent white.

Poecile Anglais. Deep crimson with deep green border.

Carolyn Whorton. Rose, darker veins, green hue. Fine for pots.

Edna. Large, glossy leaves. Brilliant red. Excellent pot plant.

Fred Bause. Red, low-growing; excellent for bedding.

Freida Hemple. Dwarf, all-purpose red.

Mrs. Arno Nehrling. Bronze turning white, pick hue, red midribs.

Dr. T. L. Meade. Bronze-red leaves; bright red midribs.

Itacapus. Spotted deep red.

Texas Beauty. Dwarf, bronze-green leaf, heavily blotched with pink.

Fanny Munson (Red Glory). Excellent, brilliant pink with deeper veins.

Lord Derby. Transparent rose with dark ribs. Bushy.

The following varieties held their color well with a minimum of burning under open-sun conditions in our West Chicago trials: *T. L. Meade, Fanny Munson,* and *Freida Hemple.*

LANCE-LEAF (STRAP) CALADIUMS

A distinct class, differing from the regular fancy-leaved varieties in leaf appearance. Strap-leaved varieties have heavier-textured, leathery leaves than other varieties. Leaves are usually narrow and plants grow shorter. Because of their heavier-textured leaves, strap-leaved varieties are generally better for open-sun planting, since their leaves and coloring do not fade or burn as easily. Strap-leaved varieties produce smaller tubers than fancy-leaved varieties and are usually priced 1 grade above their actual size, as compared to prices for the fancy-leaved varieties. Leaves of the strap-leaved varieties hold up well when cut. Culture of this class is identical to that of the fancy-leaved varieties.

Following is a representative list of varieties suitable for pot-plant or bedding purposes:

Elizabeth Lou. Magenta background with green ribs and edges.

Ace of Spades. Red, blotched with pink and green.

Pink Glow. A large, brilliantly colored pink.

Pothos. Green and white variegated.

Rosalee. Shiny red leaves with green border.

White Wings. White-green background with crimson outline.

CALCEOLARIA (Pocketbook Plant)

ANNUAL *(C. herbeahybrida)*
500,000-1,000,000 seeds per oz. Germinates in 16 days at 70°. Light.

This old-time favorite continues to be one of the most showy and interesting of all pot plants. Old-time growers would scarcely recognize the fine, modern varieties of this "lady's pocketbook." While calceolarias are rather exacting in their growing requirements, they are not especially difficult to handle if a few points are carefully watched.

To make 5 or 6-inch pot plants for Easter (early April), seed should be sown September 1. Use sterilized soil; even in this, seedlings easily damp-off if kept at all wet in hot weather. Seed is very small, so be careful with it, using soil with plenty of sand and some peat or leaf mold, and be sure the surface is level and seed not sown too thickly. Do not cover the seed with additional soil. Set the pan or flat in the coolest house you have. After germination, avoid getting seed bed very wet, for it is the combination of this condition and high temperature that damps them off. Damping-off is largely avoided by keeping the surface dry and exposing the seedlings to plenty of air circulation. As they become established, the soil will stand keeping more on the dry side. When large enough to handle, transplant to flats about 2½ inches apart, or into individual 2¼-inch Jiffy-Pots, using less sand in soil. As they begin to crowd, pot direct into 5's or 6's. While this method calls for a little care in preventing overwatering until they make new roots, it is not only perfectly safe, but produces better results with less labor. Great care should be taken when repotting. They must be potted shallow or stem rot will occur. A night temperature of 48 to 50° will agree

CALCEOLARIA BALL MULTIFLORA NANA MIX

very well with them. The seedlings or young plants can be grown at 60°, but as soon as possible in the fall the temperature should be dropped to 50°. Flower buds will not start to form until the temperature is below 60°. While plants should not be allowed to wilt, use care to avoid overwatering. An August 1 sowing will flower in early March in 4's or 5's if lighted from November 15 to December 20. The use of lights, however, has a somewhat softening effect on any growth unless balanced with at least a normal amount of sunshine. Also, except during the very depths of winter, it is very important to shelter them from the sun, which has a burning effect on both foliage and flowers. Aphids seem to enjoy them as much as we do, so be sure to keep them sprayed or fumigated.

Occasionally, there is too much heat around Mother's Day for calceolarias, though they will stand some of it in a well-shaded house. Four-inch pots in full flower for this occasion are very salable to any retailer. They can be had by sowing around October 1.

Calceolarias are more difficult to handle in the South and shouldn't be attempted until cooler weather sets in; then, started plants should be obtained from the North. As we go to press with the XIII Edition, new techniques for forcing calceolaria year-round are emerging. See GROWER TALKS, November '75 for details.

VARIETIES

Popular for many years and still widely used in the Ball Multiflora Nana Mixture with its hard, small, smooth leaves. Its superiority lies in the greater durability of flowers and foliage.

As in many other classes of plants and flowers, F_1 hybrids are being developed that are superior to existing inbred strains. Such is the case with calceolaria. In extensive trials at West Chicago, we found several strains that flowered 3-4 weeks earlier, had a more compact growth habit and flowered more uniformly than the inbred lines. These include Brite 'N Early (earliest of them all), Grandiflora Dwarf Mix and Glorious Mix.

CALENDULA (Pot Marigold)

ANNUAL *(C. officinalis)* *3000 seeds per oz. Germinates in 10 days at 70°. Dark.*

Not very widely grown anymore as a greenhouse cut crop by wholesale growers, some retail operations may find them profitable for December and January flowering. For this period, the seed should be sown the third week in August, and not before September 1 in the near South. A January sowing will bring them into flower in the spring. For best results, they should be grown in deep ground beds at a temperature of 45-50°. Best spacing is 12 x 12 inches. To obtain maximum-size flowers (4 inches), disbudding is necessary. *Ball Improved Long Orange, Ball Gold* and *Ball Lemon Queen* are the most popular varieties, with the bulk of the demand being for the orange sorts.

In some areas, calendulas are used extensively for bedding-plant purposes. These dwarf varieties grow to a height of from 10 to 15 inches, and will flower from June till frost. They do their best, though, where summer temperatures are not too extreme. Most widely used for this purpose are the *Pacific Beauties* because of their greater resistance to summer heat. The *Mix* is most popular, but they are also available in separate colors. *Orange Coronet* is a bright orange variety that is very free-flowering and grows about 12 inches high.

CALLA

Callas may be grown either as a year-round bench crop (or in pots) for cut flowers (usually the large white *Aethiopica*), or as pot plants for flowering during the spring months. There are 3 principal species of callas. *Aethiopica* is the common large white calla; *Godfreyana* (listed commercially as *Godfrey*) is a dwarf, smaller-flowered variety of *Aethiopica* grown chiefly as a pot plant. *Calla Elliottiana* is the common yellow calla. It is grown either as a pot plant or for cutting.

Calla Rehmanii Superba, known as the "Pink Calla," is a dwarf plant with flowers mostly white with a rose tint. Also grown are *Calla Alba Maculata,* a creamy white with white-spotted foliage, and *Arum pictum* (known as the "Black Calla") with a violet-black flower.

Callas are propagated by division of parent rhizomes or by "offsets" from the original rhizome. "Bulbs" are commonly produced in California and are available during the fall months. Callas may be planted as soon as received in a loose loam soil. They are native to shady locations near streams or ponds, which gives an indication of their requirements. Callas do best in a loose peat loam with plenty of water and frequent liquid fertilizing during their growing period. When planting in benches for cutting, space the plants liberally—2 feet between plants is ample. Many growers grow their cut-flower crop in large pots instead of in open benches. Callas are subject to fast-spreading root and rhizome rots that are kept from spreading if all plants are grown in pots. Callas do best in full sunlight during the winter months and in partial shade during the bright summer season. *Aethiopica* enjoys a minimum night temperature of 55°, while *Elliottiana* and *Rehmanii* do best at 60°.

The yellow Calla may be forced as a pot plant for Easter flowering by planting during late December in a flat filled with moist peat and carried at 60°. When root growth has started, the rhizomes are planted in 4 or 5-inch pots. Soil in pots should be loose with perhaps 1 part in 3 of peat added. They should be fertilized regularly during their growing season. Although callas grow best at 60°, lowering the temperature to 55° at flowering time will help the plants and flowers to last longer.

Calla bulbs are sold by sizes expressed in inches of diameter. Bulbs sold as 1½ to 2-inch, for instance, will be between 1½ and 2 inches in diameter. Commercially available bulbs of the different varieties vary in size from 1¼ to 3 inches. Generally speaking, the larger-sized bulbs produce the largest flowers and the most flowers per bulb.

The most common trouble with callas is with one or more fungus rots that affect the roots or the rhizome. Rhizomes should be inspected at the time of planting for soft, rotted areas. These areas should be cut down to living tissue and the rhizome treated with a fungicide. A 1-hour soaking in a solution of commercial formaldehyde of 1 quart to 12 gallons of water, or a 1-hour soaking in a solution of 1 pound of New Improved Ceresan in 50 gallons of water with 2 ounces of a household detergent such as Dreft added, will clean up any infections on the rhizome. Non-metal containers should be used, and the bulbs should be planted while wet. Spraying with Malathion will keep common insect infestations under control. Aphids, mealybugs or red spider are the most common offenders.

CAMPANULA (Bell Flower)

PERENNIAL *(C. species)   120,000 seeds per oz. Germinates in 15 days at 70°*

Most popular and valuable of the wide variety of plants under this heading is *C. Calycanthema,* the cup-and-saucer type, available in separate colors, but most widely used as a mix. Actually a biennial, it will reach a height of 3 feet. Their chief usage is in the perennial border and garden, but they can be forced into flower for spring cutting. Seed should be sown in March or April. Carry plants through the summer either in pots, frames or outdoor beds. After the first frost in fall, dig plants, bring them into a 40-45° house for forcing, and gradually get them up to 50°. At this temperature, they should begin flowering early in April.

CANDYTUFT

ANNUAL *(Iberis coronaria) 9,500 seeds per oz. Germinates in 8-10 days at 70°.*
PERENNIAL *(I. species) 11,500 seeds per oz. Germinates in 3 weeks at 60-65°*

Iberis is used by florists both in annual and perennial forms. Most popular are the annuals, of which there are 2 distinct forms. The *umbellata* is of rather compact, branching habit and produces its numerous flowers in small umbels. While formerly used for greenhouse forcing, this class today is largely represented by the variety *Fairy Mixture*, which is used in combination pots and for bedding purposes. It is a very dwarf variety (8 inches) and produces masses of white, pink, lavender and crimson flowers. The *hyacinth* type is the class used for greenhouse forcing and is best flowered during the early-spring months. Easily the best is the hyacinth-flowered *Ball Giant White*, carefully reselected by us for large and even flower heads. White only. This produces long, hyacinth-like spikes; flowers do not shatter like the umbellatas, and the crop can be cut over a period of a month. An October sowing grown on a raised bed in a 50° house will flower in February, but not with the fine spikes produced by a November, December, or January planting, grown cool and flowered during April or May. One set of wire and string supports, which may be raised as the crop grows, is usually sufficient. Space 6 x 6 inches. A sowing around January 15, grown cool, will hit Memorial Day, and at this time, they are particularly useful. Both classes like well-enriched soil and plenty of water during the open-spring months. An alternate plan of growing this class is in "hills." Grow 4 plants single-stem in a hill just an inch or so apart. Space hills 6 x 8 inches.

There are several hardy perennial iberis or candytuft in general use. *Sempervirens,* the most popular, is 12 inches tall with clear, pure white flowers that bloom heavily in May only, but its foliage is evergreen, and even with us, it is perfectly hardy. Much used in rock work, but don't plant where it can't be kept uniformly wet.

CARNATION CULTURE

By W. D. Holley
Colorado State University

Carnations have been a major cut-flower crop in America since the 1890's. Popularity of this crop with consumers all over the world has increased markedly since World War II. From 1949 to 1969, carnations produced and sold in the United States increased from 20 to 48 million dollars. Imports of carnations into this country are increasing rapidly with the current (1971) annual rate around 40 to 50 million blooms. Recent (1969) annual production rate is placed at 613 million blooms by the U.S. Department of Agriculture. The average price per bloom actually decreased slightly during the two decades while costs of production were almost doubling. In order to continue growing carnations as a profitable crop in spite

Carnations in Jiffy-Pots—a method that has found increased favor among carnation specialists. Left-photo cuttings just potted, center-photo ready to pinch (at pencil point), right-photo plant after 6-8 weeks, ready to bench. Cuttings grow rapidly and break well, no disease problem and, of course, pot and all can be benched, saving labor. The important point: set cuttings just as high as possible in the pot, and when benching pot and all, set the soil ball half an inch or so above the bench level. Helps prevent rot.

of stable prices and rising costs, many short-cuts and innovations have been adopted by modern carnation growers. They have had to produce more flowers per square foot of bench area and in most instances they have also improved the grade of flowers. Some carnation growers have found that moving to more favorable climates or, in some cases, changing to other crops, has been profitable. The grower of carnations on a smaller scale, for sale nearby, continues in a profitable position, for he often enjoys more favorable prices and less shipping and handling costs.

PREPARATION

Carnations grow best in a porous, well-drained soil or mixture, or in inert substrates. The base soil should be sandy loam of the best natural structure obtainable. Sphagnum peat should be added to this at the rate of 10% or more by volume. Other types of unrotted organic matter such as manure, leaves, chopped straw or wood products may be substituted for all or part of the peat. Superphosphate and/or lime should be added as needed, and the mixture thoroughly tilled and steamed before planting. Soil should be moist but not wet when steamed. The temperature required to kill disease organisms that attack carnations is a minimum of 160° F in the coldest spots for 30 minutes. Recontamination with disease organisms after steaming, especially with rhizoctonia stem rot, can be avoided by careful handling of steam covers and the sterilization of all tools and flats that may come in contact with the plants or steamed soil.

Disease-free planting stock is the other main point in this disease-control program. If clean stock is planted in properly steamed soil, most of the disease-control battle is won.

PLANTING

The purchase of planting stock from specialists is gaining in popularity each year. Few growers in Europe do their own propagating and the trend is in that direction in this country.

If a grower elects to propagate all or part of his planting stock, the use of mist and a medium such as perlite or perlite and peat usually insures success. Important advantages he may experience in purchasing planting stock are uniformity, freedom from disease and being able to get the numbers and varieties he wants at any time of the year.

There are several alternate ways of handling planting stock. More and more of the specialist growers are pulling out old plants, tilling and amending the soil, and replanting with rooted cuttings within a few days. This method requires a minimum of labor and allows the clearing out and replanting of entire houses or sections in a minimum of time. Plants usually suffer the least check in growth when handled in this manner.

The most important consideration in this type of replanting is the flowering time of the new crop. Much of the replanting is done in the U.S. from June 10 to July 1 so the new crop will flower in November and December. Some June production must be sacrificed in order to replant with rooted cuttings at this time. When planting rooted cuttings direct, the soil should be moist. Cuttings should be planted as shallow as possible and still stand up. For the first week to 10 days in summer, all of the soil should not be soaked. Watering should be done around the individual plants, leaving some dry soil between rows until new growth of the plants is evident. This light-watering period may be extended to 30 days or longer during the darker part of the winter. Excess water in the early stages often causes "root drop." Should this occur, drying of the soil followed by frequent light waterings will encourage rerooting of the plants, but not without an extreme check in growth.

PLANT SPACING

Many tests have been carried out by researchers and commercial growers on the optimum number of plants to set in a bench. The objective of the individual grower should determine the spacing used. If a heavy first crop is wanted, space 5 by 6 or 6 by 6 inches. If plants are to be grown 2 years or more, space 6 by 8 inches. More flowers can be grown the first crop with close spacing. If these flower when light is good (especially spring), they will have high quality. Few differences will be found among the several spacing distances after the first crop.

TRANSPLANTS

Many growers have found some distinct advantages to planting cuttings in Jiffy-Pots or a nursery bed in late spring and transplanting them to producing benches in late June or July. Sufficient transplants can be grown in 3-inch Jiffy-Pots to plant 4 or 5 times the area at production spacing. There is an opportunity to discard backward plants that may have disease, but the big advantage is that producing benches can be flowered several weeks longer. When planting transplants either from nursery beds or Jiffy-Pots,

A new planting of carnations in gravel, showing:
1. Automatic louvers in the background for proportioning washed air into the greenhouse;
2. False ceiling of 2-mil polyethylene film to confine cool air near plants;
3. Aspirating box housing temperature controls; and
4. one-year-old carnations on the left.

setting them ½ inch above the soil line may avoid plant losses later. Frequent light waterings around the soil ball or peat pot for 10 days, or until new roots are out in the bench soil, help establish the transplants faster. The most serious pitfall in growing transplants is that of leaving the plants in this crowded condition too long. Six to 8 weeks is the maximum time from rooted cuttings to transplanting in early summer, if serious checks in growth are to be avoided.

TIMING

Many retail growers are less interested in timing for particular periods. They would prefer a steady production for day-to-day business. Certain considerations on timing are in order, however, as time of planting and method of pinching affect the first crop and its return. A single pinch on rooted cuttings delayed until lateral breaks are well cleared will insure maximum first-crop production in a minimum of time. The pinch should be made above the top vegetative lateral—removing only the tip and any reproductive breaks present. Good rooted cuttings benched direct will produce 5 to 7 original breaks by this method. A single pinch produces a heavy first crop that flowers for about one month in summer to around 2½ months duration in winter. All first-crop flowers should be cut to lateral breaks for a return crop in a minimum of time. These laterals will be quite long when flowers are cut in spring, summer and early fall; much smaller from late fall to early spring.

Pinches on young plants in July will flower in November in most sections of the country. In general, first-crop flowers cut to breaks from September to November will return late winter to spring. The lower the winter light, the later the spring-return crop will flower.

SECOND YEAR

When carnations are relatively free of disease, it is often profitable to grow them more than one year. In Colorado, California and some other sections, two-year culture is standard. Older carnation plants tend to flower heavily in summer and lighter in winter unless cutting, pinching and lighting are used to regulate flowering time.

There are two practices that help reduce summer production thereby changing it to fall and early winter. Cutting all flowers during January, February, and March to the origin and raising the cutting level in April and May to good wood, but below breaks, help decrease summer flowers and increase those later. If this is not done, plants can be pinched in soft wood in May, June, and early July to accomplish the same thing. By taking the plants out of production during the heat of summer, many low-quality flowers can be avoided. Much better quality and usually better prices can be

First crop from single pinch ready for first disbudding. This crop is relatively short if it flowers in summer or fall; longer in winter and longest in spring.

obtained when the plants come back into bloom during fall.

In climates with the darkest winters, eighteen months is often a good period to grow carnations. Once the heavy fall-and-Christmas crop is cut, there is very little return crop until late May and June. This crop returns for September to December. Many growers plan a rotation with snapdragons or another crop to follow carnations after eighteen months and to fill in the gap before carnations are replanted in the same area the following May or June.

WATER AND NUTRITION

Healthy and fast-growing carnations require lots of water and feed. The most efficient way to apply these is together through a liquid-feed proportioner. There is no reason to change the strength of the liquid-feeding solution from one time of the year to another. The more growth the plants make (regulated by light and temperature), the more water and fertilizer they will require.

Carnations should be watered on demand. Water loss in excess of water intake (water stress) is one of the major limiting factors in carnation growth. Some water stress is probably needed to prevent growth from becoming too soft, especially when light is limited. Stress is usually greater in soil than in gravel culture, where more frequent irrigation is used. To minimize stress on soil-grown plants, the soil must be well structured so it will tolerate frequent irrigation without damage from lack of oxygen. Each soil mixture is different in its characteristics when wet or dry. Sensing the moisture content of a particular soil mixture comes with close observation and experience. A tensiometer that measures the suction with which the water is held by the soil particles is an objective method of measuring soil moisture content. Where these are used, growers obtain good growth when the soil is thoroughly soaked at a moisture tension of 10 to 30 centibars (approximately 3 to 9 inches of vacuum). The interval between waterings varies with the size of plants, the speed of growth at the time, and with the depth and moisture-holding capacity of the soil mixture. When soils are uniform and crops are in the same stage, irrigation both in frequency and time applied is easily automated. A moisture-sensing device in the soil or a solar-energy counter can be used to establish when to water.

Phosphate and lime are usually applied to carnation soils before planting as needed. Five pounds of superphosphate per 100 square feet will usually supply adequate phosphate for a carnation crop for one year or longer. Limestone or gypsum applied if calcium tests indicate low levels. Dolomitic limestone at 5 to 10 pounds per 100 square feet is used if the pH is low. Gypsum at the same rates is used if the pH is 6.5 or above.

Recent work on carnation nutrition at Colorado State University has shown the importance of ion balance in obtaining maximum yield from carnations. Optimum ion balance has been established at near the following ratios:

K	Ca	Mg	Na	NH_4	NO_3	SO_4	H_2PO_4	Cl
6	3½	3½	½	2	14	½	1	0

Calcium plus magnesium should equal 7, but each can vary so long as neither is deficient. Potassium can vary upward to 8 while NO_3 can vary down to 10 without significantly affecting yield or quality.

This solution represents the total ions available in the nutrient solution from the soil or substrate. All ions need not be added to the feeding solution, however. Some may be added to the soil while some may be in the water supply.

It is extremely important that the water analysis is known. Some irrigation waters contain large amounts of mineral salts. These must be accounted for in the final nutrient solution, otherwise the growth of the crop may be reduced because of excesses of certain ions. Calcium, magnesium, sodium, sulfates, bicarbonates and chlorides are the most common ions present in irrigation water.

A balanced feeding solution used successfully by many carnation producers on a continuous basis uses the following weights of chemicals per 1,000 gallons of irrigation water:

5 lbs. potassium nitrate

3 lbs. calcium nitrate

1 lb. ammonium nitrate

2 lbs. magnesium sulfate

1 lb. phosphoric acid

½ ounce borax

This solution is presented merely as a guide. It is a well-balanced nutrient solution for growing carnations in gravel culture, but for soil culture, several modifications may be made. Phosphate and calcium may be added to the soil prior to planting and either eliminated or reduced in the irrigation water. Calcium, magnesium, and/or sulfate may be present in adequate amounts in the water supply. Where calcium is present in the water at 60 ppm or higher, or is supplied in the soil as limestone, substitute 1 pound of ammonium nitrate for each 2 pounds of calcium nitrate. If magnesium is present in the water supply at 25 ppm or more, and sulfates in the water exceed 25 ppm, add no magnesium sulfate. If the only available water is high in salinity, growth and quality will be reduced. Carnations are tolerant to high concentrations of sulfates. Increase potassium to the level of sodium in sodic waters, i.e. those containing more than 140 ppm of sodium. Chloride levels above 70 ppm usually reduce carnation growth and tend to harden plants. High calcium and/or magnesium (levels of the two combined above 250 ppm) also reduce and harden growth. *Warning:* Know what ions and their concentrations are present in your water supply. Do *not* add ions that are already present. If you must use saline water, prepare a well-drained medium or use gravel, and leach freely at each irrigation to prevent excess-salt accumulation.

Tissue analysis is now available to all growers. Periodic leaf analysis will give you the best check on the effectiveness of your feeding program. Micronutrients are not discussed in detail here. Your state experiment station or your farm adviser can inform you of the likelihood of micronutrient deficiency in your area. Tissue analysis also reveals micronutrient levels. Most micronutrient deficiencies reduce growth of carnations seriously, long before visual symptoms are apparent.

In general, boron is limited in the majority of soils where carnations are grown. Parts of California and Illinois are exceptions. Boron hunger is quite common where additional boron is not supplied. This should be added to the irrigation water for safest results. However, rates required by carnations may be too high for chrysanthemums. Where boron hunger has been observed in a carnation crop, an application of only 3 to 4 ounces per 100 square feet per year has corrected it. Common symptoms of boron hunger are shortened internodes and a slight clubbiness to the flower stems. Stimulated branching on the upper flower stems and malformed flowers are also present. In extreme cases, most of the petals may be missing and the flowers are extremely crippled. Similar symptoms are produced from flue-gas injury, but boron hunger is seldom seen during the heavy-heating season.

TEMPERATURE AND LIGHT

These two factors are the greatest influences on carnation quality, while light is the predominant factor, affecting yield. Since temperature is much more controllable by the grower, it will be discussed first.

TEMPERATURE

Successful growers are particularly careful with temperature control for carnations. They supply temperature conditions for their plants that change gradually from day to night and back to day. They control the spread between day and night temperature and they change from summer to fall to winter to spring as light increases or decreases. A guide to this temperature pattern follows:

	Summer	Fall	Winter	Spring
Day	70° F	65°	60°	65°
Night	56-60° F	55°	50-52°	55°

All day temperatures are those at which ventilation or cooling is used. Night temperatures should be considered maximum for the majority of varieties presently being grown. It is not possible to give more than a guide for the many growing conditions and climates used for carnations. An individual grower will modify these for his own set of conditions. Generally, when carnation flowers are small, leaves narrow and branching is poor, there is a good chance that day temperature is too high. When stems are weak and flowers are small but have good color, high night temperature is indicated.

Summer cooling has been one of the most valuable developments for the carnation grower in recent years. Where summer humidities are not excessive during midday, evaporative cooling can be used to advantage. Excess summer heat hardens and greatly delays carnation growth and reduces quality of flowers. Even 10° of cooling will pay for itself on carnations. During the hottest part of the day, the humidity is generally lowest; hence, an evaporative cooling system can be successful in so-called "humid" climates.

Winter ventilation is another important phase of temperature control. The

The author examines a pot of carnations. Good dwarf varieties would be a welcome addition for pot growing.

introduction of too much cold air and the sudden chilling of flower buds will cause additional whorls of petals, leading to bullheaded flowers or split calyxes. Carnations are best in an environment where temperature changes gradually. The development of the translucent plastic convection tube for use with exhaust fans to let in cold outside air for winter ventilation has almost eliminated split and malformed flowers during the period it can be used. This draft-free system consists of one or more exhaust fans and one or more fresh-air inlets in gable walls. Thin tubes extend from the inlets the full length of the greenhouse. The tubes are suspended on wire near the ridge or well above the plants, and have holes punched along the entire length at regular intervals. The tubes are closed off at the far end in shorter houses, attached to inlets at both gable walls in houses 150 feet or longer. This system is easily automated to come on at a desired temperature. As the fan turns on, the slight vacuum in the house causes the tube to inflate and fresh air is discharged through the small holes in the tube to all parts of the house. There is a thorough mixing of the outside air with the warm air inside and the temperature inside the house is amazingly uniform. When the desired temperature is reached, the fan shuts off, the tube collapses and the ventilation stops. No worker can ventilate as well, even if he is in the house constantly.

There are several advantages to providing air flow inside the greenhouse when no outside air is being introduced. Temperature variation within the house (hot and cold spots) may be largely eliminated and much more accurate temperature control by the thermostats achieved. Peaks in relative humidity are avoided, thereby giving some disease control. Carbon dioxide is probably made more available to the leaf surfaces. Jay Koths of the University of Connecticut advocates horizontal air flow over vertical air flow with small fans to boost the air along. Cost to move air may be only a third as great with horizontal flow. He suggests 4 1/10 hp motors with 18-inch blades for an area of 3000 square feet. Air velocities of 100 to 300 feet per minute accomplish good results and tend to equalize plant and air temperatures. Packaged heating, ventilating and air-circulating equipment are now available for those who want to accomplish several jobs with one piece of equipment.

LIGHT

Light is the source of energy and the overriding factor responsible for plant growth. It is doubtful that light can be too strong for carnations since they are among the plants having the highest light requirements known. Since heat always accompanies light from the sun, excess heat is often a problem when sunlight is intense. While glass houses are still standard structures for plant-growing, several plastics are increasing in popularity for carnations. Most of the construction in Colorado for the past 10 years has been of fiberglass materials. Improved quality under these covers is probably due to the diffusion of heat and light and the reduction of water stress. Fiberglass coverings for greenhouses have been greatly improved by the manufacturers. Currently, the best product is a good panel with a thin layer of Tedlar® laminated to the outer surface. These panels will probably last for 20 years or more without serious degradation. Polyethylene has proved to be a good cover for carnations in many parts of the world. Many other plastic films have been tried and discarded for one reason or another.

The distribution of yearly light energy varies with location and determines the yield patterns—the speed of return crops, etc. Anytime a heavy crop is flowered in a low-light period, the quality and stem strength will be low. A grower produces the best carnations when he works with the light he has and not against it. Clean coverings inside and out, and modern light structures oriented E-W in 35-50° latitude, offer important advantages of more winter light to the grower.

While shading compound on the roof is controversial among carnation growers, it is necessary to hold quality on flowering benches in summer. Most growers agree that light shade, or none at all, is best for young plants. When applying shade to the roof, it should be kept in mind that light is reduced much more than heat by any density of shade.

LIGHTING FOR CROP CONTROL

Research during the past 20 years, first in England and later in this country, has shown a definite and useful response of carnation to extended day length. Lighting was first done, as it is with chrysanthemums, either adding to the day to get 16 hours of light or interrupting the night by lighting from 10 p.m. to 2 a.m. While the carnation responded to this, it was found that lighting all night with low-intensity light gave the greatest response. This latter method of lighting is done and advocated by Gordon Koon, a leading carnation producer of Colorado. He, and other growers who follow his method, use GE PS-30 incandescent lamps 8 feet above the soil level and 14 feet apart to cover 4 carnation beds. Lights are turned on from dusk to dawn for specific lighting periods.

Flower-bud initiation is hastened by lighting and the resulting crop is bunched more closely than for unlighted crops. This type of lighting also elongates internodes and inhibits lateral branching. Growers who have used lighting most successfully light for periods of from 2 to 4 weeks to produce a given crop or cycle. When a lighting period is started, the shoots with 6 and 7 expanded leaf pairs are initiated within a few days. Those having 3, 4, or 5 leaf pairs may develop to the initiation stage during the lighting period if it is continued 3 or 4 weeks. Lights are then turned off to let another crop of shoots develop to the proper stage and to avoid excessive stem elongation and weak stems.

Lighting should produce a crop 12 weeks after August lighting starts—16 weeks after November lighting—if susceptible shoots are present in the 3-7 leaf-pair stage. Lighting from February 1 should produce a crop in 14 weeks. There is a second effect that can be just as important: another crop begins with the start of new shoots as soon as lighting is stopped. The gap between these two crops is 2 to 3 weeks. While this gap of low production has not been used intentionally, it could be a way of dealing with short-but-poor marketing periods.

Lighting is especially effective on plants in their second year when crop control is more difficult. Successful management of this technique includes an ability to control the time when susceptible-sized breaks are present for lighting. For example, a heavy crop of *Red Sim* is wanted for Valentine's Day on second-year plants. This crop must be shoots with 3-7 expanded leaf pairs on October 1. This means that these plants should have produced a September-October crop to have the proper-sized shoots for lighting.

Lighting also stretches the internodes on flower stems in the later stages of development. Midwinter lighting weakens the stems of flowers in their final growth. Lighting during the summer and early fall tends to increase stem length and flower grade on fall and early-winter crops.

The start of new laterals is inhibited during the lighting period, so there is a lag of 2 to 4 weeks between a lighted crop and the next one to come. This fact can be used to advantage, if poor markets are experienced following a holiday. It is also a beneficial effect on single-crop carnations, since it reduces competing shoots on the flower stems.

A shortened timing schedule worked out by Gordon Koon for Colorado is:

Lights on (3) weeks	Main cropping period
August 15	November 15 - December 25
October 1	January 5 - February 10
November 15	February 15 - March 15
January 1	April 10 - May 10

SINGLE-CROPPING

Availability of reliable cuttings at any time of the year and lighting have caused more interest in growing single crops of carnations to flower for specific holidays. The economics of this practice are particularly attractive in eastern markets where prices of specific colors sometimes double for brief periods.

While the success of single-cropping remains to be demonstrated, many possible advantages can be listed.

1. A uniform, high-quality crop can be produced.

2. The grower should have much more control on timing, quantity, and color mix.
3. Harvesting, support of plants, and pest control should be easier.
4. Cost of planting stock would increase, but hopefully would be more than covered by additional income.

Chrysanthemum growers should be particularly adapted to single-cropping of carnations. They are familiar with the methods required and have the lighting equipment and heating capacity for 60° F nights. In fact, single-cropping of carnations may fit especially well into schedules with chrysanthemums, snapdragons, or other short-term crops.

Single crops involve planting a bit closer with uniform cuttings, and giving one pinch with the goal of 16-20 shoots per square foot. When the shoots reach the susceptible stage, they are lighted for 4 weeks to initiate flower buds uniformly and to effectively bunch the crop. In spite of these goals, most commercial trials with this method have not produced the calculated number of flowers for the specific period. A possible reason for this is that we have no varieties developed specifically for single cropping. Also, shoots in excess of 4 per plant should be removed by pinching off the lower ones.

Two temperature responses should be mentioned in connection with single-cropping of carnations. Harry C. Kohl, Jr. of the University of California at Davis has demonstrated that carnation shoots can be grown at 60° F nights until the calyx-opening stage and finished the final 30 days at 50-52° F. This resulted in good-quality flowers in about 70% of the time. Abou Dahab, working in Holland, reduced the time to produce a carnation flower to 70-80% by exposing the shoots at the 6-7 leaf-pair stage to 40° F for 3 weeks. This exposure period coincides with the stage that ordinarily

Automatic watering system for gravel culture, including Toro hydraulic valve and Chapin Twin-Tube delivery; tubes between rows of plants have 4-inch hole spacing. DuPont flower support netting barely visible. Two or more layers are placed on the bench and the plants set through the right spaces, netting raised as the plants grow.

would be lighted. Several temperature and lighting manipulations are possible when we think of single-crop carnations that may be grown in separate houses.

CUTTING AND GRADING

Most retail growers cut their flowers too open to realize maximum life from them. While tight flowers do not open under refrigeration, they open beautifully at room temperature and the consumer may realize two days more of life from them. Grading has proved to be a profitable practice in almost every instance. The set of S.A.F. grades now in the process of wide adoption includes Extra Fancy (Blue) grade with 22-inch-long stems and large (2¾-inch) flowers, free from damage or malformation. The second or Fancy grade (Red) has minimum stem length of 17 inches and strong stems with slightly smaller (2¼-inch) flower diameter. Number 1 grade (Green) has minimum stem length of 10 inches. White grade includes all flowers that are split— even though mended. Grading facilitates trading flowers without the buyer seeing each bunch, and it almost always increases the grower's average return.

BUD-CUTTING AND STORAGE

Research done in the past ten years has revealed possibilities for cutting carnations (and other flowers), in a tight-bud stage, storing or shipping the buds, and opening the buds at distant markets or even in the retail flower shop. There are many advantages to this method, the greatest being that the consumer can enjoy better flowers if all is done correctly.

Peonies and gladioluses have always been harvested in tight buds, primarily because open blooms cannot be handled through our marketing systems. The first to use tight-bud cutting and shipping on a large scale may be those who export carnations to the United States and to Europe. Larger shippers of carnations to distant markets in the United States may follow shortly. Selling buds to retail florists will always be difficult, so the larger shippers of carnations will probably harvest and ship the carnation buds to wholesale outlets which they own in terminal markets. The buds can be stored for several weeks before opening, or they may be opened and placed in regular marketing channels immediately.

Advanced buds showing ½ to 1 inch of color are highly satisfactory for bud opening. Temperatures of 70° to 75° F and selected flower-opening solutions are the remaining requirements. Carnation buds in these stages open in 2 to 4 days and have better quality than when opened on the plants. Buds have longer storage life and withstand stress during shipment better than open blooms.

Bud-cutting may be a bit ahead of its time, but it will be useful when it is needed.

VARIETIES

The variety *William Sim* is the parent of almost all standard carnation varieties grown throughout the world. The *Sim* sports are tall-growing with

ELEGANCE

Miniature. Flushed deep pink, blending to white. Note spray formation.

good-sized flowers of high quality most of the year. A breakthrough to a better family of varieties has been most difficult for breeders, but will probably come in time. Percentages of the various colors for each greenhouse or area cannot be standardized. Usually, white is most popular in American markets at from 30 to 40%. The reason for a high percentage of white is that as much as ¼ of the whites in some markets are dyed exotic colors not found in the natural product. Red and light pink are currently being grown in almost equal percentages of about 25%. This leaves a maximum of 20% for all other colors. Novelty colors are less important in most shops, though some make a specialty of having colors and varieties not commonly available. As more and more carnations are sold in mass markets and on street corners, the popularity of novelty colors will make itself known. While there are several hundred varieties of carnations, a brief listing should include:

White: *White Sim* in an infinite number of selections.
Light Pink: *Light Pink Sim* in many selections, *Linda, Coquette, Dusty.*
Dark Salmon: *La Reve, Flamingo, Shocking Pink.*
Red: *Scania, Red Gayety,* many other selections of *Red Sim.*
Yellow: *Braun's Yellow Sim, Pajee, Yellow Dusty.*
Orange: *Tangerine, Quinn's Orange, Sunset Sim.*
Purple Frosted: *Orchid Beauty, Safari, Caribe.*
Variegated: *Gayety, S. Arthur Sim, Mamie, Blaze, Pink Mist.*
Miniatures: *Elegance, White Elegance, White Royalette, Exquisite, Goldilocks, Lemon Drop, Orange Elf, Starfire, Sweetheart, Silvery Pink, Tinkerbell, Twinkle,* and many others.

INSECT TROUBLES

The effective insecticides and methods of application are constantly changing. The major pests of carnations remain the same.

Aphis or greenfly is currently being controlled by Vapona applied as smokes, aerosols or sprays. Insufficient dosage is the major cause of poor kills. It is quite safe on carnations. Cygon and similar aphicides are being used successfully by many growers, although slight tip scorch may be caused if applied too strong.

240

Red spider mite is being controlled by systemics in the soil such as Meta-Systox, by wet sprays such as Pentac. Severe infestations of mites are very difficult to control by aerosols or fogging.

Thrips are usually not a problem in cold weather so control of these should be concentrated between April and October. Dieldrin at ½ pint per 100 gallons of pad water is used weekly by those who have evaporative cooling systems. A top spray of Dieldrin at ½ pint per 100 gallons at weekly intervals is an even better control measure. Growers who use fogging devices in their insect-control program have obtained good thrips control by starting in late April or early May with weekly applications of their regular Vapona or other insecticides to which is added Dieldrin emulsion 18% at the rate of 3 parts Dieldrin to 7 parts of the regularly used fogging formula. Six pints of Dieldrin per acre of greenhouses per week during the thrips season should effectively control this pest.

Insecticides have not been improved greatly in the past 5 years due in part to the current scare on pollution of environment. There is some improvement each year, so alert growers should keep up with these developments through current trade papers.

LOOKING AHEAD—CARNATIONS, 1980

The number of carnations produced will continue to increase along with rather large increases in imports from Latin America. This means that more carnations will be available each year. Fortunately, we are seeing some significant changes in marketing methods. Flowers are gradually becoming easier to buy. Most supermarkets are anxious to sell flowers, or anything else that is profitable. Whether flowers are sold from a produce counter, a special flower area within the supermarket, or on street corners, more flowers are being sold, even in 1975. This trend will continue at an accelerated rate. The carnation is one of the best flowers for mass-market sales.

Supplying these sales outlets is not going to be easy. They require shorter grades at stable prices. The pricing structure leaves little room for the conventional commission wholesaler. Ideally, the producer or a group of producers should supply the flowers directly to the seller so minimum marketing costs are passed on to the consumer.

Mass-marketing of flowers has been researched, talked about and tried for many years. An inadequate and unstable supply of flowers, especially in winter and at holidays, has been the major reason for late developments of mass-market sales in floriculture.

Increased sales that are sure to come will require more and more carnations. More of our domestic producers will locate branch facilities in Latin America and ever-increasing imports will lend stability to the flower supply. U.S. producers are giving a lot of thought to modifications they can make to produce the types of flowers needed for consumer sales. Shorter stems, more colors and even multiple blooms per stem may be needed. Cost per bloom must be minimized to gain maximum sales and profits. This may require innovative methods of cutting and plant control to obtain fast crops on possibly taller plants. There is work here also for the plant breeder, for surely, more productive strains with large flowers and shorter stems are possible. As mass-marketing is developed, new opportunities will arise for producers, buyers and supplying agents for chain stores, and for a multitude of handlers and sellers at the consumer level.

CARNATIONS—OUTDOOR TYPE

ANNUAL & PERENNIAL *(Dianthus caryophyllus)*
14,000 seeds per oz. Germinates in 2-3 wks. 70°

The so-called "annual" varieties are actually biennial, but they are not winter-hardy. They will live over for several years in mild climates.

The types which we know today were mostly bred in the south of France. The earliest strain is *Enfant de Nice,* used chiefly today as a formula mixture. They will flower within five months from sowing. Most other strains take about six months to flower, such as the famous *Chabaud* strain, with its free-flowering habit, available in many colors. This is the preferred strain for bedding.

All range in height from 12 to 20 inches, with the tallest being the *Chabauds.* Flowers in outdoor carnations are from 90 to 95 per cent double type. The best outdoor annual carnations will be had in moderately warm sections of the country. In recent years, dwarf strains have become available. Growing to a height of only 12-14 inches, they are excellent for bedding purposes and require no support. Dwarf *Fragrance* is the best of these newer dwarf varieties.

For pack sales in May, seed should be sown from late January through mid-February. After transplanting, pinch once and grow at 50°.

The so-called "hardy" carnations are the *Grenadin* strain. This strain features many of the good points of the annuals, including the fact that they can be had in flower from a spring sowing the first season. They are, however, not fully winter-hardy in the North. They can also be started to good advantage for larger plants and earlier blooms from an outdoor summer sowing.

CELOSIA

ANNUAL *(C. argentea cristata)* *28,000 seeds per oz. Germinates in 8-10 days at 70°*

One of the showiest and most dependable of annuals for cutting, garden decorations, bedding, borders or pot plants. Currently, they are showing increased usage, for they are exceedingly attractive from late summer until frost. Celosias are easy to grow if a few simple rules are observed. They are heat-loving plants, and no attempt should be made to handle small plants for bedding unless a night temperature of at least 60° (preferably 65°) can be maintained. Even under these conditions, seed should not be sown earlier than 6 weeks before time for selling and planting out (after all frost danger

▲ CELOSIA JEWEL BOX
The dwarfest of the Cristata celosias, only 4-5 inches tall. Large combs in a mixture of white, yellow, pink, red and purple.

◄ GOLDEN TRIUMPH
A tall bushy Plumosa type.

has passed and nights are dependably warm). If their growth is checked in any way, either by cold temperatures, or by remaining too long in their growing containers, they will produce small flowers prematurely, and will likely remain permanently stunted. Celosia plants for beddings sales *must not* be allowed to come into flower before planting out, nor should they be pinched.

The two main types of classes are the *cristata* or *coxcomb*, producing the large, curiously shaped heads and the *plumosa* or "feathered" type of flower. The *cristata* may be had in both tall (2-3 feet) and uniformly dwarf strains (10-12 inches), that make showy, 3-4-inch pot plants, as well as bedding plants. Dwarf strains of *cristata* in colors, especially *Dwarf Empress Imp.*, come quite true in every way. *Kardinal* is a very popular bright red. Dwarfest of all is *Jewel Box* (4-5 inches). It has large combs in a color mix from white and light yellow to pink, red and purple. The taller *cristatas* are used where appropriate colors are wanted in fall decorative work. Outstanding in this class are the varieties *Toreador* and *Fireglow*. *Toreador* (18-20 inches) has extremely large combs of a bright red color while *Fireglow* reaches a height of 20-24 inches and produces large, globular combs of a brilliant scarlet-red color. The *plumosa* class is also available in tall and dwarf strains. Most popular tall one is *Golden Triumph*. Reaching a height of 2 feet, it has golden-yellow plumes and bright green foliage. *Forest fire* (2½ feet) has been very popular for some time with its fiery, orange-scarlet plumes contrasted with bronze foliage. A semi-dwarf class (18-24 inches) is also now available. Outstanding in this class is the variety *Red Fox*. Its flowers are bright carmine red, freely borne on bushy plants.

The popular dwarf one is *Fiery Feather,* bright red (1 foot), which makes a good pot plant or can be used for edging. *Golden Feather* is a deep yellow of similar habit.

CENTAUREA (Cornflower)

ANNUAL *(C. species) 7,000 seeds per oz. Germinates in 10 days at 65°. Dark.*

A cool-temperature, hardy annual useful for cutting both in and outdoors. Also, several dwarf dusty millers come under this heading. Most valuable for cutting is *Centaurea cyanus* or Bachelor Button. A September sowing on a raised bed in a 50° house can be flowered in February, but the more natural

CENTAUREA CYANUS
Useful for cutting either under glass or outdoors.

and better time to flower all the centaureas is the spring months. This is done through planting from November to January, or even February, if well-started pot plants are used. While a late or spring-flowering crop can go on ground beds, we prefer raised or shallow beds especially for the cyanus class because of the heavy, almost unmanageable growth they make in deep, rich soil. They should be spaced at least 12 x 12 inches. In the early stages of their growth, a low temperature will naturally be good for them, because it permits building up a strong root system that responds better to higher temperatures later.

After the centaureas get well-started, 50° nights suit them very well. In the latitude of Cincinnati, Ohio, a late-September sowing outdoors will make established little plants before the ground freezes up. If drainage is right and some coarse covering used, they should winter-over and flower earlier in spring than will a spring sowing outdoors. This goes for annual larkspur, as well. By far, the best color is blue. *Blue Diadem* is a good strain, representing an improvement in flower size and color over other existing blues.

For bedding purposes, there is a lower-growing strain available (10-12 inches). They are well adapted for use in a mixed border or for general bedding purposes. *Polka Dot Blue* and *Snowball* are varieties commonly used in this class.

Used for bedding purposes is another variety commonly referred to as a dusty miller. With its silvery-white foliage, it provides an excellent contrast to many colorful annuals when used as an edger. *C. Candidissima* (6 inches) is a slow-growing variety that should be started early. This variety is being replaced rapidly, however, by the cineraria types of dusty miller.

CHRISTMAS PEPPER
A nice holiday plant.

CHRISTMAS CHERRY AND PEPPER

ANNUAL *(Solanum pseudo-capsicum)*
12,000 seeds per oz. Germinates in 15 days at 70°
(capsicum species) 9,000 seeds per oz. Germinates in 12 days at 70-80°

Due to their ease of culture and the attractiveness of well-fruited 5 or 6-inch pot specimens, Christmas cherries find a ready market during the Christmas holiday season. Sow the seed early in February, carrying them along in pots in a 50° house. They prefer a soil which is not too rich and must be pinched back occasionally, although not later than July 1. Don't let them get pot-bound. As soon as danger of frost is over, most growers prefer to set plants outdoors, usually in 4-inch pots. By plunging the pots deep into the soil, the plants will root through the drainage holes. However, the restriction of the pots will keep them from going into a rampant growth that will lose leaves when lifted. In September, take them up and make the final shift into a 5 or 6-inch pot. Shortly afterward, they should be setting fruit which should be a bright orange red by Christmas or earlier.

Cherries can also be summered-over in the field without pots, digging and potting in the fall. Plants handled this way make fine large specimens, but lose leaves and wilt some when potted, due to disturbance of their rather large root system. For maximum fruit set, they must be grown outside during the summer. Most widely used varieties are the *Ball Christmas Cherry* and *Red Giant* which has somewhat larger fruit.

Christmas peppers are handled the same as cherries in most respects; however, several cultural differences should be noted. They should be sown in April or May, depending on final pot size; and they are much better off summered-over in pots than when planted right out, not seeming to mind the restriction at their roots as much as do the cherries. A possible variation in their culture would be sowing made in June, potting off into 2-inch pots, and in the fall, planting four of them into a 6-inch pan—nice holiday material. Do not top them if started this late. Most suitable and widely used variety is *Ball Christmas Pepper*.

A very dwarf, compact variety for possible mass market sales in 4-inch pots is *Fips*.

An interesting arrangement for semi-automatic black cloth application—at Brater-Brockwell's, Oak Ridge, Tennessee, Don Brater in the photo. Note the large overhead polyethylene tube, upper right. Just above the tube and to the left, if you look carefully, you'll see a roll of black cloth. In the evening, this roll is simply allowed to unroll down the slanted wires (one of them held by Don Brater) until they reach the gutter. Then, a 6-foot drop curtain is lowered by hand from the gutter to the ground. In the morning, the roll of black polyethylene is rolled back up to the ridge of the greenhouse by a small electric motor which draws small wire cables up and around the roll of poly.

CHRYSANTHEMUM

Year-round mums continue to be an undisputed No. 1 among cut-flower crops—the most dollars wholesale value. Year-round pot mums must certainly hold the same No. 1 spot among major pot crops.

Mums are big business in our world of ornamentals and are continuing to get bigger.

Some interesting things are happening to the different segments of the mum industry:

POT MUMS

Really bullish! For example, an almost 50 per cent increase in production, 1966-'70 (11.1 to 16.2 million pots). And, believe it or not, a 9-cent price increase ($1.43 to $1.52). This, per USDA. You know an important part of this increase is going into various mass-market thrusts. They fit the bill—colorful, long shelf life. They are the most profitable of the major pot crops—per many large pot-plant growers.

STANDARDS

For the 4-year period, 1966-'70, production up 16 per cent in dollars, 11 per cent in flowers. Prices up only a shade. The figures (USDA):

	Per Stem	Dollar Sales	Stems Sold
1966	17.4¢	$23,200,000	133,300,000
1970	18.3¢	$26,900,000	147,000,000

They are a big crop—and profitable when well grown and well marketed. Considerable expansion among West Coast growers, steady in the Midwest and East.

POMPONS

Again, substantial increase in bunches sold (1966-'70), up 14 per cent; up 21 per cent in dollars. The figures:

	Per Bunch	Dollar Sales	Bunches Sold
1966	78¢	$22,000,000	28,300,000
1970	82¢	$26,700,000	32,400,000

Again, a big crop. We see a steady volume of production in the East and Midwest. Fair increase in Florida and California. The West Coast has become a major pompon producer—mainly plastics competing with the Florida cloth house.

A good sign—substantial breeding interest in both pot and cut mums by such specialists as Yoder's and Pan-American Plant (Shoesmith). Some really major improvements. The mighty *Indianapolis* family is finally giving way to a new winter race. Name: *May Shoesmith*. But in pots, *Bright Golden Anne* (also by Shoesmith) is still No. 1.

Year-round mums are big in Europe, too—even in Japan (in a very different way). European year-round sales are clearly larger than the U. S.

How interesting to speculate on the ingredients that have gone into the remarkable success story of year-round mums in our country. The basic concept of controlling flowering with day length was born among our university research people. And yet, without the major contribution of the propagator, would the year-round mum ever have made it? Not only has the reliable regular supply of good cuttings on schedule been vital, but also the work in disease control and in breeding new year-round varieties.

And, of course, there had to be the American businessman-grower, ready to risk the capital and management effort on a new unproven entry. He finally said, "Go!"—and made it work.

Where does the year-round mum go from here? It is not meant for us to know the future. But it does seem likely that the mum will continue to be a stable, major crop in the U. S. (and across the world) for many years to come. What else can be done other than for research people, propagators, and growers to do their best to improve the crop, sell it as effectively as they can—and see what the future holds.

GENERAL CULTURE

WHAT'S THE TRICK?

Occasionally you will hear someone say, as they admire a really good job of growing, "What is the trick you used to get such beautiful results?" Some special fertilizer, for some reason, is often suspected.

There aren't many things we claim to *know* about this business of growing. One thing, though, that seems clear is that good growing isn't a "trick." It's

247

more likely the day-in and day-out attention to dozens of little well-known details. It's that extra spraying a bench of newly planted cuttings gets on a hot afternoon, keeping after planting crews' shallow planting of cuttings, getting shade off the roof promptly in the fall—and so on down the list. Of course, to some extent, a man must have a "feel" for plants—he must instinctively hurt a little bit inside when he walks by a dry plant. But mainly, good growing is just doing the little things that are not secret—doing them all day, *every* day.

We hope that these remarks about mum culture will help guide those really interested to many of the little points that make for good mums.

ABOUT MUM SOILS

There isn't any one type of soil that mums particularly favor. There are some rules of soil *management* that are quite important. Most important of these is the matter of humus. A hard, poorly aerated soil just won't grow good mums. A good mum soil should have a loose, open texture. When water is applied, it should soak into the soil, not run off. It should be possible to push one's fist down into a bench of mum soil. A good mum soil won't crack as it dries.

Almost any reasonably good field or garden soil can be made into this kind of a porous, open growing medium by additions of humus, peat, and inorganics, such as perlite. Coarse peat moss is a readily available, weed-free, reasonably disease-free source of humus for both pot and cut-mum soils. Straw is used by many cut-mum growers before most crops for aeration and improved soil structure with accompanying steam sterilization, which is important. Rice hulls, unsalted peanut hulls, sugar cane stems, and occasionally, sawdust, provide other sources of organic humus to cut-mum soils, less often used on pot-mum soils, as decomposition rates are slow.

Field Soils

Where new benches are being filled, or where soil is changed annually, outdoor-field soil must be used. Any good field soil that has been growing

Problem: Should old mum plants be removed between crops? More and more growers are finding that if the tops are ground up and if thorough steam sterilizing is practiced, these old stumps can actually contribute considerable organic matter to the soil—and certainly cause no problem. Here's a grinder we are using in West Chicago that seems to do the job well. It's a Mott Hammer Knife®, costs about $175, available from the Mott Corporation, Box 278, La Grange, Illinois.

good farm crops can be brought into the bench, 1½ inches of peat or other humus added, the soil steamed, and it will be ready to plant. Better results will often be had if the land to be used is planted to a cover crop several years in advance of its use. Rye or bluegrass are both excellent. It takes about two years to build up organic matter in soils in this way—and the amount of humus won't increase much after that. Fertilize the cover crop regularly. Post recommends 800 pounds of 5-10-10 per acre the first year, if no manure is used. After that, 200 pounds of ammonium sulfate per acre, applied each spring, is recommended. Acidity must be checked, lime added if necessary. Tops are cut each year at the bloom stage.

Such cover crops should be turned under about one month before soil is needed in the bench. Since rotting of the roots, etc., in these soils tends to take up available nitrogen, it is important to watch nutrient levels the first few months such soils are in the bench. Manure or peat may be added just before plowing field soils under—and will help in many cases.

Reusing Greenhouse Soils

The majority of cut-flower growers now keep their bench soils in more or less permanently. It is almost standard practice to steam the soil at least annually. Many growers on year-round mum programs steam before each crop—three times a year. Humus is maintained by regular additions of peat, sometimes well-rotted manure, or both. Nutrients are usually supplied in liquid form, sometimes dry.

By and large, the system works well. It saves the tremendously expensive task of wheeling out hundreds of yards of soil during the hot summer weather. It eases the ever-increasing problem of finding good fresh topsoil. A sterilized soil is free of weeds, soil-borne insects and diseases. With modern methods, steaming is really not too much of a job. Full details on sterilizing soils on page 91.

Several points should be watched. Most important is to insure that adequate humus is added. Most soils will benefit from about 1 to 1½ inches of peat (domestic or imported) annually. Peat can be overdone—resulting in a soil that stays too wet, aerates poorly. Mums won't grow in a peat bog. But, more often, the error is the other way. Some growers add the peat as a mulch on cuttings benched in warm weather. Many current soil-management programs incorporate several sources of humus during a year's rotation to take advantage of the varied benefits each may provide.

It's hard to put a limit on reusing greenhouse soil—five or six years of continuous cropping with mums might bring the grower close to trouble. Try half a bench of fresh soil—do they grow better?

FERTILIZER AND GOOD MUMS

Mums, being heavy, leafy plants, tend to be heavy feeders during the period of most vigorous growth. However, it is just as easy to overdo on feeding as it is to cut them too short.

It is difficult to offer any suggestions on how much of what type of fertilizer to apply—and when. The only answer to this question is a soil test. Roughly, the following nutrient levels should be maintained, in our experience.

Nitrates	20-40 parts per million, Spurway
Phosphorus	3-5 parts per million
Potash	20-40 parts per million
Calcium	150-250 parts per million
pH	6.4-7.0

In general, it is desirable to start out newly planted cuttings at levels some-what below those given above. However, even the newly planted cuttings must have nutrients.

Few growers actually do their feeding strictly according to soil tests. The more common practice is to set up a regular feeding routine that from previous experience is known to be about adequate. Then, the benches are "spot checked" by means of soil tests every month or two. The feeding program can then be adjusted if nutrients are found to be too low or too high.

Actually, most commercial mum growers today feed both cut-flower and pot-mum crops using fertilizer injectors—feeding applied along with each watering. It is virtually a labor-free operation, insures that crops get a little fertilizer each time water is applied, seems to do a good job. For full details on these injectors and notes on using them, see page 164.

Some Cautions on Feeding

First, as any grower experienced in the northern dark-winter country knows, both feeding and watering must be drastically reduced during dark weather. As a very general guide, mums on a ground bed in midwinter will need perhaps 1/5 as much of both fertilizer and water as the same crop in midsummer. Of course, the crop should not be allowed to wilt—nor should it be starved for nitrogen. But it will need so much less of both water and feed during the short, sunless days of January that, with reasonable care, this shouldn't happen.

In general, fertilizer should not be applied to a dry soil. Better water lightly first, feed, then soak well.

A problem sometimes associated with feeding (overfeeding) is an excess of soluble salts in the soil. We are concerned here with an excess of the *total of all soluble salts* in the soil. The soil solution simply becomes so concentrated that roots cannot take up moisture. Solu Bridge readings will indicate quite accurately whether total salt concentration is too high. Where do these salts come from? Usually from a very hard water that constantly adds salts, and from heavy fertilizing. Cure: leaching 3 to 5 gallons of water per square foot. Be sure soils drain well. Be sure that water penetrates completely through the soil to run-off each time it is irrigated to help regularly flush through accumulations of salts. If the problem is too serious, it may be more practical to change soil.

DIRECT-BENCH CUTTINGS!

It gives so much more rapid growth than any other way of handling them—and it's so much less work besides. We have direct-benched all of our mums for years; losses even in hot weather have been negligible.

However, it's one of those operations that must be done right. The rules are simple, easy to follow, but failure on any important point can mean real loss. Here are the "rules" that we follow:

Nutrient levels must be low to medium, especially nitrogen and potash. Too-high levels will burn roots; too low starves the plants. Occasional Solu Bridge tests will tip you off to excesses of salts. Tender roots of new cuttings aren't very tolerant!

Aeration. Provide a good, open soil structure by the addition of peat moss or other kinds of coarse humus with or without inorganic additives such as perlite, vermiculite, or calcinined clay. Good aeration and drainage must be assured before planting. They cannot be developed after the crop is in the bed.

Steaming. We have for several years made it a rule to *steam all beds the day prior to benching of cuttings.* Many other growers follow this practice on mums and other crops. Where peat has been applied and where salts are at reasonable levels, it will work almost 100%. Somehow, the cuttings take off exceptionally well in the newly steamed soil—even if it's still warm.

6 DAYS AFTER BENCHING
If the rules of direct benching are followed closely, roots like these should be typical within 7 to 10 days after planting cuttings. This one was direct-benched the day after soil was steamed.

Bone-dry soil. Tender roots of new cuttings planted in bone-dry soil will wither and die. Soil must be medium moist.

Plant shallow. Mum cuttings must be set just as shallow as possible. Even if a few are knocked over by the first watering, they can easily be set up again. Setting the root ball down 2 to 3 inches deep will guarantee a slow start—and often trouble with rotting of cuttings. Firming soil before planting helps keep them shallow.

Watch your planting crew. It's so important!

About misting. Where cuttings are direct-planted in hot weather, it is very important that they be misted—sprayed overhead lightly—3 or 4 times on the first few days. Keep the foliage moist.

Cold storage of cuttings. If cuttings have been stored at a low temperature, be sure to warm them up gradually—12 hours at room temperature is best—before setting them in a hot greenhouse. Incidentally, storage, even under ideal conditions, doesn't improve a cutting. Plant just as soon as possible after receiving the cuttings! If they must be stored, do so as near 32-36° F as possible.

Exposure of roots. Those little roots on a cutting are *delicate.* Five minutes exposure to strong sun will wither them. Watch planting crews to be sure they don't take a lot of cuttings out of the boxes and lay them out along the bench for the planters. It can spell disaster.

Plant a good cutting. Whether it's mums, or carnations, or what have you, it's hard to make direct-benching work unless the cuttings are good ones.

That means 3½ to 4½ inches long, husky yet succulent (brittle), roots 1 to 1½ inches long. A weak cutting just won't make it.

SPACING CONTROLS STEM WEIGHT

If your crop is producing too many heavy pompon sprays and too-large standards, space closer. If you're getting a lot of culls, give them more room.

For normal-season pompons where a uniform quality spray is desired, space 6 by 7, prune to 2 stems per plant, 3 on outside rows. This will give very few culls, and you'll be averaging 6 stems per 9 to 10-ounce bunch.

Some growers space 7 by 8 or 8 by 8 inches, prune to 3 (outside rows, 4). This gives more culls, less uniform cut, a few more stems per foot.

Standards: the trend seems to be away from a 6 or 7-inch mum. They bring little more than good, clean, 5-inch blooms. We are spacing our pinched standards 7 by 8, 2 stems per plant (outside rows, 3), 7 by 9 in winter.

Single-stem spacing for fall crops: pompons 6 by 4; standards 6 by 5. Winter quality will be improved when pompons are afforded spacing up to 6 by 5 inches, and standards, a spacing of up to 6 by 6 inches.

PINCHING—AND TIME PINCHING

Time pinching simply means pinching plants on the pinch date given in the catalog. To have normal-season (fall) mums ready to pinch on the catalog pinch date, plant cuttings about two weeks prior to that date. Then, pinch on the date given in the catalog.

Pinching on the correct date generally assures pompons with good, open spray formation. Standards pinched on the correct date will not usually throw crown buds—thus eliminating doglegged necks.

Single-stem: ordinarily produce good spray formation if cuttings are planted on the catalog pinch date.

Softly, Please

You'd be surprised how much better results you'd get by just pinching out the top ½ inch. Pinching down hard means that new shoots must come from old, hard wood.

SUPPORTING THE EASY WAY

One layer of wire-cross strings will support any ordinary bench of pompons or standards. The one layer must be moved up every week or two, but if properly set up, it takes only minutes.

Better than this, though, is the use of wire mesh or plastic. Already in general use among western and southern mum growers, it seems to be quite practical. Between crops, it is raised overhead out of the way for plowing, etc. Wire mesh eliminates:

1. Unrolling and stretching individual lengths of wire.
2. Winding them up after the crop.
3. Stringing, too!
4. Plastic mesh is lightweight and easy to handle.

INSECTS

For detailed suggestions on control of insects, see page 118.

MUM DISEASES

For simplicity, the preventive sprays for control of septoria leaf spot, mildew, petal rots, etc. were included under the insect section (page 125).

Here's a brief run-over on mum diseases:

Petal Rot. These rots can ruin an otherwise fine crop—and in a hurry, too! Suggestions:

1. Under glass: fairly heavy summer shade, especially on standards flowered in midsummer, will prevent sunburn injury. Ample ventilation, even a little heat on during summer evenings, helps prevent botrytis—keeps petals dry. Also, of course, Parzate spray on flowers from the time they show color. A very effective preventive spray is the use of Benlate at the rate of 8 ounces per 100 gallons of water. Initial overhead application at the time the buds begin to show color and every 5 to 7 days thereafter gives good results.

2. Outdoors: spray programs (above) are effective. Parzate as a dust kept on opening flowers has given even better control for growers on the Gulf Coast.

Septoria Leaf Spot. Worse on outdoor crops. Clean cuttings plus the preventive spray program (above) will give good control.

Verticillium. Clean (cultured) cuttings planted in sterilized soil will eliminate it.

Stunt. A virus that will stunt occasional plants to ½ to ⅔ normal height—and bleach flowers of red and bronze varieties. Again, clean cuttings in sterilized soil ordinarily eliminate this problem. Buy from reputable propagators who culture-index their stock plants.

Foliar Nematode. Tiny worms feeding within the leaf tissues cause this condition. Especially under outdoor or any warm, wet conditions, it can spread very rapidly. A spray of Meta Systox-R is best control.

Control: preventive spray program (above).

Dodder. Pale, yellow to orange threads (vines) growing very rapidly over stems, leaves and flowers—that's dodder. It has no leaves—being a parasite. It can ruin a bed of mums in 2 weeks. Usually it comes in with peats, soils, or manures from outdoors. Steam kills it. Once a bench is affected, it is cheaper to remove and burn all affected plants.

CLOTH-HOUSE ANGLES

Top-quality pompons are flowered under cloth from August 1 into October—if frost protection is available. Pointers:

1. Schedules—the regular tables apply.

2. Diseases are something more of a problem than under glass. The preventive sprays outlined above will keep them clean ordinarily, though.

3. Cloth. Cotton or aster cloth is more effective in keeping leafhoppers and small insects out than plastic (saran). The saran is more expensive but will last many seasons. If saran is used, specify amber—*not* the green. The green makes too much shade—reduces production.

4. Varieties. In general, those recommended for August-October flowering

Production of mum cuttings in Florida—above photo at Pan-American Plant Company, Cortez. The high levels of sunshine and favorable temperatures during the winter in southern Florida produce a cutting that is hard to beat! Interesting fact: The "soil" here is almost pure sand. However, with heavy additions of peat moss, mums seem to be very happy in it.

are excellent for cloth-house flowering. In many areas, growers use some of the 11-week pompons in October. They tend to be heavier, better quality.

SHADE ON THE GLASS?

Opinions among growers vary plenty here! Our own experience has led us to these conclusions:

1. The less shade, the better as far as growth, production, quality of mums (or snaps, or carnations) is concerned.
2. Standards flowered during the hot summer months will usually show petal rot or burn unless shaded fairly heavily (during flowering only)—and given regular Benlate sprays. Muslin or aster cloth stretched above beds in flower doesn't seem to do as much good as actual shade on the glass— although a combination of light shade on the glass plus cloth over the bed is often used.
3. We have *not* been shading newly planted cuttings. It seems unnecessary if they are sprayed overhead lightly several times daily until established.
4. There are times when it just gets so hot under glass that if you expect people to stay in there and work, you have to put a light shade on. It does help cut down watering. And it reduces temperature under the sateen covers in late afternoon.
5. Pot-mum specialists who flower through the summer months generally carry a light shade on plants in flower.
6. Tests at Michigan State University showed that ordinary aster cloth (46% light reduction) cut production very substantially on greenhouse

A neat job of automatic black-cloth application. Identification of the range not available. Black cloth is moved from the left sidewall, across the house, overhead, mechanically.

A close-up of the means of suspending the black cloth—on the installation shown above.

pompons. *Different varieties produced from 10% to 55% fewer bunches per foot under the cloth compared to full sun in the greenhouse.* Makes you want *not* to shade.

Shading—and cooling—of summer greenhouses bring up the very important question of mechanical cooling. For growers who are flowering either pot or cut mums in summer-early fall, and who are having trouble with heat, this cooling technique has much to offer. Heat delay can be almost eliminated, and ill effects on quality during hot weather can be largely avoided. For details, see page 267.

TAKING THE BUD

Which bud to let flower on big mums?

Now that we grow mums on definite schedules, this, too, can be reduced to simple rules.

The rule: If the crop is planted and pinched on or near the recommended dates, flower the first bud that appears. In other words, as soon as a bud of any kind appears, remove all side shoots and let the center bud flower.

Crowns and Terminals

Under long summer days (14 hours), a mum will remain "vegetative"—will produce "blind" growth tips free of buds. As the days gradually shorten towards fall, the mum becomes "reproductive"—and produces a cluster of flowering buds at the growth tip.

When a plant is physiologically midway between vegetative and reproductive growth, it may produce a so-called *crown bud*—a single flowering bud surrounded by blind or vegetative shoots. It might be called a half-hearted flowering bud—produced by a plant not yet fully reproductive.

As days shorten still further, the same plant will become fully reproductive and produce a *terminal bud*—cluster of flowering buds.

Some of these halfway-vegetative crown buds can be left on and will make good flowers; some can't. You can't tell by looking at them. The point is that if the crop is planted, pinched and grown according to recommendations, even though a crown might appear, it will almost always be a "good" one. Hence, our recommendations to flower the first bud that appears—crown or terminal.

The rule applies to both normal and off-season crops.

A Possible Exception. Under certain conditions of day length, temperature, etc., some varieties of standards (or pompons) can produce a crown bud 3-4 weeks or less after planting. Such crowns, produced while the plant is less than 18-20 inches tall, we remove, and allow one vegetative side shoot to grow on.

On normal-season standards, a crown that appears earlier than these dates is best removed:

Varieties that flower	Remove crowns that appear before
Oct. 15-Nov. 5	Sept. 5
Nov. 5-30	Sept. 25
Dec. 1-15	Oct. 5

DISBUDS—SHORT AND OTHERWISE

Disbuds today are a quite small part of the American mum crop—but we believe that the trend will be up in the future. Not necessarily "short" disbuds, but more of regular 3½-4 inch flowers on at least 25-28 inch stems—produced year round.

Production per square foot of such disbuds is almost double that of regular "standard" mums—which means that cost is roughly half as much. In other words, where standards are being grown for $4.00 per dozen, the same bench could produce disbuds at $2.50 per dozen—and at a better profit.

It's not that these disbuds should or will replace standards or any other part of the mum crop. Actually, they are in effect a different facet of the mum crop and will be used in ways distinctive from standards. They are excellent for lower-priced basket work—funeral, hospital, church, and home decorations. Because they ship well, are long-lasting, and easy to arrange, they are a natural for low-markup, cut-flower outlets.

DISBUD SCHEDULES

Schedules in outline form for year-round disbuds are given below. These schedules should produce a minimum of around 25 inches of stem on most varieties around the year. If longer stems are desired, 1 or 2 more weeks of long days should be given.

For Flowering Period	Weeks plant to pinch	Weeks pinch till start of short days	Weeks start of short days till flowering	Response group that can be used
Jan. 1 to Mar. 15	2	3	11	10-11
Mar. 16 to Apr. 15	2	3	10	10
Apr. 16 to Apr. 25	2	2	10	9-10
Apr. 26 to May 30	2	1	10	9-10
June 1 to June 15	2	1	10	9-10
June 16 to July 31	2	0	10	9-10
Aug. 1 to Oct. 15	1	1	10	9-10
Oct. 16 to Oct. 31	2	1	10	9-10
Nov. 1 to Nov. 30	2	2	10	9-10
Dec. 1 to Dec. 15	2	2	10	10
Dec. 16 to Dec. 31	2	3	10	10

The above time can be reduced a total of one week where CO_2 is used in fall, winter and spring.

SPACING—DISBUDS

For winter crop, 6 by 5, two stems per plant. In summer-fall, 6 by 6, three stems per plant. Same temperatures as for standards.

As with other mum crops, the very best results will be achieved if a separate "program" is set up for growing disbuds—so that just the right number of long days, etc., can be provided for each crop—and so that no time is wasted. However, it is quite practical to combine year-round disbuds (using

Gt. #4 Indianapolis White flowered on March 12 at West Chicago—as a disbud, 3 flowers per plant. A pinched crop, but no more weeks plant-to-flower than a regular single-stem crop of standards. It looked somewhat better in terms of dollars per foot than regular standards flowered at the same time.

schedules given above) with regular year-round standard mums. Quite a few growers are going after disbuds in just this way—half a bench once or twice a month combined with their regular standards.

Our Mum Planning Service will be glad to work out a disbud program tailored to fit in with your other mum crops.

Pot-growing of cut flowers is seen more and more. Example: Southern Floral at Houston, Texas, Will Weatherford shown in the photo with Nobhill, photo early March. It's done most often in ranges where both pots and cuts are grown—to permit the grower to move back and forth from pots to cuts by season. Actually, pots grow every bit as good quality mums as are grown in the open bench— sometimes better.

VARIETIES—DISBUDS

There are many fine ones, and several excellent novelties this year. Among the very best:

	Dec. 1- Apr. 15 Winter	Apr. 15- June 15 Spring	June 15- Sept. 15 Summer	Sept. 15- Dec. 1 Fall
WHITE				
White Marble	X	X	X	X
Divinity	X	—	—	X
Gt. #4 Ind. White	—	X	—	X
Independence	X	X	X	X
Starburst	X	X	X	X
Iceberg	—	X	X	—
Polaris	X	X	X	X
YELLOW				
Brt. Gold. Anne	X	X	X	X
Cream Yel. Pr. Anne	X	X	—	X
Golden Starburst	X	X	X	X
Florida Marble	X	X	X	X
Yel. Divinity	X	—	—	X
Gt. #4 Ind. Yellow	—	X	X	X
PINK				
Pr. Anne Superb	X	X	—	X
Brilliant Anne	X	X	—	X
Vedova	X	X	—	X
Venoya	X	X	—	X
Escapade	—	X	X	X
Lydia	—	X	—	X
Regal Anne	X	X	—	X
Valencia	X	X	—	X
BRONZE				
Onward	—	X	X	X
Gay Ann	X	X	—	X
Bronze Marble	X	X	X	X
Copper Anne	X	X	—	X
Festival	X	X	—	X
Trident	X	X	—	X
Wildfire	—	X	X	—

YEAR-ROUND CUT MUMS

PRO

The overwhelming consideration in favor of year-round mum production is simply that most growers find them profitable. This in turn depends on market demand. To some extent, there's no accounting for the long-range changes in the public's tastes. It does seem, though, that the flower-buying public is more critical of lasting quality than ever before—and mums do keep well. Also, unlike most other cut flowers, mums offer such a wide variety of sizes, flower types, and colors. This variety and contrast make them more desirable from the designer's viewpoint than the other important cut flowers.

A good example of the superior quality of standards that can be grown in pots—with Chapin irrigation. The growers: Walt (left) and Art Maton of Webb Brothers, Pana, Illinois. The crop is grown with 4 cuttings per 6-inch pot, spaced to allow for a normal cut-flower spacing per plant. Photo in late August. Variety, Dignity, which was doing a good job for summer flowering here.

Another critical factor in selling any flower is the grower's ability to produce the grades and types that are wanted—and at the *time* they are wanted. The year-round mum producer can vary his proportions of colors and types from week to week. To some extent, he can build up his production for certain periods. Always, he can plan his production—and know that what he plans for a certain week will be there for him. An unseasonably warm spell in April won't suddenly double his cut.

The year-round greenhouse-mum grower can, in most sections of the country, be on the market 52 weeks out of the year with acceptable-quality flowers. Some other cut flowers deteriorate so badly in quality during the summer that they more or less go off the market.

An interesting trend has been the increasing number of medium to large-size retail-growing ranges that have entered year-round production. They do business every week of the year—and they like having mums always there as sort of a "backbone" on their cut-flower supply.

Then there are the purely management aspects of year-round flowering that make it attractive. Biggest point—the uniform workload. No seasonal rush. Cuttings to plant and flowers to pick *every* week. Another point: space utilization. Benches are idle between crops an average of 1 to 2 weeks. On regular programs, a few days after a bench is cut out, cuttings arrive to replant it—no worry about what to "follow up" with.

Mums take less labor than most of the other major cut-flower crops. They lend themselves to mechanization—automatic watering and feeding, single-layer wire mesh support, direct-benching of cuttings.

AND CON

So much for the advantages. What are the problems, shortcomings?

For one thing, year-round production is not recommended where the grower is not equipped to maintain a minimum of 60°. A night or two of unusually severe weather that takes the house down below this won't hurt, but by and large, it takes 60° to set those buds.

One of the factors that has kept year-round flowering from being overdone is the investment necessary before the first flower is cut. For a rough figure, it takes about $200 to buy black cloth, install lights, and plant up a bench 4 by 100 feet. The crop will pay, but like so many other things, it takes dollars to make dollars.

High summer temperatures under glass have created problems. As pointed out above, the fact that good mums can be produced under summer greenhouse conditions has been a real advantage to the year-round grower. However, especially farther south, there have been problems of delay, and in extreme cases, failure to flower during occasional spells of very hot weather. Fortunately, the technique of evaporative cooling of greenhouses, when properly applied, can definitely solve this problem. Growers are adopting it rapidly.

Lastly, year-round mum production takes good growing. All the problems of soil management, disease and insect control, getting and training help and marketing are there just the same as for any crop. Year-round mums aren't a cure-all for everyone's troubles. They do offer a real opportunity for those qualified to handle them.

LIGHTS—WHY AND HOW

The chrysanthemum is a "short-day" plant. That means it will set buds when it is exposed to a short (12 hours or less) day. Mums naturally flower in the fall because the days are shorter.

With this in mind, it is apparent that a cutting planted in midwinter will promptly set bud—due to the very short day length. To delay this bud setting until sufficient stem length develops, we extend the length of the natural day with artificial light (technically, we shorten the night rather than lengthen the day). Buds will not form on mums as long as the periods of uninterrupted darkness are not over 7 hours long.

How to Light (with separate reflectors)

	Watt	Spacing	Height above soil
One 4-ft. bed	60	Every 4 ft.	60 inches
Two 4-ft. beds } One row of lights }	100	Every 6 ft.	60 inches
Three 4-ft. beds } One row of lights }	150	Every 6 ft.	60 inches

Reflectors must be held up off the bulb. Built-in reflector bulbs may be used. For a 20-foot wide house, a single row of 300-watt reflector bulbs facing down at a 45° angle, spaced every 10 feet, will do it. Bulbs should be staggered on alternate sides of ventilators—not directly under because of rain damage to bulbs. Figure about 1½ watts per square foot of ground covered. Indoor-type bulbs may be used if covered with metal protectors to keep water out.

Supplemental lighting really does boost winter-quality pot mums in dark areas. Here are lights installed at Maekawa's, Seattle. They provide 400 foot-candles, 6 a.m. to 6 p.m. for the 30 days before flowering. In the photo, Kay Maekawa. For further details see MUM TALKS, February 1, 1971, page 6.

Use flood not spot bulbs.

It takes 7 foot-candles to prevent bud formation.

On large installations, half the beds may be lighted before midnight, half after. This halves the demand cost.

220-volt lines reduce main sizes greatly.

Hours of Light Per Night

Latitude 35-40°
North of Charlotte, N. C.; Memphis, Tenn.; Bakersfield, Calif.

June 15-July 15	No
July 15-July 30	2
Aug. 1-Aug. 31	3
Sept. 1-Mar. 31	4
Apr. 1-May 15	3
May 15-June 15	2

Latitude 25-30°

Dec. 1-Mar. 31	4
Apr. 1-May 31	3
June 1-July 31	2
Aug. 1-Sept. 30	3
Oct. 1-Nov. 30	4

The above hours of light should be provided as near to the middle of the night as possible. For example, if 4 hours of light is called for, light should be turned on from 10 p.m. till 2 a.m. If the lights were turned on from 6 p.m. till 10 p.m., there would be a period of darkness from 10 p.m. till 7 a.m. (in winter)—which would total 9 hours. The maximum allowable period of un-interrupted darkness to prevent buds is 7 hours.

Likewise, if half the beds are lighted before and half after midnight, be sure to apply both periods as near to midnight as possible. For example, light from 8 p.m. till midnight (4 hours) leaves a period of darkness from midnight till 7 a.m.—just within the allowable 7 hours.

About Light Leakage

There have been cases where light "leaking" onto the crop by accident from some nearby source, in effect, delayed flowering of a crop. The effect is like heat delay. The tip-off nearly always is the area affected. Plants nearest to a window of a nearby home—light shining out at night—or, in some cases, light used on main walks by night men.

It is obviously important in year-round flowering to carefully "cage in" light being applied to a bench of young plants. If a bench is being lighted and the benches on either side are not being lighted, then the light must be confined to the one bench by means of sateen curtains. Light that "leaks" to other benches will cause blindness—failure to flower.

SHADING DETAILS

Why do we shade?

The chrysanthemum plant will set bud only if exposed to a short day (not over 12 hours)—and to a temperature of 60°. We, of course, artificially shorten the day when necessary by means of black sateen.

For years, it was common practice to apply sateen cloth in late afternoon—just before closing time. Often, this meant that the first covers went on as early as 4 p.m. daylight-saving time—which is 3 p.m. by standard time. Applying shade for longer than 12 hours per night is definitely harmful to the crop. First, if shade is put on at 4 p.m. during hot weather, it will become very warm under the covers, thus further aggravating the hot-weather-delay problem. Even during cooler periods, this midafternoon shading has a light-reduction effect—much like carrying a heavy shade on the glass, only worse. Result: substantially reduced production, flower size, etc.

We therefore strongly recommend not applying shade till 6 or 6:30 p.m.—and leaving it on to provide 12 hours of darkness to all beds. It may cost over-time to get it done in the evening, but it will be worth it—in our experience.

Dates to Start and Stop Light and Shade
    Latitude 25-35°

Response Group	Lights		Shade	
	Start in fall	Stop in spring	Start in spring	Stop in fall
7-8 Weeks	Continuous		Mar. 29	Sept. 20
9-11 Weeks	Continuous		Mar. 15	Oct. 1

Mum breeding—Pan-American Plant, West Chicago, November 4. Here are close to 45,000 new seedlings—pot and standard candidates. The first task is to select a very small per cent for further evaluation. In the photo: Len and May Shoesmith, in charge of mum breeding for Pan-American.

Latitude 35-45°
North of Charlotte, N.C., Memphis, Tenn., Bakersfield, Calif.

	Lights		Shade	
Response Group	Start in fall	Stop in spring	Start in spring	Stop in fall
7-8 Weeks	July 15	June 14	Mar. 15	Sept. 15
9-11 Weeks	July 15	June 14	Mar. 15	Sept. 25
12-14 Weeks	July 15	June 14	Mar. 15	Oct. 20

Lighting until June 14 and the resumption of lighting on July 15 help insure thorough maintenance of vegetative growth.

INTERRUPTED LIGHTING

A means of opening up clubby sprays on pompons, and doubling up standards that tend to be small and show center in winter.

Big trouble so far seems that each variety must be more or less "interrupted" on a schedule worked out to suit that variety. Under commercial conditions where half-dozen or more varieties are grown under the same lighting schedule, it is generally impractical to interrupt—for the reason outlined above. Interrupting January-February standards (especially *Indianapolis*) comes the nearest to being a practical deal.

We recommend the following initial schedule for interrupted lighting and suggest, in practice, it may be modified in the individual growing situation for various varieties. To establish an interrupted lighting schedule, count back 12 days from recommended "lights-out" date in our schedule. Leave lights out for 10 days, after which the lights are on for an additional 12 days. The crop will be delayed a week or 10 days from the scheduled flowering date, but some growers have found that the increased quality is worth the extra crop time. Interrupted lighting should not be attempted unless at least a 60-62° F night temperature can be maintained. Accurate temperature control is imperative during lights-off and lights-on phases.

COLORS AND VARIETIES—YEAR-ROUND CUT-FLOWER CROPS

	Jan.-April	May-Sept.	Oct.-Dec.
% Pompons	40	60	60
% Standards	60	40	40

Color Percentages of Pompons

	Jan.-Mar.	Apr.-May	June	July-Aug.	Sept.-Oct.	Nov.-Dec.
% White	45	45	50	40	30	35
% Yellow	25	25	25	35	30	25
% Pink	20	20	15	15	15	15
% Bronze	10	10	10	10	25	25

Note: Southern markets seem to prefer less white.

Color Percentages of Standards

	Jan.-Mar.	Apr.-May	June	July-Aug.	Sept.Oct.-	Nov. Dec.
% White	55	45	40	40	30	35
% Yellow	30	30	35	35	35	30
% Pink	15	15	15	15	15	15
% Bronze	—	10	10	10	20	20

Note: Southern markets seem to prefer less white.

SINGLE-STEM OR PINCH?

Most year-round or continuous-flowering programs are operated on a single-stem basis. Main reason: it enables the grower to realize an extra crop a year from about half the benches on a program.

Even beyond this, though, there is a certain vigor and quality of growth on the direct-benched unpinched crop that's hard to get when pinching is practiced. This is especially apparent on winter-spring crops of standards.

WHAT IS AN "EIGHT-WEEK" VARIETY?

Note that all mum varieties are classified under a response group heading—"8-week varieties"—9-week, 10-week, etc. What does it mean and why is the term used?

It is primarily a term of use in connection with controlled flowering—under lights and shade. It refers to the number of weeks of short days needed to make the variety flower. For example, an 8-week variety is one which will "respond" (or flower) 8 weeks after short days are started. Starting short days is accomplished in summer with black cloth, in winter simply by discontinuing lights at night.

The response group classification is of use to the normal-season grower, too. The 7 to 8-week varieties are generally the garden or hardies (flowering in late September through October). The 10 to 11-week kinds are the November-flowering ones, the 12 to 15-week kinds are the lates—December-flowering. Nearly all cloth-house crops take the 9 to 11's. Most pot-mum growers use 9 to 11-week kinds, too.

CONTINUOUS-FLOWERING SCHEDULES

Actually most off-season-mum growing is done on so-called year-round-flowering programs. A given area, usually not less than 6-8 benches, is put on

Here's an exceptionally well-done job of starting chrysanthemums in peat pots. Cuttings are grown in 3-inch square peat pots for a maximum of four weeks—all under long days, then set into the flowering bench. Result: five-and-a-quarter crops per year—and certainly no penalty in quality as the job is done here. The grower (above right) Lloyd Bachman, of Bachman's, Minneapolis—on the left, Bob Whitman, G.J.B., Inc.

a continuous rotation, each bench producing 3 crops during the year. Thus, an 8-bench house would produce 24 benches of flowers each 12 months. The advantages of steady cut, steady return, and even workload are obvious.

Because such programs are nearly always tailor-made to fit local conditions, none are included here. If interested, write our Mum Planning Dept. for details.

ABOUT SPACING

You sometimes hear a grower complain that his pompon sprays are too heavy—even as little as four stems make too big a bunch. The retailers complain at as little as four stems per bunch—even though they may get a giant head of flowers. This fellow is simply allowing too much space per stem. On standards, it's the same story—except that too-wide spacing will produce a lot of 7-inch blooms that are lovely to look at—but bring little if any more on the market than 5-inch ones. They're spaced too far apart!

What is the correct spacing? That depends on three things:

1. Time of year—the high-sunshine conditions of summer and early fall make it possible to space considerably closer than midwinter, yet retain uniformity and quality.
2. One stem per plant—or two or three? It has been our experience that you can get more stems per square foot where crops are grown single-stem than you can where three or four stems are grown on each plant. It's logical when you stop to realize that under single-stem culture, each stem has a direct private line to food and water.
3. Difference between growers—a man who is doing a topnotch job of soil management, feeding, watering, etc., can get by with closer spacing.

Our recommendations for year-round flowering under reasonably favorable conditions (for no-pinch culture):

Crops to Flower	Spacing	Sq. Inches per Stem
Jan. 1–Mar. 15	6 x 5 in.	30
Mar. 15–June 1	7 x 4 in.	28
June 1–Nov. 15	6 x 4 in.	24
Nov. 15–Dec. 31	7 x 4 in.	28

Two stems per plant can be grown on roughly the same area *per stem* as one. Example: for late-summer pompons, we recommend 6 by 8 inches for 2 per plant (24 square inches per stem), or if single-stem, space 6 by 4 inches— also 24 square inches. Where 3 stems are grown per plant, add roughly 10% to the amount of bench area per stem. Reason: 3 stems sharing the same root system!

HEAT DELAY

Unusually severe heat in the summer, especially in the South and Southwest, has caused much trouble with summer crops of mums. The crop *grows* normally and well in spite of severe heat, and will even set buds. However, greenhouse temperatures running 95° and higher may *delay* bud development several weeks or more. In severe cases, flowers may be crippled— or buds may never even open.

Means have been developed to cool greenhouses enough to overcome this problem. For details on this, see page 129.

TEMPERATURES FOR YEAR-ROUND CROPS

Maintaining correct temperature is one thing about year-round flowering that must be done right—within rather close tolerances. It is important that growers understand *why* a certain temperature must be held. It is even more important that they be able to recognize the symptoms of too-high or too-low temperatures. More than any other major crop, year-round mums will quickly and quite obviously show the effects of being too warm or too cold. The growers must know these symptoms.

In our opinion, more year-round crops fall short of expected quality and production because of incorrect temperatures than for any other reason.

60° Will Do It

Before we go further, let's make it clear that a good job of producing year-round standards or pomps *can* be done in a northern greenhouse maintained at 60° day and night all winter long (plus or minus 1 or 2 degrees). Many year-round crops are operated entirely in one house, with crops in all stages of growth necessarily sharing the same temperature. However, even this type of year-round production can be done better by the grower who knows the symptoms of too-high and too-low temperatures.

The larger year-round program often permits some adjusting of temperatures. If done properly, such shifting of temperatures can produce larger flowers with better keeping quality.

"Too Warm" Symptoms

The following symptoms commonly appear when winter-spring standards and pomps are grown too warm:

1. Especially on the midwinter northern greenhouse crops where the 13-14-week response group of pompon varieties is used, carrying too warm a temperature will cause delay or even complete failure of bud development. The bud will *set* and grow to perhaps a ¼-inch size, but if grown too warm, will simply stall from then on. In mild cases, the crop will just flower a week or two later than scheduled. Where still higher temperatures are applied, sprays will "compound" (produce 10, 15, or even 20 flowers per spray. Flowering will be delayed 3 or even 4 weeks, and the plants will be 4 or even 5 feet tall. In still more severe cases, the crop will just go into completely "wild" uncontrolled growth with not even color showing. Varieties differ in this respect.

   The late pomps such as *Silversmith* and *Corsair* are the most sensitive to high temperatures during bud development. This problem can be greatly relieved by use of several newer varieties that are less critical as to temperatures. Examples: *Icecap* and the *Iceflos*.

   A commercial range held at 60° twenty-four hours a day all winter would flower even *Revelation* successfully. However, if this same grower boosted his cloudy-day temperatures to 68°, sunny days to 75°, he would have serious delay trouble. A boost to 65° on sunny days only would probably not interfere—there are few sunny days in winter up North, anyway!

   In a very general way, the 11 and 12-week kinds and the *Divinitys*, *Galaxys* and *Elegance* are less prone to this delay and interference from high temperatures, but are still to be watched. Many of the 10-week kinds will delay several weeks if finished in the 70's. Generally, the 9 and 10-week kinds are much less susceptible to this high-temperature delay.

   These are rather broad generalizations, but if followed, should at least avoid trouble or loss due to too-high temperatures during bud development.

2. Aside from the high-temperature stall described above, there is a very definite drop in *quality* where standards and pomps are flowered too warm. As would be expected, this difference tends to be more serious during dark weather. *Silversmith,* for example, flowered in January-February, will develop considerably more flower size if it is cooled to 55° after buds show—as compared to holding it at 60° or better, clear through till cut. Equally serious, the *Silversmith* flowered warm will last perhaps half or less as long (after cutting) as a crop finished at 55°.

   Indianapolis mums seem to produce their best quality if held at straight 60° clear through. Much cooler temperatures produce flatter, more spiny flowers.

3. There is a third symptom of too-warm temperatures during development of mum buds. Mainly on the pink and bronze varieties—colors tend to fade at higher temperatures. Maximum color intensity develops at quite cool temperatures—50° or even cooler. It isn't practical during winter and spring flowering to finish crops this cool (reasons later), but certainly, there is a practical and important difference between the color that develops at 55°

A good example of very efficient hand-shading of mums. The grower: Len Holmberg, Fairhope, Alabama. It's simply a sheet of black polyethylene drawn from gutter to gutter on overhead wires. For a closer look at the wiring, see photo at left. In the photo, Len Holmberg. Note the cooling pad installation—some light leakage, up to one week delay for the first 5-6 feet from the pad. Len says that 2 men can shade an area 72 by 256 feet in 15 minutes. By the way, cool air can be drawn from pad to fan under the shade at night. More details, GROWER TALKS, November 1969, page 14.

as compared to 65°. Once again, 58-60° night and day will develop fair color intensity, but the crop that can be cooled to 55° after buds show will show appreciably better color. Dropping to 50° for the last two weeks before cutting will still further intensify the color—and improve flower size and keeping quality, too, on many varieties.

"Too-Cold" Symptoms

There are very definite limitations on the other side of the scale! Winter-spring crops not kept warm enough will "object" in the following ways:

1. Crops grown too cold from planting till time for buds to appear will simply fail to show buds. The old "safe" rule was a minimum of 60° to insure getting even bud set on all varieties year round. The height of the thermometer or thermostat at which a crop temperature is read is of vital importance. We have seen house temperatures read on a thermometer 6 feet above the growing top of the plant. The temperature difference may be as extreme as 10° lower in a situation such as this. The same points pertain to the location of a thermostat. Though certainly, for practical reasons, it's necessary to keep a themostat high, the problem can be overcome by locating a thermometer in the growing area of the plants and calibrating the

Len and May Shoesmith of Pan-American Plant Company, shown with May Shoesmith — the leading white standard for winter production across the U.S.

thermostat to demand heat to maintain the proper temperature at growing level.

The most important period is from the "lights-off" date till buds definitely appear. However, keeping the plants warm enough from benching till lights off helps insure prompt bud set.

2. Another symptom of too-*low* temperatures: tight, clubby sprays on pomps. Winter-spring crops of pomps grown too cold both before and after lights off tend to this fault. Actually what happens is that the peduncle (little stem on which individual flowers are borne) fails to stretch to normal length. Clubby sprays usually go hand in hand with few and small flowers—and correspondingly low production in bunches per foot.

How cool will do this? On a midwinter crop, dropping to 55° will usually not affect spray formation. Going down to 50° just before or shortly after lights off on winter-spring crops will almost surely cause clubbiness on many varieties. Several years ago, tests were run at several schools on the idea of growing pomps in carnation-house temperatures (50° nights). On nearly all varieties, sprays were clubby and production was low.

Of course, our time-honored November "normal" crop of pomps—grown without light or shade—has always been grown at 50° nights. Remember though—day temperatures during the growth of this crop were usually quite warm—offsetting the lower night temperature.

3. A third effect of too-low temperatures after buds appear on the winter crop: flower discoloration. Certain white standards and pomps especially will develop varying degrees of "pinking" if finished too cool. *Indianapolis White* is probably the most sensitive of all. *Snowcap*, and *Jupiter* pomps will show pinking. Some yellow varieties will show bronziness if finished too cool—*Yellow Iceberg* is a good example. It's actually an overintensifying of the color.

This pinking and bronzing will usually not appear on crops held at 55° or higher. It seems to develop starting about the time the buds are perhaps ¼-½ inch across. If *Indianapolis* is too pink several weeks before cutting, it can be whitened-up quite nicely by just raising the temperature perhaps 3 or 5 degrees.

Pot growers find that Y*el. Mandalay* will develop a somewhat heavy or bronzy cast in midwinter if finished too cool.

Bumping Temperatures

Carnation growers traditionally carry 50° nights, 57° cloudy days, 63° sunny days—give or take a few degrees. If a mum grower carries 60° nights, bumps his temperatures 7° for cloudy days (to 67°), and 13° for sunny days (to 73°), he is asking for trouble, especially on those heat-sensitive winter pomps. Remember, the buds simply won't develop at anything much above 60°. Remember, too, that the mum "remembers." If a house of *Corsair* and *Silversmith* is run 60° nights, and 73 or 75° on a week or so of sunny days in February, it will probably be about the same average temperature effect as if the house were held at 65° night and day through the period. That means delay and compounding on those winter pomps.

In setting our temperatures for winter and spring standards and pomps, we are of necessity riding a fine line between the "too-cool" symptoms listed above and the "too-warm" ones. We feel that bumping temperatures more than perhaps 5° for sunny days is not good practice under the circumstances.

Everyone is trying to mechanize the harvesting job. Here, John McCormick of Carolina Wholesale, Sanford, North Carolina, has an interesting approach. A bit hard to see—but the 3 or 4-foot tray, shown below, left, is moved back and forth across the greenhouse on the overhead monorail shown above. In effect, the tray goes up and down the benches, standards are loaded onto it as it passes by, and are carried into the grading room where the grading girls unload them. The trays are in continuous operation around the houses and into the packing shed. For good measure, John moves the benches up near the packing shed as they come into flower—to make the harvesting more efficient and convenient. In the photo, on the left, John McCormick, and on the right is Norm Lamberg, G.J.B., Inc.

Chapin tube irrigation—almost standard among U.S. and European pot-mum growers today. The little ⅛-inch tubes leading from the main center tube provide irrigation and feed individually to each pot on the bench. Now the grower can water a bench of pot mums in just minutes. Actually, this installation was at Brater-Brockwell's, Oak Ridge, Tennessee, and is used for watering cut mums grown in pots—the same idea as for pot mums.

Most of all . . .

Try to get the "too-cool" and "too-warm" symptoms firmly in mind. Watch for them on your own crops. Often, a warm or cool end of a bench will show a marked difference in one of these very points—a sure tip-off as to which way temperatures should be adjusted to improve the crop.

It's one of the real tricks in successful year-round mum flowering!

VARIETIES—BEST OF THE PROVEN AND THE NEW

The following notes—or rather tabulation—of mum varieties is intended as a rather general guide. With year-round flowering as widely developed across the U. S. (and around the world) as it is, to attempt to recommend the "best" variety for each given climate each time of the year would take a book by itself!

The tabulation on page 273 is intended to recommend varieties for each season for the northern grower—the Chicago-New York latitude. Growers farther south can easily adapt this table to their situation. Take pompons, for example. Growers in the Memphis-Raleigh, North Carolina latitude do not use the 13 to 14-week pompon varieties, even in midwinter. Instead, they tend to use the 11-week kinds from early January through most of March, and 9 and 10-week varieties the rest of the year.

Still further south, in Florida, the 9 to 10-week pompons are used the year round.

Of course, the 9 and 10-week pompons can be flowered even in Minnesota right through the winter—and are in a few cases. But the grower who is seriously shooting for quality will be flowering 12 to 14-week pompons in the northern area in January and February.

The same generalization applies to both standards (football) mums and to pot mums. The 12 to 14-week kinds are not used in winter in the North in either case, but the varieties used in winter are different from those used in the summer. And the same application of the northern tables to southern climate would apply as was the case in pompons. For example, mid-South growers would tend to use varieties for their midwinter crop which are recommended for late fall and early spring in the North.

The little table that follows presents this idea graphically—example No. 1, the case of year-round pompons for all areas of the U. S.

| | Year-Round Pomps for the United States | | | |
| | We Suggest | | | |
To Flower	Chicago Boston	Kansas City Washington, D.C.	Dallas Atlanta	Fort Myers Stuart, Florida
Midwinter	12-14-Wk.	10-11-Wk.	10-Wk.	9-10-Wk.
Spring	10-11-Wk.	10-Wk.	9-10-Wk.	9-10-Wk.
Summer	9-10-Wk.	9-10-Wk.	9-10-Wk.	9-10-Wk.
Fall	10-11-Wk.	10-11-Wk.	9-10-Wk.	9-10-Wk.

POMPON VARIETIES

Color:	9-Week	10-11-Week	12-14-Week
WHITE	Nimrod	Polaris	Icecap
	Arctic	Iceberg	Iceflo
	Pinocchio	Dawn Star	
	Tinsel	Hurricane	
	White Marble	#2 Shasta	
		Iceland	
		Divinity	
PINK*	Dolly	Dark Delight	Delmonico
	Belair	Carillon	
	Imp. Bluechip	Deep Telstar	
	Blue Marble	Delmarvel	Debutante
		Caravelle	Alvoda
BRONZE*	Showoff	Tuneful	Beau Brummell
	Bronze Marble	Dillon Beauregard	Galaxy
	Dazzler	Beauregard	Red Brummell
	Bronze Belair	Stingray	
		Thelma	

*Bronzes and pinks not recommended for hot-weather flowering without cooling, due to fading.

YELLOW	Yellow Showoff	Yel. Iceberg	Goldflo
	Statesman	Yel. Beauregard	Yel. Galaxy
	Cavalier	#2 Yel. Shasta	Goldcap
	Florida Marble	Imp. Yel. Hurricane	
		Yel. Polaris	
		Yellow Divinity	

Here's the Krause potting machine from Germany—set up for demonstration at West Chicago recently. Pots are fed from the diagonal stack at the right into a fork, then moved to the revolving drum at the right. Here they are filled with soil, then moved to the left. Just to the left of the young lady in the photo is the equipment which punches the holes to accommodate either the soil ball or mum cuttings, whatever is to be potted. They then move off to the right of the young lady and down the belt where cuttings, or whatever, are inserted into the pots. The finished product moves off to the left.

Apply B-Nine at time of pinch—not weeks after! The series pictured was done at Ohio State. Cuttings were potted October 8, short days, and pinched October 22. Plant on the left was treated with B-Nine 3 weeks after pinch. Next right, 2 weeks after pinch. Next right was treated at time of pinch, and the plant on the extreme right was the untreated check. Shows the really very good control of height possible with these retardant chemicals. The nice thing about this material: It can be sprayed on the foliage rather than going to all the trouble of mixing with soil. The man behind the plants is Howard Jones, then undergraduate at Ohio State, now growing for Alexander Masson, Kansas City, Kansas.

Year Round Standards for the United States

To Flower	We Suggest			
	Chicago Boston	Kansas City Washington, D.C.	Dallas Atlanta	Fort Myers Stuart, Florida
Midwinter	List A	List A or B	List B	List B
Spring	List B	List B	List B	List B
Summer	List C	List C	List C	List C
Fall	List B	List B	List B	List B or C

STANDARD VARIETIES

Color:	List A	List B	List C
WHITE	*May Shoesmith* *Imp. Fred Shoesmith* *Imp. Mefo*	*May Shoesmith* *Dignity* *Nobhill*	*Dignity* *Southern Comfort* *Nobhill*
YELLOW	*Brt. Yel. May Shoesmith* *Goldburst Mefo* *#2 Yellow Shoesmith*	*Brt. Yel. May Shoesmith* *Yel. Nobhill* *Yel. Dignity* *Eldorado*	*Yel. Dignity* *Eldorado* *Southern Sun* *Yel. Nobhill*
PINK*	*Deep Champagne* *Promenade*	*#3 Ind. Pink* *Deep Champagne* *Promenade*	*Promenade*
BRONZE*	*Blaze* *CF2 Ind. Bronze* *#2 Ind. Dk. Bronze*	*Blaze* *CF2 Ind. Bronze* *Onward*	*Onward*

*Bronzes and pinks not recommended for hot-weather flowering without cooling, due to fading.

POT MUMS THE YEAR ROUND

The past seasons have been continued growth in the year-round pot-mum crop. The larger wholesale-pot-plant specialists continue to find a market for what they produce. You hear more and more of $2.50 (even $3.00) for a good 6-inch. Oddly enough, the biggest development in out-of-season pot growing seems to be among small to medium-sized retail growers. A small but steady program of pot-mum production with some buildup for the spring holidays and Thanksgiving seems to be a solid deal for these retail growers.

The biggest requirement here is temperature. A 60° house will do it with certain varieties, but 62°-63° generally will give more uniform and prompt bud set. This and the usual shade and light facilities are the main requirements.

AREA NEEDED

For growers interested in an approximate amount of bench area needed for a given production of year-round pot mums (6-inch):

275

To produce 50 pot mums every 2 weeks year round, about 380 square feet of bench space will be needed. A small part of this area must be equipped for lighting; all of it must have enough heat to hold 62°-63°.

To produce 50 pots every 2 weeks, by the way, is a good minimum program for the retail grower. Much less total production and less frequent flowering are usually not too practical.

TEMPERATURE—62° DOES IT

We definitely recommend 62°-63° nights (62°-65° cloudy days, 65°-70° clear days) for off-season pot growing. We've tried 60°; you just don't get the even bud set and flower development that you do at 62°-63°.

PLANTS TOO TALL?

Much can be done to control height of pot mums by several key cultural practices—and by careful selection of varieties each season. See notes below.

However, several so-called "growth-retardant" chemicals are on the market which are of great help in this problem. The most commonly used and probably the most practical, as of now, is B-Nine. A solution of 0.25 percent B-Nine (no spreader added) simply sprayed onto the growth tips of the plant about 2 weeks after pinching will substantially retard the stem elongation of most varieties most times of the year. The application of B-Nine late in the day has proven to be the most effective time for its use.

Varietal response does vary considerably, but all varieties respond more or less. On varieties that tend to stretch after the first application, follow up with a second application, spraying the top one-third of the plant foliage with an 0.25 per cent solution of B-Nine 2 days after disbudding. An important point in spraying plants with B-Nine is to be sure that the plants are not watered overhead for about 24 hours after the application of the chemical—since it will simply wash it away before it has a chance to take effect. Otherwise, there is no delay in flowering or any other interference with the crop as a result of this material—in our experience. See photo, page 274, showing the effect of B-Nine on pot mums.

Several other pointers on why pot mums tend to grow too tall:

Here's a really convincing demonstration of the strength of the new retardant, A-Rest. The subject here is pot mum Regal Anne—the one variety that, as any pot-mum grower knows, is almost impossible to keep from getting too tall. From the left: untreated check, one application of B-Nine, A-Rest at 100 ppm, A-Rest at 200 ppm. The 200 ppm plant finished only about 8 inches tall and delayed a week or 10 days—obviously, too strong a treatment. However, the 100 ppm plant was a pleasant 12 inches high, probably 3 or 4 days delay over B-Nine, but otherwise, a first-class Regal Anne. The material is reported generally effective on mums, poinsettias, lilies, hydrangeas—not effective on all bedding plants.

Retardents play a major role in pot mum culture today. Plants finish more quickly, flowers are of uniform height and floral heads have greater conformation than those on untreated plants. Golden St. Moritz, newest pot mum from Pan American Plant, is a vigorous grower that requires tall treatment all year round. Holding the plant is Cindy Jentsch of G.J.B., Inc.

1. Crowding plants unduly makes them grow tall and chimney-shaped instead of spreading. Well-grown 6-inch pot mums need and should get 1½ square feet (15 by 15) in their final stages.

2. Azalea pots, being somewhat shorter, are usually used for pot mums.

3. Dirty glass, or anything else that restricts the amount of sunlight getting to the plant, will tend to stretch pot mums.

4. During very hot weather, the pot mum will sometimes delay flowering for several weeks beyond the normal date. This will, of course, have the effect of making the plant taller. Not much can be done about it other than to use greenhouse cooling.

5. Pinching—improper pinching in relationship to when lights are turned off also can lead to tall plants—for example, the height of such varieties as the *Princess Annes* can be controlled by pinching 1 to 2 weeks after lights are turned off. This is called a delayed pinch. Delaying the pinch is used to shorten the plant. One point—don't overdelay, that is, wait 3 weeks or more. Delaying too long, in effect, doesn't reduce height that much, but it will delay flowering considerably, so why delay too long? One to 2 weeks after lights are turned off is a sufficient delay.

SEVERAL SUGGESTIONS

1. In potting mum cuttings directly to the flowering pot (which is generally done), it helps to grade out the cuttings, putting the extra-large ones together, etc. This makes for more uniformity.

2. Most good growers arrange the cuttings in a circle around the outer edge of the pot. This leaves more air and light at the center.

3. As the cuttings are planted into the pots, set them so that they point outwards at about a 45° angle rather than straight up. This will help still

Hostess, 9-week, medium-treatment, pink pot variety —a leader in pink pot mums for fall, winter and spring. Sturdy, compact, pleasing color.

more in getting air and light into the center of the pot. It will tend to make the plant more spreading and bushy—less chimney-shaped. Try it.

PLANTS TOO SHORT?

In most sections, the retailers prefer a plant that measures 12 inches high, 12 inches across the top of the flower head—and with 12 or more flowers. Just remember, "12 x 12 x 12."

Mainly in the case of *Always Pink* and *Torch* on winter crops, plants tend to flower *too short*. Year-round pot schedules allow several weeks more of long days (lighting period) to lengthen the plants. A high soft pinch on these varieties will definitely help get them to flower taller and with more breaks per stem. The added weeks of light give the plants more time to develop substance.

ABOUT RAPID GROWTH

Needless to say, all we covered about humus, feeding, ample water, etc., under cut mums applies here—with interest! After all, we're growing a lot of plants in a handful of soil, and that takes some watching. Highlights:

1. *Soil preparation:* One-third coarse peat, ⅓ perlite, ⅓ soil. Moist peat will help develop a good, open structure as mixing is done. Steam-sterilize soil preferably just before using (within 2 days).

2. *Feeding:* Phosphate added dry as peat-perlite is mixed. Nitrate and potash applied weekly (in summer) as a liquid feed. Use same rates with 25-0-25 as for cut mums. Some excellent pot-mum specialists feed every 3 days, liquid fertilizer injected with the water.

3. *Water:* Be sure there's a good drainage, then keep them well watered, especially as they get larger. That may mean every day in hot weather (twice in hot areas). If pots are set on muddy soil, it stops up drain holes.

In potting, don't fill the pot clear full. Leaving an inch will catch more water—reduce frequency of watering. Mechanical-watering systems provide more thorough penetration, save labor, and often reduce the needed

An interesting crop of pot mums for mass markets—at Ulery's, Springfield, Ohio. The plants above are all 1 cutting per 4-inch, mostly Nobhills. The packing is innovative here, sort of a corrugated box (shown), holding 6 pots—6-inch. The entire tray of plants is then lowered into a larger corrugated box. In the photo, from the left, Phil Ulery, Carl Weals, G.J.B., Inc., Wayne Ulery, Jake Ulery.

At right, a close-up of a typical 1-cutting-to-a-4-inch pot mum produced at Ulery's. This extreme shortening of growth is achieved by frequent applications of retardant. Holding the plant: Carl Weals, G.J.B., Inc.

frequency of watering.

4. *Crop management:* The first 2 or 3 weeks' growth often determines the finished quality of a crop. Close temperature control, full sunlight, relatively high humidity and thorough watering, help insure maximum take-off and growth.

DISBUDDING

In most sections, competition demands that the 10 to 15 stems on a pot mum must be disbudded to 1 flower per stem; also, side shoots are removed down the stem. Exception: the garden varieties, or any pompon grown as a pot mum. They just won't make a bigger flower, even when disbudded. These later varieties benefit by the removal of the top center bud, however; this produces a more even flower development and a more desirable plant habit.

How open should a pot mum be before it is moved from greenhouse to retail shop? Answer: It should be at least as open as the plant held by the young lady in the photo, who, by the way, is Miss Virgina Walter, former grad student at The Ohio State University, who ran a detailed series on this question. Details in GROWER TALKS, February 1971. The point is, if the plant is moved into a flower shop while just showing color (left), it simply won't open out satisfactorily for the retail consumer.

NUMBER OF CUTTINGS PER POT

To insure a well-filled-out plant, 5 cuttings for a 6-inch pot are generally recommended (for single pinch). A few varieties that tend to break more freely can be grown 4 to a 6. Because breaks come more freely during the summer months, a few growers go to 4 cuttings per pot on those flowered from July through November. However, the competitive market during the fall in many areas requires a well-filled-out plant that can be accomplished only by use of 5 cuttings per pot. Poor breakers, like *Royal Purple 3589* and *Starburst,* are apt to be thin even then with 5 cuttings.

Incidentally, many growers in the Northwest grow as many as half of their pot mums in 5-inch pots—and even some 4's. Bill De Jong, Pella, Iowa, grows 4's in quantity, 2 cuttings per pot, 8 flowers.

ATTENTION SOUTHERN GROWERS

In any areas where winters are quite sunny, open, and warm, the schedules given in the catalog tables will tend to make excessively tall plants during the winter season. In such areas, better results will be obtained if the late-summer schedules given are used year round—with perhaps one extra week of lighting added for plants to flower between January 1 and April 1.

The taller kinds (*Winter Carnival, Princess Anne* varieties) are given no long-day period at all (even in winter) by many growers in these "sunny-winter" areas. This means no lights, and in summer, shade same day cuttings are potted. To further insure against excessive height, pinch is delayed 1 week or 2 weeks (summer-fall crops). Some good growers do not like to use a 2-week delayed pinch. Reason: plant tends to be poorly shaped. Long, obvious main stem, lot of smaller short stems coming out from the top. They prefer B-Nine if height is a problem—even 2 applications if needed.

Shorter-growing varieties (*Torch*) are given 1 week of lights on crops to be flowered December 15 through March 1. Rest of the year; no long days.

Many good growers across the South stay with 1 week of long days year round, even on short varieties. Better, heavier plant.

Single-stem growing (mostly *Indianapolis* and *May Shoesmith* varieties) is practiced extensively—no lights at any time of year. *Indianapolis* has less of a long, exposed neck grown no-pinch.

For any variety, anywhere, any time of the year, if plants are too tall, change the schedule next year to:

1. Provide fewer (or no) long days between potting and shading (or lights-off).
2. Delay the pinch. Don't forget that other things cause tall plants: crowding, dirty glass, rooting through the drain hole, heat delay in summer—and use of too-tall varieties.
3. Use B-Nine where needed—judge each crop as it develops.

ABOUT "SHORT" TREATMENT

In descriptions of new pot mums, each variety is classified as "short treatment," "medium treatment," or "tall treatment." A "short-treatment" variety is one that naturally tends to be quite short *(Always Pink, Torch)*. These varieties generally need 2 or 3 or more weeks of lights for winter flowering to make them *tall* enough. The "tall-treatment" kinds are those that are really compact-growing enough for pot use, but which tend to be taller than the really short ones, such as *Neptune*. Especially on summer-fall flowerings, they must be given no long days (shade same day they are potted)—and pinch must be delayed—to keep them from being *too tall*. The *Princess Annes* are considered "tall-treatment" types.

The tables in our bulletins are based on these "short," "medium," and "tall-"treatment schedules. They tend to make the very short ones somewhat taller in winter (more so than our former schedules)—and to make the tall ones shorter in late summer-early fall. The varieties selected are those generally considered best for the period concerned.

TROUBLES—A FEW OF THE MOST COMMON

1. *Uneven bud set?* The same problem as with cut mums—too cool. For winter-spring crops, we find 62-63° nights give much more even bud set and development than 60°. Good quality, too.
2. *Lower leaves dry up -why?* Several reasons. One very common one is foliar nematode or foliage diseases. See page 122. Generally they are worse on outdoor-grown plants.

    Two other reasons: overcrowding and underfeeding. Under good care, the leaves should stay on, and stay green clear to the bottom. Poor drainage seems to affect them, too.
3. *Can't get over 1 or 2 breaks per cutting.* As with any plant, the 3 main requirements for generous and prompt breaking are plenty of nitrate and potash, plenty of water, and ample sunlight (meaning *generous* spacing). Varieties differ. We put 1 more cutting per pot of poor breakers.

    A good, soft cutting will always break better than a hard, wiry one.
4. *Flower rot as they open.* Much the same story as with cut mums. Several

pot-mum growers report good control with Benlate spray every 5 days from color show. Some shade in hot weather helps. Thrips nymph will, when present in the opening flower bud, sometimes cause petals to rot, also. An overhead spray of Meta Systox-R, providing good penetration into the petals, will control these insects.

Year-Round Pot Mums for the United States

To Flower	Chicago Boston	Kansas City Washington, D.C.	Dallas Atlanta	Fort Myers Stuart, Florida
Midwinter	List A or B	List A or B	List A or B	List A-B or C
Spring	List A or B	List A or B	List A or B	List A-B or C
Summer	List C	List C	List C	List C
Fall	List A-B or C	List A-B or C	List A-B or C	List A-B or C

VARIETIES

Color	List A	List B	List C
WHITE	Puritan	Puritan	Puritan
	St. Moritz	St. Moritz	St. Moritz
	Independence	Bonnie Jean*	Mountain Snow
	Winter Carnival	Independence	Bonnie Jean*
	Bonnie Jean*		
YELLOW	Br. Golden Anne	Brt. Golden Anne	Goldstar
	Imp. Yel. Bonnie Jean	Yel. Mandalay	Yellow Torch
		Golden St. Moritz	Mountain Peak
		Yel. Bonnie Jean*	Golden St. Moritz
			Imp. Yel. Bonnie Jean*
PINK**	Hostess	Always Pink	Always Pink
	Brilliant Anne	Hostess	Illini Trophy
	Pr. AnneSuperb	Brandywine	Illini Hotpink
	Regal Anne	Illini Trophy	Royal Purple 3589
BRONZE**	Gay Anne	Mandalay	Torch
	Copper Anne	Torch	Mandalay
	Red Anne	Orange Bowl	Minuteman
	Dramatic*	Dramatic*	Dramatic*

*Daisy—center bud removal is suggested.
**Bronzes and pinks not recommended for hot-weather flowering without cooling, due to fading.

ABOUT SINGLE-STEM POT MUMS

We don't recommend to any grower that he go 100% to single-stem pot mums, but there are some angles to them that may fit your trade. The pros and cons as we see them:

Let's put down the disadvantages first. Mainly, more cuttings—probably 7 to a 6-inch pot against 5 for the same plant pinched. Net loss: 2 cuttings.

Interesting point about single-stem pot mums (above, left): Here's the new Dignity grown 1 cutting per 4-inch. Instead of the many applications of B-Nine used by most growers, this shortening was achieved by one application of the remarkable new A-Rest at the rate of 100 ppm.

Right: From the same A-Rest test as the picture of Dignity (left), here's a plant of Dramatic—a pot daisy. Again, Dramatic is generally too tall for a satisfactory pot variety, but one application of A-Rest made a fine plant.

On the credit side:

1. Large, showy blooms—*May Shoesmith,* for example, makes fine, large, showy blooms that would average ⅓ to ½ larger than the same variety pinched. They're really quite striking. It's a deluxe plant, but still finished in a 6. Individual flowers ran 5½ to 6 inches in our trials. If competition in pot mums is hot on your heels, perhaps this is the way to "have the best."

2. Ordinarily, no-pinch plants do not require tying. They are short, and having more plants per pot than pinched plants, tend to stand up better.

3. No more problem of getting enough breaks per plant. *Indianapolis* is bad on this, but nice grown "no-pinch."

4. You save several weeks time on the bench—and the labor of pinching and tying, too, of course.

HERE'S HOW:

Again, growth-retardant chemicals, particularly B-Nine, are a real help here. Actually, they enable the grower to use many varieties with fine, large flowers and splendid colors, but which, without B-Nine, are simply too tall grown this way. The normal spray of B-Nine, or if necessary, 2 applications, as described previously in this chapter, will do the trick. Otherwise, basic culture is simple: plant 5 to 7 cuttings per 6-inch pot, no long days in summer; 1 week of long days for winter flowering. Many growers plant 10 cuttings to a 7-inch pot or 12 cuttings to an 8-inch pot to provide a limited number of very large plants where the market demand exists.

VARIETIES FOR SINGLE-STEM POT-PLANT CULTURE

	WHITE	YELLOW	PINK*	BRONZE*
Summer	Nobhill Marguerita 773 Mountain Snow Independence	Yellow Nobhill Golden Nobhill Mountain Peak Imp. Yel. Marguerita	Escapade	Orange Bowl Copper Bowl
Fall	Nobhill #3 Ind. White Fuji Mefo Independence Mountain Snow	Yellow Nobhill Golden Nobhill Imp. Ind. Yellow Brt. Golden Anne Dark Yel. Tokyo Mountain Peak	Escapade #3 Ind. Pink Brilliant Anne Regal Anne Streamer	Festival Gay Anne Orange Bowl Copper Bowl
Winter	#3 Ind. White May Shoesmith Fuji Mefo Independence	Brt. Yel. May Shoesmith Gt. #4 Ind. Yel. Escapade Dark Yel. Tokyo Brt. Golden Anne	Streamer Brilliant Anne Regal Anne	Gay Anne Festival
Spring	Nobhill #3 Ind. White Fuji Mefo Marguerita 773 Independence Mountain Snow	Yellow Nobhill Golden Nobhill Imp. Ind. Yellow Brt. Golden Anne Imp. Yel. Marguerita Dark Yel. Tokyo Mountain Peak	Escapade Regal Anne Streamer	Gay Anne Orange Bowl Copper Bowl

*Bronzes and pinks are not recommended for hot-weather flowering without cooling, due to fading.

Specialist mum propagation—Pan-American Plant rooting operation at West Chicago, Bob Danielson in the photo. Most all of U.S. cutting production today is done this way—cuttings grown in Florida (see photo, page 254), rooting in northern greenhouses such as the above.

NORMAL-SEASON GREENHOUSE POT SCHEDULES (Two-Pinch)
(No Lights—No Shade)

VARIETY	COLOR	Pot Cuttings (4 per 6-inch pot)	1st Pinch	Final Pinch	Flowering Date
Distinctive	Pink	July 26	Aug. 3	Aug. 24	Oct. 23
Neptune	White	July 19	July 26	Aug. 17	Oct. 25
Vermilion	Red	July 19	July 26	Aug. 17	Oct. 25
Always Pink	Pink	July 19	July 26	Aug. 17	Oct. 25
Puritan	White	July 26	Aug. 3	Aug. 24	Oct. 25
Treasure Chest	Yellow	July 31	Aug. 6	Aug. 27	Oct. 25
St. Moritz	White	July 31	Aug. 6	Aug. 27	Oct. 25
Dramatic	Bronze	Aug. 6	Aug. 13	Sept. 2	Oct. 31
Orange Bowl	Bronze	July 26	Aug. 3	Aug. 24	Nov. 5
Delawares	Yel./bronze	July 26	Aug. 3	Aug. 24	Nov. 5
Torches	Bronze Yel.	July 26	Aug. 3	Aug. 24	Nov. 5
Illini Trophy	Pink	July 31	Aug. 7	Aug. 28	Nov. 5
Dark Red Star	Bronze	July 31	Aug. 7	Aug. 28	Nov. 5
Mandalays	Yel./bronze	July 31	Aug. 7	Aug. 28	Nov. 5
Bonnie Jeans	Yel./white	Aug. 4	Aug. 11	Sept. 1	Nov. 5
Winter Carnival	White	Aug. 4	Aug. 11	Sept. 1	Nov. 5
Princess Annes	———	Aug. 4	Aug. 11	Sept. 1	Nov. 5
Margueritas	Yel./white	Aug. 4	Aug. 11	Sept. 3	Nov. 7
Nobhills (single stem)	Yel./white	Sept. 1	No	No	Nov. 7
Goldstar	Yellow	Aug. 4	Aug. 11	Aug. 28	Nov. 8
Dark Yel. Tokyo	Yellow	Aug. 4	Aug. 11	Sept. 3	Nov. 8
White Ann	White	Aug. 11	Aug. 18	Sept. 5	Nov. 10
Rosamunds	Pink	Aug. 11	Aug. 18	Sept. 5	Nov. 10
Ridges	———	Aug. 11	Aug. 18	Sept. 7	Nov. 15
Cristals	———	Aug. 11	Aug. 18	Sept. 7	Nov. 15

Note: If extra-heavy plants are desired, pot cuttings 2 weeks earlier than the above dates. Make first pinch 1 week earlier than indicated, final pinch as shown above.

Single-pinch: To grow the above varieties single-pinch for normal date, pot cuttings 7 to 10 days in advance of final pinch date given above and pinch on final pinch date shown.

Garden mums flowered in May, no shade, no lights, are a "must" in any spring bedding-plant program. Very easy to grow, showy, and irresistible sales appeal are the reasons. Left to right: Penguin, Lipstick and King's Ransom.

GARDEN MUMS IN POTS

Use of the "hardies" for *spring flowering* in 3-inch and 5-inch pots is fast taking hold across the country. Reasons as we see them:

1. Besides being showy little flowering plants at time of spring sales, they can be planted outdoors for another flowering in the fall. It's easy and it works!
2. Though not as large-flowered as the regular greenhouse mums, they make up for it in showy and unusual colors.
3. Cheap to produce—a fast crop (2½ months), no disbudding. Some growers even dispense with shade and lights, especially on the later flowerings.
4. Well adapted to cash-and-carry type of trade.

SCHEDULES (for spring flowering)

Plant Cuttings	February 25	March 17
Lighting period	February 25-March 2	March 17-23
Shade	March 15	March 24
Pinch	March 10	April 7
Flower	Mother's Day	Memorial Day

Since the actual date of spring holidays varies from year to year, especially Easter, it is difficult to set down an exact schedule. Therefore, the following rule can be used as a guide for garden mums to flower for holidays such as Mother's Day, Memorial Day and Easter: count back 10 weeks from desired flowering date. This gives you your plant date. Light for 1 week; pinch 3 weeks after the plant date. Start shade March 15.

VARIETIES

WHITE

Betsy Tears
Corsage Cushion
Cloud 9
Minnwhite

Jess. Williams
Powder River
Diamond
Penquin

Garden mums as grown by Earl J. Kurtz Farms, Cheshire, Connecticut. They do 15,000 a year. A typical schedule (early lot): pot one cutting per 7-inch on May 15, 2 pinches, short days June 15. Most sales in August-early September. Prices, $1.10 to $1.20. Trend in garden mums up.

YELLOW

Minnyellow	*Jackpot*
Sunburst Cushion	*Goldtone*
Yel. Jess. Williams	

BRONZE & RED

Ruby Mound	*Lipstick*
Pancho	*Fireside Cushion*
Festive Cushion	*Flaming Sun*
	Starlit

PINK

Minnpink	*Tinker Bell*
Tango	*Mango*
Stardom	

Use only varieties that are normally very short growers.

NO SHADE, NO LIGHTS (Spring Flowering)

Garden varieties can be flowered very nicely as spring pot plants without shade or lights. They will not flower at an exact date, but by using quite a few varieties, you can have a spread of bloom from late April through May.

Simply pot cuttings direct on March 1-5. Pinch them (a soft pinch) 2 weeks after planting. No shade, no lights. The varieties listed above will flower April 25 through May. Plants must be kept at 60° till buds set. This can be done in a 50° house by enclosing the plants under sateen at night and turning heat on under the cover.

Cool temperature after buds set will intensify colors.

HARVEST GIANTS

The so-called English "early mum" is a major part of the important mum crop in England today—and has been for many years. In effect, these are

Harvest Giants shown above bring to the American gardener the first standard, or "football-" type mum that can be flowered in the gardens of northern and eastern U.S. without black-cloth shade. The September Song shown flowered naturally late September (photo September 29), made a fine showing of color from then to killing frost, 3 or 4 weeks later. They were grown in the Chicago area.

large standards (5 to 7 inches), and sometimes disbuds (3½ to 4 inches), which flower naturally through August and September. No black-cloth shade. They are grown by tens of thousands of enthusiastic amateurs in England for garden decoration, usually outdoors. They are also a major cut-flower crop among English commercial growers—again outdoors.

Repeated efforts to grow these English early mums under American conditions have not succeeded. They simply will not stand the very high summer temperatures prevalent over much of the U. S.

Several years ago, an American mum breeder, Orville Dunham, of Niles, Michigan, succeeded in hybridizing a new race of mums which carry both the fine, large flowers and strong English colors of the English early mum— and also the ability to withstand the difficult conditions of our Midwest and eastern U.S. They were introduced to the trade as Harvest Giants®. In effect, they are large-flowered standard mums (some incurved, some reflexed), with a natural flowering date of mid-to-late September and, in some varieties, early October. Since killing frost in much of the Midwest and eastern U.S. is about October 25, this means at least a month of colorful show in the American garden at a time when most annuals are going downhill.

And the strains *do* stand up well under the high summer temperatures of the U. S. Properly grown, fine large 6 and 7-inch standard, or football-type mums *can be* grown in American gardens in Chicago and New York (see photo, above). And they will produce good-quality standard mums for commercial cut-flower production from about September 15-20 on—without black cloth.

Here are the principal uses for these strains:

1. *For garden decoration.* Typically, florists, garden centers, etc., offer 2¼-

The final step in automating watering of mums. The crop shown above (Pickerell's, Elkhart, Indiana) is watered with Gates-style nozzles around each bench. However, rather than have a man stand by for hours turning the benches off and on by hand, the whole thing is controlled with solenoid valves and a time clock. In effect, the grower can set up on the control panel (photo at right) a 5 or 10-minute watering for each bench on the whole range—one after the other, in succession—all done automatically. And, best of all, it seems to work! Standards here have been, and certainly are, top quality. In the photo, from the left, Gene Pickerell and grower, Dave Thode.

inch or 3-inch plants in late May or early June. These are simply set out in the garden, in full sun, preferably, given normal feeding and watering. They should be pinched, last pinch July 15. In late August, each of the half-dozen-or-so stems on each plant must be disbudded down to one bud. Some of the varieties will require staking or some sort of support. Planting a rooted cutting even as late as June 15-25, of course, reduces the length of time for the plant to grow and minimizes the height problem a great deal. Some varieties are a good bit more compact in habit than others—see descriptions. And lastly, of course, retardants can be used. We have seen some retail growers offering plants of Harvest Giants in the spring who offered a small pack of Phosfon to be mixed with the soil around the plants.

2. *Spring-pot flowering.* One cutting potted to a 3-inch pot on March 2, pinched on March 16, grown 60°, will produce several fine 3½ to 4½-inch blooms by late May—a very salable plant! No light, no shade. These plants can be enjoyed by the homeowner as they are for several weeks, then cut back and planted outdoors to flower again in the fall and natural season. They will flower just as well as plants which have not been "spring-flowered." See photo, page 286.

Dignity—topnotch spring-summer standard. Large flower, very low percentage of culls, rarely petal burns. Good in North from mid-March through December 1.

3. *September cut flowers*. Rooted cuttings planted to the bench at normal cut-flower spacing around June 5-10, pinched not later than July 15—will produce good-quality standard mums, starting late September—no black-cloth shade. Normal disbudding the same as for any other standard is required; otherwise, no special care. Most varieties will flower quite satisfactorily right outdoors with no protection from the rain. In fact, the cool nights of outdoor exposure do much to intensify color of some of the pinks and bronzes.

4. *For fall sale in containers*. Cuttings can be planted in 5 and 6-inch containers (Herculite, for example), one cutting per pot, around June 5-10, last pinch July 15, disbudded as you would for a normal pot mum. These plants, if given good watering, feeding, and other care, should produce 4 or 5 good, large blooms for fall sale. They can, of course, be used in patio tubs, planted into borders and flower beds and enjoyed until killing frost. Cuttings can be planted right to the open field and dug for retail sales, but generally, much better results can be had if they are container-grown. Use either overhead irrigation or Chapin-type irrigation for each pot to insure ample feeding and watering. This is one of the keys to producing good plants. Use shorter varieties for both this fall flowering in containers, and for spring-pot flowering, of course.

NORMAL-SEASON CUT MUMS

WHEN TO BENCH CUTTINGS

See program outlined below for plant dates and corresponding pinch dates for each particular crop.

In general, cuttings are benched directly to the flowering bench 2 weeks prior to the pinch date. It is possible, especially on the late-December crops, to bench cuttings just before or on the pinch date, pinch 2 weeks later. Somewhat shorter stems will result, but with good flowers.

One of the biggest difficulties encountered with normal-season plantings is that of the initiation of premature crown buds. Most of this can be overcome by planting cuttings on the recommended plant date as indicated below and also pinching on the recommended pinch date. Planting too far in advance of the pinch date only invites premature crown-bud trouble.

SPACING

Most normal-season crops are grown pinched. In general, they are spaced 6 by 8 inches, with plants pruned to 2 stems per plant (3 on the outside row), or 8 by 9 inches, pruned to 3 stems per plant (4 on the outside row). For single-stem crops, plant on the pinch date.

Normal-season, single-stem crops are generally grown at a 5 by 6-inch spacing.

TEMPERATURES

Natural-season mums are grown at 50° nights, 58° cloudy, 65° sunny-day temperatures. Once buds are set, these temperatures can be lowered 10° or even 12°. This will delay flowering (several weeks on December varieties), and will improve hardness and quality. It saves fuel, too!

One caution: especially on the late-(December) flowering pompons, it is important that they *not* be grown too warm. Example: such varieties as *Illini Cascade,* ˙ grown at 60° nights, 70° days, will probably "stall"—bud development delays, buds compound, until there may be 25-35 buds per stem —but they never develop. It's a mess!

EXTENDING THE NATURAL SEASON

It is possible, often profitable, to extend the natural-season crop both ways with black-cloth shade (earlier), and lights (for later crops). We especially recommend black-sateen shading for September-October flowering. Reason: in this way, it is possible to flower the November varieties in September. They are far superior in quality to the ones that naturally flower in early October.

It is possible, by simply lighting, to also bloom these excellent November varieties up into January. Here, though, you must provide 60° till buds form. No sateen is needed.

Turn to page 294

NORMAL-SEASON SCHEDULE

	Some Recommended Varieties To Use				Plant Date	Pinch Date[1]	Flowering Period
	WHITE	YELLOW	PINK	BRONZE			
8-Wk. Pomps	Horizon	Yel. Calumet	Accolade	Dark Calumet	July 16	July 30	Oct. 15-
8-Wk. Stds.	Silver Song	Golden Promise	Touchdown	Indian Summer			Oct. 24
9-Wk. Pomps	Poloris Nimrod Cloudbank Alabaster Arctic White Marble	#2 Dandy Gold Coast Sunbeam Cavalier Yel. Keepsake Yellowchip	Bluechip Belair Dolly Pink Marble	Showoff Bronze Marble Tanfastic Dazzler Blaze Detroit News	July 23	Aug. 6	Oct. 25- Nov. 4
9-Wk. Stds.	Dignity Southern Comfort	Southern Sun Yel. Nobhill	Escapade Promenade	Onward			
10-Wk. Pomps	Iceberg #2 Shasta Dawn Star Hurricane	#2 Yel. Iceberg Yel. Beauregard Yel. Shasta Golden Bantam	Dark Delight Carillon Deep Telstar	Stingray Dark Red Beauregard Dillon Beauregard Tuneful	July 30	Aug. 13	Nov. 5- Nov. 14
10-Wk. Stds.	Imp. Fred Shoesmith Imp. Mefo Nobhill	#2 Yel. Shoesmith Imp. Yel. Mefo	Lydia	Mrs. Roy			
11-Wk. Pomps	Divinity Iceland Jupiter	Yel. Divinity Jubilee Forty-Niner Northern Lights	Delmarvel Caravelle	Beauregard Supreme Inferno Thelma	Aug. 6	Aug. 20	Nov. 15- Nov. 24

NORMAL-SEASON SCHEDULE

Some Recommended Varieties To Use

	WHITE	YELLOW	PINK	BRONZE	Plant Date	Pinch Date[1]	Flowering Period
11-Wk. Stds.	May Shoesmith	Bright Yellow May / Shoesmith	Deep Champagne	Red Balcombe Perfection / Commodore			
12-Wk. Pomps	Icecap / Iceflo	Goldcap / Goldflo / Yellow Galaxy	Delmonico	Red Galaxy / Galaxy / Beau Brummell	Aug. 13	Aug. 27	Nov. 25-Dec. 4
12-Wk. Stds.	December Glory	#3 Yel. Glory					
13-Wk. Pomps	Wintertime / Snowcrest	Goldflo / Corsair / Kingpin	Debutante / Dark Pink Minstrel	Christmas Star	Aug. 20	Sept. 3	Dec. 5-Dec. 14
13-Wk. Stds.	Smith's White	Smith's Dark Yel.					
14-Wk. Pomps	Elegance / Icebreaker	Golden Elegance	Alvoda	Christmas Greeting	Aug. 27	Sept. 10	Dec. 15-Dec. 29
15-Wk. Pomps	Ill. Cascade	Yel. Ill. Cascade			Aug. 27	Sept. 10	Dec. 30-Jan. 5

[1] For single-stem crops, plant on the pinch date.

Examples:

To flower *Iceberg, Shasta, Gt. Betsy Ross* September 12, plant cuttings June 13, start black-cloth shade July 4, no lights, no pinch. For pinched crop, plant May 30, pinch June 13.

To flower *Icecap* January 9, no pinch, plant cuttings September 19, light September 19-October 3. For pinched crop, plant September 5, light from September 5 till October 3.

It is obvious that the cultural treatments given these two Shoesmith plants were not the same. Follow the practice described in this article for quality shown on the right.

BLUEPRINT FOR IMPROVED WINTER STANDARDS

Editor's Note: Good-quality standard mums are in keen demand through the winter months—and bring premium prices. Reason: they are hard to grow under the poor light conditions of the northern greenhouse in winter. Yet, it can be done—and is done by many experienced growers.

What are the little tricks of temperature and moisture and judging that spell the difference between good winter quality—and poor? Generally these are hard things to put into the printed page. We felt, though, that the following notes tell this story exceptionally well. From Yoder's Grower Circle News.

Having trouble with Shoesmith form?

Every winter, we receive questions and comments from *Shoesmith* growers.

The warmer the winter or the less sunshine available, the more numerous the inquiries.

"All my *Fred Shoesmith* and *Yellow Shoesmith* are losing their good incurved form. Reflexing is very bad. What's wrong?"

"Stems on my *Shoesmiths* are too weak to support the flowers. The flowers are small and reflexed. Can you tell me how to improve the crop?"

"There is a firm over in (town, state) shipping to the same market I do that has had beautiful *Fred* and *Yellow Shoesmith* all winter. The size, form and stems have all been excellent. Mine are terrible by comparison. How can I grow them that way?"

"*Fred Shoesmith?* We quit. We're going back to *Indianapolis*. Even if it is smaller, the form is more reliable. Wish we knew how to grow good *Fred Shoesmith;* we need its size."

Are you growing a good winter Indianapolis?

Even with the improved size available in the *Giant #4 Ind. White* and *Yellow* and the *#2 Ind. Dark Bronze* and *CF2 Ind. Bronze,* the complaint of small-sized blooms produced during December, January and February is common.

The blueprint for consistently producing good winter *Indianapolis* is an exacting one. It requires close attention to cultural details. Because a low-temperature finish during this period with the *Indianapolis* varieties is a major contributing factor to quilled form, it cannot be used to tone up the crop and slow down flower development as is true with the *Mefos* and *Fred Shoesmith.*

Compensating properly for the lack of sunshine to conserve the plant carbohydrates is essential for good size and form and is the whole secret to successful crops.

Our experience with *Indianapolis* has convinced us that the supplemental CO_2 at a minimum of 500 ppm in conjunction with a few degrees higher day temperature to assure maximum utilization, have very significantly contributed to the more consistent production of good-quality crops. We believe 750 to 1000 ppm would be even better. Air movement provided by inside fans also greatly helps to improve the quality of winter crops.

Unquestionably, our enthusiasm for *Indianapolis* varieties in winter flowerings has increased with the use of CO_2.

Having winter difficulties with Mefo?

In northern greenhouses, it is always interesting to observe that growers who produce the best incurved form and depth on their winter crops of *Indianapolis* are the ones who complain the most that their *Mefos,* grown in the same houses, have poor, reflexed form and many culls.

The answer here is fairly simple.

The warm grower provides the optimum environment for best form for winter crops of *Indianapolis*. These warm 62°-64° finishing temperatures under low-light conditions cause *Mefo* to reflex and blow its form. *Mefo* is not quite as low-temperature tolerant as *Fred Shoesmith.*

The flower form and stem strength you obtain on your winter crops are directly determined by your ability to properly compensate for the lack of sunshine November through March. During the period of the year when light is deficient, you must pay closer attention to the careful regulation of:

1. *Soil*
2. *Plant Spacing*
3. *Soil Moisture and Humidity*
4. *Feeding*
5. *Timing*
6. *Crop Tone*
7. *Temperature*
8. *Interrupted Light*
9. *Carbon Dioxide (CO$_2$)*

SOIL

Good drainage is a must. Most growers of quality mums have solved their soil problems, and open soils are generally the rule.

Raised benches with open, well-drained bottoms are definitely preferred over ground beds. It is more difficult to produce and control winter crops in ground beds. However, good crops can be grown in ground beds if you provide open soil, excellent drainage and exercise careful moisture control.

The straw compost is excellent for opening soil and building structure. The practice of chopping in stems and leaves of a previous mum crop is not considered a good one.

Soils with low soluble-salt content are essential for best results. Test your soil regularly so that you will know what the salt reading is before planting. If it is high, leaching thoroughly before planting is recommended.

Sterilization just prior to planting is highly recommended. If you can only sterilize your soil once a year, the most benefit will be gained if this is done prior to your winter planting. Soils are more open after sterilization and usually require more frequent watering than if not sterilized.

PLANT SPACING

When the largest strains are grown, the minimum recommended spacing for single-stem from October 15 to April 15-flowering crops is 30 square inches per stem. Many growers go to 36 square inches per stem. This 6 by 6-inch spacing materially contributes to strong stems. The 36-square-inch-per-stem level holds culls to the very minimum.

Blessed with clean glass and a location in a relatively smoke-free, cloud-free area, the 30-square-inch level is usually satisfactory.

Some of the best winter crops we have ever observed were at a compromising 33-square-inch level.

We still find some northern growers holding 6 by 4-inch spacing. Their results are generally quite sad.

If you have had difficulty in the past with weak stems and poor form and were not violating the temperature recommendations excessively, you would be well advised to start with the 36-square-inch-per-stem spacing.

To a considerable extent, this spacing required per stem is directly correlated to the height of the crop. Very tall crops need wide spacing. Shorter crops are satisfactory with less space per plant. This is based on the belief that for a given variety at a given period, the greater the total leaf area per plant, the more space is required to obtain normal function of all leaves.

The center row left open improves overall quality on winter crop.

SOIL MOISTURE AND HUMIDITY

Well-drained soils seldom remain wet too long and problems of excess soil moisture are rare in such cases. The practice of "touching up" all around the edges of a bed with water is far more sound than the often-observed error of watering in the entire bench when center areas do not need it and are frequently kept too wet by it. Many growers in winter modify their bench spacing and plant arrangement to open up the center of the bed. This permits more light in the center rows and is desirable. It can create some wet spots, but these can be avoided by proper watering.

Granted that the soil is in good physical shape with low soluble-salt content and preferably just recently sterilized, the practice of maintaining relatively high humidity after planting is sound in promoting rapid crop take-off.

Humidity reduction during the finish of the crop is essential for crop tone as well as botrytis control. Good air movement through fans or a crack of ventilation during the day is important.

Withholding water at the right time and for the right duration distinguishes the professional grower from the amateur.

Reducing moisture during the period from lights-out to buds-observable improves the uniformity of response, and stiffens stems.

Running crops very dry at the finish just prior to cutting is a grave error. Maintain uniform soil moisture at this stage.

A stuffy, motionless, humid environment is ideal for soft, stretched growth and botrytis. Maintaining good crop tone under such conditions is almost impossible. Air movement is more essential than air change. There are good solutions such as the poly tube, turbulators, Dutch Mill and Modine fans. Avoid sudden cold-air changes or drafts. Mildew frequently will appear under such rapid changes.

FEEDING

Since the frequency of watering in winter is reduced, the need for higher-than-summer concentrations of liquid feed is self-evident. Maintain adequate feeding at all times.

Get your crop off to a fast start. The first 3-5 weeks are very important and you should strive to attain maximum vegetative growth during this period. Beginning with plant date, and until the crop is well established, feed plants regularly and thoroughly with a complete liquid fertilizer, or a combination of ammonium nitrate and potassium nitrate. By "thoroughly," we mean the soil must be saturated and some feed runs off and is wasted. This is necessary to help flush soluble salts from the soil. It is very vital to feed mum plants as soon as possible after planting. Our practice has been to water in with dilute feed so food will be available immediately. Early use of high-water-soluble-phosphorus fertilizers is strongly recommended to build roots.

After start of short days, we find it helps to delete the ammonium forms of nitrogen fertilizers because they have a tendency to produce more succulent growth which may result in weak stems. We finish our crops with potassium nitrate only, with excellent results.

Cutting off long-day weeks from the recommended winter timetable is a serious risk, and generally, results in short, weak stems that have not had the time to build sufficient leaf area needed to provide the carbohydrates required for top-quality blooms. Very skillful growers can do it, but by and large, it must be recognized that a large flower requires a good, strong plant. To produce this quality, it requires time to grow. It cannot be overemphasized that good flower size and form in winter must have a strong, well-grown plant.

CROP TONE

Experience has demonstrated that combining correct adjustments of soil moisture and fertilizer results in a better and more rapid toning of the winter crop than either one alone. If you are experiencing weak stems, try the following recommendations:

1. Feed dilute early. Attain maximum growth while crop is under long days. Do not allow the crop to dry out.

2. Taper off on water and feed when short days or lights-out starts.

    Continue to hold off on thorough watering until the stems have hardened up and become whippy or semiwoody. The plants normally take on a dark green color. Apply only enough moisture to keep the plants from suffering permanent wilting injury to the foliage.

3. Once the buds have begun to swell, and all soft, vegetative aspects have disappeared, feed and thoroughly water the crop to encourage large flower and petal development.

4. During the process of toning plant growth and developing the flower buds, maintain as much air movement as possible to reduce atmospheric humidity.

TEMPERATURE

The temperature chart on page 300 indicates the ideal temperatures to maintain at various stages of crop growth for *Mefos, Shoesmith* and *Indianapolis* crops planted November through March.

By "ideal," we refer to temperatures that can be maintained on crops grown in programs where these varieties do not require a compromise in temperature. Where chrysanthemum crops are grown at various stages in the same house or where there are other flower crops within the same house, a temperature conflict generally results and ideal temperatures are impossible to maintain.

We fully realize that most growers today are unable to maintain such ideal temperatures because of the physical plant and cropping-program limitations. However, it is our aim to point out the ideal and encourage you to come as close as possible. Also, these figures may be of value when planning new areas or analyzing growth problems that can occur where less-than-ideal temperatures are involved.

If you are unable to maintain these ideal temperatures, we would suggest maintaining minimum temperatures of 60° night, 60° cloudy, and 65° bright throughout the crop duration.

Growers often make a mistake in the fall months of carrying temperatures too high too early. This only causes crops to respond early, develop shorter-stemmed crops and small flowers. It is not necessary to hold a 60° minimum night temperature on crops in September and October. Plants being grown at this time are from cuttings harvested during the high temperatures of August and September and have a built-in carry-over temperature. It is a very responsive cutting and will give best results when grown at night temperatures around 55°F until approximately November 15 to offset these high-temperature effects. This temperature manipulation can be readily followed when we have a warm fall, which is so often the case. When a cooler-than-normal fall is experienced, a 60°F night temperature should be maintained at an earlier date.

For best winter results, *Indianapolis* should not be grown with *Shoesmith* and *Mefo* because *Indianapolis* requires higher finishing temperatures than *Shoesmith* or *Mefo* for best size and form (see chart next page). Under *Indianapolis* finishing temperatures, the *Mefos* and *Shoesmiths* will readily shatter, reflex, and blow their form.

Advance flowering by using CO_2 on Indianapolis Bronze.

Another important point to remember when ideal temperatures can be maintained: Reduce the temperature after bud color on *Mefo* and *Shoesmith* by 4°, gradually (2°F each week), until you reach 56°. Do not drop the temperature 4° all at one time. If the temperature is dropped too rapidly after bud color, the *Shoesmiths* may pink. This drop in temperature will improve crop tone and keeping quality.

IDEAL TEMPERATURE RANGES

Growth Stage	← Long Days →						← Short Days →								
	Start			Vegetative			Bud Initiation			Bud Development			Bud Color To Cut		
	Night	Cl	Br	Night	Cl	Br	Night	Cl	Br	Night	Cl	Br	Night	Cl	Br
Without CO₂ Mefo's Shoesmith's	62°	62°	67°	60°	60°	65°	62°	62°	67°	60°	60°	65°	56°	56°	61°
Indianapolis	64°	64°	69°	62°	62°	67°	64°	64°	69°	62°	62°	67°	62°	62°	67°
With CO₂ Mefo's Shoesmith's	62°	68°	75°	60°	66°	73°	62°	68°	75°	60°	66°	73°	56°	62°	69°
Indianapolis	64°	70°	77°	62°	68°	75°	64°	70°	77°	62°	68°	75°	62°	68°	75°

Start (Warm)—The period from plant date to plant establishment. Generally a 1-2 week period, depending on the season.

Vegetative (Cool)—The period from plant establishment (1-2 weeks after planting) to lights out or start of short days.

Bud Initiation (Warm)—This is the 3-week period immediately following lights-out or start of short days. This is a very critical period affecting uniformity of flowering.

Bud Development (Cool)—This is the period immediately following the bud-initiation period (buds visible) to bud color. Be careful not to reduce temperature before you are sure of uniform bud set.

Bud Color to Cut (Warm)—Indianapolis (Extra-Cool)—Shoesmith and Mefo.

CARBON DIOXIDE (CO₂)

We have had first-hand experience in winter with chrysanthemums grown and flowered in CO₂-enriched greenhouses.

There are some observers who believe that when the blueprint as given in steps 1 to 8 is followed to the letter, the crop will not be improved by the use of CO_2.

There are other observers who believe that the high temperature plus CO_2 costs are not recovered in the resultant crop. It must be realized here that much of the higher temperature is day temperature obtained simply by not ventilating until house temperature reaches 75°F. This in itself is a fuel saving.

We believe that without access to CO_2, a grower in the Ohio and other northern areas has very narrow limits for error in regulating the environment for top-quality chrysanthemums.

We believe that with the use of CO_2, much wider limits of error are possible with no detrimental effect on the crop.

A minimum level of 500 ppm was used from 8:00 a.m. to 5:00 p.m. The period of critical need appears to be from 11:00 a.m. to 2:00 p.m.

The grower who is using additional CO_2 on his crops should be cautioned on using it beyond the point of color show. We have found that flower texture is softer and more susceptible to botrytis if CO_2 and tight ventilation are carried to full crop maturity. We would suggest at this period that the use of CO_2 be discontinued and adequate ventilation be applied to reduce relative humidity and temperature. This suggestion is based on our results with the use of additional CO_2 in winter.

There is increasing evidence that with the use of CO_2 and the resultant growth improvement, there is a need for stepping up the feeding program. Further experience is needed before any detailed recommendations can be made, but it is evident that unless this is done, the maximum benefits from CO_2 are not always realized.

While there is much yet to be learned, we are convinced that the use of CO_2 can be considered a valuable supplement for sunshine in the light-deficient areas.

INTERRUPTED LIGHT

An additional suggestion for the perfection and retention of good form in winter standards is the use of interrupted light. When properly done, this will add up to 50% more petals to the flowers.

Formula:

From the *scheduled lights-out date,* count back 12 days and stop lights. Then apply 9 short days. Follow this with 12 days of lights on. Thereafter, maintain lights out to cut. This is the recommended *9-off, 12-on* formula for interrupted lighting. This will slow down the crop by about 9 days, but results in a size and form improvement that cannot be equalled with just abrupt lights out.

Since the larger strains of *Indianapolis* are more open in their form and the short days of winter tend to reduce petal count, the practice of interrupted lighting is beneficial in increasing petal count. It should be emphasized that it is not essential. This is especially true when CO_2 is used. It does work well and can be recommended when the given area is all the same variety and the lighting system permits it. *Accurate temperature control* during the lights-off, lights-on period is essential.

We continue to see growers shade beds all winter to reduce light interference. Generally, this is done by those who string their lights too high, and lower light levels are preferred. When full-bench shading is necessary, it should never be done at the expense of reducing normal daylight. It should be applied very late and removed very early. Do not shade for less than 12 hours.

Keeping the glass clean, planting shallow, properly controlling insects and disease, providing adequate plant support, disbudding on time, and cutting the crop when prime, are minor but important points when added to the master blueprint.

CINERARIA IMPROVED FESTIVAL

CINERARIA

ANNUAL *(Senecio cruentus)* *150,000 seeds per oz. Germinates in 10 days at 70°*

Cineraries are very colorful, inexpensive pot plants to produce, and are still much in demand from January through April.

For midwinter and Easter plants in 5 or 6-inch pots, most seed is sown during August and September. Nice 4-5-inch pot plants are made from a sowing about October 1, while a December sowing will produce excellent 3-inch for mass-market sales. Just when they will come in from any sowing depends, of course, on winter temperatures. A night temperature of 48-50° will keep them in good shape. Cinerarias are cool-temperature plants and will not set buds at night temperatures above 60°. Normally it takes 3 to 4 weeks at temperatures of 55° or lower to set buds. These will then develop and mature regardless of lower or higher temperatures.

To avoid damping-off, transplant the seedlings as soon as they can be handled. We prefer to plant them into 2¼-inch Jiffy-Pots or similar containers in light soil with little or no fertilizer in this stage. They dry out so fast in small clay pots that it is usually impossible to maintain that uniform moisture that is easier to do in Jiffys. When they begin to crowd, pot direct into 5's. We find that while this method calls for a little care in preventing overwatering until they make new roots, it produces better results with less labor. When they become pot-bound, the main point to watch is the watering. They dry out fast, and on bright days, might easily wilt. Also, they should be protected from strong sun, but during the short days, they can stand all we usually get. Since cinerarias are subject to verticillium, all pots, flats and soil should be sterilized. Light feedings of liquid commercial fertilizer, after buds show, will also be beneficial.

VARIETIES

Probably the most widely used variety in America is *Improved Festival*. It combines compact, well-rounded habit with large heads of medium-sized flowers. Another valuable point is the small foliage.

Dwarf Giant Exhibition Mixture is a dwarf strain with a wide color range containing both solid colors and white "eyes." It is more dwarf than *Improved Festival* with slightly larger flowers.

Varieties in the multiflora nana class, better suited for smaller pots and mass market sales include *Starlet,* an extra dwarf compact grower with a wide range of flashy colored flowers, and *Gold Buttons,* unique, because of the bright gold center in each floret.

One of the finest of the dusty millers also belongs to the cineraria clan. It's *C. Maritima Diamond,* and is an excellent bedding plant.

CLEOME (Spider Plant)

ANNUAL *(C. spinoso)* *12,500 seeds per oz. Germinates in 12 days at alt. 70-85°*

Widely grown years ago in old-fashioned gardens, spider plants, as cleomes are commonly known, seem to be staging a come-back. This is due principally to the popular, large-flowered variety, *Rose Queen,* and the equally large, pure white *Helen Campbell.* With their 6 to 7-inch heads of attractive flowers, and heavy hedgelike growth reaching a height and width of 4 feet, they are well suited for planting along walls or to hide unsightly spots. They are easily grown and bloom throughout the summer until frost. Seed should be sown indoors in March or April for May bedding-plant sales. Other varieties are available, but the two named are by far the best.

COLEUS

ANNUAL *(C. blumei)* *100,000 seeds per oz. Germinates in 10 days at 65-75°. Light.*

This is one of the most useful of all colored foliage plants, suited for growing in shaded and semishaded areas. There are two or three classes, their distinction being based on the size of their leaves. Probably the most used is the well-known, small-leaved class in which there are numerous named varieties which are propagated by cuttings. Next in foliage size we might call the "rainbow" class. The foliage of this type is medium in size and the plants, while rather large and vigorous, are quite free-branching and bushy. It is easily and economically grown from seed which is available not only in mixture but in separate colors which come quite true to type.

While the above 2 classes are being grown yet on a limited scale, by far and away the market is switching over to the use of a vastly improved strain called *Carefree*®. Developed by Claude Hope, it is a self-branching, dwarf bushy type. Small, narrow leaves are closely spaced with deep and finely lobed edges, providing a ruffled appearance. A superior bedding plant for pots and paks. Available in the full range of coleus separate colors as well as a mixture, color preference lies in the red and scarlet shades.

303

CAREFREE® COLEUS

Other types or classes currently being used include *Exhibition* type, a large leaved strain typified by the variety *Red Monarch*.

Fringed type sold as *Fringed Mixture* and *Magic Lace*. 90% true to type, color shades are largely rose, bronze, green and salmon.

Salicifolius-Duster series. Very narrow leaves with serrated edges. At present available in 2 colors, red and yellow.

Coleus, being of tropical origin, will grow freely only in a warm house, and this requirement, of course, very much extends to the germination of its seed. If grown in a 60° house, a January sowing should make good 3-4 inch pot plants by around Easter. An early-March sowing is about right for mid-May bedding-plant sales. You can recommend *Carefree* coleus highly for semishaded areas.

COSMOS

ANNUAL *(C. bipinnatus)* *4,000-5,000 seeds per oz. Germinates in 5 days at 70°*

This popular, fast-growing annual will provide an abundance of cut flowers throughout the summer. Although of limited commercial value as a bedding plant overall, growers in some areas do have a ready market for cosmos in packs. The *Sensation* type (3 feet), very early, is largely used as a mixture, but can be had in separate colors. *Diablo*, a *Klondyke* type, producing 2-inch large, semidouble flowers in a rich burnt-orange color, is a recent introduction.

A good example of a potted crocus —just as it comes out of the rooting room. Cultivar is Remembrance.

CROCUS FORCING

August De Hertogh
Michigan State University

GENERAL ASPECTS

All crocuses used for forcing are grown in the Netherlands. The flowering season for crocuses extends from late December to early March. To have high-quality plants for this season, it is necessary to have a controlled-temperature rooting room. The information provided below is designed for a forcer who has such a facility. Those forcers who continue to use outdoor-rooting beds will have to make adjustments based on experience.

To assist the forcer, the flowering season has been divided into four flowering periods (Table 1). These periods are abbreviated "C-1" to "C-4." It should be noted there is no sharp dividing line between these periods and they may be adjusted according to individual needs and facilities. The season has been divided to take advantage of both precooled (PC) and nonprecooled (NP) bulbs and the characteristics of the cultivars. Since the minimum cold requirement for both types of bulbs is 13 weeks, the planting dates are changed to provide the highest-quality plants.

Crocuses for forcing are usually 10/11 centimeters in circumference. This size bulb forces well and has large flowers, usually 2 per bulb.

In general, there are few problems associated with the forcing of crocuses. Normally, any insects or diseases can be controlled by using commercially available insecticides or fungicides.

FORCING INFORMATION

The forcer's responsibility begins immediately on arrival of the bulbs. As soon as they arrive, the bulbs should be ventilated, inspected and stored at the proper temperature. If it is time for precooling, place them at 48° F, otherwise, store the bulbs at 60-63° F until either precooled or planted.

Crocus corms are normally planted in special crocus pots. They can, however, be planted in 4 or 6-inch pans, depending on the market to be supplied. When planting the bulbs, use a well-drained soil mixture, one similar to that used for potted chrysanthemums or poinsettias. After planting, place them in the rooting room and water thoroughly. Keep the plants moist throughout their time in the rooting room.

Table 1
Programming Guide for Crocus

Flowering Period	Start of Precooling	Time of Planting	Rooting Room	Dates into Green- house	Approxi- mate Flowering Date	Weeks of Cold
C-1	Aug. 28-31 (48° F.)	Oct. 1 to 7	A	Dec. 8 Dec. 15 Dec. 22 Dec. 31	Dec. 30 Jan. 2 Jan. 6 Jan. 12	14 15 16 17
C-2	—	Sept. 28 to Oct. 5	A	Dec. 31 Jan. 7 Jan. 14	Jan. 20 Jan. 25 Jan. 29	13 14 15
C-3	—	Oct. 16 to 20	B	Jan. 20 Jan. 27 Feb. 3 Feb. 8	Feb. 5 Feb. 10 Feb. 13 Feb. 18	13 14 15 16
C-4	—	Nov. 10 to 15	B	Feb. 11 Feb. 18 Feb. 25	Feb. 21 Mar. 1 Mar. 6	13 14 15

The program (Table 1) described for crocus-forcing utilizes 2 rooting rooms in order to obtain quality plants for the entire flowering season. Rooting room "A" has a temperature sequence of 48° F to November 5 to 10, 41° F to January 1 to 5, then 33-35° F. Rooting room "B" has a temperature sequence of 48° F to December 1 to 5, 41° F to January 1 to 5, then 33-35° F. The criteria for making the changes in temperature are as follows. The change from 48° F to 41° F is dependent on the development of the roots. The 48° F temperature should be maintained until the roots grow out the bottom of the containers. Be sure to check each cultivar, since cultivars can react differently. The change from 41° F to 33-35° F is dependent on the length of the sprouts. The 41° F temperature should be maintained until the sprouts become about 1½ inches long. The 33-35° F temperature is used to retard sprout growth so that a quality plant is produced in the greenhouse. Table 2 lists the cultivars used for forcing and their flowering-period usage. Crocus bulbs for "C-1" should be precooled while those for "C-2" to "C-4" should be nonprecooled.

Crocus 1 (C-1): Bulbs for this period should be precooled at 48° F. This should start about August 28 to 31. A forcing temperature of 58-60° F is preferred for this period.

Crocus 2 (C-2): For this and all succeeding periods, only nonprecooled bulbs need to be used. A forcing temperature of 55° F is preferred.

Crocus 3 (C-3): A forcing temperature of 55° F is preferred.
Crocus 4 (C-4): A forcing temperature of 55° F is preferred.

Table 2
Crocus Cultivars for Forcing

Cultivar	C-1	C-2	C-3	C-4
Flower Record	PC	NP	NP	NP
Peter Pan	PC	NP	NP	NP
Pickwick	PC	NP	NP	NP
Purpureus Grandiflorus	PC	NP	NP	NP
Remembrance	PC	NP	NP	NP

PC—Precooled   NP—Nonprecooled

STORAGE OF FINISHED PRODUCT

At times, it is necessary to store the finished product prior to sending it to market. If this is to be done, store the plants at 33-35° F at the first sign of any color in the flower. Also, it is advisable to treat them with a protective fungicide prior to storage.

CROSSANDRA

ANNUAL *(C. infundibuliformis) 4,000 seeds per oz. Germinates in 3-4 wks. at 70-85°*

This is an unusual and attractive pot plant and came originally from India. Introduced to the American trade by our firm, it has become quite popular in many localities, and while it does require a rather high temperature for germination and growth, the results are well worth the additional precautionary measures. The plants have glossy, gardenia-like foliage with flower spikes of overlapped, clear salmon-orange florets. It may be sown almost anytime, but is probably more easily started in early spring. A minimum temperature of 75 to 80° will be necessary for satisfactory germination with a

CROSSANDRA
An unusual and attractive pot plant.

minimum of 65° for later stages. It needs rather rich, well-drained soil and will flower in 7 to 9 months after seed is sown. Germination usually starts 10 to 14 days after sowing and will continue slowly and irregularly over a period of a month. Transplanting, therefore, must be done at intervals as the plants appear and when they are large enough to handle. Use care in transplanting so that the ungerminated seeds will not be disturbed. The plants may also be grown from cuttings rooted in sand over good bottom heat, with some protection, so that a condition of high humidity is maintained.

CYCLAMEN

ANNUAL *(C. indicum giganteum) 2,500 seeds per oz. Germinates in 7-8 wks. at 60°*

This attractive plant continues to maintain its position near the head of the list of popular winter pot plants—and few plants are more showy during the dark days of midwinter. In Europe, where they are even more popular than here in the States, nearly 40% of the production is for cut flowers. Growers there make a practice of pulling the first several flowers from each plant and slitting the end of the stem for this purpose, later selling the blooming plants. With 12-inch stems, cyclamen are as attractive as sweet peas in table arrangements and hold up much better—and their use doesn't hinder the sale of the plant later.

If one's facilities for culture of cyclamen plants are limited, chances are it would be a mistake to attempt their production, for the specialized care their culture demands is considerable. In fact, there are a number of florist pot plants that belong in this class, and in these cases, the buying-in of partly-grown plants is a distinct advantage. However, that "specialized care," in the case of cyclamen, is usually a matter of knowing the fundamentals and watching them.

Probably the most important sowings are made during September-October for flowering as 6's in late November through February (12-14 months later). They can be sown in June to make 8-inch specimen plants—or as late as

CYCLAMEN
F₁ HYBRID DOUBLE MIXTURE
The first of the F₁ hybrids. Fully double flowers in pink, rose and salmon shades. Makes a showy, long-lasting house plant.

early February to produce nice salable 4's the following January-early February. Generally, growers are swinging to later sowings because the lower-priced, somewhat-smaller plants sell better.

FAST CROP CYCLAMEN

Over the past few years a great deal of research by Professor Widmer and his associates at the University of Minnesota has led to the development of a fast crop program or schedule whereby a finished crop can be produced in 8 or 9 months from an April sowing, thus reducing crop time by 25-30%. Copies of this schedule are available.

Germination, in our experience, is best done in a neutral peat. The peat used for this purpose (and for soil mixtures for later shifts) is about pH 6.8. Some soil may be added, but it isn't necessary for sprouting, in our experience. Best practice: make a "dibble board" that will punch holes in the soil surface spaced 1 x 1 inch. Drop a seed into each hole—it shouldn't be more than ¼ to ½-inch deep. Carry flats at 60° till they sprout, then drop back to 55°.

SPRING CARE

As soon as seedlings start to crowd, they should be transplanted. They can be potted to 2¼'s but more common practice is to transplant them to flats at a spacing of 3 x 3 inches. They're a lot easier to keep watered, and in general seem to grow better. Some growers even set them right out on an open, raised bench. Soil mixtures here (and clear through), in our experience, should be mostly nonacid peat, leaf mold, or rotted cattle manure—with perhaps ¼ to ⅓ soil. Superphosphate should be added. Such mixtures as 2 parts soil, 2 parts peat, and 1 part manure are common. Sterilizing is important to eliminate nematodes, weeds, and rot fungi. "Curing" of soil after steaming for a few weeks is a must for us.

They should have full sun during the early spring, 50-52°, and light liquid feeding as soon as root action starts.

Shifting schedules? Here, there seems to be much difference of opinion. Some growers—and good ones, too—will pot a heavy transplant or 2½-inch plant directly to a 5 or 6-inch pot. Most others go from transplant to 3 inch, then to 5 inch; or from transplant to 4 inch, then to 6 inch. The direct shift *will* work, but growers who have had limited experience with cyclamen will usually do better with an extra shift. Where direct shift to larger sizes is practiced, plants must be kept on the dry side (but never wilting)—and not fed—until roots show through to edge of the pot.

SUMMERTIME—HARD ON CYCLAMEN

Cyclamen are lovers of cool, moist climates, so the summer—particularly in our Midwest and in the South—is a trying period at best. Much can be done, though, by keeping the plants in a well-shaded and ventilated area frames—and by spraying them overhead on all hot afternoons to keep up humidity. This spraying is a real help in control of mites—they hate moisture.

We are now approaching final shift date. This date is **critical** because it affects flowering dates. In general, plants given their final shift by mid-August will be in bloom during November-December. If final shift is delayed till September 10, most plants should flower for Christmas. Final shifting in early October means plants in flower during January-February, when they aren't in as good demand. Plants should be fairly pot-bound by mid-October if they are to flower for Christmas.

FINISHING THEM OFF

Approaching frost dates in late September should see most cyclamen back under glass. Night temperatures here vary between 50-55°. Feeding program should be held off unless plants absolutely need it, during October—and till plants are definitely setting buds. Heavy feeding and watering encourage leafy, rank growth—and no buds. No shade during budding and blooming— and again, plenty of space.

In recent years, the demand for good cyclamen has been brisk for November, Christmas, and even up to Valentine's Day. From then on, they seem to be less wanted. Hence, the importance of getting them to bloom early. It's mostly a question of culture. Here are what seem to be the critical points.

First, sow early enough—as per previously mentioned schedules. Final shift dates discussed earlier are very important, too. Cyclamen, to a considerable extent, flower when they get pot-bound—which is governed by final shift date. During the fall when you are looking for buds, carry them a bit dry, and avoid nitrate feeding as much as possible. Temperature during late fall affects flowering date: 50° nights is best in our experience; 55° may flower them a bit sooner, but with certainly no better quality.

Lastly, it is true that strains will vary in their earliness. In evaluating our flowering trials and selecting the best sources, we keep an eye on the strains that are first in bloom.

Mites are a headache. You have to fight them from the very start—a mite-infested plant is so deformed that it won't sell. Even a light infestation severely reduces the keeping quality of the plant. They aren't easy to keep out, but good growers do it. They are almost too small to see without a hand lens, but you'll know their presence by the twisting and deforming of growth tips. They cause flowers to be deformed and streaked.

The best mite-control program probably consists of the use of several different insecticides. Malathion and Kelthane are both effective. Red spider and thrips are sometimes also encountered on cyclamen. Aramite is effective against spider, and Dithio does a good job on thrips.

Crown rot is probably the most troublesome disease. This can be largely eliminated by allowing good air circulation around the plants at all times, by being careful not to overwater, and by placing the top of the bulb or corm above the surface of the soil when shifting to the finishing pot.

The bulk of cyclamen-seed demand is in the following varieties: *Improved Bonfire, Halo, Pure White, Glory of Wandsbek* and *Rose of Zehlendorf*. The recently introduced *F₁ Hybrid Double Mixture* adds a new dimension to cyclamen and leads the way to even better varieties.

KING ALFRED DAFFODIL
Most popular forcing variety.

DAFFODIL FORCING

August De Hertogh
Mich. State University

Daffodils used for forcing are grown either in the Pacific Northwest or the Netherlands. The earliness, and to some extent, the usage of the various cultivars will vary according to the locality in which they were produced. In general, the U.S.-grown bulbs can be forced 3 to 4 weeks earlier than Dutch-grown bulbs. For this reason, a cultivar-selection guide is not presented. Forcers should check with their bulb suppliers for cultivar selection and usage.

Daffodils are forced either as potted plants or cut flowers and a distinction must be made between the forcing techniques for these products. The reasons for this are threefold. First, the desired length of the cut daffodil is markedly different from that of the potted plant. Second, pot and cut daffodils intended for the same market period, e.g., Valentine's Day, are shipped at different times. Third, the cold requirements of the two crops may differ by as much as 3 to 4 weeks for some cultivars.

The flowering season for potted and cut daffodils extends from late December to early April. To have high-quality plants throughout this season, it is necessary to have a controlled-temperature rooting room. The information provided below is designed for a forcer who has such a facility. Those forcers who continue to use outdoor rooting beds will have to make adjustments based on experience.

To assist the forcer, the flowering season for potted and cut daffodils has been divided into five flowering periods (Tables 1 and 2). These periods are designated "PD-1" to "PD-5" for pot daffodils, and "CD-1" to "CD-5" for cut daffodils. It should be noted that there is no sharp dividing line between these periods and they may be adjusted according to individual needs and facilities. The season has been divided to take advantage of precooled (PC) and nonprecooled (NP) bulbs. The planting dates are changed to compensate for the cold requirements of the specific cultivars and usage.

Daffodils used for forcing are normally double-nosed bulbs. They are listed as Double Nose I, Double Nose II, etc. They will vary in the number of flowers produced by each size. The Double Nose I produces the greatest number of flowers.

The most serious problem encountered with forcing of daffodils is basal rot. Bulbs should be checked carefully both before precooling and before planting.

FORCING INFORMATION

GENERAL

The forcer's responsibility begins immediately on arrival of the bulbs. As soon as they arrive, the bulbs should be ventilated, inspected and stored at the proper temperature. Bulbs for precooling should be placed at 48° F while nonprecooled bulbs, if not ready for planting, should be held at 55-60° F.

Potted daffodils are usually planted in 6 or 8-inch pots, while cut daffodils are planted in flats. When using flats, be sure to use a size which is not excessively large so that it will be relatively easy to handle. Pallets are useful in both types of production. When planting the bulbs, use a well-drained soil mixture, one similar to that used for potted chrysanthemums or poinsettias. After planting, place the plants in the proper rooting room and water thoroughly. Keep the plants moist throughout their time in the rooting room.

POT DAFFODILS

In the production of potted daffodils, it is desirable to produce a plant which is 10 to 14 inches tall at the bud stage of development. The final plant height is affected by 3 factors. First, the overall length of the cold treatment used is important; overcooling tends to produce tall plants. This is why the precooling and planting dates are staggered for the different flowering periods. Second, the selection of the cultivar itself is important. For example, *Golden Harvest* can be a pot plant when forced early, and a cut flower later. Third, the selection of forcing temperature is important. Potted daffodils should be forced at 60-62° F. This will produce shorter plants than will lower forcing temperatures.

The forcing program for potted daffodils is outlined in Table 1. It utilizes only one rooting-room temperature sequence. Rooting room "B" sequence is 48° F to December 1 to 5, 41° F to January 1 to 5, then 33-35° F. The criteria for making the changes in temperature are as follows: The change from 48° F to 41° F is dependent upon the development of the roots. The 48° F temperature should be maintained until the roots grow out the bottom of the containers. Be sure to check each cultivar, since cultivars can react differently. The change from 41° F to 33-35° F is dependent on the length of the sprouts. The 41° F temperature should be maintained until the sprouts become about 2 inches long. The 33-35° F is then used to retard sprout growth so that a quality plant is produced in the greenhouse.

Pot Daffodil—1 (PD-1): Bulbs for this period should be precooled. They should be placed at 48° F during August 26 to 31. A forcing temperature of 60-62° F is preferred.

Pot Daffodil—2 (PD-2): For this flowering period, some cultivars should be precooled; others can be used as nonprecooled bulbs. Precooled bulbs should be placed at 48° F September 1 to 7. Their planting date is October 6 to 10. Nonprecooled bulbs should be planted September 20 to 25. A forcing temperature of 60-62° F is preferred.

Pot Daffodil—3 (PD-3): For this period and all succeeeding periods, only nonprecooled bulbs need to be used. The planting date should be October 15 to 20. A forcing temperature of 60-62° F is preferred.

Pot Daffodil—4 (PD-4): Planting date should be October 26 to 30. A forcing temperature of 60-62° F is preferred.

Pot Daffodil—5 (PD-5): Planting date should be November 5 to 10. A forcing temperature of 60-62° F is preferred.

Table 1
Programming Guide for Pot Daffodils

Flowering Period	Start of Precooling	Time of Planting	Rooting Room	Dates into Green- house	Approxi- mate Flowering Date	Weeks of Cold
PD-1 (PC)	Aug. 26 to 31 (48° F.)	Oct. 1 to 7	B	Dec. 1 Dec. 8 Dec. 15 Dec. 22	Dec. 25 Dec. 31 Jan. 6 Jan. 12	13½ 14½ 15½ 16½
PD-2 (PC)	Sept. 1 to 7 (48° F.)	Oct. 6 to 10	B	Dec. 30 Jan. 5 Jan. 12	Jan. 18 Jan. 24 Jan. 30	16½ 17½ 18½
PD-2 (NP)	—	Sept. 20 to 25	B	Dec. 30 Jan. 5 Jan. 12	Jan. 23 Jan. 29 Feb. 2	14 15 16
PD-3 (NP)	—	Oct. 15 to 20	B	Jan. 20 Jan. 27 Feb. 3 Feb. 10	Feb. 7 Feb. 11 Feb. 17 Feb. 24	14 15 16 17
PD-4 (NP)	—	Oct. 26 to 30	B	Feb. 17 Feb. 25 Mar. 2	Mar. 1 Mar. 6 Mar. 13	16 17 18
PD-5 (NP)	—	Nov. 5 to 10	B	Mar. 8 Mar. 15 Mar. 22 Mar. 29	Mar. 19 Mar. 26 Apr. 1 Apr. 7	17 18 19 20

Rooting-room temperature sequence is 48° F. to Dec. 1 to 5, 41° F. to Jan. 1 to 5, then 33-35° F.

CUT DAFFODILS

In producing cut daffodils, it is desirable to obtain flowers which are at least 14 inches in length in the "gooseneck" stage of development. Stem length is controlled by the length of the cold treatment and the cultivar used. The forcing temperature is also important. Cut daffodils should be forced at 50 to 55° F to obtain the longest stem length. Greenhouse temperatures above 60° F should be avoided.

The forcing program for cut daffodils is presented in Table 2. The entire flowering season requires only one rooting room. Rooting room "B" has a temperature sequence of 48° F to December 1 to 5, 41° F to January 1 to 5, and then 33-35° F. The criteria for making the temperature changes are the same as those described for the potted daffodils. (See above.)

Cut Daffodil—1 (CD-1): All bulbs for this period should be precooled. They should be placed at 48° F on August 20 to 25. Planting date should be October 1 to 7. A forcing temperature of 55° F is suggested.

Cut Daffodil—2 (CD-2): All bulbs for this period should be precooled. They should be placed at 48° F on September 1 to 5. Planting date should be October 6 to 10. A forcing temperature of 55° F is preferred.

Cut Daffodil—3 (CD-3): For this and all succeeding periods, only non-precooled bulbs need to be used. Planting date should be September 20 to 25. A forcing temperature of 55° F is preferred.

Cut Daffodil—4 (CD-4): Planting date should be October 20 to 25. A forcing temperature of 50-55° F is preferred.

Cut Daffodil—5 (CD-5): Planting date should be November 5 to 10. A forcing temperature of 50-55° F is preferred.

Table 2
Programming Guide for Cut Daffodils

Flowering Period	Start of Precooling	Time of Planting	Rooting Room	Dates into Green-house	Approximate Flowering Date	Weeks of Cold
CD-1 (PC)	Aug. 20 to 25 (48° F.)	Oct. 1 to 7	B	Dec. 1 Dec. 8 Dec. 15 Dec. 22	Dec. 26 Dec. 31 Jan. 5 Jan. 10	14 15 16 17
CD-2 (PC)	Sept. 1 to 5 (48° F.)	Oct. 6 to 10	B	Dec. 30 Jan. 5 Jan. 12	Jan. 17 Jan. 25 Feb. 1	16½ 17½ 18½
CD-3 (NP)	—	Sept. 20 to 25	B	Jan. 20 Jan. 27 Feb. 3 Feb. 10	Feb. 7 Feb. 11 Feb. 17 Feb. 24	17 18 19 20
CD-4 (NP)	—	Oct. 20 to 25	B	Feb. 17 Feb. 25 Mar. 2	Mar. 4 Mar. 10 Mar. 15	17 18 19
CD-5 (NP)	—	Nov. 5 to 10	B	Mar. 8 Mar. 15 Mar. 22 Mar. 29	Mar. 20 Mar. 27 Apr. 2 Apr. 8	17 18 19 20

Rooting-room temperature sequence is 48° F. to Dec. 1 to 5, 41° F. to Jan. 1 to 5, then 33-35° F.

STORAGE OF FINISHED PRODUCTS

Pot Daffodils. When potted daffodils are to be stored prior to being shipped to market, they should be placed at 33-35° F in "pencil" or "goose-neck" stage of development. They should be treated with a protective fungicide prior to storage.

Cut Daffodils. The cut daffodil must be stored in the "gooseneck" stage of development. They should be placed dry, in an upright position, at 33-35° F.

DAHLIA BORDER JEWELS

DAHLIA

ANNUAL *(D. pinnata) 2,800 seeds per oz. Germinates in 10 days at 70°*

In certain limited areas of the country, the taller-growing, large-flowered varieties are used for cut-flower purposes by some florists. If used for cutting, the ends of the stems must be seared to avoid "bleeding" and consequent wilting.

The most profitable part of the dahlia business lies in the growing of the dwarf varieties for sale in the spring, either as potted or bedding plants in packs. These are best and easiest grown from seed, usually sown as a mix.

For Mother's Day in 4-inch pots, we suggest an early-December sowing. An early-February sowing will provide 2½ or 3-inch pots for use in combinations for Mother's Day, also. Sow in late February and early March for pack sales in May. If well-fed and amply spaced, they require no pinching.

The dwarf strains grow to a height of from 15-24 inches and produce an abundance of brightly colored flowers in a range of 2 to 3 inches across. Flowers are semidouble and double. *Early Bird* and *Border Jewels* are the most popular varieties used in that order. Comparable to *Border Jewels* but with bronze-red foliage is a newcomer named *Redskin.*

DAISY

PERENNIAL *(Chrysanthemum maximum)*
21,000 seeds per oz. Germinates in 12 days at 60-65°

While many varieties of plants are loosely referred to under this heading, what most of us have in mind by this term is *Chrysanthemum maximum,* commonly known as *Shasta daisy.* This is the largest and best of the perennial daisies for cutting and is easily grown from seed, after which particularly good specimens may be propagated by divisions. If sown February 1, planted outdoors in enriched soil, a few late-summer flowers will be produced, the best crop coming the following season; and with us, this is usually the last one. Our winters are too severe, without enough snow protection to carry them beyond 2 seasons.

Sown in January and February, excellent plants are produced for spring sales along with annuals in packs or pots. Most widely used is the variety *G. Marconi,* which produces double flowers of a large size with long stems.

DELPHINIUM

PERENNIAL *(D. elatum) 10,000 seeds per oz. Germinates in 18 days at alt. 70-85°*

Today's stately delphinium is, without question, the number one perennial as far as commercial importance is concerned. While they are admittedly one of the most valuable hardy perennials for outdoor cutting, they also respond well to forcing. Outdoors, they seem to be profitable from Canada to Florida, though the finest flowers are produced where summer temperatures are moderate. In Florida, they are largely grown as an annual. Some southern growers find it best to use well-established seedlings that are started farther north.

While they seem to do well in all types of soil, if a choice is available, we

"Six Best" delphinium. Left to right, Guinevere, Galahad, Summer Skies, Black Knight, Blue Bird and King Arthur.

prefer a moderately heavy loam for all perennials. Such material retains fertility as well as moisture better than soil largely made up of sand. In Florida, where sandy material prevails, growers overcome the leaching tendency from such soil by top-dressing lightly but frequently with balanced fertilizer.

We find the best plan for producing strong plants to set out in spring is to sow about September 1 in finely prepared soil in a cold frame. Be sure the soil is perfectly level and well-watered, and don't spread the seed too thickly unless you plan to transplant (which we find unnecessary). After the soil is frozen, remove the sash and cover with any coarse material to prevent too much thawing and freezing. Ordinary straw, we find, is inclined to pack and rot what it is supposed to protect. Cornstalks are ideal for protection. As it warms up in spring, remove this material and replace the sash, but don't soften them through lack of air; let them come slowly and be hardened off. Set out as soon as they are well in growth. Plant out in deeply prepared, fairly enriched, drained soil. Avoid using the same soil over, for they are susceptible to various rots that are carried over in the soil. Another commonly used method of starting this crop is to sow indoors in January. With seed well-matured and temperatures cool at that time, germination should be at its best. Seedlings can be transplanted about 3 inches apart in flats, grown cool, and set out early to harden before planting in the open. Some growers sow the seed direct into the open ground as early as it can be handled; and this, too, is a good plan, for it combines a minimum of labor with an unchecked start that promptly gets into rapid growth.

For forcing, the *Giant Pacific* strains are best. Sow the seed not later than August 1 in flats set in the coolest spot available and later, transplant the seedlings into frames. In late November, after they have had a short rest, they are taken up and planted in a cold house, spacing 6 x 8 inches. About February 1, they are started into growth by a minimum temperature of 40-45°; as spring advances, this is increased to 50° nights. This schedule gets them into full crop by Mother's Day and they continue producing nice stock well into July, after which they are discarded to be followed by other crops. If the *Belladonna* type is used, and they are excellent, space them 6 x 6 inches.

There are 2 distinct types of delphinium—the species *elatum,* to which most of the *Giant Pacifics* belong, and *cheilanthum,* which includes the bella-donna types. The latter are not so strong in growth or as long-stemmed as the hybrids, but are more free-flowering. *Belladonna Imp.* is a very choice light blue. But little of the dark *Bellamosum* is wanted. *Connecticut Yankees,* an All-America Selection, produces bushy well-branched plants with very large florets in shades of lavender and blue. Decidedly, the best strain of giants is known as the *Giant Pacific Court* series, which was developed from, and offers the same fine quality as, the original *Giant Pacific strain* (no longer available) originated by Frank Reinelt. They are available in a fine line of colors from light to the darkest blues, lavenders, mauve, and white. The best varieties in the leading colors are *Galahad,* white; *Guinevere,* lavender; *Summer Skies,* light blue; *King Arthur,* royal violet; and *Blue Bird,* a mid-blue. *Astolat* contains lavender-rose shades, some of which are near pink. Most of them have a conspicuous center or "bee," as it is called. Nearly all come remarkably true to color. Also, they are quite mildew-resistant. While this strain is at its best under the ideal climate of its native state, it does remarkably well in the middle states.

DIANTHUS
F₁ MAGIC CHARMS
MIX
All-America winner.

DIANTHUS

ANNUAL *(D. chinensis)* *25,000 seeds per oz. Germinates in 7 days at 70°*
PERENNIAL *(D. species)* *28,000 seeds per oz. Germinates in 10 days at 70-80°*

Dianthus or pinks, as they have been called for generations, comprise quite a large and very useful genus. Altogether something over 250 species are recognized, but not more than 2 or 3 dozen are of any commercial importance. Varieties under *D. caryophyllus* comprise our popular greenhouse carnations; aside from this group, nearly all dianthus are grown outdoors as garden plants for cutting, borders or edging work, etc. Most dianthus species used today are perennial and, if not wintered-over in too-wet ground, are very hardy. Any good, fairly light garden soil will suit them; they lean to alkaline rather than acid soil. Most of the perennial dianthus are easily propagated from seed that produces flowers the second season from sowing. Division by cuttings or roots is practiced in the case some large double forms that don't propaga   ie from seed.

The annual form   dianthus *(D. chinensis)* are very showy and interest in their usage has quickened in recent years. The majority of the varieties bloom throughout the summer, and for bedding-plant sales, should be handled the same as petunias. Generally, they gr   to a height of 6-12 inches, although the variety *Wee Willie* (annual sweet william) grows to only a height of 3 or 4 inches and makes a fine display of color in packs. Outstanding is the recently introduced F₁ *Charm* series. Plants are 6 inches high, bushy and uniform. Five separate colors available as well as a mix. 12 weeks from sowing to bloomir   aks.

D. barbatus or sweet   illiam is one of the best known of the "old-fashioned" garden flowers. It grows 18 inches high and is propagated most commonly and easily from seed. Sweet williams are, strictly speaking, biennials, but are commonly used as perennials. They enjoy a fully-exposed location and are shown to best advantage in massed plantings. The most commonly used varieties are double-flowered and sold as mixed colors, ranging from red through pink and white. An extra-dwarf (6-8 inches) is available and sold as *Double Midget Mix.*

There are many other attractive dianthus species and varieties that space doesn't permit describing. The outdoor carnations *(Chabaud, Enfant De Nice,* etc.) and the hardy *Grenadin* types are treated under carnations.

EUPHORBIA

PERENNIAL *(E. species) 7,000 seeds per oz. Germinates in 4-5 wks. at alt. 70-85°*

The euphorbia family consists of a great number of plants varying widely in form, habit and use. There are, however, only a few euphorbias that are of importance to the commercial grower. *E. pulcherrima,* poinsettia is a major pot-plant crop and is discussed in detail beginning on page 402.

The annual *snow-on-the-mountain* is *E. variegata,* also known as *Marginata,* and is of some use to retail growers for summer cutting. *E. heterophylla* is sometimes referred to as annual poinsettia or Mexican fire plant because of the red shading on the upper leaves. *E. polychroma* is an attractive perennial rock-garden plant. Bushy plants 15-18 inches high produce bracts of a bright yellow color changing to rosy-bronze.

TROPICAL FOLIAGE PLANTS

Robert McColley
Bamboo Nurseries

Several years ago the term "foliage plants" was thought of as a comparatively small group of non-flowering outdoor plants, such as alternanthera, coleus, etc. By 1950, the industry producing foliage plants was known as the "green-plant" industry. It was during the 1950's the demand for foliage increased greatly and led to an unhealthy situation—best illustrated by one northern buyer's statement to a southern grower—"If it is green, looks DIFFERENT, and is in a pot—send it!" This led to an oversupply of poor varieties, diseased plants, and trash in general being dumped on over-eager consumers.

The early 1960's saw the pendulum swing the other way. The plastics people cashed in on a market weary of low-quality plants. Many a producer of the poor-quality plants was forced out of business and those remaining added one word to describe their product—"QUALITY" foliage plants.

Now, in the early to mid 70's, we have seen this same pendulum swing in the opposite direction once again. Foliage plant sales are really booming. Net value of sales in '74 was up 64% from the year before. Once again this greatly increased demand can lead to an oversupply of poor, diseased material, which really hurts the industry.

Bob McColley, Bamboo Nurseries, Orlando, Florida. Bob is a foliage plant grower and has done important breeding in this area. Here he is with his Red Princess.

A foliage plant is a plant used because of its decorative shape, size, color, and leaf character and not because of flowers. Therefore, a "QUALITY" foliage plant is one that has all of these and will remain decorative over a long period of time under the adverse conditions supplied to it by the consumer.

This section on foliage will confine itself to a few fundamentals of growing for the small grower who has many other crops in his greenhouse. Foliage plants are easy to grow—"QUALITY" plants can only be grown IF certain basic conditions are provided.

Generally speaking, the smaller producer of foliage plants is economically ahead by buying small plants or rooted cuttings rather than attempting to propagate his own. Specialist producers in Florida, for instance, grow *philodendron cordatum* by the acre under lath or cloth protection. They do a much better and less expensive job of producing rooted cuttings or small plants than can be done in northern greenhouses. Buying cuttings instead of propagating has the additional advantage of shortening the time the plants occupy valuable greenhouse space. Today, the trend is for growers to buy large, established plants and keep them just long enough to establish the plants and condition them in selling containers. Quick turnover is one of the "secrets" of making money with foliage plants. However, the most important point in "quality production" is to start with *CLEAN* material. This point cannot be overemphasized. Unless the plants you start with have a sound, disease-free root system, your production can never be profitable. With clean cuttings, sterilized soil and benches, you will eliminate a lot of later troubles.

There are 5 basic requirements that must be provided in the successful growing of tropical foliage plants. They are easily understood if we consider for a moment the native environment of the plants. Most are native to the tropical parts of the world. They put their roots down into tropical forest soil that is predominantly organic matter or humus. They grow in the shade of larger trees or on the comparatively "dark" tropical forest floor. The climate provides temperatures the year around in the 70's at night and 80's or 90's during the day. Rainfall is heavy and humidity high. To anyone who has traveled in the tropics, the term "steaming jungle" is a most appropriate term for tropical humidity. Hence, the 5 points:

1. SOIL

A very loose, well-drained, STERILIZED soil is a must for quality production. Many producers use straight peat moss as a growing medium. Excellent results are being obtained by many growers using a mixture of 50% sphagnum peat and 50% horticultural perlite. There are many good combinations that are variations of a soil/sand/peat formula. Regardless of which formula is used, the medium must not pack, and must provide adequate soil aeration. Most tropical foliage plants do very well in acid soils with pH from 4.0 to 5.0. Many foliage-plant troubles, both in greenhouses and in homes, are easily traceable to a heavy, water-logged soil. Better to err on the side of a too-loose soil rather than a too-heavy one. Since more and more foliage plants are being bought by growers as established plants in containers, it is a wise policy, when repotting or shifting, to pack moist peat or peat and perlite around the ball rather than a soil mixture. This will prevent the original ball from drying out unduly. This of course does not apply to cacti and other succulents which require a medium that doesn't hold too much moisture.

2. LIGHT

Most of our tropical foliage plants in commerce are happiest in at least partial shade. Most other crops grown in northern greenhouses suffer from spells of cloudy weather and our naturally dark winters. Not so with foliage plants. With a few exceptions, they are best grown in 1,000 to 3,000 foot-candles of light intensity. This means shading out ⅔ of the light on a bright summer day and perhaps ⅓ to ½ during the winter. Tropical plants should never be exposed for long periods during the day to direct sunlight. Many producers in Florida, Puerto Rico, or southern California use lath houses. There are a few notable exceptions. Aglaonema or Chinese evergreen, fern, maranta and fittonia should be grown in comparatively heavy shade—50 to 500 foot-candles. These exceptions will be noted in the notes on specific plants later in this article. For those growers not experienced with foliage plants, a light meter reading in foot-candles is a good investment. If you sell foliage plants at retail, your customers will appreciate being guided in their selection according to the light intensity of the intended location of the plant. Generally, people should be encouraged to place their "house plants" in as light a place as possible—barring direct sun, of course. A north window could be considered ideal. Most tropical foliage plants are chosen and promoted on the basis of their ability to withstand dark home locations, but this doesn't mean they don't do better with more light. Fifty to 100 foot-candles of light intensity is considered minimum for satisfactory maintenance of most foliage plants in homes.

3. TEMPERATURE

Most tropical foliage plants should be grown at a 65° minimum night temperature. They grow fast in this temperature and develop that all-important glossy foliage that the ultimate buyer looks for in foliage plants. Some growers prefer 70°. A 60° night temperature is high enough for holding and excellent for conditioning most foliage plants that are ready for sale, but is not high enough for good growth during production.

4. WATER

A constant supply of water is one of the keys to success with most tropical foliage plants. Some growers use lukewarm water in their foliage-plant houses. This, of course, MUST be combined with loose, well-drained soil. A foliage plant grown in the greenhouse must never receive the check that results from allowing the soil to dry out to the point of wilting. Quite to the contrary, however, instructions to the retail customer should be to keep the soil just a bit on the "dry side," except during the first week the plant is in its new environment, when it should be well-watered to compensate for air movement and evaporation due to heating and air-conditioning fans. Under low-light intensity and dry-air conditions of a living room, most of our foliage plants last longer if kept just above the wilting point. High humidity is also a requirement. One of the largest and most successful producers of foliage plants in Florida grows most of his plants under high-pressure mist and in straight peat moss. His plants are constantly literally "dripping" wet; however, plants grown in this manner need a "hardening-off" period before going to the consumer. A 70 to 80% relative humidity is considered a reasonable minimum for best production. There are several notable exceptions to this "the-more-the-water-the-better" rule. Peperomia and sansevieria are happiest on the "dry side."

5. FERTILIZER

A grower can well afford to add 3 to 5 pounds of dolomite and 3 to 5 pounds of a fertilizer similar to a 6-6-6, 50% organic, to each cubic yard of potting mix. This is excellent for potting rooted cuttings or shifting-up. As the plants grow and one feels the nitrogen is becoming depleted (the new leaf a little pale is a good indication), then 1 pound of 30-10-10 in 100 gallons of water should be used. Additional feedings every 1 to 4 weeks (according to growth rate) may be needed. It is usually beneficial to leach the soil between feedings. A 2-1-2 ratio soluble may be alternated with the 3-1-1, but one needs to always beware of phosphate build-up, as repotting is the only solution when this happens.

Insects are usually not a serious problem in growing foliage plants. Aphids, thrips, red spider, mealybug and scale can be problems, but can be eliminated easily by appropriate sprays and dusts such as malathion, Chlordane, Sevin, Diazinon, etc. Always refer to manufacturer's charts.

Certain diseases can be serious problems. Pythium root rot is extremely hazardous to philodendron, dieffenbachia, aglaonema, anthuriums and only slightly less dangerous to other foliage crops. It can best be detected by lightly grasping a blackened root between thumb and forefinger and pulling away from the base of the plant. If the outer layer of root slips off leaving only thin inner core, then Pythium is present. Terraclor is helpful as a control, but a new chemical, Truban, looks extremely good and seems to have a residual effect of from 2 to 3 months. Rhizoctonia is a problem only slightly less prevalent and usually works from the soil surface up the stem. Terraclor usually gives satisfactory control.

By far, the best solution to disease control is to buy only clean cuttings, use sterilized soil, pots and benches and KEEP EVERYTHING CLEAN. Water, if possible, only during morning hours and make every effort to have foliage dry before night.

Containers for foliage-plant growing are usually clay or plastic—either is satisfactory, provided drainage holes are opened. Jiffy-Pots are excellent for most small rooted cuttings and the cuttings do not wilt when replanted as they sometimes do when bare-rooted. Containers for sales vary as much as one's imagination. Just remember, drainage is all-important and if the container has no drain, then a liberal amount of charcoal in the bottom of the pot will usually prolong the useful life of the plant by helping to delay souring of the soil.

For anyone interested in more information on foliage plants, Alfred Graf's *Exotica,* published by Roehrs Co., Rutherford, N.J., is the most complete reference book available.

Following are descriptions and growing notes on some of the more important of the many hundreds of decorative tropical foliage plants in use today. Where certain plants require conditions different from those outlined above, these exceptions are noted.

AGLAONEMA (Chinese Evergreen)

One of our most satisfactory house plants because of its low-light-intensity requirements. Should be grown under 50 to 500 foot-candles and can tolerate down to 10 foot-candles under home conditions. Can be grown in shallow water gardens. Propagated either from single-node stem divisions or tip cuttings. Commercially available in propagating canes (stems), rooted or unrooted cuttings, or potted plants. Cuttings are usually sold in grades by inches of height and number of leaves. *Simplex* is the common, all-green Chinese evergreen. *Commutatum* is similar, except that leaves are mottled with silvery grey.

CHINESE EVERGREEN

Roebelini is a large-leaved, extremely tough species with silvery-grey patches on dark green foliage.

There are several new selections now available: *Silver King, Silver Queen, Fransher* and *Pseudo-Bracteatum.* All are very tough as well as attractive. Use aglaonemas for those dark spots.

APHELANDRA (Zebra Plant)

A compact-growing plant of the Acanthaceae family. Its leaves are shiny, emerald-green, elliptical and of medium size with prominent white veins and midrib. Most species and varieties have bright yellow flowers. The aphelandras require more water than most plants, with about 30% shade. If the plants should wilt, water frequently until growth is re-

ZEBRA PLANT

vived. Fertilize lightly about every 2 months, unless plant is in rapid growth, and then fertilize lightly every 2 to 4 weeks.

DIEFFENBACHIA

A very handsome, large, decorative plant. Commonly propagated by cutting stems into sections containing one or more eyes or by rooting tips under mist. Commercially available in propagating canes, unrooted cuttings, rooted cuttings, or established pot plants. *Amoena* has large, broad and pointed leaves, deep green with cream-white bands and blotches, and is most widely used. *Bausei* has a large pointed leaf, yellowish-green with dark green and white spots and a dark green edge. *Hoffmannii*, a comparatively new variety, has pointed leaves. Deep green with leaves and petioles marbled and spotted white. White midrib. *Picta* has light green, oval leaves with ivory-white marbling and blotching. Petioles dotted pale green. *Rudolph Roehrs* (Roehrsi), a variety of *Picta*, has leaves yellow and ivory with white blotches; midrib and borders dark green.

DRACAENA

Dracaena constitutes a large family of attractive house plants. The Hawaiian ti plant is a close relative. *D. indivisa* is propagated from seed. Propagated mostly by rooting tip cuttings, although a few of the lesser-used kinds such as *Massangeana Tricolor, Eugene Andre* and *Fire Brand* are propagated by cutting up old canes that root at each leaf axil. Unrooted canes of these varieties are also available, in addition to rooted plants. Catalogs usually list small cuttings or plants by number of leaves, number of tiers of leaves, or inches of height. Their growing medium should be kept quite wet.

Godseffiana usually has several wiry spreading stems. Thick, leathery leaves grow in pairs or whorls and are liberally spotted yellow or white. *Sanderiana* is a particularly nice plant in small sizes. It grows upright and has long, narrow leaves that are sometimes twisted slightly. Leaf color is deep green with prominent marginal white band. *Warnecki* is a particularly good plant for dark locations. It has large, sword-shaped, leathery leaves. Each leaf has a milky-white streak down the center and another translucent white band on each side, bordered by a narrow, bright green edge.

FICUS (Rubber Plant)

Most attractive as comparatively large specimens. They are propagated by specialists, mostly by the air-layering method, in which a layer of moist peat moss is wrapped around a section of stem from which part of the outer "bark" has been removed. Roots result in several weeks and the stem is then cut just below the roots to produce a "tip cutting." Ficus is occasionally propagated by tip cuttings, but this method is much more expensive. Small plants are available as "air layers" or "mossed rooted cuttings," and most catalogs specify number of leaves per plant. *Elastica* is the original and very durable rubber plant. It grows into a 100-ft.-high tree in its native Malaya or India. Its close relatives supply the world with natural rubber. *Elastica* has deep, glossy leaves with a rosy sheath enclosing newly formed leaves. There are several newer and superior varieties of *Elastica*. One is *Decora,* an *Elastica* seedling with broader heads and heavier leaves. New leaves are borne in red sheaths. This is by far the most popular variety in use today. *Doescheri* is a variegated variety of *Elastica* that originated in New Orleans. Leaves are variegated with gray, creamy yellow, or white. *Pandurata* is sometimes known as the "fiddle-leaf plant" because of its fiddle-shaped leaf. Leaves are quilted and wavy with attractive yellow-green veins. Grows more upright than the *Elastica* family.

Do not allow any of the ficus to become dry, or the plants will drop a number of their lower leaves.

MARANTA

Maranta and its close relatives, the calatheas, are an attractive group of small, low-growing, decorative foliage plants. Their one drawback is that they

DRACAENA SANDERIANA

NEPHTHYTIS GREEN GOLD

require conditions of quite-high humidity—higher than is found in the average home. They make excellent subjects for glass terrariums or home greenhouses, however. Commercially available as unrooted cuttings, rooted cuttings, or established pot plants. Catalogs usually specify number of leaves per plant. *Kerchoveana* is probably the most common of the marantas—popularly known as the "prayer plant" because its leaves point down toward the ground and fold up at night. Leaves are a pale, grayish-green with prominent chocolate or dark green blotches. *Makoyana*, properly listed under *calathea*, is a bushy plant with beautiful feathery designs on both sides of its oval leaves. Colors are opaque olive-green lines and ovals in a field of pale yellow-green. Leaves are purplish-red beneath.

NEPHTHYTIS

Properly listed as *Syngonium*, nephthytis is a climber in its native habitat. They are attractive plants in small sizes before they begin to creep or climb. Older plants are used on poles. An excellent house plant because it seems capable of withstanding no end of abuse. One of the common troubles in growing nephthytis is that its leaf colors don't develop properly. This is usually due to insufficient light and/or temperature. Nephthytis should be grown in a 75° temperature and comparatively high-light intensities. Propagated commonly by single-node stem cuttings. Commercially available as rooted cuttings (catalogs usually specify number of leaves) or established pot plants. Propagating vines are also available for those growers wishing to root their own cuttings. *Emerald Gem* is the commonly grown, all-green variety, with arrow-shaped leaves. This variety can be grown from seed which is highly perishable, and thus available only at crop-harvest time. *Green Gold* has leaves marked with whitish centers. *Imperial White* is a mutant of *Green Gold* and improves its parent with better coloring and a more compact habit. *Imperial White* is more bushy and doesn't begin to climb as quickly as other varieties.

PALM

One of the more miniature palms represents its large family in the decorative foliage-plant field. *Neantha bella* is a comparatively inexpensive miniature palm tree, very attractive even in small sizes. Usually grown by specialists from seed. Approximately 5 months is required to produce a 2¼-inch pot at 70°. Plants are available as seedlings in sizes measured by number of leaves (usually 2 or 3/5) or transplants that usually have 5 to 10 leaves. Also available as established pot plants.

PEPEROMIA

One of the outstanding exceptions to the "constant-water" rule. One of the main troubles encountered in growing these plants is a root or stem rot that is encouraged by overwatering. Allow soil to become moderately dry before watering. Propagation is by leaf, stem, or tip cuttings. The overwatering problem also extends to the propagating bench. Most specialists propagate peperomia cuttings in sharp sand because of the extra drainage thus afforded. Commercially available as unrooted tip cuttings, usually with 3 to 5 leaves, rooted cuttings, or established pot plants. *Obtusifolia* is the standard all-green kind. *Variegata,* a creamy-white variegated form of *Obtusifolia,* makes a most attractive pot plant even in small sizes. The amount of coloring in variegated peperomias varies considerably. Most specialist producers carry on a constant process of selection to improve their stock. In some cases, these selected plants are marketed under special names. *Emerald Ripple* is a sturdy and very useful little plant from Brazil. Leaves are heart-shaped and attractively rippled. Produces upright-flowering stalks of greenish-white flowers. Available as rooted cuttings or established pot plants.

PHILODENDRON

Undoubtedly our most important tropical decorative plant family. Grow at their best under typical tropical conditions as described earlier. However, most philodendrons are very tolerant of dry air and low-light intensities found in most homes. Most philodendrons are strong climbers in their native habitat, which makes them ideally suited to totem-pole work.

There are over 100 kinds being grown today, and there are many more species, mutants and hybrids that are making their way into the marketplace.

Cordatum is probably the most important single decorative foliage plant in the trade. Estimates run to a hun-

PHILODENDRON PANDURAEFORME

dred million or more grown each year. They are propagated by rooting sections of stem with the roots coming from leaf axils. They are commercially available as propagating vines which are cut up and rooted, started eyes that are calloused cuttings just beginning to root, rooted cuttings with 2-4 or 3-5 leaves each, or as established pot plants—sometimes with 2 or 3 plants in a pot. *Cordatum* is sold to retail customers in all sizes, from the familiar "rooted cuttings in a plastic pot" in dime stores to mature specimens on large totem poles, or in hanging baskets.

Hastatum is one of the many large-leaved, climbing species. Leaves are arrow-shaped. Propagation is by tip cuttings, rooting of stem sections, or by cutting up stems that throw aerial roots. Commercially, they are available most commonly as 3 and 4-inch pot plants, but also as rooted and unrooted cuttings. Very salable in smaller sizes.

Propagated and available same as *hastatum, panduraeforme* has large, fiddle-shaped leaves. A good climber and a very durable house plant. Propagated and available same as *hastatum, pertusum* is probably the most widely

Philodendron cordatum stock plants in Florida. This is by far the most popular foliage plant.

sold of the large-leaved philodendrons. It is a fast climber for totem-pole work. Its first leaves are almost solid, but as the plant develops, "character leaves" with typical indentations begin to develop. *Monstera deliciosa* is a *pertusum* plant that has grown to maturity with deeply cut leaves. *Selloum* is one of the best arborescent or "tree-like" philodendrons, which means it is not a climber. These nonclimbing types make large plants, suitable only for large, roomy locations. Leaves are deeply lobed and cut. *Selloum* likes higher light intensities and slightly cooler temperatures than most other philodendrons.

Some of the new hybrids that have already proven they are excellent house plants are *Emerald Queen, Red Emerald* and *Florida. Emerald Queen* is a bright green with arrow-shaped leaves. *Red Emerald* is similar in shape and growth, but has darker green leaves with red stems and petioles. *Florida* has anchor-shaped leaves with red petioles.

Red Princess is a new patented hybrid that is outstanding as a keeper in the home. It has heart-shaped, undulating leaves of medium size with red stems and petioles.

All of the varieties listed above with the exception of *pertusum* and *selloum* can be used in dish gardens and small planters, if grown from single-eye cuttings. The cane of an overgrown plant can be cut up: Use about 2 inches of cane with a leaf attached, and plunge in peat with 70° temperature. In 10 to 12 weeks, one has a compact rooted cutting that makes an excellent small pot or dish-garden plant.

POTHOS aureus

Sometimes listed as *Scindapsus aureus*. A very satisfactory and easily grown climber. Similar in general habit and growing to philodendron *cordatum,* but somewhat coarser in form. Sometimes, northern growers have trouble establishing rooted cuttings received from Florida during the winter. Maintaining high humidity and watering with warm water will help. During the first week or two, rooted cuttings should be watered sparingly until new roots are established. Cold drafts during these first few days should be avoided. Sold extensively, both as small potted plants and in more mature forms on totem poles. A "giant-leaf" offering of *pothos* means that the plant has been held until the leaves are large—6 to 8 inches—as compared to the normal 2 or 3 inches. In its native habitat in the Solomon Islands, *pothos* leaves are 2 feet or more wide. Commercially available as propagating vines for growers who root their own cuttings. Vines should be cut up into "eye" sections and rooted. Be careful to keep the leaf axil or leaf stem of each eye above the soil or sand level. Also available as rooted cuttings, unrooted cuttings, or established pot plants. Started eyes are calloused cuttings that have just started to root; they are a particularly good buy for large growers. *Wilcoxi* or *Golden* have leaves marked with yellow blotches or streaks. *Marble Queen, Orange Queen* and *Silver Marble* are marked with white instead of yellow. Specialists are constantly selecting their stock for better colored markings and some improved strains are marketed under special names.

SANSEVIERIA

One of our most common and durable house plants. Will stand almost no end of abuse EXCEPT (1) overwatering, or (2) sudden chilling. Should be grown a bit on the dry side, and this is particularly true under home conditions. There are a dozen or more attractive species and varieties. The most common fall into three main headings. *Zeylonica* is the one with light green to grayish-white cross-bands on its leaves. Normally propagated by root (rhizome) divisions or by cutting leaves into 2 or 3-inch sections and rooting them as cuttings. *Laurentii* has yellow bands across its leaves. In order to maintain its yellow markings, *Laurentii* must be propagated by root (rhizome) divisions. Leaf cuttings as outlined for *Zeylonica* will revert back to the green-and-white *Zeylonica* coloring. Both this and *Zeylonica* are commercially available in grades expressed by the length of leaves. The normal range is from 4 to 6 inches to 18 to 24 inches. These are bare-root plants. These grades are available in plants having 2 leaves, 2 to 4 leaves, or 3 to 5 leaves. Also available as established pot plants. Miniature plants are very small and suitable for small dish-garden planting. *Hahni,* the third type, is a comparatively small plant, growing only in a rosette form with no long, sword-like leaves such as has *Zeylonica* or *Laurentii. Hahni* is a sport of *Laurentii* and has light green cross bands on its leaves. *Silver Hahni,* a sport of *Hahni,* has leaves almost entirely pale, silvery-green. *Golden Hahni,* another sport of *Hahni,* has broad cream-to-golden-yellow bands across its leaves. The *Hahni* types are commercially available as bare-root plants listed as small, medium, or large, and also as established pot plants.

SCHEFFLERA actinophylla

Attractive, fast-growing plant, and salable in either small or large sizes. Large, compound leaves with 6 to 9 leaflets. Usually propagated from seed. Available either as seedlings, transplants, or established pot plants.

FREESIA

ANNUAL *(F. hybrida)* *3,000 seeds per oz. Germinates in 25 days at 65°*

The majority of freesias in this country are propagated from corms which are planted in flats, benches or pots from late August to late November. Fifty degrees is the optimum growing temperature. Tip burn will result if plants are allowed to dry out.

Improved seed strains have made it possible for the grower to sow directly outdoors in beds in the spring, moving them inside in the fall, and to flower a crop the same winter. Thus, greenhouse space is tied up for a comparatively short period of time. Rub the seeds between the hands to remove the outer coat, then soak seeds for 24 hours before sowing. Germination should be done in a 65° temperature and will require about 3 weeks. If seeds are sown in the spring, the flats of untransplanted seedlings may be plunged outdoors during the summer in peat moss in a frame and kept in good growth with sufficient moisture and liquid fertilizer as required. In early September, water should be withheld and the flats put in a dry place until the tops die down. After a few weeks rest, remove the small bulbs from the soil and repot in pans or space 3 x 3 inches in flats of fresh soil. Given usual care, they will bloom in January or February. The *Super Giant* strain, used most commonly for this purpose, is now facing competition from a new improved strain called *Super Emerald,* which has larger flowers in a wider range of bright colors.

FUCHSIA

ANNUAL *(F. hybrida)* *70,000 seeds per oz. Germinates in 4-6 wks. at 65-75°*

Occasionally grown from seed. Fuchsias are largely propagated from tip cuttings.

These cool-temperature plants enjoy a rather light soil with some organic material. The trailing varieties are fittingly used in hanging baskets or porch boxes; and the more upright growers are used for pot plants and bedding, but where summers are hot, they must have considerable protection from the sun. This gives them special value with us for boxes and baskets that are usually in at least partial shade. For strong 3 to 4-inch plants in spring, propagate from cuttings early in January and for larger specimens, the preceding September. In some areas of the country, there is considerable demand for 6-inch pots for Mother's Day. Three 2¼-inch plants are placed in a 6-inch pot around the first of February. Grown at 55° and given a last pinch around mid-March, fine-flowering specimens will be ready for sale by Mother's Day. To develop bushy plants with compact growth, pinching is necessary. The more popular varieties include *Bagdad, Black Prince, Lord Byron, Mrs. Marshall, Hollydale* and *Pride of Orion.* Varieties especially suited for hanging baskets include *Curtain Call, Dark Eyes, Swingtime* and *Southgate.* In a climate such as is enjoyed in California, they grow into fine, large specimens in the open and sometimes withstand some frost.

GAILLARDIA

PERENNIAL *(G. grandiflorum) 9,500 seeds per oz. Germinates in 20 days at 70-75°*

There is an annual form of gaillardia, but the perennial is very much the better for cutting, and when well-grown, is profitable for this purpose. They need plenty of water, and will suffer if they have to endure much hot, dry weather. Under our conditions, they rarely last more than 2 seasons, so must be treated as a biennial. By sowing seed early in February, strong plants can be planted out after hard frosts are over. Such a planting should flower some late in summer and be in heavy the following season. Plant in well-enriched, deep soil and space at least 12 inches in the row.

Of the available varieties or strains, the *Monarch Strain* is largely called for and grown. However, it is really a large-flowered mixture of red and yellow in varying proportions. Other varieties and strains in different colors can be obtained, but the *Monarch* strain is most popular.

GERANIUM (Pelargonium hortorum)

CUTTING-PROPAGATED GERANIUMS

Popular for many years and still becoming more popular, the geranium is the sixth most important flower crop in the United States today. In many

TOREADOR
An Iowa State introduction.

areas, it is the No. 1 pot plant. Current economic trends indicate that the demand for geraniums is still on the increase. One of the chief reasons for its great popularity is its ability to grow and flower under adverse and varying conditions of temperature, soil, light and moisture. It is very versatile in its usage and adapts itself well to the average homeowner's idea of what a plant should do; namely, flower all summer long without much care or bother.

Over the years, specialist producers and experimental workers have awakened a new interest and future for geraniums. They have discovered that geraniums respond beautifully to proper growing conditions. Briefly, these conditions consist of a well-drained soil combined with plenty of water, 60 to 65° temperatures, and a steady program of feeding. By proper spacing, timing, and pinching, the geranium can be developed into a beautiful, well-branched plant in a minimum of time.

For many years, growers rooted geraniums in late fall and early winter, and after potting them up, would place them in a cold house (45-50°) where they were kept dry till spring when they were forced and finished. This was done mainly to provide sufficient cuttings to meet their needs. Today, however, these methods are rapidly changing, and the method used by an ever-increasing number of growers evolves around the idea of producing a plant in as short a time as possible. The factors involved in this rapid-production method include cultured cuttings, soil, temperature, timing, water and feed, and varieties. These factors will be considered further on in this writing.

There are many growers today who still find it profitable to propagate their own cuttings from stock plants produced by them. Each grower must determine for himself whether the stock plants and cutting production fit into his overall program. Stock plants can be selected from a grower's regular crop, or cultured-indexed cuttings, purchased from a specialist propagator, can be used to produce stock plants. Culture-indexed cuttings are disease free, but are not immune to disease and must be handled with care to prevent infection. Regular spray programs and strict sanitation should be used.

Producing cuttings from stock plants begins with the rigid selection of plants during the spring as the plants come into flower. Plants should be selected for uniformity, earliness and free-flowering ability, trueness to varietal characteristics, and absolute freedom from all diseases. Stock plants should be selected BEFORE any plants are sold. Plants should be planted in June, 10 or 12 inches apart, on raised beds in the greenhouse. A suitable soil should consist of about 1 part in 4 of peat moss. If the maximum number of high-quality cuttings is to be had, high levels of nitrogen, potash and phosphorus should be maintained. Feeding can be done every 2 weeks in the winter and once a week during the summer, using a 20-20-20, or 25-0-25 soluble fertilizer at the rate of 2½ to 3 pounds per 100 gallons of water. A minimum night temperature of 65° appears to be most desirable.

Stock plants should be kept well watered. A moist soil helps to produce a vigorous growth for maximum cutting production. Cuttings can be taken from September on. After each crop of cuttings, remove all dead or broken leaves and flower buds to keep foliage diseases in check. Spraying stock plants regularly with Benlate, Termil and Exotherm is a good disease-prevention program. Stock plants can be kept over for as long as 2 years. However, many growers discard their plants after the last batch of cuttings is taken. Terminal or tip cuttings 2½ to 4 inches long are best. Leaf-bud cuttings require a month longer to produce flowering plants. The less trimming of leaves from cuttings, the better. At least 3 full and perfect leaves should remain on each cutting when it goes into the sand. Cuttings can be cut or broken from the stock plant, either at nodes or between nodes, since there is no appreciable difference in rooting either type.

The typical good rooting medium for geraniums is coarse sand or a peat-perlite mixture that provides ample drainage. Media should be sterilized between batches of cuttings to prevent the spread of disease organisms. Cuttings should be spaced approximately 2 by 4 inches in the propagating bed. Geranium-propagating benches should be run on the dry side, but kept turgid for the first week or 10 days, until cuttings have developed a callus; thereafter, more moisture will encourage rooting. A media temperature of 75° is about optimum—never allow temperature to go above 80°.

While cuttings will root without the use of a hormone, in some cases, it will hasten the rooting. A fungicide such as Benlate can be used in combination with the rooting hormone. Bottom heat will speed up the rooting. Use mist to maintain turgidity, but do not overmist.

When utilizing cultured plants for stock, it is possible to increase yield 100% over uncultured stock. Many programs are possible, depending upon space and time available. Stock can be planted anytime from June on. Stock planted in the summer should yield 30-50 finished plants per stock plant the following spring, if the first few flushed are potted for additional stock. Stock planted late December-January should yield 2-6 finished plants for spring sales. To obtain these yields, bottom heat, mist, direct sticking, and minimum night temperature of 65° must be adhered to. CO_2 will enhance growth only when all other factors are at optimum levels.

The single-stem tree-type stock-plant production prescribed by Dr. Marlin Rogers (University of Missouri) is one method of production which will supply a grower with a greater number of cuttings at one time. Some growers have used this method very successfully. Cuttings or plants are either benched directly, or planted to a container. The plant is staked and tied as the terminal growing tip grows up. This terminal tip should be pinched only once, about a month before cuttings are wanted. As the lower lateral branches grow out, they should be pinched, leaving 2 or 3 basal leaves. Additional shoots will develop from these pinches. When propagation begins, the terminal cuttings are removed and the remainder of the plant is cut up into single-eye stem cuttings. By using this method, the maximum number of cuttings are produced. If the cropping is performed by the middle of February, the stem cuttings will produce quality 4-inch pots for Memorial Day sales. However, rapid production methods must be used.

Some growers avoid the propagating bench and the labor connected with it by placing unrooted or calloused cuttings directly into pots. Some place cuttings in a 2¼-inch Jiffy-Pot for rooting, and then shift into a 4 or 5-inch flowering-size pot. Others place cuttings directly into flowering-sized pots. This method has two advantages and one disadvantage: It avoids the expense of putting cuttings into a propagating bench and then potting them; it also results in faster growth because the plants grow continually without the inevitable checking of growth that comes from the root disturbance of moving plants. The disadvantage lies in the fact that the cuttings take up more greenhouse space during their earlier stages—particularly if cuttings are put right into flowering-sized pots. If this method is used, the potting-soil mixture should be very light and well drained. A mixture of ⅓ each soil, peat and sand is ideal.

The rapid-production method of growing 4-inch geraniums which is being employed by many growers today necessitates a change in cultural methods which were used by growers for many years. To obtain rapid growth, the soil must provide good drainage, aeration, and good moisture and nutrient retention. Some growers are using a mixture consisting of equal parts of loam, peat and perlite. Others use 2 parts soil, 1 part peat, and 1 part sand. Regardless of the combination of ingredients used, it must afford the conditions mentioned above. The pH should be between 6.0 and 7.0. Geraniums must have a constant supply of moisture. Keeping the plants on the dry side reduces growth and delays flowering. Water should be kept off the foliage.

A relatively new program being followed is to buy cultured cuttings from the geranium specialist in early April (after Easter) and potting directly in 4-inch pots spaced 4 per square foot. Cultural practices that must be used are minimum 65° night temperature, constant feeding at 200 ppm N and K, a light, well-drained medium (1 part peat, 1 part perlite, 1 part soil), and never allow plants to dry out. These plants are ready for sales from May 15 with an early Easter. A late-Easter planting will yield plants for Memorial Day sales.

A 60° night temperature should be used with a sunny-day temperature of 65-70°. With this temperature range, it is imperative that maximum light reaches the plants. A light shading applied only after the buds are well above the foliage will prevent sunburn on the flowers.

With the use of a lighter soil, higher temperatures and increased watering, adequate fertilization is a must. A liquid feeding every 2 weeks of 20-20-20 or 25-10-10, used at the rate of an ounce to 2 gallons of water, will keep the plants in good growing condition. Some growers add an organic-base dry fertilizer to the soil mix before potting for insurance. Adequate ventilation must be used to avoid disease troubles and soft growth. Plants must also be lifted regularly if grown on soil to prevent rooting through.

Spacing must be regulated in part by the type of plant required by a particular grower's market. Crowding produces leggy plants and invites disease problems. For the production of a quality plant, a spacing of 6 by 8 inches should be sufficient.

There are growers today who feel that in order to produce a well-branched plant, pinching must be practiced. However, it seems to be generally believed that a heavy, well-branched plant can be produced without a pinch when properly grown and spaced. If pinching, the last hard pinch should be made around February 15, and the last soft pinch in late March for Memorial Day flowering.

The time required to produce a 4-inch pot will generally vary according to the type of cutting used and the available sunlight. Many pot-plant growers today take a 2¼-inch pot, and shift to a 4-inch pot after Easter. If Easter is early, some plants will flower for Mother's Day, and all of them should make Memorial Day. If Easter is late, some of the plants will flower for Memorial Day, and the remainder will hit early June. Still other growers pot a calloused cutting to a 2¼-inch Jiffy-Pot, and when it roots through the pot, shift to the 4-inch pot. Potting a calloused cutting direct to a 4-inch pot is also practiced. Overall flowering time thus will be about 10 to 12 weeks when starting with a calloused cutting. Thus, by potting a calloused cutting around March 1, some of the plants will be in bloom for Mother's Day and all would be in flower by Memorial Day. Pinching would not be practiced in any of the above methods.

VARIETIES

The matter of varieties varies considerably between growers, markets, and parts of the country. Generally, a crop consisting of 60-70% red, 20% pink, and the balance in white and other assorted colors will satisfy most market demands. Following is a representative list of the most important varieties as measured by sales. There are, of course, many other excellent varieties.

RED: *Red Perfection.* Dark red. Olympic seedling.
    Imp. Ricard. A dependable, large-flowered brick red.
    Irene. An excellent, bright scarlet red.
    Sincerity. Dark orange red.
    Cardinal. Robust dark red.

PINK: *Skylark.* Large medium pink.
    Genie. A free-flowering rose pink.
    Penny. A semidouble neon pink.
    Didden's Imp. Picardy. Good salmon pink.
    Salmon Irene. A medium salmon; excellent.
    Enchantress Fiat. An excellent light salmon pink.

WHITE: *Snowmass.* One of the better whites.
    Summer Cloud. A white Irene.

Dr. Griffith J. Buck, Iowa State University, Ames, Iowa, has a continual breeding and development program for better geraniums. Several of his more popular introductions are *Toreador,* deep red, and *Skylark,* medium pink.

INSECTS & DISEASES

The disease that tops any geranium grower's list is commonly called stem rot or blackleg. It manifests itself by blackened, rotted areas of the stem.

Blackleg usually starts at or near the soil line, but it can also start in the upper stem and leaf tissue or in the roots. It is caused by a complex of one or more fungus organisms—usually one or more of the pythiums or fusariums are the principal offenders. There is also a bacterial blight that results in much the same symptoms. One or more of these organisms may be in the plant tissue awaiting favorable conditions to develop, or they may enter from infected soils. There are two general procedures that, if used together, will keep these diseases from causing trouble:

1. Using disease-free stock to begin with. There are today quite a few specialists from whom cultured or index-cultured cuttings are available. These cuttings are pathogen free. The grower who grows his own stock plants should exercise extreme care in selecting only his cleanest plants. Any diseased plants that appear should be immediately destroyed.

2. A strict sanitation program will keep infections from developing and spreading. Using a fungicide, such as Benlate, on cuttings, and sterilization of propagating material, are musts. Be sure to use a well-drained potting-soil mixture; a soggy soil encourages development of these organisms. Sterilizing potting soil and pots insures disease-free soil to start with. Generally, healthy and rapid growth seems to keep plants from developing symptoms. Underfeeding, overfeeding, or using an unbalanced fertilizer (particularly excesses of nitrogen) seems to bring on symptoms of blackleg. If cuttings are taken with a knife, spread of disease organisms from one cutting to another from the knife blade is often a common source of infection.

Several viruses infect geraniums. They evidence themselves with such symptoms as crinkled leaves with translucent spots, yellow spots on leaves, or mottled leaves. There is no known cure for any of these virus infections. Growers should destroy carefully any plants showing these symptoms. Generally, keeping plants in a healthy, rapid-growing condition tends to enable the plants to "out-run" the virus infection so that a plant matures before symptoms become objectionable. Botrytis is seemingly becoming a greater problem. It causes blossoms to fade prematurely and dry. Also, it affects leaves, producing brown, water-soaked areas. It is best prevented by keeping humidity down, practicing strict sanitation, keeping water off the foliage, and spraying regularly with Captan, Benlate or Daconil. The same holds true for preventing rust, except that Maneb and Zincb be used to help prevent spread.

The common insect enemies of geraniums are mealybugs, whitefly, leaf roller, and red spider. Sevin, Morestan and/or Malathion are effective controlling insecticides.

The needs of the geranium industry today are far ahead of breeding. However, breeding has made rapid progress in the last few years, and it is an established fact that uniform, high-quality plants in several colors can be produced from seed. Disease resistance is still of the utmost importance and requires more time to develop than other characteristics. Nevertheless, breeders feel that it will not be too far off when disease-resistant varieties will be available.

Seed Geraniums adapt well to the bedding trade—and perform extra well outdoors. Here's Sooner Red—in Cell Paks.

GERANIUMS FROM SEED

With the introduction of Sprinter Scarlet in 1974, pack and pot production of hybrid seed geraniums became an economic reality. To be sure, Nittany Lion and the Carefree series were being used successfully in many areas but they were late to bloom and often were sold green in packs.

With fuel prices soaring, it's becoming more difficult to carry mother plants for cuttings through the winter. Hybrid seed offers an alternative. They can be scheduled better to meet specific sale dates, and you can have the seed on hand when you want it. Being seed propagated, hybrids do avoid the problem of disease in propagating stock. Especially in the South, outdoor performance of seed varieties is generally well ahead of cutting types. They do present a problem at times due to petal shatter, especially if plants are dry — or stored overnight in boxes on delivery trucks with closed doors.

Sprinter shaved 3-4 weeks off the crop time of its predecessors, and is now as much as 2 weeks later than some of the more recently developed hybrids. In recent Michigan State University pack trials, Allan Armitage and Dr. Will Carlson reported that Smash Hit was the earliest to flower of 36 cultivars (100 days from sowing) with Sooner Red close behind (101 days).

TWO PRINCIPLE USES OF SEED GERANIUMS:

A. Sold as 2¼ inch, or in packs, as a bedding plant. Lower cost makes them a contender for mass plantings along with Petunias, Marigolds, Impatiens, etc. Newer varieties will flower in such uses.

B. Hybrids, sown around January 15th, will produce saleable 4-inch geraniums in flower for the mid-May trade in the North (late April in the South).

GERMINATION

1. Use loose, sterile medium: Such as Jiffy-Mix.
2. Seed spacing: ¼ inch apart in row, 1½-2 inches between rows. Cover seed with ⅛ inch loose, sterile sowing medium.
3. Soil Temperature Critical: Maintain 72° soil temperature. Use propagating mat and soil thermometer at seed level in sowing flat (5-8° difference in temperature between bottom and top of germination flat).
4. Maintain Moisture — Critical: Best germination occurs under mist system. Otherwise, water flat with fine spray, then cover with glass or plastic. Remove cover immediately upon seed emergence.
5. Germination will be complete in 2 weeks. Wide temperature changes will delay germination. Under proper conditions most of the seed should germinate within a week and show true leaves within two weeks.
6. We do not recommend sowing directly into Jiffy-7s or any 2¼-inch container, as poor germination may result: due to difficulties in maintaining uniform soil temperatures and proper moisture levels.

TRANSPLANTING FOR PACK SALES—2¼ INCH

1. As soon as they can be handled (about 2 weeks after sowing), put plant in well drained soil mix. Plant them to base of seed leaves — they won't flop over.
2. Drench with Dexon and Terraclor immediately. Follow label instructions carefully. Use only one application of Terraclor. Damp-off can also be controlled by application of Truban and Benlate.
3. Grow on at 62° night temperature.

GROWTH RETARDANT TREATMENT — 18 DAYS TO 3 WEEKS AFTER TRANSPLANTING

1. Why? Improves basal branching habit, produces shorter plants, flowers 3-7 days earlier, depending upon variety.
2. Water several hours before and allow leaves to dry before spraying.
3. A-Rest Concentration Rate: Use a 200 ppm solution. Mix 24 fluid ounces of A-Rest with 8 ounces of water to make a quart. Use fine spray setting on sprayer. 1 quart solution will cover between 30 to 40 Handi-Flats.
4. Cycocel Concentration Rate: Use a 1500 ppm solution. Mix 1¾ ounces of Cycocel with one gallon of water. Spray evenly over plants. 1 gallon solution will cover between 120 and 160 flats. A second application could be sprayed on one week later for more effective height control and early flowering. Check varietal recommendation. We recommend Cycocel over A-Rest. It's less expensive to use.
5. Apply as spray, evenly covering leaves with spray until leaves are wet.
6. B-Nine is not effective as a growth retardant on geraniums.
7. Do not water plants for 24 hours after treatment. Overwatering after applying a growth retardant can lead to rot problems. They can be kept slightly drier than normal.

POT UP IN 4″ CONTAINERS

1. 4 to 6 weeks after growth retardant spray, pot in 4-inch container.
2. The plants should be rosetted and dark green.
3. Put plant flush with soil line in pot. Avoid deep potting.

FERTILIZING PROGRAM

1. After established in 4-inch pots, begin regular fertilizer program. Plants can be fed with each watering — 200 ppm of nitrogen and potassium plus additional amounts of minor elements.
2. Plants can be fed by using 14-14-14 Osmocote or MagAmp. Mix 10 to 12 pounds per square yard or roughly ½ pound per bushel with soil before potting. With Osmocote, do not mix and store — use immediately.
3. Water plants thoroughly so that some leaching occurs at each irrigation. Otherwise a soluble salts problem could develop. This fertilizer/soil mixture will provide fertilizer for up to 6 months.

GROWING ON TO FLOWER

1. Maintain 62° temperature until last 4 weeks of production when temperatures can be dropped to 50° to produce larger flowers and stockier plants. The lower temperature may cause later flowering however.
2. Apply Dexon drench every three weeks at the one-pound-per-100-gallon rate.
3. Provide enough space for growing plants. Plants grown pot to pot will bloom unevenly. Space as necessary while growing. Crowding will delay flowering of those plants in the middle receiving less light and restricted air movement.

WHAT VARIETIES TO GROW?

There are dozens of hybrid geraniums to choose from and more being added to the list each year. Here is the Ball Seed Company's list of recommendations for 1981. (See page 340).

FLOWERING SCHEDULE

Here's a partial list of the number of weeks required to produce saleable 4-inch pots in flower.

North:

14 weeks	15 weeks	16 weeks	17 weeks
Dynamite	Encounter Red	Cherry Glow	Capri Brick Red
	Fire Flash	Jackpot	Playboy Cherry
	Knockout	Mustang	Red
	Orbit Red	Picasso	Playboy Scarlet
	Red Express	Scarlet Flash	Sprinter Deep
	Ringo Scarlet	Sprinter Scarlet	Red
	Smash Hit		Capri Deep Red
	Sooner Red		

18 weeks
Carefree Crimson

South: Reduce crop time above by 1-2 weeks.

To help avoid shattering of the petals during shipping, some growers have found a partial solution by reducing air temperatures to 40° about 24 hours before loading and watering in well. Good air circulation in transit also helps.

For more information on hybrid geraniums, see Grower Talk issues dated February, 1980, and August, 1979.

BALL'S 1981 HYBRID GERANIUM RECOMMENDATIONS

FOR THESE
CONTAINERS: BALL RECOMMENDS:

	RED	SALMON	PINK	WHITE	BICOLOR
PACKS 32, 36, or 48 Per Flat	Smash Hit Ringo Scarlet	Sooner Deep Salmon Ringo Salmon	Ringo Rose	Snowdon	Razzmatazz Heidi
PACKS 18 or 24 Per Flat	Smash Hit Ringo Scarlet Sooner Red	Cameo Encounter Salmon	Ringo Rose Rosita	Snowdon Ice Queen	Razzmatazz Heidi
4½ inch pots for a strong, full plant and good heads	Sooner Red Fire Flash Mustang Sprinter Scarlet Smash Hit	Cameo	Rosita	Ice Queen	Razzmatazz Heidi
4 inch pots grown tight	Smash Hit Ringo Scarlet Sooner Red	Cameo	Ringo Rose Rosita	Ice Queen	Razzmatazz Heidi
Great Outdoor Performers	Smash Hit Fire Flash Sprinter Scarlet Red Express	Cameo Encounter Salmon	Deep Rose Flash	Ice Queen	Razzmatazz Heidi

GERBERA (Transvaal Daisy)

ANNUAL *(G. Jamesoni) 6,000-7,000 seeds per oz. Germinates in 10 days at 70-75°*

Gerberas, or "Transvaal daisies," as they are sometimes known, make an excellent cut-flower crop. While the bulk of the crop today is produced outdoors in California and Florida, some growers are able to produce a crop of superior quality under glass and thus find them a profitable item.

Gerberas are a deep, strong-rooting crop and should be planted to a ground bed with at least 6 inches of loose, well-drained soil with plenty of organic matter. The usual plant spacing is 12x12 inches.

Propagation of gerberas is usually from seed or divisions, which should be made during June. If seedlings are used, and most of them will give very good results, sowing should be done in January so that seedlings will be in 3's or 4's by June, sown in a warm house with complete germination expected in 10-12 days. Not the best, but very good results are had by growing young stock in the open field and planting indoors in the fall. When planted in June, they, of course, have an established start as the shorter days set in; and this means longer stems. For best results, plant indoors in June. When planting to the bench, care should be taken to see that they are planted shallow with the crown of the plant above the soil level. Partial covering of the crown will result in rot. To help avoid crown-rot problems, it may be advisable to grow the plants in ridges across the bench so that watering is done between the rows, allowing the crowns of the plants to remain above the general soil level. Dexon is very helpful in controlling crown and root rots.

Gerberas should start out in fairly well-enriched soil, perhaps a little stronger than you would make it for other crops. They enjoy a slightly acid soil (pH 6 to 6.5); but will tolerate a pH of 7. When in full growth late in winter and spring, they will stand liberal feeding. They are subject to some rotting, so the best growers will lose a few indoors. Keeping decayed foliage picked out and surface soil clean will help prevent its spread. Mildew must be anticipated, for gerberas are very susceptible. We can suggest nothing better than keeping them covered with sulfur. Mildex spray is also effective. 45-50° nights will produce but few winter flowers. They seem to rest partially in that temperature. Sixty degrees will keep them in active growth, and with it must go more ventilation than is necessary for most crops, for that temperature will soften them unless toned up with fresh air. This is especially true during dark weather when the stems will soften and bend over. If dark weather is prolonged, gradually drop the temperature some to offset its weakening effect. The cut flowers ship well and are long-lasting, but must be cut at the proper time, which is when the first outer row of a staminate flower bears pollen. If cut before this time, they will wilt. They should not be placed in cold storage.

We have tried a number of strains, and in our opinion, the *California Duplex Hybrids* with their double rows of petals rate tops in quality and attractiveness. Growing 2-2½ feet tall, they produce large, 5-inch flowers with many more petals than the ordinary strain.

There are also available 2 more refined strains of the California type. One of these is the *Crested Mixture,* which includes double, semidouble and crested flowers with a small percentage of duplex types. The other is a hand-pollinated strain of the most brilliant selected colors known as *Florist Mixture.*

The European strains have stiffer stems and flowers. Petals are under and shorter. Flowers have large centers. Most popular is the *Jungenelen* strain.

GEUM

PERENNIAL *(G. varieties) 7,000 seeds per oz. Germinates in 3 wks. at alt. 70-85°*

Species and varieties of geum are quite widely used for decorative garden work in borders, beds and in the rock garden. They are of comparatively easy culture and most varieties flower from early May or June throughout the season. Their clear scarlet, orange and yellow shades are hard to beat in our common selection of summer-flowering decorative plants. The double varieties, like *Mrs. Bradshaw,* are suitable as cut-flower subjects.

For garden decorative work, geum should be spaced 6 to 8 inches apart and established in a fairly loose, well-drained location, although ample moisture is desirable during the summer-growing months. Partial shade is desirable for most varieties. Geum are perfectly winter-hardy if some protection is provided. Propagation can be effected by root division and several varieties, as noted, reproduce quite readily and with fair certainty from seed in a soil temperature of 70° to 85°.

There are over 50 species of geum described; most are native to our temperature and northern climates. Only a very few, however, are in common use. Most of the common taller garden varieties are, botanically speaking, varieties of *G. chiloense (G. atrosanguineum)*. These varieties grow to about 2 feet tall. *Mrs. Bradshaw Imp.*, double fiery scarlet, is perhaps the most popular.

GLOXINIA

ANNUAL *(Sinningia speciosa) 800,000 seeds per oz. Germinates in 2-3 wks. at 65-75°*

While gloxinias are grown more quickly and easily from tubers, and should be when small quantities are wanted, they are more economically produced from seed; and when grown in quantity, that might be a consideration. Also, if a leaf with stem is inserted in sand, the base of the leaf will root and form tubers. But this method of propagating is slow and not used much. When grown from seed, gloxinias can be made available for almost any season of the year. While formerly thought of as spring and summer pot plants, their usage at various other times is becoming more prominent. There are quite a few specialist growers today who have seedlings or small potted plants available for shipping at most times of the year. Close care is necessary to germinate such fine seed as gloxinia. In a warm, moist house, 65-70° nights, 4-6-inch flowering plants are produced in 6 to 7 months from sowing, and they are largely grown this way abroad, especially for the following season's tubers. A December or early-January sowing is nicely flowered in June. A June 1 sowing will make Christmas, while for Valentine's Day, seed should be sown in late July. When seedlings are large enough to handle, they can be either transplanted to another flat, spaced about 1½ inches each way, or potted direct to a 2¼-inch Jiffy-Pot. From the 2¼-inch pot, they can go directly to a 5 or 6-inch pot for finishing. If seedlings are transplanted to another flat from the seed flat, usual procedure is to transplant them directly from the growing-on flat to a 4-inch pot in which they are finished.

The same soil used for tuberous begonias will suit gloxinias. When shifting or potting, it is important to remember that gloxinias like a loose, open soil mix and therefore, the soil should not be packed around the plant. Quite often, the seedlings have a tendency to stretch up before shifting to the finishing pot. Generally, we find that these can be set down deeper in the pot and thus will produce a shorter, more compact finished plant. It should consist of ⅓ peat moss, ⅓ light organic soil, and ⅓ sand. This same mixture can be used as they are moved along in pots. If light but overall shade is used, we never note any harm from water on the foliage; but if water is hard or full of sediment, better keep it off. However, water should

John Holden G.J.B., Inc., and Lyle Cox, Iowa grower, checking over trials of gloxinias in our West Chicago greenhouses.

not be allowed to remain on the crown of the plant overnight.

In growing gloxinias, any approach to dryness, especially to the point of inviting red spider, is disastrous. Mite can be a serious pest—Rotenone or Malathion sprays or parathion aerosols will give control. Failures are usually traced to lack of attention to these vital points: plenty of heat, moisture, and light shade. In Europe, they are grown to the highest perfection in low, old houses protected with portable shade, carefully applied and removed as conditions demand. Watering is done with a can, and 2 or 3 times daily, the house is wet down, though its need is not nearly so great with us. Gloxinias develop large, coarse leaves which necessitate proper spacing to avoid stretching. Brittleness of these leaves can be reduced by growing at a 70° night temperature and by providing a high relative humidity. It's that careful attention to well-known details that counts with gloxinias, as with other choice stock.

Lighting the plants often results in earlier flowering when grown at 60°; 100-watt bulbs spaced 4 feet apart will do the job when turned on for 4 or 5 hours. This is not due to a photoperiodic effect.

The most popular varieties by far when it comes to seed-grown gloxinias are the reds or scarlets, typified by such hybrid varieties as *Superb, Menning Red, Edelrot,* and *Ultra Scarlet.* The *Ultra* series, available in a whole range of separate colors, seems to be gaining popularity. Generally speaking, the F_1 varieties are more uniform and free-flowering than the inbreds, although considerable quantities of the latter are still grown, often in formula mixes. There also are on the market a few double-flowered varieties that as yet have varying percentages of singles in them.

GOMPHRENA (Globe Amaranth)

ANNUAL *(G. globosa)* *5,500 seeds per oz. Germinates in 2 wks. at 65-70°. Dark.*

Easily grown and quite heat-resistant border annuals, the "everlasting" gomphrena clan is seen quite often, especially in the South and Middle West. Seed is sown in March and the plants transplanted out to the border in late May. A fair check on drought resistance was a spell of 100° weather at our West Chicago trials, and gomphrena continued to look as well as even the vinca after such abuse. The dwarf variety, *Buddy*, a bright reddish-purple, growing to a height of 9 inches, makes a fine, dwarf, uniform plant for bedding.

To aid in germinating the seed, soak in water for 3 or 4 days, and then spread the wet, cottony seed mass over the top of the soil thinly.

The taller forms (18 inches) are not nearly as widely used. They are usually sold as mixtures in shades of purple, white, pink and red, and can be used for cutting and drying.

GRASS (Ornamental)

ANNUAL *(Pennisetum ruppelianum)*
14,000 seeds per oz. Germinates in 3-4 wks. at 70-80°

Pennisetum grass (fountain grass) adapts itself well for group planting, bordering and temporary hedging.

There are dozens of species of grasses cultivated, although the several species of pennisetum account for most cultures of them. Most popular is *P. ruppelianum*, fountain grass. It reaches a height of 3-4 feet, has green foliage with showy, graceful, purplish plumes, which are nice for fresh and dried arrangements.

Propagation of most pennisetum is by seed each year. A sowing made in February and carried along in pots furnishes material to plant out by June. Seed comes through promptly in 70-80° soil.

There are many species of *Eulalia*, perennial grasses, offered in American nursery catalogs. Among them will be found *Zebra Grass (E. Japonica zebrina)*, 6 to 10 feet with broad yellow bands across its leaf; *Japan Rush (E. gracillima univittata)*, 6 feet, bright green with silvery midribs; and *E. japonica variegata*, a very ornamental, variegated leaf type. Then, too, there is pampas grass that produces great clusters of silvery plumes reaching a height of 12 feet. It is also known as "plume grass," and is botanically *Erianthus ravennae*. All these species are propagated by division only. There are other species in this group, such as *Elymus glaucus* (blue lyme grass), that stay below 18 inches.

Most of the common grasses can be dried and used very effectively in winter bouquets; pampas grass is much used for this. For best results, cut as soon as pollen appears and store in a cool, shady, dry place, hung upside down.

GREVILLEA (Australian Silk Oak)

ANNUAL *(G. robusta) 3,000 seeds per oz. Germinates in 3 wks. at 80°. Light.*

Used in some areas as a filler for plant combinations and boxes, its chief commercial value had been in its use as a filler for poinsettia pans. With the development of improved, long-lasting "points," which are able to retain their foliage, this usage has declined. It's primary use now is as a foliage houseplant. Seed should be sown from mid-June to a month later. If they get too tall for the poinsettias, pinch about August 1. Don't figure on their breaking much. A sowing made July 15 will get up around 6 inches in 2½'s and should be about right for smaller poinsettias. In the final panning of poinsettias, plunge empty 2¼-inch pots where the grevilleas are later to be planted; in September or October, remove the empty pots and in the openings, insert the grevilleas. If grevilleas are panned earlier with the poinsettias, they are inclined to grow too fast and overcrowd, causing a loss of poinsettia leaves.

A spring sowing of grevillea should be ready to shift to 3-inch pots by mid-September, where they can remain in a 50° house or cooler. Shift to 4's by early March, and you will have strong plants for larger work. To make 2½-inch stock for midwinter work, sow in August or early September.

GYPSOPHILA (Baby's Breath)

ANNUAL *(G. elegans) 24,000 seeds per oz. Germinates in 10 days at 70-80°*
PERENNIAL *(G. species) 34,000 seeds per oz. Germinates in 10 days at 70-80°*

Both the hardy perennial and the annual forms are of considerable commercial importance. Both classes call for completely drained and not over-enriched soil. The perennial grafted varieties do best in rather gravelly or coarse material. In our fairly heavy soil that is well tilled but rather flat, grafted plants gradually all die out. The dry, calcareous soil of cool Colorado is where it seems to do best, though some eastern nurserymen make out very well with it. Several strains or selections are offered and all seem equally valuable. The grafted varieties seem to dry and are preserved better than seed-grown stock that also can be dried for future use by hanging the bunches up in a cool, dry shed. The perennial *G. paniculata Double Snow Flake* does well in most soils, but with us, it, too, dies out after a few years. However, being grown from seed, it isn't costly to have stock coming on. About 50% of this variety will come double, though they vary some in size. *G. paniculata* is the perennial single. *Repens Rosea* is a very compact grower with light pink flowers that make an excellent ground cover for sunny areas. The indispensable, easily grown annual form is *G. Elegans. Covent Garden Market* is large and partly 6-8 petalled, with petals almost completely filling the space between them. This is the ideal flower the breeder selects in any strain, but it is difficult to get uniformity. In growing the annual form, some effort should be made to control its growth by planting in shallow and not overenriched soil. Flats are used to advantage, as they can be moved about as wanted. A 4-inch-deep flat filled 3 inches will give the roots all the moisture they require. Space the plants 3 to 4 inches. May be sown from December to April, flowering in about 3 months from seeding.

HELICHRYSUM

ANNUAL *(H. bracteatum monstrosum)*
36,000 seeds per oz. Germinates in 7 days at 70°. Light.

Strawflowers are useful to most every florist who does a retail business, and it's not difficult to grow and dry your own. Where summers are long and hot, we can't grow such helichrysum as are grown and shipped from California; but if the seed is sown in well-enriched, deep soil as soon as the ground can be worked, they make a very good showing with occasional watering when the soil is dry. The tall form (2-3 feet) is most commonly used. There is also available a dwarf type (12-14 inches) that can also be used for bedding purposes.

HELIOTROPE

ANNUAL *(Valeriana officinalis)* 50,000 seeds per oz. Germinates in 3 wks. at 70°.

Richly fragrant, the old-fashioned heliotrope is largely used as a bedding plant today in the country. However, it can be grown as a pot plant and would make a good specimen planting.

In Europe it is grown into standards that are richly attractive when in full flower. It is not at all difficult to produce this attractive form of growth; simply run the first or main growth up to any desired height. Before stopping it, rub out all side growths except about the top. Some trimming is necessary as well as tying to a secure stake. They are quickly grown into 4-inch pot plants from seed sown around February 1, or cuttings put into warm sand in March. When planted out in the open, heliotrope is sometimes inclined to make blind growth; allowing the plants to become pot-bound before planting out will help to harden them into flower. Here in the Midwest it performs admirably through the summer. Since most forms have a sort of loose-type growth habit, they should be pruned early in the growing season to produce a tighter, more compact form.

Probably the number one variety is *Marine* (12 inches) which produces extra large, fragrant flowers of a deep violet color.

Note on germination information: "Light" means that best germination is obtained when seeds are exposed to light. "Dark" indicates that seeds germinate better without light. "Alt. 70-85°" indicates that this crop should be grown at an alternating temperature of 70° nights and 85° days.

HOLLYHOCK

ANNUAL *(Althea rosea)* 2,000 seeds per oz. Germinates in 2-3 wks. at 60°
PERENNIAL *(Althea rosea)* 3,000 seeds per oz. Germinates in 2-3 wks. at 60°

This old-fashioned garden favorite has been greatly improved and modernized with double flowers and an array of rich colors. They are usually sown in April, potted as soon as they can be handled, and either planted out or sold as pot plants. They can also be sown out in the open in May and if kept thoroughly cultivated, will grow into strong plants by fall. An early March sowing will usually flower some the following late summer. Hollyhocks are usually rather short-lived perennials, so must occasionally be replanted. This may not be true of old varieties, but we find it so of the finer strains. Under our trying winter conditions—temperature extremes and irregular snowfall—hollyhocks should be given the protection of any rough loose material. If growth is vigorous and free as it will be in deep, well-drained soil, little will be noted of the rust that sometimes overwhelms them. When transplanting, care should be taken to see that the roots go straight down into the soil with the crown about 2 inches below the soil level. This will assist the plant in obtaining good anchorage and prevent wind damage. The double colors or varieties are by far the most popular and their color range is complete.

In addition to the perennial class, annual forms blooming in 5 months from seed are also available. *Silver Puffs,* an All-American winner, grows about 2 ft. tall and produces silvery-pink flowers on bushy plants with many flowering side shoots.

Another AAS winner is *Summer Carnival.* Five to 6 feet tall, it is a dependable producer of large double flowers in a wider color range than available in other strains. *Triumph Supreme* produces extra-large, fully double fringed flowers in unusual delicate shades.

For years the only perennial double Hollyhock available has been Chater's, which is still widely used.

Hollyhock Summer Carnival.

A good example of forcing pot hyacinths and tulips—Burt Beelen, Minneapolis pot plant grower. Burt, who does the job well, says that the main cause of unevenness here is lack of water. He urges several heavy waterings immediately after potting. Then, be sure to keep them well watered in the cold-storage chamber.

HYACINTH FORCING
August De Hertogh
Michigan State University

GENERAL ASPECTS

All hyacinths used for forcing are grown in the Netherlands. The flowering season for hyacinths extends from mid-December to mid-April. To have high-quality plants throughout this season, it is necessary to have a controlled-temperature rooting room. The information provided below is designed for a forcer who has such a facility. Those forcers who continue to use outdoor rooting beds will have to make adjustments based on experience.

To assist the forcer, the flowering season has been divided into six flowering periods (Table 1). These periods are abbreviated "H-1" to "H-6." It should be noted that there is no sharp dividing line between these periods and they may be adjusted according to individual needs and facilities. The season has been divided to take advantage of the fact that the Dutch bulb grower provides two types of hyacinths—prepared bulbs for early forcings and regular bulbs for later forcings. Since the minimum cold requirements for prepared and regular hyacinths are 10 to 13 weeks respectively, the planting date is changed for the various flowering periods to maximize the use of a given cultivar and to provide the highest-quality plants.

Hyacinth bulbs are sold in sizes ranging from 15/16 centimeters in circumference to 19/20. All sizes can be forced. The size to be used will depend upon the market for which the plants are intended, e.g., supermarket or retailer, and the individual characteristics of the cultivar.

In general, there are few problems associated with the forcing of hyacinths. Normally, any insect or disease can be controlled by using commercially available insecticides or fungicides. Spitting or loose-bud has been a problem for some forcers. This disorder can be avoided if the bulbs are never frozen, or if frozen, they are allowed to thaw very slowly and then forced at low temperatures for several days.

FORCING INFORMATION

The forcer's responsibility begins immediately on arrival of the bulbs. As soon as they arrive, the bulbs should be ventilated, inspected and stored at the proper temperature. Prior to planting, prepared bulbs, which are obviously meant for early forcings, should be stored at 48 to 55° F. Regular bulbs should be stored at 60 to 65° F. When storing these bulbs, keep in mind the total number of weeks of cold that they require for the intended flower period. Hyacinths can be planted anywhere from 1 to a pot to 7 or 8 to a pot, depending on the market usage. When planting the bulbs, use a well-drained soil mixture, one similar to that used for potted chrysanthemums or poinsettias. After planting, place them in the rooting room and water thoroughly. Keep the plants moist throughout their time in the rooting room.

The forcing program for hyacinths has been set forth in Table 1. The cultivars and their flowering-period usage are presented in Table 2. Hyacinth bulbs have a distinct advantage in that a forcer need use only one rooting room to produce plants for the entire season. On the other hand, tulip forcers need a minimum of two controlled-temperature chambers. In discussing the programming of tulips, we will be referring to rooting room "A" and rooting room "B." The temperature sequence for rooting room "B" is exactly the same for tulips as for hyacinths. As a result, all references to a rooting room for hyacinths call for the use of rooting room "B."

A good example of potted hyacinths—flowers in the "green-bud" stage of development. Cultivars are: on the left, Delft Blue; on the right, Anna Marie.

The rooting room "B" sequence consists of maintaining a temperature of 48° F until the period of December 1 to 5. The exact date must be determined by the forcer and is dependent on his judgment of the condition of the plants. The roots of the last plantings should be coming out of the bottom of the container. Temperature is then lowered to 41° F and maintained to January 1 to 5. Again, the judgment of the forcer comes into play. Sprouts should be about 2 inches in length. At that time, the temperature should be lowered to 33° to 35° F.

The reason all flowering periods can be incorporated into one rooting-room temperature sequence is due to the fact that prepared hyacinths require less cold than regular hyacinths and will develop more quickly at 48° F than at any other temperature. Note that with the hyacinths, the length of time to force is different for each flowering period.

Hyacinth Flowering Period 1 (H-1): Prepared hyacinths must be used for this period. In addition, a rooting room must be used. To have plants in full flower at Christmas, the bulbs should initially be forced at 73° F for 10 to 14 days. After that time, and for other forcing in this period, a greenhouse temperature of 65° F is satisfactory.

Hyacinth Flowering Period 2 (H-2): When a rooting room is used, some prepared and regular hyacinths are needed for this period. For outdoor root-

Table 1

Programming Guide for Hyacinths

Flowering Period	Type of Bulb	Time of Planting	Rooting Room	Dates into Greenhouse	Approximate Flowering Date	Weeks of Cold
H-1	(PR)	Sept. 17 to 22	B	Dec. 1	Dec. 20	10
				Dec. 8	Dec. 28	11
				Dec. 15	Jan. 3	12
				Dec. 22	Jan. 11	13
H-2	(PR) and (RG)	Sept. 25 to 30	B	Dec. 26	Jan. 14	13
				Jan. 5	Jan. 21	14
				Jan. 11	Jan. 27	15
				Jan. 17	Feb. 3	16
H-3	(RG)	Oct. 24 to 28	B	Jan. 26	Feb. 9	13
				Feb. 2	Feb. 14	14
				Feb. 9	Feb. 21	15
H-4	(RG)	Nov. 10 to 15	B	Feb. 17	Mar. 1	15
				Feb. 24	Mar. 7	16
				Mar. 2	Mar. 13	17
H-5	(RG)	Nov. 10 to 15	B	Mar. 10	Mar. 19	18
				Mar. 16	Mar. 25	19
				Mar. 23	Apr. 1	20
H-6	(RG)	Nov. 10 to 15	B	Mar. 30	Apr. 10	21
				Apr. 6	Apr. 16	22

PR—Prepared Bulbs, RG—Regular Bulbs
Rooting-room temperature sequence "B"—48° F to Dec. 1-5, 41° F to Jan. 1-5, then 32-35° F.

ing beds, prepared hyacinths are preferred. The forcing temperature should be 65° F. If needed, higher temperatures can be used.

Hyacinth Flowering Period 3 (H-3): For this and all succeeding periods, only regular hyacinths should be used. A forcing temperature of 65° F is preferred.

Hyacinth Flowering Period 4 (H-4): For this group, a forcing temperature of 60-62° F is preferred.

Hyacinth Flowering Period 5 (H-5): The forcing temperature should be 60° F.

Hyacinth Flowering Period 6 (H-6): The forcing temperature of this period is the same as the previous period—60° F.

STORAGE OF FINISHED PRODUCT

At times, it is necessary to store the finished product prior to sending it to market. If this is done, store the plants at 33-35° F in the "green-bud" stage of floral development. Also, it is advisable to treat them with a protective fungicide prior to storage.

Table 2

Hyacinth Cultivars for Forcing

Color	Cultivar	Flowering Period and Type of Bulb Needed					
		H-1	H-2	H-3	H-4	H-5	H-6
Red	Jan Bos	PR	RG	RG	—	—	—
Pink	Amsterdam	PR	RG	RG	RG	RG	RG
	Anna Marie	PR	RG	RG	RG	—	—
	Delight	—	RG	RG	RG	—	—
	Eros	—	PR	RG	RG	RG	RG
	Lady Derby	—	—	RG	RG	RG	—
	Marconi	—	—	—	—	RG	RG
	Pink Pearl	PR	RG	RG	RG	RG	RG
	Princess Irene	—	RG	RG	RG	RG	—
	Queen of the Pinks	—	—	—	—	RG	RG
	Vuurbaak	—	PR	RG	RG	RG	—
Blue	Bismarck	PR	RG	RG	—	—	—
	Blue Giant	—	—	—	RG	RG	—
	Blue Jacket	—	—	RG	RG	RG	RG
	Delft Blue	PR	RG	RG	RG	RG	—
	Marie	—	—	—	RG	RG	RG
	Ostara	PR	RG	RG	RG	—	—
	Perle Brillante	—	—	RG	RG	RG	—
White	Carnegie	—	PR	RG	RG	RG	RG
	Colosseum	—	RG	RG	RG	RG	RG
	L'Innocence	PR	RG	RG	—	—	—
	Madame Kruger	PR	RG	RG	RG	RG	—
Violet	Amethyst	—	—	—	—	RG	RG

PR—Prepared bulbs, RG—Regular bulbs

Saran shade for starting young plants, getting better breaks, and increasing summer growth. In the photo, Professor James B. Shanks, University of Maryland.

HYDRANGEAS
by James B. Shanks
University of Maryland

The absence of recent census information makes comment on the relative position, importance, or trends in hydrangea production rather difficult. Most would agree, however, that hydrangeas have declined somewhat over the past 10 years. Yet, at the present time there is an upsurge of interest in this crop and reason to believe that the hydrangea will again take an important place as a spring-flowering plant.

Several factors have contributed to the decline as well as the potential increase in hydrangea popularity which need to be considered. The hydrangea is not a cheap plant to grow, as it has a plant-production phase of growth as well as a rather long forcing period with a generous bench-space requirement. Yet, it began being considered a "cheap" plant and possibly was one of the first flowering potted plants sold in chain stores on the spring market. Poor understanding on the part of producer, distributor and sales outlet, plus attempts to produce flowering plants more cheaply, have resulted in the presence of plants on the retail market of unbelievably poor quality. In addition, many presumably good-quality hydrangeas have been produced under a "the-bigger-the-better" philosophy which resulted in a large, showy plant which was frequently "under-potted" or otherwise not adapted **to** holding up satisfactorily under modern home conditions, as the hydrangea has a large water requirement and can be permanently damaged by high moisture stress. Thus, many factors have contributed to the poor image of the hydrangea in the eyes of sales personnel and the general public.

Increased interest in hydrangeas can be felt in many quarters and increased production can be expected due to certain recognized factors. First is the relatively good economic position of potted-plant production in the broad northern, central, and eastern portions of the country. Second is the need in the potted-plant industry for variety, and for plants with certain characteristics which the hydrangea easily meets, such as distinctiveness, pleasing colors, wide appeal, long-lasting potential, and most important, the capability of being predictably forced in large numbers for a holiday market.

The hydrangea at this time is in need of being upgraded in the eyes of the retailer and the consumer as a high-quality, long-lasting potted plant, for which they should be willing to pay a price commensurate with the costs of production, and as an exceptional value if properly cared for. The situation could be likened to the position of the poinsettia some 10 years ago, before the introduction of varieties better adapted to survival in the home; or to the rose industry before concentrated efforts by a national group, through research, education, and introduction of better varieties, helped a lagging industry gain the position it so justly deserved.

Specifically, efforts by those seriously interested in hydrangea production could well be centered on:

1. Research and education on the care and keeping qualities of hydrangeas.
2. The production of uniform quality in the greenhouse with consideration for lasting in the home.
3. Introduction of varieties better adapted to the home, and means of controlling water loss and water supply for this plant.
4. Research of procedures which would extend the period for the availability of blooming plants to at least the winter, spring, and summer months.

Botanically, the hydrangea is known as *Hydrangea macrophylla* (Thunb.) and is a member of the *Saxifrage* family or *Saxifragaceae*. It is a woody shrub growing to about 12 feet in its native habitat of Japan, where the species is generally hardy to about 10° F. The large panicles of flowers (the inflorescense of flowers is "cymose" in formation) are formed in the apical buds or at the tips of the stems in the late summer or early fall and, when growing outside, flower the following summer. The true petals of the flower are inconspicuous. Flowers are showy only in the case of the staminate flowers (bearing pollen, but incapable of bearing seed) and in these staminate flowers it is the sepals which are petallike and showy. The fertile, complete flowers are hidden in the inflorescence in the common florist varieties, but form the center part of some of the outdoor varieties known as "lace-cap" hydrangeas.

The color of the hydrangea flower is due to the anthocyanin contained in the flower parts of the pink-blue varieties. The white varieties contain essentially no pigment, although some may develop with age. Anthocyanin is normally red, but in hydrangeas, is capable of forming a complex with certain metals and so changes to a blue pigment. For all practical purposes, the substance responsible for the color change in hydrangeas is aluminum because of its solubility, low toxicity, and relative abundance in all soils. The amount of anthocyanin changed from pink to blue depends on the amount of aluminum available in the pigment-containing cells of the sepals, and so a partial color change in flowers without adequate aluminum is possible. The effect of incomplete color change is considered unsightly in some varieties, but with others, as *Merveille* and *Rose Supreme,* an intermediate color is acceptable or frequently desirable on some markets. The concentration of anthocyanin determines whether the variety has pink or red flowers (or light or dark blue).

REQUIREMENTS AND RESPONSES

GENERAL

Hydrangeas grow best in slightly acid soil (pH 5.5 to 6.5), but because of the effect of soil acidity on the availability and uptake of aluminum, the soil acidity is controlled more for the effect upon the flower color than for growth considerations. When growing at a pH where flowers readily stay pink (pH 6.0 to 7.0), there will be more tendency for lack of iron uptake with the resulting iron chlorosis.

Plants respond well to nitrogen fertilization with the exception of periods of extremely hot weather. It is desirable to restrict fertilization during the summer-growing period, fertilizing regularly to maintain leaf color and stem vigor, but not so as to result in lush growth or an overly vegetative condition. This should be continued until plants are dormant to assure flower-bud initiation. During the forcing period, the use of maximum rates tolerated by the plant will assure best leaf color and flower color where pink flowers are desired. Experiments have shown a rather low requirement for phosphorus and potassium for good growth and a 2-1-1 to 3-1-1 ratio of nitrogen-phosphate-potash is excellent for consistent use. As was the case with soil acidity, so in the case of fertilization the flower color takes precedence over plant growth in practice. Pink flowers are favored by high nitrogen, high phosphorus, and low potassium during the forcing period. Aluminum assimilation and the formation of blue flowers are favored by low nitrogen, low phosphorus, and high potassium fertilization during the forcing period.

Photoperiod (day length) exerts a certain degree of control on vegetative growth, flower formation and forcing. Rapid, vigorous growth with the formation of long internodes occurs with long days. With the short days of late summer (dark periods longer than 10 hours), terminal growth slows and internodes do not elongate so that terminal or winter buds form and flower primordia are induced more readily. The use of additional light during forcing can counteract the effect of insufficient cold storage with longer stems and slightly earlier flowering, but has little effect on plants that have had an adequate storage period.

The temperature during midsummer is frequently excessive for hydrangeas and growth may be checked on certain susceptible varieties (as *Strafford*); and if the plant has been recently pinched or heavily fertilized, injury may occur. Although it has been shown that the flowers on hydrangeas will form at warmer temperatures, they will form more readily at night temperatures of 60-65° F. Cool temperatures restrict growth, and flower buds may be inhibited at temperatures too cool for growth to occur.

During the forcing period, a cool temperature produces long stems and large flowers provided the plant has had adequate storage to permit growth at a low temperature. At temperatures higher than 60° F, growth will be more rapid, but stems will be short and flowers small. This will be especially noticeable at 70° F. A combination of initial forcing at 70° F, followed by 55-60° F after flowers are visible, will produce short plants with large flowers. Initial forcing temperatures higher than 70° F have been responsible for flower-bud abortion and care must be exercised in the use of high-temperature initial forcing.

CHEMICAL REGULATION

Growth-retarding chemicals have been useful in reducing the internode length or "stem-stretch" of hydrangeas both in the summer-growing period and during forcing in the greenhouse. Currently available materials have not affected earlier flower formation on hydrangeas as they have on certain other plants, neither have recommended dosages interfered with flowering if made in September. Trials with such late applications have demonstrated a dwarfing effect on stem elongation during forcing without reducing the size of the flower heads or inflorescences, which is usually to be expected following application during the forcing period. Treatments made in mid-summer, shortly after growth has resumed following pinching, can be repeated in the late summer to further restrict growth if so desired.

Many varieties of hydrangeas become taller than desirable during the

Applications of B-Nine made during the summer can have a desirable shortening effect on the plants at forcing (plant on the right).

355

summer, particularly if heavily fertilized. This excessive height can be controlled by late pinching, but early pinching may be desirable to assure early flower initiation for early forcing, to assure fullest bud development and flower size where small flowers may be a problem, as with the variety *Merveille*, or to avoid heat injury on susceptible varieties such as *Strafford*. Particularly vigorous varieties such as *Rose Supreme* could well be routinely retarded for height control.

The chemical retardation of stem elongation can be useful during forcing of vigorous varieties or in forcing for late-spring flowering where excessive vigor is permitted by the long storage period. Treatment is made shortly after growth resumes in the greenhouse and adequate leaf and stem area is present to absorb the chemical. This is usually between the second and fourth week of forcing. The reduced space requirement of treated plants is an important consideration in using retarding chemicals.

Alar (B-Nine) is effective in reducing internode length in hydrangeas and summer applications are made by spraying to run-off with a solution containing ½ to ¾% active ingredient while application during the forcing season is usually at ¼ to ½% active ingredient.

Ancymidol is a newer growth retardant (Eli Lilly Co.) which has been very effective on hydrangeas. Ancymidol has been extremely effective on many herbaceous plants when applied to the soil, but current tests indicate that this may not be true for hydrangeas, perhaps due to the woody nature of the stems and reduced translocation to the top of the plant. Spray applications of ancymidol have had desirable dwarfing effects at concentrations of 50 to 100 ppm. Two to 4 milligrams of ancymidol applied to a 6-inch pot should constitute an effective soil application.

Gibberellin is effective on hydrangeas and the common gibberellic acid (GA-3) or potassium gibberellate (K-GA) can induce stem elongation at very low rates of application. The effects of GA-3 on hydrangeas are very similar to the effects of shortening the dark period with incandescent light. In fact, the use of the two together can very easily lead to overtreatment with such adverse effects as plants becoming too tall, malformation of flowers, long peduncles, light green leaves, and a tendency to shed lower leaves. Attempts to substitute GA-3 for the cold-storage treatment of hydrangeas have not been entirely successful because of the likelihood of detrimental side effects as described, and also the small margin of time that can be gained in forcing. If, however, it is known or becomes evident during the forcing period that the plants have not had sufficient cold storage to force freely, the treatment with GA-3 may become useful. Upon removal from storage, or as soon as is evident from a failure to develop normally that treatment is needed, a series of weekly sprays (probably never to exceed 4 in number) of 5 ppm GA-3 can be initiated and continued until plant growth resumes. The point of overtreatment may vary with many

Butyne-diol as a defoliant, control plant on left. Picture taken one week following sprays of (left to right) ½, 1, and 1½% of butyne-diol.

factors and caution is advised. A formulated concentrate containing ½% active GA-3 would be diluted 1 part to 1,000 (approx. 1 tablespoon to 4 gallons plus wetting agent) to prepare a solution of 5 ppm active ingredient.

Chemical defoliation of hydrangeas has proven useful in a number of situations. Fumigation can be done if plants are in a storage room or can be covered with a plastic sealed at the edges. Fumigation in a greenhouse would be essentially limited to a relatively short fumigation period because of leaks and ventilation. Standard storage treatments aimed at de-greening of citrus or ripening of bananas with ethylene would no doubt efficiently induce defoliation of hydrangeas even though representing wide variations in dosage. During a period of reasonably warm temperature (60-70° F), ethylene gas is released in the room periodically so that 5 ppm of the gas is present. Banana-ripening is done by releasing a cubic foot of ethylene gas for each 1,000 cubic feet of storage space. With hydrangeas, these conditions have been conveniently provided in a practical way by placing a bushel of apples in the storage room for each 400 cubic feet of storage space and letting the apples provide the ethylene.

Vapors from the soil fumigant Vapam are an effective defoliation agent, but overdoses can be injurious to the flower buds and caution must be exercised. The Vapam is diluted in water to aid in distribution and is sprinkled over the floor area (not on the plants) at the rate of 50 milliliters (approx. ⅕ cup or 10 teaspoons) per 1,000 cubic feet of storage space. If the storage is not tight, it is safer to apply a second fumigation one week later than to increase this dosage; and if the storage room is considered tight, this dosage might be reduced by half.

Plants in the field or a greenhouse where it is not considered practical to fumigate can be defoliated by a spray with 2-butyn-1,4-diol. Butyne-diol crystals are available from chemical supply houses and dissolve readily in water. Matured and budded hydrangeas should defoliate in about 7 days following a spray of 1% butyne-diol (1 pound in 12 gallons) depending upon temperature.

The use of auxins to promote rooting of cuttings is almost universal and standard preparations are available containing indolebutyric or naphthaleneacetic acids or derivatives are available. Treatment of the base of cuttings with a dust of 1,000 ppm or a liquid solution of 500 ppm active ingredient is suggested.

PHASES OF GROWTH

VEGETATIVE

The production of budded hydrangea plants is carried on under outdoor conditions in most areas and moderate summer temperatures plus high humidity are conducive to best results. In areas of high temperature and low humidity, the use of partial shade from cloth or lath will permit better growth; or air-conditioned greenhouses may be used under extreme conditions. Full light intensity is usually provided during the period of flower initiation. Reduced light is particularly important as young plants are becoming established, or immediately following pinching, for the encouragement of new shoots. Full light intensity is usually provided during the period of flower initiation or at least by September 1. Pinching not only induces branching for the production of multiple-flowered plants, but also prevents the formation of summer flowers. Overvegetativeness should be avoided during this period of growth.

FLOWER INITIATION

Flower formation will eventually occur under all conditions. It is important that the plant be growing, healthy, and supplied with fertilizer. Early pinching assures early flower formation. The buds form naturally under the conditions of gradually shortening days and cooler temperatures of early fall. Under experimental conditions, about 6 weeks of short days and temperatures of 65° F or cooler are required. Under natural conditions at College Park, Maryland, best results have been obtained by putting plants in cold storage no earlier than October 25. Earlier storage has been successful with well-grown plants of early varieties. Flowers are present in terminal buds of early varieties by September 25 but not for another 4 weeks on late varieties.

DORMANCY OR REST

The conditions conducive to flower formation in hydrangeas also cause a gradual reduction in the rate of growth until all visible growth ceases. The plant is said to be dormant and no amount of temperature, water or fertility will start growth until the buds of the plant have gone through their rest period. As the dormancy is partially overcome, some growth will occur, but higher temperatures must be used and the stems are short and the flowers small. As this resting stage is completed, the plant is able to grow vigorously under a broader range of conditions and so is capable of growing more efficiently. The rate of growth is faster, stems will be longer and flowers larger.

The factors responsible for hydrangeas to complete their rest are exposure to cool temperatures and to a certain extent, defoliation. Cold temperatures (32-35° F) are best for long-term storage, but a warmer temperature is more desirable for early forcing and 40-45° F is close to optimum while temperatures above 50° F are not effective.

More storage is required for early forcing than for later forcing. Unfortunately, plants put in cold storage too soon will not respond to the treatment and will still be in a resting condition when removed from the cold temperature. A certain degree of flower initiation and exposure to short days seem necessary before rest. Plants which have initiated flowers are usually ready for storage. An accumulated period of 1,000 hours or 6 weeks is required for efficient forcing of well-matured plants, but 8 weeks of storage may be necessary for plants placed in cold before they are fully responsive to the treatment.

FORCING

It is not necessary to start plants in a cool house and gradually increase the temperature; rather, it is desirable to permit them to remain in cold storage as long as possible and then bring them directly to forcing temperature. Approximately 80 to 100 days are required for forcing, depending on the variety, at an average forcing temperature of 62° F. If large, well-colored flowers are to be obtained, a relatively cool temperature must be maintained after flower buds are visible. Adequate ventilation must be given at all times to keep the humidity low so that plants will withstand flower-shop and home conditions and prevent mildew, which is a serious problem on many varieties.

Full light intensity should be given until flower color shows and for early forcing, full light can be given at all times. For Easter and later forcing, and in the southern areas, a light shade on the glass or from the use of aster cloth inside the house should be used to prevent fading and sunburn of flowers.

During the forcing period, fertilization should be heavy to make the most of the plant's potential in flower size and leaf color. Particular attention

The mistake of removing plants from cold storage too soon. The plant on the left was removed December 9, plant on the right removed December 23. Both forced at 62° F nights. At least 6 weeks of temperature below 50° are necessary for hydrangeas to force efficiently.

Vegetative shoots for propagation wood can be made into one tip cutting plus several single-eye or two-eye cuttings, as shown on the right.

must be given to color control during this period.

PLANT PRODUCTION

The production of budded plants ready for greenhouse forcing is shifting to specialists or to large growers who produce more budded plants than required for their own forcing needs. Successful forcing depends upon the quality of growth made the previous summer and in preparation for forcing by proper cold-storage treatment. Many hydrangea forcers are now finding it profitable to buy plants ready for forcing from these specialists who may be more favorably located with respect to soils, summer growing conditions, or facilities for providing the correct cold treatment. A disadvantage of "buying-in" plants is that these are usually produced in smaller pots to reduce handling and shipping costs. Such plants may become very pot-bound, making the successful shifting to larger-sized forcing pots more difficult.

PROPAGATION

Propagation wood is frequently obtained from West Coast sources with the limiting factor frequently being the delay in obtaining the propagation stock so that there is not enough time to get growth under way before hot weather starts in the central and eastern portions of the country. Specialists usually grow their own stock plants and produce their own propagation wood, permitting them to both propagate early and to constantly reselect their stock. Plant forcers have the opportunity to obtain ample cuttings at the time of pruning and shoot selection and leaf-bud cuttings are ideally taken at this time. This practice, however, results in a longer growing period with increased production costs.

Stem cuttings can be made from the tips of vegetative shoots and the lower nodes of long shoots utilized for 2-eye (butterfly) cuttings or single-eye (leaf-bud) cuttings. Budded or flowering shoots are not satisfactory for stem cuttings, but the 3 to 4 midstem pairs of leaves make satisfactory 1-eye or 2-eye cuttings. Terminal or stem cuttings should be taken by mid-May to be rooted by early June for pinching by mid-July. Taken in June, they will make single-stem plants for 1 bloom at forcing or for panning in the late forcing period to make up multiple-flowered pans.

Single-eye cuttings are useful in producing pinched plants, but must be taken by mid-April because of the long growing period required to attain the stage desirable for pinching. They are very desirable for this purpose due to the greater number of nodes close to the soil, and frequently branch more freely than do terminal cuttings.

Butterfly cuttings taken from stock plants 10 to 14 days after removal of a terminal cutting are almost certain to produce 2-budded shoots, but taken at the same time as the terminals, the 2 buds may not develop as uniformly.

From the standpoint of best plant growth during forcing, it is desirable to produce plants in the pots in which they will be forced. In moving plants into and out of cold storage, and in shipping plants, the larger pot and ball of soil increase the cost of handling, shipping, and the amount of space required for storage. If it is feasible to develop a system requiring little plant movement, then plants grown by the forcer can well be produced in the full-sized pots required for forcing.

Plants grown for shipping are grown in 3, 4, 5 or 6-inch pots depending upon the size of plant produced. Clay pots dry rapidly and are frequently plunged into the soil of well-drained beds, while plastic pots can be put on the surface of any well-drained area. Young plants can be taken out-of-doors as soon as frost is past and given a spacing so that stem stretch will not result from crowding. They can then be placed on any well-drained bed, gravel, or paved area. Up to 50% light reduction should be given, depending upon the stage of growth and local climatic conditions as already discussed.

Since hydrangeas require an abundant supply of water but are intolerant of high soil moisture or poor drainage, it is essential that soil be light and the pots have several center or side drainage holes. The inclusion of up to 50% coarse peat moss in any soil enhances both the drainage and moisture-holding capacity while up to 25% perlite could further enhance the drainage and aeration of the soil. Ground limestone is added at the same time as other amendments to adjust the soil acidity to pH 6.5, or if blue flowers are desired, the necessary acidification to pH 5.5 should be made. Eight ounces of 5% active chlordane per cubic yard of soil will adequately control soil grubs, such as the Japanese beetle larvae. Slow-release fertilizers can be added after soil-steaming, but make later soil tests of questionable value. Excessive amounts which remain in or on the soil in an active nutrient-releasing state during cold storage may cause toxic fertility levels before forcing is started.

Fertilization should be started as soon as the cuttings are rooted. Rates

Flower buds are visible and the size of a pea 8 weeks before full bloom, the size of a nickel 6 weeks, and the size of a 50¢ piece 4 weeks before flowering at a temperature of 62° F.

should increase during the peak vegetative growing period of late July and August and continue at reduced rates until plants are placed in cold storage or defoliated. Constant injection fertilization at 60 ppm nitrogen (3 ounces of 25-10-10 in every 100 gallons of irrigation water) should meet plant requirements. For a periodic fertilization program, the use of one pound of 25-10-10 per 100 gallons of water at 2-week intervals during the early growth stages, weekly in mid- and late summer, and at biweekly intervals in October should also prove satisfactory. This periodic fertilization will also need to vary with pot size, as small pots will require more frequent applications.

The amount of slow-release fertilizer necessary to provide nutrients for good growth will also vary with the soil-volume to plant-size ratio. Osmocote 18-6-12 has been most satisfactory at 8 to 16 ounces per bushel of soil, depending on the size of pot.

Plants cannot be put in naturally cooled storages until temperatures can be maintained below 55°, and should be cooler when possible. Where put in cold frames for storage, they must have light until the weather is cold and then the plants can be darkened.

Grey mold causes severe loss to hydrangea buds in cold storage unless the humidity is kept low. Fans which circulate air to all parts of the storage are helpful, particularly where they are designed to bring in cold dry air from the outside. Artificially cooled storages normally have a low humidity. Early removal of the leaves from the plants is also beneficial in preventing grey mold. It is not desirable to remove leaves before early November so removal before going into storage should not be attempted.

FORCING

Hydrangea forcers should develop a philosophy of growing aimed at producing a blooming plant most adapted to home conditions. Among the factors which might be considered are the following:

1. The pot regulates the water reservoir supplying available water to the plant in the store and in the home:
   a. Plastic will not dry as rapidly as clay.
   b. Force plants in a larger pot, or return to the older practice of shifting into the next-size pot, using a peat-moss medium just before sale.
2. A high-quality but restricted type of growth should not wilt, nor suffer permanent damage from water stress as rapidly as a soft plant:
   a. Space plants, use plenty of ventilation, *grow* on dry or wire-bottom beds, and never syringe during the growing period.
   b. Use a retardant.
   c. Harden plants before sale.

REPOTTING

When shifting to a larger finishing pot immediately upon the start of forcing, it is considered best to slightly crush or otherwise "rough-up" the soil ball of pot-bound plants. This original root ball must also be thoroughly watered at the time of replanting. If shifting is done at the end of the second to third week of forcing, new root growth should have already begun and this practice should not be followed. Soil for shifting may be the same as for growing, or even better, the new medium can be moistened peat moss to which has been added up to 1 pound of ground limestone per bushel when pink flowers are desired. The following rule may help in selecting the final pot size:

Single-bloom plants	— 5½-inch pots
2-bloom plants	— 6-inch pots
3-bloom plants	— 6½-inch pots
5-bloom plants	— 7-inch pots

Hydrangeas force more rapidly at a warm temperature (plant on left), but stems and flowers will be small. The plant on the right, grown at a cool temperature, will be much taller and have larger flowers.

(The variety *Rose Supreme* might well be forced in the next-larger-size pot.)

Space requirements will vary depending upon variety and other factors, but single-bloom plants should finish on 10-inch centers, 2-bloom plants at a spacing of 12 x 14 inches, and 3-bloom plants on 14-inch centers.

TEMPERATURES AND TIMING

The rate of forcing depends to a great extent on temperature. Plants that force in 80 days at 66° F have forced in 87 days at 60° F and in 110 days at 54° F. As stated earlier, it is best to use a warm temperature, such as 64-68°, until buds are visible and then reduce the temperature to 56-60°. Such plants finished cool are hardened simply by reducing moisture where practical, and permiting the flowers to become well developed.

The flower buds should be plainly visible after 4-6 weeks of forcing. It is well to prune plants at this time and remove all blind shoots and early or late-developing buds, leaving only the desired number of shoots which will form a symmetrical plant. Very young shoots can be removed, rooted under mist and forced on the new roots in 4-inch pots. Staking and tying can be done shortly after the selection of flowering shoots.

At 60° F, it takes about 8 weeks for buds to flower which have just become visible (size of a pea); 6 weeks for buds the size of a nickel, and heads should be larger than a half dollar at 4 weeks before flowering. When finishing plants at 54° F following initial forcing at 66° F, this schedule is altered. Buds will be the size of a pea in 3 weeks, about the time of temperature change, and 10 weeks before flowering. The variety *Rose Supreme* develops more slowly, and approximately 7 additional days should be allowed for forcing.

COLOR CONTROL AND FERTILIZATION

Fertilization should be started as soon as the plants are placed in the greenhouse. The initial fertilization should be with 25-10-10 at 2½ pounds per 100 gallons of water. Subsequent applications should be made the third week and should follow at weekly intervals until flowering. Where injection fertilization is being done, the irrigation water should contain 6-8 ounces 25-10-10 per 100 gallons for each watering during the forcing period. To assure pink flowers in non-limestone areas, a mixture of equal parts of ammonium phosphate and 25-10-10 can be used as suggested above, or the ammonium phosphate used alone on alternate weeks.

In the production of plants with blue flowers, the soil should not be limed the previous summer, or if in a limestone area, it should have been acidified as previously suggested. In addition, 3 or more applications of aluminum sulfate should be applied during the forcing period at a dilution rate of 12 to 15 pounds per 100 gallons. Fertilization should be at half the rate specified for pink-flowered plants with no additional phosphorus being added. To increase the potash level, 2-4 ounces of muriate of potash can be added to each pound of 25-10-10 used.

Hydrangeas! The grower: Stanley Moncrief of Baxter Springs, Kansas. There are about 50,000 of them in the photo, some flowered here, the majority sold dormant. Stan's cultural practices generally match up with this chapter. He does prefer to do the winter repotting soon after removal from storage, likes to "rough up" the old root ball. He feels a severe roughing will help a lot in getting new root action started. Recommended soil for repotting: one part each soil, peat, and perlite. Start feeding when new root growth begins. Stan is a heavy and frequent feeder of the plants during the summer growing season.

The use of slow-release fertilizers during the forcing period must pretty well be confined to surface applications, as a limited amount can be in the soil used in shifting to a larger pot. Because of the very high fertility requirements for pink-flowering plants, this can prove valuable as a supplement to regular liquid or injector-fertilization programs. While urea formaldehyde nitrogen has been used successfully, Osmocote 18-6-12 has given best results, and the use of 1 tablespoon per 6-inch pot has given good results without additional fertilization.

VARIETIES

Rose Supreme is an excellent light pink or light blue hydrangea with large flowers, but is inclined to be a tall grower. Although flower buds form in late fall, the shoots are seldom blind when given recommended culture. It requires about 7 days longer to force than other standard varieties. It withstands hot weather well in both the growing and forcing seasons, and is popular with southern forcers.

Merritt's Supreme is noted for excellent-quality, medium-pink flowers. The flower heads are large, but the plant is not as vigorous and does not require as much bench space as *Rose Supreme*. Can be grown for pink or blue.

Merveille is an extremely versatile variety, suitable for pink or mauve shades, and is a recommended variety for blue. The buds form in midfall. This variety tends to have small flower heads unless pinched early. It is susceptible to grey mold during storage and mildew during growing and forcing.

Todi is an early forcing variety which responds very well to later-winter flowering. Although it grows and branches well in the summer, it does not seem to withstand hot temperatures at forcing, and so is better adapted to northern greenhouses. Growth is short, flower heads are large and of good quality, and the flower color is a deep salmon pink. This variety forces 7 days earlier than *Strafford* and *Merveille* and 14 days earlier than *Rose Supreme*. It makes a dark blue.

Strafford has declined in popularity because of difficulty in growing in summer. It is only suitable for pink flowers, as it turns blue with difficulty. Growth is tough and the quality excellent. Flower buds form late in the fall. This variety will not withstand heat. Plants must be pinched early in the summer and even then may not branch freely.

The white varieties available are not as good quality as the pink-blue varieties mentioned above. All are inclined to be rank-growing and soft. Buds form early and plants force readily. *Regula* tends to be an "off-white" when fully open. *Sister Therese* is pure white, but the flowers are softer than *Regula*.

TROUBLES

PHYSIOLOGICAL

"Blind wood" can usually be attributed to poor growing conditions in the summer, less than optimum conditions in the fall (poor light, early storage, early defoliation, early frost, early onset of temperatures too cool for growth, nutrient deficiency), or overly vegetative growth. Hydrangeas are readily injured by frost prior to flower initiation, but later, acquire some cold hardiness.

Many growers consider that enlarged terminal buds contain flower primordia and that larger buds are more developed and somehow more desirable than smaller buds. The formation of buds is a response to short days, but does not necessarily indicate the initiation of flowers. Buds may be cut open or dissected under a lens to ascertain the actual stage of floral development.

Inadequate storage problems are common and are recognized by failure of flowers to develop rapidly, stems to elongate, or leaves to attain size. Such plants require higher temperatures and remain dwarfed unless GA-3 (gibberellin) treatments are given, or plants are returned to cold storage for additional cold treatment. Give plants additional storage time for an early Easter rather than bring them into the greenhouse too soon.

Dropping of lower leaves may be due to crowding, hardening from accumulated spray material, or insect-and-disease-related problems. Deterioration of flower heads not related to disease has been noted under conditions of excessive phosphorus fertilization and high humidity. The presence of leaves within an inflorescence is a sign of overvegetativeness at the time of initiation, but may be remedied simply by removal at a very young stage of floral development. Green sepals result in bronzed flowers, but cause and control have not been demonstrated.

Interveinal chlorosis is usually caused by an interruption of the supply of iron to young developing leaves and may be due to poor aeration, cold soil, high salts, alkaline soil, or root injury from any cause. Plants frequently grow out of this condition, but the underlying cause should be sought and corrected. Re-greening of leaves can be hastened by sprays of several iron compounds: iron sulfate at 1 ounce to 2 gallons of water, iron chelate at 1 ounce to 10 gallons of water or Rayplex iron at 1 ounce per gallon of water plus ½ ounce of low-biuret urea.

PESTS

Aphids are most common during forcing and can be controlled with a number of insecticides of which Vapona, Diazinon, Malathion, and Meta-Systox-R are recommended. "Red spider" mites occur most frequently during the summer. The controls listed above for aphids are also miticides, but in addition, Pentac may be used if resistant mites are present. Snails and slugs may present a real problem during forcing and should be controlled during the early stages of growth. Sprays or dusts containing metaldehyde and aimed primarily at the pots, lower stems, and benches have been effective controls.

DISEASES

The common "damping-off" pathogens may be troublesome during propagation, but are seldom serious if attention is given to the steam sterilization of the rooting medium and other sanitation procedures. Likewise, soil used in potting should be treated for the control of these common fungi in addition to the elimination of weeds. Mildew is common in late summer and fall. A severe infestation may induce leaf-drop or otherwise reduce photosynthetic efficiency and contribute to the failure to form flower buds. Septoria leaf spot, indicated by purplish blotches on leaves, can also be a problem in the fall. Late-summer and fall sprays with a fungicide can correct these problems. Mildew may also become a problem during forcing, if leaves remain wet or humidity high, due to lack of ventilation and air movement. Benlate has been reported to give excellent results as a mildew control on hydrangeas.

Botrytis or grey mold is responsible for bud rot and is primarily a problem in cold storages without air circulation or cooling systems to keep the humidity low. The early removal of dead leaves following defoliation is helpful. Benlate sprays at 2-3-week intervals have given control, as have Daconil and Termil.

Several virus diseases have been recognized on hydrangeas, but have not posed serious problems. Ring-spot symptoms appear as yellowish blotches on the lower leaves just before flowering, or occasionally as reddish-brown or green rings on yellowish leaves. Commercial varieties are assumed to be tolerant to ring spot, as stock has been shown to be generally infested, but with little effect on performance.

Aster yellows, most recently not considered a true virus, has appeared on hydrangeas, presumably carried into plants by leafhoppers during summer culture. The symptoms are dramatic (dwarfed and malformed growth, plus malformed greenish-yellow flowers followed by ultimate death), so careful roguing of plants can eliminate this disease before attempts are made either to force or to propagate infected plants.

IMPATIENS (Sultanas)

ANNUAL *(I holsti and sultani)*

50-60,000 seeds per oz. Germinates in 18 days at 70°. Light.

Well known for many years largely because of its ability to produce flowers under poor light conditions, the impatiens has really come into its own as a popular bedding and pot plant, filling the need for a plant that will continue to thrive and flower under conditions of heavy shade. Another reason for its rise to prominence has been the development of new and vastly improved dwarf forms, such as the F_1 *Elfin* series. As an annual for shaded spots, it ranks with the begonia. Its growth is quite succulent, cuttings root very easily, and will make nice 2½-inch pot plants in a month or 6 weeks. Cuttings or seedlings can also be planted in packs or flats where they will outgrow weeds. In a few days after lifting and potting from open soil, they are on their way again.

Impatiens are quite easy to grow from seed; however, they should be germinated at a minimum temperature of 70° under full-light conditions. Sown around February 15, 2¼-inch pots will be ready for May sales if grown at 55 to 60°. For pack sales, sow March 1 to March 15. One pinch is usually necessary. To obtain plants with maximum number of flowers and limited

Impatiens Elfin Mix—an F_1 hybrid variety. Growers' top choice for shade annuals.

vegetative growth, we suggest leaving the seedlings in the germination flat as long as possible, and restricting the amount of feed and water given to the plants.

As mentioned above, the prime reason for the vastly increased usage of impatiens as bedding plants has been the development of the F_1 strains. Briefly, here are the advantages:

1. Better seed germination;
2. Increased vigor;
3. Produce more flowers;
4. Have better habit (dwarf); no pinching needed.

Heading the list of these F_1 hybrids is the *Elfin* series (8-10 inches). Compact, free-flowering and available in the 9 separate clear colors listed as well as a mixture, it is rapidly taking over the No. 1 spot. Currently available are *Elfin Orchid, Crimson, Fuchsia, Orange, Pink, Rose, Salmon, Scarlet, Blue* and *White*. Also being widely grown is the F_1 *Imp* series. Early, free-flowering with a dwarf habit, it comes in about the same range of separate colors as the *Elfin* series. The F_1 Minette series is similar to the Elfin but a little more vigorous. Grandé Mix, a recent addition, is unique in that large 2 inch flowers are produced on dwarf plants.

Bicolors are rapidly gaining prominence. Outstanding is the F_1 Ripple series. Large flowered with a uniform star pattern, they are available in scarlet and rose separate colors as well as a mix. F_1 Stars and Stripes is a novel mix of bicolors with about 20% solid colors. Inbred varieties (12-14 inches), still being used heavily in some areas, include *Dwarf Mix, Dwarf Bright Orange, Scarlet Baby* (a brilliant scarlet), *Dwarf Bright Rose, Blaze* (an orange-scarlet with dark foliage), and *General Guisan,* a novel red and white bicolor. The taller-growing *Holsti* type (20 inches) is sold largely as a mixture in shades of pink, rose, orange, salmon, red, lavender and purple.

All impatiens are sold predominantly as color mixtures; where separate colors are used, preference is for white, scarlet, orange and crimson.

Currently stirring up quite a bit of interest are the so called New Guinea Hybrids. Available only as rooted cuttings or small plants presently, they represent a radical departure from common, widely used strains in that many of them have variegated or multi-colored foliage. Original stock was released by the U.S.D.A.

See "Balsams" for another species of impatiens.

FORCING IRIS

Many growers, both retail and wholesale, find it profitable and not too difficult to force iris during the winter months. Here, we refer strictly to forcing varieties classed generally as Dutch iris. These bulbs are grown in Holland and Japan as well as in our Pacific Northwest. However, with the excellent quality produced in this section of our country, it is wise for a grower to limit his purchases to the American-grown bulbs.

Bulbs should be planted in deep flats (4-5 inches) or into a bench. The top of the bulb should be level with the surface of the soil. Iris must be kept moist and should never be allowed to dry out. Since, in flats, iris form a thin matted layer of roots on the bottom, thorough watering is a must. Placing of the flats too near the heating pipes will cause rapid drying out and subsequent bud blasting. A spacing of 3 by 3 inches is recommended. Some growers mark the flat or bench at this spacing after thoroughly watering the soil, and then push the bulbs into the soil covering them with an inch layer of peat which is again watered. If placing flats on a bench, it is a good idea to allow a 1-inch air space between them. Iris need plenty of light and ample ventilation with uniform temperatures. The bulbs should be planted in an ordinary loose, well-drained soil without any special fertilizer added.

Due to the excellent work which has been done by the U.S.D.A. and other experiment stations, fairly accurate schedules are available today which allow the grower to plan his crop by selecting the proper variety, size, temperature and treatment to force a crop from mid-December through May.

If, at the time of planting, temperatures are still too high in the greenhouse, flats can be placed in a cool cellar or may be buried outside for about 2 weeks until the greenhouses have cooled off. The bulbs should not be left outdoors after the top growth has reached 6 inches. Because of the precooling treatment that bulbs are given now to obtain accurate timing, they can be started off in the greenhouse at forcing temperatures.

Bulbs are usually dug in July and immediately given a 10-day curing period at 90°, which accelerates the formation of flower buds. Immediately

IRIS WEDGEWOOD

upon arrival at warehouses, all iris that are to be shipped to customers for planting after mid-November are put into a heat-retarding chamber at 80°. They are left in this chamber until they go into precooling, which is approximately 4 to 8 weeks before planting, depending on variety and size. Those bulbs that are to be planted before mid-November can be left in open storage for about 30 days until they go into precooling. By precooling, the bulbs force more quickly and uniformly. Bulbs are placed in a 48° precooling storage at the proper time so that they can be removed at planting time. Precooled bulbs must be planted immediately, since a delay will nullify the precooling effect. Some growers have facilities to do their own precooling, and thus use regular or heat-treated bulbs, depending on the intended planting date. Generally, these are shipped 6 weeks prior to planting. However, the time of precooling varies from 4 to 8 weeks, depending upon the time of the season, variety and size of bulbs. If a grower is in doubt about this, he should consult those firms where scheduling

370

services are available.

The types of bulbs now available for accurate timing of crops are as follows: *Regular*—for the grower who wants to do his own precooling or planting prior to mid-November; *precooled*—for growers who have no precooling facilities, but who plant prior to mid-November; *retarded*—for the grower who desires to do his own precooling and planting after mid-November; *retarded/precooled*—for growers who do not have precooling facilities but who will plant after mid-November; and *special/precooled*—for the grower who has no precooling facilities and who wishes to flower a crop prior to Christmas.

There are many newer varieties of iris available for forcing, but *Wedgewood* is still the most popular, and is the only one that can be used for flowering before February 1. Other varieties used that can be accurately timed are *Blue Ribbon,* a deep blue; *White Perfection;* and *Golden Harvest.* For flowering from February-on, using heat-cured and precooled bulbs, there are quite a few excellent varieties available: *White Perfection, Snowdrift, White Superior, Pacific Gold, Moonlight.* Flowering a few weeks later are *Yellow Queen, Joan of Arc, The Orchid, Van Vliet* and *Imperator.* Iris come in sizes measured in centimeters of diameter: 6/7, 7/8, 8/9, 9/10, 10/11 and 11/up. Iris can be forced in a wide range of temperatures (from 45-60°) and the forcing temperatures are dependent upon the size and variety of bulb used. Higher temperatures (55-58°) are used for forcing 10/11 bulbs only. For Christmas flowering, use 10/11 *Wedgewood* that have been precooled from September 1 to October 13, plant no later than October 20, and force at 55-58°. Following are some rules that apply to selection of varieties, sizes and growing temperatures:

1. Use *Wedgewood* 10/11 for flowering between December 24 and February 1 at 55-58°. *Wedgewood* 9/10 can be flowered after January 13, but only at 50-53°.

2. *Wedgewood* or *Blue Ribbon* 9/10 size are not recommended to flower at a 55-58° temperature.

3. *Blue Ribbon* in any size should not be flowered before February 1 because of grassiness and bud-blasting. The 9/10 size of *Blue Ribbon* should not be flowered before March 1.

4. *White Perfection* and *Golden Harvest* should not be forced for flowering before February 1, and for accurate scheduling of these varieties, only the 8/9 size should be used.

The preceding discussion has dealt largely with precooled and retarded/precooled iris. Regular iris cannot be timed accurately, so only the grower with precooling facilities will be interested in the regular bulbs.

There are 2 principal troubles encountered in the forcing of iris. *Bud-blasting* is generally caused by too-high temperatures in forcing (about 60°), overcrowding in the bench, not enough water or light. An aphid infestation on the bulbs can also cause blasting. If bulbs are infested with aphids at time of planting, a parathion or methyl bromide treatment before planting will solve the problem unless the bulbs are already damaged. Blasting is more common in the early-forced crop than in later plantings. *Blindness* is generally caused by too-early digging of the bulbs and too-early precooling and planting. Blindness should not be excessive if bulbs are dug and cured by August 15, precooled September 1 to October 15, and planted on October 15. Although it is possible to harvest flowers from 95 to 100% of the bulbs planted, percentages of 80 to 90 should be considered satisfactory for the earliest crop.

An outdoor cold-frame crop of iris can be flowered in May or June. Plant bulbs in a cold frame in mid-November or before the ground freezes. Use smaller-sized bulbs and plant 4 to 6 inches deep and 3 inches apart. Water thoroughly at the time of planting and cover with several inches of straw. Remove the straw in late March. Naturally warm spring temperatures will bring the bulbs into flower in late May or June.

When iris flowers are destined for long-distance shipping, they should be cut in the bud stage just as their true color begins to show. For local selling, flowers should be cut nearly wide open.

KALANCHOE

ANNUAL *(K. blossfeldiana)*
From Seed: 1,000,000-2,500,000 seeds per oz. Germinates in 10 days at 70°. Light.

This attractive and long-lasting plant with its showy heads of bright red flowers is especially valuable for Christmas and is easily flowered for that occasion by the use of black cloth shading for about 6 weeks, starting September 1, if grown at 60°. It blooms naturally in January if grown at a 60° night temperature, or for Valentine's Day if grown at 50°. It may be had as early as October with black cloth treatment. Seed may be sown from January till July for finishing in 2¼ to 5-inch pots.

Various shadings of a 60° crop from the same sowing date will result in different flowering dates and pot sizes. Shading July 20 to September 20 will produce flowering plants in mid-October. Shade August 15 to October 1 for flowering in early December. Apply black cloth shade daily from 5 p.m. to 7 a.m. Usually seedlings are transplanted to 2¼-inch pots, and then when ready for shifting, are moved to a 6-inch pot using 3 (2¼'s) per finishing pot. Final pinch should be made in late June.

Kalanchoes are not too particular in their soil requirements and will do well as long as the soil used is well drained. Since they are subject to stem rot, all soil and pots should be sterilized. The plants should be grown in full sun to prevent stretching of the flowering stem.

Tetra Vulcan is the best variety for pots, being naturally dwarf and bushy in growth with large flower heads. Used to a much lesser extent are the taller growing *Swiss Strain* varieties, which require frequent pinching. *Ramona*, a vivid scarlet, and *Swiss Rose* are two varieties commonly used.

From Cuttings:

Intensive breeding efforts in numerous areas have led to the development of new hybrids which are vegetatively propagated and sold, usually out of 2¼" or 2½" pots, under license agreement. Best known are the *Irwin Hybrids*. Consisting, at the present, of eight different varieties ranging in colors from light yellow through apricot and orange into reds and pinks, they are sold as 2½″ pots and can be flowered year round. On the average they will flower from 10 to 14 weeks after the start of black cloth shade. The flowers will develop under long days after 5 or 6 weeks of black cloth treatment.

LANTANA

ANNUAL *(L. camara)*

Very useful for spring bedding sales. These colorful, free-flowering plants will perform well under many varying soil conditions. They do, however, like warm temperatures.

While a mixture of colors and habit can be had from seed, uniformity in these important characteristics can only be had from cuttings. Thus, the wide majority grown are vegetatively propagated. They are easily rooted in September if taken from outdoor plants. Perhaps a better plan is to lift such plants and plant them in a 55° house. If the old plants are trimmed back some and not watered much till they get into growth, plenty of cuttings will become available as spring approaches. If strong, 4-inch pot plants are wanted, fall cuttings should be used. Lantanas will not do well without some heat— this is why they flourish during the heat of summer and make such an attractive showing in the South. In the greenhouse, they should be grown at a minimum of 60°. A wide range of varieties and colors are available from propagating specialists.

LARKSPUR

ANNUAL *(Delphinium ajacis)*

8,000 seeds per oz. Germinates in 20 days at 55°. Dark.

The half-hardy nature of the larkspur can be taken advantage of by outdoor growers in the near South. If a sowing is made in the open in this section 6-7 weeks before the ground freezes, plants well enough established to winter-over should be produced. An exceptionally severe winter will sometimes destroy them, but usually they come through very well. Most growers find that a covering of even coarse material tends to rot them. With perfect drainage and some coarse covering, a fall sowing outdoors does usually come through nicely for us if made late enough to avoid germination before the ground freezes. The advantage of such a sowing lies in the promptness with which it germinates in early spring. Such a sowing will flower at least 2-3 weeks earlier than if sown out after the ground dries in the spring. In figuring seed requirements for an extensive planting, do so on the basis of 25 ounces of seed covering an acre; this is figured on double 8-inch rows spaced 3 feet apart. Spacing plants in the rows is not so important. They will fill out the row if spaced 10-14 inches, but will do so more promptly if allowed half that distance. Some growers plant out March 1-sown seedlings, usually getting good results, but we believe that if the fall sowing comes through, it will be more profitable because of the cost of greenhouse plants and transplanting. If you are depending on spring sowings, 2 should be made 2-3 weeks apart. By all means, get the first one in as early as possible and use deep, fairly well-enriched soil, and it will pay to irrigate during dry

LARKSPUR
BALL FLORIST MIXTURE

weather if it can be done.

As a greenhouse crop, larkspur is grown on a limited scale. Basic principles of good culture must be followed to avoid serious disease problems. These principles include the use of sterilized soil, adequate ventilation, and careful watering, which should be done on bright days and only when the soil is on the dry side.

Larkspur can be used to follow fall mums. Well-started 3-inch plants should be ready when the bench is empty and are produced by a September sowing in pots or bands set in a cold frame. We prefer raised beds for most greenhouse crops, especially for larkspur, but if ground beds are well drained and care used in watering, very good results are had with them. Larkspur growth will become heavier and more susceptible to rot on such beds. For this reason, we prefer to space the plants at least 12 by 12 inches. On raised beds, 10 by 10 inches should be ample. A night temperature of not over 50° should be maintained.

VARIETIES

The *Regals* and *Supremes* are the two classes widely used today, and are a great improvement over those varieties formerly used. Important characteristics of these improved types are their more vigorous growth, longer, better-formed flower spikes and larger, more fully double florets.

Among the many varieties, we consider the following the finest: *Dark Blue Supreme, Lilac Supreme, White Supreme* and *Regal Rose*. White is by far the most widely used color.

Another class that some growers like is known as hyacinth-flowered. This is nonbranching, producing 1 long, heavy spike. If this is grown cold or in a ground bed, its heavy, hollow stem becomes so easily broken that it is unprofitable to handle. If planted on a raised bed and forced into flower at a 50° temperature, we find it excellent. For early flowering, it should be preferred. Available in all larkspur colors, but used mostly as a mix.

ACE LILY
The most popular and widely used lily for Easter flowering. Compact foliage allows for closer spacing.

LILIES FOR EASTER POTS

Edited by Robert Hastings, Harbor, Oregon

Lilium longiflorum (white trumpet, or Easter Lily) is, by far, the most valuable and popular of the species when it comes to florist production. American production of Easter lily bulbs came into being when the supply of "gigs," which are Japanese-grown *Giganteum*, was cut off during World War II. This production now rests largely in *Ace* and *Nellie Whites; Ace* being the most popular strain for Easter forcing at a ratio of better than 1.75 to 1 *Nellie White*.

The various strains of *longiflorum* lilies each has its own individual characteristics. A decade ago, *Croft* was, by far, the most popular and widely used type. Due largely to its leaf-tip burn difficulties, and its requirement for additional bench space, it was overtaken by *Ace*, which is nearly exempt of tip burn and requires less bench space. *Ace* also gives additional buds under normal forcing conditions. The strain *Nellie White* has come into being in recent years in a good number. *Nellie Whites* are shorter growers than most other strains, have nice, broad foliage and very upright, strong-growing habits. The *Georgia* strain, which was used for many years for cut flowers, has become increasingly more interesting for pots due to its ability to produce a large number of buds and blooms. The grower must be very careful when forcing the *Georgia* strain not to get too tall a plant, as its natural growth habit is to grow taller than *Ace* or *Nellie Whites*. The *Georgia* type has many blooms per bulb size, but bloom life is of shorter duration than any of the other varieties.

Ace and *Nellie White* lilies are produced in the Pacific Northwest. The largest concentration of production is on the California-Oregon state line, centering between the cities of Crescent City, California, and Brookings, Oregon. The forcing-size bulbs are the result of 3 years growing in the field. The first year, they are "bulblets"—small, thumb-sized bulbs produced by the lily plant on that part of the stem below the ground and above the top of the bulb. These bulblets are removed from the stems in the fall, replanted into the field, and the second year become "yearlings." The "yearlings" are generally removed from the fields after one year. At the time of this removal, they run from 4 to 7 inches in circumference. The "yearlings" are then planted back and the following year, "commercials" are dug, which are the forcing-size bulbs.

Bulbs are normally dug in late September or early October, immediately graded, and shipped to the eastern storage houses. Bulb grades are designated by the measurement of the bulb's circumference—their largest girth—and referred to in inches. The grade 9/10, for instance, con-

A fine crop of Crown Nellie White lilies at Podesta Plant Acres, Half Moon Bay, California, the late Andy Podesta in the photo. Picture taken April 1969; bulbs used were 9/10 and 10/up.

An example of what can happen if precooled bulbs received in the fall are not placed in cold storage or potted immediately on arrival. The taller plant was potted December 17 directly from the cold storage treatment. The bulb of the short plant was exposed to room temperature from December 17 to January 3, then potted.

tains bulbs that measure 9 to 10 inches around. There is not much leisure time in the lily fields during harvest; as the top growth is removed, the bulbs are cleaned, graded and packed, all in a matter of a few days. The Northwest-grown lilies are packed and shipped in near-standard cases which consist of 300 bulbs, size 6½/7 (Ace only); 250 bulbs, size 7/8; 200 size 8/9; 150 size 9/10; 100 size 10/up. This "white gold," as they were called in the mid-forties, when they sold for $1.00 each, are packed in peat moss of a standardized moisture consistency so that they do not dry out excessively in the case while in transit and in storage.

Immediately after packing, the bulbs are loaded into refrigerated trucks for shipment to cold-storage houses for precooling. Precooling of lilies means storage of the bulbs at 33° to 38° F for a minimum of 5 weeks. The length of precooling varies from year to year due to the fluctuation of the Easter date. The precooling (cold storage) has the effect of bringing the bulbs into flower in less time than if they were *not* precooled, and gives more uniformity. For this reason, most good lily growers desire their lily bulbs with only 5 weeks of precooling on late Easters, a minimum of 6 weeks precooling on early Easters. The longer lilies are precooled, the faster they respond; therefore, the minimum of 6 weeks precooling. Late Easters allow the forcers to develop a better root system before top growth starts; thus, when time is sufficient, 5 weeks of precooling is ample. Some growers have their bulbs delivered immediately without any precooling whatsoever. Nearly all of the West Coast forcers pot up nonprecooled bulbs and increasing numbers in the eastern section of the United States are potting up nonprecooled bulbs. They actually accomplish the precooling effect by potting immediately upon receipt, and placing the pots in straw-covered cold frames or other locations where the temperatures are comparatively low—50° F or less. This early-potting method has the advantage of giving the bulb more time to make its root system before terminal growth starts and the results are generally higher bud count than with the proverbial precooled bulb.

Recently, the "C.T.F." (Controlled-Temperature Forcing) method has been receiving more and more attention from growers. This technique, developed by Dr. August DeHertogh of Michigan State University, has several advantages for the grower with available controlled temperature. Among these are high leaf and flower number and long basal leaves. The following recommendations for C.T.F. for Easter, early April, were published by H. F. Wilkins and R. E. Widmer of the University of Minnesota. The varieties which respond to this treatment are the cultivars *Ace* and *Nellie White*.

PROCEDURE

1. Noncooled bulbs are used.
2. Bulbs arrive approximately October 10-20.
3. Pot immediately. Place the bulb deep in the pot in case of possible premature sprouting. Keep pots moist at all times. Potting should be completed by October 23.
4. Use a well-aerated, porous soil. See University of Minnesota's fertilizer recommendations in the above-mentioned report.
5. Keep temperatures at 63°F for 3 weeks. This temperature allows roots to form. Hence, pot as soon as possible upon receipt. It is felt that this rooting

These 2 plants show strikingly the results of Dr. Stuart's cold-frame culture of lilies—compared to long-term storage and refrigeration. Plant on the right was potted to a 4-inch peat pot August 24, set up in a cold frame, kept above freezing. It was shifted to a 6-inch pot, moved to 60° on December 10.

Plant on the left went to 35° storage from August 24 to December 10, then was potted, moved to a 60° greenhouse. Both plants drawn from 7 to 8-inch double-nose Georgia bulbs. Note, even at this early stage, the heavier growth, more leaves on the cold-frame plant. It will make many more buds.

On the left, Dr. Stuart; on the right, Bill Franklin of G.J.B., Inc.

period is responsible for the high bud counts produced under this technique. If there are signs of premature emergence upon opening the case, or during this period, proceed to step 6 immediately.

6. On November 9, drop the temperature to 35°-40° F for *Ace* and 40°-45° for *Nellie White*. Place thermometers in the soil next to the bulb and record temperatures daily.

7. Bring potted bulbs into the greenhouse between December 20-24.

8. Day or night temperatures should not go below 60° F, nor should day temperatures go above 65° F until January 22. Lower temperatures may decrease flower count and root development. Higher temperatures at this stage may delay flowering. Forcing at any temperature above 70° F should not commence until after February 5. Flower buds do not develop until plants are 4-6 inches tall and flower buds are formed. Until this time, temperatures near 70° F and above may delay flowering.

9. Upon emergence, the long-day insurance policy can go into effect as described in University of Minnesota Easter Lily Research Report (Paper No. V; December, 1969 and Paper No. IX; December, 1970, Minnesota State Florists' Bulletin). Use long days immediately upon shoot emergence for 2 weeks at 15 foot-candles from 10 p.m. to 3 a.m. (5 hours).

10. Follow the leaf-counting technique for scheduling temperature forcing of the plants as described in University of Minnesota Easter Lily Research Report (Paper No. VIII; December, 1970, Minnesota State Florists' Bulletin).

Lily forcers should not leave their bulbs lying around in their packing sheds after they are delivered, but should pot them immediately. The erratic temperatures and atmospheric moisture in the packing or boiler shed are not conducive to good bulb performance; therefore, one of the cardinal rules when growing Easter lilies is "pot upon arrival."

What size bulbs should be forced? Most experienced forcers have very decided preferences. The bud count desired by the forcer is the largest influence in answering this question. Under proper growing conditions, one should expect on *Ace* lilies an average of 4 flowers for 7/8's, 5 flowers for 8/9's, 6 flowers for 9/10's, and 7 flowers for 10/up. The actual bud count on lilies is controlled by the forcer, as the bulb does not have flower buds in it when planted. These flower buds are developed when the vegetative growth is from 2 to 4 inches, as will be explained later. Some forcers grow chiefly for a mass-market outlet and are therefore satisfied with an inexpensive plant. In such cases, the 7/8 *Nellie White* and the 6½/7 *Ace* are generally used. Forcers who use the 6½/7 *Ace* and 7/8 *Nellie White* must bear in mind that should any difficulties arise during the forcing period, where they lose a bud or two, they may well end up with an undesirable, nonsalable plant—too few blooms, no reserve. Many growers feel they would rather use a larger bulb and have more flowers than needed for their trade than take a chance of having too few. The larger bulb size has a better chance under adverse forcing conditions to produce a salable Easter lily plant.

Potting of *Ace* and *Nellie Whites* for pot-plant sales is generally done in a 5½ or 6-inch standard pot. Since lilies are "stem-rooting" bulbs (they produce roots both from the bottom of the bulb and from the plant stem below the soil surface), they should be potted a *minimum* of 2 inches below the soil level. It is of vital importance that the lily crop be planted at a uniform depth, as there is experimental evidence which supports the claims that the depth of planting controls to some extent the time and evenness of bloom. This area between the soil surface and the tip of the bulb gives the stem roots an opportunity to develop so that they can help the basal roots produce a desirable plant. Stem roots on lilies are desirable for several reasons. (1) They help support the plant, thus minimizing staking. (2) Aid in supplying moisture and food. (3) Stem roots have brought many a crop through.

An even emergence of the vegetative growth is most desirable. This can be accomplished by uniform depth of planting the bulb, uniform temperatures, uniform soil mix; and probably most important, uniform moisture. Some forcers are getting more even emergence by covering the pots with black polyethylene during the period between initial potting and placement on the bench (3-5 weeks).

Soil for potted lilies should have an ample supply of humus material. It should be well-drained, and should contain the basic supply of not-too-quickly available plant food. Typically, a good *Ace* or *Nellie White* potting soil might consist of 1/2 coarse peat, 1/4 vermiculite or perlite, and 1/4 good-structured greenhouse soil. Steam-sterilized soil is most desirable. The pH of lily soil should be from slightly acid to neutral—pH 6.5 to 7.0. When the pH is less than 6.5, sufficient lime should be added to bring it up to a minimum of 6.5. Quickly available soluble fertilizers should not be used until the plant root system is well-established. Good drainage is a "must" when growing Easter lilies for pot plants—some growers put a handful of coarse gravel on the bottom of each and every pot. Others are sure that the drain hole is never plugged up by putting drainage material over it. Regardless of the method, the forcer must be assured that excess water has an avenue of escape, as lilies with wet feet for only a few hours become inferior lilies.

Timing of lilies for Easter centers around a basic rule that the bulb requires approximately 120 days from potting to flowering. There are many variations to this rule—location, north vs. south, available light, and simply the forcer's cultural practices. *Ace* and *Nellie White* can be planted at the same time. If the two varieties are grown in the same house, *Ace* should preferably go to the warm end of the bench, *Nellie Whites* next. *Ace* requires a little more heat than *Nellie White* during the same forcing period, whatever its length. Some growers are placing their lilies in a 60° F house immediately upon potting. They then govern their timing nearer development. Other growers, immediately after potting, place their bulbs in a temperature of 50°. When this is practiced, additional days from potting to flowering are required or additional temperature in the later stages of development is required. If *Ace* lilies are potted 130 days before the Easter holiday and are kept at a 50° temperature until 105 days before Easter, the bulbs have an opportunity to produce a root system that will help the plant during its initiation and later .

forcing period. Simply more time, more roots. Earlier potting as opposed to late potting will definitely result in a higher bud count. Experimental work has shown that buds are initiated at the time the plant's top growth is 2 to 4 inches high. For this reason, it is imperative that the plant be in a vigorous growing condition before this stage. A plant that lacks a good root system or that is otherwise in a poor growing condition will not initiate as many buds (or produce as many flowers) as one that is in a healthy growing condition during its early stages. The number of flowers that a bulb produces is influenced more at the early stage, when it is initiating buds, than at any other.

"The man on the hose grows that lily," is quite true. Watering of lilies should be complete and thorough at the time of potting. During early root-forming period, they should be kept moist. Thereafter, "on the dry side" is the usual expression, but be careful of your interpretation of "on the dry side." Some growers overhead syringe quite often; others pot water only on demand, then water thoroughly. A heavy, waterlogged soil will interfere with the all-important development of roots that are so necessary for bud initiation and successful forcing. These should never be so dry as to allow them to wilt—a good, thorough watering when the soil ball is only slightly moist is desirable.

Regardless of the time of potting, *Ace* and *Nellie White* should be run at 60° F nights and 70-75° F days beginning about 100 days before Easter. They should be given all the sunlight possible and be watered and fed regularly. During the forcing period, spacing of the plants is of vital importance —crowded conditions generally cause lower leaf loss.

One hundred days or so before the Easter date, the forcing process must begin in earnest. By this time, the plant should have a good root system and its terminal growth should be emerged from the top of the bulb. Ninety-five days before Easter, the forcing shoot should be showing above the soil line of the pot. At this point, it is desirable to place the slower plants in the warm end of the bench and the more advanced plants at the cooler end of the bench. About 85 days before Easter, the terminal shoot should be 2 to 4 inches tall. It is at this stage (when the shoot is 2 to 4 inches above the ground) that the buds are actually initiated in the plant. A well-established, vigorous root system helps to determine the initial bud count. However, the care that is given the plant during the succeeding forcing period determines how many of these buds ultimately produce flowers.

When the root system is well developed and the top growth has started, it is time to begin commercial feeding. Most forcers are using a balanced fertilizer, low in phosphates, or straight nitrogen, alternating between the two in their regular feeding program. Too high a concentration of any fertilizer will burn the roots, thus weakening them, and root loss is nearly always inevitable; therefore, it is desirable to take particular caution when fertilizing lilies. A typical feeding routine involves watering the plants every two weeks with a solution made up of 1 pound of calcium nitrate to 40 gallons of water. This is an alkaline fertilizer and should help keep the pH of the soil up. If the pH gets much over 7.0, switch to ammonium sulfate at the same rate or use both—1/2 pound each to 40 gallons of water. Temperature should be kept at a 60° minimum at night (except for further-advanced plants that are separated out) and all plants should be given full sunlight.

About 75 days before Easter, the forcer should again sort out his most-advanced plants and place them in a cooler area—the slower plants in the warmer area. It should be kept in mind that when lilies are forced in a temperature of 70° and above, equal percent of atmospheric humidity should be present. Example: 75° temperature, 75% humidity. If a high humidity is not maintained along with a high temperature, bud blasting and aborting of small buds are nearly always inevitable.

In the low-light areas in colder climates, buds should be visible in the growing tip 50 days before Easter. Three weeks before Easter, the largest bud on a plant should begin its point-down and should be 2 inches in length. A bud which has swollen and become creamy white is from 4 to 7 days from opening at a 55 to 60° temperature. Throughout the forcing period, feeding should be continued on a regular basis right up to the flowering time—and more-advanced plants should be cooled down, whereas the backward plants should be moved to warmer houses or areas. Some growers claim that the last 3 weeks of the forcing period are the most critical, as it is in the spring of the year when weather conditions fluctuate greatly; therefore, the manipulating of temperatures is important to take care of these unforeseen irregularities. It must be kept in mind that lilies are of little value Easter Sunday—it is quite evident that more money has been lost on lilies developing too late than has been lost on their being too early.

Height of Lilies. A standard lot of *Nellie White* or *Ace* bulbs can be finished very short or very tall, depending upon the forcing procedures. The most desired pot lily seems to be from 18 to 24 inches above the pot rim. Some factors contributing to short plants are:

1. Ample space on the bench. Crowded plants tend to draw up.

2. Ample light from clean glass will keep lilies down in height.

3. Overwatering or too heavy a soil mixture tends to produce taller lilies. *Ace* and *Nellie White* should be watered heavily when first potted; thereafter, water only when the soil is just slightly moist.

4. All factors being equal and constant, feeding will keep *Nellie White* and *Ace* shorter than when they are starved. A starved plant tends to stretch, producing weak flower petioles, long internodes, and a very undesirable-appearing plant.

5. Once more, early potting tends to keep *Nellie White* and *Ace* short because they develop a good root system BEFORE top growth starts, and as a result, they don't have to be forced as hard to make Easter. Forcing at higher temperatures (about 60°) will tend to produce taller, stringier plants.

Blasted buds are generally due to poorly rooted plants or too much high-temperature forcing. Insufficient atmospheric moisture (same humidity percentage as temperature is a good rule) will invariably blast lily buds in nearly all stages. Lack of sufficient light, root injury, simply not enough water, and any other plant shock, will cause buds to blast.

Loss of lower foliage, or yellowing of lower foliage, is usually due to nitrogen starvation, poor aeration and insufficient light due to crowded conditions. Poor root action or not enough water are also contributing factors.

Insect Control. Aphids are the chief problem. Parathion, malathion, or Lindane are recommended. Systox, more commonly known as Demeton, is also used as a soil drench. One pint 23% Demeton per 100 gals. of water, to be applied once when the plants are 2 to 4 inches high. There should be a ½ to ¾-inch space between the soil surface and top of the pot. Three to 6 ounces of diluted Demeton per pot should not be exceeded. There is no excuse for aphid infestation of *Nellie White* or *Ace.* They are easy to find and the above-mentioned materials are specific and easy to obtain. Nicotine insecticides are apt to produce a leaf burn—watch out! Splitting of flowers is often caused by a heavy infestation of aphids after the buds have cleared.

Leaf scorch (burn of leaf tips) is a problem that is not fully understood; however, research work indicates that the governing factor is the pH level. Therefore, it is recommended that the pH of the lily potting soil be between 6.5 and 7.0. Leaf scorch is more prevalent in acid (low pH) soils than it is in alkaline soils. Scorching is sometimes found in low-nitrate and/or high-phosphate potting soils. If a forcer will avoid phosphate fertilizers, control the pH of his soil, and keep his nitrogen feeding program going as recommended, he is doing about all that he can. Leaf scorch, as a problem, is practically nonexistent on *Ace* and *Nellie White.*

Root-rot trouble. Root rot on Easter lilies has been with us for some time and most likely will continue; however, there are several steps that can be taken to help prevent its occurrence. Root-rot prevention is far better than the cure. It is known that most of the troubles come from three groups of fungi: fusarium, pythium, and rhizoctonia. Where these organisms come from, why they are more destructive in some cases than in others, and what should be done about them are still problems to be solved. Most authorities and forcers agree that the use of sterilized soil and good sanitary greenhouse practices greatly reduce root-rot problems. It is quite evident that a loose, well-drained and structurally good soil, combined with care in not overwatering, nearly eliminates this problem. It is better to slightly underwater *Lilium longiflorum* (not to the point of wilting, however) than it is to overwater. As a precautionary measure, many of the better lily-forcing operations throughout the country have put into practice in recent years the act of "breaking the soil-ball pot seal" by simply knocking out and giving the plant and its soil ball a quarter-turn 2 or 3 times during the forcing season. As a precautionary measure, it is recommended that this quarter to a half-turn be done 9 weeks before Easter and again 5 weeks before Easter. This physical action actually increases soil aeration and drainage. If you have root-rot problems, give it a try—it may improve your crop. It is quite evident that high salts is also a factor in creating root-rot difficulties. Should this be the case, the best solution here is to leach the soil thoroughly—get the salts out of the soil ball before they weaken the plant and allow root difficulties. In addition to the above precautionary steps, it is recommended that the following treatments be exercised.

1. Drench soil with a solution of 4 ounces of Dexon 70% W.P. and 4 ounces of Terraclor (PCNB) 75% W.P. in 100 gallons of water. Apply drench at first watering after initial pot watering. A Dexon drench of 4 ounces of 70% W.P. per 100 gallons every 14 days until buds are 2 inches long is an excellent preventative measure for root rot. A combination of 8 oz. each of Benlate and Truban in 100 gallons of water can also be used.

2. Add to the potting soil after steaming a mixture of 4 ounces each of 75% Terraclor and 50% Captan per cubic yard of soil.

3. Immerse the bulbs for 5 to 15 minutes before potting in a lukewarm solution made up of the following: per 100 gallons of water, 2 lbs. Terraclor 75% and 2 lbs. Fermate 76%.

These chemical treatments may not solve the problem entirely but they certainly will not hinder. Generally speaking, a good lily grower uses a structurally good, well-drained soil; sterilizes; watches his watering; and follows good sanitation measures, such as placing pots on a clean, non-infested surface, which reduces his root problems. A weakened plant is prone to increase susceptibility to infectious organisms over a strong, healthy plant.

FORCING

There are many acts a forcer can perform to speed up his forcing of lilies. The degree of tardiness in the timing governs the intensity and number of the following which should be performed at one time:

1. The use of 35 foot-candles supplementary light for a period of 5 to 8 hours a night with temperatures of 60-65° will hasten flowering, but taller plants will generally result.

2. Temperature manipulation the last 100 days of forcing.

3. Increase the temperature, as well as the humidity, to speed up flower development.

4. Water with lukewarm water to hasten flowering.

Too-far-advanced lilies can be controlled by lowering the temperature to 45-50°. Much below 45°, the check on the plant development will be so great that it will be hard to get the plant moving again. Many growers place advanced lily plants in a dark refrigerator at a temperature of 36-38° for as long as two weeks without any adverse results, so long as when the plants are placed in refrigeration, the bell has not opened. When using the refrigerator to hold plants, it should be kept in mind that the pots should be well-watered before refrigeration and taken out in ample time to acclimate to more normal conditions before being sold. Lily bells which are placed in refrigeration, or open in refrigeration, are generally of poor texture when removed, thus their keeping period is reduced—and the consumer does not get satisfaction.

EASTER LILY TERMINOLOGY

basal plate. Perennial, shortened, modified stem which has a growing point and to which scales and roots are interjoined.

basal rot. A chocolate-colored rot of lilies, caused by *Fusarium oxysporum* Schlecht, f. sp. *lilii* Imle., and usually confined to warm climates. Possible symptoms of this disease are stunting, yellowing, and premature dying with the eventual rotting of the entire bulb.

bulb. A specialized plant organ consisting of a greatly reduced stem (basal plate) surrounded by fleshy, modified leaves called scales.

bulb dealer (jobber). Individual or firm who stores, ships and distributes bulbs.

bulb forcer (flower grower). Individual or firm who produces flowers or potted plants from bulbs.

bulb grower (producer). Individual or firm who propagates bulbs for wholesale purposes.

bulb size. Transverse circumference measurement of the bulb.

commercial. Bulb of a size suitable for commercial forcing.

devernalization. Negation of a vernalizing stimulus by temperatures above a critical level.

dormancy. A physiological state of a healthy bulb characterized by a temporary delay in the sprouting or elongation of the daughter stem axis.

flower blasting. Phase of flower-bud abortion occurring after flower differentiation is completed. When blasting has occurred, visible signs of the floral organs are evident.

flower bud abortion. Cessation of floral-bud development at any stage.

flower induction. An unobservable, preparatory step which occurs prior to visible flower-bud initiation.

flower initiation. Visible organization of flower primodia at the stem apex.

forcing. Acceleration of flowering by manipulation of environmental conditions; refer to **programming** and **greenhouse phases.**

long-day treatment (LDT). Use of light (10:00 p.m. to 2:00 a.m.) at the time of shoot emergence to promote rapid flowering.

maturity. Measure of capacity of a healthy daughter stem axis to sprout without delay and to respond to flower-inducing treatments.

natural cooling. Technique in which nonprecooled commercial bulbs are planted immediately on arrival and grown under cool natural conditions, but with frost protection, prior to being placed in the greenhouse.

nonprecooled bulb (NP). Bulb which is delivered direct to the forcer and has not received a cold treatment.

precooling (PC). A cold-moist treatment prior to planting which induces rapid shoot elongation and flowering. Usually bulbs are packed in moist peat.

programming phase. The portion of the forcing program in which the bulbs are induced to flower. The methods used are **precooling, natural cooling, controlled-temperature forcing** and/or **long-day treatments.**

root rot. Condition of lily roots which may be caused by several organisms either singly or in combinations. Usually includes such fungi as *pythium*, *rhizoctonia*, and *fusarium*. Nematodes and mites may also be involved.

stem root. Adventitious root produced on the underground portion of the stem.

summer sprouting. Premature sprouting of the daughter axis before normal scale complement and bulb size are achieved.

vernalization. Cold-moist treatment applied to a bulb or plant to induce or hasten the development of the capacity for flowering.

LOBELIA

ANNUAL *(L. erinus) 700,000 seeds per oz. Germinates in 20 days at 70°*
*(Exception: Variety **Heavenly** best at 50°)*

Although more at home in a moderate climate such as England's, lobelias are used throughout the U.S. for their brilliant blue effects in combination boxes, pots, and for borders. With the development of many delicate-toned varieties, lobelias have gained in popularity and are highly valued as edging plants in shady or semishady areas.

Culturally, they are not difficult. Being a bit slow-growing, they should be started not later than February 1, if flowering pot plants are wanted for Memorial Day. The seed is very fine; don't cover. A moderate temperature, say 45-50°, will keep them moving without undue softening. They stand transplanting satisfactorily, and do well in any ordinary garden soil. If you can give them some shade, they will stand heat much better.

Most popular in the dwarf class is *Crystal Palace*—a very dwarf, deep blue with dark, bronzy-green foliage. *Blue Gown* is a strong, deep blue with a very slight eye; *White Lady* is clear and showy. *Heavenly* is a deep sky-blue with large flowers and compact habit. *String of Pearls* is a mixture blended from separate colors. All of the above varieties will stay below 8 inches.

There is a trailing class known as *pendula* that works out well for trailing over porch boxes, etc. Outstanding are *Hamburgia*, sky-blue with white eye and bronzy foliage, and *Sapphire,* deep blue with white eye and light green foliage.

LUPINE

PERENNIAL *(L. polyphyllus) 1,000 seeds per oz. Germinates in 30 days at alt. 70-85°*

At one time, the annual form of lupine *(L. hartwegii)* was used as a cut-flower crop under glass. Today, however, it is seldom used for this purpose, and the perennial form has greater commercial value.

The perennial species generally grown is known as *polyphyllus* and is not dependably hardy under our climatic conditions, though they will come through if covered with coarse material. Like the entire lupine family, the *polyphyllus* class resents such temperatures as we occasionally meet with during June, their flowering season. They reach their highest state of perfection in England. There are favored locations here—mild winters and moderate summers—and under such conditions, they should be used. They delight in a loose, rather sandy soil that must be well drained. By far, the best class of hardy lupines is the *Russell* strain. All garden forms grown previous to the introduction of this strain were superseded by its development. Producing large blossoms and shapely spikes in an extensive range of color, they provide a brilliant display in the early perennial border.

MARIGOLD

ANNUAL *(Tagetes patula and erecta)*

9,000-10,000 seeds per oz. Germinates in 7 days at 70-75°

One of the most showy and easily grown annuals, useful for bedding, pots, and cutting purposes, the marigold continues to grow in popularity. Responsible to a great degree for this continued rise in popularity is the development of new and improved varieties to such an extent that there are types and varieties available today that would fit nearly every gardening need. (See chart below.) While they are native to warmer countries they do not perform at their

Showboat is a bright golden dwarf triploid that performs well in the pack and garden. Ultimate height of 12-15 inches make the plant useful in containers and beds.

best during periods of extreme heat such as we often experience here in July and August. For greenhouse cut-flower use, we recommend a night temperature of 50-55°. A January or February sowing spaced 4 by 4 inches and grown single-stem will flower in April and May, while an August sowing will produce flowers for December and January cutting. Seedlings should be

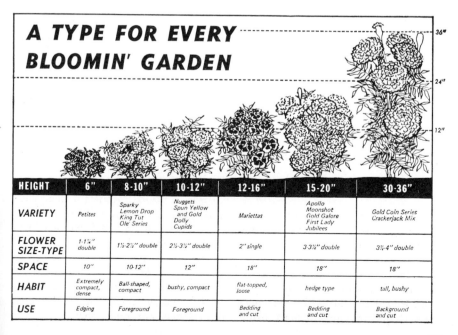

A TYPE FOR EVERY BLOOMIN' GARDEN

HEIGHT	6"	8-10"	10-12"	12-16"	15-20"	30-36"
VARIETY	Petites	Sparky Lemon Drop King Tut Ole' Series	Nuggets Spun Yellow and Gold Dolly Cupids	Mariettas	Apollo Moonshot Gold Galore First Lady Jubilees	Gold Coin Series Crackerjack Mix
FLOWER SIZE-TYPE	1-1½" double	1½-2½" double	2½-3½" double	2" single	3-3½" double	3½-4" double
SPACE	10"	10-12"	12"	18"	18"	18"
HABIT	Extremely compact, dense	Ball-shaped, compact	bushy, compact	flat-topped, loose	hedge type	tall, bushy
USE	Edging	Foreground	Foreground	Bedding and cut	Bedding and cut	Background and cut

transplanted direct to a raised bench. The giant-flowered varieties fit this purpose well. Included in this group are the F_1 Gold Coin series, and Crackerjack Mixture, an excellent inbred, double-carnation-flowered type.

With the wide selection of types and sizes available today for general bedding-plant purposes, the most feasible descriptive type of classification is simply to group them into dwarf and tall varieties.

DWARF MARIGOLDS:

Most useful for pots and bedding-plant sales. For 2¼-inch pots for Mother's Day, sow about February 15. For blooming plants in packs for May sales, sow 8 to 10 weeks before selling season and grow warm. Following is a listing of those varieties that are time-tested and have proven to be most popular in their class, along with a few new ones showing great promise.

The "double petites" are an extra-dwarf strain (6 inches) used in a mixture as well as separate colors with the yellow being most popular. *Sparky* (8-10 inches) presents a striking combination of gold and red flowers 2½ inches across. Similar to *Sparky* is *Bolero*, an All-America Award winner in the 8-10-inch height class that produces flowers with bright maroon petals tinged gold at the center. *Lemon Drop* (9 inches) with fully-double, small, lemon-yellow flowers, continues to hold its own and is most dependable. An interesting, more recently introduced class are the *Nuggets* which are dwarf triploids, growing about 12 inches high with 2-inch blooms. They flower more freely through the summer, since they produce no seed. Germination is somewhat reduced and they do produce a small percent of taller types. They are available in the usual range of marigold colors. *Moonshot, Apollo* and *Mariner* comprise the F_1, Dwarf Giant Double Space Age series. Growing to a height of 14 inches, they produce large, 3 inch double flowers. *Moonshot* is yellow, *Apollo*, orange and *Mariner*, gold. *Space Age* is a mixture of the three. All will bloom in the pack at a height of 10 inches, 10-12 weeks from a February sowing. *Dolly* is an extra-dwarf (10 inch) large-flowered (up to 4 inches) type in a mixture of orange, yellow and primrose colors. Similar to *Dolly* but improved with the addition of orange colors is *Guys and Dolls*. *Golden Boy* is a golden-yellow version of *Petite Gold*, having a similar habit, but larger flowers. *King Tut*, in the same height class, has a golden-yellow crest with deep red guard petals, similar to *Spry* but much larger.

In the super double crested class are two series: The *Royal Crested* and the *Moon* series. The former consists of 4 separate colors and a mix, *Honeycomb, Autumn Haze, Gold Rush* and *Stardust*. These grow to a height of 8-10 inches and are essentially shades of gold, yellow and orange tinged or edged with maroon or red. The *Moon* series consists of *Harvest Moon*, an orange, *Honey Moon*, a yellow, and *Pagan Moon*, a gold and red. These will flower about 2 inches taller than the *Royal Cresteds*. *Firelight* is bright red with a gold center, while *Sunlight* is a bright maroon flecked with crimson. Both produce 2½-inch flowers. Not to be forgotten is the single-flowered *Dainty Marietta* (12 inches high), which freely produces 2-inch single, golden-yellow flowers with dark red eyes.

**MARIGOLD F₁ HYBRID
HAPPY FACE
AAS—'73**
Most recent addition to the very
popular "hedge" type.

TALL MARIGOLDS:

The newer F_1 hybrids are rapidly crowding out the inbreds which were formerly grown in large quantities. Because of their hybrid vigor, they are better able to withstand midsummer heat and produce a continuous show of color throughout the season. Most sowings of this type should be made about 6 weeks before the selling season begins. If they tend to get too tall, they can be pinched back without any ill effects. The following method is being used by some growers to produce earlier-flowering plants: Sow seed about 6 weeks before intended selling date, and as soon as it sprouts, limit the day length to 9 hours by the use of black-shade cloth. Continue the use of black cloth for 30 days after the seeds have emerged. At this time, remove the black cloth and market as desired. At this stage, bud tips are in evidence and their development will continue normally. This crop must be grown at 65°.

For flowering pots for Mother's Day, sow in mid-February. Use the above short-day-treatment plan, and transplant 8 seedlings to a 6-inch pot. Plants should be treated several times with B-Nine, the last application being made when the plants are disbudded. Plants treated in this manner will continue to flower normally throughout the summer. Best suited for this purpose is the "semitall" or "hedge-type" group, which includes *First Lady, Gold Galore, Happy Face* and the *Jubilee* series.

Probably the best of the tall-growing F_1 hybrids is the *Gold Coin* series, which, in addition to a mixture, consists of *Double Eagle,* a pleasing light orange; *Doubloon,* a bright yellow; and *Sovereign,* pure gold. These vigorous, uniform hybrids produce large double flowers on 2½-foot-tall plants. Second to the *Gold Coins* in popularity is the F_1 *Climax* series which is similar in habit and is available in a mix and also separate colors of yellow and orange *(Toreador). Crackerjack Mixture* (30-36 inches) is an excellent inbred, fully double, carnation-flowered variety. The flowers are 100% double and are produced in shades of orange, yellow and gold.

The most significant development produced by intensive breeding efforts on marigolds in recent years has been the introduction of the "hedge-type" or semitall F_1 hybrid group. Growing to a height of from 15 to 20 inches, they are densely branched with a very compact habit, and produce large flowers in abundance all over the plant. They have the ability to stay upright throughout the season without staking. Included in this type are the *Jubilees* (18-20 inches), *Diamond, Golden, Orange* and a mix; *First Lady* (15-18 inches), a bright yellow; *Gold Galore* (16-18 inches), and *Happy Face*, the newest addition to this group. It is a large deep gold that produces a continuous crop of flowers even through extremely hot periods.

MATRICARIA (Feverfew)

PERENNIAL *(M. capensis) 145,000 seeds per oz. Germinates in 15 days at 70°*

Though there are dwarf forms of matricaria available for bedding-plant purposes, it is more commonly used as a greenhouse cut flower. Formerly used in considerable quantity as filler material, its usage has been declining. Although usually flowered in May from an October or November sowing, a crop may be had in flower as early as the first of March.

The early flowering is accomplished by lighting with 60-watt lights, spaced 4 feet apart. For a normal Easter and around the middle of April, the seed (*Ball Double White Imp.*) should be sown in mid-October, benched in the latter part of January, and lighted 4 hours per night from February 5 until buds show. An earlier or later flowering would have to be varied correspondingly. A February 1 sowing, planted out after hard frosts are over, will flower heavily in June.

The culture is easy—any good soil will do. Although normally a heavy feeder, be careful of overfeeding or overwatering during winter—especially on ground beds. Use 10 by 12-inch spacing for raised beds or 12 by 12-inch for ground beds. A 50° night temperature is desirable. Red spider likes feverfew, so watch for it. The *Ball Double White Improved* makes very fine long stems for cut-flower work.

Feverfew can be grown from cuttings, but seed is most reliable and more commonly used.

MORNING GLORY

ANNUAL *Morning Glory (convolvulus species)*
650 seeds per oz. Germinates in 7 days at 65°

Popular as these showy vines are, we occasionally get complaints about "all vines and no flowers." There are 2 reasons why this sometimes happens: too much moisture or excessive soil fertility. For bedding plants, use in 3 or 4-inch Jiffy-Pots, sow 4 or 5 weeks before time to sell. Band or pot seedlings 1 week after germination to prevent transplanting shock, and insert a short stake in the center. *Heavenly Blue* is, in our opinion, the showiest and the best seller. A more-recent introduction is the variety *Early Call*, an All-America Selection. It is a dependable, large-flowered bright rose.

MYOSOTIS (Forget-Me-Not)

ANNUAL *(M. oblongata) 44,000 seeds per oz. Germinates in 10 days at 55°. Dark.*

Because of its blue color and ease with which it can be grown, myosotis or forget-me-not can be used by growers, chiefly retail, as a good, short-stemmed, cut-flower crop. It flowers over a long period of time and does not require a great deal of space. While they are a cool-house crop, they are probably more profitable in a 50° temperature when grown for cutting. Some growers plant them along the edge of a carnation bench, to which there is no objection if the walks are not too narrow.

Economical and easy to grow from seed, myosotis can be sown any time from June to August. If planted on a bench, space them about 10 by 10 inches for they make quite a spread during the winter. Because it is early and free flowering, the variety *Ball Early* (bright blue) is best suited for this purpose. It can also be used for pots. For spring pots, a sowing should be made in December or January.

Considerable business is done in spring with plants carried over and grown as are spring pansy plants; but they are frequently not so hardy as pansies, so they should be planted in frames and covered with some loose straw and a sash.

Largely used this way are the perennial forms. Of these, the *Victoria* strain, because of its dwarf compact habit (6-8 inches), is very popular. Available in a number of separate colors, its greatest demand lies in the blues.

Cynoglossums are sometimes referred to as Chinese or summer forget-me-nots, but are not related to myosotis and wilt after cutting though placed in water.

NASTURTIUM

ANNUAL *(Tropaeolum majus) 175 seeds per oz. Germinates in 10 days at 65°.*

While the ordinary kind is sometimes very effectively used for bedding, it is not, on the whole, much of a florist item. But they are popular with the gardening public who buy tons of seed for outdoor planting. Of much more interest and value is the *Double Gleam* type. Of a trailing or climbing habit, they produce fragrant, double, long-stemmed flowers in rich colors. They are well suited for greenhouse cutting or outdoor use.

More suitable for outdoor bedding purposes because of its dwarf, rounded, compact habit, *Jewel Mixture* is widely used. It produces large, double flowers of the *Gleam* type in a brilliant assortment of colors.

NEMESIA

ANNUAL *(N. strumosa suttonii)*
90,000 seeds per oz. Germinates in 10 days at alt. 55-65°. Dark.

There are two distinct classes of this showy annual. *Grandiflora* is the name of the taller strain that can be used as a novelty greenhouse cut flower and will draw up to a height of about 2 feet.

Of much greater value is the *Nana Compacta* type. Its dwarf habit, 10 inches in the greenhouse, makes it popular to use in combinations. For this purpose, it should be sown in January and February for April and May flowering in 2¼ or 3-inch pots. While available in separate colors, it is chiefly used as a mixture. The *Hi Fi Mixture* is a most excellent strain, which is more heat resistant and will remain in flower several weeks longer.

NICOTIANA (Flowering Tobacco)

ANNUAL *(N. affinis) 300,000-400,000 seeds per oz.*
Germinates in 15 days at 70°. Light.

Several ornamental species of the tobacco family have been improved to the point where they are quite attractive for garden decoration. They are a taller-growing annual and adaptable to a wide variety of planting compositions. In sunny areas, they will give a continuous display of color over a fairly long season. Easily grown from seed, they should be sown about the middle of April for late-May pack sales. *Sensation Mixture* is a strain that contains all colors from white through cream and pink to crimson and purple. Recently introduced is the F_1 hybrid *Nicki Series*, 16 to 18 inches tall, self-branching, free flowering with fine fragrance. *Nicki* represents a great improvement over existing strains. Its currently available in three separate colors, pink, rose and white.

NIEREMBERGIA (Cup-Flower)

ANNUAL *175,000 seeds per oz. Germinates in 15 days at 70°*

The variety *Regal Robe* is a tender perennial form that flowers early and freely the first summer after sowing. It is of compact growth, keeping itself completely covered with purple-blue flowers throughout the season, even in strong sunlight. We have noted second-year plants in California grow to 18 inches, but nierembergia doesn't grow over 6-10 inches with us, though it is somewhat spreading. While it is reported to endure 10-15° frost, it isn't at all hardy in our locality and probably should be handled as an annual in most areas.

Not as widely used as it could be, it is a good bedding plant here in the Midwest, and is especially valuable for edging. A January sowing will provide blooming material for combination and bedding sales in May.

PANSY F₁ HYBRID GOLDEN CHAMPION
Typical of the new improved F₁ hybrid pansies appearing on the market.

PANSY (Viola Tricolor)

ANNUAL *(Viola tricolor) 20,000 seeds per oz. Germinates in 10 days at 65-70°. Dark.*

Pansies continue to rate high on the list of American gardeners' favorite bedding plants. Coming into bloom early in the spring in a wide and interesting color range, a quality pack or flat of pansies in flower is hard for the home gardener to resist. Adapted to a wide variety of planting uses, they are a most consistent performer, even under conditions of high pollution. With the advent of F_1 hybrids, showing apparent ability to flower in the heat of summer, their future potential appears well insured.

WHEN TO SOW

Midsummer has long been the traditional sowing time, generally late July or early August in the North. But any pansy plants which must grow from August 1 to April or May before being sold—about 9 months in all—encounter many conditions that can reduce quality. Their worst testing time is usually during winter, when exposure to weather can harden and damage outside leaves, even though the heart of the plant comes through in good shape. Good-looking pansies can be grown from summer sowings, though, by keeping the plants well watered and fertilized during their growth and giving thorough winter protection. One other point: This system usually produces the heaviest plants.

The method being used by more growers each year calls for a December or early-January sowing. Pansies can be grown steadily straight through to selling time with no dormant period. There is no hot-weather trouble during seed sowing and no damage from winter injury. Plants are either taken straight through in a 50° greenhouse, or else shifted to frames when weather permits, usually early March. The greenhouse growing is often on shelves

Pansy packs—always a very popular early-spring sales item. With the development of new F₁ hybrid strains which have the ability to produce flowers throughout the hot summer, the continued popularity of this item would seem to be assured.

and racks or in little-used cold houses; heated frames also work well. This minimizes use of expensive greenhouse space.

Seedlings started in November or early December and carried around 40° or 45° make good, heavy plants, which often bring more than enough to justify the added time and expense. At the other end of the scale are late sowings made up to March 1. These produce young stock for sale with annual bedding plants, and can increase your overall pansy business. Southern growers frequently purchase seedlings shipped down from the North instead of trying to grow their own, since pansy seed can be difficult to germinate in extremely hot weather. August sowings are the most common, whether for spring sales in the mid-South or midwinter sales in the Deep South.

CONTAINERS

Consider for a moment the labor it takes to sell pansy plants. Making up baskets is a time-consuming job that must be done when you can least afford the time. A good many growers are shifting over to the bedding-plant method of handling—growing them in the selling container. They find that top-quality plants can be grown in their own choice of the many pack sizes and types available. Trends in containers seem to be toward greater use of the multiple-unit type where the seedlings are grown as individual plants, separated from each other, and yet handled as one unit. The Jiffy-Strip is an example of this type. Another widely used type is the Cell-Pak, a vacuum-formed plastic unit that is available in a wide range of configurations. Four to 6-plant units are becoming more common. In these size units, ample space is provided to finish extra-heavy plants.

Customer satisfaction should reach new highs when they discover that there is no transplanting shock and each plant has a large intact root system. Pansies, it is being found, will bloom well into summer with this treatment. With either of these containers, beds or benches should have a root-discouraging surface, such as a layer of polyethylene or pea gravel. This keeps the pack clean and attractive, and easily restrains the root system in Jiffy-Pots (pansies are fairly light rooters).

SEED STARTING

Pansy germination requirements include:
Temperature: 65°-70°.
Medium: Something sterile, well drained and low in fertility, that will not pack.
Covering: Enough to hide the seed.
Moisture: Constant. Intermittent-mist systems work well, as do plastic sleeves over the seed flats. (See snapdragons.)
Air and light: Little at first, to retard drying; plenty as soon as seedlings are up.

In the greenhouse, these requirements are met much the same as for snaps, and you may wish to check the snap story for some of the details.

Night temperatures of 65° to 70° are best until seed is up, when you can begin dropping to 50° by a week or so after germination.

A fine, friable soil mixture is suitable for a germinating medium. You can use sand-peat, perlite, leaf mold and other ingredients as well, just so you come up with a mix that meets the physical and chemical requirements.

Whatever means you employ to keep the seeds moist while sprouting, they should not dry out at all. After they are up, they do need plenty of air and light, and the soil surface can get quite dry between waterings.

Germinating pansy seed outside in frames is quite an art, practiced successfully by many careful growers. Sowings are made right in the frame where the seed bed has been carefully prepared and leveled. After thoroughly soaking the soil, about ½ inch of screened neutral peat is added. Beds are then steamed or treated with chemical sterilants. Steam is best. Seed is broadcast *thinly*, one ounce to 75 square feet. A very thin layer of sterilized neutral peat, or a mixture of 2 parts peat and 1 part soil (sifted) is used to cover the seed lightly. Constant moisture must be retained after sowing. Any period of dryness during germination is usually fatal. Germinating time is usually 10 to 14 days, depending on weather conditions.

Frames are covered with burlap and a double layer of lath to preserve moisture, which means that usually no watering is needed before sprouting. As soon as seed is well sprouted, the cover starts coming off, and within a week or so, they are receiving full light and air.

GENERAL GROWING

Pansies can get too soft. Watering, feeding, temperatures, light, ventilation, soil, spacing, all are influenced by this fact. Fifty degrees is usually considered the maximum night temperature, and this during good weather. In dark, cloudy periods, growers may favor dropping the temperature a few degrees below 50°.

At these cool temperatures, water requirements will be modest. Letting the plants dry to the point of slight wilting before giving water promotes the deep green foliage customers like to see. Feeding is usually light or nonexistent during winter. Summer-started plants, or those sown in the greenhouse later on, should get enough feed from the original planting soil until bright spring weather arrives, when 1 or more applications of 25-0-25 at 1 ounce to 3 gallons of water will help in finishing them.

Pansy soil should be loose, with plenty of organic matter—1 part peat to 3 parts soil, or a 2-inch layer worked into the top 6 inches of soil in frames or beds. Twenty per cent superphosphate is usually added, 5 pounds per 100 square feet, or 2 pounds per cubic yard.

Full light develops the best pansies. In fact, some growers use the sash all winter with frame-grown stock, even when plants are dormant and frozen. More conventional protection is loose straw or salt marsh hay applied only after freeze-up. Along with plenty of light, they like plenty of air. Except for frost protection, sash should be left off altogether once plants are in active growth. In greenhouses, pansies need maximum ventilation to keep from getting too soft.

In outdoor beds or frames, pansy spacing varies from 4 by 4 to 9 by 9 inches, 6 by 6 is a rough average. Flat and pack growers generally space them much closer, since they are growing smaller, younger plants. They find that as soon as a few flowers pop, the packs are salable, and thus it is not necessary to grow the plants to an extra-large size. In Jiffy-Pots, pansies usually are rim to rim—sizes ranging up to 4 inches make several spacings available.

VARIETIES

Based on our yearly flowering trials at West Chicago, here is the way pansy varieties stack up.

Ball Giant Mixture. Our most popular dwarf bedding strain. Contains principally a *Swiss Giant* mixture, with separate colors added to insure a well-rounded balance of all bright pansy shades.

Roggli Giant Elite Mixed has a color richness not equalled by any other strain. This original *Swiss* strain also excels in dwarf habit and large flowers with excellent substance.

F₁ Majestic Giants. Rapidly increasing in popularity, this large-flowered, early-blooming giant blooms well throughout the summer. Flowers have conspicuous blotches.

Super Clear Crystals. An improvement over the regular *Clear Crystals* strain, with larger flowers. Flowers are in clear colors without the dark center blotch in shades of red, blue, yellow, orange, lilac, purple and white.

Steele's Jumbo Mixture. Large flowers, early, vigorous grower. Always popular. Does well in South.

Four Aces Formula Mixture. Combines by formula blend these best sellers:

PANSY F₁ HYBRID MAJESTIC GIANT MIX
Ever-increasing in popularity, this giant-flowered pansy displays well the advantages of an F_1 hybrid: Greater vigor, earlier flowering and heat tolerance.

Ball Giant Mixture, Roggli Giant Elite Mixed, Steele's Jumbo Mixture, and *Oregon Giants.*

Color Carnival. The closest thing to the originator's *Roggli* strain. Excellent color blend. American-produced.

Ruffled Rainbow. Unusually heavy ruffling gives this strain a special appeal. Fine color balance.

Early Season Mix. A very early F_2 strain with good range of colors, both clear and with blotch.

King Size. Color range and size similar to *Roggli* but several weeks earlier.

Masquerade. An F_2 strain of *Steele's Jumbo* with typical *Jumbo* colors. Early.

There is considerable demand for pansies in separate colors, and many growers offer them this way to give a distinction to their line. While they are available in many separate colors, demand is greatest for white, yellow and blue. Most popular in the F_1 separate colors are: *Mammoth White,* ivory with small yellow eye; *Azure Blue,* a rich azure color with lighter petals at the top; *Sunny Boy,* a bright yellow with a dark blotch—very dwarf. *Golden Champion,* the largest flowered clear golden yellow. *Imperial Giant Blue,* (AAS) a light lavender-blue with yellow eye; *Imperial Giants Orange,* Bright orange. Widely used inbreds include *Coronation Gold,* a clear golden yellow; *Pay Dirt,* large yellow with black lines; *Thunersee,* dark blue with blotch; *True Blue,* light mid-blue shades; *Paper White,* pure white with a yellow eye.

Winter-flowering pansies for cutting have a definite place as inexpensive gifts and for home decoration, and can be used in the same manner as sweet peas. Sown around August 1, they will flower at 50° from December to late spring. They require from 10 to 12 inches of space each way, and support by wire and string.

PETUNIA WHITE CASCADE
The No. 1 petunia in popularity. Excellent for hanging baskets. Great for bedding.

PETUNIA

ANNUAL *(P. hybrida) 285,000 seeds per oz. Germinates in 10-12 days at 70-80°.*

The many and important cultural aspects of petunias are covered in some detail in the bedding-plant section of this book (page 3).

Not covered in that section, though, is the very important question of what's best in classes and varieties of petunias. The following is a resume of "best in class" for each of the various colors and types as of today:

CLASSES AND THEIR USES

Grandiflora Doubles. Well known for their value as pot plants, the grandiflora double petunias do very well as bedding plants, too. New varieties with 3 to 4-inch flowers provide an ever-widening range of solid colors and two-tone combinations for every taste. "Best in class"—*Fantasy,* variegated blue and white; *Blue Crown,* dark blue; *Canadian Queen,* rose-pink; *Salmon Bouquet,* light salmon-pink; *Sonata,* white; *Valentine,* red; and *Circus,* a salmon-red and white bicolor.

Good doubles in 4-inch pots for early April are best produced from a late-November sowing, growing them at about 45°. For later May flowering, 3-inch pots are usually preferred. Early-January sowing will bring these along for Mother's Day or Memorial Day gifts or combinations. The grandiflora doubles require a little more attention than the other petunia classes. They cannot develop to their full potential if grown half starved or too cold. Growing them under these conditions will often produce semidouble or poorly developed flowers.

Multiflora Doubles. Free-flowering and showy, they bloom more freely than the grandiflora doubles, when planted outdoors. Compact in growth, they produce many miniature carnation-like flowers in a good color range, and provide an outstanding show of color, even under the difficult conditions of the midwestern summer. "Best in class"—*Cherry Tart*, #1 multiflora double, rose-pink and white bicolor; *Plum Tart*, penciled bright orchid; *Apple Tart*, coral; *Salmon Delight*, light clear salmon-pink; *Snowberry Tart*, pure white; *Red and White Delight*, white and strawberry red.

As with grandiflora doubles, these should be sown earlier than the other types to sell at the same time.

California Giants. Recommended mainly for spring pots. *Can-Can*, an F_1 hybrid mix of many shades of colors, gives a high percentage of huge flowers. The variety *Ball Dwarf Giant #1* is noted for extra-early flowering on dwarf, compact plants. Flowers often reach 5 to 6 inches in diameter. While declining each year in popularity, there still is considerable demand for this class. However, these appear to be giving way to new and larger-flowered single grandifloras. Sowing dates: same as for all doubles.

Single Grandifloras. This class, with its large and attractive individual flowers, continues to lead in popularity and includes all the "fancy" single types—petals are ruffled or fringed or both; flower size is medium or large. Virtually all the key varieties are F_1 hybrids, which are available in every petunia color, with many bicolors and other unusual flower forms. Certain grandifloras are best suited for pots, with a dwarf, early-blooming type of growth. Others, having a more vigorous growth habit, find their best use in beds. A good many varieties, including *Pink Magic* and *White Magic*, give top performance either way. "Best in class"—*Calypso*, variegated scarlet and

Breeding of annuals at Pan American Seed Company, Bradenton, Florida. This work has created such important garden flowers as Carefree Geraniums and a wide variety of petunias such as the Cascade series, El Toro, Red Magic and Pink Snow.

PETUNIA CHERRY TART
The finest and most popular of all multiflora doubles.

white; *Royal Cascade,* a deep blue; *Red Baron,* a large, early bright red; *Red Cascade,* a close #2 in reds; *Pink Magic,* a smooth bright pink; *Coral Cascade,* coral-rose; *White Cascade,* giant, pure white; *Sunburst,* ruffled light yellow; and *Sugar Daddy,* bright orchid with deep-red veins.

One of the outstanding series in the F_1 single grandiflora class is the *Cascades.* While, with their vigorous growth habit and extra-large flowers they are ideal for bed planting and pots, their most popular usage is for hanging baskets, window boxes, etc., where their cascading habit is a "natural."

Single Multifloras. Here is the traditional bedding class of petunia. F_1 hybrids provide vigorous plants of excellent, compact habit in all major petunia shades, with starred and striped varieties as well. Early-March sowing means salable plants in flats or packs by about mid-May.

"Best in class"—*Starfire,* scarlet and white; *Sugar Plum,* orchid with wine-red veins; *Paleface,* white with small creamy eye; *Pink Salmon,* rose-pink; *Comanche,* scarlet-red; *Coral Satin,* coral-rose; and *Moon Glow,* rich creamy yellow.

PETUNIA RED BARON
Major hybridizers have produced many new improved varieties in recent years. One of the most promising of these is the brilliant Red Baron.

PHLOX

ANNUAL *(P. drummondi) 14,000 seeds per oz. Germinates in 10 days at 65°. Dark.*
PERENNIAL *(P. paniculata) 2,500 seeds per oz. Germinates in 3-4 wks. at 65-75°.*

A very showy, colorful annual that probably requires a little more attention than common annuals, such as petunias, when planted to outdoor beds. They will easily make satisfactory-sized bedding plants for spring sales by sowing about the middle of March.

There are both a tall and a dwarf class of phlox, known as *Grandiflora* (15-18 inches) and *Nana Compacta* (6-8 inches), respectively. The former can be used where cut flowers are wanted, but the dwarf forms are most popular and of greatest commercial value.

Best in the *Nana Compacta* group are: *Beauty* and *Ideal Bedding Mixture,* however, the most widely used dwarf forms are *Globe Mix* and *Twinkle.*

The former has an almost perfectly rounded ball-like growth habit and an exceptionally free-flowering characteristic. It branches out beautifully from the base of the plant in marked contrast to the other types of annual phlox, and has a good range of showy colors. *Twinkle,* an early bloomer, produces an abundant amount of dainty starred flowers with pointed petals.

Then there is the whole class of perennial phlox, about which a separate *RED BOOK* might be written. Briefly, though, the most important group is the summer phlox *(P. decussata, P. paniculata, P. maculata,* etc.). There are dozens of brilliant reds, purples, salmons, and varicolored varieties propagated by divisions and root cuttings in this group. They like a fairly well-enriched soil and should be kept fairly moist. Let each clump have 4 or 5 square feet to develop. Their normal flowering season is mid-July to September. *Beltsville Beauty* is a blend of *P. paniculata* types under the name of *Beltsville Beauty.* Seed should be exposed to freezing weather for several weeks for best germination.

For rock-garden work, the dwarf perennial *Phlox subulata,* variety *Nelsonii,* makes a brilliant showing. They are division-propagated, flower early in May, and make a mat of bright green foliage clear through the season. In addition to *Nelsonii,* there are a dozen or so other choice varieties varying from white through bright pink, red, and crimson. All of this *subulata* group are procumbent, under 3 inches, and are used for carpet plantings, rockeries, etc.

Note on germination information: "Light" means that best germination is obtained when seeds are exposed to light. "Dark" indicates that seeds germinate better without light. "Alt. 70-85°" indicates that this crop should be grown at an alternating temperature of 70° nights and 85° days.

A striking demonstration of the case for growth retardants on poinsettias. The plant on your right was treated with Cycocel. Plant on your left (the tall one), no treatment. The variety: Elisabeth Ecke. Holding the plant, Mr. Paul Ecke, Sr.

POINSETTIA CULTURE

Paul Ecke, Jr.
Paul Ecke Poinsettias

GENERAL REQUIREMENTS AND CHARACTERISTICS

Cultural programs have changed substantially in poinsettia production over the past decade due to the differences in growth habit of the new varieties. Fortunately, most of the changes in variety characteristics have made it easier to produce a quality plant.

As new varieties are developed, tested and introduced into the trade, there will undoubtedly be new approaches employed in their handling. However, certain basic characteristics of poinsettias will prevail, regardless of developments, and it is the purpose of this publication to provide both background and practical-application information on handling this crop in particular.

The poinsettia is a short-day plant which is grown in greenhouses to produce colored leaves called "bracts" rather than the flower itself, which is a relatively inconspicuous organ. It has been demonstrated that in the northern hemisphere, flower-bud initiation occurs in early October, and, under favorable temperature conditions, results in flowering at or near Christmas. Some of the varieties may flower faster and others slower than the average. One of the attractive features of poinsettias for Christmas production is that there is little or no need for day-length control. For other blooming periods, day length must be artificially controlled. In general, it can be assumed that the bract development will be completed 2 to 3 months after initiation.

Although all aspects of the mechanism have not been clearly demonstrated, it appears that there is a certain minimum day-length requirement for the first stage of initiation. If this critical day length remains constant, the plant may tend to split as if it had been pinched, and proceed to produce 3 vegetative branches. However, if the day length is gradually reduced from time of initiation, the tendency then is to produce a single stem terminating in bract and flower. Thus, under normal conditions, initiation occurs when days are just short enough to stimulate this reaction and as days gradually become shorter, they automatically satisfy the second requirement.

Poinsettias have been, and currently are being grown in a wide variety of media. There is little question that best root development and subsequent growth occur in soil mixes of high porosity. It has further been demonstrated that poinsettias thrive under conditions of high fertility and high moisture supply. The tendency has been to use very high fertility programs, but it is questionable whether they actually need to be any higher than for many other common pot-plant crops, such as pot mums and Easter lilies. The poinsettia is sensitive to high pH, with values below 6.0 considered ideal.

Susceptibility to unfavorable conditions of salinity, high boron, and high sodium are no greater than for other pot-plant crops, and, if anything, somewhat less. Domestic water containing chlorine and/or fluoride is not harmful to poinsettias.

Disease prevention deserves constant and persistent attention if successful production is to be attained. For most growers, the primary problems of disease are those which result in root deterioration during the development stages, and botrytis during the finishing stages. The latter becomes particularly important when temperatures are reduced. Normal precautions, such as are exercised for any other flowering pot-plant crops, are applicable to poinsettia production. Propagation is a particularly sensitive stage and is frequently the source of problems for the grower who does his own rooting.

Facilities required for pot-plant production of poinsettias include an ability to supply heat with minimum temperatures of no lower than 60°F and preferably capability for higher minimum temperature. The facilities should also include means of controlling excessive temperatures, though this condition usually occurs only in the earlier forcing stages. Optimum daytime temperature in 80-85°F, though the plants will tolerate considerably higher temperatures. Extremely low temperatures will tend to retard growth and incite chlorosis, while extremely high temperatures with limited light encourage stretching and thin growth. It is sometimes desirable to keep different varieties in separate houses so that they can be exposed to their own optimum temperatures.

Growth regulators are often used to restrict stem elongation, though this has become unnecessary or nearly so for some of the new varieties. The use of a growth regulator is sometimes employed for "toning" the plant. Leaf color is darkened by this treatment. Another "toning" practice is that of reducing temperatures in final stages of development, particularly for purposes of creating deeper bract color.

The typical Christmas crop is grown either as a single-stem plant terminating in bract and flower, or as a multiflowered plant with each branch resulting from the pinch producing its own bract and flower head. New varieties make the multiflowered plant highly attractive, both physically and economically. A properly grown modern variety will have a large bract and heavy stems, requiring no staking. *Eckespoint C-1* will long be remembered as a first in demonstrating these desirable characteristics.

SALES

Historically, poinsettias have been marketed through flower shops and, in some sections of the country, garden shops. With the introduction of the long-lasting varieties, poinsettias are being marketed in other sales outlets and it appears that this trend will continue. Because many of the longer-lasting varieties bloom earlier than the older varieties, sales are starting at Thanksgiving time. It is possible to insure end-of-November flowering by black-clothing from September 15 for 3 weeks. Naturally early-blooming varieties will not require this treatment.

The pricing of poinsettias varies greatly, depending on many factors. In New England, where the investment in greenhouses is high and where the fuel bill is a factor, it is obvious that these producers must get more for their plants than those in Florida growing in the field under saran covering. Many growers have tried to sell their crop by the bloom, particularly when plants were grown as single-stem. Now that there are good varieties producing excellent multiflowered plants, more growers will be marketing the plants "by the pot." In either case, it would seem that the producer should determine the cost of production and then attempt to sell the plants based on cost and reasonable return. Many wholesale growers are now planning to gross at least $2.50 per sq. ft. of finished bench space on their Christmas crop. A rule of thumb used by some growers is to figure a minimum return of 50¢/square foot/month for bench space. Spacing and time to produce a salable crop then become the deciding factors in establishing the sales price.

SHOP CARE

All varieties must be handled carefully when being wrapped and packaged in the greenhouse for delivery to retail outlets. The use of paper sleeves is common practice and is recommended. Cellophane sleeves, if used, should be perforated to avoid possible condensation of moisture on the inner side and subsequent botrytis infection of the bracts. Upon arrival at the retail outlet, the plant should be unsleeved, watered, and the appropriate care-tag attached. The retailer as well as the consumer should follow the care-tag instructions. A typical care-tag is shown on opposite page.

It has been demonstrated that poinsettia plants will last longer in the shop and in the home if at least one small light is kept burning during the entire night.

Do *not* use fluorescent lamps for displaying plants, as this light source

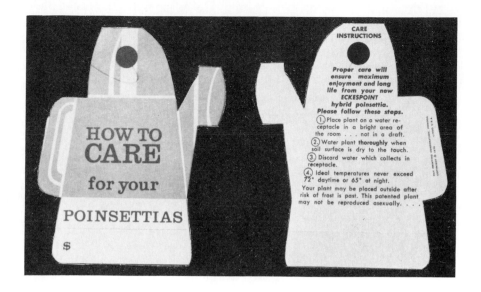

distorts the true color of bracts and leaves. Most homes are lighted with incandescent filament lamps. Light your plants with the same kind of lamp . . . the consumer will see what he is getting.

POINSETTIAS ARE NOT POISONOUS

For years, there has been adverse publicity during holiday time concerning the alleged poisonous nature of poinsettia plants. Recent research at the Ohio State University has disclosed that laboratory rats are not subject to any ill effects from eating leaves and bracts. This research indicates that the poinsettia are not harmful to humans and animals, though, of course, it is not recommended that they should be taken internally.

STOCK PLANTS

To produce flowering plants true to variety, poinsettias are vegetatively propagated using mother plants of selected quality. The use of seedlings is confined to breeding in the constant search for plants of better color, better structure, greater vigor and overall improved quality. Fortunately, the climatic conditions in southern California are particularly favorable for year-around growing and breeding of poinsettias. The bulk of the plants used in commerce originate from this area.

Not all growers produce their own cuttings. Many purchase rooted, unrooted or calloused cuttings directly from a specialist propagator, who, in turn, grows the stock plants. Specialists produce greenhouse-grown cuttings where controlled environment insures high production at periods of maximum requirement and also availability of vegetative plants the year around.

Where cutting production is to be carried out by the grower, the procedure of developing stock plants starts with purchased liners—usually 2¼-inch

405

pot-size plants or rooted cuttings—from a specialist propagator in March, April, May, or June. The specialist propagator, by virtue of controlled environment, including artificial lighting for his own stock plants, can provide vegetative plants whenever the grower might want them.

Liners received for stock-plant production should be planted as soon as possible into beds or containers in which they will be grown throughout their period of production. Placing a small liner in a large container will result in greater total growth than shifting it up from one size pot to another. Growing medium and feeding program should be the same as for Christmas-crop production. Night temperatures of 65°F and day temperatures between 80° and 90°F will favor healthy development.

Spacing of plants placed in beds must be determined at the time of planting as opposed to container planting, where later spacing can be provided according to need. The earlier the stock is planted into beds, the wider the spacing should be. The earlier the stock is planted into containers, the larger the container should be. Since cultural practices as well as varietal characteristics will determine optimum handling in any given situation, only guideline approximations can be suggested below (Table 1).

TABLE 1. STOCK PLANT BED SPACING/CONTAINER SIZE GUIDELINES

	Beds		Containers	
Month Planted	Min. Spacing	Sq. Ft./Plant	Min. Diameter	Final Spacing
March	18" x 18"	2.25	12"	18" x 18"
April	15" x 15"	1.55	10"	15" x 15"
May	12" x 12"	1.0	8"	12" x 12"
June	8" x 8"	0.44	6"	8" x 8"

There are many different and potentially successful approaches to the use of liners as a source of stock plants, but for purposes of illustration, a typical program is outlined.

1. Upon receipt, liners should be immediately potted into sterile containers of steamed or otherwise decontaminated soil of *high* porosity. Synthetic mixes have been very successful. At this time, and throughout the life of the stock plants, it is important to maintain high humidity in order to encourage maximum growth and maximum number of breaks.

2. Upon planting, drench with fungicide using the following:
   AMOUNT PER 100 GALLONS WATER
   4 ozs. Dexon 35
   4 ozs. Terraclor 75% W.P. or Benlate 50% W.

3. Maintain high fertility as for forcing of pot plants, using constant liquid feed or one of the other alternatives.

4. Provide medium shade during establishment with 65° to 70°F night temperatures, continuing to maintain high humidity during daylight hours. After plants are well established, the shading may be reduced slightly. Day temperatures should be 80° to 85°F, if possible to control.

5. As soon as liners are established, make a soft pinch (remove tip, including one fully expanded leaf). Depending on variety, three or more breaks should arise from nodes below the pinch.

6. When new growths have attained a mature state (leaves fully expanded as opposed to being paper-thin and light-colored), and when there is a minimum of 4 fully-developed leaves on the shoot, it can again be pinched in the same manner as above. This will leave 3 mature leaves and respective nodes from which additional breaks can arise. Frequently, only 2 breaks arise from the second and later pinches.

7. To avoid possible flower-bud initiation, use night lighting for 4 hours at 10 foot-candles until May 15.

8. Harvesting and propagation of cuttings can start about July 15 and proceed through the last of September. Many growers finish propagation by mid-September. Earliest propagations should be designated for branched plants or specimen plants and may require growth-regulator treatment, depending on variety. The early propagations are more subject to "splitting" unless they, in turn, are pinched.

9. The grower who wishes to produce his own cuttings from stock plants will first want to estimate the number of stock plants required to produce the desired number of cuttings. There is no substitute for experience in this regard, since so many factors enter into the calculation of production potential. Such items as time of planting, growing conditions, efficiency of pinching, efficiency of harvesting, success in propagation and, above all, the characteristics of the variety, must be considered. A table of procedure and production based on strictly theoretical considerations of a typical variety is provided (Table 2) for illustration.

In practice, it is generally found that the first pinch and the second pinch can be fairly accurately predicted. However, growth rates of some branches will be different from others. Also, it is not uncommon to obtain more than the theoretical number of breaks. For this reason, after the second pinch, it becomes necessary to examine the stock plants at about weekly intervals and pinch those stems which have matured sufficiently in the interim. The result is that stems ready for harvesting of cuttings will reach this stage at different times after any theoretical starting point. From the time that cuttings are harvested for propagation, it is usually desirable to repeat the cutting harvest at weekly intervals until the deadline date, which is frequently established as September 15.

TABLE 2. THEORETICAL STOCK-PLANT PRODUCTION

Plant Liners	March 15	April 15	May 15	June 15
1st pinch (at 2 weeks) 3 breaks	March 30	April 29	May 29	June 29
2nd pinch (at 6 weeks) 6 breaks	April 29	May 27	June 26	July 27
3rd pinch (at 10 weeks) 12 breaks	May 25	June 24		
4th pinch (at 14 weeks) 24 breaks	June 22			
Harvest 1st cuttings, Aug. 13 number	24	12	6	3
Harvest 2nd cuttings, Sept. 17 number	48	24	12	6
Total cuttings/stock plant	72	36	18	9

PROPAGATION OF SOFTWOOD CUTTINGS

The term "softwood cuttings" applies to vegetative branch tips carrying one or more mature leaves. This is different from hardwood cuttings, which are taken from mature stems with or without leaves, and usually stripped of leaves if they exist.

There are basic criteria which must be satisfied if success in propagation is to be assured. These include:

1. Absolute freedom from disease.

2. Elimination of moisture stress once cuttings have been removed from the mother plant.

3. Adequate bottom heat (70°-72°F) during rooting.

Conditions during propagation are highly favorable to spread of and infection by disease organisms. The program of sanitation must be directed toward eliminating disease rather than attempting to suppress it. This program must start *before* cuttings are taken from the stock plants.

In the outline to follow, 1 or more of the 3 criteria listed above are involved in each step. Normally, cuttings can be considered internally clean when removed from the mother plant. Surface-carried, inactive spores may be a source of contamination if not eliminated. Procedures listed below have given excellent results in propagation. This does not mean that deviations and alterations of these procedures will not also be successful. Common sense and constant attention to sanitation are primary requisites for success.

1. Use a spray program on stock plants at 1-week intervals occurring 1 or 2 days before the cuttings are to be taken. The objective is to provide protection against possible surface contamination being carried into the propagation bed.

The following combination has been successfully employed as a fine-mist coverage:

AMOUNT PER 100 GALLONS WATER

8 ozs. Captan 50% W.

2 ozs. Terraclor 75% W.P. or Benlate 50% W.

1 fl. oz. wetting agent

or

Household bleach to give 50 ppm

active ingredient (dilute at 1:1000)

1 fl. oz. wetting agent

It is of interest that wetting agents materially improve the ability of subsequent mist to thoroughly wet leaf surfaces. There is some variability with varieties. Also, it appears that the improved wetting results in improved color retention.

2. Rooting medium can be any clean and well-drained combination of sand, peat, perlite, vermiculite, or other available materials of similar properties suitable for soil-mix composition. Preformed media are also available and can be used. The medium should have a pH of 5.5 to 6.0 for best results, since excessive acidity slows rooting and excessive alkalinity contributes to chlorosis. Fertilizers as used in regular potting media incorporated into the rooting medium do not seem to inhibit rooting. Cuttings can be rooted in pots or pans containing soil mix in which they will be finished, thus saving 1 or 2 steps in handling and avoiding additional opportunity for contamination. This procedure is termed "direct rooting" and is rapidly attaining popularity for starting multiple plant pans. The procedure saves approximately 1 *week* in the forcing schedule and will produce uniform pots, if carefully managed. The procedure is fairly simple but does require special care in handling cuttings. Uniformity is most important. Cuttings should be of the same age (taken from the shoots of equal length). They should be similar in length, caliper, and color and should be stuck to the same depth. Finally, uniform mist coverage is required to produce plants of equal size and growth rate.

3. Cuttings should be removed from stock plants by means of a clean, sharp knife, making the cut anywhere between the third and fourth fully expanded leaves on a mature shoot. Ideally, the cut will leave at least 2 mature leaves on the mother plant stem as a source of new growth and subsequent cuttings. Do *not* remove leaves from the cuttings, as this reduces the stored food reserve and provides additional injury for possible infection.

4. Collect cuttings in sterile containers. Plastic containers prerinsed with diluted bleach are ideal (1 gallon 5% household bleach diluted to 10 gallons with water is satisfactory).

5. Avoid any moisture stress by undue exposure to dry air during period of collection. Ideally, though not always practical, cuttings should be taken in the evening, at night, or very early in the morning when moisture stress is minimal.

6. For efficient and rapid handling, do not collect too many cuttings at any one time. Transport each batch under sanitary and moist conditions to the propagation area. Stick cuttings as soon as possible in steamed or otherwise decontaminated rooting media. Start mist as soon as possible to minimize moisture stress.

7. All personnel handling cuttings should thoroughly wash hands with soap and water followed by a rinse with a hospital or dairy-type disinfectant. The product LF-10 used at 3 fl. ozs. per 5 gallons water has been fairly popular. Other materials are equally satisfactory and non-irritating. Shallow tubs or basins of disinfectant should be kept handy for frequent rinsing of hands and/or tools.

8. If cuttings are to be spread out on any surface for handling, be sure that such surfaces are sanitary. Plastic covering is desirable and can be disinfected easily by washing with one of the hospital disinfectants or with bleach. Any cuttings which accidentally fall to the floor or contact non-sterile surfaces should be discarded.

9. Cuttings should be stuck by placing in preformed holes or by simply pushing into soft media. Do *not* flood them in after sticking, but *do* commence mist or other humidity supply immediately upon sticking. Flooding causes rooting medium to compact around the stem, increasing the moisture and reducing the air in this zone. This condition is highly conducive to bacterial soft-rot infection, which can occur within the first 2 or 3 days after sticking.

10. Mist frequency and duration should be such that leaves always have a film of moisture covering them. A satisfactory program in California has been 5 seconds of mist at 5-minute intervals on bright, sunny days. Should drying conditions occur at night, it may be necessary to use mist during this period. In very bright weather, moderate to heavy shading is required to protect against rapid drying and high-light-intensity bleaching of the foliage.

11. At the end of 1 week, there should be evidence of callous formation. At this time, fertilizer plus fungicide can be employed as a protective drench and a means of setting the medium around the cutting. Callous formation seems to occur best when there is a large amount of air surrounding the cutting, but root initiation occurs most rapidly under slightly less open conditions. Choices of fungicide and/or fertilizer are numerous with the following having been satisfactorily employed:

AMOUNT PER 100 GALLONS WATER APPLIED
4 ozs. Terraclor 75% W.P. or Benlate 50% W.
2 lbs. Captan 50% W.P.
8 ozs. Ammonium nitrate

12. At 14 to 21 days, root initiation should be at a stage which permits reduction or elimination of mist. If day temperatures can be controlled adequately, mist should be turned off, since surface-applied water does have a bleaching and nutrient-leaching effect on the foliage. All effort should be

exercised to maintain good fertility in the rooting medium as soon as callous and root initials appear. If stretching and bleaching are problems, spray with Cycocel at 1500 ppm to reduce stretch and hold color.

13. Transplanting should occur as soon as practical after roots are established in order to minimize shock due to root disturbance.

Use of fertilizer in mist is practiced by many growers and has been advocated by numerous researchers. Experience to date indicates considerable variation in results due to materials and methods employed. Unless previous experience has provided the necessary background, the grower is advised to approach this program on a trial basis. Elements most rapidly leached from the foliage by mist are nitrogen and potassium. Phosphorus seems to encourage stretching. As a guide for initial trials, the following mist-water composition is suggested.

AMOUNT PER 1,000 GALLONS WATER APPLIED
4 lbs. Ammonium nitrate
2 lbs. Potassium nitrate

As previously mentioned, rooting can take place in a variety of media and containers. Preformed rooting media, which are rapidly appearing on the market, are being successfully used. Any *new* approach should be given adequate trial before being used on a large scale. Rooting in beds is quite common, but care must be exercised in lifting cuttings to avoid injury to roots.

Where rooting media are shallow, there is frequently an interface effect which results in waterlogging in the zone occupied by the base of the cutting. Such a condition will cause darkening and deterioration of the stem and give the appearance of disease, even though disease organisms may not be present. The reaction is actually due to lack of oxygen. To minimize this possibility, rooting beds should be 6 inches or more in depth. Where direct rooting in containers is practiced, they should preferably be nested in sterilized sand, perlite or vermiculite to effectively increase the soil column height of shallow containers. Good contact with a wood surface can also provide a certain amount of "blotter" effect causing free water to move out of the bottom of the pot.

Excessive crowding of cuttings in the propagation bed should be avoided in order to reduce soft growth, stretch, and slower rooting. In bed-rooting, allow at least 12 square inches (2 inches x 6 inches) per cutting. For rooting in 2¼-inch pots, allow 15 square inches (3 inches x 5 inches) per pot.

Although rooting hormones are not used by all propagators and are not essential to root initiation of poinsettia cuttings, experience has indicated that they do speed up the rate of rooting and improve uniformity. Normal acceleration is several days to a week or more.

One of the most convenient methods of hormone treatment is to provide a quick dip of cutting base in liquid solution. Indolebutyric acid has been successfully employed at 2500 ppm strength. A calculated risk in employing this treatment is the possibility of spreading disease from one infected cutting to all other cuttings dipped in the same solution. An insurance practice which has been shown to be beneficial is to add 10 drops of household bleach per pint of hormone solution. The use of hormone powders reduces the chance of cross contamination, particularly if some Captan is mixed with the powder. Dusting the powder on the base of the cutting is less apt to spread disease than dipping the cutting in powder. However, the use of powder provides less uniform treatment than the liquid quick dip.

Some growers use air-conditioning in their propagation areas. This is hardly necessary where frequent mist cycles are in use, but may be helpful under some circumstances. Ideally, the foliage of the cuttings should be kept cool and humid while the stem in the rooting medium should be kept warm, but not waterlogged. The ideal mist system would maintain air humidity at near 100%, but would supply little or no free water to the rooting medium. Some compromise is commonly necessary in practical procedure.

VARIETIES

STANDARDS

Within this group the principal series is the beautiful *Eckespoint C-1* which is available in *Red, Pink* and *White*. The culture of this entire group is the same, because the pink and white are sports of the original seedling.

These medium-height growers do make good branched plants, if soft-pinched properly. They are considered 9 to 10-week varieties, and must be finished at a warmer temperature to insure early to mid-December blooming, unless they are black-clothed starting September 15 for 3 weeks.

Eckespoint Reddy Light (H-15) is a medium tall grower that blooms in 10 to 11 weeks at 3°-4° lower night temperatures than C-1 in November and December. It cannot be sold on the green side as is the case with C-1.

The *Paul Mikkelsen* variety and its various sports are tall growers and were the original long-lasting type.

MULTIFLOWERING VARIETIES

The most important group in this category is the Norwegian introduction, *Annette Hegg*, and its many sports. The sports of this family are medium-short growers, and include *Dark Red Annette Hegg, White Annette Hegg, Pink Annette Hegg* and *Marble Annette Hegg* (bicolored pink and white bracts). There are many promising sports currently under trial that appear to be improvements over the current varieties, including *Annettee Hegg Supreme,* which is a more brilliant red.

Annette Hegg Diva and *Annette Hegg Lady* can be forced at lower night temperatures than any of the other sports of *Annette Hegg*. These two will flower at about the same time as *Dark Red Annette Hegg* when grown at a 1°-2° lower night temperature.

Annette Hegg and its sports are considered to be 8 to 9-week varieties. They can be produced with considerably less heat requirement and, in fact, must be finished near 60° during November and December to insure the best color in the bracts.

This family of sports has a particularly strong root system, seems to be very resistant to ordinary root rot, and can generally stand a lot of abuse before and after blooming.

A typical well-done "multiflowered" poinsettia—one cutting per pot, pinched and branched.

C-1 RED

Other multiflowering varieties within this classification are the *Mikkel®* *Rochford* and *Mikkel® Scandia*.

Currently, there are many hybridizers working to improve the variety list.

PRODUCING A CHRISTMAS-SEASON CROP

Although detailed discussion of specific phases of plant handling is provided in sections to follow, it may be helpful to have a generalized program in mind and at hand when reviewing subsequent chapters, if only for use as a point of departure. There can be many successful alterations to any outlined program including that to follow.

The first step in planning the Christmas crop is to determine the desired final product in terms of:

1. Pot sizes.
2. Varieties.
3. Blooms per pot.
    (a) Single-stem.
    (b) Branched.
4. Date ready for sale.

A production plan can then be drawn up and compared with space available in order to make final decisions on the intended inventory. It is quite important to be certain that there will be sufficient space at each stage of production, since crowding will definitely reduce quality. Table 3 provides a typical worksheet for this purpose.

Following the preparation of the plan, a "deadline" log should be prepared to indicate exact dates for completion of action for each phase of production. Since growing conditions are variable as to both location and facilities, this portion of the planning should be carefully reviewed by experienced per-

TABLE 3
POINSETTIA PRODUCTION PLAN
FOR_____
(Variety)

CONTAINER SIZE	4"	5"	6"	7"	_____
SINGLE STEM					
Total Pots					
Plants/Pot					
Cuttings Required					
Final Space (sq.ft.)*					
Sales Price/Pot					
Theoretical Gross					
BRANCHED					
Total Pots					
Plants/Pot					
Cuttings Required					
Final Space (sq.ft.)*					
Sales Price/Pot					
Theoretical Gross					

Total cuttings required _____

Total bench space required _____sq. ft.

Total theoretical gross $_____

*See Table 7. Select 2 or 3 flowers/sq. ft. spacing. For branched plants, program pinch to produce 3 or 4 flowers/plant.

sonnel and adjusted to suit the particular conditions anticipated.

All plants for the Christmas crop should be established in their final container by September 25. A possible exception would be the 4-inch pot or smaller size, where direct rooting can be started as late as September 25 in order to assure short plants. Earlier propagations are required for large-size containers to attain desired height at time of maturity.

Where single-stem, multiple-plant pots are to be produced by direct rooting, it is essential that all cuttings be uniform if a uniform finished plant is to be produced. Cuttings should be selected from stems of *equal* length to insure equal stage of maturity, and should be equal in length, stem size, leaf number, and color. Finally, they should be stuck in the rooting medium to the same depth.

Branched plants can be programmed to produce a desired number of flowering stems, particularly in the case of the free-branching *Hegg* varieties.

TABLE 4
CUTTING-PROPAGATION AND PINCHING DATES

Pot Size and Form	Direct Rooting In Finish Pot	2¼" Pot Rooting	Pinch
7"—SS—5-7 plants	Sept. 1	Aug. 25	
7"—Br—1-3 plants	Aug. 17	Aug. 10	Sept. 7
6"—SS—3-5 plants	Sept. 1	Aug. 25	
6"—Br—1-2 plants	Aug. 20	Aug. 13	Sept. 15
5"—Same as 6"			
4"—SS—1 plant	Sept. 22	Sept. 15	
4"—Br—1 plant	Sept. 7	Sept. 1	Sept. 21
Smaller pot sizes—same as 4"			

SS = Single Stem, typical *Eckespoint C-1*
Br = Branched, typical *Annette Hegg*

This is accomplished by removing the top of the plant at a point which leaves the desired number of nodes above the soil line. Each node will produce a flowering stem. Where this procedure is used, earlier propagation or transplanting can be employed since height will be controlled by removal of more of the top of the plant, should it be excessively tall.

Where cuttings are rooted in 2¼-inch pots, panning should be scheduled for approximately 4 weeks from time of sticking. By this time, roots should be well established and yet not root bound.

In order to avoid stretch, all finished containers should be placed at final spacing as early as possible and no later than October 1.

Feeding should be carried out, preferably as constant liquid feed, from the earliest date possible after roots appear. At each stage of transplanting, the new pans or pots should be drenched with a fungicide solution as a matter of precaution against accidental contamination. Subsequent drenches with Dexon should occur at minimum 30-day intervals. The first drench should include Terraclor or Benlate, but these materials can be omitted in subsequent drenches unless a particular problem arises, requiring their use.

In producing branched plants, the top should be removed at an early enough date to provide sufficient growing time to produce the length of stem required for the pot size. Immediately following the pinch, it is very important to maintain high humidity by frequent misting until branches have started to develop (approximately 1 week). Temperatures should be about 80° F in the daytime, and no lower than 65° F at night. Moderate shade will help in maintaining humidity. Care should be taken to avoid excessive water application to the roots, since plants will use less moisture due to fewer transpiring leaves. Water-logged soil will cause new leaves to be yellow.

The period of flower initiation will start between September 23 and October 10. High temperatures seem to counteract the stimulus to initiate flowers, so temperatures during this period should be reduced. Night temperatures of 64° F or lower are considered satisfactory for normal development with day temperatures not exceeding 80° F.

Since some varieties flower earlier than others, consideration must be given to providing proper temperatures and/or special treatment, depending on variety and desired date of maturity. Typical examples are *Annette Hegg*, as an early-flowering type, and *Eckespoint C-1*, as a normal-flowering type.

If the early-flowering type is being grown, a night temperature of 64° F after initiation will bring it in for Thanksgiving (November 23—November 27). If flowering is desired for Christmas for these early-flowering types, the night temperature should be no higher than 62° F until November 1, and then reduced to 60° F. Another method of delaying the crop is to provide long-day lighting from September 1 to October 10, using appropriate temperatures thereafter.

Where a normal-flowering type is being grown, it will be necessary to use black-cloth shading from September 15 to October 10 to obtain earlier initiation for a Thanksgiving crop. After initiation, night temperature should be approximately 65° F with day temperature about 80°F. Obviously, it will be necessary to advance the propagation and planting schedules where normal-season varieties are being shaded for early flowering.

In the period following flower initiation, it is desirable to apply growth regulators as a spray or a drench. This practice seems to improve plant quality by darkening foliage and strengthening stems, even though varieties being grown may be naturally short. Varieties which tend to grow tall may need several applications. Spray treatment, using 1500 to 3000 ppm Cycocel, should occur prior to October 10. If desired, a drench may be used instead at 3000 ppm. Spray applications may cause temporary foliar yellowing, but they do offer an opportunity to even up the plant growth. Taller plants or branches usually receive more growth retardant under a spray program. Selective spraying is sometimes used to check the growth of overly vigorous stems. Treatment can be applied up to November 15, if growth characteristics indicate a requirement. Late applications will tend to reduce bract size and delay bract development.

Some temperature manipulation may be required as plants reach maturity to insure their being in prime condition when sold. Lower temperatures during the final one to two weeks of forcing will enhance bract color. The one adverse feature of lower temperatures is the risk of botrytis infection. Protection can be afforded by providing good air circulation at night along with some heat and ventilation to dry out the air. Also, certain fungicides can be used at regular intervals (usually once per week) to present a barrier against botrytis infection.

Air-conditioning can be used during periods of extremely high temperatures and will, under these conditions, have a very beneficial effect. However, it is important that day temperatures be in the range of 80°F for best plant performance. If the crop should appear to be ahead of schedule, air-conditioning can be used to drop the temperature to 70° or 75°F and hold the crop back. Usually, this is not practiced until fairly late in the production

TABLE 5
ECKESPOINT C-1
3-BLOOM, SINGLE-STEM-6" PAN
A TYPICAL PRODUCTION PROGRAM*

DATE	Temperature (°F) Night	Day	CULTURAL PROCEDURE
Sept. 1	72	80	Direct-stick uniform unrooted cuttings close to pot edge. Rooting is slower below 70°F soil temperature. Use automatic mist during daylight hours. Use medium shade. *Do not water in.*
Sept. 7	72	80	Water in with: *AMOUNT PER 100 GALLONS* 8 ozs. ammonium nitrate 4 ozs. Dexon 35W 4 ozs. Benlate 50%W. Continue mist.
Sept. 15	68	80	Reduce mist. Start constant liquid feed *(CLF)*. See Table 10.
Sept. 23	64	80	Space 15 x 15 inches. Spray with Cycocel @ 3000 ppm. Avoid water-logging. *CLF.* Lower temperature for uniform bud initiation.
Oct. 10	66	80	Start of forcing period. *CLF.*
Oct. 15	66	80	Spray with Cycocel @ 1500 ppm. Drench with Dexon @ 4 ozs./100 gals. *CLF.*
Nov. 7	66	75	Color showing in upper leaves. Use Termil once each week until sale to protect from botrytis. If possible, ventilate and heat at night to reduce humidity. Use internal circulation of air. *CLF.*
Nov. 15	66	75	Drench with Dexon @ 4 ozs./100 gallons. *CLF.*
Dec. 5	62	75	Bracts approaching maximum size. Lower night temperatures will enhance color. *CLF.*
Dec. 10	60-62	75	Ready for sale. Can be held in good condition for at least 2 weeks. *CLF.*

NOTE: If direct-rooting of unrooted cuttings is not used, then plant 2¼-inch liners or rooted cuttings in 6-inch pans on Sept. 15, drench with Dexon, Benlate, and ammonium nitrate. Then follow the schedule.

*Based on OHIO conditions. Northern areas may require earlier programming, with later programming for southern areas.

cycle. If temperatures are too low during the bract–maturation period, size may be adversely affected.

SPACING FOR FLOWERING PLANTS

For best quality, plants should be spaced early in their growing period to final location on the bench. This avoids temporary periods of crowding, re-

TABLE 6
ANNETTE HEGG
MULTIFLOWERED, 5 OR 6" PAN
A TYPICAL PRODUCTION PROGRAM*

DATE	Temperature (°F) Night	Day	CULTURAL PROCEDURE
Aug. 20	72	80	Direct-stick uniform unrooted cutting in center of pot. Rooting is slower below 70°F. soil temperature. Use automatic mist during daylight hours. Use medium shade. *Do not water in.*
Sept. 1	72	80	Water in with: *AMOUNT PER 100 GALLONS* 8 ozs. ammonium nitrate 4 ozs. Dexon 35W 4 ozs. Benlate 50%W.
Sept. 7	68	80	Commence constant liquid feed *(CLF)*. See Table 10.
Sept. 15	68	80	Program pinch to leave 4 or 5 nodes above the soil, depending on how many flowers are desired. Maintain high humidity. Avoid waterlogging. *CLF.*
Sept. 23	64	80	Lower temperature for uniform bud initiation. *CLF.*
Oct. 1	64	80	Breaks should be about 1 inch long. Space to 15 inches x 15 inches. Drench with Dexon @ 4 ozs./100 gals. *CLF.*
Oct. 5	64	80	Spray with Cycocel @ 1500 ppm. *CLF.*
Nov. 1	62	75	Color development well under way. Use Termil once each week until sale to protect from botrytis. If possible, ventilate and heat at night to reduce humidity. Use internal air circulation. *CLF.*
Nov. 25	60	75	Ready for early sales. *CLF.* Can be held cool for several weeks.

NOTE: If direct-rooting of unrooted cuttings is not used, then plant $2\frac{1}{4}$-inch liners or rooted cuttings into 5-inch or 6-inch pans on Sept. 1, drench with Dexon, Benlate, and ammonium nitrate. Then follow the schedule.

*Based on OHIO conditions. Northern areas may require earlier programming, with later programming for southern areas.

duces labor, and permits use of automatic irrigation for maximum period of time.

As a rule of thumb, maximum density for a high-quality product of the *large*-bract type should be figured as 2 flowers per square foot with square patterns most commonly employed. Depending on variety, method of handling, and market acceptance, up to 3 flowers per square foot can be produced.

A guide for spacing distance (Table 7) is provided as a convenient means of determining the number of plants that can be grown in a given area. This approach assumes that planting into the final container size will have occurred by September 30. Where quality is less important than quantity, later planting and closer spacing can possibly be employed. Growth-regulator sprays and drenches can be used to minimize stretch, which does occur under close-spacing conditions. Usually, the flower head is smaller and plants are less vigorous with weaker stems when spacing has been reduced.

TABLE 7
SPACING GUIDE FOR POINSETTIAS

Pot Size (inches)	Plants/ Pot	Treatment*	2 Flowers/Sq. Ft.		3 Flowers/Sq. Ft.	
			Spacing (inches)**	Sq. Ft./Pot	Spacing (inches)**	Sq. Ft./Pot
4	1	none	9 x 9	0.56	7 x 7	0.34
4	1	pinched	15 x 15	1.56	12 x 12	1.00
5	2	none	12 x 12	1.00	10 x 10	0.67
5	3	none	15 x 15	1.56	12 x 12	1.00
5	1	pinched	15 x 15	1.56	12 x 12	1.00
6	3	none	15 x 15	1.56	12 x 12	1.00
6	4	none	17 x 17	2.00	14 x 14	1.35
6	1	pinched	15 x 15	1.56	12 x 12	1.00
6	2	pinched	21 x 21	3.05	17 x 17	2.00
7	4	none	17 x 17	2.00	14 x 14	1.35
7	5	none	19 x 19	2.51	15 x 16	1.67
7	7	none	22 x 23	3.50	18 x 18	2.25
7	2	pinched	21 x 21	3.05	17 x 17	2.00
7	3	pinched	25 x 25	4.33	21 x 21	2.90

*Assume 3 strong breaks/plant; with multiflowered, there will be more.
**Approximate—rounded off to nearest inch.

CHEMICAL HEIGHT CONTROL OF POINSETTIAS
With the advent of new naturally-short-growing varieties, the importance of growth regulators and their effect on height control have been somewhat reduced. Most used in the past has been Cycocel. New products are being rapidly introduced and tested with a strong possibility that new approaches will soon be employed.

One of the most recently introduced and effective growth regulators is A-Rest. Used as a drench, ¼ pint of A-Rest should be mixed in 16 gallons of water and then apply 8 ounces of this solution per 6-inch pan, 2 times, one week apart. It should be applied to the Heggs and Rochfords no later than October 7. If the plants are lighted, extend this date till October 17.

Although it has not been labeled for use as a spray, many growers have

Dr. Marc Cathey of the U.S.D.A., checking results of his experiments on growth retardants. Treated plant on the left; untreated check on right. New products are being rapidly introduced and tested with a strong possibility that new approaches will soon be employed.

used A-Rest successfully this way. Recommendation is to mix one pint A-Rest to 3 pints of water and apply this solution to one square foot, 2 times, one week apart.

Factors affecting the action of growth regulators include concentration of active ingredient, quantity applied, time of application in relation to flowering date, stage of root development at time of application, temperature and humidity prior to and after treatment, plant moisture content, interaction of other spray materials, and method of treatment, whether by spray or drench. In general, growth regulators are *less* effective when temperatures are high, moisture supply and humidity are high, light is reduced as from crowding, and when nitrogen supply is largely ammonium or urea.

There are possible undesirable side effects from treatment. These include reduced bract size, crinkling of bracts, blotchy yellowing of leaves, marginal leaf burn, and delayed flowering. By early application under favorable environmental conditions, these problems will not develop. With spray applications, the yellow blotching which sometimes occurs will gradually disappear. Soil application seldom produces these undesirable reactions. However, foliar application permits best opportunity to even up the height of the plants.

Methods of application include soil drench or foliar spray with Cycocel. The soil drench application will usually provide greater height control than spray application per treatment. Cost of material and labor of application are higher with soil-drench procedure.

Solutions of desired strength (Table 8) should be made by measuring the appropriate quantity of growth regulator into an empty container and then adding enough water to make the desired final volume.

Soil-drench application should be made as early as practical after plants are well rooted in the container. Late applications affect bract size and form. In northern areas, it is not recommended that application be made later than October 15. In southern areas, applications have been successful as late as

TABLE 8—CYCOCEL GROWTH-REGULATOR SOLUTION PREPARATION
(BASED ON 11% CONCENTRATE)

Desired Concentration		Fluid ounces to make:		Dilution Ratio
%	ppm	1 gallon	10 gallons	
0.1	1,000	1	11	1:116
0.15	1,500	1½	16	1:80
0.2	2,000	2	22	1:58
0.25	2,500	3	28	1:46
0.3	3,000	3½	32	1:40
0.5	5,000	5½	54	1:24
0.6	6,000	6½	64	1:20
0.75	7,500	8	82	1:16
1.0	10,000	11	108	1:12

NOTE 1: Fluid ounces rounded off to nearest ½ ounce.
8 fl. ozs./cup   32 fl. ozs./quart
16 fl. ozs./pint   128 fl. ozs./gallon

November 1. Treatment of branched plants should occur approximately 2 weeks after pinching.

Treatment by foliar spray should be completed by November 1 or earlier. Spray should be applied to the top side of all foliage of the plants for maximum benefit. Some growers make a practice of treating individual plants in multiplant containers in order to equalize the height. Spray treatment should be given only when plants are well supplied with moisture and when rapid drying will occur. Further moistening of foliage should be avoided for at least 24 hours. This permits maximum absorption.

Rates (Table 9) are usually higher in strength for early applications than for late. Numerous variations on treatment have been tried by researchers and growers with results equal to those advocated here. When a program is providing desired results, no changes should be made except by comparative trial. Since the spray approach is most apt to cause leaf yellowing or burn, it is desirable to test-spray a few plants one week ahead of the intended general

TABLE 9—TYPICAL RATES FOR GROWTH-REGULATOR APPLICATION

	August	September	October
Cycocel Soil Drench*	3000 - 6000 ppm	3000 ppm	3000 ppm
Cycocel Foliar Spray	3000 ppm	3000 ppm	1500 ppm

*2 fluid ozs./3" pot   4 fluid ozs./5" pot   8 fluid ozs./8" pot
3 fluid ozs./4" pot   6 fluid ozs./6" pot

treatment as a check on possible damage. Even this precaution is not foolproof.

FERTILITY MAINTENANCE

Methods of supplying fertilizer to plants vary greatly. All possible combinations and types of programs cannot possibly be covered, but the principal approaches are listed below. The best program is, of course, one which requires the least amount of labor and permits the least opportunity for error. Also, economics is a factor, though fertilizer cost is usually not considered a major part of production costs. A number of typical approaches are listed below:

Liquid Fertilizer at Every Irrigation

In recent years, this has become the most popular of programs and is probably the most foolproof as well as most economic. It automatically limits the quantity of fertilizer applied in case of underwatering and prevents excessive buildup, even under conditions of overwatering. If all irrigation water contains fertilizer of desired concentration, there are no problems in administration of the feeding program. When water is required, fertilizer is automatically supplied. A single formula can be satisfactorily employed for the entire production period under most circumstances. A good poinsettia program is likely a good Easter lily and/or pot-mum program.

Liquid Fertilizer at Fixed Interval

A popular approach that varies from the above is to inject fertilizer at weekly or other fixed periods, using higher concentrations than for the constant liquid program in order that levels will not be depleted too much during the interim when clear water is being applied. This type program may require adjustment of concentration at different stages of growth due to increasing frequency of interim irrigation as plants attain large size and utilize more water. The intensity of watering can have a substantial effect on the average fertility level.

Top Dress with Dry Fertilizer

This approach requires care and experience where fertilizer is fast-acting or highly soluble, but may have much the same effect as constant liquid feed where slow-release fertilizers are employed. Again, differences in irrigation intensity can greatly affect the levels attained. Also, temperatures are sometimes a factor in rate of release. Higher temperatures can increase the rate of nutrient release.

Incorporation of Slow-Release Fertilizer in Mix

This procedure has gained some favor and prominence as better products have become available. Again, it is similar in effect to the constant-liquid-feed program except that the control over fertilizer availability is subject to such factors as rate of application, temperature of soil and intensity of irrigation. In some instances, the addition of the slow-release fertilizer must be made *after* steaming to avoid excessive release at the outset (except for MagAmp). Soil with slow-release fertilizer added *cannot* be held for later use, since excessive soluble-fertilizer salt buildup can occur during storage.

Combination Liquid/Slow-Release Fertilizer Programs

Much of the research which has been carried out in evaluating slow-release fertilizers in recent years has employed a program of infrequent or constant use of liquid feed plus incorporation of a slow-release fertilizer in the soil mix. It is a little difficult to understand the philosophy of this approach since *liquid feeding capability* provides *complete* control by the grower of the fertilizer levels. Incorporation of a slow-release product subjects the grower to a set of conditions over which he has less control. It would seem that if liquid-feeding capability is available, this would be chosen as the system for maintaining fertility. If it is not available, it would seem wise to consider a slow-release fertilizer system which would approach constant liquid feeding in its effect. The *combined* approach is an unnecessary complication. (Editor's note: for a different point of view here, see *Grower Talks*, August, 1971, page 1).

Poinsettias in particular seem to require a substantial rate of nitrogen applicaton with modest phosphorus and modest potassium rates. It has been observed that very low soil potassium is still sufficient to supply the requirements of poinsettias. Apparently, this plant is capable of extracting potassium with greater efficiency than many other crops. In order to provide a simple and straightforward selection of liquid-fertilizer programs, an outline of several approaches (Table 10) has been provided. Molybdenum has been included in several of the formulas, since this element has been found to be quite important in poinsettia nutrition, particularly in synthetic mixes.

Where liquid-feeding facilities are not available, many growers may wish to use dry fertilizer. Rates should be relatively high for poinsettias compared to many other crops. A program which has proved successful should not be replaced by a new program without appropriate trial. Where a grower wishes to try one of the newer slow-release fertilizers, experience to date suggests that Osmocote 18-9-9 is a suitable formula for poinsettias. For top dressing after planting into pans or pots, 1 level tablespoon per 6-inch pot is a reasonable rate, if the soil is well drained and if irrigations are thorough. Lower quantities should be used where light irrigations are practiced, or where soil textures include substantial silt and clay. Addition of slow-release fertilizer to the soil mix prior to planting can again utilize the same material at a rate of 7 to 10 lbs. per cubic yard. Slow-release Osmocote should not be added until soil has cooled *after* steaming. Rates most appropriate for a particular condition will have to be determined by trial and error, and will be affected by soil temperature as well as irrigation frequency and intensity. Osmocote seems to provide continuous nutrition for about 12 weeks. It will, therefore, carry the crop through the entire forcing period when added about mid-September.

In making small quantities of fertilizer solution, it may be helpful to have some idea of quantities to use (Table 11). Since quantities less than an ounce are difficult to weigh, volume measure is more commonly used for this range, but is subject to greater error.

Turn to page 425

TABLE 10—POINSETTIA LIQUID-FEED PROGRAMS

	AMT./1000 GALS. WATER APPLIED	PPM IN WATER N — P — K
CONSTANT LIQUID FEED		
Make your own:	3 lbs. ammonium nitrate 5 lbs. calcium nitrate 3 lbs. potassium nitrate 16 fl. ozs. 75% food-grade phosphoric acid 1½ fl. ozs. molybdenum stock solution	259 — 43 — 132 +0.1 ppm Mo
Prepared Mixes	13 lbs. 16-4-12 or 8.5 lbs. 25-10-10	250 — 27 — 158 250 — 44 — 85
INTERMITTENT LIQUID FEED (Every 2nd or 3rd irrigation)		
Make your own:	6 lbs. ammonium nitrate 10 lbs. calcium nitrate 6 lbs. potassium nitrate 1 qt. 75% food-grade phosphoric acid 3 fl. ozs. molybdenum stock solution	518 — 86 — 264 +0.2 ppm Mo
Prepared Mixes	26 lbs. 16-4-12 or 17 lbs. 25-10-10	500 — 54 — 316 500 — 88 — 170

molybdenum stock solution: Dissolve 1 lb. sodium or ammonium molybdate in 5 gallons water.

TABLE 11—AMT. OF FERTILIZER TO MAKE A SOLUTION OF 250 PPM NITROGEN

Fertilizer Formula	Final Volume of Solution (Gallons)				
	1000	100	50	5	1*
25-10-10	8 lbs. 5 ozs.	13 oz.	6½ ozs.	4 t	1 − t
16-4-12	13 lbs.	21 oz.	10½ ozs.	2 T	1 + t
34-0-0 (ammonium nitrate)	6 lbs. 4 ozs.	10 oz.	5 ozs.	4 t	1 − t
15.5-0-0 (calcium nitrate	13 lbs. 6 ozs.	22 oz.	11 ozs.	2 T	1 + t

t = teaspoon	*1 − t = slightly less than level full
T = Tablespoon	1 + t = slightly more than level full

ACCIDENTAL BUD-SET DELAY

Each year, more and more growers are having trouble getting poinsettias to set bud properly in the autumn because of unnoticed extraneous lights shining into the greenhouses at night. The proximity of well-traveled highways, new and improved street lighting, and large, well-lighted shopping centers near poinsettia-producing greenhouses impose new threats. If it is impossible to eliminate the unwanted light source, it is necessary that black cloth be pulled starting October 1 to insure a 14-hour dark period for at least 3 weeks. Black-clothing will insure bud set if the temperature is not above 65°F at night.

PHYSIOLOGICAL CHARACTERISTICS OF POINSETTIA

AVAILABLE FORMS OF NITROGEN

Nitrogen can be utilized by plants directly as urea, ammonium nitrogen, or as nitrate nitrogen. The poinsettia reacts unfavorably to excessive quantities of ammonium or urea. Poor root development, yellowing of foliage, leaf-drop and stunting have been observed in commercial and university trials. As a rule of thumb, no more than half of the nitrogen supplied to poinsettias should be in the form of ammonium, and urea is preferably omitted completely.

Another effect of nitrogen that has repeatedly been observed is a difference in height when ammonium nitrate is compared with calcium nitrate as the sole source of the element. Plants supplied ammonium nitrate are consistently taller.

MOLYBDENUM DEFICIENCY

With the use of synthetic mixes, fertilizers of high purity, plastic pipes, and intensively grown stock plants, there have been numerous occurrences of molybdenum deficiency. The characteristic symptoms observed in many parts of the U.S. and recently reported in Europe have been those of young, mature-leaf yellowing, sometimes confused with nitrogen deficiency or iron deficiency. The symptoms may progress to include some leaf-edge burn. The leaves characteristically curl upward in just the opposite manner from moisture stress. Since molybdenum deficiency results in *nitrate accumulation* in leaves, a test for nitrate nitrogen in dried leaf tissue is an indirect method of assessing the molybdenum status. No symptoms have been observed where nitrate nitrogen was less than 3000 ppm in dry-leaf tissue. Severe symptoms have been associated with values of 6,000 to 14,000 ppm nitrate nitrogen.

LEAF CRIPPLING, DISTORTION, PUCKERING

For many years, leaf deformity seen in some stock plants, and sometimes appearing on pot plants in greenhouses, has been suspected of being a virus disease. However, the presence of a virus has never been demonstrated and it now seems that the problem is one of environment.

The observed symptoms are extremely variable. In some cases, damage has occurred only at the tip of the immature leaf and it will give the appearance of having been chopped off at a later stage of development. Where the entire margin of the leaf has been affected in earlier stages, later growth of all except the margin causes a "puckered" appearance, as if a drawstring around the leaf margin had been pulled up tight.

Many plants, including poinsettias, have leaf structures which include hydathodes or vein endings opening along the edges, tips and sometimes leaf surfaces. Under cool, humid conditions, with ample soil moisture supply and elevated soil temperature, the pressure of fluids in the conducting system may cause guttation (the formation of small drops of liquid along the leaf edges, tips or surfaces). If a rapid rise in temperature and drop in humidity occur *simultaneously,* as frequently does happen in the mornings of bright days, the liquid droplets will rapidly dry. Dissolved contents will become more concentrated. Sudden use of air-conditioning fans or natural movement of air from wind can cause much the same effect. This concentrated solution may be strong enough to cause cell damage and, when sudden stress on the plant occurs simultaneously, the concentrated fluid may be drawn back into the vein endings and cause damage to cells in and around this area. Since the phenomenon occurs only on immature leaves which are still undergoing expansion, subsequent growth in areas of cell injury will be inhibited and developing leaves will be distorted.

A complicating factor is frequently that of infection of injured tissue by botrytis, when temperatures at night are sufficiently low.

Control of this leaf-edge damage can best be attained by maintaining low humidity at night and avoiding conditions of rapid drying in the morning. Syringing of foliage in the early morning may also aid by removing the droplets before drying commences.

LATEX ERUPTION

Plants belonging to the Euphorbia family contain latex which is exuded upon cell injury. This became a problem in poinsettia production when *Paul Mikkelsen* and its sports first became popular. Of varieties currently in use, they seem to be the most susceptible. The malady was aptly termed "crud." The mechanism was one of bursting cells resulting from high turgor pressure with latex spilling over the tissue and, upon drying, the creation of a growth-restricting layer. When this occurs at developing stem tips, distortion or stunting of growth results. The exuding of latex has also been observed on fully expanded leaves, sometimes giving the appearance of mealybug infestation due to the white splotches scattered over the leaf surface.

All contributing factors have not been clearly defined, but several obvious ones include high moisture availability and high humidity, both of which result in high fluid pressure within the cells. Low temperature is an important contributing factor. Mechanical injury from rough handling or from excessively vigorous air movement may also increase injury to cells. High rates of photosynthesis may contribute by building up a high osmotic pressure in cells from carbohydrate accumulation.

Control is best attained by using growing media which dry out in a reasonable length of time and avoiding extremes of high humidity, particularly during the night. Moderate shading in extremely bright weather may also aid. Sudden lowering of temperature can trigger the reaction. Fortunately, most varieties are not highly sensitive to this problem.

STEM-SPLITTING

Under certain conditions, poinsettias which do not normally branch unless pinched will suddenly produce stem branches at the growing tip. Careful examination will reveal that the true stem tip has stopped growth or aborted. This first became a prominent factor in 1964 when the *Paul Mikkelsen* variety was being heavily propagated. Many growers encountered splits and splayed flower heads. The phenomenon is not peculiar to *Paul Mikkelsen,* but was brought about by a major change in cultural practice at that time. Propagators soon learned the reason for splitting and have taken steps to eliminate it.

Splitting is actually a first step in flower initiation. The stimulus to flower increases with age of stem, with lengthening of night, and with low temperatures. Even with short nights and normal temperatures, splitting can be expected if the stem is permitted to grow until 20-30 leaves are present. Stem tips which are continuously propagated carry an increasing tendency to flower. To insure against this, lights should be supplied to stock plants until May 15. Propagations prior to July 15 should be grown for multiflowered or branched plants with the tip discarded. Probably no hard and fast rules can be laid down, since new varieties may exhibit new tendencies. It is always good insurance to discard early pinches instead of trying to propagate them. Also, stems which are heavily shaded by a canopy of higher foliage may be subjected to enough reduced light to cause them to split even in periods when day length would be considered adequate.

LEAF-DROP

The older varieties were much more prone to sudden loss of leaves than are modern varieties. There are several indirect causes of leaf-drop. Under conditions of moderate to severe stress, it is not uncommon for older leaves to form an abscission layer at the juncture of the petiole and the supporting stem. This is believed due to loss of auxin from the leaf blade under the stress conditions. Once started, the reaction is irreversible and the leaf petiole is virtually severed from the stem. Also, when plants are kept under very low light intensity for a period of several days, lower leaves will yellow and drop.

Many of the older varieties were very susceptible to leaf-drop. Before better sanitation reduced or eliminated disease problems, leaves would frequently drop in the greenhouse as root disease reduced the ability to supply water to the top of the plant. A parallel contributing factor was also the deliberate attempt of growers to carry the soil dry in an effort to restrict disease activity. Even with healthy roots, many of the varieties would drop leaves within a day or two after being moved from the humid glass house to a warm and dry living room. The change in environment induced more water stress than the leaves could tolerate. The moisture loss exceeded the ability of the roots to supply water.

Modern varieties are far more resistant to leaf abscission, though not completely immune. Modern methods of sanitation should make it unnecessary to impose dry soil conditions in the greenhouse or the home. Healthy poinsettias thrive under high-moisture availability and moderate to high light. Waterlogging should be avoided, however.

BRACT BURN

Although botrytis causes an injury which is typically observed as a burn, all such injury is *not* necessarily due to the fungus disease. Severe bract burn has been encountered where extreme rates of fertilizer, particularly slow-release, have been used. Under these conditions, the leaves may show no damage. It is theorized that during growth, there is a diluting effect of plant-absorbed fertilizer, but at flowering, new tissue development has virtually ceased and the fertilizer salts accumulate in the youngest mature and most sensitive tissue—the bract. This accumulation causes cell damage usually starting on the bract edges.

Where slow-release fertilizers are used, the rate should be modest and application should be early enough to insure almost complete depletion at time of flowering. It may also help to increase intensity of irrigation in the finishing stages to insure adequate leaching and removal of accumulated salts.

INSECTS

With the present emphasis on ecology and the effects of pollution, it becomes necessary to know what greenhouse pests are infesting the poinsettia and how best to control these infestations. The present federal regulations governing the use of pesticides make it doubly difficult to know what material can be used.

One of the most important practices is that of keeping the greenhouse immaculately clean. Experience has shown that growers with the fewest problems are those with the cleanest operations.

Poinsettias are subject to attack by various pests under greenhouse conditions. Where warm, humid conditions prevail, plants are always under constant threat of being infested.

BIOLOGICAL CONTROL

This is the use of parasites, predators and diseases of insect pests. Unfortunately, the "good" insects are sometimes more susceptible to the insecticides. Many of them are host-specific. They do not necessarily eradicate the undesirable pests and may only reduce the population.

CHEMICAL CONTROL

With new federal regulations and the ever-changing list of pesticides treatment control as outlined here can only serve as a temporary guide.

TABLE 12—POINSETTIA PEST-CONTROL CHART

Pests	Materials	Formulation	Dosage Per 100 Gals.	General Remarks
ANTS	Diazinon	50% W. P.	1 Pound	Apply on bench legs, wall bases, walls & soil.

TABLE 12—POINSETTIA PEST-CONTROL CHART

Pests	Materials	Formulation	Dosage Per 100 Gals.	General Remarks
APHIDS	Dimethoate (Cygon)	2 E.	1 pint	1 spray application or 1 drench application
	Meta-Systox®	25.2% E.C.	1 pint	1 spray application or 1 drench application
ROOT APHIDS	Dimethoate (Cygon)	2 E.	1 pint	1 drench application
	Meta-Systox®	25.2% E.C.	1 pint	1 drench application
FUNGUS GNATS	Dithio (Sulfotepp)	Aerosol or smoke	Follow directions on label	2 applications 1 week apart to control ADULTS
	Diazinon	50% W.P.	1 pound	Spray under benches, on walls and on top of plants to control adults and drench for "worms"
	Dimethoate (Cygon)	2 E.	1 pint	For heavy infestation of WORM STAGE in plant tissue—1 drench application only
MEALYBUGS	Dithio (Sulfotepp)	Aerosol or smoke	Follow directions on label	4 applications, 3 days apart—repeat every 3 weeks until control obtained
	Diazinon	50% W.P.	1 pound	3 spray applications 10 days apart
	Dimethoate (Cygon)	2 E.	1 pint	2 spray applications 14 days apart
OLIGO-CHAETS	Diazinon	50% W.P.	1 pound	3 applications 14 days apart
SCALES	Dithio (Sulfotepp)	Aerosol or smoke	Follow directions on label	(FOR CRAWLER STAGE ONLY) 4 applications 3 days apart
	Diazinon	50% W.P.	1 pound	2 spray applications 14 days apart
	Dimethoate (Cygon)	2 E.	1 pint	2 spray applications 14 days apart
	Sevin	50% W.P.	2 pounds	2 spray applications 14 days apart

TABLE 12—POINSETTIA PEST-CONTROL CHART

Pests	Materials	Formulation	Dosage Per 100 Gals.	General Remarks
SLUGS and SNAILS	Metaldehyde	20% Liquid	1 quart	1 spray application to soil
	Metaldehyde	Dust or Granules		Follow directions on label
SPIDER MITES (red spider)	Kelthane	18½% W.P.	1 pound	3 spray applications 10 days apart
	Chloro-benzilate	25% W.P.	1 pound	3 spray applications 10 days apart
	Dithio (Sulfotepp)	Aerosol or smoke	Follow directions on label	4 applications 2 days apart
	Pentac	50% W.P.	½ pound	2 thorough spray applications 10 days apart
WHITEFLIES	Dithio (Sulfotepp)	Aerosol or smoke	Follow directions on label	4 applications 3 days apart, repeat every 3 weeks until controlled
	Thiodan	50% W.P.	1 pound	2 spray applications 10 days apart
	Cygon	2 E.	1 pint	1 spray application
	Diazinon	50% W.P.	1 pound	2 spray applications 14 days apart
WORMS	Sevin	50% W.P.	1½ pounds	2 spray applications 10 days apart

CAUTION

It is always wise to ask local university extension personnel for any locally-preferred recommendations*.

When using unfamiliar materials, trial a small portion of crop. When practical, allow 3-4 weeks for possible plant damage to show up before treating entire crop*.

All pest control should be completed by November 1 before bracts show color, if at all possible. Following this procedure will avoid the possibility of fading or injury to the bracts*.

After color shows, only smokes are advisable*.

E.C. = Emulsifiable concentrate

W.P. = Wettable powder

SPRAY - Means apply material with full coverage to top and bottom side of foliage. When using wettable powder, it is good to fog off the accumulated material on the upper side of the leaves immediately after application. This will eliminate the residue problem that may develop when the material dries.

DRENCH - Means apply material as a thorough watering to the soil. Soil should be moist before drench is applied. Plants should not be under water stress. Apply at the rate of 8 ozs. mixture maximum per 6-inch pot.

*Certain resistant strains of any pest may develop which will require different materials than those mentioned above.

GREENHOUSE POINSETTIA DISEASES

Pathogens of primary importance include fungi and bacteria. For disease to occur, the organism and the host plant must be in close proximity. Fungi infect plants through wounds, natural openings such as stomates and intact epidermal surfaces. Bacteria infect primarily through wounds or natural openings including stomates, lenticels, nectaries, hydathodes, and glandular hairs. Under favorable conditions, wounded tissue is quickly covered by a suberin film which protects against bacterial infection.

Disease *control* can *only* be attained by using clean plants, clean soil, complete sanitation, and providing appropriate environment. All other procedures must be considered as *suppression*—not control! The use of chemicals anticipates that the control measures will not be, or have not been, properly executed.

The diseases described below include pertinent information on the ecology of the pathogen. This background often provides the most important basis for planning control measures and preventing infection.

Where chemicals are to be used, limited trials should be employed before treating an entire crop, unless there has been adequate prior experience.

RHIZOCTONIA SALANI (Stem and root rot)

Plant Symptoms:

Brown rot of stem at soil line; roots may have brown lesions and leaves can become infected under mist propagation where they touch soil. Infected plants are stunted with leaves yellowing from the bottom and sometimes dropping. Complete plant collapse under severe conditions.

Organism Characteristics:

A fungus which carries over in the soil or on infected plants. Easily spread by water. No airborne spores. Favored by moderately-high available moisture, high temperature, and factors which weaken the host, such as salinity.

Suppression:

Rogue infected plants and avoid scattering debris from infected plants. Drench with fungicides such as Terraclor 75%W.P. (PCNB) at 4 ozs. per 100 gallons, Magnacide D at 1 fl.oz. per 100 gallons, Benlate at 4 ozs. per 100 gallons. Keep soil on dry side.

PYTHIUM ULTIMUM (water-mold root rot)
Plant Symptoms:

Root tips and cortex rotted. May advance up stem. Plants stunted, lower leaves yellow and drop. Entire plant may collapse. Soil tends to stay wet, since roots are incapable of removing moisture leading to the erroneous diagnosis—"too much water."

Organism Characteristics:

Carries over in soil or infected plants and is spread in water. No airborne spores. Requires high moisture availability. Active at cool temperatures. Inactive spores may live in dry soil for several months.

Suppression:

Rogue obviously infected plants, taking care not to spread debris to healthy plant areas. Maintain low soil moisture. Drench with fungicides such as Dexon 35 at 4 ozs. per 100 gallons, Magnacide D at 1 fl.oz. per 100 gallons.

THIELAVIOPSIS BASICOLA (black root rot)
Plant Symptoms:

Roots develop black rotted areas. Stem may accumulate black sclerotia which form in the pith area. Plants show lack of vigor, leaf yellowing, leaf drop, and sometimes sudden collapse, particularly after temperatures have been lowered below 60°F.

Organism Characteristics:

A fungus having long life in soil as sclerotia resting stage. Favored by cool, moist environment. Slow growth at elevated temperatures and in highly acid soils (pH below 5.5). No airborne spores.

Suppression:

Rogue infected plants, avoid low soil temperatures, use acid soils and acidifying fertilizers. Drench with Benlate at 8-12 ozs. per 100 gallons.

BOTRYTIS CINEREA (gray mold)
Plant Symptoms:

Rotting of tissue, frequently starting on young leaf edges or other immature tissue. Sometimes causes damping-off symptoms at or near the soil line. Red varieties develop purplish color on infected bracts. Difficult to distinguish from edge burn due to chemicals or salts when bracts are affected.

Organism Characteristics:

A fungus whose spores are airborne and can be assumed to be present everywhere at all times. Not an aggressive parasite unless favored by injured, aging, or succulent tissue, moderately low temperature, and 100% humidity at site of infection. Thrives on plant debris on floor of greenhouse.

Control:

First line of defense is control of environment. Avoid physical injury to plants, maintain air circulation at night, use night heat plus ventilation to lower humidity, keep temperatures above 60°F if at all possible. Remove all dead plant material. The dense habit of multiflowered types presents a special problem of leaf and bract overlap.

Suppression:

Numerous fungicides are effective as inhibitors to germination of spores and growth of mycelium. New developing plant tissue must be repeatedly covered to provide continuous protection. Materials which leave no residue are preferred to maintain saleability. Fungicides employed include Termil fumigation, Daconil spray at 1 lb. 75% W.P. per 100 gallons, Tutane spray at 2 fl.ozs. per gallon, Captan 50% W. at 1½ lbs. per 100 gallons, and Benlate 50% W. spray at 4-6 ozs. per 100 gallons. Termil programs have been widely used with little or no reported damage.

ERWINIA CAROTOVORA (bacterial soft rot)
Plant Symptoms:

Rot of covered stem in propagation. Occurs within three days after sticking cuttings. Callous and rooting sometimes occur above rot. Rot usually stops at or near the soil line.

Organism Characteristics:

This bacterium is not particularly aggressive except under highly favorable conditions. Wounded tissue, water-logging, and high temperatures are very favorable. The organism is prevalent on dead plant material and can be carried on wind-blown dust, non-sterilized tools, and unwashed hands. Readily spread in water.

Control:

Grow stock plants under glass or other controlled environment. Spray stock plants with bactericide at regular intervals. Avoid water-logging of rooting medium. Add bactericide to rooting hormone, particularly if liquid. Use extreme sanitation throughout harvest and propagation of cuttings.

Suppression:

If other sanitary precautions are not taken, dip cuttings in chlorine (500 ppm) and drench rooting medium with chlorine (50 ppm) immediately prior to and after sticking of cuttings. Streptomyacin is not too effective and does tend to bleach the foliage.

CORYNEBACTERIUM POINSETTIAE (bacterial canker)
Plant Symptoms:

Black, elongated, and water-soaked streaks occur on green stems. Stem tips abort or bend over. Spots or blotches occur on leaves. In a favorable (warm, humid) environment, disease progresses rapidly, resulting in death of stem above infection and/or entire plant. Not a common disease except during hot, humid weather, such as found in summer climate of midwestern, eastern and southern U.S. It has shown up in other areas where innoculum was present and environment favorable.

Organism Characteristics:

A bacterium transported in water, soil, on contaminated tools and on the hands of workers. Enters plant through stomates or wounds. Spreads in plant through thin-walled parenchyma cells.

Suppression:

Severe roguing should be practiced and all overhead irrigation or syringing avoided. Humidity should be kept as low as practical and excessive temperatures should be avoided. Plants should be protected from wind and/or rain. If stock-plant infection is suspected, sterile knives should be used in removing each cutting to avoid spread.

NOTE:

A number of additional diseases are reported as occurring on poinsettias, but these are primarily of concern in outdoor or landscape plantings. The following is a brief listing of the principal ones.

Sphaceloma poinsettiae (scab)—a fungus disease of stem and leaf
Phymatotricum omnivorum (Texas root rot)—a fungus disease of roots
Uromyces euphorbiae (rust)—a fungus disease of leaves

SANITATION HINTS—

1. Hose end off floor.
2. Hand rinse before handling plants.
3. Copper naphthanate on all wood, metal or composition surfaces.
4. Presteam all soil or sand benches.
5. Steam or fumigate all soil mixes.
6. Avoid inoculation from dust.
7. Use a tool dip to decontaminate.
8. Never pick up cuttings or tools from the floor where they may have fallen. Discard cuttings, rinse tools.
9. Remove soil from tools, pots, benches before treating with LF-10, Clorox or other disinfectant.
10. Eliminate weeds and debris which can harbor disease and insects.
11. Think "clean."

POPPY (Papaver)

ANNUAL *(P. nudicaule) 275,000 seeds per oz. Germinates in 12 days at 70°. Dark.*
PERENNIAL *(P. orientale) 140,000 seeds per oz. Germinates in 12 days at 70°. Dark.*

It is interesting to reflect that from the same genus can come the flaming *Oriental* poppy in springtime perennial gardens, the charming little *Iceland* and *Shirley* species that fairly cover acres with color—and the dreaded opium poppy, responsible for so much misery and human degradation. These and over a hundred more species come under the head of *Papaver,* but only the *Oriental, P. orientale* and the *Iceland, P. nudicaule,* are important in horticulture.

The *Icelands (P. nudicaule),* native to Arctic regions, are perennials, but are usually grown as annuals. They might well answer the quest for "something different" in spring-forcing annuals. Sow in January, either directly into pots or into the bench where they are to flower; if allowed to flower in 4-inch pots right where they are, they will come in earlier as a result of the check. A 50° temperature and ordinary garden soil are O.K. Flowers cut full-blown during the day will drop their petals in an hour; if cut early in the morning in the bud stage, and if the cut ends are burned, they will keep several days; in fact, they are even shipped in this loose bud stage. Several named varieties are available in this group, but mixtures are by far the most popular. *Sanford's* and *Gartford's* are two of the best.

Papaver rhoeas includes the *Shirley* poppies and the so-called annuals, among which are some very showy doubles. They are all strict annuals and are generally handled much the same as the *nudicaules.* Two distinctions are: first, the *Rhoeas* group includes some really brilliant scarlets not found in the *Icelands;* second, the *Shirleys* carry their foliage on up the stem, while the *nudicaules* have a "rosette" of foliage that stays near the ground. In cultural needs and flowering dates, they are much the same as the *Icelands.* Most popular in the *Iceland* class is *Champagne Bubbles,* a more-recently introduced F_1 hybrid. Far superior to the inbreds, it produces flowers 2 to 3 times as large on bushier, compact plants (1 foot) and flowers over a much longer period of time. It has an extremely wide color range, including bicolors.

Once a year, in early June, we are treated to the large, gaudy, scarlet blooms of the *orientals (P. orientale).* What they lack in extended flowering season is made up many times by the brilliance of their flowers. Their use is primarily for perennial borders: flowers just aren't satisfactory for cutting. Sow almost any time during open weather, but figure on 2 seasons for established flowering clumps. They have no special cultural requirements beyond a good loam; usual height about 3 feet. The outstanding seed strains are *Brilliant,* a fiery red; and *Beauty of Livermore,* a dark oxblood. Named varieties from seed other than red are inclined to vary in color. There are many other named varieties from both seed and divisions.

Of curiosity interest is *P. somniferum,* the opium poppy. The drug is taken from the bleeding of shallow cuts on the immature capsules. It is said to have gorgeous flowers rivaling even the *Oriental.*

Portulaca—a showy ground-covering annual requiring a minimum of care.

PORTULACA (Moss Rose)

ANNUAL *(P. grandiflora) 280,000 seeds per oz. Germinates in 10 days at 70°*

One of the most popular and colorful annuals, moss roses are widely used today because of their ability to thrive under adverse conditions. They are truly procumbent and quite spreading, so a few plants cover a good bit of ground. While portulaca can be sown directly where they are to flower, as early as the ground is warm in early May, your customers will eagerly buy started young plants, and it's here that the profit lies. They flower in a month or 6 weeks from sowing date, and require no special care beyond fairly moist soil during germination.

Many growers will either sow the seed direct into the selling container, or transplant several seedlings to one spot in the pack to allow for better color balance in a mixture. Sowings are commonly made for mid-February through March.

Most popular is the *Double Mixture,* a showy blend of white, primrose-yellow shades, orange, red, lilac and mauve. Single strains are still available and used on a limited scale, but these are rapidly being replaced by the more showy doubles. The *Sunglo* series, eight separate colors and a mix, is the first F_1 on the market. *Sunnyside Mixed* is a recently introduced large flowered double strain.

PRIMULA

MALACOIDES

ANNUAL *(P. malacoides) 385,000 seeds per oz. Germinates in 3-4 wks. at 70°. Light.*

This baby class of primula is much easier and more quickly grown than the *obconica* and is not irritating to the skin. With the advent of a new and vastly improved series called the *Rhinepearls* (see picture), interest in their production and sales has quickened. From our trials here in West Chicago, they would seem to be particularly well adapted to mass-market outlets.

First sowings are usually made in June for flowering in 5 or 6-inch pots shortly after the first of the year and carry through well till Valentine's Day. Later sowings will produce correspondingly smaller sizes, which can be used for make-up pots (3 or more per pot) and combinations. Sowings made after October 15 will usually result in blind growth without flowers.

Preferring cool temperatures (40°-45°) for greenhouse growing, they do suffer during the midsummer heat and often are very difficult to germinate at this time. Thus, it is advisable to get them started before the heat, or wait till September. Seed can be sown in a mixture of equal parts of leaf mold, sand and soil or in a mix of equal parts of peat, soil and vermiculite. Keep the seed flat in the coolest spot possible. When the seedlings are large enough to be transplanted, they can be spaced out (1 inch each way) in another flat, or shifted directly to a 2¼-inch Jiffy-Pot. Primulas like a light, well-drained soil with a good percentage of humus added to it. However, stay away from ingredients with an acid reaction, since chlorosis caused by acidity can be troublesome. Many growers have found it advantageous to buy-in young plants (2¼-inch) from a specialist grower, rather than attempt to start them from seed.

From 2¼-inch Jiffies, the plants can be shifted directly to the finishing pot. Frequently, fertilization is necessary to keep the plants in active growth. When shifting to a larger pot, care should be taken to see that the crown is set just above the soil line. If set too low, rot can result; if too high, the plant will topple over. If grown under glass during the summer, shading is required. Also, the application of a light shade during late winter can intensify the flower colors at times.

One of the common ailments of primula is yellowing of the foliage. This can be caused by the soil being too acid, too wet, or poorly drained. It can also be caused by deficiencies of nitrogen and/or potash, or spraying with certain insecticides.

The *Rhinepearl* series is, by far and away, the finest available today. Compact, base-branching, with flowers borne close to the foliage, they are available in a mix as well as separate colors of *White, Rose* and *Carmine*.

PRIMULA MALACOIDES
RHINEPEARL WHITE
Tops in the malacoides class—
well suited for mass-market pot-
plant sales.

OBCONICA

ANNUAL *(P. obconica) 130,000 seeds per oz. Germinates in 3-4 wks. at 70°. Light.*

This large-flowered type is not nearly as widely grown today as the small-flowered *(malacoides)* type. This is undoubtedly due to the longer time required to produce a crop, and also to the rash that it can cause on some people. A January sowing will finish for Christmas in a 5 or 6-inch pot, while an October sowing will make good 4-inch pots for spring sales. General culture for *obconicas* is similar to that of the more popular *malacoides,* except for the fact that they can be grown several degrees warmer (45-48°). They are mostly grown as color mixtures today.

HARDY PRIMULA

PERENNIAL *(P. veris) 28,000-35,000 seeds per oz. Germinates in 3-4 wks. at 70°.*

There are many, many species of hardy primulas, but only a few which are of importance to the grower today. These varieties and strains belong to the *veris* group. When given a sheltered position in a shaded spot with light winter protection, they will overwinter in this part of the country and are well adapted for the perennial border. In addition, they make an excellent pot plant for early-spring sales. An August sowing, wintered in frames, or grown in a cold greenhouse, will make attractive-flowering 3 or 4-inch pots for sales from mid-February through April. They must not be exposed, though, to high temperatures; as with other species of primulas, they do their best in a light, well-drained soil, high in organic matter. When in the greenhouse, they should be lightly shaded.

Renewed interest in perennial primulas for spring sales is, to a great extent, due to the *Pacific Giant* strain; with beautiful, clear, large flowers on longer stems, they are excellent for bedding and pot plants. While the *Blue Shades* are most popular, they are available in *Pink, Rose, Red, White* and *Yellow Apricot* as well as in a *Mixture.* Representing an improvement in uniformity of color, habit and performance is the *Laser* series. Available in six separate brilliant colors and a mix, it probably has the greatest potential. *Jewel Mixture* is an improved dwarf form (4 inches) containing the same vivid colors as the regular strain. *Colossea* is also a good strain, which is hardier outdoors than most. It can be treated as *Pacific Giants* with respect to general culture.

PRIMULA VERIS
JEWEL MIX
A dwarf Pacific
Giant strain for
pot-plant growing.

PYRETHRUM (Painted Daisy)

PERENNIAL *(P. roseum) 18,000 seeds per oz. Germinates in 2-3 wks. at 60-70°.*

Among the most valuable and best known of these easily grown perennials is *P. roseum* or "painted daisy." It includes a number of useful, long-stemmed, cut-flower varieties which bloom heavily in June with a few scattering flowers during summer. In England, named varieties that are propagated by divisions are very popular, the climate there enabling them to be marketed on heavy 2 to 3-foot stems. We have tried some of this division-propagated stock, but found they die out shortly, while seed-grown plants will do well for 3 to 4 years. Double strains of pyrethrum have been developed and they improve upon the single form, but the strength of at least 2-year-old plants is necessary to produce double flowers. The first year, nearly all will be singles. While there are separate-color varieties available, the *Double Mix* strain is most popular. Another English strain known as *Robinson's Mixture* produces large, single, attractive flowers.

ROSE

CUT FLOWERS

Rose growing by a retail grower has sometimes been avoided because of the extra care and cost of growing this very perishable crop. On the other hand, many retail florists have made this the backbone of their business. "What is sold here is grown locally and cut fresh daily." Roses should be considered a prestige flower, and a good business can be built around this fact. It is also reasonable to expect that if you are the only florist growing roses locally, you will have the edge on your competitors who do not grow roses.

Rose growing has long been assigned to the specialist, and rightly so, for it does adapt itself to a large operation with many thousands of plants. Producers of cut roses need a constant supply of blooms during all seasons of the year. In order to do this, you need a large number of plants to produce enough roses to grade out fancy, long, medium, and short lengths for the various needs of the florists. As a producer, you need a selection of varieties that will give you types (hybrid teas and sweethearts), as well as the color classes (red, yellow, pink, white, and bicolors). It is obvious, then, that 1,000 or 2,000, or even 5,000 plants will hardly carry on all the needs of one flower shop. However, one retail grower can profitably supply a lot of the roses he needs with a small planting.

Rose plants are very particular in their requirements and therefore should be more or less isolated to one house or area where this can be achieved. They are more exacting in their light, temperature, and moisture requirements than are most other crops. It would be very difficult to control disease and

FOREVER YOURS
Leading rose in the U.S. for cutting.

insect problems if they were not restricted to a given area.

As a retail grower with this limited number of roses, you would have to decide what varieties to grow. You should grow those that you use most in your retail shop. The varieties you have just an occasional demand for should not be considered. It will be the constant supply from your greenhouse and constant demand from your customers that will make this a profitable part part of your business.

STRUCTURES FOR GROWING ROSES

The most practical type of structure is one which will give full sunlight to all plants in the house. There should be no shading from other greenhouses, buildings or trees. Preferably, the greenhouse should have adequate ventilation so it can be ventilated during all seasons of the year without cold drafts. The house should have at least 7-foot gutters so that the roses will not touch the glass when they are at their highest level of production.

Whether roses are grown in ground beds or raised benches makes little difference as long as good drainage is supplied. Those grown in ground beds are generally easier to manage and generally give more long-stemmed flowers.

Roses are generally planted 4 plants across a 42-inch to 48-inch-wide bench with a 12-inch spacing down the bench. This planting gives you approximately 1 square foot of area for each plant.

The heating of a rose house should be adequate to supply 60°F in the coldest weather. The source of heat should be from the floor of the house, which creates rising air currents that will give you the maximum circulation. You should also have pipes around the house which can be left on at all times to keep plants dry at night. Roses grown in ground beds may have the pipes around the perimeter of the beds, thereby giving even heat to the house. Controlling the temperature is a very important part of rose culture, especially on timing and quality. The rose structure should supply warm, humid atmosphere with high light intensity during the daytime, and at night, a lower humidity with an even, warm 60° to 62°F. Good-quality roses can be grown with a cooler night temperature, but production will be reduced.

PLANTING STOCK

The time to plant roses is usually between January 1 and June 15. It is generally believed a better practice to plant in January or February and bring the plants into production in the early summer. This gives you time to build a large plant to go through the following winter.

Budded plants are the most widely used at the present time. The rose variety is budded on a root stock of superior type for vigorous root growth. The budding usually takes place on the West Coast during May and June. Some of the buds take earlier than others, and these usually become your started-eye plants. The buds which do not begin to grow the first year become dormant-eye plants. Actually, the new growth the plant makes from the eye is vigorous and strong and the individual grower's ability to get dormant eyes to break with strong canes determines his success with a new crop. On started-eye plants, this new-growth budding already has taken place and they usually break out from this growth a little earlier than dormant-eye plants. The object of any rose planting is to produce 3 to 5 working canes per plant that will give you maximum production per square foot.

Rose plants should be ordered from the producer at least 6 months to a year ahead of time of delivery. This usually amounts to a substantial reduction of price, and assures you of the best-quality plants.

The plants will arrive in large cases and should be opened for inspection on arrival. If the plants are dry, water thoroughly and cover up to put moisture back in them. If you leave the plants set in a warm room (70°-80°F) for 3 or 4 days, the buds will swell and the roots will begin to make feeder roots. The roses are now ready to plant.

When planting, the soil should be moist, but not to the point that it packs. The plants should be taken out of the box and roots pruned back about 1 inch from the root tip. The canes of started eyes are pruned back to about 6 inches; dormant-eye plants are planted without pruning. Some started-eye plants may be branched, and all weaker growth should be removed and the canes trimmed back to 6 or 8 inches.

The bud graft on a plant is very noticeable and the plants should be set in the soil with this union about 1 or 2 inches out of the soil. This will allow the root system good aeration near the soil surface. It will also allow room for a mulch as the plants come into production.

When planting, a trench may be dug across the bench and the root system spread out across the bench. The soil is then packed in around the roots. This system gives maximum root development and is much easier than planting individually.

SOIL AND PLANTING

The soil used for roses should meet drainage, moisture-holding and fertilizer-retention requirements. It has also been found that roses will grow in a wide range of soils, but this will depend on the grower's ability. In general, a good loam soil with plenty of organic matter will give them their best year-around growth. We must remember these plants are going to be in this soil up to 4 years, and because of this, the soil must be able to hold its properties. Before the soil is put in the bench, drainage capacity must be supplied through tile or naturally. In concrete benches, drainage capacity should be supplied through a "V" bottom with coarse gravel to cover the tile laid down the center. In wooden benches, the boards should have ½ inch between them. Soil that will not or cannot drain will soon destroy the plants placed in it.

Roses are very heavy feeders, and as they grow and produce, the soil should have a good supply of the necessary elements. When soil is placed in the bench, room at the top should be left for a mulch which can be applied later as the plants begin to grow. The bench should be filled to a depth of at least 6 inches. Leaving room for 1 or 2 inches of mulch on the bench is always necessary. At this time, 5 pounds of 20% superphosphate per 100 square feet should be applied to the soil. If possible, the pH should be adjusted to 6.5. This may be done by adding flowers of sulfur to the soil. As the plants begin to grow and become fertilized, the pH can be controlled by the addition of fertilizers that will control the soil reaction.

The first 6 weeks of the new rose planting is very important to your success. The plants should be watered thoroughly several times and then they should not be watered until the soil has dried out thoroughly, or there is sufficient top growth. Instead of watering plants, the top should be syringed 4 or 5 times a day during this period. This practice will induce top growth. Rose plants at this time are not losing water to transpiration, and any water tends to reduce the amount of air in the soil. The grower should strive to get maximum root growth to drive new vegetative growth out of the new eyes breaking above on the plant. A rose plant which develops top growth without root growth will soon die.

It is very important that all of the plants on the bench break at one time so that the bench can be watered and fed as the new growth begins to mature. Any plants which hold back will soon be lost because the bench needs are that of growing plants. Slow-breaking plants should be covered with a plastic bag to control humidity around them. To build up a plant for production of cut flowers, all new growth must be pinched when buds appear. This soft pinching is usually practiced at this time. Pinch all new growth back to the second 5-leaflet leaf. The new growth resulting from this pinch will be pinched, and so on, until a high level of production is reached. If plants are started in January, a partial crop may be had for Mother's Day by selecting a few of the stronger canes to flower at this time. At no time should a heavy crop be taken from young plants. Rose plants should be at their maximum growth during September and October in order to produce during the winter months. The recommended practice is to build plants up during the summer and fall and cut down on the wood during January through May.

SUPPORTING THE PLANTS

The usual method of supporting rose plants is to string layers of wire down the bench and cross them with bamboo canes tied to the wire. This makes a maze to support new breaks on the plants.

WATERING

Watering of a rose crop is very important and a number of factors enter into the amount of water they need at any one time. If the plants have a lot of top growth and are coming into crop, water requirements are high. The bench dries out quickly and watering should be adequate to prevent checking of the growth. In general, a rose crop should be watered thoroughly and then allowed to dry. If roses are cut back or if a crop is taken off, the water requirements will be less than a full-production crop. Rose plants should require considerably less water in winter than in the summer months. Mulching will tend to reduce the amount of water necessary during the summer months. It will also tend to keep the soil open and aerated. A soil that is not mulched soon becomes compacted from the great amount of water applied. Mulches or corncobs, hulls, peat, or other similar material can be applied at almost any time. Cattle-manure mulches must be applied at a time when the houses can be ventilated adequately, from early March through September. Care should be taken not to put much manure in the house at one time, or an ammonia buildup will occur which will burn the foliage and leaves and give your plants a real setback. When mulch is applied, or even manure, an application of nitrogen is needed to offset the reaction caused by the decomposition of the mulch. A good practice is to apply one pound of ammonium sulfate per 100 square feet. Then go ahead with your regular feeding program. Watering can be done either by hand with a full-flow breaker or by an automatic system, such as Gates or Skinner. Either system works as long as enough water is applied to soak soil thoroughly.

FEEDING

Feeding roses is again based largely on the time of the year and amount of top growth. You may follow an injector feeding program based on soil tests and supplement this with special applications of lime, sulfur or gypsum to adjust the pH of the soil.

Liquid Feed Injector. 200 ppm N & P

	Fertilizer Used:	Pounds per 50-gallon stock solution	
		Injector ratio 1:100	Injector ratio 1:200
	20-20-20	42 lbs.	84 lbs.
	20- 0-30	42 lbs.	84 lbs.
	25- 5-20	34 lbs.	68 lbs.
ammonium nitrate	33- 0- 0	18 lbs.	37 lbs.
potassium nitrate	13- 0-44	18 lbs.	37 lbs.
ammonium nitrate	33- 0- 0	25 lbs.	50 lbs.
muriate of potash	0- 0-60	14 lbs.	28 lbs.
ammonium sulfate	20- 0- 0	28 lbs.	56 lbs.
potassium nitrate	13- 0-44	18 lbs.	37 lbs.

Dry feed applications.

Reaction	Fertilizer	Analysis	Rate
Neutral	ammonium nitrate	33-0- 0	1 lb./100 sq. ft.
Acid	ammonium sulfate	20-0- 0	1 lb./100 sq. ft.
Alkaline	sodium nitrate	16-0- 0	1 lb./100 sq. ft.
Alkaline	calcium nitrate	16-0- 0	1 lb./100 sq. ft.
Neutral	muriate of potash	0-0-60	1 lb./100 sq. ft.
Neutral	potassium nitrate	13-0-44	1 lb./100 sq. ft.
Acid	sulfur flowers or dusting		1-3 lbs./100 sq. ft.
Alkaline	limestone dolomite		5 lbs./100 sq. ft.
Neutral	gypsum		5 lbs./100 sq. ft.
	10-10-10		3 lbs./100 sq. ft.
	10- 6- 4		3 lbs./100 sq. ft.

Feeding is usually discontinued during the darker months of winter and again during the warmer months if roses stop growing. A very good practice is to discontinue feeding during December and January, and test your rose soils regularly.

All roses should maintain 40-60 ppm nitrates, 5-10 ppm phosphorus, 25-50 ppm potassium—Spurway. The pH of the soil should be on the acid side—6.5. When watering roses, you should water thoroughly at all times to eliminate soluble-salt problems. If soluble salts do become a problem through overfeeding, leaching several times with large amounts of water will bring the soil back to normal.

DISEASES AND PESTS

The health of rose plants depends largely on success in controlling diseases and insect pests in your plantings. In contrast, we should say that all these factors work hand in hand. Red spider must be controlled, since roses simply will not produce on starved and spider-infested plants. You must have a regular scheduled program of *prevention* to control insects and diseases. Spraying is generally preferred to eliminate spiders. The following sprays should be used regularly: Kelthane, Meta-Systox, and Pentac. Spraying on the undersides of leaves is a must. Aphids, thrips and midge can be controlled by a number of aerosol bombs. They should be used on a weekly program, and more often as infestation appears. Some of the aerosols that could be used on roses are: parathion, Chlorobenzilate, Hepachlor, malathion, Dithio and Vapona.

Mildew is the worst disease problem and can ruin a rose crop unless checked. Spraying with Parnon, Benlate, or Actidione will clear up the problem: but by careful ventilation and watching for drafts from broken glass, it can be prevented.

Rose plants will often lose mature leaves if sprayed or gassed when the soil moisture is low. Leaves will ripen and fall when the soil is allowed to dry out too much between waterings. When applying insecticides, the condition of the plants should be watched carefully. Never use a spray that has not been carefully tested by you before subjecting your whole crop to it.

ROSE CUTTING

Rose cutting is a very important part of rose production. Where you remove the rose from the plant largely determines the ability of your plant to produce. Many systems of cutting have been used, the most common being to cut to the second 5-leaflet leaf on the new wood. This will assure you of another rose within 7 weeks from this cut. This type of cutting in the summer and fall will tend to build your plants up. The hooks produced by this type of cutting can be removed by cutting below the hooks in the late winter and spring months. Another method is to soft-pinch all breaks as they appear and cut the rose back below the pinch. With this method of cutting, you will have a long stem and better quality, but production will be reduced.

As a retailer, you must decide on the length of roses you can best make use of in your shop. Long-stemmed roses have a certain demand for cut flowers, but a short length will often be more desirable for much of the design work. Roses are very versatile and fine used for corsages, centerpieces funerals, and as cut flowers. As a retail grower, you do not necessarily need all long roses, and you can very well control the number and quality of roses you cut.

Roses must be cut twice a day to assure that none will open on the plant and be lost. It is also important that benches be cut at the same time every day, since 1 or 2 hours will result in a lot of blasting. These roses cannot be held, but must be used immediately.

Roses cut at the right stage of development will last 5 to 7 days under refrigeration at a 42°-45°F temperature. Sweetheart roses and some hybrid teas will last well over a week. Varieties such as *Forever Yours, Promise Me,* and *Carina* will outlast old standbys such as *Better Times* by several days.

As the roses are cut, they should be placed in water as soon as practical. The water should be room temperature and deep enough to immerse all the stems in 8 to 10 inches of water. They can then be placed in a cooler at 42°- 45° F for a few hours to take up water. The roses should be graded some time during the day by length and quality. You may be using these roses in your own shop, but to do so efficiently, you must grade them. This will also give you a record of what you cut and the quality.

RESTING ROSES

It can be very desirable at times to rest roses. This will give you an opportunity to clean out the old wood and bring a more vigorous plant into production. The first practice is to dry the soil until it cracks and the plants seem to be almost dormant. You would then cut back all the plants to between

18 and 24 inches above the soil; also, be sure to remove all the dead wood from the plants. It usually takes about one month to dry rose plants back for pruning. Immediately after pruning, give plants several very good waterings, soaking the soil thoroughly. Once the soil is absolutely soaked, you may return to normal watering. Rose plants will break out in new growth at once, and again, these shoots have to be pinched to bring the wood up to a new productive level. You will be back in production in September if you dry plants back in June.

Once planted in the bench, plants can very well last for 4 years with good growing practices. They should be gone over regularly to pinch out blind shoots, remove the dead wood or die-back, and return long, irregular growth to a good production level. If this is done, rose plants may never have to be rested, but can be kept in steady production.

TIMING OF THE ROSE CROP

There is always an increased demand for roses for Christmas, Valentine's Day, Easter and Mother's Day. To meet this demand, you must pinch off enough of your crop prior to the holiday. This is done by determining when you wish to start cutting, probably 5 to 7 days before the holiday. Soft pinches are generally several days later than hard pinches. It is a good practice to soft-pinch earlier and hard-pinch later when timing a crop.

The Christmas pinch date is based on 49 days for most varieties. You would then pinch your roses on the last 2 days of October and the first 2 days of November for the Christmas cut.

Valentine's Day would largely depend on the return crop from what you cut at Christmas, since only 7 weeks separate the two holidays.

Both the Easter and Mother's Day crops would result from a pinch 45 days before the cut date.

Weather has a very definite effect on the timing of roses. Cold and cloudy weather will slow the crop down considerably. Likewise, warm and balmy weather will speed it up. As the case may be, you may have to raise or lower your night temperature to offset this weather condition. You must watch and study your crop to see how far along the buds are, and determine what you can do to bring them in on time. Rose buds should be the size of a pea 3 weeks before cut date.

SUMMARY

The rose grower must not neglect his planting at any time. He must schedule his work so that he has time to fit all the needs of the rose crop into his daily routine.

The night temperature should be 60° F for most varieties. This temperature should be adjusted as soon as possible at the close of the day. In mild weather, some air should be left on the houses at all times. Under no condition should the house be closed without at least some heat being given to it. This can be accomplished by having at least one heating pipe around your house on at all times. The heat from this pipe keeps the foliage dry and the air movement optimum for rose growing. Bright and sunny days call for the ventilators to be cracked or open. Mildew is always present in rose houses where cold drafts are not avoided. The temperature of the house on sunny days should run about 8° to 10° over night temperature. On cloudy days, the day temperature should only be raised about 5° over night temperature.

In the daytime, the humidity of the house should be raised by wetting the walks and with normal watering of the mulched beds. This should not be done too late in the day, because low humidity is desired at night to control mildew.

The cutting of roses should be one of the first and last jobs of the day. Never cut so tight a bud that it will not open or take up water. Secondly, do not let buds open too far on the plant. As a grower, let the people who use roses tell you how far open to cut the buds. The stage at which the bud is cut is very important to the life and usability of the rose.

It is a good practice to carry a light shade on rose houses during late May through August. Shading of the house will keep the temperature to where the flowers will not be burned by the sun's rays.

The foliage of roses can become very tender during periods of dark weather, and because of this, should always be watered on the first sunny day. If you have a large number of buds almost ready to cut, you must watch to see that they are not injured by changing weather conditions. The people cutting these roses must always be careful not to injure the buds and foliage when cutting.

The rose grower must continually have a planned control for aphids, spiders and mildew to grow quality roses.

CARBON DIOXIDE—New practices would involve the use of carbon dioxide during the winter months or when the houses are closed to increase production. It is an established fact that roses produce more breaks under higher concentrations of carbon dioxide.

FAN-AND-PAD COOLING—Air-conditioning of rose houses for summer production has proved to be very beneficial. The constant movement of air through the rose plants has made it possible to grow quality roses all summer.

AUTOMATIC WATERING—The use of Gates watering systems around the perimeter of the bench can save the grower many hours of hand-watering. The spacing and type of nozzle used should cover all parts of the bench for a thorough watering.

ROSES, INCORPORATED—Roses, Incorporated, an organization of commercial rose growers, has done much to promote the rose industry. This organization should be supported by every rose grower for the promotion and sale of his product and return of worthwhile information on culture and handling. For details, write to:

James C. Krone, Executive Secretary
1152 Haslett Rd.
Haslett, Mich. 48840

VARIETIES

It would be very difficult to recommend any one variety to a given grower. New varieties are being introduced every year to the industry and some of these will become popular. Some varieties that have remained popular are:

Hybrid Teas

Red: *Forever Yours, Cara Mia, Yuletide.*

Yellow: *Golden Fantasie, Town Crier, Golden Wave.*

White: *Promise Me, Snowsong Supreme, White Butterfly.*

Pink: *Carina, Caresse, Sonia, Pink Sensation.*

Sweethearts

Red: *Mary DeVor.*

Yellow: *Golden Garnette, Coed*

White: *Jack Frost.*

Pink: *Carol Amling, Junior Bridesmaid, Bridal Pink.*

Orange: *Can Can*

R.D.

GARDEN ROSES

This article deals with starting garden roses by the florist to sell as established plants to retail customers.

Few, if any flowering plants for the home garden exceed garden roses in interest and demand, and with good reason. Roses are widely adaptable and not difficult for the average home gardener to grow. They certainly produce a beautiful assortment of cut flowers for the home.

OREGOLD
Lemon yellow hybrid tea rose. AARS 1975.

Roses were formerly sold exclusively by mail-order and local nurseries Later, grocery stores and chain outlets started handling them in dormant bare-root form, wrapped in foil or polyethylene bags. However, today's customer is more sophisticated, wants to see what he is buying, and wants to see it growing before he spends his money. This is where the retail florist with growing facilities enters the picture. Many have found that a good selection of well-grown roses attracts a larger clientele than do bedding plants alone. The best of the growers soon become known in local gardening circles as "rose specialists," a fact which gives them worthwhile word-of-mouth advertising over a wider area than they could normally expect. And hand in hand with these increased rose sales go increased sales of bedding and pot plants.

Thus, the retail-grower florist enjoys a very great advantage over mail-order houses and the corner grocery store in the garden-rose business. He can offer his customers rose plants already growing. This not only cuts the retail customer's loss to practically nothing, but gives him flowers within a few weeks after he buys the plant. Started rose plants don't have to be purchased by home gardeners early in the spring; they can be bought and planted out in the garden anytime during the summer and still enjoy a good life expectancy and produce cut flowers before frost.

There is no problem in starting potted roses, providing a few rules are followed exactly. In our business of selling dormant, bare-root garden-rose plants to florists, we have found a considerable lack of basic information concerning their requirements. From our own experience, the following rules are applicable for starting potted roses.

1. Order your bare-root dormant plants for delivery at least 2 months before you want to sell them as started growing plants. For your own convenience, you can order your plants delivered in more than one shipment to spread out your workload and to give you a succession of plants to sell throughout the spring and summer. We will discuss the question of varieties later in this article. Rose plants do not have to be sold as soon as they are started. A plant properly started will remain in saleable shape for several months.

2. When your rose plants arrive, you will find them packed in containers and in material which protects them from frost and drying out. If the shipment arrives damaged, be sure to file a claim with the trucking company immediately. If your plants arrive frozen, it is wise to file a claim, even though there is a good chance of thawing them out with no loss. If, when you open the shipment (and it should be opened immediately upon arrival), you find the plants frozen, pack them up again and store the shipment in a cool (temperatures between 34 and 40° are ideal), dark place for 2 or 3 days, especially if frozen hard. This will give the plants a chance to thaw out gradually, which is the secret in salvaging frozen rose plants. Dormant rose plants can stand considerable frost, IF they are thawed out gradually.

The most important, basic point in handling rose plants is to be sure the plant is NEVER allowed to dry out—either its roots or canes. As soon as roses are dug in the growing field, they are pruned, graded, and packed in moist packing material immediately and put into cold-temperature, high-humidity storage. If, when you receive them, they are allowed to stand out in the open sun and wind for a few hours, all this careful handling will have been for nothing and the plants may die. Even if they do not die, they will be sufficiently injured to cause slow starting and poor subsequent growth. It is a good idea to soak the plants in water for an hour or two as they are unpacked. In case the plants have dried out a little in transit, this dip will replenish their supply of moisture.

3. Rose plants should be pruned and potted IMMEDIATELY upon receipt. If you can't get to them immediately, leave the plants in their shipping container until you are ready to pot them. However, don't leave them packed any longer than necessary—a day or two at most.

Pruning rose plants is a second important fundamental. At the time of potting, the plants should be cut off to within 6 or 8 inches of the crown of the plant. This should leave 2 to 4 "eyes" from which growth will start. Don't be afraid to cut most of the cane off. Long canes produce weak new growth and small blooms. Also, the plant will be more subject to injury from dessication. Remember that until new root hairs are produced, the plant has no way of compensating for moisture lost from the canes, and the longer the cane, the greater the loss. Grading by the American Nurserymen's Association requires, among other things, canes of a certain length, which is the reason canes are left long when shipped to you. Also, trim off any damaged roots or any roots that are excessively long. The finer roots are the important ones—heavy, thick ones do not produce the all-important white roots that the plants need to start growing.

This pruning procedure applies to all varieties and types of roses, including the climbing varieties.

4. There are several types of rose pots available. They should be at least 6 or 8 inches wide at the top and 8 or 10 inches deep, and should have a hole in the bottom to insure good drainage. Soil used for potting should be of a loose consistency to provide aeration and drainage. Peat moss incorporated into a heavy soil will help. Add NO fertilizer to the potting soil except superphosphate, if it is needed. Apply nitrogen and potassium only after the plant has started into active growth and can make use of it. Water, not fertilizer, is the "mother's milk" of a starting rose. Rose plants should be potted to a depth so as to just barely cover the bud union. This is the thickened part of the stem from which the canes grow.

Firming the soil around the roots of the plant during potting is important. Place a handful of soil in the bottom of the pot and then put the plant in the pot. Fill up the pot with soil, frequently firming the soil as the pot is being filled. If the soil isn't firmly tamped around the plant roots, air pockets may dry out the roots before they have had a chance to get into the soil. Fill pot to within an inch of the top.

5. IMMEDIATELY AFTER POTTING, the pots should be thoroughly soaked with water. This can be done by repeated hose waterings until the soil in the pot is completely saturated. The pots should be placed on a surface that allows drainage out of the bottom of the pot. Gravel, for instance, is a good material to place pots on. Newly potted rose plants must be protected from wind and sun until root action starts. The best method of getting strong initial growth is by using WHITE opaque polyethylene. Cover the plants completely and tuck the plastic under the outer pots. When growth starts and the first leaves have appeared, the sides of the poly can be folded back to allow the plants to become adjusted to a lower humidity gradually, and then removed completely after a couple of days. Caution:

CARLA
Clear pink hybrid tea rose.

Where air temperatures are likely to exceed 80°, do not use clear poly-ethylene unless you spray it with shading compound. Should high temperatures follow within 48 hours of potting, heat build-up under clear poly will sometimes result in the plants being killed outright. Once the roots are active, they can tolerate any temperature to be experienced in a greenhouse. Roses started outdoors under plastic should present no problems.

During the growing period, the soil and the pot should be kept wet and not allowed to dry out at any time. Varieties vary in the time required to start growth. Some will begin to break within a few days. Others may take a week or more. Slow-starters may be aided by being separated and covered with polyethylene until growth starts.

You can sell a started rose pot plant to your retail customer with every confidence that it will continue to grow when planted out in the garden. Just caution the customer not to break up the root ball when removing the pot. Nothing helps rose sales more than to have one or two plants showing color, and if you have the facilities, it is worthwhile starting plants early so that their flowering coincides with your peak selling period. If these are kept on display, they will be found to be a real assistance in selling roses that are not yet in bloom. You should also not be afraid to charge extra for a potted growing plant over and above the dormant bare-root price. You have put your skill, time and effort into producing a growing plant and the customer will not object to paying extra for this service. Most homeowners have had sufficient experience in trying to start dormant roses to be only too glad to leave that job to you, the professional.

6. Once the rose plants are growing, the only care they need are an occasional spraying and feeding. Blackspot and mildew are the principal diseases of roses, both of which can be easily controlled with modern fungicides. Blackspot is a defoliating disease which does not often occur in a sales lot, but it is well to be on the safe side and practice prevention. Mildew, on

the other hand, under certain weather conditions, can appear and will be disfiguring to the foliage. Both mildew and blackspot can be controlled by spraying at 14-day intervals with Benlate, or a combination of Folpet and Actidione.

Rose plants which remain on the sales lot after midsummer may become infested with aphids or spider mites. Tedion is one of the most effective outdoor miticides. Malathion or Diazinon are two materials which will control aphids and also nonresistant mites. At the first signs of either of these pests, a spray application should be made, as it takes very little time for them to build up into a major problem. Occasionally, carpenter bees may make their home in rose canes by boring in from the cut end. Dabbing tree paint or cane sealer on the cut ends will stop their activities, as will the use of the more prosaic thumbtack.

Once your plants are actively growing, they can be fed either by an application of soluble 20-20-20 during your normal greenhouse feeding, or they can be top dressed with one of the many rose fertilizers or plain agricultural 10-10-10.

Feeding and spraying will help to keep your roses looking in their best shape over a long selling season, and it should not be necessary to have to cut prices because of their poor appearance.

The choice of varieties will be dictated to a degree by your location and climate. AARS Award winners are usually satisfactory nationwide, but some introductions by rose nurseries may be of regional adaptability. This is where your salesman should be helpful in providing such information.

An average rose order should consist of at least 50% patented varieties. Hybridists are steadily improving the breed, and the newer patented varieties are generally quite a bit superior to those of 20 years ago. It is to these newer roses that your type of customer will gravitate.

Today, roses come in almost every color range. In making your variety selection, you should take into account customer preferences. As an example, last year, our customers ordered their roses by color in these percentages—patented varieties: 33% red, 25% pink, 15% yellow, 5% white, 12% multicolor, 5% orange, 5% lavender. In the standards, they ordered 43% red, 21% pink, 24% yellow, 6% white, 5% multicolored, 1% lavender. The large percentage of yellow is accounted for by *Peace* being included in this color category. This variety is still one of the largest selling of any. However, it is wise to bear in mind that preferences change from year to year, albeit slowly, and it is always hard to predict exactly what will sell in colors.

FORCING POT ROSES

This article is concerned with producing specimen rose pot plants in flower for Easter and Mother's Day.

Roses for pot forcing should be dormant, 2-year-old budded plants. These plants are received from production fields during December. Planting for Easter should be done about 3 months before the holiday occurs. The grower should request delivery of plants at the time they are to be potted. Roses should be stored as near 31° F as possible, and in very high humidity—conditions that most growers do not have readily available. Therefore, it is better to have the dealer from whom the plants are purchased keep the plants in storage until time to pot.

As soon as rose plants are received, they should be unpacked, immersed in water for a short time, or wet-down thoroughly and covered over completely with moist burlap for a day or so, and then potted. If plants arrive in a frozen condition, chances are they can be successfully thawed out by leaving them in their packing cases and storing the cases at 35 to 40° for 3 or 4 days. This will effect a gradual thawing out that will not harm the plants. If freezing is suspected, immediately notify the transportation company that delivered them, so that a claim may be filed later if the plants are damaged.

At the time of potting, dormant plants should be pruned back to within 6 or 8 inches of the bud union—the swollen section of the lower stem from which the canes grow. Generally speaking, higher pruning will result in more branches and bushier plants, while lower pruning (6 inches) will result in fewer and taller branches. Any good greenhouse soil with about 1 part of peat moss or rotted manure is satisfactory. Be sure to firm the soil well, as plants are potted so that no air pockets form around the roots. A 6 or 7-inch pot is required for proper root growth. During potting, roots should be pruned as little as necessary. Bear in mind that the fine, fibrous roots are the ones that help the plants off to a quick start. If any root pruning is necessary in order to get the plants into a pot, cut off the heavier or damaged roots.

Immediately after potting, rose plants should be placed in 50° and kept well watered in high humidity. At this temperature, the plants will start root development quickly. After 2 weeks at 50°, roots will have become established and the temperature should be raised to encourage top growth. Rose plants require plenty of water (both in the soil and in the atmosphere) during their first 2 to 4 weeks to encourage shoots to break and grow. Again, as in garden roses, white polyethylene will give superior results in getting roses off to a good start. High atmospheric moisture can be accomplished by frequent syringing or misting, while some growers cover plants with wet burlap to serve this purpose. However, any covering should be removed as leaves begin to open.

As soon as shoots are well started (2 to 3 weeks), the plants can be moved into full sunlight. Feeding with soluble nitrogen or a balanced fertilizer should be done about 3 times during the plant's growth with the first application about 6 weeks after potting.

The question of whether or not to pinch pot roses varies with growers. Some growers do not pinch at all. Others use pinching not only to develop more flowers, but also to help time their crop. For instance, if an April 1 Easter crop is planted January 1 and given a soft pinch February 1, the plants should be in flower by April 1—8 weeks after pinching. A Mother's Day crop should be pinched 7 weeks before flowering. Control of flowering time is also possible by adjusting temperatures. The basic forcing temperature should be 58°, but the crop can be advanced with a higher temperature (62°)

or retarded with a lower temperature (55°). Bear in mind, however, that temperatures above 58° are apt to result in loss of quality in the finished plant. For instance, flowers grown on plants forced at too-high temperatures are much more apt to shatter than those grown at lower temperatures.

A crop of pot roses for Mother's Day should be potted the first week in February. Otherwise, the same cultural practices apply as for the Easter crop. Plants unsold for Easter may be pinched back for a later crop. A pinched-back plant should flower in about 6 weeks from an Easter pinch.

Pot rose plants are available in three size grades. "XXX" plants have at least 4 strong canes, and are used to produce the largest specimen plants. "XX" plants have at least 3 strong canes, and are suitable for medium-sized finished plants. "X" plants (available only in the standard or non-patented varieties) have at least 1 strong cane. This smallest grade is used only for small plants suitable for special uses.

VARIETIES

Practically all pot roses forced today are of the small-flowered floribunda type. Following is a list of the more important varieties.

Garnette is the most widely grown pot rose variety. This is the same variety grown for cut flowers. Its attractive bronzy-green foliage and red flowers combine to produce a beautiful and salable plant.

Triomphe Orleanais is the "old standby." It is an easy forcer and very free-flowering. Flowers are semi-double and a carmine or cherry red.

Margo Koster is a salmon-orange with globular shaped flowers.

Mother's Day is a red sport of *Margo Koster* and excellent for either Easter or Mother's Day.

Carol Amling, the light coral-pink *Garnette* sport grown for cut flowers, is increasingly grown as a pot plant.

Tammy* is a clear pink sport of *Mother's Day* and a recent introduction.

Other good and important varieties are *Thunderbird**, a brilliant, velvety-scarlet sport of *Garnette; Bright Pink Garnette*, a bright, deep pink sport of *Garnette; Dick Koster,* bright salmon-rose; *Starina**, orange-red; *Chipper**, coral pink, and *Scarlet Gem**, scarlet.

Potted rose plants are popular for Mother's Day and Easter sales.

Miniature roses are also grown as forced pot plants. Varieties such as *Cinderella**, cream-white; *Pixie**, double white; *Red Imp**, crimson; and *Sweet Fairy**, pink, force very well. These varieties are all supplied as own-root, cutting-propagated plants, and are available in a dormant condition in either the spring or fall. They are used in outdoor miniature-garden plantings and are very hardy. In a 60° night temperature, these miniature varieties will force in about 6 weeks. Some judicious pruning is sometimes necessary, as the plants develop, to prevent "leggy" shoots from developing. Gaining rapidly in popularity is *Marmalade*. Dwarfer than other strains, (18-22 inches), it produces 3 inch single orange flowers with small dark eyes. *Patented varieties.   *I.M.*

RUDBECKIA (Coneflower)

PERENNIAL *(R. hirta burpeii) 40,000 seeds per oz. Germinates in 3 wks. at 70°.*

Often called "coneflowers," rudbeckias are easy to grow and will produce long-stemmed flowers excellent for cutting. Easily grown from seed and an excellent perennial for spring-plant sales to go with annual plant offerings, the *Gloriosa Daisies* make a fine bedding display and are also excellent for cutting. They will flower the first summer from a February or March sowing. The *Double Gloriosa Daisy* is in much greater demand than the single, which is a *tetraploid*, producing large single flowers in shades of yellow and mahogany-red. Producing large (4-inch) and many fully double flowers of golden yellow, the *Double Gloriosa Daisy* fits well into the hardy border.

SAINTPAULIA (African Violet)

ANNUAL *(S. ionantha) 1,000,000 seeds per oz. Germinates in 25 days at 70°. Light.*

African violets are grown by the hundreds on window sills by amateurs across the country. There are very few other plants which are easier to grow and will flower more freely than the African violet hybrids. Propagation is by well-matured leaf cuttings inserted in sand at around 70°. A well-established, 3-inch flowering pot plant is produced in about 6-8 months from inserting the cuttings. An ordinary, not-too-heavy compost soil, to which is added ¼ leaf mold, has been found to be the best material for growing this plant. All material used in growing this as well as other choice pot plants should be steam-sterilized. A light intensity of 800-1,000 foot candles is necessary. The temperature of the water used on African violets is very important. Since cold water causes leaf spotting, the use of tempered water, 70°-75°, is a must. A minimum 70-72° night temperature should be maintained for *Saintpaulia*. In addition to leaf propagation, several varieties are available from the seed, which is extremely tiny and requires great care in germination and during early growth stages. A flowering plant is produced from seed in approximately 10 months.

Revitalized interest and demand for foliage, or house plants, has stimulated commercial production of African Violets. Propagated by specialists and sold as transplants, equivalent to a 2 inch or 2¼ inch plant, growers can finish a crop in 10-12 weeks in 4 inch pots. The *Fischer Ballet*® series is outstanding and currently available in 12 different color varieties. Also widely used is the *Rhapsody* series.

SALVIA

ANNUAL *(S. species) 7,500 seeds per oz. Germinates in 12-15 days at 70°. Light.*

The immense popularity enjoyed by this brilliant red "scarlet sage" for many years shows no signs of declining. They are of special interest to the florist because, while they are seed-propagated, few home gardeners have the heat to sprout the seed—so they buy plants.

Biggest call is for bedding-size stock in packs or 2¼-inch pots for planting out during May. An early-March sowing should have no trouble making this size by mid-May if carried at 55°. An early-February sowing should easily make 3's or 4's for May sales—and there is call for that size from folks who want to make more showing in a hurry, or they are also useful in combination pots. Our trial-ground salvia that makes a fine showing for us is not actually sown until early April.

SEED GERMINATION

Certainly not hard, but salvia germination failures are more frequent than average—because their requirements are not understood. We never have trouble sprouting good salvia seed if:

1. Seed flats are soaked thoroughly at time of sowing, covered with paper or glass to hold moisture, and not watered till seed sprouts, unless surface of soil is absolutely dry (it shouldn't get dry before seed comes through). Excellent results can also be had by germinating under a mist system.

2. Seed flats are kept in a minimum of 70° till seed sprouts. It just won't come through at 50°—and that's likely the biggest reason for failure.

3. Seeds are not covered.

Note: Salvia seed is sensitive to methyl bromide-treated soil.

Lastly, we move the flats to a cooler house (55°) as soon as seed is well through—it helps prevent damp-off that can wreck them in a hurry if conditions are right.

Cultural needs beyond this are simple—an average, good garden soil lightened with peat, as you would do for any annual, and the usual routine spray program to control spiders that are especially fond of them. They like full sun all the way, but we have seen them make a fine showing outdoors where they had sun only till noon.

ABOUT VARIETIES

There are quite a few of them, and obviously a lot of misunderstanding as to exactly what each one is supposed to look like. After many seasons of flowering the best domestic and foreign strains in our trial grounds, here is our classification. Note that the more dwarf sorts are the earliest. The mid-season kinds have more vigorous growth, and may look somewhat better than the earlies late in the season.

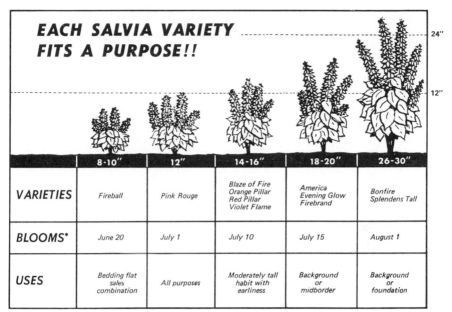

EACH SALVIA VARIETY FITS A PURPOSE!!

	8-10"	12"	14-16"	18-20"	26-30"
VARIETIES	Fireball	Pink Rouge	Blaze of Fire Orange Pillar Red Pillar Violet Flame	America Evening Glow Firebrand	Bonfire Splendens Tall
BLOOMS*	June 20	July 1	July 10	July 15	August 1
USES	Bedding flat sales combination	All purposes	Moderately tall habit with earliness	Background or midborder	Background or foundation

*Blooming date from April 1st sowing—Chicago

Earliest and most dwarf are *Fireball,* about 10 inches; *Red Hussar,* 9 to 10 inches and later than *St. John's Fire; St. John's Fire,* under 12 inches; and *Blaze of Fire,* about 14 inches, in flower by early July, exceptionally even, dwarf, and fine. Next comes *Firebrand,* in flower a few days later and reaching a height of perhaps 15 to 18 inches. *Red Pillar,* a deep red with beautiful foliage, flowers about mid-July at a height of 14 inches. *America* at 20 inches (July 20). *Bonfire* flowers late July, grows about 26 inches, and is followed about the middle of the month by *Splendens Tall,* which grows 30 inches. The later-flowered sorts do have a more intensive coloring, and it must be said that, especially during unfavorable seasons, the extra-early sorts get ragged before frost.

Leading the scarlet-red varieties in popularity and usage are *St. John's Fire* and *Red Pillar. Evening Glow,* a brilliant old-rose color, and *Pink Rouge,* a dwarf salmon pink rose, are used to a much lesser extent. *Violet Flame,* a dark violet purple, grows about 15 inches high. *White Fire,* a dwarf, creamy white, flowers early and is probably the most popular white. Latest introduction belonging to the *splendens* type is *Orange Pillar* (14 inches), which has the same bushy, uniform habit and spikes that *Red Pillar* has; the flowers are orange-red to rich salmon in color.

Salvia farinacea (blue-and-white salvia) has become increasingly popular in recent years with the introduction of dwarf or compact varieties with more intense color. Useful for border work and cutting, *Regal Purple* (2 feet) is widely used along with its white counterpart, *Regal White.* Recently introduced is *Catima* (2 feet), a deep midnight-blue with a uniform, bushy plant habit. *Royal Blue* grows to a height of about 3 ft.

SCABIOSA (Pincushion-Flower)

ANNUAL *(S. atropurpurea) 4,500 seeds per oz. Germinates in 12 days at 70°.*
PERENNIAL *(S. caucasica) 2,400 seeds per oz. Germinates in 18 days at 60°.*

Often called "pincushion-flower," the annual form of scabiosa is another outdoor summer-cutting item that produces reasonably long stems under trying outdoor conditions. Should be drilled out as early as soil will permit. Fall sowing under favorable conditions is even better. Annual scabiosa also does well forced for spring flowering in a cool house (50°), but in a warm house or during warm weather, the naturally slender stems draw up rather weak. For May flowering, the seed should be sown in March and benched in April. For cutting purposes on a small scale, the *Giant Imperial Mix* is a good strain.

The perennial form, like the annual, is a cool-temperature plant. While both suffer in excessive summer heat, the perennials are inclined to die out if it gets too trying. Probably for this reason, they are not widely used in the Midwest, but are very choice where summers are more moderate. The variety known as *House Mixture* is very popular. Flower size is 3 inches with colors ranging from white to deep blue.

SCHIZANTHUS (Butterfly Flower)

ANNUAL *(S. species) 60,000 seeds per oz. Germinates in 15 days at 60°.*

These are easily grown plants that literally cover themselves with a brilliant mass of showy blooms. Schizanthus is useful both for cutting and for that "something different" in pot plants.

Sow late in August, for 5 or 6-inch pots. A 45-48° house should get them in. Also, schizanthus can be sown for 3 to 4-inch pot plants up to February 1. Remember that even the earliest sowing date will not flower until well into spring conditions, unless their roots are checked by becoming pot-bound. Don't overlook this: an early-August sowing carried along in pots, and planted out in a shallow raised bed of a 48-50° house, will get into nice flower by mid- or late winter. But the soil should not be much over 4 inches deep. While they are fragile and will shatter if handled much or shipped, they will last a remarkably long time if undisturbed.

While the dwarf types are perfect as pot plants without pinching, the stronger-growing, medium-dwarf ones should be topped back when up 6-8 inches. The tall ones, fit only for cuttings, should also be topped.

VARIETIES

Ball Giant Flowered is the finest all-purpose variety. It makes a choice pot plant, especially for exhibition, if pinched several times. It should also be used for cutting.

458

Greenhouse snaps—largely because of fuel shortages, this traditional favorite is making a comeback. The variety, Rainier (white).

SNAPDRAGON

GREENHOUSE

ANNUAL *(Antirrhinum majus)*
180,000 seeds per oz. Germinates in 1-2 wks. at 65-70°

Snapdragons continue to be one of the florist's major cut-flower crops. During the past ten years, tremendous strides forward have been made in developing varieties and timing schedules which have made possible the production of snaps on a year-round basis with fairly accurate timing. More growers each year are going to the single-stem-replant method, where in previous years many growers would take 2 or even 3 crops off the same plant. To grow profitable crops under this newer and advanced method of growing snaps, it is essential that close attention be paid to all of the various factors involved in the culture of this crop.

GENERAL CULTURE

Seed Germination—Any medium which has the following properties is suitable for germinating—good drainage, good aeration, uniform texture, and adequate moisture-holding ability. Very commonly used is a mixture of ⅓ peat, ⅓ sand, and ⅓ soil; or ½ peat and ½ soil. Another good medium would consist of ½ peat and ½ vermiculite. By using this last-mentioned mixture, a feeding of the seedlings would be necessary before transplanting. Thorough steam sterilization at 180° for one-half hour is a must. This is best done by placing the filled flat on the bench where the seed is to be germinated, and then steaming the bench, flat and medium at one time. Any tools, labels or markers used in conjunction should also be steamed.

The use of an intermittent-mist system is probably the most satisfactory method of watering the seed flat during germination. We have used it here for several years and find it most satisfactory. Its operation is controlled by both a 24-hour time clock and a short-span timer that controls the misting interval. During the dark days of winter, we have used 5 seconds of mist to every 15 minutes from noon till 4 p.m. only; while with the coming of longer and brighter days, the system would be set to provide 5 seconds of mist every 10 minutes during the daylight hours. The big advantage to this system is, of course, the fact that you don't have to worry about the surface drying out, and also that the seed is exposed to full light, since it is not necessary to cover the seed. We do use a light shade on the glass during the brightest times of the year. The other most common method used for germinating snap seed involves the use of a plastic sleeve. After the seed has been sown and thoroughly watered in, the flat is merely slipped into this poly sleeve and the ends folded under. The flat does not have to be watered again until after seed has germinated and the sleeve opened. After germination, it is important that the sleeve be removed promptly, since delay will result in weak, spindly seedlings.

Greenhouse snap seeds are packeted to contain approximately 2,000 seeds per trade packet. Proper sowing will provide at least 800 uniform seedlings. This figure allows for close selection of uniform seedlings at transplanting time. Sowing at the rate of ½ trade packet per 14 x 22-inch flat will give the seedlings sufficient room until they are ready for transplanting. By sowing the seed in rows rather than broadcasting, control of damp-off is made easier if it does occur. Many times, it can be controlled or confined to one row of seedlings. In addition, row seeding seems to give more uniform seedlings.

While snap seed will germinate at 65°, a soil temperature of 70° is desirable. With this higher soil temperature, germination is much more rapid and uniform.

After the seed has germinated, the seedlings should gradually be conditioned by reducing humidity and watering and placing them in a cooler house where they will receive maximum ventilation. It may be necessary to shade the newly germinated seedlings lightly for a few days before exposing them to full light. Some growers will carry the seedlings at 60° right up to transplanting time. Seedlings should be transplanted as soon as the first true leaves are well developed, or when the plant is about 1 inch in height. The sooner the seedlings are transplanted, the less chance for damp-off to occur in the seed flat, and the less shock from transplanting. Prompt transplanting produces earlier, more uniform flowering.

Super-Seedlings®. For the grower who does not have good germination facilities, specialist-produced seedlings, for example, Super-Seedlings, offer

Super-Seedlings being conditioned under 24 hours of light and a controlled temperature-humidity environment.

an ideal solution. By ordering in advance, a grower can have top-quality seedlings of the varieties wanted delivered to his door on the scheduled date for transplanting.

Soils—Of utmost importance in the production of snaps is the use of a well-drained and aerated soil. Quality snaps cannot be grown in a bench or bed that is not properly drained. Many times, drainage is blocked in raised benches by the cracks in the bench bottom swelling, plugging of the drainage holes, or insufficient drainage space in the bench to begin with. The best way to check this is to water the bench thoroughly and then check to see if the water drains through the soil and not at the sides of the bench. The drainage in ground beds may be somewhat more of a problem, and it may be necessary to install drain tile or to use a good layer of coarse gravel at the bottom of the bed. Sometimes, where cropping is continuous, the repeated use of a Rototiller will form a hard pan at the base of the soil, which can be broken up every so often by hand spading the bed. The use of ground beds versus raised benches is largely a matter of preference of the grower, if the same temperature can be provided at both levels. Usually, we find that raised-bench crops will flower up to 3 weeks earlier in the wintertime. This is no doubt due to a somewhat-higher temperature and slightly improved light condition. Proper drainage is somewhat more of a problem on ground beds than it is on raised benches. Many growers feel that better control of moisture and nutrients is obtainable on ground beds.

A soil with a loose, porous structure is an absolute essential in the production of quality snaps, particularly during the winter when rapid drying of the soil is essential. To provide an open, well-aerated soil, it is necessary to add organic matter to the average field soil. This can be done by the use of cover crops in the field. In addition to this, peat moss and manure will aid in loosening a tight soil. The addition of coarse sand or coarse perlite will increase the porosity of the soil without increasing the water-holding capacity. This brings up one of the difficulties involved in using peat moss as a soil additive. While peat moss is excellent for loosening up a soil, at the same time, it increases the water-holding capacity, which is undesirable during the winter. Thus, the addition of peat to the bench soil is probably best made prior to the planting of the summer crop. Other organic materials used are wood shavings, peanut hulls and cattle manure, which is excellent for this purpose, but must be well rotted so as to prevent possible burn from ammonia.

The bench should be thoroughly steamed before planting each crop—180° for one-half hour. Seedlings should be transplanted into the bench as soon as it cools.

Direct Benching Versus Jiffy-Potted Seedlings—There are advantages and disadvantages to both of these methods of handling the seedlings, and generally, successful crops can be produced by either method. Which method to use is largely determined by various economic factors peculiar to each grower. The chief advantage in using Jiffy-Pots is, of course, the fact that it enables a grower to squeeze in an additional crop when flowering on a year-round schedule. Using this method, it is possible for a grower to save about a month per crop. This naturally varies according to the time of the year. For the grower who has bench space available which is not suited for cut-flower production, the use of Jiffy-Pots is ideal. This space can be used as a nursery-bed area where the seedlings are grown from the time of potting

Snaps in a northern winter greenhouse, nine weeks from bench to flower! Drastic reduction in bench time accomplished by use of Jiffy-Pots. Note, by the way, that Jiffys are not "planted"—actually are just on top of the soil. In the photo: Professor J. B. Gartner, head of Floriculture, University of Illinois.

until a bench is cleared. Thus, a savings in valuable crop-production area. By "Jiffying," a grower does have better control over the selection of seedlings at the time of transplanting. Both the 2¼-inch and the 1½-inch Jiffy-Pots are suitable for this purpose. A standard 14 x 22-inch flat will hold 50 2¼-inch pots. Maximum time for holding the seedlings in Jiffy-Pots is 3 weeks in the summer and 4 weeks during the winter. If growing a pinched crop and using pots, the plants should be established in the bench before pinching, since a plant handled this way will produce more and stronger breaks.

The big advantage to the direct-bench method lies in the labor saving of less handling and no pot cost. Some growers feel that direct-benched plants produce a slightly higher-quality crop than the potted ones.

Growing Temperatures and Light—Snaps are still basically a 50° crop. This is the night temperature, and the basis used for timing and scheduling year-round programs. On cloudy days, a temperature of 55° should be carried, while on bright, sunny days, 60-65° will do. After germinating, the seedlings are normally carried at 60° for a short period of time; then, they are gradually hardened by slowly dropping the temperature. Currently, there are some authorities who feel that seedlings should be grown at 60° till benching time, claiming that more rapid growth is promoted in a shorter production time.

Snaps should be exposed to full light at all times. Special effort should be made to see that the glass is clear, since the quality of snaps is so dependent on light conditions. The one possible exception to this might be a summer-flowering crop coming in under excessively high summer temperatures which are uncontrollable. Here, a light summer shade may be necessary.

Fertilization—In general, low-to-medium nutrient levels must be maintained in the soil to produce a decent crop. These levels are as follows: nitrogen, 25-30; phosphorus, 5-10; potassium, 25-30; and calcium, 150-200 ppm, using the Spurway method (see page 161). A pH of 6.0 to 6.5 is desirable. An addition of 3-4 lbs. of superphosphate at the time of soil preparation will be enough to take care of phosphorus requirements for the year. The use of 3-4 lbs. of MagAmp or a similar slow-release fertilizer can be very beneficial in getting plants off to a good start. Excellent results are being obtained by feeding with a dilute fertilizer at each watering. Five ounces of a complete fertilizer per 100 gallons of water is a good starting point. If phosphate had been incorporated at the time of soil preparation, a 20% nitrogen material plus muriate of potash can be used. There are a number of good proportioner or injector-type fertilizing machines on the market today which do an excellent job. High levels of nitrogen during the winter are undesirable, while in spring and summer with rapid growth, a good level of nitrogen is necessary. The injector system of fertilizing in a way automatically controls the varying amounts of fertilizer required at different times of the year. During that period of the year when temperature and light are high, more frequent watering is necessary, and thus, fertilizer is more frequently applied. If using this system, it is important to water thoroughly each time, providing some leaching action and prevention of soluble-salt buildup which snaps are particularly susceptible to. More troublesome in the seedling or early stages of growth, it is suggested that a soil test and Solu Bridge reading be taken before benching the crop. Frequently, high-salt trouble occurs when following a mum crop with a crop of snaps. On the winter crop in particular, it is important that the amount of nitrogen be reduced as buds are being formed. Some growers stop feeding at the time the buds appear, while others have good results by feeding until the buds start to expand. The point here is to watch the nitrogen feeding closely at the time that vegetative growth slows down. Just one extra shot of fertilizer can cause weak stems, grassiness, and soft growth.

Watering—It is not necessary to soak the bench thoroughly immediately after transplanting young seedlings in the winter. Once the seedlings take hold and begin to grow, thorough watering is necessary to prevent soluble-salt buildup. Young plants must be kept moist to allow maximum vegetative growth. If plants are allowed to wilt badly, the growth is checked. Frequency

Automatic watering will do a good job on established seedlings.

of watering is determined largely by the time of the year, the soil mixture used, and the growth stage of the crop. The decision as to when to water is largely a matter of the grower's experienced judgment. During the low-light periods, watering should be done less frequently after the buds appear. However, holding back the water in the hot summer months will cause a growth check.

There are a number of automatic-watering systems available today that are being used with a high degree of success. Watering by hand requires excessive labor costs, and often the job done is not as good or as uniform as an automatic system. The automatic-bench system using a twin-wall hose has given very satisfactory results. The Chapin System is popular.

Insects and Pests—*Aphids*—Cause distorted foliage on young plants and old. Control: Vapona aerosol, malathion spray, and Cygon and Systox as systemics.

Thrips—Injure florets during warm-weather season. Control: Air-cooled houses can use Dieldrin in the water flowing through the pads. Malathion is very effective when used as a mist spray over the flowers.

Mites—Often do considerable damage. Control: Kelthane and Tedion sprays.

Whitefly—Not too common on snaps, but are seen at times. Control: Thiodan or Lindane sprays.

Garden Symphylan—Control: Soil sterilization, Lindane drench.

Cabbage Looper—Control: Sevin, Zectran and Thuricide HPC sprays.

Bees—Pollination will cause florets to drop prematurely. Control: Screen vents if possible. Use shatterproof varieties.

Diseases—Wilt and botrytis are two of the most damaging diseases of snapdragons. Although they both produce the same symptom (wilting), they are brought on by different causes. It seems quite well established that a major cause of "wilt" in snapdragons is related to the soil fungus, pythium, most commonly seen in December and January. The best preventive measures consist of avoiding soft growth, using that all-important well-aerated soil, and adopting a complete and thorough sterilization and *sanitation* program. The latter is the best preventive control for botrytis, which is a fungus disease causing serious damage at flowering time. Often, the stem is attacked by the fungus, and will eventually girdle it, causing complete wilting. Since botrytis is spread by spores which require condensed moisture to germinate, it is necessary to ventilate properly to avoid condensation on the foliage. By watering in the morning, foliage will be dry by evening when the temperatures start to drop and condensation occurs.

Rust is not nearly as troublesome on greenhouse snaps as it was a few years ago. It appears in the form of blisters on the foliage which emit brown, powdery spores spread by air currents which require moisture to germinate. Best control lies in keeping water off the foliage. Spraying with *zineb* will control it.

Stem rot will attack snaps, especially during warm weather. Plants are usually attacked right at the soil line. Best preventive control is steam sterilization for ½ hour at 180°. A drench of Dexon-Terraclor or Benlate-Truban immediately after planting will usually prevent loss.

Powdery mildew can largely be prevented by using the same measures suggested for botrytis control. In addition, sulfur can be used as a spray or dust in preventing its occurrence. Thorough coverage is necessary.

SINGLE-STEM OR PINCHED CROP

Today, the majority of snap growers is interested in a quick, uniform, high-quality crop; thus, the greater preference for, and use of the single-stem method. The big advantage to the single-stem method is that it affords a much faster method of producing a crop. A 3 to 4 week saving in time allows a grower to produce 3 to 4 crops a year on a given bench, while only 2 crops are possible using the pinched method. A single-stem crop will produce more uniform quality and is more easily timed. Crops grown single-stem can be flowered year round, while pinched crops should not be flowered from June 15 through November 1.

Snap variety trials in our West Chicago greenhouses—Group II varieties flowered in February, March and April.

Despite the fact that production of snaps is swinging over more and more to the single-stem method of growing, there yet remain many growers, particularly retail, who grow the pinched crop and find it advantageous. Briefly, using this method requires less labor and less plants. Having the crop spread out over a longer period of time is advantageous to many retail growers.

Spacing on a pinched crop should be 7 x 8 inches. If it is not possible to bench seedlings direct, the plants should not be pinched until they have taken hold and are established in the bench. Pinching prior to benching reduces the number of breaks produced. Plants should be pinched back to 3 good pairs of leaves when they are about 8 inches high. Four good breaks per plant are generally desirable, and any above this amount should be pruned out.

There are growers who take a second crop from an initial planting. After the first crop is cut, which, incidentally should be quite low to produce strong basal breaks for the second flowering, the developing shoots are thinned out to 4 or 5, and plants are kept in active growth by watering and feeding.

Accurate timing of pinched crops is more difficult than with a single-stem crop. However, we have found the schedule below to be fairly accurate in our northern latitude when using varieties normally flowered at the season indicated.

PINCHED SCHEDULE—NORTH—RAISED BENCHES—MINIMUM 50°

Sow	Flower
July 20	Dec. 15
Aug. 1	Jan. 15
Aug. 20	Feb. 15
Sept. 5	Mar. 1
Sept. 20	Apr. 15
Nov. 15	Mid-May

DEBUTANTE
Group II light pink.

RAINIER
Pure white, Group II snap.

From our own trials here in West Chicago, the following **Group II** varieties proved very satisfactory when grown as a pinched crop and flowered in spring.

McKinley	*Maryland Pink Imp.*	*Treasure Chest*
Golden Spike	*Jackpot*	

YEAR-ROUND FLOWERING

Largely responsible for the rapid development of snap production on a year-round basis is the introduction of new improved varieties and refined classification of varieties into response groups. This classification is based on a variety's reaction to temperature, light intensity and day length. Group I includes those varieties that produce quality stems and spikes at 50° minimum temperature under the low-light and short-day conditions of midwinter. Group IV, on the other hand, includes those varieties which do their best under high temperature, high-light intensity and long days, such as we normally experience during the summer months. Thus, this classification allows a grower to select the best varieties for the time of the year he wishes to flower his crop. By proper selection of varieties, a grower can produce snaps on a year-round basis. Advance planning is necessary when considering going into snap production on this basis, and our Sales Service Dept. is well qualified to completely plan and set up a year-round-flowering program, and also will schedule snaps in combination with other crops. For example, here is a typical year-round program based on an 8-bench rotation, designed for a northern grower—growing single-stem snaps on raised benches at 50° night temperature.

Typical Year-Round Snap Schedule

BED NO.	SOW	BENCH	APPROXIMATE FLOWERING PERIOD
		First Rotation	
1	Nov. 2	Nov. 27	Apr. 16-26
2	Nov. 17	Dec. 17	Apr. 27-May 7
3	Dec. 5	Jan. 5	May 8-13
4	Jan. 3	Feb. 3	May 19-24
5	Jan. 30	Mar. 2	May 30-June 4
6	Feb. 24	Mar. 24	June 11-16
7	Mar. 18	Apr. 18	June 22-27
8	Mar. 30	Apr. 30	July 3-8
		Second Rotation	
1	Apr. 16	May 6	July 15-20
2	Apr. 27	May 17	July 24-29
3	May 3	May 23	July 30-Aug. 4
4	May 14	June 4	Aug. 8-13
5	May 26	June 14	Aug. 20-25
6	June 8	June 26	Sept. 3-8
7	June 19	July 7	Sept. 11-16
8	July 1	July 18	Sept. 23-28
		Third Rotation	
1	July 12	July 30	Oct. 8-18
2	July 21	Aug. 9	Oct. 22-Nov. 1
3	July 26	Aug. 14	Oct. 29-Nov. 9
4	Aug. 5	Aug. 23	Nov. 20-Dec. 5
5	Aug. 17	Sept. 5	Dec. 17-Jan. 7
6	Sept. 1	Sept. 18	Jan. 28-Feb. 18
7	Sept. 8	Sept. 26	Feb. 10-Mar. 1
8	Sept. 20	Oct. 8	Feb. 26-Mar. 18

The big advantage of year-round flowering is, of course, the steady and continuous production that a grower can supply to his customers or the market. This enables a grower in many instances to book standing orders. Peak prices are generally obtained from December through February and many growers hit this period with extra production by the use of additional benches over and above those regularly used in the year-round program. Very often, these benches are then used for bedding plants. While there is great fluctuation between prices received for snaps on the market during February and June or July, the high-low price periods, it must be remembered that comparative production costs must be related to market returns.

Following are timetables that can be used as guides in planning a snap schedule. Unfortunately, there are many factors involved which can alter these schedules, and it behooves the grower to standardize his cultural practices and keep accurate records so as to insure himself reasonably accurate timing. For example, an extended spell of cold, dark weather during the winter can greatly delay a crop. Improper soil mixtures, poor watering practices, and the flowering of varieties out of season will have quite an effect on the flowering date.

Single-Stem—Raised Bench—North

SOW	FLOWER	SOW	FLOWER
Group I		**Group III**	
Aug. 16	Dec. 16 - Jan. 1	Feb. 25	June 10 - June 15
Aug. 28	Jan. 20 - Feb. 10	Mar. 10	June 18 - June 23
Group II		**Group IV**	
Sept. 17	Feb. 23 - Mar. 15	Mar. 31	July 3 - July 8
Oct. 6	Mar. 16 - Mar. 31	Apr. 20	July 18 - July 23
Oct. 25	Apr. 5 - Apr. 20	May 5	July 31 - Aug. 5
Nov. 14	Apr. 25 - May 5	May 25	Aug. 20 - Aug. 25
		June 10	Sept. 5 - Sept. 10
Group III		**Group III**	
Dec. 11	May 10 - May 15	July 3	Sept. 24 - Sept. 29
Jan. 2	May 19 - May 24	July 17	Oct. 16 - Oct. 26
Jan. 20	May 26 - May 31	**Group II**	
Feb. 9	June 3 - June 8	Aug. 1	Nov. 10 - Nov. 19

Generally, the dividing line between North and South is considered to be the 38th parallel. Since this line is approximate, adjustments in scheduling would have to be made by growers on the fringe areas of this line.

Recommended spacing, North: November to May 15 flowering—4 x 5 inches. May 15 to October flowering—3 x 5 inches.

Single-Stem—Raised Bench—South

SOW	FLOWER	SOW	FLOWER
Group II		**Group IV**	
Aug. 25	Dec. 9 - Dec. 29	Mar. 26	June 21 - June 26
Sept. 8	Jan. 13 - Feb. 2	Apr. 21	July 16 - July 21
Sept. 29	Feb. 17 - Mar. 7	May 6	Aug. 1 - Aug. 6
Oct. 28	Mar. 21 - Apr. 6	May 27	Aug. 22 - Aug. 27
Dec. 9	Apr. 16 - Apr. 26	June 21	Sept. 16 - Sept. 21
Group III		**Group III**	
Jan. 17	May 6 - May 11	July 12	Oct. 8 - Oct. 18
Feb. 22	May 28 - June 2	Aug. 11	Nov. 14 - Nov. 29

Recommended spacing, South: November 15 to April 15 flowering—4 x 5 inches. April 15 to November 15 flowering—3 x 4 inches

Varietal Recommendations—North

DECEMBER 10-FEBRUARY 15 FLOWERING

White	*Sierra, Citation, Pennsylvania, Oakland, Teton*	Rose	*Wisconsin, Rosita*
		Red	*Vulcan*
		Lavender	*Señorita*
Yellow	*Chicago, Doubloon, West Virginia*		(from Jan. 1-Mar. 1)
Pink	*Spanish Lady, New Jersey*		

FEBRUARY 15-MAY 10 FLOWERING

White	*Snowman, Rainier, Oakland*	Pink	*Debutante, New Jersey, Pink Ice*

| Yellow | Montezuma, Chicago, Golden Spike, West Virginia | Rose | Maryland Appleblossom, Baltimore |
| Bronze | Gallant Fox | Red | Navajo, Apache |

MAY 10-JUNE 30 FLOWERING

| White | Panama, Oakland, Virginia | Pink | Pan-American Summer Pink, Winchester |
| Yellow | Tampico, Potomac Yellow | | |

JULY 1-SEPTEMBER 10 FLOWERING

| White | Panama, Texas, Potomac White | Yellow | Tampico, Potomac Yellow |
| | | Pink | Miami, Winchester |

SEPTEMBER 10-OCTOBER 25 FLOWERING

| White | Panama, Oakland, Virginia | Pink | Pan-American Summer Pink |
| Yellow | Tampico, Potomac Yellow | | |

OCTOBER 25-DECEMBER 10 FLOWERING

White	Snowman, Oakland, Rainier	Pink	Pink Ice, New Jersey, Idaho, Debutante
Yellow	Golden Spike, Montezua, West Virginia	Rose	Treasure Chest, Maryland Appleblossom
		Bronze	Michigan
		Red	Navajo

Varietal Recommendations—South

OCTOBER 1-NOVEMBER 30 FLOWERING

White	Panama, Oakland
Yellow	Tampico, Potomac Yellow
Pink	Pan American Summer Pink

DECEMBER 1-APRIL 30 FLOWERING

White	Ranier, Snowman (from Feb. 1)	Bronze	Michigan
		Pink	Debutante, Pink Ice, New Jersey
Yellow	Chicago, Montezuma, Golden Spike (from Feb. 1)	Rose	Treasure Chest, Baltimore
		Lavender	Lavender Lady (from Feb. 1)

MAY 1-JUNE 10 FLOWERING

White   *Panama, Virginia, Oakland,*
                San Francisco
Yellow   *Tampico, Potomac Yellow*
Pink   *Winchester, Pan American*
                Summer Pink

JUNE 10-SEPTEMBER 30 FLOWERING

White   *Panama*
Yellow   *Tampico, Potomac Yellow*
Pink   *Miami, Winchester*

◄ MONTEZUMA
Deep yellow Group II variety. One of the best
yellows we've seen in years.

SUMMER SNAPS

Many growers, who for some time have realized that June is an excellent month for snaps—particularly white—are discovering that continued production through the summer can be profitable. While the quality and return of the crop is not equal to crops produced at other times of the year, summer-flowered snaps can be profitable if produced with top cultural care. The summer crop is a fast one and production costs at this time are relatively low. At this time of the year, there is a definite need for a spike-type flower to offer variety to a cut-flower line.

Because summer snaps mature in a hurry, it is necessary to grow these single-stem. An attempted pinched crop will result only in short stems which are not profitable.

Cooling during summer is certainly advantageous and will produce a crop of much higher quality. Group IV varieties must be used for summer flowering.

OUTDOOR SNAPS

FOR SPRING PLANT SALES

ANNUAL *(Antirrhinum majus)*   *180,000 S.*   *1-2 weeks*   *65-70°*

There are few spring-plant sales items which have increased in popularity with the home gardener as rapidly in recent years as snaps. With the introduction of the All-America Award-winning F_1 *Rocket* series several years ago, gardeners for the first time were able to produce snaps in their own yard during the summer of a quality comparable to those grown in greenhouses at other times of the year. Well-known is the F_1 *Floral Carpet,* an extra-dwarf bedding strain. Thus, from the tall *Rockets,* tops for cutting, down through the other varieties available in varying heights, to the extra-dwarf *Floral Carpets* for edging, there is a variety or strain available to suit

ROCKET SNAPDRAGONS
Photographed at West Chicago August 2. This is second crop from February sowing. First crop bloomed mid-June.

practically any purpose that the home gardener may have.

Because of their extra vigor, uniform habit and color, plus their ability to branch and bloom more freely, the F_1 hybrids are most widely used and accepted. In order to have stocky, well-branched plants available for spring sales, the seed should be sown early, and the plants grown at cool tempera-tures. Pinch the plants when ready leaving 3 sets of true leaves. Pinched plants that have well-developed breaks offer much more sales appeal when grown in pots or packs. For 3-inch pots for early-spring sales, a late-January sowing is satisfactory. For heavy 2¼-inch pot and pack sales, February 15 is about right. A sowing of the *Floral Carpets* at this time will have them flowering in packs for mid-May sales.

Outstanding for cut-flower purposes are the F_1 *Rockets,* producing stems from 2½ to 3 feet tall. Available in *Bronze, Red, Yellow, Orchid, Rose, Pink, White, Cherry, Frosty Rose,* and *Lemon,* as well as a formulated mixture. They are effectively used as background material for plantings.

Also available is the F_1 *Pinnacle* series. These have many of the qualities of the *Rockets,* but are somewhat shorter and bloom a bit earlier. The same color range as in *Rockets.*

The *Butterfly* has a unique flower form. The florets are open-tubular, resembling pentstemon. Three classes are presently available within the *Butterfly* series: *Bright Butterflies,* 2½-foot cut-flower type; *Madame Butterfly,* 2-3-foot azalea-flowered double; and *Little Darling,* a 12-inch, semi-dwarf, bushy type. All the *Butterfly* types are available in a blend of colors ranging from crimson, deep rose, bronze, through terra cotta and pink to golden yellow, primrose yellow and ivory white.

In the medium height class are the F_1 *Sprites.* This class grows from 14 to 18 inches high, and can be used for cutting and bedding purposes. Available in separate colors as well as in a mix, the *Sprites* break well from a pinch.

F_1 *Coronette Mix* grows 20 to 40 inches high and produces very bushy, free-flowering plants.

F_1 *Promenades* are a 12-inch, bush-flowering class, very uniform in their flowering and good for edging as well as bedding.

F_1 *Floral Carpet* is an extra-dwarf bedding snap, growing only 6 to 8 inches high, an excellent, showy edging plant that will flower in packs. Colors include *Bronze, Orchid, Pink, Red, White, Yellow,* and *Rose.* Also available in a *Formula Mixture.* The tetra or tetraploid snaps (30 inches) are still used for bedding as well as the F_2 strain, *Panorama Mixture,* also 30 inches tall. **RR**

STATICE (Sea Lavender)

ANNUAL or PERENNIAL *(Limonium species)*
13,000 seeds per oz. Germinates in 15-20 days at 70°.

Botanically, the genus *Statice* is no longer recognized, the various species now belonging to either the genus *Armeria* or *Limonium.* However, the term "statice" has been used so long that we shall continue to refer to them under this name. Principal use of statice is to furnish dried material for winter bouquets, wreaths, etc. The annual type, *S. sinuata,* is grown by the acre in Florida, while the perennial types are found all over this country and Europe, and are handled as hardy perennials.

Sinuata is sown in Florida during the midsummer, usually in late July or early August. This crop will flower during midwinter—January and February—right outdoors. The flowers are used both for the tourist trade, and for shipping to northern markets. Later sowings keep a succession of bloom until spring. Incidentally, it requires about 3 pounds of annual statice seed to plant an acre.

Sinuata can also be grown as a spring greenhouse crop in the North; sow in January, and plant into a deep ground bed for a fine crop of flowers in May. Sown outdoors late in May in the Midwest, it will flower nicely later in the summer. Under good culture, it should reach a height of 2½ feet. Best varieties are *Iceberg, Rosea Superba, Gold Coast, Blue Bonnet, Kamp's Blue Improved* and *Grand Stand Mixture,* which is a blend of the aforementioned varieties, in addition to several others of minor colors.

The Russian, or rat-tail statice, known as *Suworowii,* produces lavender spike-type flowers that can be sown in October, spaced 8 by 8 inches in a light soil mix, grown at 45°, and will flower from late February through May.

Of the perennial sorts, *Latifolia* is probably the most popular. It is handled as almost any other perennial, requires 2 years to flower, and is very hardy. It dries well, and may be dyed after being thoroughly cured. The color is a clear blue, and its usual height is 30 inches. *Dumosa* is a silvery-gray variety; *Perezi* produces exceptionally large, fine, rich blue heads, but is not dependably hardy here.

STOCK

ANNUAL *(Mathiola incana)*

16,000-20,000 seeds per oz. Germinates in 2 wks. at 65-75°.

Columnar, or nonbranching stock, at one time a major greenhouse cut-flower crop in the midwestern, eastern and southern parts of the country, is largely produced today outdoors in California and Arizona. To compete with this market, the greenhouse grower must produce stocks of the finest quality. Toward that end, the following cultural information is presented.

SOWING DATES

Based on our own records kept over many years, the following table will give a close idea of when to sow to flower at a given time. Note that, for the Midwest and East, sowing stocks prior to July 10 or later than February 15 may mean blind, worthless growth—a result of high temperatures.

To flower	Ground beds, seedlings, transplanted, 45° nights through dark months of winter	Raised benches direct-sown 50° minimum temperature	Remarks
January	6½ months sow to flower	5½ months sow to flower	Buds won't set if temperature is above 65° for 6 hours per day
March	6¾ months sow to flower	5½ months sow to flower	For XX quality, allow 7 months at 35-40° nights
April (Easter)	6½ months sow to flower	5¼ months sow to flower	Buds should show 9 weeks before cutting date
May (Mother's Day)	4½ months sow to flower	3¾ months sow to flower	
Early June	4 months sow to flower	3¾ months sow to flower	

Above sowings are based on eastern and midwestern greenhouse conditions. Growers in near South (Tulsa, Nashville) find growth more rapid—Easter stocks 4 months from sowing, for example.

Minimum spacing should be 3 by 6 inches. Seed may be sown direct in the flowering bench, placing 3 seeds at each spacing, and later thinning out to the strongest-growing seedling.

Stock must have a porous, loose soil. A light, slow-drying soil will not do the job. A pH range of 5.5 to 7.0 is satisfactory. Regular liquid feeding is necessary. Frequency should be determined by soil tests. Since stocks have a high potash requirement, readings should be kept at the following levels:

$$\text{nitrates} \quad - \quad 2.5 \text{ ppm}$$
$$\text{phosphorus} - \quad 5.0 \text{ ppm}$$
$$\text{potash} \quad - \quad 30.0 \text{ to } 40.0 \text{ ppm}$$

Potash deficiency is common and shows up as a brown burning on the margin of older leaves.

Stem rot (rhizoctonia) is the big disease problem. Steam sterilization, the use of Terraclor as a drench 10-14 days after benching at the rate of 1 tablespoon per gallon of water, plus proper watering and ventilating practices, will go a long way towards eliminating this problem.

The best, most widely used varieties are:

No. 16 Ball White—Medium-tall. Large-flowered, pure white.

No. 1 Lilac-Lavender—Clear lavender.

No. 22 Ball Supreme—A long-stemmed silvery rose.

BRANCHING STOCKS

There are several strains of branching stocks which can be used successfully as cut-flower material, particularly by the retail grower. This type produces a center spike with numerous side branches from 10-12 inches long which can be useful in small vases and arrangements. Spacing on these should be 6 by 8 inches, and plants should be topped when 6 inches tall.

An unusual race is the *Trysomic Hi-Double,* which, under California field conditions, produces about 85% doubles with no seedling selection being necessary. According to our greenhouse trials, the percentage of doubles is but little higher (5 to 10%) than regular stocks. It is available in most separate colors as well as in a mixture.

OUTDOOR BEDDING STOCK

The *7-week Trysomic Dwarf Double* strain is rather widely used for bedding plants in some sections of the country. Growing to a height of 12 inches, it is the only strain that will flower under high temperatures. Plants will usually throw a central spike in May and then produce numerous side shoots which will flower later. It can be flowered in the pack. Seed should be sown in February. As soon as seedlings become established, they should be moved to a cold house. Chiefly grown as a color mixture, the strain is also available in separate colors.

SWEET PEA

ANNUAL *(Lathyrus odoratus)* *350 seeds per oz. Germinates in 15 days at 55°*

A major cut-flower crop at one time, today, "peas" are largely grown on a small scale by retail growers who still find them profitable. Their decline has largely been due to the development of longer-lasting cut flowers and the labor necessary to harvest the crop. With their sweet scent and beautiful pastel shades of color, they certainly add that "something different" to a retailer's offerings. Some growers with limited space will plant a few peas around purlin posts in benches which are producing other crops.

THE WINTER CROP

While not the easiest to grow, the winter crop seems to be the best-paying one. Sowings are usually made in July and picking extends from November into February. A mid-August sowing will flower from Christmas through March.

Peas do their best in a well-drained soil that is slightly alkaline. If the soil is on the acid side, hydrated lime should be incorporated to correct the pH. Generally, ground beds are preferred, since peas are deep-rooting and require 6-8 feet of head room. Soil must be steam-sterilized to avoid rot problems.

Sow seed direct to the flowering bed in a trench 1-1½ inches deep. Space seeds about 1 inch apart, and later, thin out to a single seedling every 2 inches. Cover the seed with moist soil, over which newspaper or a board can be placed to prevent drying out until the seedlings have emerged. Most peas are grown in double rows, 6 inches apart, with 3-foot walks between the double rows. As soon as plants are 10-12 inches high, they must be supported by string and wire. Wires are run at ground level and at a height of 7-8 feet the length of the bed. Strings are then run between the two every 2 or 3 inches apart.

Sweet peas do require a great deal of water, but care must be exercised with its application during the winter. Constant wet conditions promote bud drop and other diseases. Maximum light must be provided. The cooler peas are grown, the higher the quality, and the lower the production. Thus, a compromise between quality and production is necessary. We suggest a night temperature of 48° till dark weather sets in, then drop it down to 45°. Run cloudy days about 50-52° and sunny days 60-65°. Provide an abundance of fresh air, but don't subject the plants to rapid temperature changes. For this winter-flowering crop, use the *Ball Florist Mixture*.

Midwinter isn't the easiest time of year to flower good peas. Furthermore, the spring crops will usually reward your efforts with longer stems—but— the winter crop seems to be the one that pays off. Big point here is that flowers of all kinds are a lot more scarce in December-January and up to Valentine's Day, and that's just when this crop comes in.

PEAS IN THE SPRING

Of all the months of the year, certainly no finer peas are grown than during March, April, and May. The sunshiny weather that is usually enjoyed in the East and Midwest at that time brightens the colors, makes longer stems, larger florets, and marks an end to the bud-drop problem that is with us more or less through the dark winter months.

Ordinarily, a November 1 sowing of winter varieties can be counted on to be well in flower for an early-April Easter—to keep on blooming through May. An October 1 sowing will normally flower February 15-25, and will be of usable quality through Mother's Day. The heat of late May deals harshly with pea vines, especially the older crops. A December 1 sowing will start flowering about April 15-25, and is normally good through May. Sown January 1, they will bloom from early May through Memorial Day.

Don't overlook the value of including some of the spring-flowering peas. *Royal Mixture* is an improvement over the *Cuthbertson* strain, and will provide good, long-stemmed flowers through May and June, after the earlies are finished.

Very interesting and useful for bedding purposes and as pot plants is the dwarf class of sweet peas. The plants are upright and form low, rounded, non-vining mounds 2-2½ feet high. They require no support and bear 5 to 7 flowers on each stem, which is fairly long. Best performer in this class is *Knee-Hi Mix*.

THUNBERGIA

ANNUAL *(T. species) 500-1,100 seeds per oz. Germinates in 12 days at 70°.*

Where a splash of real color is wanted in annual climbers, porch boxes, or hanging baskets, you'll find *Alata* hard to beat. It's easy and cheap to propagate, fast-growing, and has lots of black-eyed orange, buff and yellow flowers. It is also very useful as a screening material when planted to open ground and allowed to cover a trellis or fence. Sow in early February for 2¼ or 3-inch-pot sales in flower for May. Grow at 60°. *Gibsoni Orange Lanterns* has flowers of a deep orange color, twice the size of *Alata*, but isn't quite as free-flowering in our trials.

THUNBERGIA ALATA

Fine for hanging baskets, which are becoming more and more popular.

TORENIA (Wishbone Flower)

ANNUAL *(T. fournieri) 375,000 seeds per oz. Germinates in 15 days at 70°.*

Once used as a summer pot plant, torenias are chiefly used today as a summer bedding annual, where they make a surprisingly bright showing, flowering from June until frost. They can also be used as a midwinter pot plant, at which time their bright blue blooms are most welcome. Pinching will help develop a bushy plant.

Torenias are perennial, but are almost always cultivated as rapid-growing annuals propagated from seed. Sown in early February and kept in a fairly warm house, at least 50°, they will make nice-sized pot material for sale as bedding stock—or for combination pots. They have no particular soil preference; grown outdoors, they do best in cool, moist, partly shaded places, but make a surprising showing in full hot sun.

The most important commercial variety is *Fournieri Compacta Blue*, dwarf form generally preferred for pots or bedding. In addition, a white form of *Compacta* is also available.

TULIP FORCING
August De Hertogh
Michigan State University

GENERAL ASPECTS

Most tulips used for forcing are grown in the Netherlands. There is, however, a limited amount of production in the northwest U.S. and Japan. Basically, the same techniques are used for all tulip bulbs, regardless of source.

Tulip bulbs are forced either as potted plants or cut flowers, and a distinction must be made between the forcing techniques for these products. The reasons for this are threefold. First, the desired length of the cut tulip is markedly different from that of the potted plant. Second, pot and cut tulips intended for the same market period, e.g., Valentine's Day, are shipped at different times. Third, the cold requirement of the two crops may differ by as much as 4 to 5 weeks for some cultivars.

The flowering season for potted and cut tulips extends from early January to mid-May. To have high-quality plants throughout this season, it is necessary to have a controlled-temperature rooting room. The information provided below is designed for a forcer who has such a facility. Those forcers who continue to use outdoor-rooting beds will have to make adjustments based on experience.

To assist the forcer, the flowering season for potted and cut tulips has been

Cut tulips are moving up again in the U.S.—due mainly to new techniques of prestoring at lower temperatures. This permits direct planting into the flowering bench—and much faster forcing than was the case before. The above photo on Long Island, the variety is Apeldoorn. Note uniform crop and good stem length.

divided into seven flowering periods (Tables 1 and 3). These periods are designated "PT-1" to "PT-7" for pot tulips and "CT-1" to "CT-7" for cut tulips. It should be noted that there is no sharp dividing line between these periods, and they may be adjusted according to individual needs and facilities. The season has been divided to take advantage of precooled (PC) and non-precooled (NP) bulbs. The planting dates are changed to compensate for the cold requirements of the specific cultivars and usage.

Most tulip bulbs for forcing are 12 centimeters and up in circumference; sometimes 11/12 centimeters can be used.

Problems such as aphids, botrytis and penicillium can be controlled with commercially available insecticides and fungicides. The serious problems with tulips are fusarium, blindness and flower-blasting. Bulbs infected with fusarium must be eliminated both before precooling and at planting time. There is no fungicide which is effective once the bulb is infected. The symptons to look for are a *white* mold on the skin, soft bulbs, or very light bulbs. Blindness can occur from either "heating in transit" or by precooling the bulbs prior to the time the bulbs reach the "G" stage of development. (See page 483). All cultivars must be checked for the stage of floral development before precooling. "Heating in transit" can sometimes be observed by cutting a few bulbs prior to planting and looking for aborted floral buds. There are many causes for blasting, e.g., lack of sufficient water, "heating in transit," forcing a cultivar too early, and ethylene damage.

FORCING INFORMATION

GENERAL

The forcer's responsibility begins immediately on arrival of the bulbs. As soon as they arrive, the bulbs should be ventilated, inspected and stored at the proper temperature. Bulbs for precooling should be checked for stage "G" of floral development. If they have not reached "G" stage, store them at 55 to 63° F until it is reached. They should be precooled at either 45 or 48° F (see Tables 1 and 3). Nonprecooled bulbs for pot-plant use should be stored at 60-63° F, while nonprecooled bulbs for cut-flower use should be stored at 55-60° F.

Potted tulips are planted anywhere from 4 to a pot to 10 or 12 in a pot, depending on the market usage. Cut tulips should be planted in flats which hold approximately 50 bulbs each. Pallets are useful in both types of production. When planting the bulbs, use a well-drained soil mixture, one similar to that used for potted chrysanthemums or poinsettias. After planting, place the plants in the proper rooting room and water thoroughly. Keep the plants moist throughout their time in the rooting room.

POT TULIPS

In the production of potted tulips, it is desirable to produce a plant which is from 10 to 14 inches tall at the bud stage of development. At the same time, it is desirable to obtain a plant with large flowers. Both of these factors are affected by the length of the cold treatment. Thus, it is important to shift the planting date for the various flowering periods in order to maintain the proper plant height and flower quality. A 15-week cold treatment is suitable for most cultivars.

The forcing program described for pot-tulip production (Table 1) utilizes 2 rooting rooms in order to obtain quality plants for the entire flowering season. Rooting room "A" has a temperature sequence of 48° F to November 5 to 10, 41° F to January 1 to 5, then 33-35° F. Rooting room "B" has a temperature sequence of 48° F to December 1 to 5, 41° F to January 1 to 5, then 33-35° F. The criteria for making the changes in temperature are as follows. The change from 48° F to 41° F is dependent on the development of the roots. The 48° F temperature should be maintained until the roots grow out the bottom of the containers. Be sure to check each cultivar, since cultivars can react differently. The change from 41° F to 33-35° F is dependent on the length of the sprouts. The 41° F temperature should be maintained until the sprouts become about 2 inches long. The 33-35° F is used to retard sprout growth so that a quality plant is produced in the greenhouse. Table 1 shows which flowering periods and type of bulbs are to be placed in the individual rooting rooms. The cultivars available for forcing, and in reasonable supply, are described in Table 2.

Tulip bulbs designated for pot-plant production should be precooled for period PT-1. Some cultivars for period PT-2 need to be precooled whereas others can be nonprecooled. Bulbs for all other periods should be nonprecooled. Rooting room "A" should be used for flowering periods PT-1, PT-2, and

PT-3. Rooting room "B" will accommodate flowering periods PT-4, PT-5, PT-6, and PT-7.

Pot Tulips 1 (PT-1): Bulbs for this period should be precooled as soon as possible after they reach the "G" stage of development. This should be about August 26 to 31. A forcing temperature of 65° F is suggested.

Pot Tulips 2 (PT-2): For this period, most cultivars are precooled. There are some, however, which can be used as precooled bulbs. For this period, a forcing temperature of 65° F should be used.

Pot Tulips 3 (PT-3): For this period and all succeeding periods, only non-precooled bulbs need to be used. The first group which is intended for the Valentine's Day market can be brought into the greenhouse on January 18 and should be forced at 65° F. Succeeding groups in this period should be forced at 60-62° F, since forcing will become easier as time goes on.

Pot Tulips 4 (PT-4): A forcing temperature of 60° F is preferred. This is the first period for using rooting room "B."

Pot Tulips 5 (PT-5): A forcing temperature of 60° F is preferred.

Pot Tulips 6 (PT-6): A forcing temperature of 60° F is preferred.

Pot Tulips 7 (PT-7): As in all periods, beginning with PT-4, the preferred temperature for this period is 60° F.

CUT TULIPS

In producing cut tulips, it is desirable to obtain flowers which are at least 14 inches in length and at the same time, maintain a large flower. In forcing tulips, both stem length and flower size are affected by the length of the cold treatment as well as the degree of cold used. Studies have shown that for use as cut flowers, most tulips require a cold treatment in the range of 15 to 19 weeks. Some cultivars require less, others more. The forcing program described takes this basic requirement into consideration and also attempts to integrate other factors which are essential to the production of high-quality bulb flowers.

The forcing program described for cut-tulip production (Table 3) utilizes 2 rooting rooms in order to obtain plants for the entire flowering season. Rooting room "A" has a temperature sequence of 48° F to November 5 to 10, 41° F to January 1 to 5, then 33-35° F. Rooting room "F" has a temperature sequence of 48° F to December 1 to 5, 41° F to January 1 to 5, then 33-35° F. The criteria for making the temperature changes are the same as those described for the potted tulip (see above).

The cultivars available for forcing, and in reasonable supply, are described in Table 4.

Tulip bulbs designated for flowering in periods CT-1, CT-2, and CT-3 should be precooled. Some cultivars usable for period CT-3 need not be precooled. Rooting room "A" will be used for CT-1, CT-2, CT-3, and CT-4. The use of rooting room "A" is optional for CT-5. Bulbs for this period may use rooting room "A" or "B." Bulbs for periods CT-6 and CT-7 should use rooting room "B."

Cut Tulips Flowering Period 1 (CT-1): Bulbs for this period should be precooled as soon as possible after they reach the "G" stage of development.

This should be about August 23 to 28. For this period, a forcing temperature of 65° F should be used. Covering of the plants during the first few days in the greenhouse may be valuable.

Cut Tulips Flowering Period 2 (CT-2): A forcing temperature of 65° F is preferred here. Again, covering of the plants could be of value.

Cut Tulips Flowering Period 3 (CT-3): Mostly precooled and a few non-precooled bulbs are used for this flowering period. The first group for this period is intended for the Valentine's Day market and should be brought into the greenhouse on approximately January 10. A greenhouse temperature of 65° F should be used for Valentine's Day flowers. After that time, a temperature of 60-62° F is preferred, since forcing will become easier.

Cut Tulips Flowering Period 4 (CT-4): The preferred forcing temperature for this period is 60° F.

Cut Tulips Flowering Period 5 (CT-5): This period is designed primarily for early Easter. Again, a forcing temperature of 60° F is preferred.

Cut Tulips Flowering Period 6 (CT-6): This period is primarily designed for late Easter, and a forcing temperature of 60° F. is preferred.

Cut Tulips Flowering Period 7 (CT-7): Forcing for Mother's Day falls within this period. As with all periods following CT-4, a forcing temperature of 60° F is preferred.

STORAGE OF FINISHED PRODUCTS

Pot Tulips: When potted tulips are to be stored prior to being shipped to market, they should be placed at 33-35° F in the "green-bud" stage of development. They should be treated with a protective fungicide prior to storage.

A good example of a pot of tulips in the "green-bud" stage—ready for sale as a flowering plant. Cultivar is Peerless Pink. Photo courtesy August De Hertogh, Michigan State University, East Lansing, Mich.

Cut Tulips: There are two methods to store cut tulips prior to marketing. In either case, the tulips should be removed from the greenhouse in the "half-green-bud" stage of development. Those flowers which are to be stored for only a few days should have the bulb removed, graded, wrapped and boxed. The flowers should then be stored dry in a horizontal position at 33° F. If the flowers are to be stored for extended periods of time, they should be removed from the forcing trays with the bulb left attached. They should then be placed upright in buckets and stored dry at 33° F. Prior to shipping, the bulbs should be removed and the flowers graded, wrapped and boxed.

ABOUT STAGE "G"

Development of Bulb Flower

Spring flower bulbs, at harvest time, do not (except for narcissi) have their floral parts fully developed. To achieve this stage of development requires storage at prescribed temperatures. Without going into too many details, we can point out that the several stages of development of a flower bulb have been given arbitrary designations such as I, II, P_1, P_2, A_1, A_2, and G. Each of these symbols indicates a specific stage of development of the floral parts within a bulb. Temperature treatments at the bulb-production source usually start at a high level and are lowered when specific stages are reached. By the time bulbs reach the forcer, they have usually achieved Stage G or, at least, have passed Stage A_2.

Stages "A_2" and "G"

The 2 stages that flower growers should become familiar with are Stages A_2 and G. Stage A_2 is that in which all 6 stamens have been formed (Figure 1). Stage G is that in which the stamens and pistil are fully formed and well defined (Figure 2). The ability to determine when tulips have achieved Stage G is particularly important for flower growers who plan to precool their bulbs. Precooling of tulips must not begin before Stage G has been reached.

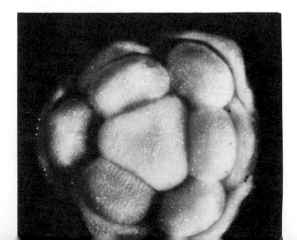

Figure 1 ▶

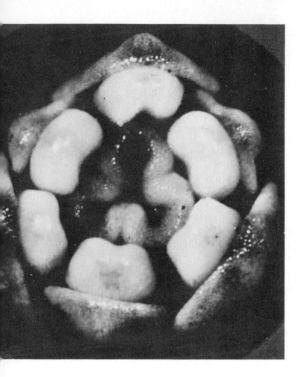

◄ Figure 2

Figures 1 through 3 reprinted from "Bulb Forcers Handbook," Second Edition, September, 1967, Associated Bulb Growers of Holland.

Checking for Stage "G"

The procedure to determine whether Stage G has been reached is demonstrated below (Figure 3). Basically, the procedure consists of cutting the bulb into a block approximately ¾ inch square, containing the floral bud in the center. The scales are cut until the yellow tips of leaves are seen. The tips of the leaves are then carefully cut, exposing the floral parts. By placing a drop of blue or black ink on the floral parts and then blotting the ink, the floral parts can be made more evident. It is suggested that a hand lens or binocular microscope be used for identification purposes. When the characteristic 6 stamens and trilobed pistil are seen, Stage G has been achieved. If Stage G has not been reached, the bulbs should be stored at 55 to 63° F until Stage G is achieved.

Figure 3

Table 1

Programming Guide for Pot Tulips

Flowering Period	Start of Precooling	Time of Planting	Rooting Room	Dates into Green-house	Approximate Flowering Date	Weeks of Cold
PT-1 (PC)	Aug. 26 to 21 (45° F.)	Oct. 1 to 7	A	Dec. 10 Dec. 17 Dec. 24	Jan. 1 Jan. 8 Jan. 15	15 16 17
PT-2 (PC)	Sept. 1 to 7 (48° F.)	Oct. 6 to 10	A	Dec. 30 Jan. 5 Jan. 12	Jan. 20 Jan. 28 Feb. 5	16½ 17½ 18½
PT-2 (NP)	None	Sept. 18 to 22	A	Dec. 30 Jan. 5 Jan. 12	Jan. 20 Jan. 28 Feb. 5	14½ 15½ 16½
PT-3 (NP)	None	Oct. 1 to 7	A	Jan. 18 Jan. 25 Feb. 1	Feb. 8 Feb. 16 Feb. 23	15 16 17
PT-4 (NP)	None	Oct. 24 to 28	B	Feb. 8 Feb. 15 Feb. 22	Mar. 1 Mar. 8 Mar. 15	15 16 17
PT-5 (NP)	None	Nov. 6 to 11	B	Feb. 28 Mar. 6 Mar. 13	Mar. 20 Mar. 26 Apr. 1	16 17 18
PT-6 (NP)	None	Nov. 10 to 15	B	Mar. 16 Mar. 22 Mar. 28	Apr. 4 Apr. 10 Apr. 17	18 19 20
PT-7 (NP)	None	Nov. 10 to 15	B	Apr. 1 Apr. 8 Apr. 15	Apr. 21 Apr. 28 May 3	20½ 21½ 22½

(PC)—Precooled bulbs   (NP)—Nonprecooled bulbs

Rooting-room temperature sequence for "A" is 48° F. to November 1 to 5, 41° F. to January 1 to 5, then 33-35° F. Rooting-room temperature sequence for "B" is 48° F. to December 1 to 5, 41° F. to January 1 to 5, then 33-35° F.

Table 2

Tulip Cultivars for Pot-Plant Use

Color	Cultivar	Flowering Period and Type of Bulb Needed						
		PT-1	PT-2	PT-3	PT-4	PT-5	PT-6	PT-7
Red	Albury	—	—	—	—	NP	NP	NP
	Atom	—	—	—	—	NP	NP	—
	Bing Crosby	—	PC	NP	NP	—	—	—
	Cassini	—	PC	NP	NP	—	—	—
	Charles	—	PC	NP	NP	—	—	—
	Couleur Cardinal	—	—	—	—	NP	NP	NP
	Danton	—	PC	NP	NP	NP	NP	—
	Diplomate	—	—	—	NP	NP	—	—
	Olaf	—	PC	NP	NP	—	—	—
	Paul Richter	PC	PC	NP	NP	—	—	—
	Prominence	PC	PC	NP	NP	NP	—	—

Tulip Cultivars for Pot-Plant Use

Color	Cultivar	Flowering Period and Type of Bulb Needed						
		PT-1	PT-2	PT-3	PT-4	PT-5	PT-6	PT-7
Red	Red Giant	—	—	—	—	NP	NP	—
	Robinea	—	—	—	—	NP	NP	NP
	Stockholm	—	PC	NP	NP	—	—	—
	Topscore	—	PC	NP	NP	—	—	—
	Trance	PC	NP-PC	NP	NP	—	—	—
Pink or Rose	Blenda	—	PC	NP	NP	—	—	—
	Christmas Marvel	PC	NP-PC	NP	NP	—	—	—
	Palestrina	—	—	—	—	NP	NP	NP
	Peerless Pink	—	—	—	—	NP	NP	NP
	Preludium	—	PC	NP	NP	—	—	—
	Virtuoso	—	—	—	—	NP	NP	—
Yellow	Bellona	—	PC	NP	NP	—	—	—
	Christmas Gold	—	PC	NP	NP	—	—	—
	Kareol	—	—	NP	NP	—	—	—
	Makassar	—	—	—	—	NP	NP	—
	Monte Carlo	PC	NP-PC	NP	NP	—	—	—
	Ornament	—	—	—	—	NP	NP	NP
White	Blizzard	—	—	—	—	NP	NP	NP
	Hibernia	—	PC	NP	NP	—	—	—
	Pax	—	PC	NP	NP	NP	—	—
Lavender	Attila	—	PC	NP	NP	NP	—	—
	Prince Charles	—	PC	NP	NP	—	—	—
Orange	Orange Sun	—	—	—	—	NP	NP	—
	Princess Irene	—	—	—	—	NP	NP	—
Apricot	Apricot Beauty	PC	NP-PC	NP	—	—	—	—
Bicolors	Carl M. Bellman	—	—	—	—	NP	NP	NP
	Comet	—	PC	NP	NP	—	—	—
	Denbola	—	—	—	—	NP	NP	NP
	Edith Eddy	—	—	—	—	NP	NP	NP
	Golden Eddy	—	—	—	—	NP	NP	NP
	Invasion	—	—	—	NP	NP	NP	NP
	Karel Doorman	—	PC	NP	NP	—	—	—
	Kees Nelis	—	PC	NP	NP	—	—	—
	Madame Spoor	—	PC	NP	NP	—	—	—
	Merry Widow	—	PC	NP	NP	—	—	—
	Mirjoran	—	PC	NP	NP	—	—	—
	Paris	—	—	—	NP	NP	NP	—
	Thule	—	PC	NP	NP	—	—	—

PC—Precooled bulbs   NP—Nonprecooled bulbs
Varieties not shown as either PC or NP for a given flowering period are generally not suitable for that flowering period.

Table 3

Programming Guide for Cut Tulips

Flowering Period	Start of Precooling	Time of Planting	Rooting Room	Dates into Green-house	Approxi-mate Flowering Date	Weeks of Cold
CT-1	Aug. 23 to 28 (45°F.)	Oct. 1 to 7	A	Dec. 10 Dec. 17 Dec. 24	Jan. 3 Jan. 10 Jan. 17	15½ 16½ 17½
CT-2	Aug. 26 to 31 (48°F.)	Oct. 1 to 7	A	Dec. 30 Jan. 7	Jan. 23 Jan. 30	17½ 18½
CT-3 (PC)	Sept. 3 to 7 (48°F.)	Oct. 6 to 10	A	Jan. 10 Jan. 17 Jan. 27	Feb. 3 Feb. 10 Feb. 17	18 19 20
CT-3 (NP)	None	Sept. 18 to 22	A	Jan. 10 Jan. 17 Jan. 24	Feb. 3 Feb. 10 Feb. 17	16 17 18
CT-4	None	Sept. 25 to 30	A	Feb. 2 Feb. 9 Feb. 16	Feb. 24 Mar. 2 Mar. 10	18 19 20
CT-5	None	Oct. 16 to 20	A or B	Feb. 23 Mar. 2 Mar. 9	Mar. 16 Mar. 23 Mar. 30	18 19 20
CT-6	None	Nov. 6 to 11	B	Mar. 16 Mar. 23 Mar. 30	Apr. 5 Apr. 12 Apr. 19	18 19 20
CT-7	None	Nov. 6 to 11	B	Apr. 6 Apr. 13	Apr. 26 May 3	21 22

(PC)—Precooled bulbs, (NP)—Nonprecooled bulbs

Rooting-room temperature sequence for "A" is 48° F. to November 1 to 5, 41° F. to January 1 to 5, then 33-35° F. Rooting-room temperature sequence for "B" is 48° F. to December 1 to 5, 41° F. to January 1 to 5, then 33-35° F.

Table 4

Tulip Cultivars for Cut Flower Use

Color	Cultivar	Flowering Period and Type of Bulb Needed						
		CT-1	CT-2	CT-3	CT-4	CT-5	CT-6	CT-7
Red	Abbe Pierre	—	PC	PC	NP	—	—	—
	Albury	—	—	—	—	—	NP	NP
	Apeldoorn	—	—	PC	NP	—	—	—
	Atom	—	—	—	—	—	NP	—
	Bing Crosby	—	—	PC	NP	—	—	—
	Cassini	—	—	PC	NP	—	—	—
	Charles	—	—	—	NP	NP	—	—
	Diplomate	—	—	—	—	NP	NP	—
	Dix' Favourite	PC	PC	NP	NP	—	—	—
	K & M's Triumph	—	—	PC	NP	NP	NP	NP
	London	—	—	PC	NP	—	—	—
	Most Miles	PC	PC	NP	—	—	—	—
	Orient Express	—	—	PC	NP	NP	NP	NP
	Oxford	—	—	—	NP	NP	—	—

In the upright class *Rainbow Mixture,* in a wide assortment of colors, is most popular. Because of its earliness and habit, it is valuable for pots and combination work. Similar to *Rainbow* is *Regalia Mix,* a recent introduction.

VINCA LITTLE PINKIE ▶

VINCA (Periwinkle)

ANNUAL *(V. rosea) 21,000 seeds per oz. Germinates in 15 days at 70°. Dark.*

An excellent bedding plant gaining rapidly in its popularity with home gardeners, *Vinca rosea* will make a continuous show of color throughout the summer under hot, dry conditions. Even in areas of high pollution, it will thrive with a minimum of care. For 2¼ and 3-inch pots in bloom for sale in May, we suggest a late-January/early-February sowing. For pack and flat sales, sow from February 10-20. The plant is easily seed-propagated. If grown in a 60° house, they should fill out into good-sized flowering plants by Memorial Day. They can be hardened-off for 2 or 3 weeks at 55°, but should not be grown at temperatures below this. Vinca seedlings are slow starters and will quickly yellow and die off if grown under cold or wet conditions. Outdoors, the plants will bloom continuously until frost, if given fair exposure to the sun.

The most desirable class for general bedding-plant purposes is the dwarf (10 inches). Tops in this class is the *Little* series. It consists of the following 4 varieties and a mixture of the 4:

    Little Bright Eye—White flower with red eye.

    Little Pinkie—A rosy pink.

    (The above 2 account for about 75% of all those sold.)

    Little Delicata—Pink with rose eye.

    Little Blanche—Pure white.

In the semitall class (15-18 inches), a mixture is commonly used.

Very popular, too, among the vinca clan, are the forms of V. *major,* a foliage vine usually seen in its variegated form. It is the traditional edging for window-box and urn plantings, and, like its close relative V. *rosea,* it stands heat and drought exceptionally well. Propagation here is by cuttings, either tip or 3-inch sections of old stems. Finished 3 or 4-inch stock takes 2 years growth which adds to its cost, but its exceptional and lasting popularity stands it well. The cuttings are stuck in October or November; as soon as rooted, they can be potted to small pots in which they will hold through the spring. From here, they usually go outdoors, over the summer until fall. Clumps are then dug, divided, tops cut back to 4 or 5 inches, and heeled in closely in a cool house. About January 1, they are potted into 3's or 4's, set up along the southern edge of a bench, vines hanging downward, where they make their final growth. Frequent feedings of nitrogen-bearing fertilizer help fill them out. It is very important to break the taproot that forms through the drain hole frequently during this stage, or the plant will suffer greatly when moved out.

Most popular type grown is *V. major Variegata,* a green and white variegated sort; next in popularity is *Reticulata,* green and yellow variegated. The pure green species is sometimes seen but not highly prized.

A third, and again highly useful vinca is *V. minor.* Unlike both *major* and *rosea,* it is completely hardy, and makes a fine ground cover, especially in deeply shaded places. It flowers profusely, having a heavy crop of 1½-inch single blooms during spring and early summer. Propagation is usually by stem cuttings rooted in June. Old clumps may be divided as a further means of propagation. The plant is also a favorite for rock gardens; often, it is commonly referred to as "myrtle" or "common periwinkle."

VIOLA (Miniature Pansy)

PERENNIAL *(V. cornuta) 24,000-43,000 seeds per oz. Germinates in 10 days at 65°.*

Invaluable as edging plants, violas are also very effective when used in mass plantings to front a shrub border. Although not as large as pansies, they are freer-flowering and may be obtained in a wide range of colors—yellow, red, purple, lavender, apricot and white. Their culture is much the same as for pansies; late-summer or fall sowings are, if anything, even more successful because of their unusual hardiness. Violas will do very well in light shade, although they prefer full sun. They will do well in any good garden soil, but in order to do their best, they should be planted in a fertile soil with a good supply of organic matter. There are some varieties not ordinarily seed-propagated; simply cut the plant back in midsummer, take cuttings from the bushy growth that returns, and root them in a frame provided with some shade. They offer no particular difficulty handled in this way.

Among the most popular varieties in the seed-propagated group are *Jersey Gem,* an attractive violet blue; *Arkwright Ruby,* a bright maroon with dark center; and *Lutea Splendens,* a clear, golden yellow. For apricot, we prefer *Chantreyland. White Perfection* is a clear white; *Blue Perfection,* a large-flowered medium blue.

The so-called "jump-ups" are distinctive for smaller but very-freely produced blooms. They are in constant color from early spring till frost. *Helen Mount* is a violet, lavender and canary-yellow combination.

ZINNIA

ANNUAL *(Z. elegans) 2,500-10,000 seeds per oz. Germinates in 7 days at 70°.*

Zinnias' big claim to fame—they're really showy and they do stand summer heat! And heat is one thing you'll find plenty of during most summers in the majority of our states. If given reasonably good soil and water, they will yield quantities of the brightest-colored of all summer cut flowers. They are easy to grow.

Florists' main interest in them: sale of pack-grown or 2¼-inch plants in May for outdoor planting—and second, their use as a summer cut flower. Properly grown, they can be money-makers on both scores.

FOR SPRING-PLANT SALES

Sow 4 to 5 weeks before desired selling time in order to have good, husky plants for pack or 2¼-inch pot sales. Exception to this is the extra-dwarf variety, *Thumbelina,* which should be sown about a month earlier to have plants in flower for pack sales. The big trick—seed flats *must* be kept at 70°,

ZINNIA F₁ HYBRID FRUIT BOWL GIANT CACTUS FLOWERED
Fast becoming the most popular of all as new colors are added each year. Medium-sized, bushy plants (24 to 30 inches tall) are covered with huge blooms of delicately twisted petals, alleviating the appearance of stiffness usually attributed to zinnias.

at least, till seed is through the ground. Most complaints on zinnia germination are the result of trying to germinate the seed at 50° or lower; they just won't come through—and, in fact, will soon rot in the ground. After seedlings are through, the flats may be carried along at 50°, and the trayed or potted plants will be "huskier" if grown in this temperature.

Plant breeders have done some excellent work with zinnias in recent years and have developed new and improved varieties to such an extent that today there is nearly a type, size or color available for any conceivable garden use (see chart listed below).

AS CUT FLOWERS

Most popular handling for the retail florist is a late-March sowing of pot or pack-grown plants carried in a 50° house and planted out in late May. These plants, if given water outdoors, will give a good crop from early July on through the summer. They should be spaced 12 by 12 inches outdoors. The "dahlia" and "cactus-flowered" classes are preferred, although the tiny "lilliputs" are often included to provide variety.

A direct sowing made outdoors June 1 will be in flower by late July—they grow very rapidly if given good soil and water as needed. Sow in rows 2 feet apart, thin to about 6 inches in the row, making it easier to cultivate than if a 12 by 12-inch spacing is used. Later sowings may be made on through

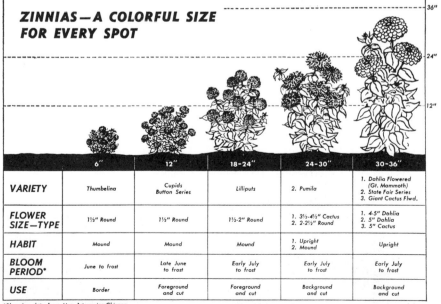

ZINNIAS—A COLORFUL SIZE FOR EVERY SPOT

	6″	12″	18-24″	24-30″	30-36″
VARIETY	Thumbelina	Cupids Button Series	Lilliputs	2. Pumila	1. Dahlia Flowered (Gt. Mammoth) 2. State Fair Series 3. Giant Cactus Flwd.
FLOWER SIZE—TYPE	1½″ Round	1½″ Round	1½-2″ Round	1. 3½-4½″ Cactus 2. 2-2½″ Round	1. 4-5″ Dahlia 2. 5″ Dahlia 3. 5″ Cactus
HABIT	Mound	Mound	Mound	1. Upright 2. Mound	Upright
BLOOM PERIOD*	June to frost	Late June to frost	Early July to frost	Early July to frost	Early July to frost
USE	Border	Foreground and cut	Foreground and cut	Background and cut	Background and cut

*Blooming date from May 1st sowing-Chicago

ZINNIA F$_1$ HYBRID PETER PAN ORANGE
An AAS 1974 addition to the *Peter Pan* family.

June. Disbudding will greatly improve the quality of the flowers.

Zinnias may be forced into flower in the greenhouse by late April or early May. Sow February 15, space 4 by 4 inches, and disbud to 1 flower per plant. A 60° temperature will do the best job.

TYPES AND VARIETIES

The "giant cactus-flowered" class has rapidly developed into one of the most popular types. It produces huge flowers up to 6 inches in diameter with long, curved petals, irregularly arranged in a pleasing manner. Largely responsible for their great popularity has been the development of F$_1$ hybrid varieties. Prominent in this class are two series, the *Fruit Bowl* and the *Zenith*. Available in a mixture as well as in 4 and 5 separate colors, they are truly outstanding and are rapidly gaining popularity over the inbred varieties. Varieties in the *Fruit Bowl* series include *Winesap*, a deep scarlet red; *Tangerine*, bright orange; *Nectarine*, rich rose pink; *Carved Ivory* (AAS), a rich, butter-cream color, and *Wild Cherry,* a two-toned bright red. Tops in the *Zenith* series are *Firecracker*, brilliant scarlet red; *Torch*, a rich orange; and *Yellow Zenith*, a clear midyellow. *State Fair Mix*, a giant *tetraploid* (30-36 inches), produces 5-6-inch flowers with broad petals in a full range of bright colors. While also available in separate colors, as a mixture, it probably outsells all other varieties in the large-flowered class. The "dahlia-flowered" or "giant mammoth" class is usually sold as a mix, although separate varieties are available in the complete zinna color range. *Gold Medal Mix* is probably one of the best formulations available in this class.

The most recent outstanding additions to the zinnia family are the F_1 hybrid *Peter Pans,* currently available in 4 colors—*Peter Pan Pink,* a coral pink; and *Peter Pan Plum,* a rose, *Peter Pan Scarlet,* a brilliant scarlet, and *Peter Pan Orange.* These free-flowering All-America Winners produce extra-large, fully double, 3-inch flowers on very bushy plants only 10 to 12 inches high.

The *pumilas* (2-2½ feet) are between the "giants" and *lilliputs* in flower size, the latter being more widely used. It produces small pompon-type flowers (2 inches) on bushy plants, 1½ to 2 feet tall. Both of these, largely grown as color mixes, are available in separate colors. However, an outstanding variety in this class is *Scarlet Ruffles* (AAS), a deep scarlet, ruffled type flower with 2½ inch flowers.

Another up-and-coming member of the zinnia clan is the "dwarf" (6-12 inches) Cupid-type *Button* series—*Cherry,* cherry red; *Pink,* bright salmon-pink; and *Red,* bright red. They produce masses of 1½-inch double flowers. They are useful for cut flowers as well as bedding plants.

Thumbelina (6 inches) is an extra-dwarf formulated mixture of bright colors that is particulary well adapted to edging. The compact, uniform plants flower early in packs and pots. In this same height class are two separate color varieties, *Mini-Pink Coral Rose,* and *Mini-Salmon,* a bright salmon.

Single flowered varieties are once again gaining in popularity. Heading the list currently are *Sombrero* (18 inches), a bright colored red and gold; *Chippendale Daisy* (15 inches), 2-inch mahogany blooms with gold tipped petals, and *Classic* (8-10 inches), golden-orange with 1½-inch blooms.

SPECIAL DATES

	1980	1981	1982
New Year's Day	Jan. 1	Jan. 1	Jan. 1
Lincoln's Birthday	Feb. 12	Feb. 12	Feb. 12
Valentine's Day	Feb. 14	Feb. 14	Feb. 14
Ash Wednesday	Feb. 20	Mar. 4	Feb. 24
Washington's Birthday	Feb. 18	Feb. 16	Feb. 15
St. Patrick's Day	Mar. 17	Mar. 17	Mar. 17
Palm Sunday	Mar. 30	Apr. 12	Apr. 4
Passover	Apr. 1	Apr. 19	Apr. 8
Easter Sunday	Apr. 6	Apr. 19	Apr. 11
Secretaries Day	Apr. 23	Apr. 22	Apr. 21
Mother's Day	May 11	May 10	May 9
Memorial Day	May 26	May 25	May 31
Father's Day	June 15	June 21	June 20
Rosh Hashana	Sept. 11	Sept. 29	Sept. 18
Yom Kippur	Sept. 20	Oct. 8	Sept. 27
Sweetest Day	Oct. 18	Oct. 17	Oct. 16
Election Day	Nov. 4	Nov. 3	Nov. 2
Thanksgiving Day	Nov. 27	Nov. 26	Nov. 25
Christmas Day	Dec. 25	Dec. 25	Dec. 25

CALENDAR

1980

JANUARY
S	M	T	W	T	F	S
		1	2	3	4	5
6	7	8	9	10	11	12
13	14	15	16	17	18	19
20	21	22	23	24	25	26
27	28	29	30	31		

FEBRUARY
S	M	T	W	T	F	S
					1	2
3	4	5	6	7	8	9
10	11	12	13	14	15	16
17	18	19	20	21	22	23
24	25	26	27	28	29	

MARCH
S	M	T	W	T	F	S
						1
2	3	4	5	6	7	8
9	10	11	12	13	14	15
16	17	18	19	20	21	22
23	24	25	26	27	28	29
30	31					

APRIL
S	M	T	W	T	F	S
		1	2	3	4	5
6	7	8	9	10	11	12
13	14	15	16	17	18	19
20	21	22	23	24	25	26
27	28	29	30			

MAY
S	M	T	W	T	F	S
				1	2	3
4	5	6	7	8	9	10
11	12	13	14	15	16	17
18	19	20	21	22	23	24
25	26	27	28	29	30	31

JUNE
S	M	T	W	T	F	S
1	2	3	4	5	6	7
8	9	10	11	12	13	14
15	16	17	18	19	20	21
22	23	24	25	26	27	28
29	30					

JULY
S	M	T	W	T	F	S
		1	2	3	4	5
6	7	8	9	10	11	12
13	14	15	16	17	18	19
20	21	22	23	24	25	26
27	28	29	30	31		

AUGUST
S	M	T	W	T	F	S
					1	2
3	4	5	6	7	8	9
10	11	12	13	14	15	16
17	18	19	20	21	22	23
24	25	26	27	28	29	30
31						

SEPTEMBER
S	M	T	W	T	F	S
	1	2	3	4	5	6
7	8	9	10	11	12	13
14	15	16	17	18	19	20
21	22	23	24	25	26	27
28	29	30				

OCTOBER
S	M	T	W	T	F	S
			1	2	3	4
5	6	7	8	9	10	11
12	13	14	15	16	17	18
19	20	21	22	23	24	25
26	27	28	29	30	31	

NOVEMBER
S	M	T	W	T	F	S
						1
2	3	4	5	6	7	8
9	10	11	12	13	14	15
16	17	18	19	20	21	22
23	24	25	26	27	28	29
30						

DECEMBER
S	M	T	W	T	F	S
	1	2	3	4	5	6
7	8	9	10	11	12	13
14	15	16	17	18	19	20
21	22	23	24	25	26	27
28	29	30	31			

1981

JANUARY
S	M	T	W	T	F	S
				1	2	3
4	5	6	7	8	9	10
11	12	13	14	15	16	17
18	19	20	21	22	23	24
25	26	27	28	29	30	31

FEBRUARY
S	M	T	W	T	F	S
1	2	3	4	5	6	7
8	9	10	11	12	13	14
15	16	17	18	19	20	21
22	23	24	25	26	27	28

MARCH
S	M	T	W	T	F	S
1	2	3	4	5	6	7
8	9	10	11	12	13	14
15	16	17	18	19	20	21
22	23	24	25	26	27	28
29	30	31				

APRIL
S	M	T	W	T	F	S
			1	2	3	4
5	6	7	8	9	10	11
12	13	14	15	16	17	18
19	20	21	22	23	24	25
26	27	28	29	30		

MAY
S	M	T	W	T	F	S
					1	2
3	4	5	6	7	8	9
10	11	12	13	14	15	16
17	18	19	20	21	22	23
24	25	26	27	28	29	30
31						

JUNE
S	M	T	W	T	F	S
	1	2	3	4	5	6
7	8	9	10	11	12	13
14	15	16	17	18	19	20
21	22	23	24	25	26	27
28	29	30				

JULY
S	M	T	W	T	F	S
			1	2	3	4
5	6	7	8	9	10	11
12	13	14	15	16	17	18
19	20	21	22	23	24	25
26	27	28	29	30	31	

AUGUST
S	M	T	W	T	F	S
						1
2	3	4	5	6	7	8
9	10	11	12	13	14	15
16	17	18	19	20	21	22
23	24	25	26	27	28	29
30	31					

SEPTEMBER
S	M	T	W	T	F	S
		1	2	3	4	5
6	7	8	9	10	11	12
13	14	15	16	17	18	19
20	21	22	23	24	25	26
27	28	29	30			

OCTOBER
S	M	T	W	T	F	S
				1	2	3
4	5	6	7	8	9	10
11	12	13	14	15	16	17
18	19	20	21	22	23	24
25	26	27	28	29	30	31

NOVEMBER
S	M	T	W	T	F	S
1	2	3	4	5	6	7
8	9	10	11	12	13	14
15	16	17	18	19	20	21
22	23	24	25	26	27	28
29	30					

DECEMBER
S	M	T	W	T	F	S
		1	2	3	4	5
6	7	8	9	10	11	12
13	14	15	16	17	18	19
20	21	22	23	24	25	26
27	28	29	30	31		

1982

JANUARY
S	M	T	W	T	F	S
					1	2
3	4	5	6	7	8	9
10	11	12	13	14	15	16
17	18	19	20	21	22	23
24	25	26	27	28	29	30
31						

FEBRUARY
S	M	T	W	T	F	S
	1	2	3	4	5	6
7	8	9	10	11	12	13
14	15	16	17	18	19	20
21	22	23	24	25	26	27
28						

MARCH
S	M	T	W	T	F	S
	1	2	3	4	5	6
7	8	9	10	11	12	13
14	15	16	17	18	19	20
21	22	23	24	25	26	27
28	29	30	31			

APRIL
S	M	T	W	T	F	S
				1	2	3
4	5	6	7	8	9	10
11	12	13	14	15	16	17
18	19	20	21	22	23	24
25	26	27	28	29	30	

MAY
S	M	T	W	T	F	S
						1
2	3	4	5	6	7	8
9	10	11	12	13	14	15
16	17	18	19	20	21	22
23	24	25	26	27	28	29
30	31					

JUNE
S	M	T	W	T	F	S
		1	2	3	4	5
6	7	8	9	10	11	12
13	14	15	16	17	18	19
20	21	22	23	24	25	26
27	28	29	30			

JULY
S	M	T	W	T	F	S
				1	2	3
4	5	6	7	8	9	10
11	12	13	14	15	16	17
18	19	20	21	22	23	24
25	26	27	28	29	30	31

AUGUST
S	M	T	W	T	F	S
1	2	3	4	5	6	7
8	9	10	11	12	13	14
15	16	17	18	19	20	21
22	23	24	25	26	27	28
29	30	31				

SEPTEMBER
S	M	T	W	T	F	S
			1	2	3	4
5	6	7	8	9	10	11
12	13	14	15	16	17	18
19	20	21	22	23	24	25
26	27	28	29	30		

OCTOBER
S	M	T	W	T	F	S
					1	2
3	4	5	6	7	8	9
10	11	12	13	14	15	16
17	18	19	20	21	22	23
24	25	26	27	28	29	30
31						

NOVEMBER
S	M	T	W	T	F	S
	1	2	3	4	5	6
7	8	9	10	11	12	13
14	15	16	17	18	19	20
21	22	23	24	25	26	27
28	29	30				

DECEMBER
S	M	T	W	T	F	S
			1	2	3	4
5	6	7	8	9	10	11
12	13	14	15	16	17	18
19	20	21	22	23	24	25
26	27	28	29	30	31	

SPRAY DILUTION TABLE

We find this table a real time-saver in figuring spray dilutions. Note that dilutions are figured both in tablespoon-teaspoons and in cubic centimeters (cc.). The cc. is simpler, more accurate. Cylinders graduated in cubic centimeters (10 cc., 50 cc. or 100 cc.) may be obtained from Central Scientific Co., 1700 Irving Park Blvd., Chicago, Ill.—or probably from your local druggist.

The table is from the Ohio Florist Association Monthly Bulletin No. 198.

t. = teaspoonful   T. = Tablespoonful

	1 to 50	1 to 100	1 to 200	1 to 300	1 to 400	1 to 500	1 to 600	1 to 800	1 to 1000	1 to 1600
1 Gal.	72.5 cc. or 5 T. plus 1/4 t. or 2.56 ozs.	36.2 cc. or 2 T. plus 1 3/4 t. or 1.28 ozs.	18.1 cc. or 3 3/4 t. or .64 oz.	12.2 cc. or 2 1/2 t.	9.1 cc. or 2 t.	7.3 cc. or 1 1/2 t.	6.0 cc. or 1 1/4 t.	4.5 cc. or 1 t.	3.6 cc. or 3/4 t.	2.3 cc. or 1/2 t.
2 Gals.	144.9 cc. or 10 T. plus 3/4 t. or 5.12 ozs.	72.5 cc. or 5 T. plus 1/4 t. or 2.56 ozs.	36.2 cc. or 2 T. plus 1 3/4 t. or 1.28 ozs.	24.1 cc. or 5 t.	18.1 cc. or 3 3/4 t.	14.5 cc. or 3 t.	12.2 cc. or 2.5 t.	9.1 cc. or 2 t.	7.3 cc. or 1.5 t.	4.6 cc. or 1 t.
3 Gals.	217.3 cc. or 15 T. plus 1 t. or 7.68 ozs.	108.7 cc. or 7 T. plus 2 t. or 3.84 ozs.	54.3 cc. or 3 T. plus 2 1/2 t. or 1.92 ozs.	36.2 cc. or 2 T. plus 1 3/4 t. or 1.28 ozs.	27.2 cc. or 1 T. plus 2 3/4 t.	21.7 cc. or 1 T. plus 1.5 t.	18.1 cc. or 3 3/4 t.	13.4 cc. or 1 T.	10.9 cc. or 2 1/4 t.	6.9 cc. or 1.5 t.
5 Gals.	362.2 cc. or 12.8 ozs.	181.1 cc. or 6.4 ozs.	90.6 cc. or 6 T. plus 1 1/4 t. or 3.2 ozs.	60.3 cc. or 4 T. plus 3/4 t. or 2.13 ozs.	45.3 cc. or 3 T. plus 1/2 t. or 1.6 ozs.	36.2 cc. or 2 T. plus 1 3/4 t. or 1.28 ozs.	30.3 cc. or 2 T. plus 1/2 t. or 1.07 ozs.	22.6 cc. or 1 T. plus 1 3/4 t.	18.1 cc. or 3 3/4 t.	11.3 cc. or 2.5 t.

10 Gal.	22.6 cc. or 1 T. plus 1¾ t. or .8 oz.	36.2 cc. or 2 T. plus 1¾ t. or 1.28 ozs.	45.3 cc. or 3 T. plus ½ t. or 1.6 ozs.	60.3 cc. or 4 T. plus ¾ t. or 2.13 ozs.	72.5 cc. or 5 T. plus ¼ t. or 2.56 ozs.	90.6 cc. or 6 T. plus 1¼ t. or 3.2 ozs.	120.8 cc. or 8 T. plus 1½ t. or 4.27 ozs.	181.1 cc. or 12 T. plus 2½ t. or 6.4 ozs.	362.2 cc. or 12.8 ozs.	724.5 cc. or 25.6 ozs.
25 Gal.	56.5 cc. or 4 T. or 2 ozs.	90.6 cc. or 6 T. plus 1¼ t. or 3.2 ozs.	113.0 cc. or 8 T. or 4 ozs.	150.8 cc. or 10 T. plus 2½ t. or 5.33 ozs.	181.1 cc. or 12 T. plus 2½ t. or 6.4 ozs.	226.4 cc. or 16 T. or 8 ozs.	302.8 cc. or 10.7 ozs.	452.8 cc. or 16 ozs.	905.6 cc. or 32 ozs.	1811.2 cc. or 64 ozs.
30 Gal.	67.8 cc. or 4 T. plus 4½ t. or 2.4 ozs.	108.6 cc. or 7 T. plus 2 t. or 3.84 ozs.	135.9 cc. or 9 T. plus 1½ t. or 4.8 ozs.	180.9 cc. or 12 T. plus 2 t. or 6.39 ozs.	217.5 cc. or 15 T. plus 1 t. or 7.68 ozs.	271.8 cc. or 19 T. or 9.6 ozs.	362.4 cc. or 12.81 ozs.	543.3 cc. or 19.2 ozs.	1086.6 cc. or 38.4 ozs.	2173.5 cc. or 76.8 ozs.
50 Gal.	113.2 cc. or 8 T. or 4 ozs.	181.1 cc. or 12 T. plus 2½ t. or 6.4 ozs.	226.4 cc. or 8 ozs.	302.8 cc. or 10.66 ozs.	362.2 cc. or 12.8 ozs.	452.8 cc. or 16 ozs.	602.8 cc. or 21.33 ozs.	905.6 cc. or 32 ozs.	1811.2 cc. or 64 ozs.	3622.4 cc. or 1 gal.

PART II. CULTURAL NOTES BY CROPS

The following product names are registered trademarks of Geo. J. Ball, Inc. or Divisions of Geo. J. Ball, Inc.

CONTAINERS

Jiffy-Pots	Ballet Violets
Jiffy-Strips	Handi-Flats
Jiffy-7	Handi-Paks
Jiffy-9	Cell-Paks

OTHER ITEMS

Super-Seedlings	Carefree (Geraniums)
Ball Crown (Lilies)	Elfin (Impatiens)
Harvest Giant (Mums)	Jiffy-Mix (Soil substitute)
Tag-Along (Plastic Labels)	

Other registered trademarks mentioned herein:

Fertilizer: MagAmp

Insecticides: Thuricide HPC, Meta-Systox-R

Fungicides: Benlate, Dexon, Exotherm Termil, Truban, Mertect 16 Thiabendazole, Terraclor, Pipron, Termil

Growth Retardants: Cycocel, A-Rest

Chemical Pinching Agent: Off-Shoot-O

Rooting Material: Hormex Rooting Powders

Anti-Fogging Material: Sun Clear

Geo. J. Ball, Sr.—founder of the Ball company, creator of THE BALL RED BOOK—in a 1934 photo with his then-famous Ball Calendula.